DATE DUE

Mar 19 69			
May 1 '69			
Apr 2 '71			
Apr 21 '71			
Apr 24 '72			
May 9 '72			

MANUAL ON
INDUSTRIAL WATER AND
INDUSTRIAL WASTE WATER

SECOND EDITION—1966 PRINTING
WITH NEW AND REVISED METHODS

Sponsored by
ASTM COMMITTEE D-19
ON
INDUSTRIAL WATER

Reg. U. S. Pat. Off.

ASTM Special Technical Publication No. 148-I

Price: $17.25; 30 per cent discount to members

Published by the
AMERICAN SOCIETY FOR TESTING AND MATERIALS
1916 Race St., Philadelphia, Pa. 19103

NOTE—The Society is not responsible, as a body, for the statements
and opinions advanced in this publication.

*Nothing contained in any publication of the American Society for Testing
and Materials is to be construed as granting any right, by implication or
otherwise, for manufacture, sale or use in connection with any method, apparatus or product covered by Letters Patent, nor as insuring anyone against
liability for infringement of Letters Patent.*

Printed in Baltimore, Md., U.S.A
January, 1960
Second Printing, February, 1961
Third Printing, February, 1963
Fourth Printing, February, 1965
Fifth Printing, April, 1966
Sixth Printing, March, 1967

43–91

FOREWORD TO FIRST EDITION

Committee D-19 on Industrial Water of the American Society for Testing and Materials has long believed that something more than standard methods of testing are needed by those who look to the Society for aid. A general discussion of the nature and uses of industrial water should illuminate these prescribed procedures and specifications.

The inception of a Manual on Industrial Water occurred before World War II, but the actual preparation was begun by a section of Committee D-19 in 1946. This section consisted of R. C. Adams (chairman), A. A. Berk, T. H. Daugherty, O. M. Elliott, J. A. Holmes, C. E. Imhoff, A. K. Light, F. U. Neat, F. R. Owens, and A. H. Reynolds. Each member of the section drafted an assigned portion of the Manual with more or less assistance from his associates and from other members of Committee D-19. These drafts were modified, correlated, and assembled by the entire section so that the resulting Manual is the product of group effort in the Society tradition, not a compilation of individual authorships. Many persons not in the section contributed to the Manual. Particular acknowledgment should be made to Max Hecht, L. K. Herndon, E. P. Partridge and C. K. Rice.

This first edition of the Manual will be revised to keep it up to date, and subsequent editions should appear periodically. Any errors noted, or suggestions for revision and improvement, should be brought to the attention of the Society at its headquarters.

January, 1953.

FOREWORD TO SECOND EDITION

The first edition of the Manual on Industrial Water and Industrial Waste Water was reprinted three times. This widespread acceptance has demonstrated the need for a publication devoted to industrial water. Each printing of the Manual was brought up to date by inclusion of all current ASTM methods for the examination of water. The editorial matter, however, was reprinted without revision.

Committee D-19 has taken note of the fact that interest in the characteristics of water is not confined to its suitability for process use, but continues after its final discharge from the plant. This continuing interest arises from the potential effects of certain waste waters on downstream uses. It was decided therefore that a new edition of the Manual should contain information on waste water as well as process water.

Preparation of the second edition was assigned to a task group of Committee D-19, consisting of F. N. Alquist,[1] R. A. Baker, G. D. Beal, F. E. Clarke, E. F. Davidson, B. W. Dickerson, D. K. French, A. S. Goldin, J. E. Kinney, W. W. Leathen, S. K. Love, W. A. Moore, F. R. Owens, J. K. Rice,

---

[1] Deceased.

C. C. Ruchhoft,[1] R. K. Scott, J. M. Seamon, J. B. Smith, F. N. Speller, R. F. Weston, and R. D. Hoak, chairman. The new edition was composed in the same manner as the first one. Thus it represents a real collaborative effort entailing group responsibility for all the chapters. Acknowledgment should also be made of the contribution of C. K. Rice who, as the D-19 Standards Advisor, was responsible for the editorial form of the methods in Part II.

Successive editions of the Manual will be published from time to time. Any errors of fact, or suggestions for revision or improvement, should be brought to the attention of the Society.

January, 1960.

FOREWORD TO ADDITIONAL PRINTINGS OF SECOND EDITION

In the following printings of the Manual, Part II has been enlarged and brought up to date by the inclusion of the new and revised methods and definitions issued since the last printing.

There have been no changes in Part I of the Manual.

PRINTING	DATED
1960	December, 1960
1962	December, 1962
1964	December, 1964
1965	December, 1965
1966	December, 1966

CONTENTS

---

* Approved as **USA Standard** by USA Standards Institute.

v

For Contents in Numeric Sequence, see p. xi.

For Contents in Numeric Sequence, see p. xi.

Methods of Test for: PAGE

For Contents in Numeric Sequence, see p. xi.

INDEX

CONTENTS IN NUMERIC SEQUENCE

OF

ASTM STANDARDS RELATING TO INDUSTRIAL WATER AND INDUSTRIAL WASTE WATER

* Approved as **USA Standard** by USA Standards Institute.

MANUAL ON INDUSTRIAL WATER AND INDUSTRIAL WASTE WATER

INTRODUCTION

This Manual is intended as a brief reference source of information for three types of users: executives and plant designers; individuals engaged in industrial operations involving the use of water; and analysts, operators of special instruments, engineers, and consultants. It will not replace an adequate library on the subject for any of these users, but it does provide basic information for routine use and cites references to the technical literature, thus serving as a point of departure for more specific and detailed studies.

For executives, plant managers, designers, and similar technologists and administrators, it offers information on the influence of water on industries in which it is used either as a raw material or in conjunction with manufacturing processes. The influence of water on various industries ranges from that in paper manufacture, for example, where very large volumes are used and its quality is of great importance, to small industries where only incidental supplies are needed. At no level, however, can the amount and nature of the available water be disregarded lest a plague of supply failure, contamination, corrosion, scaling, or other difficulty arise to interfere with the manufacturer's operations and to sap his profits. The Manual should serve as a guide to the nature of water planning required at the supervisory and investment levels.

Operating personnel will find in the Manual a guide to the significance of the treatment they are applying. Combined with general discussion of the problems arising from industrial use of water are details of specific control procedures and instructions for such critical operations as sampling water under the various conditions and in the several forms in which it is employed. The Manual will be useful as a text for training plant operators and for the indoctrination of technologists from other fields.

Chemists and other technologists having special knowledge of water can use the Manual as a reference for specific information not assembled elsewhere. Standard methods for sampling, analysis, reporting, and testing water that have been developed cooperatively by ASTM Committee D-19 on Industrial Water are included for ready reference, together with constants, names, and factors of immediate usefulness to water practitioners. The techniques that have not yet achieved standardization are discussed to aid the water specialist in keeping abreast of new developments.

It is hoped that the Manual also will be used as a text in technical schools and colleges. While this was not the prime purpose of its preparation, the material presented should be suitable for classroom use. Suggestions for improvements in this respect will be particularly welcome for inclusion in later editions.

Despite the extensive use that can be made of the Manual, it should not be expected to replace competent and well-trained technologists. It will give general

1

information to some and detailed information to others, but the design and efficient application of the treatments and techniques discussed require experience that no books can supply.

The first two chapters provide general information about industrial uses of water. The first chapter discusses the uses themselves and the factors that must be considered in selecting a source of water; the second reviews the kinds of difficulties that may be caused by various impurities in industrial supplies. Chapter III is a new one that gives a brief account of the mechanism by which streams assimilate wastes. The next chapter introduces the more technical portion of the Manual by defining various terms and presenting the technologist's conception of water and water deposits. Chapter V comprehensively covers the treatment of process water and waste water and cites many references to technical literature where details of particular processes may be found. Chapters VI to IX deal with the procedures and

precautions to be observed in sampling analysis, and examination of water and water-formed deposits and the reaction and corrosion products of water. Rapid expansion of industrial use of radioactive nuclides pointed to the desirability of including information on this subject in a new chapter which concludes Part I of the Manual.

Part II contains, in numeric sequence, all methods for the examination of water that are currently accepted by the American Society for Testing Materials. This section of the Manual is preceded by an introduction to laboratory practices which contains helpful advice for analysts, whether experienced or not. An Appendix provides certain data commonly needed by water analysts.

This edition of the Manual represents a substantial expansion of the first edition. It has been designed to satisfy the growing need for dependable information about water and the problems its use entails. The authors hope that it will properly serve the intended purpose.

INTRODUCTION TO SECOND PRINTING OF SECOND EDITION

This Second Printing of the Second Edition is essentially identical with the first printing, with the addition of two new methods and the inclusion of all revisions of methods. Several of the revisions are the outgrowth of cooperative efforts of Committee D-19 and other organizations. ASTM Committee D-19 is one of twelve member organizations engaged in a cooperative effort to bring about uniformity in methods of water examination. This activity is directed by the Joint Committee on Uniformity of Methods of Water Examination (JCUMWE). The objectives of JCUMWE are, (1) to review the methods of water examination published by member organizations for the purpose of obtaining

uniformity in sampling, testing, reporting test data, terminology, and in applications; and (2) to provide a mechanism for the exchange of information on these matters by member organizations.

The member organizations of JCUMWE are: Association of Official Agricultural Chemists, American Public Health Association, American Petroleum Institute, American Society of Mechanical Engineers, American Society for Testing Materials, American Water Works Association, Manufacturing Chemists Association, Technical Association of the Pulp and Paper Industry, United States Pharmacopeia, United States Geological Survey, United States Public Health Service, and Water Pollution Control Federation.

PART I

INDUSTRIAL WATER—GENERAL USES AND PROBLEMS OF SAMPLING AND ANALYSIS

CHAPTER I
Uses of Industrial Water

CHAPTER I—USES OF INDUSTRIAL WATER

Water is accepted, almost universally, as an abundant and commonplace material in the life of Man. This same misconception of the importance of water exists, to a slightly smaller degree, in our industrial life. The necessity of guarding and conserving this great natural resource is imperative today, not tomorrow.

Man's industrial progress can be traced by studying his utilization and exploitation of the earth's watercourses. Our future industrial progress will, in a large measure, be determined by our rational use of water. Industrial operations entail a demand for water both in quantity and quality. These two requirements vary not only between different types of plants but also for different uses within each plant. A secure water supply must be a basic consideration in the selection of a site for any industrial plant. It is essential that the supply be adequate to serve all the intended uses.

The water requirements of a plant may be broadly classified as industrial and sanitary. This Manual is primarily concerned with industrial water, which may be defined as water (including all its impurities) used directly or indirectly in an industrial process. Potable water is that which is intended for immediate or ultimate human consumption; publications of the Public Health Service provide full information about such supplies.

Many industrial uses are made of water in a modern plant, and frequently there are differences in the characteristics of the waters required. Efforts should be made to employ the untreated natural water for all possible uses and then to supply the remainder of the plant requirement by the minimum and most economically satisfactory treatment. Thus untreated sea water can be used for condenser-cooling water and for partially regenerating zeolite softeners, but the salt content is far too high for it to be used as boiler feedwater or for numerous other phases of the plant water cycle. Where sea water is available, it would be economical to use it insofar as possible and to supplement it with a more expensive untreated or treated fresh water for the remaining uses.

BASIC INDUSTRIAL WATER USES

Industrial uses of water may be grouped in seven basic categories. These seven basic uses are: steam generation, heat transfer, solvent action, carrier, raw material, kinetic energy, and nuclear energy. Every plant will not necessarily use water in all seven ways; water use varies widely among different types of industry.

An industrial plant must also have available an ample supply of water for fire protection. This should not be classed as an industrial use; the source is often a municipal supply.

The powerhouse of any industry is a large user of water. Although a pound of water must be evaporated to form a pound of steam, the water make-up to the boilers is seldom the largest water use in modern plants. Much of the steam, particularly in public utility stations, is condensed and re-used in the boilers. Usually the greatest water use is for condensing steam and for cooling. A large utility may use an amount of water

7

equivalent to the total flow of the stream which supplies it, even though only a small fraction of this volume is employed as make-up boiler water. Lesser quantities of water are used for such power purposes as cooling pump glands, regenerating zeolite softeners, and backwashing filters.

Washing operations are required by all industries, even if only for cleaning the plants periodically. Equipment must be washed more or less frequently. Raw materials require washing to remove foreign matter, and the products in various stages of manufacture require washing to remove spent chemical residues and unwanted by-products.

Industry makes use of water to transport raw materials, to dispose of wastes, and to separate substances of different specific gravity. The kinetic energy of water is utilized in hydroelectric plants, in hydraulic mining, and as high-pressure sprays for debarking lumber and descaling steel.

Air conditioning, now becoming commonplace, requires large volumes of water for cleaning, cooling, and humidity regulation of the air. Ice, still widely used, is made directly from water, with some water wastage to remove dissolved salts.

Heat exchangers require steam or water. Frequently they are used to remove heat evolved in chemical reactions or added heat that is undesired in subsequent steps. If possible, the heated water is conveyed to some other operation where heat is required, thus improving efficiency.

Nuclear energy, industry's potential giant, uses water for radiation shielding, reactor moderation, steam generation, and to dilute radioactive wastes. Although the quantity used in this field may be limited, problems associated with quality and waste disposal present a real challenge to engineers and technologists.

In addition to these uses of water, which are largely common to all industry, each industry has special water uses of its own. These individual uses and variation in emphasis on common uses make the problem of water supply peculiar to each industry. The nature of water requirements for several major industries is discussed as examples below.

The Chemical Industry

Unquestionably, water is used in the chemical industry in every known way. Each individual process employs water in a number of different ways, and processes differ widely from one another in the volume used. Overall, however, the use of water for condensing and cooling ranks first in volume. Separation and purification of substances are quite frequently effected by a change in phase which requires heat input. A change in phase occurs when a solid is converted into a liquid by heating, as in the mining of sulfur when it is melted with steam and the liquid forced to the surface with pressure. A change in phase also occurs when a liquid is converted to a gas, as in the distillation of alcohol from fermented grain or in the fractionation of petroleum to produce lubricating oils, kerosine, gasoline, and other distillates. Heat must be extracted to regain these purified products in forms stable at normal temperature and pressure. Large volumes of cooling or condensing water are employed for removing this heat in many chemical plants.

Another important use of water is as a reactant, that is, a substance that contributes its atoms to the final product. Thus quicklime, CaO, reacts with water, H_2O, to form slaked lime or calcium hydroxide, $Ca(OH)_2$. Similarly, phosphoric acid, H_3PO_4, is manufactured by reacting phosphorus pentoxide, P_2O_5, with water. Another type of reaction is the hydrolysis of animal fats to produce glycerine and fatty acids for soap manufacture. Water itself can be split by electrolysis to make hydrogen and oxygen gases. Water reacts with calcium carbide to form acetylene, the raw material for a large organic chemicals industry.

Natural waters containing large quantities of dissolved salts (brines) are used as sources of these salts for manufacturing various chemicals. Thus, bromine, magnesium, and magnesium compounds (such as milk of magnesia) are derived from sea water. Lake and well brines are sources of various useful compounds of potassium, sodium, and boron. Chlorine is made from a water solution of sodium chloride by electrolysis.

Water finds many applications as the cheapest and most universally available liquid. Such uses include: the classification (separation by flotation) of minerals and ores; the sealing of gas holders; the disintegration or milling of clays; the quenching of molten products, such as caustic soda from waste-lignin furnaces; the emergency drowning of reactions out of control, such as might occur in the manufacture of trinitrotoluene (TNT); and the fluming or carrying of materials in water suspension from one operation to another.

Water is an almost universal solvent, and this action, particularly on acids, bases, and salts, is the basis for many uses. Washing and rinsing operations are the commonest application of this solvent ability. Washing is the removal of water-soluble impurities from raw materials, intermediate products, and final products. Special names are applied to different washing processes, based upon the manner in which the water is used. Thus, dialyzing is the dissolving of soluble compounds from materials of high molecular weight through a porous membrane, such as the removal of salt from gelatin contained in a cellophane bag which is dipped into water. Extraction is a washing operation in which water is passed through a confined mass of material to dissolve soluble impurities. Decantation and the washing of filters, thickeners, and centrifugal separators are other types of washing operations. Water-soluble constituents in gas streams are frequently removed in scrubbers or absorption towers in which gas is passed countercurrent through water. Crystallization is often a washing operation by which crystalline substances are freed from impurities through the use of water.

Many chemical reactions will not proceed rapidly enough unless the reactants are dissolved in a mutual solvent, which in innumerable cases is water. Conversely, water is used to dilute reactants in order to reduce and control the rates of reaction.

Water in the form of steam is widely used to supply heat to chemical processes. Typical operations are: distillation of volatile materials (oils, organic solvents); liquefaction of solids (waxes, sulfur, gums); sterilization or pasteurization (milk); digestion, cooking, or steeping (cereals); blending (molding compounds); curing (plastics); vulcanizing (rubber); and dehydration (foods), evaporation (sugar), concentration (acids), or drying (nitrocellulose, salts). Steam jets find occasional use, as in the manufacture of rock wool and in inducing vacuum by means of an eductor. Steam is also a reactant, as in the manufacture of synthetic ammonia and water gas, and the synthesis of styrene.

The rapid growth of the chemical industry has been broadly influenced by a plentiful supply of water—a substance of great versatility.

The Steel Industry

The principal use of water in steel mills is for cooling. There are many such applications in addition to condenser cooling in the powerhouse. The reduction of iron from its ore; the compounding of this iron into pig iron, wrought iron, carbon steels, and alloy steels; and the forging of these products into usable shapes are processes that require tremendous amounts of heat at high temperatures. Water is used for cooling parts of the furnaces, such as the tuyères of blast furnaces, and the doors and side walls of open hearth furnaces. Also, the rolls must be cooled with a water spray, and the skid rails for hot billets by internal water circulation. Finally, the billets are descaled by means of high-pressure water jets, which provide a combination of thermal shock and mechanical action. Clean cooling water is generally re-used for inferior purposes, such as gas-scrubbing.

Water is used to condense coal distillates, to scrub gases, and to quench the product in the manufacture of metallurgical coke. In electrostatic precipitators, which separate dust particles from gases, water is employed to rinse the collected dust from the surfaces on which it deposits.

Steel is pickled in a strong acid solution to remove mill scale. Sheet steel is pickled and rinsed by being fed at high speed through successive tanks containing the pickle liquor and the rinse water. When steel is to be tinned, galvanized, or chemically coated for corrosion protection, it is passed through successive tanks containing alkaline detergent solution (to remove roll lubricants) and rinse water.

The Food and Beverage Industries

Water is a raw material in these industries, and they employ large quantities in a wide variety of ways. Quality of the process water is vitally important, with freedom from bacteria, toxic substances, malflavors, and turbidity being of most importance. Water used in products

for human consumption must meet the standards for potability. Examples[1] of special quality requirements are: low alkalinity, high sulfate-hardness, and absence of nitrates, nitrites, ferrous iron, copper, and fluoride ions for brewing; zero hardness for canning peas and beans, and for dairy wash water; low mineral content for gelatin; and low microorganism count and low sodium and magnesium chloride content for alcohol distilleries. Fluorides tend to concentrate in spaghetti, beans, and cereals, and copper decreases the shelf-life of package foods.

While washing, blanching, and cooking of raw fruits and vegetables are among the operations requiring larger volumes of water in the industries devoted to products for human consumption, two lesser volume uses distinguish these industries. One such use is sterilization, in which hot water or steam supplies the heat necessary to kill all living organisms. The other is the flume system in which water serves to transport foodstuffs through the various plant operations, from washing to blanching, peeling, sorting, grading, inspecting, cooking, or to other steps as required.

Each food product has one or more characteristic water uses. Fruits and vegetables are blanched or surface heated with steam or hot water, and sometimes are peeled by use of steam or high-pressure water jets. Vacuum freezing of fruits and vegetables employs a steam-jet aspirator to produce the vacuum. Cereals are steam-exploded to produce the many physical forms of breakfast foods or are wet-milled and separated into fractions in water suspension, such as in the tabling process for cornstarch. Some meats are injected with, or pickled in, water solutions of salts. Beverages

---

[1] W. L. Faith, "Plant Location in Agricultural Process Industries," *Chemical Engineering Progress*, Vol. 45, p. 313, May, 1949. See also publications of the American Public Health Assn. and the American Water Works Assn.

are malted, boiled, cooled, and fermented by means of water and steam. Sugar is decolorized in, and crystallized from, water solution.

Thus, in the production of the multitude of food and beverage products, practically every conventional water use is employed somewhere.

The Paper Industry

Most paper mills are located on rivers or lakes and use is made of flowing water to float the logs from the forests to the plant. The first operation on the logs is debarking, which is usually done mechanically, but is sometimes effected by high-pressure water jets. The logs then are chipped and the chips are fed to digesters where water, steam, and chemicals are added. The digested fibers are blown into pits, where they are washed and then flushed onto screens where knots and larger pieces of wood are removed. Digestion before screening is by the sulfite, the sulfate, the soda, or the semichemical process. After screening, the pulp is chlorinated and then extracted with mild caustic to remove chlorinated lignins. After further washing, it is bleached in a solution of hypochlorite, chlorine dioxide, or peroxide, washed, and passed to the beaters where more water is added. From here it is blended in stock pits, treated in Jordan mills to separate the individual fibers, and passed to the paper machine with the addition of water to reduce the consistency. The pulp is flowed uniformly onto a continuous wire screen through which the water drains. The wet sheet is picked up by a continuous felt which presses it against a series of steam-heated cylinders to produce a dry sheet. The sheet is then calendered and rolled.

A groundwood mill differs from the chemical processes in that the debarked logs are ground between stones with sufficient water to produce the desired pulp consistency. The pulp is bleached with a peroxide solution and then flumed to the beaters.

Thus water in very large quantities is used by paper mills for floating the logs to the mill, for hydraulic debarking, as a solvent for reactants, for dissolving spent chemical residues, and as a carrier for the pulp. Steam is employed for raising temperatures of reacting mixtures and for drying the final product. Many paper mills generate a portion or all of their electricity in steam powerhouses. Even when ample water resources are at hand, considerable re-use of water is practiced to prevent wastage of chemicals and pulp. The paper industry has studied water quality extensively and has set standards for making each grade of paper.

The Leather Industry

The first use of water in a typical tannery is for soaking the hides for rehydration and reconstitution, and for removing salts and dirt. The hides are then worked in a water suspension of lime, sulfides, and other chemicals to remove globular proteins and loosen the hair. The next step is mechanical unhairing. The hides are washed and then bated in a steam-heated water solution of enzymes for improving the grain. After another water wash, the hides go either into a vegetable tanning solution or into an acidic salt water solution for pickling and thence into a chrome tanning solution. (Tanning solutions require water of low iron content.) After tanning, they are washed again, a process which is often followed by dyeing in a water solution, fat liquoring or stuffing, and drying. The leather is then damped and staked with a small amount of water which serves to lubricate the fibers. The final finishing operation may involve either a water-suspended pigment or a dye-topping solution.

THE TEXTILE INDUSTRY

The principal products of the textile industry are wool, cotton, and a variety of synthetic fibers. Each of these requires considerable water in manufacturing and finishing. Water of excellent quality is necessary for textile manufacturing; at many mills the standards for potable water are met or exceeded. Hardness greater than 50 ppm is undesirable because it may precipitate certain dyestuffs or cause soap-bound stains. Most mills use ion-exchange resins or phosphate treatment to reduce hardness. Manganese should not exceed 0.1 ppm, iron 0.3 ppm; these metals affect dye color. Color should be low, but pH may be in the range 6.5 to 8.5. Corrosion is sometimes a problem, largely because it may introduce ferrous ions.

Many textile mills have had to install air conditioning, humidity control, and air cleaning. This requires a huge amount of water, and the need for such water usage is steadily increasing.

Wool is first scoured in a steam-heated caustic solution to remove soil and natural grease. It is then dried, oiled, spun into yarn, and woven or knitted into fabric. The fabric is shrunk in a fulling mill, which requires water as a carrier for soap. It is again scoured in a steam-heated water solution and thoroughly rinsed. It then passes into a carbonizing bath which consists of water and acid, following which it is rinsed and the acid neutralized in an alkaline water solution. The next step is dyeing in a steam-heated dye solution. Final steps are rinsing, hydroextraction, drying, and tentering.

Cotton is first singed and then desized in a steam-heated enzyme solution. It is next kier-boiled, a process which requires both water and steam, rinsed, bleached in a hypochlorite solution, washed, soured in a bisulfite solution, mangled in

water to remove the sour, and dried. The next step is mercerization, which requires water and caustic soda to improve the strength and luster. The cotton is then washed, dyed in a steam-heated solution, mangled in water to remove excess dye, and dried. Some dyed materials require a soaping after dyeing. The finishing or sizing of cotton is conducted in water, after which the goods are steam-calendered and rolled or folded.

Water use in manufacturing and processing synthetics differs somewhat among the several fibers. All need a great deal of water, and its use is roughly similar to that for natural fibers.

THE MINING INDUSTRY

Hydraulic mining of ores and minerals uses great volumes of water to flush the desired material from its natural location in the earth. The water-borne material is separated from earthy matter by a classification process called flotation.

The coal mining industry uses a large amount of water for washing the product to prepare a clean-burning fuel. Water is also used to classify coal and to carry away fines and particles of slate. Some producers treat their coal with a water solution of dye to identify their product.

At most coal mines the problem is to get rid of surplus water. Ground water drains into nearly all mines and must be pumped away to permit mining; for every ton of coal produced, from 10 to 30 tons of water may have to be pumped out of the mines.

Water is converted to steam for power supply at many mines. This energy is needed for shaft hoists, conveyors, and general mining purposes.

THE PLANT WATER BALANCE

These varied demands, in both quantity and quality, make it apparent that an adequate and economical water supply can be assured only by careful planning.

Preparation of a water balance is the most logical way to accomplish this.[2]

The first step in evaluating the water situation is the preparation of a flow diagram for the entire water requirement of the plant, in conjunction with the flow diagram for the other raw materials to be used in the manufacturing process. This diagram should include the water used in the process and incorporated in the product; that required for generation of steam for prime movers and for heating; that required for cooling, air conditioning, fire protection, and cleaning; and that required for sanitary purposes. Due allowance for future expansion should be included.

The second step is the formulation of the characteristics of the water required for each phase of the process or separate use of water. These include the limits and nature of suspended matter, dissolved solids, dissolved gases, and other contaminants. Where the water is to be used in connection with products for human consumption and for the portion of the intake to be employed for sanitary purposes, provision must be made for meeting the standards for potable water. Where cooling towers, spray ponds, or reservoirs are contemplated, the problem of biological growths in the water must be considered. Similarly, where salt water is to be used, corrosion, marine growths such as barnacles, water hyacinth, and water lily constitute problems.

The third step is the estimation of the quantity and quality of water available at or near a given site. This includes appraisal of seasonal or other variations of quantity and temperature, and the concentration ranges of suspended matter, dissolved substances, and viable organisms present. The preparation of an

accurate estimate is not easy. Full advantage must be taken of all accumulated information available from local, state, and federal agencies on analyses; on measurements of precipitation, natural storage, water level, stream-flow rates and run-off rates; on temperature variations; on present demands for water from other users; and on the geological structure of the area. In addition, new analyses of representative samples, new measurements of quantities, and even test borings should be made to confirm the findings of earlier investigations. Consultation with the technical staffs of existing nearby plants will not only substantiate and supplement these data but may provide information on the types and costs of successful treatments.

The possibilities for conserving water by re-use should be thoroughly explored. Frequently it is possible to reduce materially the over-all cost and amount of water required by re-use of water. Savings also result from less piping and pumping, smaller filter capacity, fewer chemicals, less equipment for treatment, and smaller storage facilities. Increasing legislation against stream pollution points to the necessity for treatment of waste liquors before discharge, and such treatment can produce an effluent that may economically be recycled. In certain areas, the available water supply is limited or is seasonally curtailed, and here re-use to the maximum extent practical is a necessity rather than a desirability. A factor seldom considered is the appreciable cost of pipeline maintenance where the supply may carry high concentrations of sand or silt. Most streams are quite turbid after a rainfall.

Knowing the type or types of water available at the site, the fourth step is the estimation of the capital and operating cost of suitable water-treating processes for the situation. Equipment may

---

[2] S. T. Powell and L. G. Von Lossberg, "Relation of Water Supply to Plant Location," *Chemical Engineering Progress*, Vol. 45, p. 289, May, 1949.

include settling basins, filters, softeners, pumps, storage tanks, cooling towers, and piping necessary to process the required volume of satisfactory water, and then to deliver it to the various points of use and to dispose of the plant effluent to waste or to re-use. Operating costs should include labor, maintenance, supervision, and overhead in addition to chemical costs.

After these four steps have been taken, it can be decided whether the site possesses a watershed adequate for the needs of the projected industry and capable of supplying water that can be treated satisfactorily and economically for the desired uses. Comparison of the flow diagram of the plant, which shows quantities and qualities of water required, with the estimate of the quantity available and the estimate of the probable cost for the required qualities will show whether the proposed installation is feasible and economical.

An existing plant should have a water-balance diagram. It will be faced with the same reevaluation problem as a new plant when modifying or expanding its operation or when diversifying into other lines. The water balance should never be regarded as finished but should be revised continually as changes occur, either within the plant or external to it. Within the plant, the water balance is affected by each increase or decrease in water consumption of an existing process, by each new process or new water-using unit installed, and by each change of water treatment. Improvements in corrosion resistance of equipment, in processes of water treatment, and in waste water disposal can improve the water economy of the plant if properly utilized. Externally, the water supply can change materially by intrusion of other industries, which either consume water or pollute the supply, and by surface or subsurface deterioration in the quantity or quality available. The water plan may be regarded as a picture of the water supply, distribution through the plant, treatment, uses, and disposal at a given time. When any one element of the water situation changes or is changed, the water plan must be changed to depict the new situation. An important use of a well-prepared and up-to-date water plan is to forecast what natural changes in the water situation may occur and what changes can or cannot be made when some new move is being contemplated. From such a forecast, the necessary changes in supply and in treatment can be anticipated.

The water requirement per unit of different products varies widely, but the range of this variation is astonishing. There are a number of reasons for this wide range. Water used per unit of product is often based on the total intake volume; re-use of water therefore will reduce the volume per unit. Sometimes use is computed from the volume metered to specific unit operations. Differences in equipment and processes will affect the volumes used per unit in the same or different plants. The breakdown of water uses may not be accurately known, even though the over-all use is recorded correctly. All these possibilities together are responsible for the great variation in reported use of water per unit of product.

A summary of published data on the quantities of water and steam required per unit of various products is given in Appendix I. These data are not complete, and a given plant may require for its product more or less water and steam than are recorded there. The data should be used only for comparing existing operations; it would be hazardous to use the data for estimating waste disposal requirements for a new plant.

Summary

This résumé of water uses in industry is necessarily concise. It should, however, lead to a true conception of the very important functions of water in industry. The industrial uses of water are legion and the demands on water vary over wide limits. Each industry has its individual problems, but a suitable supply of water requires careful planning to achieve economy. An essential tool in this planning is a plant water balance, completely prepared and continually maintained. Water losses, through lack of equipment maintenance and indifferent personnel, can be an appreciable item in operating costs.

CHAPTER II

Effects of Impurities on Water Uses

CHAPTER II—EFFECTS OF IMPURITIES ON WATER USES

Water is essential to practically all industrial operations, but it cannot always be used just as it is drawn from stream, lake, or well. The impurities in raw water can seriously affect both equipment and product if appropriate precautions are not taken. Cooling is by far the largest industrial use of water, and for this purpose its quality can generally be quite poor. Corrosion, erosion, and slime growths comprise the major problems where untreated water is used for cooling. Water quality becomes an important consideration where water comes in contact with products; sometimes only traces of certain substances will affect products adversely.

Absolutely pure water is a laboratory curiosity. As a result of its almost universal solvent action, all natural water contains various foreign substances. The most common impurities in water are dissolved gases, such as carbon dioxide and oxygen, and soluble mineral matter, including such metal ions as calcium, magnesium, iron, and sodium in chemical balance with such anions as sulfate, bicarbonate, carbonate, hydroxyl, chloride, and others. These substances are dissolved as water flows over or percolates through the ground. Water usually carries variable amounts of organic material, depending upon its source. Typical examples are drainage from peat bogs and cypress swamps, runoff from farms, and decomposition products from aquatic plants and animals killed by changes in weather or environment. Most organic matter persists over relatively short distances in streams because of the purifying capacity of stream organisms that utilize organic matter as food. Some organic substances, for example, humates and tannates, are very resistant to biochemical destruction, and color from them may persist almost indefinitely. In a strict sense these various impurities might be called "natural pollution," but the term pollution is generally reserved for contamination resulting from the activities of mankind.

INDUSTRIAL AND MUNICIPAL POLLUTION

The natural accumulation of impurities in water is a result of the chemico-physical constitution of our world, and very little can be done to prevent it. On the other hand, pollution from the discharge of municipal and industrial wastes can be controlled to protect the interests of downstream users.

Pollution of streams has been going on ever since the appearance of settled communities. People found it expedient to dispose of unwanted materials in natural watercourses because they were quickly carried away. Stream pollution did not become a problem in America until the Industrial Revolution and the introduction of water carriage of sewage began to exert their effects. Pollution steadily increased as the manufacturing industry expanded and communities grew larger.

There are many definitions of pollution, primarily because it is a relative term, but also because those who write the definitions often reflect their own special interests. In the simplest possible language, pollution exists when the con-

19

centration of contaminants interferes with a downstream use of water. The self-purification capacity of streams has been exceeded in some areas; these waters have become septic and unfit for any but the lowest kind of industrial use. It is obvious that there is gross pollution in such instances. However, as the degree of pollution becomes smaller, it becomes increasingly difficult to distinguish rationally between objectionable pollution and that which represents a reasonable demand upon the assimilative capacity of streams. Broadly speaking, conclusions about the effectiveness of current pollution abatement programs depend upon definitions of pollution. Thus there is no general agreement on whether pollution control is gaining upon, keeping pace with, or falling behind in the struggle to improve surface water quality.

In the past, organic and inorganic materials were considered to be the only substances responsible for pollution, but now heat must also be regarded as a significant pollutant. Temperature increases in some streams have seriously impaired their value for industrial cooling water, have decreased their capacity for assimilating wastes, and have destroyed aquatic life.

The Water-Supply Industry

Supplying water to meet the requirements of mankind is a large industry in itself. Waterworks range from simple pumping stations to elaborate purification plants with extensive storage for raw and treated water. Certain industries need process water of much higher purity than would be satisfactory for domestic use; this requires expensive purification equipment and expert operation.

Personal and domestic demands for water range from 15 to 50 gal per capita per day (gcd), averaging about 35. Commercial and industrial uses range from 10 to 55 gcd, averaging about 40. Public uses and actual water losses add another 10 to 55 gcd, for an average addition to total water use of about 30 gcd. Thus, the urban use of water in the United States averages 105 gcd. Water for fire protection must be added to this figure; a community of 1000 may have to provide as much as 1450 gcd, but the requirement will approximate 50 gcd for cities of 500,000 or more.

Use of water on farms has been increasing with the gain in acceptance of supplemental irrigation to insure crop growth. This use has become notable, even in the "humid" East. Irrigational use of water is almost completely consumptive; a small amount may percolate into ground-water aquifers and some may run off into streams. Farm water is ordinarily provided by the farmer himself from wells or storage reservoirs. Water for farm livestock is used in the range of 20 to 35 gal per milk cow per day, 8 to 15 gal per beef steer per day, 1 to 2 gal per sheep per day, and 4 to 10 gal per 100 chickens or turkeys per day.

Estimates of water use are often misunderstood because of the inference that water used is used up and gone forever. Actually, most of the water withdrawn by industries and municipalities is discharged for re-use downstream. Records of the city of Milwaukee show that an average of 19 per cent more water is discharged through the municipal sewer system than is pumped from Lake Michigan by the water works. This results from infiltration into the sewers and operation of private wells; it is likely that this situation is duplicated in many cities. Water-use is thus a usufruct; that is, it is the right to enjoy the advantage of using a thing belonging to another, so far as this is compatible with the substance of the thing not being destroyed or injured.

Consumptive use is defined by the American Water Works Association as "water used in connection with vegetative growth, food processing, or incidental to an industrial process which is discharged to the atmosphere or incorporated in the products of the process." Irrigation is the largest consumptive use of water because nearly all of it is lost to the atmosphere by evapotranspiration.

Circular 398 of the U.S. Geological Survey reports that the total withdrawal of water, excluding hydropower, was about 240,000 million gal per day in 1955. This included withdrawals for public, industrial, rural, and irrigational supplies. This figure represents gross, rather than net, withdrawal because part of the total volume was used more than once as the water flowed downstream.

Types of Pollution

A watercourse can be polluted either directly or indirectly, and the causes may be physical, chemical, biological, and radiological. Although these species of pollution can be identified, it would be an unusual case that could be classified wholly under one particular form. The only exception to this might be instances of pollution by radioactive substances.

Physical pollution can be caused by sludge deposits, flotant debris, scum and foam, turbidity, color, taste, odor, and temperature, to name some of the more common kinds.

Chemical pollution can take many forms. Increases in hardness, salinity, and acidity or basicity are commonly encountered. Discharge of toxic metal ions, such as chromium, copper, lead, mercury, silver, and zinc, is not uncommon, although their value often warrants recovery in waste treatment plants. Iron, manganese, and aluminum are present in most mine waters and various industrial wastes. Cyanides, fluorides, and odorous organic compounds may be present in waste water. In fact, every chemical manufactured or used in industry may be present to some extent in streams receiving industrial waste water.

Biological pollution from pathogenic or nuisance organisms can be quite serious. In most cases pathogens get into watercourses through sanitary sewers and sewage plant outfalls or diversion manholes, but they can be present in pharmaceutical and slaughterhouse wastes. Nuisance organisms, such as yeasts, molds, algae, plankton, and bacterial slimes, may be present in the waste waters themselves, or their proliferation may be induced by substances providing a source of food or synergistic reactions.

The advent and rapid expansion of uses for radioactive elements has generated an awareness of the possibility of pollution of water by radioactivity. The great potential danger of this kind of pollution was promptly recognized and the problem of waste disposal was studied in advance. As a result, no cases of serious pollution have occurred. This has rarely been the case with other types of wastes.

Effects of Pollution

Wherever treated or untreated wastes are to be discharged to a watercourse, it is both a municipal and an industrial responsibility to preserve good public relations. An aroused public often is an unreasonable public; irritation over pollution can result in demands for needlessly elaborate waste treatment. It is thus essential for industry to survey its position to determine how pollution problems can be satisfactorily handled. An industrial executive recently said: "The maintenance of good public relations is essential to the survival of the free enterprise system. A lack of responsibility in preventing damage or nuisance by pollution may provide one more irritation leading to adverse public opinion."

One of the anomalies of pollution control is the fact that frequently a public that demands treatment of industrial wastes that can be seen, smelled, or tasted will object to paying for sewage treatment to destroy bacteria that transmit disease.

The attitude of the courts toward water use was expressed in an opinion of of the U. S. Supreme Court in a case involving a dispute over Delaware River water: "A river is more than an amenity, it is a treasure. It offers a necessity of life that must be rationed among those who have power over it."

Although this statement was prompted by an interstate problem, its philosophy is also applicable to individual and corporate riparian rights and responsibilities. State supreme courts have upheld legislation governing water pollution abatement and have sustained punishment imposed on offenders.

Politicians have included pollution abatement programs in the platforms on which they campaigned for office. The popular appeal of such programs is evidenced by the fact that all political groups now embrace them. The days of laissez faire are over; pollutional matter can no longer be discharged without sufficient treatment to make it compatible with downstream uses.

Hygienic and esthetic considerations are closely allied to public relations and can seriously affect the well-being of a community. Anthrax, a disease transmitted by *Bacillus anthracis*, could come from improperly treated wastes from wool processing, tanning, meat packing, or manufacture of pharmaceuticals. Brucellosis or undulant fever is caused by *Brucella melitensis* or *B. abortus*, and bovine tuberculosis by *Bacillus tuberculosis*; these organisms can come from

tanning, meat-packing, and related wastes. Pathogens may be present in wastes from pharmaceutical production of toxins, antitoxins, and serums, and there is always the danger of infection from pollution by untreated sewage.

Although disease-causing organisms are important factors in public hygiene, other material may be significant. The introduction and wide acceptance of many synthetic organic chemicals may cause unidentified hygienic effects. Present knowledge of these compounds indicates that they are not physiologically dangerous in the concentrations found in streams, but the situation could change in the future. Levels of radioactivity now considered safe for human exposure fall in this category.

Impurities in natural water affect recreational uses. Water for bathing should be of the same relative quality as drinking water. Boating does not require water of such high quality, but various kinds of pollution increase the cost of maintaining boats and detract from the pleasure of being on the water. Hunting and fishing may be affected by impurities in water. The flavor of the flesh of fish and animals can be spoiled by the presence of such substances as phenols, hydrocarbon oils, and sulfides in the water they use. Gross pollution has been responsible for destruction of fish and wildlife in some areas.

While impurities may affect the recreational use of streams, of far greater importance is their effect on commercial fishing and trapping; in these instances the actual livelihood of a portion of the population is impaired. Commercial transportation is another industry that can be adversely affected by heavy pollution. The cost of maintaining boats and barges increases, and immersed concrete structures may be damaged.

In addition to the active forms of aquatic recreation, clean streams perform the esthetic function of providing for rest and relaxation in scenic surroundings. This use of watercourse is not usually injured by the presence of natural contaminants, but it can be seriously affected by industrial wastes, some of which interfere with the aquatic balance of a stream. This imbalance may cause unsightliness from decaying plants and animals which, in turn, usually give rise to unpleasant odors.

Impurities in water used by the power industry, the nation's highest-rate water user, can be disastrous when they reach a certain level. The high rate of use makes it impossible to treat water used for once-through cooling. Consequently, excessive amounts of such things as chlorides, ammonia, acidity, and organic matter increase the rate of corrosion of cooling systems. In addition to corrosion, the high degree of industrial use of some streams raises their temperature so much that downstream power plants have to use progressively larger volumes of water every year to achieve the same net cooling.

The economics of water supply is a variable that is dependent on the ultimate water use. The relative concentration of impurities that must be removed from raw water is an important economic factor. The cost of providing water with a low concentration of dissolved solids rises as the concentration of such material increases. But treatment costs are also dependent on the type of impurity to be removed. For example, chlorides and sulfates are more costly to remove than similar concentrations of hardness or suspended solids.

Quality Criteria

The definition of acceptable water quality is a major economic variable in domestic and industrial water supply. The quality of domestic supplies is governed by the "Drinking Water Standards" of the U.S. Public Health Service. A water that meets these standards will be potable, but it may be quite unsatisfactory for those industrial uses that need water of exceptionally high or special quality. The differences in quality criteria for various industrial uses are so pronounced that it is possible only to establish general criteria for each specific type of industry. Quality requirements often vary from plant to plant within a given industry. In addition, water for

TABLE I.—DRINKING WATER STANDARDS (1946).

Constituent	ppm
Maximum permissible limits for specific constituents:	
Lead	0.1
Fluorine	1.5
Arsenic	0.05
Selenium	0.05
Hexavalent chromium	0.05
Suggested limits for specific constituents:	
Copper	3.0
Zinc	15.0
Iron and manganese	0.3
Chloride	250
Sulfate	250
Phenolic compounds, as phenol	0.001
Total solids	500[a]
Magnesium	125

[a] Total solids may be as high as 1000 ppm if water of lower mineral content is not available.

agriculture often must be of a still different quality.

Water quality is thus a relative term that depends upon desired uses. It is generally accepted that a domestic water supply should be free of turbidity and color, pleasant to taste, of reasonable temperature, neither corrosive nor scale-forming, free of minerals that might cause physiological disturbances, and free from pathogens. The U.S. Public Health Service established its "Drinking Water Standards" to meet these requirements. The limits for specific mineral constituents are given in Table I.

Quality criteria for industrial water

TABLE II.—WATER QUALITY TOLERANCES FOR INDUSTRIAL APPLICATIONS.

Industry	General[a]	Na2SO4 to Na2SO3 Ratio	CaSO4, ppm	OH, ppm	HCO3, ppm	CO3, ppm	F, ppm	Cu, ppm	SiO2, ppm	Al2O3, ppm	Fe + Mn, ppm	Mn, ppm	Fe, ppm	Ca, ppm	Total Solids, ppm	pH	Alkalinity, ppm	Hardness, ppm	Odor	Dissolved Oxygen, ml per liter	Color + O2 Consumed, ppm	Color, ppm	Turbidity, ppm
Air conditioning[b]	A, B										0.5	0.5	0.5					[c]					10
Baking	C										0.2	0.2	0.2									10	
Boiler feed:																							
0 to 150 psi		1 to 1		50	50	200			40	5					3000 to 1000	8.0+		75		2	100	80	20
150 to 250 psi		2 to 1		40	30	100			20	0.5					2500 to 500	8.5+		40		0.2	50	40	10
250 psi and over		3 to 1		30	5	40			5	0.05					1500 to 100	9.0+		8		0	10	5	5
Brewing:[d]																							
Light	C, D		100 to 200				1				0.1	0.1	0.1	100 to 200	500	6.5 to 7.0	75		low				10
Dark	C, D		200 to 500								0.1	0.1	0.1	200 to 500	1000	7.0	150		low				10
Canning:																							
Legumes	C										0.2	0.2	0.2					25 to 75	low				10
General	C										0.2	0.2	0.2						low				10
Carbonated beverages[e]	C										0.3	0.2	0.2		850	f	50	250	0		10	10	2
Confectionery											0.5	0.2	0.2		100				low			10	
Cooling[g]	A, B						1	0.2	10		0.5	0.5	0.5					50	low				50
Food, general	C										0.2	0.2	0.2				30 to 50		low				10
Ice (raw water)[h]	C										0.2	0.2	0.2		300							5	1 to 5
Laundering											0.2	0.2	0.2					50					
Plastics, clear, uncolored											0.02	0.02	0.02		200							2	2
Paper and pulp:[i]																							
Groundwood	A										1.0	0.5	1.0					180				20	50
Kraft pulp											0.2	0.1	0.2		300			100				15	25
Soda and sulfite											0.1	0.05	0.1		200			100				10	15
Light paper, HL grade	B										0.1	0.1	0.1		200			50				5	5

24

Rayon (viscose) pulp:																
Production	5	5	...	...	...	100	...	...	...	0.05	0.03	0.05	8.0	...	25	...	5
Manufacture	0.3	...	...	...	...	...	...	...	...	0.0	0.0	0.0	...	...	...	...
Tanning[j]	20	10 to 100	...	...	50 to 135	...	50 135	7.8 to 8.3 / 8.0	...	0.2	0.2	0.2	...	...	...	...
Textiles:																
General	5	20	...	...	20	...	20	...	...	0.25	0.25	...	...	...	...	...
Dyeing[k]	5	5 to 20	...	...	20	...	20	...	...	0.25	0.25	0.25	...	...	...	...
Wool scouring[l]	...	20 70	...	low	20	...	20	...	...	1.0	1.0	1.0	...	...	...	...
Cotton bandage[l]	5	5	...	...	20	...	20	...	...	0.2	0.2	0.2	...	...	...	...

[a] A, No corrosiveness; B, no slime formation; C, conformance to federal drinking water standards necessary; D, NaCl, 275 ppm.

[b] Waters with algae and hydrogen sulfide odors are most unsuitable for air conditioning.

[c] Some hardness desirable.

[d] Water for distilling must meet the same general requirements as for brewing (gin and spirits mashing water of light-beer quality; whiskey mashing water of dark-beer quality).

[e] Clear, odorless, sterile water for syrup and carbonization. Water consistent in character. Most high quality filtered municipal water not satisfactory for beverages.

[f] Hard candy requires pH of 7.0 or greater, as low value favors inversion of sucrose, causing sticky product.

[g] Control of corrosiveness is necessary as is also control of organisms, such as sulfur and iron bacteria, which tend to form slimes.

[h] $Ca(HCO_3)_2$ particularly troublesome. $Mg(HCO_3)_2$ tends to greenish color. CO_2 assists to prevent cracking. Sulfates and chlorides of Ca, Mg, Na should each be less than 300 ppm (white butts).

[i] Uniformity of composition and temperature desirable. Iron objectionable since cellulose absorbs iron from dilute solutions. Manganese very objectionable, clogs pipelines and is oxidized to permanganates by chlorine, causing reddish color.

[j] Excessive iron, manganese or turbidity creates spots and discoloration in tanning of hides and leather goods.

[k] Constant composition; residual alumina 0.5 ppm.

[l] Calcium, magnesium, iron, manganese, suspended matter, and soluble organic matter may be objectionable.

cannot be generalized in this manner because of specific requirements for particular uses. However, water meeting the standards for drinking water would be highly desirable for most industrial uses.

The standards for drinking water were last revised in 1946. These standards have been widely criticized; some have complained that the limits are too low, others that they are too high. The standards are currently in process of revision by the Public Health Service with the assistance of a committee of experts.

The limits given in Table I are supplemented below with a brief résumé of the physiological effects of the more common substances found in natural water.

Aluminum.—Originally thought to be harmful, but now known to be harmless at normal solubility concentrations. There is thus no necessity for a limit on it.

Boron.—Concentrations above 30 ppm may interfere with digestion of food.

Cadmium.—Reported to be toxic where concentrations exceed 13 ppm in water.

Nitrates.—High nitrates are usually associated with pollution of water with sewage, but nitrates can also come from natural sources. Normally up to 40 ppm (as NO_3) can be tolerated without ill effect, but methemoglobinemia (of which "blue babies" is one example) has occurred at concentrations above 44 ppm.

Phosphates.—No definite physiological effects have been traced to phosphates in water.

Sulfates.—High concentrations have a laxative effect.

Sodium.—This element is important only to persons with high blood pressure or those on a low-sodium diet. In such cases 200 ppm of sodium is considered to be the maximum permissible limit.

Tin.—No physiological effects are known.

Nickel.—No physiological effects in concentrations normally found.

The Public Health Service standards for drinking water primarily govern physiological factors, but they also serve to control palatability to some extent. Although various factors can affect palatability, there are frequent instances in which the nature of the offending substance is peculiar to specific circumstances. Consequently, only local conditions can be used to define the limiting concentrations of such substances.

Corrosion and scale formation by water often cause difficulties in industry. Corrosion from oxygen dissolved in water is often severe; sodium sulfite is sometimes added to water to overcome this effect. Scale formation is not likely to be troublesome in low-temperature uses if the total alkalinity does not exceed 400 ppm and the pH is in the range of 8.0 to 9.6. The alkalinity should not exceed 160 ppm for a pH of 10.6. Scale is formed by substances other than carbonates—silicates, for example—and as the temperature of the water increases such material can cause acute problems, especially in steam power plants.

Quality criteria for public water supply are directed primarily toward palatability and physiological effects, but these factors are normally of little concern in an industrial supply. A major exception is the food processing industry. The lack of interest by industry in the physiological effects of certain impurities in water does not preclude a sharp interest in substances that affect particular processes. In fact, it has been this interest that has provided detailed knowledge of methods for controlling the effects of many specific substances.

Water quality criteria for a number of industries are given in Table II. This table illustrates the great diversity of quality requirements and the number of ions of interest to industry. The figures in Table II are general averages and they cannot be applied to individual cases without regard for local conditions.

Agriculture is an industry that uses a very large amount of water. Quality criteria for agricultural water differ from those for industrial supplies, and it is convenient to classify them separately.

The major use of water in agriculture is for irrigation and livestock, of which the former is by far the greater. Approximately 124 billion gallons was used daily for irrigation in 1957; this was roughly equal to industrial use. The quality of irrigation water is governed by four major characteristics: (1) total soluble salt concentration; (2) sodium concentration, and the ratio of sodium to the total calcium and magnesium ion concentration; (3) bicarbonate concentration; and (4) toxic concentrations of minor elements.

The concentration of dissolved salts may range from 70 to 3500 ppm. With the higher salt concentrations, there must be careful control of the rate of deposition of salts to the rate of leaching by runoff to avoid a buildup of salts that would ruin the vegetative property of the soil. This is a particularly acute problem in some western areas where waters have a low total salt content but a high bicarbonate concentration. In such cases, accumulations of sodium in the soil are converted to sodium carbonate, which raises the pH and makes crop growth difficult. Crops having a high salt tolerance are beets, kale, asparagus, spinach, potatoes, and eggplant. Crops with a low tolerance include radishes, celery, grean beans, and vine crops. Among the ions most likely to cause crop damage are sodium, chloride, bicarbonate, and sulfate. In isolated cases, such ions as selenium, lithium, and fluoride may cause crop damage. Even low concentrations may have a bad effect on livestock that feed on the vegetation. Boron is toxic to many agricultural products. Handbook 60, of the U.S. Department of Agriculture, notes that concentrations of boron below 0.7 ppm are considered safe; from 0.7 to 1.5 ppm marginal; and above 1.5 ppm unsafe. Citrus fruits of all kinds, English walnuts,

pecans, apples, pears, and plums are listed as sensitive to boron. Concentrations above 1.5 ppm will cause defoliation of broccoli, cabbage, and cauliflower.

The quality of water consumed by livestock should in general be equivalent to that of domestic water. Since livestock is not subject to most of the pathogenic diseases of mankind, it is not essential that bacterial quality be carefully controlled. Gross contamination by domestic sewage is, however, to be avoided. There is a possibility that virus infections not measured by bacterial counts may be transmitted to animals by water. The mineral content of water for livestock is subject to much the same limitations as for domestic water, but limiting concentrations of such ions as chromium, lead, zinc, and cyanide must be scaled up or down according to the relative body weights of the animals.

Summary

This chapter has outlined the effects of various impurities on water use. These effects are quite diverse, depending upon specific uses.

The uncontrolled discharge of wastes to a watercourse may have deleterious effects on downstream users, but the controlled use of streams for waste disposal should not be denied to industry. The proper use of the capacity of streams for self-purification can provide many industries with an economical method of waste disposal. Balancing the equities between those who discharge wastes to streams and those who use them for water supplies requires an intimate knowledge of individual problems. In general, it must be emphasized that pollution which has a deleterious effect on a watercourse is not only a source of irritation to people and industry, but it also lowers the value of the area as a site for future industrial expansion.

CHAPTER III

Self-Purification of Streams

45-43

CHAPTER III—SELF-PURIFICATION OF STREAMS

Water is the most plentiful liquid on earth. It is a requirement for all life, whether it is used in metabolic processes, as a solvent of minerals, or in the disposal of waste. Indeed, it is difficult to name a natural phenomenon in which water, in one form or another, has not had a role.

Nature has provided for the conservation of this abundant and valuable liquid by endowing it with a considerable capacity to rid itself of foreign substances. This process, known as self-purification, is an inherent property of water. The water may be moving in streams or be relatively static as in lakes and ponds, but the natural processes of purification are similar. Advantage is taken of this intrinsic ability of water to purify itself by using it as a final stage in the treatment of sewage and industrial wastes.

Streams polluted by domestic wastes (those derived from human populations) or industrial wastes (the liquid wastes of wet-process industries and acid mine drainage) may be rendered stable by self-purification. In most instances, such polluted water becomes relatively innocuous biologically and again serves nature in one role or another. This purification is accomplished by a combination of physical, chemical, and biological forces. The extent to which each force operates is dependent upon the type of contamination. Physical forces dispose of suspended solids; chemical forces cause reactions which render unstable wastes innocuous; and biological forces contribute to the stability of the stream by enhancing both physical and chemical phenomena. The biological forces are the most active, and the most important, in the equilibration of a stream.

ESTABLISHMENT OF A DYNAMIC EQUILIBRIUM

Water, as vapor, is present in the air in amounts that we express as relative humidity. Condensation of this vapor causes the formation of droplets of water which are pure until they fall to the earth as rain, hail, or snow.

The atmosphere contains a number of pollutants, especially in industrial areas. Such pollutants may be in either the gaseous or the solid state. Some solids, such as dusts, are laden with bacteria, yeasts, and molds. In addition, the air contains the spores of microorganisms which exist in the atmosphere without benefit of being attached to solid particles. Some bacteria and viruses, also, occur in the atmosphere as free-floating agents. Thus the atmosphere possesses a distinct and variable microbiologic flora.

The microflora of the atmosphere provides one of the sources of living matter constituting a normal stream biota. When the water of the atmosphere falls to the earth, the microorganisms of the air are washed out and settle upon the ground. Many of these microorganisms become entrapped in the soil, while others are carried directly into streams with rainfall runoff. In addition, the water picks up microorganisms that are indigenous to the soil, which nearly everywhere is teeming with microscopic forms of life. In this manner, water accumulates a wide variety of microorganisms by the time it flows as a natural stream.

31

After water has formed one of the surface streams of the earth, a very characteristic microbiologic flora is established. The stream comes to equilibrium with the environment, or becomes a part of the area through which it runs. The stream reflects, by changes in its microbiota, changes in the waters it receives. If such waters contain domestic or industrial wastes, the stream will endeavor to react to rid itself of these unnatural substances. This ability of the stream biota to change in order to re-establish the contaminated stream to its original state of purity may be termed "dynamic equilibrium." The forces of self-purification—physical, chemical, and especially biological—are constantly changing to maintain the purity of water.

Normal Stream Life—The Balanced Aquarium:

Nature always attempts to provide healthy, or clean, streams. This is accomplished by the development of well-balanced flora and fauna, both in the water and on the bed of a stream. This may very well be compared to the conditions existing in a balanced aquarium.

The many forms of aquatic life, from the smallest bacteria to the largest fishes, are distributed in a stream in accordance with the environment. The environment influences both the number and the species present in any one portion of a stream. By creating such a balance, nature provides for each species of aquatic life, without an overabundance of any one form.

Each type of both plant and animal life is dependent upon the existence of other species within the same realm. For example, the presence of organic matter or other oxidizable compounds is required for bacterial growth. Protozoa depend upon such bacteria, as well as algae, for continuation of life. The rotifera and crustaceae utilize all of these microscopic forms as a source of food, while in turn, the large aquatic plants and animals require certain forms of the smaller members of the stream biota for their existence. Thus nature provides for an interdependence and balance of life forms in a stream.

General Characteristics of Polluted Streams:

A balance of biological forms is normal for all streams. Though various species of plant and animal life may predominate in each stream, no two streams are identical. Clean, pure streams, however, have certain characteristics in common. One property of such a stream is its ability to dispose of a reasonable amount of pollution. This may be accomplished without an appreciable disturbance of the normal biota. If a stream receives an unusually large amount of waste, the biota will change in an attempt to stabilize such pollutants. However, if the quantity of such foreign materials exceeds the capacity of the stream biota to render them innocuous, the aquatic life may be completely destroyed. In such cases, the stream becomes noisome and is little more than an unsightly drainage ditch.

RECOVERY OF POLLUTED STREAMS

Forces of Self-Purification:

Fortunately, the forces of self-purification usually prevent such complete destruction of one of mankind's greatest assets. These forces, closely related and mutually dependent, are physical, chemical, and biological in nature.

The physical forces include the action of gravity, light, aeration, dilution, and turnover. By gravity, the heavier suspended impurities are removed by sedimentation of individual particles. Finely divided suspended solids and colloidal matter settle out of the water as aggregates or coagulated masses. Photosynthesis causes the removal of carbon dioxide and increases the concentration of dissolved oxygen. Color is removed from water by the bleaching action of sunlight and by adsorption on colloids. Turbulence in a stream, as by flowing over a rocky bottom, causes aeration which adds oxygen to the water by adsorption from the atmosphere. Carbon dioxide and gases of decomposition escape to the atmosphere by the same phenomenon. Influents consisting of water from tributaries, domestic sewage, and industrial wastes are diluted by the receiving stream. Such dilution assists in the rapid recovery of a stream. The turnover of pools in a stream, similar to that which occurs in lakes, is another physical factor which aids stream recovery.

The chemical forces of stream self-purification include oxidation, reduction, neutralization, and coagulation. Oxidations render suspended and dissolved organic matter harmless, the products generally being mineral matter and gases. Incompletely oxidized mineral matter may be oxidized to completion, or hydrolyzed and deposited, by precipitation, on the bed of a stream. Likewise, chemical reductions may result in the liquefaction or gasification of organic matter in the process of anaerobic decomposition. Mineral matter may be put into solution by such reductions. Ground or stream water containing dissolved carbon dioxide, in contact with carbonate rocks, dissolves calcium and magnesium carbonates as their bicarbonates. This contributes alkalinity to the water, serving either as a pH buffer or as an actual neutralizing agent for organic or mineral acids. A stream is usually dependent on entering water of recent subsurface origin for maintenance of its alkaline reserve. These neutralizations tend to maintain optimum conditions for the biochemical

reactions of stream purification. Coagulation causes the precipitation and deposition of dissolved and colloidal substances on the stream bed. The removal of such materials permits other forces of stream purification to become more active.

The biological forces are not only the most important but are the most active forces; they are closely associated with the food requirements of the microbiota present.

Bacteria known as heterotrophs can cause the degradation of practically any organic substance. Many groups of such bacteria have relatively specific nutritional requirements, and their demands for sources of food material greatly assist in the purification of a stream. Fats, carbohydrates, and proteins are all converted by aerobic or anaerobic processes to products of a simpler chemical nature. Often several groups of bacteria cooperate to degrade such compounds in a series of interdependent steps.

Other bacteria, known as autotrophs, live in inorganic environments and complete their life cycle without the benefit of preformed organic matter. The sole sources of carbon for such microorganisms are carbon dioxide, carbon monoxide, or carbon suboxide. Minerals essential for the continuation of life are obtained from inorganic salts. The autotrophs are divided into groups that have specific nutritional requirements. Some live by oxidizing elemental sulfur, sulfides, thiosulfate, or tetrathionate. Others reduce sulfates to sulfide or to elemental sulfur. Nitrifying bacteria convert ammonia to nitrate. Iron organisms oxidize ferrous iron to the ferric state. Other groups of autotrophs are capable of oxidizing phenols and cyanides. In fact, as our knowledge of autotrophism grows, it is realized that there are few, if any, unstable inorganic compounds that cannot be converted to stable products by such microorganisms.

As in other reactions caused by bacteria, this conversion often proceeds through a series of individual reactions resulting in a specific product, which in turn is utilized by another group of microorganisms. An example of this is the oxidation of ammonia to nitrate, where *Nitrosomonas* oxidizes ammonia to nitrite, and *Nitrobacter* oxidizes the nitrite to nitrate. The autotrophic bacteria thus can convert many unstable compounds to stable material which can be utilized by higher forms of life.

The action of bacteria-destroying agents, known as bacteriophages, has a very important role in ridding a stream of pathogenic microorganisms. Such bacteriolytic viruses are present in sewage and in the intestinal tract of man and animals. They specifically destroy, by lysis, certain pathogenic bacteria, especially the etiologic agents of the typhoids and dysenteries. Also, the pus-forming bacteria, staphylococci and streptococci, are rapidly destroyed under favorable conditions. Present knowledge does not indicate that bacteriophages have any effect upon the microorganisms normally occurring in streams.

The algae utilize carbon dioxide, an end product of bacterial decomposition, and liberate oxygen. This aids in the reaeration of streams and induces rapid stream recovery. In addition, certain inorganic and nitrogenous substances, also occurring as the result of bacterial activity, are converted to cellular material. The algae then serve as a source of food for many of the higher forms of aquatic life.

The protozoa live on organic and nitrogenous matter. Many species prey upon bacteria, while other species find that the algae provide all of the nutrients necessary for their life processes. Some protozoa contain chlorophyll, and are similar to the algae.

The rotifera, the next higher form of aquatic life, prey upon the protozoa and consume algae. Many are saprophytic organisms and feed upon decaying organic material. This group serves as a source of food for other members of the stream biota.

The crustaceae, consisting of aquatic arthropods, feed upon many of the lower forms of life, especially the algae and smaller aquatic plants. Such animals serve to maintain a balance between the lower and higher forms in the stream biota.

Rooted forms of aquatic plants utilize the organic and mineral matter in bottom deposits. Also, such forms assist in the aeration of the stream by utilizing carbon dioxide and liberating oxygen. Aquatic plants create excellent habitats for fish and other forms of stream life.

Large aquatic animals burrow in mud deposits in search of food. The bottom sediments are disturbed and thus made more satisfactory for growth of smaller organisms. One aquatic animal will survive by devouring another. By such carnivorousness, the animal life of a stream is kept in balance.

Living things in streams are dependent upon many variables. If some extraneous factor causes an unusual increase in population of a particular group of the flora or fauna, another portion of the biota will arise to diminish this abnormality. The ability of the forces of self-purification to return a stream to its normal condition, or to adjust itself to a new condition, represents a real dynamic equilibrium.

Zones of Pollution and Self-Purification:

A whole series of events occur when pollutants, such as domestic and industrial wastes, are discharged into a stream. These changes take place along the course of the stream, usually in zones that are not sharply divided but that gradually blend into one another. Such areas shift with meteorological and hydrographic conditions. Despite this variability, classical zones of differentiation have been established that are of interest in the natural purification of streams.

The first area after the entrance of a pollutant is the zone of degradation. If the pollution is a domestic or an organic industrial waste, the water becomes dark and turbid. Sunlight is shut out. Coagulation may occur and suspended matter settles to the bottom. A deposit of sludge is formed and decomposition starts. The bacterial flora increases greatly and reduces the supply of dissolved oxygen. There is an increase in carbon dioxide. Fish may be very active, especially if the waste will serve as food. If the pollutant is an inorganic industrial waste, its toxicity might inhibit most of the aquatic life. When this occurs, dilution must take place before any stream can begin to recover. The water flora typical of this zone appears as decomposition progresses. Specific groups of bacteria will predominate, depending upon the type of waste. Algae may develop; if so, they will consume carbon dioxide, and help to replenish the supply of oxygen. The presence or absence of odors will depend upon the efficiency of reaeration. The growth of green plants is inhibited by the color and turbidity of the water, which reduce photosynthetic activity. The number of microorganisms, other than bacteria, decreases because of unfavorable conditions.

Eventually the zone of degradation gives way to a zone of active decomposition. Here, the dissolved oxygen is nearly depleted and aerobic microorganisms gradually disappear. An anaerobic condition may result, and putrefaction will occur, with accompanying foul odors. Bacteria will continue to flourish, anaerobic microorganisms taking up the work of the aerobes as the supply of dissolved oxygen is entirely used up. But as soon as the stream becomes partially reaerated, the aerobes will again predominate. The growth of algae will rid the stream of excess carbon dioxide and help to reestablish a favorable oxygen balance. Large aquatic plants and animals will be present only in areas of favorable oxygen supply.

Following this zone is the area of recovery and clean water. The water gradually becomes clear, and the bottom deposits do not evolve offensive odors. The dissolved oxygen increases probably to saturation. There is enough carbon dioxide to supply a normal aquatic flora. Bacteria decrease in number as the predatory microorganisms develop. Various protozoa, rotifera, and crustaceae are present. Algae become established, and the larger aquatic plants reappear. The more tolerant fish are present, until the zone of clean water is reached. The clean water is characterized by the normal flora and fauna previously discussed.

In natural streams, there is a considerable overlapping of these zones. Some zones are completely eliminated. At times, certain zones may cover extensive portions of a stream. The whole cycle of self-purification is adaptable to innumerable conditions. The process may be retarded, interrupted, or accelerated by the entrance of new waste materials or tributary waters. Each stream operates under conditions peculiar to it alone.

EFFECT OF POLLUTION ON DYNAMIC EQUILIBRIUM

The dynamic equilibrium, or the capacity of a stream to recover after receiving pollutants, is affected by domestic and industrial wastes. Streams receiving domestic wastes such as sewage undergo the classical cycle of zonal self-purification. The same is true, in most instances, for organic industrial wastes.

A notable exception, of course, is organic chemical wastes. Such wastes may be extremely toxic and inhibit, or prevent, the operation of stream purification processes. The same is true of many inorganic wastes.

Acid mine drainage is a pollutant that is indigenous to bituminous coal regions. It is characterized by being highly acidic and containing large concentrations of ferrous iron. It is formed by the oxidation of sulfuritic materials (represented by the formula FeS_2) of both operating and abandoned bituminous coal mines. A chemosynthetic autotrophic bacterium (*Ferrobacillus ferrooxidans*) enhances the reaction several fold where the pH of the water is in the range 2.8 to 3.5. Dissolved oxygen is utilized by these ferruginous effluents through the oxidation of ferrous iron to the ferric state. Owing to the presence of *Ferrobacillus ferrooxidans*, which increases the oxidation rate, the area in which dissolved oxygen is being consumed is kept to the shortest possible stream distance. After the deposition of iron, as basic ferric sulfates and hydrates, the stream makes a rapid recovery and supports most of the normal forms of aquatic life.

IMPORTANCE OF A WELL–ADJUSTED STREAM

From the public health aspect alone, it is essential to have well-adjusted streams. Such a stream, owing to its dynamic capacity to respond to the entrance of foreign materials, will quickly rid itself of pollutants. It will remain a clean, healthy stream, and will be a distinct asset to the community. But the capacity of the stream to respond to pollutants can never be exceeded without paying the penalty of retarding the self-purification process.

A normal stream, through its inherent capacity for purification, will be free of disease-producing bacteria, and will not be toxic for any normal aquatic flora or fauna. In addition, the recreational benefits derived from healthy streams will be well worth the care and effort required for their maintenance.

WATER QUALITY CRITERIA

It is difficult to establish exact criteria for the measurement of water quality. There is a wide variation in the mineral content of natural waters. Water from an unpolluted well in the Corn Belt, pumped into an Appalachian stream, would constitute a contaminant in the minds of most persons familiar only with Appalachian ground water. Water entirely suitable for human consumption may require treatment for use as boiler feedwater. Essential industries may produce critical wastes. The use of non-man-contaminated natural water may need to be hedged about with as many restrictions as those applying to sanitary or industrial waste.

Biological reactions provide one of the most important means for stream purification. A water treatment plant or a waste disposal plant, sewage or industrial, requires machinery and control devices, trained operators, and waste land for the disposal of residues. A stream, given half a chance, performs the function of these man-built plants with no equipment or supervision whatever. All that is required is some intelligence in controlling the concentration and rate of addition of domestic or industrial effluents to a stream.

CHAPTER IV

Composition and Classification of Industrial Water and Water-Formed Deposits

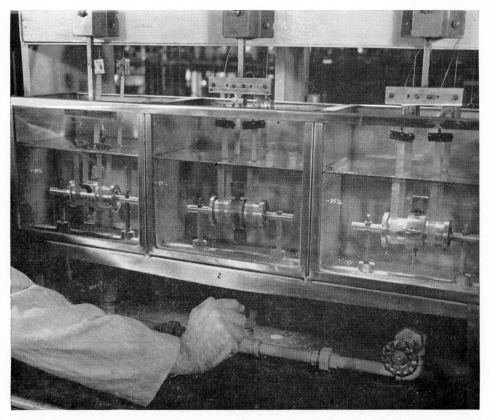

15-45

CHAPTER IV—COMPOSITION AND CLASSIFICATION OF INDUSTRIAL WATER AND WATER-FORMED DEPOSITS

A discussion of the composition of industrial water and water-formed deposits must include the terms used by different industries, methods of reporting results of analyses, methods of interpreting these analyses, and systems for converting results of analyses into other terms that may be better understood by the users of water. In addition, the composition of water must be classified so that a particular user can choose the best supply for his purpose or forecast what difficulties might arise from the use of the water available. A user should know the general composition of his water and how it changes with the seasons. If deposits occur, he should be able to identify or classify the type of deposit formed so that he can trace its source and decide upon remedies.

The range of composition of industrial water and of the deposits formed by these waters varies tremendously. Water is relatively pure when formed in clouds, but it absorbs gases from the air, such as oxygen and carbon dioxide, during its fall as rain. Upon reaching the earth, water dissolves materials with which it comes in contact; these depend upon the composition of the soil or rocks in the locality. Water also becomes polluted with industrial wastes and sewage from factories and cities. Water flowing in surface or underground streams continues to pick up substances. Accumulations of insoluble material derived from water, or formed by the reaction of water with surfaces in contact with it, are called water-formed deposits.

It is often the duty of the chemist to analyze water intended for use and, from this analysis, to attempt to forecast what deposits or other undesirable conditions it might cause.

INDUSTRIAL WATER

REPORTING RESULTS OF ANALYSIS OF INDUSTRIAL WATER

In water analysis, the dissolved constituents, consisting principally of ionic components, are determined to provide information about the chemical characteristics of a specific water. These ionic components carry one or more positive or negative electric charges and are referred to as cations or anions, respectively.

A water analysis also includes determination of undissociated materials such as dissolved gases, suspended solids, and organic substances.

Methods for analysis and for reporting results of analysis are given in Part II of this Manual and in the 1966 Book of ASTM Standards, Part 23. Method D 596[1] gives definitions of the terms used, how various constituents should be reported, what information is necessary for a complete report, and the accuracy to be expected. Method D 596 is not the only procedure that can be used, but it describes the best procedure so far devised for reporting analyses of industrial water. Since an incomplete re-

---

[1] Appears in this publication.

45-44

port can be misleading, it is advisable to report as nearly as possible in accordance with the procedure given.

The ASTM standards cover only the reporting of the analysis and make no attempt to interpret the results. Most dissolved solids in water are in true solution, that is, in ionic form, and chemical analysis determines the amounts of such substances in terms of cations and anions. For example, sodium chloride (common salt) dissociates in water to form sodium ions (cations) and chloride ions (anions) as follows:

$$NaCl \rightarrow Na^+ + Cl^-$$

Similarly, calcium sulfate (gypsum) dissociates:

$$CaSO_4 \rightarrow Ca^{++} + SO_4^{--}$$

Each ion bears either a plus or minus electrical charge that is numerically equal to its valence. Thus, sodium and chloride ions, each having a valence of 1, carry a charge of $+1$ and -1, respectively, whereas calcium and sulfate, each having a valence of 2, carry a charge of $+2$ and -2 respectively.

It is incorrect to state that ions in true solution are combined, and any analysis expressed in terms of salts (compounds) is only conjecture. Such combinations are commonly referred to as probable combinations or hypothetical combinations. These terms will be described below.

Units of Expression:

Water analyses have been expressed in many units. Until about two decades ago, grains per gallon was the unit commonly used by many industrial and municipal laboratories in the United States to express concentrations of substances dissolved in water. The unit parts per million (ppm) is now the most widely used term for this purpose. It is a convenient unit numerically and it is readily understood. A part per million is one part

by weight of a dissolved substance in one million parts by weight of water.

Parts per million is satisfactory for expression of concentrations up to about 7000 ppm. For concentrations in excess of 7000, a correction factor must be applied to compensate for the effect of increasing specific gravity.

Another unit that is commonly used is milligrams per liter. A milligram per liter is 1 mg (weight) of dissolved substance in 1 liter (volume) of water. This unit has the advantage that values reported are correct no matter what concentrations are involved. No correction factor need be applied for high concentrations. In many respects this unit is preferable to parts per million but its use is restricted to the metric system. Also, parts per million is so widely accepted by both industry and governmental agencies that it does not appear appropriate to make any change at this time.

In order to evaluate an analysis of water and also to compare analyses of different waters, it is convenient to convert concentrations of cations and anions from parts per million to equivalents per million (epm). An equivalent per million is one unit chemical equivalent weight of dissolved substance in one million unit weights of water solution. Equivalents per million are calculated by dividing the parts per million determined in analysis by the combining weight of the ion in question.

The combining weight of an ion is its molecular weight divided by its valence. For example, to convert 10 ppm of Ca^{++} to epm, divide by the combining weight of calcium (20.04) and obtain 0.499 epm of Ca^{++}. This amount, 0.499 epm, is equivalent to or will combine with 0.499 epm of any anion. Thus, by converting all concentrations from ppm to epm, the resulting values are chemically equivalent.

Evaluation of the accuracy and reliability of a water analysis is simplified by comparison of the total cations and total anions in equivalents per million, determined in the analysis. Inasmuch as be equal within the limits of the accuracy of the methods used. If these sums are not essentially equal, then a recheck of the determinations is indicated.

TABLE I.—ANALYSES OF TYPICAL SURFACE AND GROUND WATERS
IN THE UNITED STATES.

From U. S. Geological Survey Water-Supply Papers 1251, 1299, and 1300 (parts per million).

Analysis Number[a]	1	2	3	4	5—South End Well No. 7	6—Well No. 33	7—Well No. 14	8—Well No. 2 Bradley
Date of collection	6/4/1952	6/1951	...	...	2/11/1952	5/20/1950	6/13/1951	1/9/1946
Silica (SiO_2)	2.5	0.4	...	8.0	16	23	34	12
Iron (Fe)	0.03	0.05	...	...	0.0	...	...	2.1
Calcium (Ca)	5.3	27	59	79	7.2	70	26	72
Magnesium (Mg)	1.7	7	16	28	2.5	24	10	33
Sodium (Na)	1.4	} 3[b]	47	99	147	} 12[b]	138	} 358[b]
Potassium (K)	0.6		...	4	0.4		1.6	
Carbonate (CO_3)	0	1	0	4	0	...	0	...
Bicarbonate (HCO_3)	10	99	189	137	328	179	170	293
Sulfate (SO_4)	11	13	144	290	2.6	135	70	560
Chloride (Cl)	2.6	7	13	79	51	8	139	195
Fluoride (F)	0.1	...	...	0.4	0.8	...	...	2.5
Nitrate (NO_3)	0.3	0.2	4.7	0.2	0.0	...	0.0	1.1
Dissolved solids	34	130	415	661	392	392	503	1380
Total hardness as $CaCO_3$	20	98	213	315	28	276	106	316
Noncarbonate hardness	6	16	58	197	0	126	0	76
Specific conductance (micro-mhos at 25 C)	53.4	...	621	1040	651	...	867	...
Color	1	...	...	...	10	...	...	0
pH	6.9	8.1	...	8.4	8.0	7.6	7.9	...

[a] Analyses numbers are identified as follows:
    1 = New York City. Catskill supply (finished).
    2 = Detroit, Mich. Detroit River (raw).
    3 = Missouri River at Nebraska City, Nebr. Average composition, 1951 to 1952.
    4 = Los Angeles, Calif. Colorado River (raw). Average composition, 1950 to 1951.
    5 = Houston, Tex. Well 1932 ft deep.
    6 = Jacksonville, Fla. Well 1064 ft deep.
    7 = El Paso, Tex. Well 703 ft deep in Downtown Field.
    8 = Galesburg, Ill. Well 2450 ft deep.
[b] Computed by difference in epm and reported as sodium.

most waters are in chemical equilibrium with respect to ionic concentrations, it follows that the sum of the cations must be equal to the sum of the anions. If essentially all of the ionic constituents have been accurately determined, then the sums of the cations and anions should

Some waters, particularly waste waters that are lightly buffered or that contain organic substances, are not in chemical equilibrium. Disagreement in the sums of cationic and anionic constituents may not be significant in analyses of such waters.

Probable Combinations:

Prior to the widespread adoption of the practice of reporting water analyses in ionic form, it frequently was customary to report analyses in the form of chemical compounds. Thus, in place of reporting 10 ppm of calcium and 24 ppm of sulfate (which are equivalent chemically), 34 ppm of the compound calcium sulfate would be reported. Although it is now generally recognized that ionizable compounds do not occur in solution as compounds, analysts are still required on occasion to report analyses in the form of probable combinations. Directions for calculating probable combinations can be found in most texts on water analysis.

CLASSIFICATION OF INDUSTRIAL WATERS

Attempts have been made to classify industrial waters into groups having similar characteristics, but no completely satisfactory classification has been devised. Those unfamiliar with water chemistry, however, need some basic information about the substances waters may contain, how they may vary in composition, and what is to be expected when a water of a certain type is used.

Waters vary in composition from those that contain practically no dissolved solids, such as rain water, to those that are nearly saturated, like brines. Concentration of dissolved solids may range from less than 10 ppm to as much as 300,000 ppm or more. Most industrial waters, exclusive of those used for cooling, contain from about 50 to 500 ppm of dissolved solids. With few exceptions, the lower the dissolved solids content, the more attractive a water is for industrial purposes. With the exception of water used for cooling purposes, essentially all effluent water is more concentrated than influent water and hence may require some chemical modification or treatment prior to further industrial use.

Surface waters in general are softer and less concentrated than ground waters. However, hardness and dissolved solids in surface waters vary considerably over the period of a year and in many streams this variation is significant from day to day. Surface waters are frequently turbid, some excessively so, and with few exceptions must be filtered before use for public supplies or by industry.

Ground waters, on the other hand, exhibit essentially constant chemical composition and temperature and ordinarily can be used without filtration. They normally are harder and more concentrated than surface waters and thus less desirable for certain purposes.

The varying characteristics of surface and ground waters are illustrated by the analyses given in Table I (a more extensive tabulation will be found in Appendix I). All of the waters represented are used for public supplies at or near the location listed or by conduit from the source, such as supply No. 4. The waters represented by analyses Nos. 1 and 2 are nearly uniform in composition throughout the year. Analyses Nos. 3 and 4 are averages for a year. The composition of streams normally varies during different seasons of the year. For example, the concentration of dissolved solids in the Missouri River (No. 3) ranged from 336 to 600 ppm, but in the Colorado River (No. 4) the concentration remained fairly constant owing to impoundment of water in large reservoirs. Analyses of single samples of surface waters cannot be relied upon to represent their composition over a period of time unless the magnitude of the variation of specific streams is known.

A map is shown in Fig. 1 which portrays, by states, the average hardness of raw waters used by the larger public supply systems throughout the United States.

Hardness Classification:

For most industries the hardness of the intake water is the principal basis for classifying water. Hardness is defined (Definitions D 1129[1]) as a characteristic of water generally accepted as representing the total concentration of calcium and magnesium. Although other constituents, such as iron, manganese, and

Range in Hardness (ppm)	Descriptive Classification
1 to 60......	Soft
61 to 120......	Moderately hard
121 to 180......	Hard
180+..........	Very hard

Soft Waters.—Analyses 1 and 5 in Table I represent waters that may be considered soft, but they are very different in their content of dissolved solids.

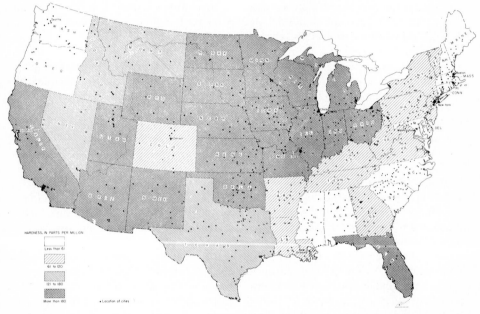

HARDNESS, IN PARTS PER MILLION

Less than 60

61 to 120

121 to 180

More than 180

• Location of cities

U. S. Geological Survey

Fig. 1.—Average Hardness, by States, of Raw Water from Public Supplies for 1315 of the Larger Cities in the United States, 1952.

other polyvalent cations cause hardness, they are usually present in such small concentrations that they do not materially affect the hardness of industrial water. Only calcium and magnesium are included in the term hardness as used in this discussion.

Any descriptive or numerical classification of the hardness of water is arbitrary. A water that is termed hard in some areas may be considered relatively soft in other areas. One classification that has been used rather widely is as follows:

Analysis 1 is typical of many surface waters and a very few ground waters along the Atlantic Coast north of Florida and in the Pacific Northwest. These waters are low in hardness and also in dissolved solids, since the igneous rock formations through which the water flows are only sparingly soluble in water. These soft waters often contain relatively high concentrations of silica which frequently amount to 50 per cent of the dissolved solids.

Analysis 5 is typical of ground waters

that have undergone natural softening. Generally, the dissolved solids in such waters consist principally of sodium and bicarbonate. It is believed that these waters originally contained principally calcium and magnesium bicarbonate, but in passing through naturally occurring softening material such as glauconite (greensand) the calcium and magnesium were exchanged for sodium, thereby changing them from hard to soft. Ground waters of this type are found in the Atlantic and Gulf coastal areas (excepting Florida), extensively in much of Texas, and parts of the Great Plains. Although they are soft, these waters frequently contain several hundred parts per million of dissolved solids. Soft waters having a high content of dissolved solids are not desirable for use in boilers or for most industrial uses other than cooling.

Moderately Hard Waters.—Analyses 2 and 7 in Table I illustrate hard waters of different composition. Analysis 2 represents water used for the public supply of Detroit, Mich., and is representative of the large reservoir of water in Lake Huron. Waters in this hardness range are found extensively in the Appalachian plateau of eastern United States and to a lesser extent in other parts of the country.

Although analysis 7 represents a water in the moderately hard range, it contains more dissolved solids than would normally be expected. This water undoubtedly has undergone natural softening in consequence of which the original concentrations of calcium and magnesium have largely been replaced by sodium.

Hard Waters.—Only a relatively few states yield substantial supplies of this hardness that are used for public supply systems. Lake Michigan, Lake Erie, and Lake Ontario comprise large sources in this range that are used extensively for both industrial and public supplies.

Very Hard Waters.—Waters with hardness in excess of 180 ppm are classified as very hard. Actually, waters used for public supplies range in hardness from 181 to over 800 ppm. In the North and Central Great Plains, the Southwest, California, and Florida are found waters that, on the average, are harder than 180 ppm as used directly by public supply systems. Many cities find it profitable to soften water before delivery to consumers. For practical reasons, however, hardness is seldom reduced to less than about 85 ppm.

Very hard waters are not desirable for most industrial purposes. Frequently, however, softening can be economically justified so that the hard water, which may be the only kind available, can be used by industrial plants.

Analyses 3, 4, 6, and 8 all represent waters in the very hard category but they differ considerably in other respects. Some contain large amounts of sulfate or chloride while others are high in bicarbonates. Some contain substantial amounts of sodium in addition to the hardness-forming cations—calcium and magnesium. All of these waters are unsuitable for many industrial uses and none would be used if other waters of lower hardness were available. The hardness can be reduced by softening, but the sodium and the sulfate and chloride cannot be removed economically for most purposes. Demineralization is sometimes justified but is usually employed on waters with lower concentration of dissolved solids.

Other Classifications:

Hardness is also classified in terms of the predominant anions that occur in the water together with calcium and magnesium. The customary categories are carbonate hardness and noncarbonate hardness. Waters have carbonate hardness when they contain carbonate or bicarbonate in addition to calcium and magnesium. Waters have noncarbonate hardness when the carbonate and bicarbonate present are less than the equivalent amount of calcium and magnesium. Sulfate and chloride are the principal anions associated with noncarbonate hardness.

Carbonate and noncarbonate hardness were formerly described by the terms temporary and permanent hardness. A substantial part, but not usually all, of the carbonate hardness of a water is removed by boiling at atmospheric pressure. Noncarbonate hardness cannot be so simply removed; it requires physical or chemical treatment for reduction or removal.

Other constituents, such as sodium, sulfate, or chloride, have been used to classify waters. In connection with recent interest in the conversion of saline to fresh waters, waters have been classified according to relative salinity. For the majority of industrial uses, however, hardness is the most important single characteristic of water.

Significance of Other Constituents in Industrial Water:

Although hardness is the characteristic most commonly used to classify water, other constituents may have more bearing on the suitability of water for particular uses. These constituents may be significant in terms of various objectionable effects related to industrial uses of water.

Silica in water supplies varies from less than 1 to over 75 ppm. The average concentration is in the range of 5 to 15 ppm. Silica is objectionable in boilers, especially high-pressure boilers, because it tends to form adherent deposits on heat transfer surfaces. Silica deposits also form on turbine blades, causing severe damage if not removed. For many installations, concentrations as low as 1 ppm require treatment for removal of silica.

Iron and manganese in relatively small concentrations cause staining and formation of deposits. Iron is sometimes accompanied by iron bacteria which frequently cause deposits and odors in water systems. More than 0.3 ppm of iron and 0.2 ppm of manganese (or about 0.3 ppm when considered together) are usually found to be objectionable.

Sodium and potassium do not cause hardness and are not normally associated with scale deposits. These cations, especially sodium, are concentrated in boiler water and have to be removed by continuous or intermittent blowdown. Softening of water by the zeolite process increases the sodium concentration by an amount equivalent to the calcium and magnesium removed.

Sodium and potassium in natural waters are derived from the solution of soil and rock materials containing salts of these cations. The sodium content of water varies over a wide range from practically zero to many thousand parts per million in brines. Potassium is usually present in small amounts and seldom exceeds 10 ppm.

Alkalinity in water supplies usually represents the bicarbonate ion, HCO_3^-, although it also includes carbonate, CO_3^{--}, and in water receiving certain alkali wastes, hydroxide, OH^-. Alkalinity is customarily expressed as calcium carbonate, $CaCO_3$. Practically all natural waters have alkalinity unless neutralized by acid from industrial effluents or from mine drainage. The alkalinity is related to the buffer capacity of a water, that is, the capacity of the water to receive acid without substantially lowering the pH.

Sulfate concentrations vary over a wide range in natural waters. Sulfate may be derived from leaching of gypsum, anhydrite, and shale deposits or from oxidation of sulfides. Waters in arid or semi-arid regions may contain relatively large quantities of sodium sulfate.

Sulfate in water tends to form hard, adherent scale on heat transfer surfaces. Sulfate is usually associated with non-carbonate hardness and is difficult to remove economically.

Chloride is found in all natural waters, and occurs over a wide range of concentrations. Streams along the Atlantic Coast, the eastern Gulf Coast, and in the Pacific Northwest normally contain less than 25 ppm of chloride except in tidal reaches or where polluted. Streams in arid or semiarid regions may contain several hundred parts per million of chloride.

Chloride in concentrations less than 50 ppm has no detrimental effect on most industrial uses, and higher concentrations are used rather widely. Chloride in boiler water contributes to the total concentration of dissolved solids. Thus, if the boiler feedwater contains substantial amounts of chloride, periods of blowdown will be more frequent than would otherwise be required. High chloride waters also promote corrosion of metal surfaces.

Dissolved gases, such as carbon dioxide (CO_2), oxygen (O_2), hydrogen sulfide (H_2S), or ammonia (NH_3), frequently are important, depending upon the final use of the water. While some of these gases may be combined as ions, they are usually considered as dissolved gases because they may be separated as gases by heat or agitation, and they leave no residue on evaporation. Their presence, however, should not be disregarded. Carbon dioxide is present both combined as bicarbonate ion, HCO_3^-, and as the uncombined gas, CO_2. Only the CO_2 above that needed to form HCO_3^- is reported as CO_2. Free CO_2 may be present in ground water in amounts as high as 20 ppm or more, but there is less

in surface waters unless acid is present. Oxygen ranges between 2 and 8 ppm in surface waters, and little or none in ground waters. Hydrogen sulfide can range between 0 and 15 ppm. As little as 0.5 ppm causes an odor. Ammonia ranges between zero and 4 ppm and usually is due to industrial waste or sewage pollution. The inclusion of dissolved gases in the classification depends upon whether their presence has an appreciable effect on the use of the water.

Hydrogen ion concentration, or pH (which is a measure of the hydrogen ion activity), is related to the acidity or basicity of a water. pH is sometimes used for classifying water for some industries, especially where water is carried in long pipe lines or is stored or used in corrodible equipment. The pH of most natural waters ranges between 6 and 8. Waters containing free mineral acids and those from mine drainage have pH values below 4.5. Some ground waters have pH values above 8, some below 6. The pH values of waters have a very definite bearing on the utility of supplies for many industrial purposes.

Classification According to Physical Characteristics:

Water may also be classified according to turbidity, odor, or taste, especially for domestic consumption or for the food industry. No analysis or classification is complete without a detailed physical description of the water under consideration.

Turbidity consists of suspended matter in water. It can result from either roily natural water or inadequately filtered treated water. *Color* usually results from the presence of organic matter; it may come from decayed vegetation or from municipal or industrial pollution. Colored organic material is quite troublesome, both to the analyst and to the user. Taste or flavor, being subjective, defies classification although many adjectives have been employed. There are, however, techniques for measuring the intensity of odor.

Summary:

In summary, waters may be classified as soft, moderately hard, hard, or very hard. They may also be classified in terms of the predominance of particular constituents; or according to low, medium, or high pH; or as colored or turbid; or any combination of these.

MICROBIOLOGICAL CONTAMINATION

The presence of organisms in industrial water frequently determines whether the water is satisfactory for a particular process. The three classes of micro-organisms most frequently encountered are bacteria, fungi, and algae. All can contribute to the formation of deposits and cause corrosion, tastes, and odors. These organisms may foul filters and ion exchangers, reducing flow rates. Highly polluted water is never desirable for any industrial use and should not be considered where the water is used in food or food-packaging industries.

It is difficult to analyze a water supply microbiologically and then forecast whether any organism present will cause trouble. The environment provided in the water system largely determines whether an organism will multiply sufficiently to be detrimental. Therefore, except for ordinary sterilization for human consumption or for certain food industries, microbiological analyses and studies of industrial waters usually are made after trouble has been encountered in use.

WATER-FORMED DEPOSITS

EXPRESSING RESULTS OF ANALYSIS OF WATER-FORMED DEPOSITS

Deposits formed by water in all its phases may be classified as scale, sludge, corrosion products, or biological deposits. The prevention of these deposits is one of the major problems of water treatment. Once they are formed, analysis of such deposits usually is necessary to diagnose the reasons for deposition, to determine methods of prevention, and to effect their removal.

The analysis of deposits differs from that of water in that results are reported as percentages, instead of parts per million, and special methods often are used to determine the chemical compounds that make up the deposit. Usual methods for examination of deposits are chemical analysis, X-ray diffraction, chemical microscopy, and spectrography.

The method most commonly used is chemical analysis. Results are reported in terms of basic oxides and acid anhydrides wherever possible.[2] This procedure does not provide for reporting definite molecular combinations. When such combinations are desired, it is better to rely upon microscopic or X-ray diffraction evidence than on hypothesis. Many laboratories, however, are not equipped with the necessary apparatus for such examinations, so only probable compounds can be calculated from the analytical data.

When simple compounds predominate (such as calcium carbonate, calcium sulfate, ferric oxide), the usual procedure for calculating probable combinations gives sufficiently accurate information. For more complex compounds, such as those containing silica and alumina, other methods that divulge the true identity of the compound must be used. Normally, deposits formed at low temperatures are

---

[2] Method D 933, which appears in this publication.

more easily identified by chemical analysis alone. Complex compounds, more apt to form at such high temperatures as occur in boilers, are not so easily identified. Therefore it is advisable to subject to special examination any deposits which have either an unusual chemical composition or have been formed at high temperature. Such an examination can be made by a laboratory equipped for the investigation of these deposits.

Chemical equivalents are used for calculating the probable combinations from the analysis of a deposit. For calculation, these are found by dividing the percentage of each constituent by its respective equivalent weight. The miscellaneous constituents, and all oxides except those of calcium, magnesium, sodium, and potassium, are usually reported in the percentages found. Unless present in quantities in excess of 2 or 3 per cent, nitrate, sulfite, and sulfide are reported as such. Chloride is practically always reported as NaCl.

Many systems are used for calculating probable combinations of radicals determined by chemical analysis. The one explained here is based on the comparison of hundreds of chemical analyses of deposits with the more exact X-ray diffraction and microscopic methods. One check on the correctness of a procedure is that the sum of the percentages of the various calculated compounds and remaining substances not used in the compound calculations totals approximately 100 per cent. If the calculated combinations fail to approximate 100 per cent, and there is no obvious reason based on chemistry or mineralogy, the deposit should be examined by such a method as X-ray diffraction. No method of calculating combinations can cover all cases, but the system outlined below is suggested as generally effective.

After conversion to chemical equivalents:

1. (a) Calculate SO_3 to $CaSO_4$.
   (b) Calculate remaining SO_3 to Na_2SO_4.
2. If CaO remains from Step 1(a):
   (a) Calculate CO_2 to $CaCO_3$.
   (b) Calculate remaining CO_2 to sodium carbonate.
3. If CaO remains from Step 2(a):
   (a) Calculate P_2O_5 to $Ca_{10}(PO_4)_6(OH)_2$.
   (b) Calculate remaining P_2O_5 to $Mg_3(PO_4)_2 \cdot Mg(OH)_2$.
   (c) Balance of P_2O_5 can be combined with Na_2O, Fe_2O_3, and Al_2O_3.
4. If CaO remains from Step 3:
   (a) Calculate as $CaSiO_3 \cdot H_2O$.
   (b) Refer remaining SiO_2 to Step 6(a).
5. If CaO remains from Step 4, report as CaO or $Ca(OH)_2$.
6. If MgO remains from Step 3(b):
   (a) Calculate to $3MgO \cdot 2SiO_2 \cdot 2H_2O$.
   (b) Calculate excess MgO to $Mg(OH)_2$.
   (c) Refer excess SiO_2 to Steps 7(a) and 7(c).
7. If Na_2O remains from Step 1(b), 2(b), or 3(c):
   (a) Calculate as Na_2SiO_3.
   (b) Report excess Na_2O as either Na_2O or NaOH.
   (c) Report any excess SiO_2 as SiO_2.
8. If K_2O is present handle same as Na_2O.
9. Subtract any OH or H_2O used above from combined water or loss on ignition.
10. Report all remaining oxides, acid radicals, and miscellaneous substances as such.
11. Convert all compounds from chemical equivalents back to percentage.
12. Sum of all substances should total approximately 100 per cent.

NOTE.—When appreciable amounts of such free metals as Cu or Fe are present in a deposit, the summation of determinations will be more than 100 per cent because the metals are determined and reported as oxides. The same difficulty may be caused by the presence of oxides of lower valence than are reported.

No report of an analysis is complete without a complete description of the physical characteristics of the deposit. Also, data must be included on the point and date of sampling, color, texture, method of sampling, operating conditions, and whether in the analyst's opinion it is sludge, scale, biological deposit, or corrosion product. An accompanying sketch of any peculiar laminations or structure as well as a sketch of the equipment and location of the deposit is always helpful. Given a complete report, it is possible to compare analyses and descriptions of deposits with past plant operations and to recognize conditions which cause these deposits.

Biological deposits, especially those containing both inorganic and organic matter, are often of such a complex nature that it is advisable to have an examination of the deposit conducted by a laboratory experienced in examining industrial biological deposits. Particular attention is called to methods of sampling and handling biological deposits described in this Manual.

COMPOSITION AND CLASSIFICATION OF WATER-FORMED DEPOSITS

Water picks up solids from the earth by coming in contact with many different types of materials which it may carry either in solution or in suspension. Conceivably it can deposit these as many different substances. The composition of deposits will vary with the character of the water and its use. The true identity of a deposit is often a valuable clue for determining the cause of the formation and remedies for its prevention. Thus it is desirable to have some knowledge of the types of deposits formed and where they are most likely to occur.

As stated above, scale, sludge, corrosion products, and biological deposits are the major classifications of deposits. It is common also to classify deposits according to their predominant acid radical: carbonate, sulfate, phosphate, or silicate; or as iron (rust) or slime (biological). This method is not satisfactory because deposits almost always are mixtures of several compounds. The compound present in highest percentage is not always the major cause of the deposit, because it may be cemented together by some minor constituent.

Another method of classification is a better guide to the deposits to expect under certain conditions. Water confined for industrial use may attack the surfaces with which it is in contact, or it may form deposits. The speed of these reactions depends upon concentration. Different types of deposits will form at different points in a system, depending upon biological growth conditions, agitation, temperature, and concentration. Most substances have limiting solubilities in water and when these limits are exceeded they will deposit from solution. Other substances will be occluded in the deposit by absorption or adsorption. The substances sensitive to minor changes in the water system will be the first to deposit. With increasing temperature or concentration, additional substances will deposit as their solubilities are exceeded.

Deposits are listed in the following classification according to the location in a water system where they are most likely to make their initial appearance. These substances will continue to deposit throughout the remainder of the system as long as conditions are favorable for it and there is any excess of that particular constituent remaining in the water.

Deposits Formed at Temperatures Below 100 C, with or Without Evaporation:

Deposits formed in this environment are usually from waters confined in tanks, pipe lines, once-through and recirculating cooling systems, household or industrial hot-water heaters, and other equipment where the water passes through, with or without atmospheric evaporation. The type of deposits most frequently encountered are:

Aragonite	$\gamma CaCO_3$
Calcite	$\beta CaCO_3$
Gypsum	$CaSO_4 \cdot 2H_2O$
Geothite	$\alpha Fe_2O_3 \cdot H_2O$
Hydroxyapatite	$Ca_{10}(PO_4)_6(OH)_2$
Oil (chloroform extractable)	
Carbonaceous	
Biological	

    (*a*) Non-spore bacteria
    (*b*) Spore bacteria
    (*c*) Fungi
    (*d*) Algae and diatoms
    (*e*) Crustaceans

Deposits Formed at Temperatures Above 100 C with No Evaporation:

Deposits formed under these conditions are most frequently encountered in high-temperature heaters for boiler feedwater or processes, or where water is used for cooling at high temperatures. Usually waters for this purpose are so pretreated that the scale-forming solids are reduced to a minimum. However, mere traces of such solids will form deposits at the high temperatures of the confining metal where heat-transfer rates are high. These deposits include:

All the foregoing deposits, and

Anhydrite	$CaSO_4$
Basic magnesium phosphate	$Mg_3(PO_4)_2 \cdot Mg(OH)_2$
Brucite	$Mg(OH)_2$

Magnetite	Fe_3O_4
Serpentine	$3MgO \cdot 2SiO_2 \cdot 2H_2O$

Biological deposits rarely are encountered.

Deposits Formed at Temperatures Above 100 C with Evaporation:

These deposits are formed almost exclusively in steam generators which may operate at pressures as high as 2400 psi. These waters usually have been pretreated to prevent the more common types of scale-forming solids from entering the boiler in more than minute amounts. Deposits would be very voluminous without such treatment and would consist chiefly of those mentioned above. These deposits include:

All the foregoing deposits, except biological materials, plus

Acmite	$Na_2O \cdot Fe_2O_3 \cdot 4SiO_2$
Analcite	$Na_2O \cdot Al_2O_3 \cdot 4SiO_2 \cdot 2H_2O$
Calcium hydroxide	$Ca(OH)_2$
Copper	Cu
Cuprite	Cu_2O
Ferrous oxide	FeO
Hematite	Fe_2O_3
Sodium ferrous phosphate	$NaFePO_4$
Tenorite	CuO
Thenardite	Na_2SO_4
Xonotlite	$5CaO \cdot 5SiO_2 \cdot H_2O$

Deposits Formed from Water Vapor or Steam:

These deposits are encountered on turbine blades, valves, and other equipment in contact with steam.

Amorphous silica	SiO_2
Analcite	$Na_2O \cdot Al_2O_3 \cdot 4SiO_2 \cdot 2H_2O$
Burkeite	$Na_2CO_3 \cdot 2Na_2SO_4$

Carbonaceous (coke)		Siderite	$FeCO_3$
Halite	NaCl	Sodium carbonate	Na_2CO_3
Magnetite	Fe_3O_4	Sodium disilicate	$Na_2Si_2O_6$
Oil (chloroform extractable)		Sodium silicate	Na_2SiO_3
Quartz	SiO_2	Thenardite	Na_2SO_4

Conclusion

The determination of the composition of industrial water and water-formed deposits and the interpretation of the results of analysis and examination of water and deposits have made rapid advances in the past 25 years. Through the efforts of this Society and others, the determination of the components in water and deposits has become increasingly precise. Interpretation of the results of analysis, however, and examination and application to field use is still dependent primarily upon experience gained through handling water for particular uses. Therefore, any written procedures and classifications must be of a general nature only. All the major fields of water treatment—municipal, domestic, boiler feed, cooling, and process—require special considerations. The fine points of reporting and interpreting results and applying them to practical use will vary with each specific industry.

CHAPTER V
Treatment of Process Water and Waste Water

45-49

CHAPTER V—TREATMENT OF PROCESS WATER
AND WASTE WATER

The purification of water for industrial use can be very complex or relatively simple, depending upon the properties of the raw water and the degree of purity required. There are many methods and combinations in use, but all are covered in three basic processes: physical, chemical, and physicochemical treatment.

A fourth basic process, biological treatment, is often employed where waste water must be purified before it may be discharged. This process takes advantage of the ability of living microorganisms to induce a variety of chemical and physicochemical reactions. Treatment of waste water is usually a much more complicated operation than the production of process water of appropriate quality.

This chapter discusses these processes as they are used in the treatment of industrial water and waste water and outlines some of the technical problems and basic considerations involved.

PHYSICAL TREATMENT

Physical treatment pertains to those processes in which there is separation of impurities from water without chemical change. The common methods are sedimentation, straining and filtration, multi-liquid phase separation, degasification, dilution, removal of entrainment, distillation and stripping, underground discharge, and ocean discharge.

Sedimentation:

Sedimentation is the process by which the force of gravity acts on particles

heavier than water and causes them to move downward and settle out. Surface waters contain varying amounts of suspended material, and this process is used to clarify raw water either by simple sedimentation or with addition of chemical coagulants. The tanks in which this action takes place are called sedimentation basins.

Particle size, weight, shape, frictional resistance, and viscosity play an important part in the design of such tanks. Theoretical calculations usually are based on modifications of Stoke's law and the assumption that the particles are spheres. Many factors must be considered in design, and all of these must be modified as judgment and experience dictate. The theory of design will not be given here; it will suffice to state that effective clarification can be accomplished in tanks that are properly designed and operated.

Settling basins may be constructed of earth, wood, concrete, or steel. They may be rectangular or circular. The usual period of retention ranges from 4 to 12 hr. Where the water contains large amounts of settleable solids, the basins often are provided with mechanical scrapers which move the settled sludge to a sump from which it is forced out by the hydraulic head of water in the basin. In other instances, manual sludge discharge valves are provided to remove some of the settled material; it is necessary to remove such units from service at regular intervals for thorough cleaning.

55

Inlet and outlet distribution of the fluid must provide for uniform flow in the basin if efficient operation is to be attained. In rectangular tanks the influent is distributed by a trough equipped with adjustable sluice gates or plug valves, and the effluent is usually discharged over a weir or series of weirs. Circular units are provided with a center distributor and an overflow launder at the periphery of the tank.

Short circuiting often plagues the operation of rectangular basins, thereby decreasing the theoretical retention time. This can be overcome by improving the inlet distribution or by effective use of muffle boards at the inlet and sometimes just ahead of the effluent weir.

Depending upon the character of the silt and suspended matter, plain sedimentation may provide as much as 70 per cent removal; where coagulants are employed removals may be as high as 95 per cent.

Many industrial waste waters contain organic and inorganic settleable solids that must be removed before final discharge. These solids respond to the process just described, and settling basins of similar design are used for the purpose. Retention periods are usually much shorter than for raw waters, rarely exceeding 2 to 3 hr. Long retention periods are detrimental where the solids are all organic, because bacterial action may take place. This may result in anaerobic conditions and the generation of odors. The settled sludge will have a tendency to float if considerable gas is evolved, and this will tend to nullify the operation.

Air flotation is very effective for removing flocculent solids that settle very slowly or have a tendency to float. The air is dispersed in the liquid under pressure and the pressure released just prior to discharge into a receiving basin. The finely divided air floats the solids to the surface where they are skimmed off. Effective separation is provided at minimum cost by this method.

Straining and Filtration:

Strainers and filters may be used where it is necessary to remove floating or suspended solids from water, either as a further step after sedimentation or where space precludes installation of settling basins.

Several types of strainers are in commercial use. Cloth, metal gauze, rotary drum, and rotary disk are the usual kinds. Cloth and metal gauze filters are used where the suspended materials are fairly fine and in low concentration. Cheesecloth or similar material is rolled around a perforated mandrel and installed in a cast iron housing. The water passes through the filter into the drum and the finely suspended material is retained on the cloth. When the pressure drop reaches a predetermined value the unit is taken out of service and the cloth washed or replaced. These units will do a good job of straining but are bulky and have a fairly high loss of head.

Metal gauze is becoming popular as a strainer. Here the size of the mesh can be rigidly controlled down to several microns and selective straining can be performed.

Rotary drum and disk strainers are quite widely used for coarse separations. The drum type comprises a rotating drum covered with a screen of the proper mesh size for the purpose and installed inside a housing. The drum is driven at slow speed by an electric motor. Valving is provided to backflush automatically a portion of the screen in its rotation and thereby keep it clean. These units are built to handle up to several thousand gallons per minute at a low pressure drop. This unit may be modified by replacing the screen with perforated porcelain disks.

A drum strainer is used where floating solids must be removed from a waste water. This is a drum frame covered with screen and rotated in a concrete channel. The water flows through the screen and out of the center of the drum. Provision is made for backwashing the screen as it rotates. This unit is for gravity flow only.

The disk unit is a perforated disk set at an angle in a channel where the water must flow through the disk. The solids are scraped or brushed off the portion of the rotating disk that is above the water surface. This is a gravity-flow unit.

Filtration of water is carried out in either pressure or gravity units containing graded sand, calcite, magnetite, anthracite, charcoal, or finely-divided, relatively insoluble materials such as diatomaceous earth. Silica sand is the most common filtering medium for cold, neutral waters because of low solubility, low cost, and the relatively high specific gravity of sand particles. Pressure filters are usually designed for a down-flow rate of 2 to 3 gal per min (gpm) per sq ft of surface area, and a reverse-flow back-wash rate up to 18 gpm. The filter medium usually is specified on the basis of effective size and uniformity coefficient. The effective size of filter medium is usually specified to be not more than 1.65 and is always greater than 1.0.

Crushed anthracite coal, because of its relatively low solubility, is usually specified as the filter medium where hot, strongly acid, or strongly alkaline waters must be filtered. The anthracite filter medium usually is backwashed at lower velocities than sand of the same size. Anthracite filter medium weighs only about 50 lb per cu ft, approximately one half the bulk density of sand.

Diatomaceous earth is often used as a filter medium. In one type the diatomaceous earth is supported by a porous stone or wire mesh element and removed by backwashing. In other types the filter material is deposited on a rotating filter drum in a fairly thick layer. A doctor blade continuously scrapes off a thin film and thus exposes a fresh surface. Precoated filters have the advantage of high-quality effluent, low weight, high capacity for their size, and sometimes lower first cost. They have the disadvantage of high pressure drop, high operating maintenance and repair costs, and rapid depreciation and obsolescence. Poorly designed units are often undependable in operation even in the care of a competent and reliable operator. A diatomite filter must have two to four times the filter area of a sand filter of equivalent capacity. Even with the larger area, the pumping power needed may be two to four times higher than for the equivalent sand filter. There are numerous types of precoat filters which employ a variety of precoat materials.

It should be understood that filtration will not remove true color from water. This can be eliminated only by use of a suitable coagulant dispersed in the water prior to filtration.

Multi-Liquid Phase Separation:

One or more nonmiscible liquids can often be physically separated from water as a result of differences in specific gravity. Gravity separations of this kind are performed on a small scale in laboratory separatory funnels and on a commercial scale in specially designed equipment.[1] The oil and water separator for oil refinery waste water is an example of one large-scale application of this process.[2]

Frequently there is not much difference in the specific gravities of the liquids,

[1] C. Ingersol, "Fundamentals and Performance of Gravity Separation," *Petroleum Refiner*, June, 1951, p. 1064.
[2] "Waste Water Containing Oil," *Manual on Disposal of Refinery Wastes*, Am. Petroleum Inst., Section I, 4th Ed. (1949).

and one of them may be dispersed in a finely divided, globular state. Thermal convection currents under such conditions may be strong enough to prevent efficient operation of the equipment. It is therefore always desirable to minimize thermal currents by careful design of gravity separator systems. An equalizing basin ahead of the treatment unit will minimize temperature and other fluctuations that may disturb proper operation. Agglomeration of the dispersed phase by chemical or physical means will greatly increase the efficiency of the separator.

Centrifugal equipment is used for multi-liquid phase separations where the value of the separated product justifies the relatively high capital cost of the equipment. Use of a centrifugal separator to remove traces of suspended water and solids from lubricating oil is an economical application of this process. The differential separating force between the two or more liquids can be greatly increased with such equipment. The strength and cost of the materials from which centrifugal separators are constructed place a limit on their size and capacity.

Air flotation is widely used in this type of separation. The oily water is put under a pressure of 30 to 50 psi and air is diffused into the liquid. The pressure is released just prior to discharge into a separating tank where the fine air bubbles rise to the surface carrying the particles of oil with them. A rotating skimmer sweeps the floated oil to a collecting trough from which it flows into a receiving tank. These systems can easily produce 90 per cent separation with very short retention periods, sometimes of no more than 30 min duration.[3]

Degasification:

Stripping operations, such as physical deaeration and aeration, are processes for removing undesirable dissolved gases from water. One or more dissolved gases, such as oxygen,[4] carbon dioxide,[5] ammonia, or hydrogen sulfide, are removed by exposing large surfaces of the liquid to a vapor phase deficient in the gases to be eliminated.

Degasifying equipment can be classified as ebullition, tray or drip, and spray units. In the ebullition type, a suitable gas is bubbled through the liquid for a period sufficient to change the vapor pressure equilibrium and enlarge the liquid surface. This principle was widely used in the past for hydrogen sulfide and carbon dioxide removal; it is now mainly employed to separate carbon dioxide and oxygen in deaerating feedwater heaters usually operating under a few pounds pressure.

Tray or drip gas-stripping equipment exposes large surface areas to the desired vapor pressure conditions by slowly flowing the water in thin layers over plates, channels, slats, or packing and allowing it to fall or trickle in droplets or thin sheets. Deaerating feedwater heaters operate on this principle to remove dissolved oxygen and carbon dioxide from boiler feedwater. The heaters are usually operated under a few pounds pressure and at temperatures above 212 F. Degasifiers used to remove carbon dioxide where alkalinity is controlled by acid addition, or by blending hydrogen zeolite effluent with sodium effluent or after cation exchange, operate on this principle. Closed wooden tanks containing many stacks of trays allow the water

---

[3] A. H. Beebe, "Soluble Oil Waste Treatment by Pressure Flotation," *Sewage and Industrial Wastes*, Vol. 25, p. 1314 (1953).

[4] J. R. McDermet, "The Separation of Dissolved Gases from Water," *Transactions*, Am. Soc. Mechanical Engrs., Vol. 42, p. 267 (1920).

[5] A. M. Amorosi and J. R. McDermet, "The Calculation of the Distribution of Carbon Dioxide Between Water and Steam," *Proceedings*, Am. Soc. Testing Mats., Vol. 39, p. 1204 (1939).

to drip down while air blown up through the tank escapes at the top.

Spray and spray-ebullition gas strippers utilizing atomizing nozzles, ebullition, and entrainment to divide the water into fine droplets for exposure to the desired vapor pressure conditions are finding wide use, not only in deaerating feedwater heaters, but also with vacuum deaeration of carbon dioxide and oxygen from cold water and ammonia from hot water. Vacuum deaeration is carried on in one or two stages, usually in vertical steel tanks where the vacuum is maintained by steam-jet ejectors.

With the exception of vacuum deaeration, some means must be employed to maintain the partial pressure of the undesirable gases well below the point at which stripping will cease. In a gas-stripping basin or tower, the air that is pumped or blown through the equipment carries the undesirable gas away to the atmosphere. Steam with a low partial pressure of free oxygen is the stripping agent in deaerating feedwater heaters. A vent condenser is usually included to permit the incoming feedwater to absorb most of the heat in the stripping steam.

Dilution:

High salt concentrations in waste water from the oil and alkali industries present a difficult disposal problem. Similar problems occur in other chemical plants where sodium sulfate and organic solids are present in high concentrations in effluents. Most regulatory agencies have set limiting concentrations in the receiving streams that restrict the amount of effluent that may be discharged.

Where inorganic salts such as sodium chloride, calcium chloride, and sodium sulfate must be discharged, there are two methods in use. One is by dilution with uncontaminated water, and the other is by controlled discharge. In those plants where the waste stream is small and there is available considerable uncontaminated waste water (for example, from cooling operations), the two are blended to conform with the concentration allowable in the plant discharge. Where the amount of clean water is insufficient for diluting all the concentrated waste, any surplus of the latter is held for controlled discharge.

Controlled discharge takes advantage of the increased stream flows during winter months or rainy seasons to dispose of concentrated wastes that would otherwise overload the receiving water. The wastes are stored in ponds and released during periods of heavy runoff at a rate that will not exceed the allowable concentration in the river. This operation may require large areas of land for storage lagoons, but it is often the most economical method of handling the problem.

When there is sufficient flow in the receiving stream to assimilate the biochemical oxygen demand (BOD) load from high concentrations of organic matter, dilution can be utilized to provide satisfactory stream assimilation and to eliminate areas of heavy oxygen depletion. This method has certain limitations but it has been used successfully in some areas.

The dissolved salts and sludge in evaporators, boilers, and cooling towers are concentrated in the circulating water and these concentrations must be controlled by blowdown. Blowdown is thus a dilution process whereby concentrated solutions and suspensions are replaced by more dilute water. Intermittent boiler blowdown usually discharges directly to an atmospheric drain tank, with the result that all of the heat of the liquid and of the flashed steam are lost. Continuous blowdown systems make it possible to recover this heat. Heat recovery systems are available for both high- and low-

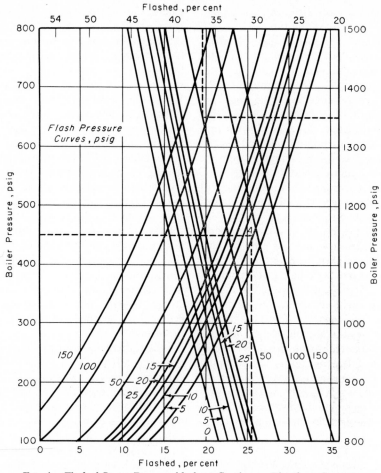

FIG. 1.—Flashed Steam Recoverable from Continuous Blowdown Systems.

NOTE.—For boiler pressures between 100 and 800 psig, use "flash" pressure curves slanting from lower left-hand to upper right-hand corner and the bottom axis. For boiler pressures above 800 psig, use "flash" pressure curves slanting from lower right-hand to upper left-hand corner and top axis.

This chart is used to calculate the percentage of boiler water discharged by a continuous blowdown system that can be flashed into steam at a reduced pressure and recoverable as low pressure steam for heating or process.

EXAMPLE.—A boiler operates at a pressure of 450 psig. Continuous blowdown amounts to 10,000 lb per hr. What percentage of blowdown water can be recovered as flashed steam at 5 psig pressure?

SOLUTION.—Locate 450 psi on left-hand axis. Follow horizontally toward the right to the intersection with 5 psi "flash" curve (point A). Drop vertically downward to the bottom axis and read 25.5 per cent. Twenty-five and a half per cent of 10,000 lb per hr blowdown = 2550 lb per hr of flash steam at 5 psig pressure.

These curves have been prepared from the formula:

$$\text{Flashed steam, per cent} = \frac{H_B - H_F}{V_F} \times 100$$

where:

H_B = heat of liquid at boiler pressure in Btu per lb,
H_F = heat of liquid at flash pressure in Btu per lb, and
V_F = latent heat of vaporization at flash pressure in Btu per lb.

temperature operation. Heat-recovery equipment for high-temperature blow-down may consist of a flask tank to salvage flash steam or of a surface heat exchanger for transferring the blowdown heat to the feedwater just before it enters the boiler. Heat-recovery flash tanks or surface exchangers for low-temperature blowdown usually transfer the blowdown heat to the cold feedwater in or ahead of the deaerating feedwater heater. Heat-recovery systems for high and low level blowdown can be used in series where the over-all heat balance of the plant makes such equipment economical.

Figure 1 shows the percentage of the boiler water that is flashed to steam as it is throttled from various pressures to atmospheric pressure. It also shows the total heat of the boiler water at various pressures.

Blowdown from cooling towers is often called purge water. Windage or other water losses are sufficient in some cases to limit the concentration of salts of the cooling tower water. Where additional dilution is required, a continuous stream of concentrated water is run to the waste water system.

Removal of Entrainment:

One of the fundamental problems in boiler design and operation is the mechanical separation of solutions and solids from the steam. All boilers must include entrainment separators. The simplest method is to provide sufficient disengaging space above the normal water line in the steam drum. It is economical for industrial steam generators to use dry pipes, baffles, or special types of separating devices to reduce the size of the steam drum. Most modern steam drums are furnished with carefully designed and proved internal equipment. Steam separator equipment is mechanical in nature and operates by gravity, centrifugal force, and surface tension or by a combination of these forces to remove liquid and solid contamination. Preliminary washing of the steam by feedwater or steam condensate may be used in steam separating equipment. Devices for overcoming entrainment of liquids in gas will not appreciably separate a mixture of gases, such as steam and carbon dioxide, or steam and hydrocarbon vapors.

Entrainment separation efficiency in a steam boiler is controlled not only by the mechanical equipment, the steaming rate, and the water level in the boiler drum, but also by the surface tension of the dissolved solids and the liquids in the boiler water. There is usually a limit for dissolved solids above which, at normal steaming rates, priming and carryover will occur. No general standard for allowable dissolved solids can cover all types of steam generators. While operators at one plant will insist that concentrations must be kept below 1000 ppm dissolved solids, operators at another plant with identical equipment, but with different water conditions, may be able to operate satisfactorily with 5000 ppm.

The same general principles apply to reduction of solids carry-over in the vapor from evaporators in process operations. This is especially important where barometric condensers are used to provide vacuum, because the tail water is usually discharged directly to the sewer and minimum solids are desirable to keep product losses and the BOD of the waste water to a minimum.

Distillation:

Distillation is the time-honored method for preparing high-quality pure water. Both dissolved and suspended solids can be removed almost completely by this purely physical process of evaporation and condensation. The condensate from a water distillation unit with good steam separator equipment,

45-51

and at normal evaporating rates, should contain no more than a few parts per million of dissolved solids and may contain only a fraction of one part per million. The suspended and dissolved solids of the feedwater remain in the evaporator salines and are removed by blowdown and descaling operations.

The high quality of its product gave the distillation process an initial advantage over other processes for the preparation of boiler feedwater. Distillation transfers a large part of the boiler water treatment problem from the plant boilers to low pressure evaporators where it can be more successfully handled. Single-effect and multiple-effect evaporators have found wide use in plants where large quantities of low level heat or exhaust steam otherwise would be wasted. Low level, or so-called waste heat, is not worthless; its cost is too often underestimated in the over-all plant heat balance and in the original plant design.

Compression distillation equipment may be economical where low level heat is not available in sufficient quantity or is being put to more valuable use. These units, employing the heat-pump principle of salvaging the latent heat of evaporation, have the heat economy of 15 or more effects of multiple-effect evaporation. Compression stills may be electrically driven or may be powered by prime movers. Diesel-driven compression distillation units can produce from 150 to 250 lb of distilled water per pound of fuel oil. With diesel fuel at ten cents per gallon, compression distillation can produce distilled water with a fuel cost of approximately 65 cents per 100 gal.

In industries where only a few parts per million of dissolved solids are allowable in the process water, either distillation or one of the deionizing processes (discussed under *Chemical Treatment*) can be used. The choice will depend largely upon the concentration of dissolved solids in the raw water.

Distillation equipment should be so designed that the scale and sludge problem can be handled with minimum labor. The problem is similar to that of a boiler except that the temperature usually is lower. Heat transfer rates at lower temperatures are more vulnerable to the insulating effects of scale and sludge deposits.

Extremely high quality distilled water can be obtained by multiple or fractional distillation. In the latter process, part of the product is condensed and refluxed to scrub entrained salts and solids from the steam being produced in the vapor generator. It is doubtful whether this quality will surpass that from a well-operated mixed-bed deionizer.

Underground Discharge:

Underground discharge is a method for disposal of liquid wastes into permeable strata in the earth. It is a satisfactory method only in areas where other methods are extremely expensive or unavailable. The permeable strata must be so located that the liquid waste pumped into them will not contaminate strata used for water supply. These permeable layers are very deep, 4000 to 5000 ft being usual. Furthermore, injection wells are very expensive.

The waste water must be sterile and free from suspended solids. Extensive pretreatment is essential to remove silt, suspended solids, oil, and emulsions. Chlorination is generally provided to make sure that it is free from microorganisms. Additional pressure above that developed by the depth to the aquifer is necessary to force the water into the strata; this may be as high as 200 to 300 psi.

This method has been used in only a few locations because of the extensive study required and the high cost of the installation. It does have its applications, however, and should not be overlooked.

Ocean Discharge:

Ocean discharge of waste water is practiced by plants in coastal locations. Actually, it is a dilution method. Consideration must be given to the path of ocean currents in the area of the outfall to insure that the waste water will not be carried to the shore and contaminate bathing beaches. The major cost for this method is construction of an outfall to such distance that safe disposal will result. Toxic wastes or those with a high BOD are usually transported by barge for release in deep water.

CHEMICAL TREATMENT

Chemical treatment pertains to those processes in which separation of the impurities from water involves chemical alteration of the contaminating material. It may include precipitation, ion exchange, sequestering reactions, gas removal, oxidation and reduction reactions, chemical control of biological growths, and sterilization.

Precipitation:

When certain soluble salts are added to an aqueous solution, some of the free ions may react to form comparatively insoluble compounds. The precipitate can be separated by filtration or by decanting the clear liquid after settling. Precipitation occurs in accordance with definite laws governing the combining weights of the reactants and their solubility products.[6] Many of the methods described below depend upon precipitation of impurities.

Softening.—The earliest commercial chemical precipitation process was the addition of hydrated lime ($Ca(OH)_2$) to water for removal of bicarbonate hardness. Lime converts bicarbonate hardness to relatively insoluble calcium carbonate:

$$Ca(OH)_2 + Ca(HCO_3)_2 \rightarrow 2CaCO_3 + 2H_2O$$

The process can be carried out in either batch or continuous equipment. In either type, close control of the lime dosage is necessary to approach the theoretical minimum hardness. Chemical cost is usually low if the lime particles are sufficiently small and good agitation is provided. Fine particles result from proper slaking of quicklime or thorough dispersion of hydrated lime.[7]

Removal of carbonate hardness by heating the water to drive off the dissolved and half-bound carbon dioxide accomplishes the same result as adding lime:

$$Ca(HCO_3)_2 + Heat \rightarrow CaCO_3 + H_2O + CO_2$$

Water containing noncarbonate hardness is only partially softened by adding lime alone. Noncarbonate hardness can be removed by adding soda ash (sodium carbonate):

$$CaCl_2 + Na_2CO_3 \rightarrow CaCO_3 + 2NaCl$$

Soda ash usually is combined with lime to remove both kinds of hardness in one step. The two reactions can be carried out simultaneously, hot or cold, in batch or continuous equipment. A coagulant generally is used to improve the separation of the solid phase.

Magnesium can be precipitated in a lime-soda softener by increasing the hydroxide alkalinity of the effluent to the point at which magnesium hydroxide is relatively insoluble. This can be accomplished with hydrated lime or caustic soda:

$$MgCl_2 + Ca(OH)_2 \rightarrow Mg(OH)_2 + CaCl_2$$

$$MgCl_2 + 2NaOH \rightarrow Mg(OH)_2 + 2NaCl$$

If magnesium is precipitated by lime, there is no appreciable reduction in

---

[6] D. S. McKinney, "The Calculation of Equilibria in Dilute Water Solutions," *Proceedings*, Am. Soc. Testing Mats., Vol. 39, p. 1191 (1939).

[7] R. D. Hoak, "How to Buy and Use Lime," *Water & Sewage Works*, Vol. 100, p. 468 (1953).

hardness unless additional soda is used to precipitate the calcium that replaces the magnesium. It is economical in some locations to use caustic soda alone instead of lime and soda for precipitating magnesium. This eliminates lime-slurry feeding problems and particle size difficulties.

Theoretically, magnesium can be precipitated only as described above. At several installations, however, where high-calcium hydrated lime alone was being used for calcium bicarbonate precipitation, it has been found that about 60 per cent of the magnesium was being precipitated, even though only a few ppm hydroxide alkalinity was present. This small amount was insufficient to precipitate the magnesium as the hydrate, but certain unusual equilibrium conditions produced the unexpected result. Total reduction of hardness was within normal limits in these instances, but the amount of calcium precipitated was less than normal. The operations were carried out in the cold in sludge-blanket units.

Most continuous process installations for lime-soda or caustic soda softening utilize accumulated sludge in suspension to promote growth of larger precipitation particles. This arrangement carries the chemical reaction and absorption processes to practical completion in a short time. The unit for performing this operation is known as a sludge-blanket precipitator. In older plants, settled sludge was mixed with the incoming water to produce the same effect. However, efficiencies were not as high as with the new units and the older method has been more or less abandoned.

Temperature plays a very important part in chemical reaction. Where low hardness is desired and hot water can be used, as in boiler feed, temperatures from 220 to 295 F are employed. A hardness of about 70 ppm is the best that can be produced at temperatures of 50 to 80 F,

but this can be reduced to about 25 to 30 ppm at 220 and to 10 at 295 F.

Zero hardness is desired for boiler feed makeup, and it is evident that the lime or lime-soda method will not provide this. Phosphate softening following hot lime-soda treatment is often used as a second softening stage; it is used for single-stage softening when the initial hardness is 30 ppm or less.[8] The theory involved is the precipitation of the calcium ion as the triphosphate, and insoluble material:

$$3Ca(HCO_3)_2 + 2H_3PO \rightarrow$$

$$Ca_3(PO_4)_2 + 6H_2O + 6CO_2$$

Any of the phosphates may be used; they are added in aqueous solution. Where the calcium hardness is mainly bicarbonate, phosphoric acid provides alkalinity control as well as lower total solids in the effluent. The reaction is carried out at a pH of 10 or higher with maintenance of a few ppm of hydroxide residual. The resultant hardness in the treated water is about 1 ppm $CaCO_3$ by gravimetric analysis. Caustic soda is used for precipitation of magnesium ion when phosphates are used to precipitate calcium.

In the past, especially in European practice, barium carbonate was used instead of lime for softening. This method has not found favor in America where it is used in only a few specific instances.

Internal Boiler-Water Softening.—Usually it is unsatisfactory to depend upon external softening alone for boiler makeup water, especially for high pressure boilers. Internal boiler water treatment may be required to convert scale-forming salts to soft sludges to be removed by boiler blowdown. Chemical compounds whose solubilities increase with a rise in temperature can be made

[8] E. W. Feller, "Fundamentals of Feedwater Treatment," *Power*, Vol. 91, p. 71, December, 1947.

to form nonadherent sludges;[9] those whose solubilities decrease with increase in temperature often form hard, adherent scale. Internal boiler-water treatment in actual practice is far more complex than these general principles indicate. This results from the wide variety of compounds and mixtures of compounds that can be formed in the boiler, and from the effects of organic matter and rates of evaporation on crystal structure.[10, 11, 12, 13]

It is not desirable to precipitate large quantities of minerals in a boiler, and internal boiler-water treatment preferably should be applied as a supplement to external chemical or physical treatment. Internal treatment alone may be satisfactory for low pressure boilers for which only moderate amounts of reasonably soft feedwater are required.

Bicarbonates and carbonates introduced with the feedwater or with internal treatment decompose in the boiler to produce carbon dioxide in the steam and to form hydroxides in the concentrated boiler water:

$$2HCO_3^- + Heat \rightarrow H_2O + CO_3^{--} + CO_2$$

$$CO_3^{--} + H_2O + Heat \rightarrow 2OH^- + CO_2$$

The hydroxides produced in this manner can precipitate the magnesium in the boiler water as magnesium hydroxide:

$$2OH^- + Mg^{++} \rightarrow Mg(OH)_2$$

<hr>

[9] Ralph E. Hall, et al., *Industrial and Engineering Chemistry*, Vol. 17, p. 283 (1925); *Ibid.*, Vol. 21, p. 826 (1929); *Technical Bulletin*, Carnegie Inst., Vol. 24 (1927).

[10] J. F. Barkley, "Questions and Answers on Boiler Feedwater Conditioning," Bureau of Mines, U. S. Government Printing Office, Washington, D.C. (1943).

[11] "Central Boiler Plants," *Technical Manual TM5-650*, Chap. 4, War Dept., U.S. Government Printing Office, Washington, D.C. (1947).

[12] "Boiler Feedwater and Feedwater Apparatus," *Bureau of Ships Manual*, Chap. 56, Navy Department, U.S. Government Printing Office, p. 56 (1948).

[13] D. S. McKinney, "Water for Steam Generation," Chemistry of Engineering Materials, McGraw Hill Book Co., New York, pp. 1–32 (1942).

During the decomposition of the bicarbonates and carbonates, some of the calcium of the boiler water is precipitated as calcium carbonate:

$$Ca^{++} + CO_3^{--} \rightarrow CaCO_3$$

The rate of decomposition of the bicarbonates and carbonates may be so rapid at boiler pressures above 5 psig that the calcium hardness is entirely precipitated and the hydroxide concentration becomes excessive. This difficulty is solved by using phosphates.[14] Internal softening with phosphates under proper conditions precipitates calcium hardness as tricalcium phosphate sludge.

Iron, Manganese, and Chromium Removal.—Iron and manganese can be removed by precipitation, using lime or caustic soda to adjust the pH to the proper range. Ground waters often contain iron and manganese that must be removed. These waters usually have very little color or turbidity except that due to those minerals. The iron is generally bound with carbon dioxide as the bicarbonate, and aeration is a necessary pretreatment to release the CO_2 and precipitate some of the iron. The addition of alkali converts the ferric iron to a hydroxide which settles out. For iron alone, a pH in the range of 8.5 is sufficient, but when manganese is present a pH above 9 is required. A coagulant is generally required to aid subsidence of the precipitate. Chlorine is often used to accelerate the rate of oxidation. Retention basins are necessary for separation of the precipitate. These may be followed by sand filters to provide a satisfactory final effluent.

Waste waters from plating operations may contain chromium, usually in the hexavalent form. Chromium in this form is toxic to aquatic and human life; it must be removed prior to final discharge.

<hr>

[14] R. E. Hall and H. A. Jackson, U.S. Patent No. 1,903,041 (1933).

The chromium is first converted to the trivalent form by lowering the pH to 2 with acid and adding reducing agent such as ferrous sulfate, sodium bisulfite, or sulfur dioxide. The chemical reaction is as follows:

$$2CrO_4^{--} + 3SO_2 + 4H^+ \rightarrow$$
$$2Cr^{+++} + 3SO_4^{--} + 2H_2O$$

The trivalent chromium is then precipitated as the hydroxide with lime and pH adjustment to some value between 7.8 and 8.5. Residual chromium can be reduced to very low limits by this method.

Emulsion Breaking or De-emulsification:

Organic oil emulsions in waste waters present a disposal problem because the emulsion will contain considerable organic matter with a high biochemical oxygen demand (BOD), and breaking the emulsion will release free oil which may not be discharged to surface streams. In many cases these emulsions can be broken by acidification below pH 4, but the resultant acid water is extremely corrosive and must be handled in acid-resisting structures. pH correction is required after sedimentation and before discharge to the receiving stream.

De-emulsification with calcium chloride and adjustment to pH 9 with soda ash is a method that has gained acceptance. The calcium chloride dosage is high, about 2000 ppm, but exceptional breaking and precipitation of the emulsion has been obtained with a resultant high percentage recovery of oil. The chemistry of this procedure is not fully understood, but full-scale installations have proved the feasibility of the process.

Ion Exchange:

It may be necessary to remove the cations or anions, or both, from water to provide a satisfactory supply for process and boiler feed uses. A preceding section described removal of cations by precipitation; this process had no effect on the anions present, and other means are required to remove them.

Certain insoluble substances possess a capacity for exchanging ions bound in their molecular structure with other ions in water. The exchanged ions are released by regeneration of the exchange resin. Negatively or positively charged ions may be exchanged, depending upon the nature of the resin. A wide variety of solid materials possess this reversible property. A characteristic difference between ion exchange and precipitation processes is that the former produces only solutions for waste disposal while the latter yields both liquid and solids. This important difference may be the deciding factor in a choice of process. Disposal of sludge from a precipitation process may make it uneconomical as compared with ion exchange. On the other hand, waste water from an ion exchange process may present a disposal problem.

Natural and synthetic substances (zeolites) have been used for many years to remove calcium and magnesium ions from water. These ions are then replaced by sodium ions when the zeolite is regenerated:

Softening:

Sodium zeolite + $Ca^{++} \rightarrow$
Calcium zeolite + $2Na^+$

Regeneration:

Calcium zeolite + excess $Na^+ \rightarrow$
Sodium zeolite + Ca^{++}

The process will operate equally well if the calcium and magnesium ions are replaced with potassium ions or with any other positive ions that can exist in a relatively concentrated neutral solution.

45-52

In the early years of the industry, zeolites were developed from natural greensand. Suitable treatment opened up the pores in the grains and hardened the surface. Exchange capacity, which was dependent upon pore area, was relatively low, about 2.8 kilograins (kgr) per cu ft. Capacities of 4.5 kgr were developed by either acid or heat treatment. The natural zeolites were not resistant to high or low pH water, and pretreatment of the raw water was often necessary because they were easily fouled by iron or organic matter. Synthetic gel zeolites were later produced and had very high capacities, but their use was rather restricted and they have gradually been abandoned in favor of the newer synthetic resins.

With advances in the art of ion exchange, carbonaceous and synthetic resin zeolites were developed that would withstand both acid and alkaline solutions and provide both cation and anion removal. Carbonaceous zeolites are limited to about 8 kgr per cu ft while the resins have a maximum of about 30 kgr.

In hydrogen cycle operation, the material exchanges hydrogen ions for calcium, magnesium, sodium, and other positive ions; it is regenerated with sulfuric or hydrochloric acid:

Hydrogen zeolite $+ Ca^{++} \rightarrow$

Calcium zeolite $+ 2H^+$

The effluent from hydrogen ion exchangers contains free mineral acidity, and it may be desirable to operate such installations in parallel with sodium cycle exchangers or to mix the effluent with untreated water to neutralize the acidity. The combination of sodium and hydrogen cycle ion exchange makes it possible to remove the hardness and reduce alkalinity at the same time. The bicarbonate hardness is converted into dissolved carbon dioxide which can be removed by degasification.

Where the anions must be removed from the water, the process is operated in two stages. The water first flows through a hydrogen regenerated cation unit and the acid effluent is then passed through an acid-absorber anion exchanger.

In this two-step process the acid effluent is usually degassed to remove free carbon dioxide before passing through the acid-absorbent exchanger to complete the deionization. The degassing step can be eliminated if a strongly basic, acid-absorbent exchange medium is used. If the hydrogen exchange of the first step is complete, the product from the final unit will be neutral and low in ionized solids. If the effluent from the hydrogen cycle contains positive ions, these ions with their negative components will pass through the acid-absorbent units and appear in the final effluent. It is therefore essential to have good operation of the hydrogen cycle in this process. Depending upon the solids in water, the two-step units will produce an effluent with a conductivity of about 1 mho. Two or more stages, or a mixed-bed unit, will be necessary if higher purity is required.

Weakly ionized materials in water passed unaffected through the older type of ion exchangers. Thus, silica was not removed by the original two-step hydrogen exchanger and weakly basic acid absorber. If the silica is converted into the strongly ionized fluosilicic acid by addition of fluorine compounds at some point in the process, the fluosilicic acid can be removed by the weakly basic acid absorber. The development of strongly basic acid absorbers has economically solved the problem of ion exchange removal of silica without the use of fluorine compounds.

In general, silica removal has been carried on along with anion removal using highly basic anion resins. Where softening and silica removal are required but not complete demineralization, the use of strongly basic anion exchangers following normal sodium regenerated cation exchangers has served the purpose economically. The capacity of anion resins for silica removal has been found to be a function of the caustic soda dosage used for regeneration. Silica reductions to 1 ppm from 35 ppm have been obtained by this method.[15]

Initial cost, process, and control problems of two-step deionization are now being reduced by the use of mixed-bed deionizers. The hydrogen exchange and acid absorbing materials are mixed intimately in a single bed in these units. A mixed-bed unit performs like multiple stages of the two-step process and can deliver water with extremely low ion content. The break-through of ions at the end of the operating cycle can be made extremely sharp with mixed bed units. During backwashing the two media separate by differential density, with the hydrogen exchanger below the acid absorber. The acid absorber can be regenerated with caustic soda and rinsed through the spent hydrogen exchange material. The hydrogen exchanger is then regenerated by introducing acid through a distributor located just below the anion absorber medium.

Ion exchange must compete with distillation for the production of high-purity industrial water. The choice between the two processes depends largely upon the total concentration of ionized and non-ionized substances in the water supply, and whether sterile water is required from the process.

Other forms of mixed-bed or multiple-bed ion exchangers are of commercial importance. One involves simultaneous sodium and chloride exchange, in which both kinds of ions in the regenerating solution serve a purpose. The sodium ions regenerate the cation exchange material, liberating calcium and magnesium ions, while the chloride ions regenerate the anion exchange material, liberating bicarbonate ions. These units will replace hardness with sodium ions and bicarbonates with chloride ions. The two ion exchange materials need not be completely mixed; the unit can be operated with the material in the layers that develop during backwashing.

This method is feasible, but it is not widely used. Two stages are employed more often, the first to remove calcium and magnesium, utilizing sodium chloride for regeneration. In the second stage, the anion material absorbs the bicarbonate ion and replaces it with chloride ion. Here a mixture of sodium chloride and caustic soda is used for regeneration. Although the salt performs the regeneration, the caustic has been found to lengthen the life of the resin, which results in higher capacity.[16]

Ion Exchange in Waste Treatment. — Ion exchange is being used to recover chromium from waste waters. The chromic acid waste is first passed through an anion exchanger to remove the chromium in accordance with the equation:

$$H_2Cr_2O_7 + R \cdot OH \rightarrow R \cdot CrO_3 + H_2O$$

The anion material is regenerated with caustic soda which releases the chromium as sodium chromate:

$$R \cdot CrO_3 + 2NaOH \rightarrow R \cdot OH + Na_2Cr_2O_7$$

The products of regeneration are then passed through a cation exchanger to

[15] S. B. Applebaum and B. W. Dickerson, "Silica Removal by Salt Splitting Without Demineralization," 16th Annual Meeting, Am. Power Conference, March 24–26, 1954.

[16] S. B. Applebaum, "Experiences with Chloride Anion Exchangers for Reducing Alkalinity Without Acid," 13th Annual Water Conference, Engineering Soc. Western Pa., October 20, 1952.

convert the sodium chromate back to chromic acid:

$$Na_2Cr_2O_7 + 2HR \rightarrow 2NaR + H_2Cr_2O_7$$

This treatment recovers the chromic acid and concentrates it for re-use.

The chromic acid content of plating waste waters varies from 100 to 500 ppm CrO_3. The recovered chromic acid has a concentration of about 30,000 ppm or 3 per cent CrO_3, which is sufficiently high for re-use. The waste water has been rid of dilute chromic acid and it can be re-used or discharged to a stream.

Ion exchange has also been used for recovery of certain ionized organic compounds. These include nicotine from water used to wash the gases from cigarette drying, and tartaric acid from winery wastes. Nonionized fruit sugars have been recovered from cannery wastes and citrus peels, and pectins from grapefruit wastes, by ion exchange. These are special applications but show the wide range of applicability of this process to the treatment of waste waters for product recovery.

Ion Exclusion.—A new technique, known as ion exclusion, has been evolved which has many possibilities in waste water treatment and certain process operations. It allows separation of ionic and nonionic materials, such as sodium chloride from ethyl alcohol, sodium chloride from formaldehyde, and sodium sulfate from glycerine. Thus, separations that were never economically possible are now quite feasible.

The method provides for alternate feeding of the aqueous solution of ionic and nonionic materials and water into an exchange column. One volume of feed solution is usually followed by one or more volumes of water. An aqueous solution of ionic material comes out of the column first, followed by an aqueous solution of the nonionic material. The separation of the ionic material from the nonionic material may be quite sharp.

Separations of this kind are possible because of the peculiar behavior of an ion-exchange bead in an aqueous solution of a mixture of an electrolyte and a non-electrolyte. In such solutions the electrolyte tends to be more concentrated around the bead, while the nonelectrolyte tends to have the same concentration within and outside the bead. This difference in concentration between the two solutes is the basis for the process. The ionic material appears to be rapidly flushed through the void spaces between the individual ion beads, while the nonionic material is retained in the column for a longer period since it diffuses through the resin beads as well as around them.

Resins used in ion exclusion do not need to be regenerated because they never become exhausted; the only operating cost is for water and pumping.[17]

Ion Retardation.—Another new ion-exchange process for separating water-soluble materials is ion retardation. This has resulted from development of a resin that has both anionic and cationic exchange sites located in the same bead. The resin will therefore adsorb both anions and cations from the feed solution. The resin sites are so closely associated, however, that they partially neutralize the electrical charges in each other; the adsorbed ions are thus weakly held and may be displaced from the resin by water alone.

Ion retardation is a column operation in which alternate portions of feed and rinse water are passed through the column, as in ion exclusion. It permits separation of two electrolytes, such as ferrous sulfate from zinc sulfate, sodium

---

[17] R. M. Wheaton and W. C. Bauman, "Ion Exclusion, a Unit Operation Utilizing Ion Exchange Materials," *Industrial and Engineering Chemistry*, Vol. 45, p. 228 (1953).

hydroxide from sodium chloride, and ammonium chloride from zinc chloride. It will also separate electrolytes from nonelectrolytes, and salts from very large nonelectrolyte molecules.

Like ion exclusion, this technique holds promise of adding another tool to the fractionation of process streams and treatment of waste waters.

Sequestering:

The sections above have been devoted to water-treating processes in which chemical constituents are removed as precipitates or by ion exchange. A third chemical method is that of sequestering the impurity into soluble complexes. In the sequestering process, certain normally positive ions, such as calcium and magnesium, are so strongly held in a complex negative ion that the equilibrium concentration of the free metal ion is extremely low. The concentration of free metal ions can be depressed by this process to the point where insoluble soaps will not form. Water so treated may have a soap hardness of zero, and it can even redissolve precipitated calcium soap.

Nearly 100 years were required between Thomas Graham's first studies of sodium metaphosphate and the general recognition that a soluble negative complex ion of calcium does exist. The discovery[18, 19] of the soluble phosphate-calcium complex was made with sodium hexametaphosphate. Many of the polyphosphates display this property in various degrees. Other chemicals have been found in recent years which are able to sequester hardness in true soluble complexes. Polysilicates are available that form soluble complexes with iron.[20]

Relatively large concentrations of treating chemicals usually are required to sequester effectively even moderate concentrations of undesirable constituents. Thus the sequestering process finds its most economic application as a supplementary or final treatment after the bulk of the undesirable constituents have been removed by a process having a lower unit cost.

Oxidation:

Surface and ground waters may contain odor- and taste-producing substances that make them unfit for drinking water and for some process uses. These substances are usually organic, and often they can be removed by oxidation.

Spray ponds provide one method for accomplishing this. Water is dispersed in the air as fine droplets by spraying it over a pond through nozzles. The intimate contact between water and air provides the desired oxidation. Usually any dissolved gases are released at the same time. A forced-draft degassing tower may be used in place of a spray pond; it should provide about the same efficiency.

Oxidation with chlorine, chlorine dioxide, or ozone can be used to convert objectionable organic matter into innocuous compounds. A short contact period, usually not over 10 min, is required for complete oxidation. Certain waste waters may contain taste-producing materials, such as phenol, in small volume but high concentration. Biological treatment under these conditions would entail a very large capital expenditure, but the operating cost would be low. The capital investment can be reduced materially by using chlorine or

[18] R. E. Hall, U.S. Patent No. 1,956,515 (1934), reissue 19,719 (1935); U.S. Patent No. 2,087,089 (1937).

[19] *Industrial and Engineering Chemistry*, Vol. 29, p. 584 (1937); *Ibid.*, Vol. 31, p. 51 (1939); *Ibid.*, Vol. 32, p. 1572 (1940).

[20] C. R. Henry, "Prevention of Settlement of Iron," *Journal*, Am. Water Works Assn., September, 1950.

chlorine dioxide, because the operation would be the equivalent of a waste treatment unit. The waste water flow would be the water supply to the chlorinator and it would be discharged as a treated effluent. The operating cost for such an arrangement might be rather high, but the low capital investment would make it attractive in many instances. The effluent will contain excess chlorine, and some retention is necessary before release to a stream.

Normal biological methods are usually prohibitive where waste waters contain more than about 3 per cent of soluble organic matter, because of the large dilution necessary for effective purification. A method known as wet combustion has been developed which provides efficient air oxidation through operation at elevated pressure and temperature.[21] The waste water is heated to not less than 350 C and the pressure raised to 2000 psi. Air is blown through the liquid under these conditions, and effective oxidation of the organic material takes place with purification efficiency well above 90 per cent. Power requirements for this process are very high, but with effective power and heat recovery, the economics of the operation are satisfactory.

A catalytic oxidation method has been developed for organic wastes plus water that are produced in the vapor phase and that can be prevented from condensing prior to treatment.[22] The waste feed is raised to 300 C and together with air in the ratio of 300 to 700 per cent of the requirement for oxidation, also heated to 300 C, is fed into a converter containing copper or manganese chromite catalyst maintained at about 600 C. The

reaction is exothermic and means must be provided to remove enough heat to hold the catalyst at 600 C. Conversion efficiencies of 90 per cent and above can be achieved by this method with organic concentrations as high as 8 per cent; the method is uneconomical at concentrations below 1 per cent.

Iron in water above 0.3 ppm and manganese over 0.2 ppm are generally objectionable. Both can be removed from most waters by lime-soda or caustic soda precipitation process. They also can be removed by oxidation, precipitation, and filtration because of the comparative insolubility of hydrated ferric and manganic oxides. Aerated water is passed through contact filters in which the filter medium acts as a catalyst for the oxidation reaction. Manganese is more dependent on catalytic contact than is iron in this process. Silica sand is often a suitable contact medium for iron removal, but complete manganese removal usually requires pyrolusite (manganic oxide) or special manganese zeolite. These manganese zeolite units are not cation exchangers but are contact oxidizers that are regenerated by treating zeolite with manganous sulfate and potassium permanganate. The higher oxides of manganese are deposited on the zeolite granules during regeneration. Contact with this material oxidizes ferrous and manganous ions to insoluble hydrated oxides which are then removed by filtration. Such units are employed most economically as a final treatment to remove the last trace of iron and manganese from effluents that already have been treated by a less expensive, but less efficient, process.

The sodium-cycle ion-exchange process will remove ferrous and manganous salts simultaneously with hardness if these metals are present as bivalent ions.

[21] F. J. Zimmerman, "New Waste Disposal Process," *Chemical Engineering*, August 25, 1958, p. 117.

[22] R. V. Green and D. V. Moses, "Destructive Catalytic Oxidation of Aqueous Waste Materials," *Sewage and Industrial Wastes*, p. 288 (1952).

Neutralization:

Neutralization of acidity or basicity may be necessary to provide satisfactory process water or for treatment of waste water. Many ground waters contain such high concentrations of carbon dioxide that the water is quite acidic. Aeration will remove most of the carbon dioxide, but not all of it, and the pH may still be so low that the water is corrosive for general purposes. Accordingly, neutralization is provided to raise the pH to the desired value.

Calcite filters, which consist of pressure vessels filled with pulverized marble, can be used if the quantity of water is small. The carbonic acid is neutralized by the calcium carbonate and the water is stabilized at the same time. Stabilization means that the alkalinity-pH ratio is automatically adjusted to provide a water neither corrosive nor scale-forming.

Alkali feeds are used where large volumes of water are needed. The solution feeder comprises equipment for continuously feeding a water solution of caustic soda, soda ash, or lime slurry. Provision is made for controlling the rate of chemical addition to maintain the desired pH value. The control may be manual or automatic, through a pH recorder-controller. Neutralization is not instantaneous and a contact period must be provided, usually not more than 5 min. The alkali solution may be fed by gravity or by pumping into the stream to be treated. Liquid storage tanks are usually designed for 12- to 24-hr operation between refills.

Chemicals may also be fed dry. Only soda ash or lime may be used in dry feeders because caustic soda is too hygroscopic to permit uniform feeding. The dry-feed machines operate either on the volumetric principle, in which a measured amount is displaced each stroke, or gravimetric, whereby the flow of dry material is weighed continuously. The dry chemical discharges into a mixing box where it forms a solution or a suspension. It is then allowed to flow by gravity, or pumped, to the point of application. These machines can be made to operate in proportion to flow rate or to pH response. Hoppers over the machines provide chemical storage of 8 to 24 hr.

Where lime or lime and soda methods of softening are employed, the effluent will contain caustic alkalinity. This excess alkalinity generally must be neutralized. This is done by adding acid, usually sulfuric or carbonic. The amount of acid fed is determined by the resultant pH value desired. The usual control is by a pH recorder-controller.

A 10 per cent acid solution is normally used to treat relatively small volumes of water. Concentrated acid is fed if the volume is large. A metering pump is to be preferred for acid feed in large-volume operations. The pump can be controlled for ratio-flow control, pH control, or a combination of both. Acid-resistant storage tanks, piping, and pumps must be used.

Both alkaline and acidic waters are encountered in waste treatment. Free mineral acids and free alkalies must be neutralized before discharging such waters. This means neutralization to the methyl orange or the phenolphthalein end point, respectively. Rarely is it necessary to go above pH 4.6 or below pH 8.3. The neutralized waste water will not reduce the total alkalinity in the receiving stream. It is very difficult to maintain pH values above 5 since slight increments in alkali feed cause wide swings in pH as neutrality is approached.

Where acid and alkali waste waters are discharged in the same plant, blending these may be all that is necessary for satisfactory neutralization. Any deficiency of one waste can be made up by a separate chemical feed and the final blended effluent can be discharged at the desired pH. The blending should be carried out in an acidproof tank providing sufficient time for full reaction. Neutralization studies in the laboratory will establish the period of retention required.

Consideration must be given to the type as well as the concentration of acids in waste waters that must be neutralized. Such acids as hydrochloric or nitric can be neutralized with lime without trouble since the salts produced are soluble in high concentrations. With sulfuric acid, there is a very definite limit if high-calcium lime is to be used; the acid concentration must be held below 0.3 per cent if calcium sulfate deposits are to be avoided. Concentrations up to 1 per cent can be handled successfully if dolomitic lime is used. If other acids are present, the resultant depression of calcium sulfate solubility must be taken into account. An example of this is a blend of neutralized nitric and sulfuric acids in which the calcium sulfate solubility was reduced to 1100 ppm from about 2000 ppm.

Acids can be neutralized by upward flow through granular limestone beds.[23] The flow rate is usually 25 to 40 gpm per sq ft of bed, and beds 3 to 5 ft in depth are placed in acid-resistant tanks. These beds are quite effective because of the turbulence created as the water is forced to flow upward. Sulfation must be avoided where sulfuric acid is neutralized or the limestone particles will cement together.

Gravity flow is necessary for handling large water volumes if high pumping costs are to be avoided. Usually both rate of flow and acid concentration will vary widely. The multistage neutralizer[24] can be used to deal with this difficulty. The neutralizer consists of several chambers in series, up to 6 in number, each provided with a mechanical mixer. The waste water flows from the top of one chamber to the bottom of the next one, thereby providing ample reaction time without short-circuiting. Lime slurry is fed at alternate chambers; the feed rate is governed by pH recorder-controllers. The first chambers of the multi-neutralizer function as equalizing units and the alternate ones as reaction vessels. Detailed reaction-rate studies must be made before designing such a system to establish total retention time, reaction time, and rate dosage.

Silo storage of burned lime is usually provided together with gravimetric feeders and slakers and effective slurry storage. The slurry, usually 10 per cent, is circulated past the feed valves and back to the slurry storage by centrifugal pumps. Provision must be made for holding constant back pressure on the feed valves. Excellent effluent control can be achieved with an installation of this kind for treating waste flows as high as 10 to 15 mgd with lime requirements of 120 tons per day.

Degassing:

Dissolved Carbon Dioxide.—Dissolved carbon dioxide can be chemically removed by adding lime, soda ash, or caustic soda to form soluble bicarbonates or relatively insoluble carbonates. This method requires careful chemical control. Approximately the same result can be obtained with less control and supervision by passing the water through a bed of material with which the dissolved carbon dioxide will react chemically to form a neutral or alkaline product. The

[23] H. W. Gehm, "Neutralization of Acid Wastes with Up-Flow Expanded Limestone Beds," *Sewage Works Journal*, Vol. 16, p. 104 (1944).

[24] B. W. Dickerson and R. M. Brooks, "Neutralization of Acid Wastes," *Industrial and Engineering Chemistry*, Vol. 42, p. 599 (1950).

most common material for this process is crystalline or granular calcium carbonate, such as crushed calcite or limestone. The calcium carbonate slowly dissolves by reaction with the carbon dioxide to form additional bicarbonate hardness in the water:

$$CO_2 + H_2O + CaCO_3 \rightarrow Ca(HCO_3)_2$$

Such a unit also acts as a filter, and periodic backwashing may be required. The initial investment is the principal cost of the process; chemical replacement and operating costs are small. The additional hardness added to the water by the process may be objectionable.[25]

Chemical Removal of Dissolved Oxygen. —To supplement physical deaeration, dissolved oxygen also can be removed from water by chemical means. Sodium sulfite is used extensively as a final treatment to consume the small trace of dissolved oxygen which is not removed by deaerating feedwater heaters. Sulfite reacts rapidly with dissolved oxygen at boiler water temperature to form sulfate:

$$2Na_2SO_3 + O_2 \rightarrow 2Na_2SO_4$$

It is easy to determine sulfite in boiler water, and the concentration and consumption of sulfite can be used as a convenient chemical integrator for checking the performance of the physical deaerating equipment. Sulfite at boiler water temperature may reduce certain chemicals, however, such as iron and copper salts, and a material balance may be slightly inaccurate. Ferrous iron salts and hydrazine have been used as oxygen scavengers. Colloidal iron, tannin, and other chemicals are also used for their oxygen-consuming properties.

Contact Reduction of Dissolved Oxygen. —Steel wool contact filters have been used in the past for dissolved oxygen re-

moval through oxidation of the metal, the products of corrosion largely remaining in the filter. Steel wool filters in some waters liberate ferrous salts which consume additional dissolved oxygen beyond the filter. The slow rate of oxygen consumption by steel wool contact filters has limited their commercial use. Contact reduction of dissolved oxygen can be brought about by a reversible oxidation reduction process using an amine exchange resin. Inasmuch as this material can be regenerated by chemicals it is similar to ion exchange.

Dechlorination and Removal of Gases by Chlorine. —Sulfite, sulfur dioxide, and thiosulfate or bisulfite can combine with dissolved chlorine in a dechlorination process. The reactions may be represented by the equations:

$$Na_2SO_3 + H_2O + Cl_2 \rightarrow Na_2SO_4 + 2HCl$$

$$SO_2 + 2H_2O + Cl_2 \rightarrow H_2SO_4 + 2HCl$$

$$2Na_2S_2O_3 + Cl_2 \rightarrow Na_2S_4O_6 + 2NaCl$$

Chemical methods usually are employed only for removing low chlorine residuals. Chlorine gas, on the other hand, may be used to convert ammonia or ammonium ions to chloramine, which can be removed from solution by aeration.

Sterilization and Disinfection:

In general, all waters, whether surface or ground, contain bacteria, the type and number depending upon existing conditions. Ground waters taken from sand strata usually are free of pathogens but may contain a fairly high count of soil organisms not harmful to man. Water taken from rock wells may or may not contain pathogenic organisms.

Surface streams are prone to bacterial contamination from both soil and man, the amount of the latter increasing greatly with sewage discharges. Other types of bacteria can be present in large

---

[25] W. J. Ryan, "Water Treatment and Purification" McGraw Hill Book Co., New York, p. 221 (1937).

numbers where industrial pollution is present.

Soil bacteria must be more or less completely removed from water for municipal supply, and pathogenic organisms must be absent. In industrial waters, small numbers of organisms can usually be tolerated, dependent upon process use. It is thus apparent that these organisms must be eliminated if satisfactory potable water supplies are to be provided.

Where small volumes require sterilization, as in the laboratory, heating to boiling temperature is sufficient. When continuous treatment is necessary, as in a water purification plant, bactericidal agents are employed. The most common of these is chlorine, either as a gas or as hypochlorite.

Feeding gaseous chlorine requires specially constructed equipment and, while the gas may be diffused into the water to be treated, the general practice is to feed an aqueous solution of it. This results in full utilization of the gas and better control. Gas chlorination is generally employed when 15 lb or more is required per day, because there is no saving in the cost of the feeding equipment below this quantity.

Bleaching powder, high-test calcium hypochlorite powder, or sodium hypochlorite solution are used where only small amounts of chlorine are needed. These solutions are fed by gravity or pumped into the system by a diaphragm pump. The available chlorine in these compounds is much more expensive than gaseous chlorine, but the low equipment cost and simplicity of operation more than offset the difference.

The amount required to provide a residual for sterilization is in general dependent upon the amount of organic matter in the water because this must be oxidized before there can be a residual. Most ground water is low in organic mat-ter, and the effluent from a filter plant is usually very low. Feed of 0.5 to 1 ppm under such conditions will provide a residual of 0.2 ppm as combined chlorine. Feed rates of 10 to 40 ppm may be required if the organic matter is high.

Chloramines are used where there is a large distribution system or a reservoir open to the sunlight, because chlorine alone may be dissipated too quickly to insure sterile water. Chloramines are formed by adding ammonia in a 1:4 ratio of ammonia to chlorine. The chloramines are not as active as free chlorine, and a minimum contact time of 15 min is required. Chloramines are very persistent, however, and they provide more satisfactory sterilization in long distribution systems.

It has been found that a combined-chlorine residual will not always destroy all of the microorganisms in the system and that tastes and odors sometimes occur in sequence. This problem is combated by maintaining a free-chlorine residual. This is done by feeding sufficient chlorine to oxidize all the organic matter, thereby to provide a residual of free chlorine. This practice is now followed at most waterworks.

Chlorine dioxide is a product that is finding favor in eliminating tastes and odors, for it is also an excellent sterilizing agent. This is produced by reacting sodium chlorite solution with a chlorine solution at pH 3.0. The resultant solution contains both chlorine and chlorine dioxide. Its use has been successful in eliminating tastes and odors in many cases when other methods have failed, and the residual appears to persist well.

Accessory equipment is required for making a solution of the chlorite and for feeding it. Furthermore, a reaction chamber is necessary for mixing the two solutions. The chlorine dioxide and chlorine combination is more expensive in terms of actual available chlorine, but with a difficult taste and odor problem it provides the only way to eliminate it.

Sterilization of water is also effected with ozone generated by passing an electrical discharge through dry air. It must be generated at the site in expensive equipment with a high electrical demand. The gas and air mixture is bubbled through the water as in a normal aeration system. The cost of installation and operation is considerably higher than for chlorinators except in large waterworks. In addition, measurement of residual ozone is nearly impossible; as a result, it has been used in very few locations.

Bromine possesses the same sterilizing properties as chlorine but it is a more difficult material to feed and control. So far, it has been used experimentally in some swimming pool installations.

Ultraviolet light can kill bacteria in clear water. The light must be generated at the point of use and the equipment is complex. A few experimental units have been installed in the past but the method has not been generally accepted.

Silver iodide has excellent disinfection properties when fed as a soluble salt. Its high cost precludes its use except during war emergencies. It was made in tablet form during World War II and was extensively used by the armed forces.

Control of Biological Growths:

Various biological growths in water may require chemical treatment, either to inhibit their growth, to kill them by sterilization, or to stimulate them with hydroponics. The objectionable organic growths in industrial water systems may include pathogenic and nonpathogenic bacteria, algae, slimes, iron and manganese bacteria, sulfur bacteria, and a host of other microscopic and macroscopic organisms. Some organic growths are dangerous to health, others cause bad tastes and odors, and still others cause clogging of equipment and piping.

Chlorination processes are effective for control of most biological growths in water.[26] Chromates and salts of copper, zinc, and silver also are used for this purpose. Organic compounds such as phenol, chlorinated phenol derivatives, naphthenates, quaternaries, and many others under a wide variety of tradenames are available for biological growth inhibition. Copper sulfate, with or without aliphatics such as citrates to keep the copper in dilute neutral solution, is used for the economical control of algae in large bodies of water such as reservoirs and lakes. Treatment with considerably less than 1 ppm of copper sulfate is usually satisfactory, depending upon the type of algae[27] and the care that must be taken not to kill fish. The amount of the treatment need only be sufficient for a limited top water layer and not for all of the water in the reservoir. For large quantities of water used only once, the economic choice for biological growth control is usually limited to copper sulfate, chlorination, and ozonation.

In smaller bodies where the water is re-used, as in circulating cooling water basins, treatment with other chemicals may be economical. Intermittent chlorination may be economically satisfactory for control of biological fouling in cooling water systems. Residual free chlorine in the order of 0.5 to 2 ppm in most cases is satisfactory for control of slimes and the spat or larval stage of larger organisms. Intermittent treatment with bromine also is used to a limited extent, especially for the control of such macroscopic organisms as mussels, which are resistant to chlorine.

---

[26] J. G. Dobson, "The Control of Fouling Organisms in Fresh and Salt Water Circuits," *Transactions*, Am. Soc. Mechanical Engrs., April, 1946.

[27] F. E. Hale, "The Use of Copper Sulfate in Control of Microscopic Organisms," Phelps Dodge Refining Corp. (1939).

Incineration:

Incineration is not usually considered as a waste disposal method but there are certain cases where it is applicable. When the volume of waste water is under 10 gpm and the soluble organic concentration above 4 per cent on a BOD basis, the waste can be sprayed into the boiler furnace for evaporation of water and combustion of organics. The boiler furnace must be large enough to handle the vapor load. Some additional fuel will be required, and the fuel-feed and burners must be of sufficient size to handle this increase. This method can generally be used only with oil-fired boilers. If the waste water contains toxic materials a modified unit provided with its own burner and fuel supply can be used effectively for destroying the compounds.

A great deal of study is necessary, followed by pilot operation, before incineration can be used effectively, but the technique does provide a satisfactory answer for certain waste water problems.

Physicochemical Processes

Several important water treatment processes depend upon combined chemical and physical action. These are coagulation, adsorption and absorption, crystal growth deactivators, additives for changing surface tension, and corrosion inhibition.

Coagulation:

Most surface waters contain suspended matter and color. Much of the suspended matter consists of particles too small to settle rapidly, even in quiet water. Color is caused by absorption of light by suspended and dissolved organic and mineral substances. A chemical coagulant, such as alum, ferrous or ferric sulfate, or sodium aluminate, will cause the finely divided and colloidally suspended materials to be gathered together into larger particles, called floc, which will settle rapidly. A flocculent precipitate which has enormous surface area per unit of volume is produced by coagulants. This precipitate removes suspended and colloidal matter from the water by electrophysical attraction, adsorption, absorption, and physical entanglement. For example, aluminum sulfate reacts with hydroxyl ions in water to form complex aluminum hydroxides that are relatively insoluble in the pH range from 6 to 8. The particles of precipitated aluminum hydroxide, with the help of suitable mild agitation, agglomerate into visible clumps which settle by gravity. The simultaneous formation, agglomeration, adsorption, and inclusion of the suspended matter and color into the floc is the physicochemical process of coagulation.

Each coagulant has a pH range in which it is most effective. The addition of the coagulant usually changes the pH of the solution at the time the floc is formed. Acidic coagulants such as aluminum and ferrous and ferric sulfates precipitate as basic compounds and reduce the pH of the water. When the natural alkalinity of the water is not sufficient to maintain the minimum pH requirement after coagulation, it is necessary to add lime or soda. The optimum range for coagulation with aluminum sulfate is between pH 5.5 and 7.0. Above 7.0 there is a tendency for some of the alum to remain unprecipitated and a small amount of residual aluminum will remain in the final filtered water. When the pH of the raw water gets above 7.2, the amount of coagulant necessary to drop the pH into the optimum band may be too great economically, especially if the coagulation pH is 6.3 to 6.4 for the water. Accordingly, sulfuric acid is added ahead of or with the aluminum sulfate to reduce the pH to the proper range for good coagulation. Sulfuric acid will lower the pH much faster and at less expense than the coagulant.

Ferric sulfate is an effective coagulant over the wide pH range of 5.5 to 10. It has an acidic reaction and lowers the alkalinity of the water. Ferrous sulfate, while effective over a wide range, is generally used between pH 8.5 to 10. In addition to requiring alkalinity for coagulation, there must be an oxidizing agent to convert the ferrous iron to the ferric state. Usually there is enough dissolved oxygen in the water to complete the oxidation; if insufficient, some form of aerating device is employed to increase the oxygen content. Chlorine also is frequently added for this purpose.

Many factors affect the amount of coagulant needed for optimum results. Among these are type and amount of suspended matter, water temperature, rate of mixing, and retention time. Coagulant dosage may vary from 5 ppm for a good water very low in turbidity and color to 100 ppm or more for a highly turbid one. Presettling is usually provided when turbidities continually run over 400 to 500 ppm, to reduce the coagulant requirement.

Continuous and proportionate feeding of the coagulating chemical is necessary for effective coagulation. In addition, control of the pH in the optimum range is essential. The coagulant can be fed dry or in solution, depending upon the amount to be fed and specific conditions. Usually quantities up to 100 lb per day are fed as a solution. Above this, dry feed machines are employed with a dissolving tank so that a dilute solution is fed; with proper physical arrangement the dry material can be fed directly into the water.

The coagulant should first be thoroughly dispersed in the stream to be treated. This is accomplished in a high-speed mixing chamber having a retention of from 0.5 to 1.0 min. After the dispersion, the finely formed flocs require agglomeration by very gentle agitation so they can develop into large masses. Slowly revolving paddles in a chamber providing from 40 to 60 min retention will bring the floc to maximum development and produce one that will settle rapidly and provide a satisfactory supernatant for filtration.

Adsorption and Absorption:

The processes of adsorption and absorption of organic and colloidal materials into flocculent precipitates with a resultant increase in sedimentation rate are used to remove color, taste, and odors from water. High silica concentrations also can be economically decreased by ferric and magnesium flocs. These processes are more efficient in terms of chemical consumption when the flocculent precipitate develops in the water than when a preformed precipitate is added.

Adsorption on ferric hydroxide can reduce the silica content to 2 or 3 ppm. The initial reduction occurs rapidly, but suitable mixing and retention time are required to attain minimum concentrations. The process operates best in the cold. Magnesium hydroxide also will remove silica and often is used in the lime-soda precipitation process for silica adsorption and precipitation. Magnesium can be added to the water as magnesium carbonate, magnesium bicarbonate, or magnesium oxide. Magnesium hydroxide requires a longer contact time than ferric hydroxide for maximum silica reduction. It differs from the ferric hydroxide process in that warming the water improves silica reduction. The pH for magnesium hydroxide formation must be above 10.2, which is the usual condition with lime-soda softening. On the other hand, the ferric hydroxide process is usually carried out separately because the pH for its most economical silica reduction is about 9.0.

Taste, odor, and some dissolved gases often can be removed from water by adsorption on activated carbon. This material can be added as a powder to the filter influent and removed from the filter bed during backwashing. Activated carbon filters of granular or powdered activated carbon are available for filtered water service. Activated carbon may be partially regenerated by steam or other gases. Activated carbon filters are also used for dechlorinating water.

Crystal Growth Deactivators:

The surface deactivation properties of numerous chemicals are employed in a variety of treatment processes for retarding or inhibiting crystal growth. The polyphosphates have this property in various degrees. Organic materials, such as tannin, lignin, and many others, have surface deactivation properties. Crystal surfaces are believed to be covered with molecular or submicroscopic films of the surface deactivator, thereby reducing, altering, or inhibiting further crystal growth.

Threshold treatment is an example in which calcium carbonate deposits are inhibited, although concentrations above the normal solubility of the scale-forming material are present. Calcium phosphate precipitation in feedwater equipment can be inhibited in the same manner. This technique is also used to retard precipitation of ferric iron in water containing dissolved oxygen; thus red-water troubles frequently can be reduced by crystal deactivation.

Surface deactivation is used as an aid in keeping trace elements in solution for hydroponics, in limiting crystal size, and for many other special uses. An ever-increasing number of surface active chemicals, under a wide variety of trade names, are available to the water conditioning engineer.

Additives for Surface Tension Changes:

Numerous chemicals have the property of significantly changing the natural surface tension of water. Chemicals which markedly decrease surface tension are called wetting agents, and those which materially increase surface tension are often spoken of as foam suppressors. Wetting agents in a wide variety of commercial forms are available for many industrial uses, such as ore-separation processes, laundry operation, fire fighting, acid cleaning, and a host of others. Numerous chemicals that increase the surface tension of water also are commercially available for reduction of foaming and priming difficulties in steam generators.

Corrosion Inhibition:

Water conditioning for corrosion control involves both physical and chemical processes operating together. Protective films that inhibit metal deterioration are physical barriers. The formation and maintenance of such films may be the result of chemical reactions. These physicochemical corrosion inhibition processes are briefly described in the following three sections.

Cathodic Protection.—The electrolytic theory of iron corrosion, as postulated by Whitney[28] and demonstrated by Walker and associates,[29] is essential for understanding the process of cathodic protection.[30] According to this theory, metals in contact with water tend to go into solution, forming positively charged ions. Positive ions can go into solution in an electrically neutral system only if an equivalent number of positive ions of some other element are plated out. In

[28] W. R. Whitney, "The Corrosion of Iron," *Journal*, Am. Chemical Soc., Vol. 25, p. 395 (1903).

[29] W. H. Walker, A. M. Cederholm, and L. N. Bent, "The Corrosion of Iron and Steel," *Journal*, Am. Chemical Soc., Vol. 29, p. 1251 (1907).

[30] J. M. Pearson, "Fundamentals of Cathodic Protection," Corrosion Handbook, p. 923, John Wiley & Sons, Inc., New York (1948).

the case of pure water in contact with a metal, such as iron, hydrogen ions are plated out at the interface. The reaction may be written:

$$Fe \quad + 2H^+ \rightarrow Fe^{++} + 2H$$

Metal   Ions   Ion   Atoms

The liberated hydrogen forms a thin, insulating film on the metal which prevents further corrosion. Thereafter the corrosion reaction proceeds at a rate that is a function of the rate of removal of the layer of atomic hydrogen. The observed effects of dissolved oxygen, temperature, pH, salt concentration, and turbulence on this protective hydrogen film on iron and steel have been found to agree with this theory.[31] Any method for maintaining the protective hydrogen film will reduce corrosion.

Galvanizing steel provides a form of cathodic protection. Here the protective hydrogen film is maintained on the exposed steel cathode at the expense of the zinc anode, which slowly goes into solution. Magnesium and zinc rods or plates suspended in water and electrically connected to the steel tank are further examples of cathodic protection. In other forms of this process, direct current is supplied from an outside source to maintain the protective hydrogen film on the steel cathode and a corrosion-resistant anode is used. A sacrificial anode, such as an abandoned pipe line, also can be used. Various types of commercial equipment are available to provide cathodic protection. Cathodic protection often is used to inhibit corrosion in cold-water tanks and pipe lines. By a variation of this process, hulls of steel ships can be protected from electrolytic corrosion caused by copper-alloy propellers.

Physicochemical Corrosion Barriers.— Any type of continuous film that is

chemically inactive in water and is tenaciously attached to the metal will inhibit aqueous corrosion. Painting and molten-metal plating are examples of physicochemical corrosion barriers. A corrosion-inhibiting film also can be developed from the metal itself by chemical action. Metal oxide finishes and chromate, silicate, phosphate, and tannate films are examples of chemically produced corrosion barriers. The art of chemically producing and maintaining uniform corrosion-resistant films on the various engineering materials is a complex field.

A well-maintained steel boiler might be defined as a clean, thin, continuous film of water-insoluble material, reinforced by steel, and used to generate vapors. The development and maintenance of this thin continuous film, usually consisting of metal reaction products, depend on many factors. Raising the pH of the water in contact with steel to between 10.5 and 11.7 to develop a more uniform protective film is common practice for steam boilers. Other conditions such as the removal of dissolved oxygen and carbon dioxide by physical or chemical deaeration will improve the uniformity and tenacity of the protective film. Filming amines are also used to provide a monomolecular protective film.[32,33] Venting of such gases as carbon dioxide[34] from steam condensate systems results in an increased pH and improves the protective film. In open cooling-water systems, chromates[35] and silicates[36] are

[31] F. N. Speller, "Corrosion, Causes and Prevention," McGraw Hill Book Co., New York, 3rd Ed. (1951).

[32] F. N. Speller, *Proceedings*, Nat. District Heating Assn., Vol. 24, p. 203 (1933).

[33] A. A. Berk, U.S. Bureau of Mines, Report of Investigation No. 3754.

[34] E. W. Guernsey, *Transactions*, Am. Soc. Heating and Ventilating Engrs., Vol. 51 (1945).

[35] Marc Darrin, "Chromate Corrosion Inhibitors in Bimetallic Systems," *Industrial and Engineering Chemistry*, Vol. 37, p. 741 (1945).

[36] L. Lehrman and H. L. Shuldener, "The Role of Sodium Silicate in Inhibiting Corrosion by Film Formation on Water Piping," *Journal*, Am. Water Works Assn., Vol. 43, March, 1951.

widely used for the development of thin, uniform protective films on steel. Organic materials such as tannin and lignin compounds are also used for this purpose.

The polyphosphates[37] under controlled conditions can form protective films on steel and cast iron. Polyphosphates, organics, and chromates are often used together for cooling-tower corrosion inhibition. Where serious deposits of calcium carbonate scale will not develop, it is sometimes desirable to increase the pH in cold, hard-water lines[38] by a controlled lime treatment to reduce corrosion. All the above processes are used for the purpose of developing and maintaining a thin, uniform, tenacious film to keep corrosion of pipe and equipment at minimum levels.

Inhibition of Biological Corrosion.— The chemistry of biological corrosion is still in its infancy. It is believed that dilute sulfuric and nitric acids can be produced on the surface of metals by biological reactions in polluted waters. Elimination of the acid-producing organisms should prevent biochemical corrosion of ferrous and copper-alloy tubing. These organisms can be controlled by the same general processes used in physical and chemical regulation of biological growths.

Liquid-Phase Separation:

With the steadily increasing demand for water, considerable thought has been given to the purification of sea water, and it is here that the liquid-phase separation is being widely investigated.

The development of ion-selective membranes has led to their use in this work. Membrane electrolysis employs a stack of alternating cationic and ionic selective membranes which provides a series of parallel cells through which the raw water flows. An electric potential across the stack causes the cations and anions to move in opposite directions and to pass through the appropriate selective membranes. As a result, ions tend to leave alternate cells and to concentrate in the cells between them. Thus the stack continuously discharges two streams, one relatively demineralized and the other proportionately concentrated in the abstracted ions. The process shows promise as an economical method for desalting brackish water.

Osmoionic demineralization is another method being studied for purifying salt water with ion-selective membranes. No electricity is required, because the method uses osmotic pressure to move ions through the membrane. The procedure is effective for desalting brines with chloride concentrations in the range of 3000 ppm.

Dialysis and electrodialysis have been used in the treatment of certain waste waters. These methods separate ionizable salts from colloidal suspensions. The ionized salt passes through a membrane and leaves the colloidal material behind. Depending upon the material to be separated and the conditions at hand, electricity may be used as an additional driving force. These methods are being used for alkali and acid separation and recovery from process liquors.

BIOLOGICAL TREATMENT

Percolation of raw surface water through a bed of fine, graded sand is one of the oldest methods of water purification. These units, after a period known as seasoning or ripening, had the ability to remove turbidity, color, and bacteria. Although primarily a straining device, the ability of these beds to remove bacteria, finely divided material, and

[37] G. B. Hatch and Owen Rice, "Factors in Formation of Protective Films upon Steel by Waters Treated with Glassy Phosphates," *Industrial and Engineering Chemistry*, Vol. 37 (1945).

[38] S. T. Powell, "Corrosion Inhibition by Lime Treatment," *Industrial and Engineering Chemistry*, Vol. 26 (1934).

color resulted from a gelatinous growth on the surface of the bed. This coating was known as schmutzdecke and comprised organic material derived from living and dead organisms such as bacteria, diatoms, algae, and lower forms of life. This material provided the major purification; the bed of sand was essentially a support for the schmutzdecke. Excellent purification resulted, although at very low rates of flow, the normal being 2.5 to 3.0 million gal per acre per day (mgad). These slow-sand filters have been almost completely supplanted by mechanical sand filters which are supplied with water from which the bulk of the suspended matter has been removed by chemical pretreatment.

Biological purification is widely used for treatment of waste water containing dissolved organic matter. Bacteria break down the complex compounds into simple, stable ones; the usual end products are carbon dioxide, water, nitrate, and sulfate. This change is brought about through the metabolism and cell synthesis of the microorganisms present. Usually these processes are carried out in the presence of excess dissolved oxygen, and the operation is then known as aerobic decomposition. Another group of microorganisms can thrive in an environment devoid of dissolved oxygen. Under these conditions the process is known as anaerobic decomposition. Although most biological treatment today is aerobic, there are some wastes which respond better to anaerobic decomposition.

There are two broad types of biooxidation equipment, trickling filters and activated sludge. The trickling filter is a bed of graded rock, usually 3 to 6 ft deep, but sometimes as deep as 10 ft. The bed diameter may vary from 15 to 200 ft. The rock is supported by an underdrain system for collection of the liquid flowing over it. A rotary distributor on the top provides for uniform spreading of the waste water on the bed. The underdrain system has air ducts which allow air to circulate through the bed by natural draft; this provides the oxygen necessary for good biological action. The stone provides a large surface for growth of the organisms that accomplish aerobic decomposition. The units are classed high or low rate depending upon the rate of operation. Up to 5 mgad is considered low rate, while 10 to 30 mgad is high rate. Biochemical oxygen demand (BOD) is the design criterion. The volume of the filter is based upon decomposition of 1 to 5 lb of BOD per cu yd of stone per day. The diameter is fixed by the rate of application and volume of waste water to be handled per day. Actual design should be developed only after pilot plant studies of the waste water in question. Efficiencies of single filter units range from 35 to 85 per cent removal of BOD. Where higher efficiencies must be provided, a second unit is installed to operate in series with the first to provide two-stage treatment. Under such conditions, 80 to 95 per cent purification can usually be obtained.

In the activated sludge process the waste water to be treated is held for a period of time in a tank in which air is blown through the liquid. This develops a lush bacterial suspension which brings about aerobic decomposition. The retention time is dependent upon the waste treated but will usually range between 4 and 24 hr. BOD in lb per day is the design criteria for these units and the loading will vary between 15 and 150 lb per 1000 cu ft of aeration tank volume. The air required is supplied by rotary compressors or centrifugal blowers. The diffuser system may be perforated pipe, nozzles, carborundum plates or tubes, and, just recently, turbo-mixers provided with a sparge ring. Purification efficiencies will range from 75 to 95 per cent depending upon the waste water and the concentration of bacteria in the aeration tank water. Higher efficiencies can generally be obtained with higher bacterial concentrations, but this must be balanced against an increased air requirement. The concentration of bacterial slime (reported as suspended solids) will range from 2000 to 5000 ppm.

Biological purification produces sludge, whether by trickling filters or by activated sludge. This must be removed from the effluent before final disposal. Settling basins providing from $1\frac{1}{2}$ to 5 hr retention permit the solids to settle. Scrapers move the settled material to a central point for removal. The sludge produced by trickling filters is removed completely from the system. In the activated sludge process, a portion is returned and mixed with the raw waste water entering the aeration tank. The excess over that necessary to maintain a satisfactory concentration of suspended solids in the aeration tank is removed from the system.

The wasted sludge must be disposed of in some manner. This can be a problem because of its fairly large volume, inability to dry readily on a sand bed, and evolution of offensive odors. Bacterial decomposition of the wet sludge under anaerobic conditions will yield a sludge that dries well and has little odor; this process is widely used for sludge treatment. Closed concrete tanks providing from 25 to 60 days retention and heated to about 90 F hold the raw sludge and allow bacterial decomposition to occur. The volatile solids are broken down from about 75 to 80 per cent to about 50 per cent and in so doing CO_2, methane, and nitrogen are given off as gases. If a sufficient volume of gas is evolved it can be burned for heating the tanks and also used for operating gas engines in the plant.

There have been many adaptations of the activated sludge process to serve particular purposes. Among the best known of these are the Guggenheim, Kraus, contact aeration, dispersed-growth aeration, and biosorption methods. These have all been described in various texts and they will not be discussed here.

Where the effluent from the treatment plant must discharge into a very small stream, the amount of organic material remaining in the treated water may be too large for inoffensive assimilation; in such cases additional purification becomes necessary. Here use is made of the oldest type of biological unit, the slow sand filter. This is simply a sand bed which is dosed intermittently with the effluent from the treatment plant. Slime growths develop on the sand and additional purification and straining take place. The effluent flowing from the underdrains is clear and has a very low BOD. The rate of flow through these filters is extremely low and extensive land areas are required, but they can do a most effective job.

Modifications of the slow sand filter are the percolation bed and spray irrigation. These use large areas of land where the soil is sandy and little or no clay is present. Percolation beds make use of the sandy soil above the ground water table and require 5 to 8 ft of depth for good operation. Low dikes are built and means provided for dosing the areas once a day Dosing is normally equivalent to flooding to a depth of about 2 in.

The waste is usually diluted with water to provide a BOD of 300 to 500 ppm and applied to give a BOD loading of 100 to 200 lb per acre per day. Under such conditions, purification efficiencies of 90 to 98 per cent have been obtained. Biological growths develop in the sand which utilize the soluble organic material in the waste water as food and thereby provide purification. Air is drawn into the soil during the dosing period; this provides the oxygen needed by the organisms.

Spray irrigation utilizes the same general principle. Rotating sprays or fixed sprays spread the diluted waste over a large area, which can be crop land or wooded areas. The spray period usually lasts from 8 to 12 hr per 24 hr. Sandy soil is a requisite, and purification is effected by biological growths in the soil. The sprayed waste water should be low in suspended solids to avoid plugging of the soil. While this method has been primarily developed for disposal of cannery and milk wastes, it is applicable to almost any easily oxidized, nontoxic waste.

A modification of the activated sludge process is the oxidation pond. In this adaptation the waste water is held in a shallow pond for a period of days. Aeration from the atmosphere takes place and bacterial growths develop. These ponds can remove 95 per cent of the BOD and kill 99 per cent of the coliform bacteria; thus purification is generally sufficient to allow discharge of the effluent into streams. These stabilization ponds have been quite widely used in the paper industry and they are gaining acceptance in the textile and chemical industries. They are used as a low cost method for municipal sewage treatment.

Summary

An attempt has been made to enumerate the principal water treatment processes serving industry at the present time. New processes will undoubtedly be developed in the future. The discussion has been limited to the main technical and economic features. Literature references have been given for readers desiring greater detail.

CHAPTER VI
Sampling and Flow Measurement of Industrial
Water and Industrial Waste Water

CHAPTER VI—SAMPLING AND FLOW MEASUREMENT OF INDUSTRIAL WATER AND INDUSTRIAL WASTE WATER

A satisfactory sample of industrial water or waste water must meet two basic requirements: it must accurately represent the large or small mass sampled and it must be of adequate size for subsequent laboratory examination. Since industrial water and waste water must be sampled under a great variety of conditions, there is no single method that can be universally applied. The method, location, and time of sampling must be coordinated so the results obtained will serve the purpose for which the sample is intended.

Industrial waters or waste waters are not fixed in their compositions but show appreciable changes depending upon their sources, seasonal precipitation, temperatures, pollutional wastes, and industrial processes. This chapter discusses variations in composition of industrial water and waste water related to environment and the mechanics of the sampling operation. These should serve as guides in determining the frequency of sampling, the appropriate points, and suitable sampling apparatus.

In the study of industrial water as an engineering material, and in the handling, treatment, and disposal of industrial waste water, flow measurement is an essential function demanding applications of many types of flow-measuring devices and equipment to suit specific conditions. A brief summary of the classes and categories of flow-measuring devices, fundamentals of flow measurement, and description of flow devices and the important points to consider in their selection is included as part of this chapter.

Manual Sampling

Types of liquid samples are broadly classified into two major groups, one called instantaneous, spot, snap, or grab samples, and the other integrated, continuous, or composite samples. A grab sample is a manually collected single portion of industrial water or waste water which serves as a spot check and is useful for investigating abnormal characteristics. A series of grab samples is necessary for tracing constituent variations. The volume of individual samples will depend on the analysis requirements. If samples are to be composited, the volume collected must be more than needed for the proportional part of the composite. To prevent serious errors in suspended solids concentration in composite samples, the original grab samples must be kept well mixed while transferring from one container to another.

Composite samples correlated with flow show the average conditions. The results are particularly useful in computing quantities of waste material discharged over a specified period of time. If the rate of flow is constant, the composite is made up of a number of uniform portions collected at frequent regular intervals. When the rate of flow varies, a weighted composite is collected. For this case, the volume of each portion is proportional to the rate of discharge at the time it is collected. Since it is generally desirable to minimize the

87

amount of analytical work, samples are composited over 4-, 8-, or 24-hr periods, depending upon conditions.

Manual sampling provides basic information useful in preparing specifications for mechanical devices designed for automatic and continuous sampling of industrial water and waste water.

CONTINUOUS SAMPLING

If it is necessary for sampling to extend over a considerable time, or when a

permit complete description of the many automatic devices suitable for continuous sampling of industrial water and waste water, the reader is referred to other sources for additional detailed information.[1,2]

SAMPLING AT ATMOSPHERIC PRESSURE

In general, industrial water has its origin in rain and melted snow reaching streams by direct runoff over the surface of the ground and by underground seep-

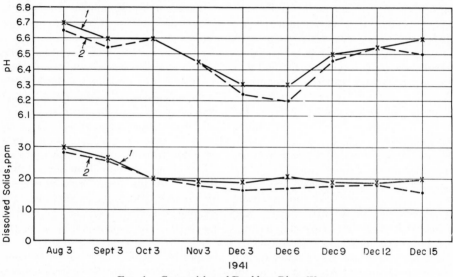

FIG. 1.—Composition of Davidson River Water.
Curve 1 = Sampling station 3 miles from mouth.
Curve 2 = Sampling station 4 miles from mouth.

continuous record of conditions at a given sampling point is required, it will be most practical to install automatic continuous sampling equipment. Correctly designed and installed, a continuous sampling devide will provide more frequent samples than is practical by manual sampling, eliminate errors due to the human element, reduce costs for supervision, and eliminate the tedious routine work required by manual sampling.

Since the scope of this chapter does not

age. It contains very little dissolved material before starting to flow on the surface or through the earth. Where the soil and surface rocks are practically insoluble, the surface and seepage waters dissolve very little mineral matter. Mountain streams usually show little variation in composition for miles. The

[1] Hayse H. Black, "Procedures for Sampling and Measuring Industrial Wastes," *Sewage and Industrial Wastes,* Vol. 24, p. 45 (1952).

[2] Ohio River Valley Water Sanitation Commission, "Planning and Making Industrial Waste Surveys," Cincinnati, Ohio, 1952.

sampling of such water, therefore, is relatively simple except during flood stages when there are rapid changes in turbidity. This is important in the operation of a filtration plant. Normally a sample taken at almost any location will meet the two basic requirements of satisfactory sampling. The data in Fig. 1[3] are an excellent example of this.

Usually water entering rivers as a result of seepage contains larger quantities of minerals in solution than water flowing over the surface of the ground, since the contact time is much longer. Hence, during periods of drought, the

sence of mixing is obvious at the junction of a muddy stream and a clear one, or of two streams of different color. An extreme example of the variation in composition from bank to bank is the Susquehanna River in Pennsylvania. The eastern branch drains the northern anthracite coal fields and is usually highly acid. The western branch drains agricultural and forested lands and is usually alkaline. More than 75 miles below their confluence, these two streams still are not thoroughly mixed. The eastern branch maintains its identity as an acid water along the left bank; the western

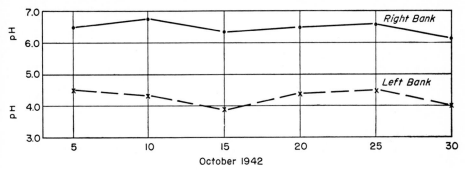

Fig. 2.—Cross-Channel Sampling of Susquehanna River Below Sunbury, Pa.

concentration of dissolved material in a river is high because most of the water flows from aquifers. On the contrary, during flood stage, the dissolved mineral content of a river water is low because it is receiving the bulk of water from surface runoff. The reverse is true with respect to suspended solids. The nature of the soil and rocks over which a river flows is an important factor in determining the kind and quantity of dissolved minerals which the stream carries.

The problem of sampling becomes quite involved for rivers flowing through highly industrialized or mining areas. Here there may be little mixing, even over a considerable distance. This ab-

branch retains its alkaline characteristics along the right bank. Figure 2[4] presents typical results of cross-channel sampling of the Susquehanna River about 60 miles below the confluence.

Complete study of water composition in a river basin would require a large number of sampling stations and samples taken at frequent intervals. The cooperative studies by the Pennsylvania Department of Commerce and the U.S. Geological Survey[5] comprise such an extensive sampling program.

---

[4] W. F. White, "Chemical Quality of Industrial Surface Waters of Pennsylvania," paper presented at the Tenth Annual Water Conference, Engineering Soc. of Western Pa., October 1949.

[5] "Industrial Utility of Water in Pennsylvania," Publication 17, Pennsylvania Dept. of Commerce, State Planning Board, August, 1947.

---

[3] Private communication from Cyrus William Rice and Co., Inc., Pittsburgh, Pa.

The sampling effort for one plant at a river location would not be so extensive. Usually a single station and daily sampling are adequate. Occasionally more frequent sampling is required, for example, during flood stage when the turbidity of river water changes rapidly. Figure 3 shows the course of such a change during a period of heavy rainfall.

The characteristics of water in a stream flowing through semiarid country usually change more rapidly than in more humid low-water periods. In the lower part of some estuaries, the salt water will remain at or near the bottom, while the fresh water flows near the tops. In such locations, an elaborate schedule of frequent sampling from many stations at various depths is required to make certain that sea water will not intrude unexpectedly.

Large lakes usually remain constant in composition over long periods of time. The Great Lakes, for example, need be

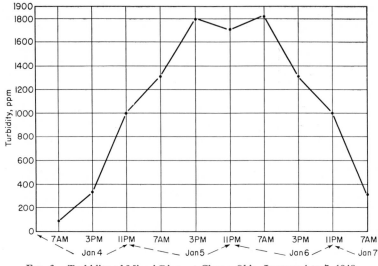

FIG. 3.—Turbidity of Miami River at Cleves, Ohio, January 4 to 7, 1949.

sections. Here the surface rocks and soil are fairly soluble, and the runoff of each storm quickly dissolves appreciable amounts of minerals. Streams in such areas should be sampled at frequent intervals during times of changing stream flow.

For industries located on streams near tidewater, the water taken from the stream must be checked frequently at various depths to insure the desired quality for the particular industrial use. Plants located far enough upstream to be free of salt during flood stage may encounter sea water intrusion during low-water periods.

sampled only three or four times a year to define their characteristics for most purposes. An exception to this would be for an industrial operation located near the discharge of a river or for some type of pollution.

Representative sampling of most small lakes will depend on the stream that flows into the lake basin. Some small lakes may be fed by more than one stream. The characteristics of the water in the streams therefore will govern the sampling schedule for the lake.

The composition of the water in a deep lake may vary considerably with depth, as shown in Fig. 4. The most favorable quality for a given industrial use should be determined by sampling at different levels.[6] Seasonal changes may make several sampling stations necessary. The concentration of dissolved oxygen and carbon dioxide varies considerably with both depth and the season.[7] Generally, the dissolved oxygen decreases as both depth and temperature increase.

Another factor that must be considered in the sampling of deep lakes is that they decided by the number and composition of streams feeding such lakes.

Reservoirs can usually be considered as lakes, but the phenomenon of a density current frequently is characteristic of deep reservoirs and occasionally of shallow basins. A density current is a stream of water that maintains its identity, with respect to both chemical composition and suspended solids, for long distances beneath the surface of the reservoir. It is caused by difference in

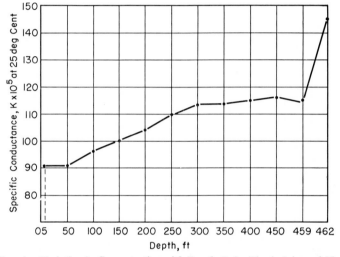

FIG. 4.—Variation in Concentration with Depth, Lake Mead, Ariz. and Nev.

turn over during the fall. As the surface water cools and becomes more dense, the lower layers, being warmer and less dense, rise and replace the former top layers. Usually this turnover is rapid, and the resulting changes in composition of the water may be considerable.

Shallow lakes do not vary much in composition from top to bottom because mixing by the winds is generally good. The problem of sampling is therefore density of the flowing water, either as a result of a difference in temperature or of the material in solution or in suspension or both. When encountered, such a density current requires a careful sampling schedule.

SAMPLING OF WATER UNDER PRESSURE

The composition of most well waters varies only slightly from year to year, and a single sampling station is sufficient. Usually two or three samples per year provide satisfactory coverage. There are exceptions, such as deep wells that have been drilled through strata containing water high in mineral content into a

[6] "Quality of Surface Waters in the United States," Paper 1022, U.S. Geological Survey, 1944.

[7] E. S. Dewey, Jr., "Life in the Depths of a Pond," *Scientific American*, Vol. 185, October, 1951.

deeper stratum that contains water of better quality. Leaking casings or poor construction can lead to contamination of the good water. A shallow well receiving water by percolation from a nearby stream may fluctuate in composition. Such conditions necessitate more frequent sampling.

The ground water in some areas varies in composition with the season. Such cyclic changes are usually related to solution channels in limestone, gypsum, or other soluble rock, and to variations

sampling station. For example, in a cooling system with or without cooling towers, a single sampling station is desirable for chemical-treatment control. Satisfactory selection of the station may require a fairly extensive initial investigation. The most desirable location is chosen by checking samples from a num ber of outlets.

A factor often neglected in locating a sampling station in pipe lines is the possibility of skin samples. An outlet that is flush with the inside wall fre-

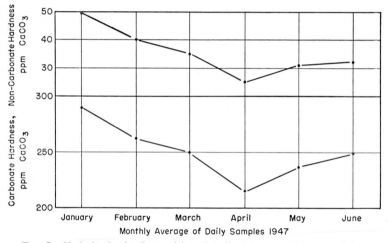

FIG. 5.—Variation in the Composition of Well Water near Matanzas, Cuba.

in rainfall. Rain water quickly reaches the water table and dilutes the higher concentrations of dissolved minerals. The concentration of the ground water is thus lower during the rainy season than during the dry season. Figure 5 shows the composition of such a well-water supply.

A new well, or one that has been dormant for an extended period, should be pumped sufficiently before sampling to guarantee that the delivered water is representative of normal conditions. This may require several days or weeks.

For sampling water from a pipe or conduit, it is desirable to choose a single

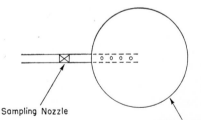

FIG. 6.—Sampling Nozzle for Pipe or Conduit.

quently will not withdraw a sample that is representative of the cross-sectional flow. Differences become more pronounced with increasing diameter of the pipe. This difficulty may be overcome by having several sampling outlets extending different distances into the pipe, using a perforated sampling nozzle such as the one shown in Fig. 6, or the steam-sampling nozzle of Method D 1066.[8] The inlets of such nozzles must face upstream. The total cross-sectional area of the holes should be such that the flow of water in the sampling line is proportional to the flow in the pipe or conduit.

Frequency of sampling should depend upon the magnitude of variations in composition of the water; that is, the schedule of samples must afford satisfactory coverage of water changes. A sampling station should not be located in any section of a pipe where the water is stagnant, such as a dead end. A sample from such a location cannot be satisfactory. Physical conditions often limit the installation of sampling stations, but the best possible ones should be chosen.

Petcocks and drain valves provide convenient sampling outlets. They are used extensively and may provide satisfactory samples from small lines or tanks, but they may yield skin samples or dead-end samples. It is advisable to test this type of sample outlet for representativeness, instead of accepting it merely for convenience.

Industrial water in a pressure system may, in many instances, be satisfactorily sampled using weir boxes, sumps, drains, and overflow as sampling stations. Such sampling devices should not be used if unstable constituents are to be determined.

SAMPLING FOR CONTROL OF WATER-TREATMENT PROCESSES

The sampling of water to control the operation of a treatment process is of major importance to all types of water-treatment plants. The nature of the raw water and the quality of the treated effluent govern the number of samples taken and the type of chemical and physical tests required. If the composition of the raw water is subject to wide and frequent changes in quality, the frequency of sampling and tests must be increased accordingly. Thus changes in chemical dosages can be performed before the quality of treated effluent is affected substantially. Similarly, sampling and testing of the treated water must be frequent enough to provide data for maintenance of water quality and to indicate any deficiency in treatment due to change in chemical dosage or variation in quality of influent.

Flowing samples of water permit the use of instruments for continuously recording certain characteristics, such as pH, conductivity, temperature, turbidity, color, chlorine residual, oxygen, hydrogen, and silica content. Instruments may be justified by the saving in costs over manpower formerly needed for time-consuming laboratory testing, and their feasibility should be examined.

All types of water treatment plants generally require sampling points on the raw water, treated water, and other miscellaneous points if the operation is to be efficient. High-flow clarification and softening plants with sludge contact or sludge blanket treatment units generally require periodic manual sampling to measure the sludge concentration and sludge level within the unit. The frequency of sampling will depend upon the variability in concentration of the constituent used as the basis for control. Samples drawn at 8-hr intervals are usually satisfactory for a water supply of fairly constant composition. On the contrary, it may be necessary to sample at less than 1-hr intervals with a supply whose composition is changing rapidly or a process that is especially sensitive.

---

[8] Appears in this publication.

Figure 7 illustrates the two types of water.

Ion-exchange units, including zeolite softeners operating on the sodium and hydrogen cycles and demineralizing units of multiple-bed and mixed-bed types, may require several sampling points for satisfactory control and for termination of the operating run before treated water quality has deteriorated significantly. of this specific treatment method. Manual samples taken toward the end of an operating run and again following regeneration and return to service are usually necessary, depending upon the type of installation and the degree of instrumentation. The time for removing these two samples must be established by sampling over a short-time interval or on a volume-of-water basis, near the end

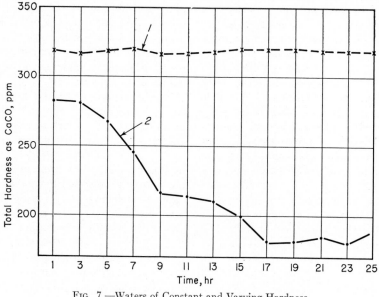

FIG. 7.—Waters of Constant and Varying Hardness.
Curve 1 = Well water near Cincinnati, Ohio.
Curve 2 = Maumee River at Toledo, Ohio.

Since this type of treatment plant lends itself to full or semiautomatic operation, flowing samples are generally employed together with monitoring instruments for continuously recording pH, differential conductivity, and hardness. Complete reliability in silica monitoring instruments must be attained in terminating the service run of demineralizers as the exhaustion point of the ion exchange material is approached. A practical silica recorder accurate in the range of 0.02 to 0.05 ppm and manual sampling are important to the successful operation of two or three demineralizing cycles and two or three rinsing cycles. The composition of some water treated by ion exchange changes rapidly toward the end of the service cycle and may require a sampling interval as short as 1 min.

SAMPLING AT ELEVATED TEMPERATURES

The requirements for sampling just discussed may also apply to hot water service, with the addition that the sample must be cooled to approximately room temperature. Failure to cool will result in flashing and an unsatisfactory sample. Figure 8 shows a suitable type of cooling coil. Another common type is a pair of concentric tubes coiled to any convenient helical diameter. The cooling water flows through the outside tube and the hot water sample flows in the opposite direction through the inner tube.

boilers to locate the most desirable one for the purpose. Method D 860[8] gives directions of this sort.

A satisfactory sample of steam, particularly from boilers operating at high pressure and temperature, is extremely important. Method D 1066[8] gives com-

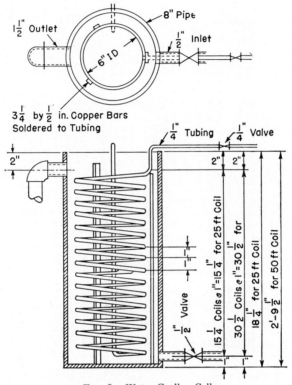

FIG. 8.—Water-Cooling Coil.

Sampling of water from boilers, feedwater heaters, or evaporators also must be accomplished under pressure using a cooling coil. Manufacturers frequently equip pressure vessels with satisfactory sampling outlets. The continuous blowdown line of a modern boiler is often used. In such cases it is advisable to locate the sampling outlet between the boiler and the flow-control valve of the continuous blowdown to avoid flashing. It is sometimes necessary to check various possible sampling stations on some

plete details of the apparatus, including several types of sampling nozzles, piping, fittings, sample condenser, and cooling coils necessary for getting a steam sample.

Because of the ease with which the approximate purity of steam condensate can be determined by conductivity measurement, this method is preferable to evaporation of large volumes of sample and is used almost exclusively for continuously recording sample purity. Ionizable gases such as carbon dioxide and ammonia dissolved in the condensed steam sample contribute to the conductivity measured, and corrections for their presence are necessary. Chemical densed fraction and a gas fraction. Solids are concentrated in a fraction comprising about one half of the original weight of steam. The measured conductivity is

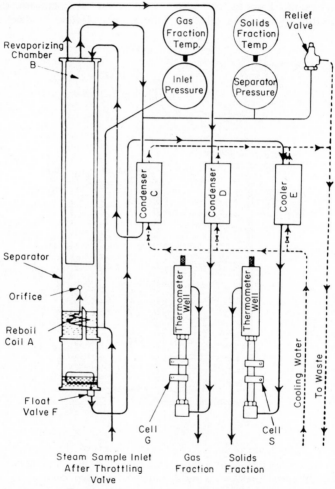

FIG. 9.—Schematic Diagram of Degasser.

analyses must be made to find their concentration in the sample. Automatic steam degassers are available which will partially remove these dissolved gases.

The schematic diagram of Fig. 9 shows the principal parts of one type of apparatus used for splitting a steam sample at nearly equal rates into a con-

multiplied by a factor of 0.5 corrected for dissolved gas content in this solid fraction to put results on an original basis.

In another type of apparatus developed to eliminate inaccuracies in conductivity measurement resulting from the presence of ionizable gases and

volatile amines, a steam sample is condensed at the atmospheric boiling point
in a condensing chamber where practically all the free carbon dioxide and a
small percentage of the ammonia is
removed by venting. The effluent from
this chamber passes through a conductivity cell and a small hydrogen

of conductivity measurement for mineral
carry-over in steam is increased.

For maximum accuracy of steam
purity determination, the sodium content of a condensed sample of saturated
or superheated steam is measured by
flame photometric techniques. It is possible to measure the sodium content of

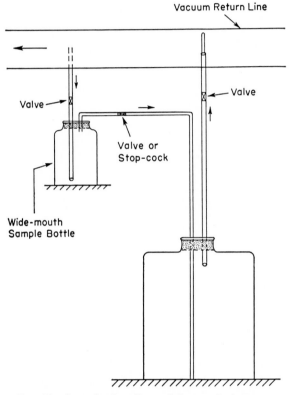

Fig. 10.—Setup for Sampling at Subatmospheric Pressure.

exchange unit. Hydroxide and carbonate
alkalinity, volatile amines, and ammonia
are removed in this step. Cations of
mineral salts are replaced by hydrogen
ions. Passage through a reboil chamber
eliminates bound carbon dioxide and
provides a constant-temperature final
sample for a second conductivity cell.
Since the conductivity of the corresponding acids is several times greater than
the original mineral salts, the sensitivity

condensed steam with a precision of 0.4
ppb where suitable apparatus and
proper technique are used. Method D
1428[8] describes the method and apparatus.

Sampling at Subatmospheric Pressure

It is often necessary to sample water
at reduced pressure, as in vacuum-return
systems or condenser hot wells. Here a

different physical arrangement is required for sampling, and extreme precautions must be taken against leakage. Minor outleakage from a pressure system will not necessarily impair the sample, but inleakage to a sample under subatmospheric pressure will contaminate it. Leakage from pressure systems is visible, but inleakage to a subatmospheric sample is not. Satisfactory physical equipment for subatmospheric sampling is shown in Fig. 10.

SAMPLING OF WASTE WATER

Many of the problems in sampling waste water are similar to those discussed in this chapter for sampling industrial water. In particular, information covering sampling in rivers and streams (flowing waters) entering larger bodies of water, in deep and shallow lakes (standing waters), and in tidal basins is applicable. These discussions should be reviewed as prerequisite to the added precautions outlined in this section. Objectives may differ somewhat in the case of waste water, because it is necessary not only to obtain representative samples but to study the waste load, methods of treatment, and the possibility of recovering materials at a profit. Rigid specifications for the quality of water-borne wastes being formulated by state and interstate commissions controlling pollution throughout the drainage areas adjacent to industrial plants make a carefully supervised sampling program of plant waste waters mandatory.

Objectives:

Common objectives in a sampling program should serve a number of purposes including the determination of quantities of industrial wastes to be discharged, location of major sources within a plant, character of wastes, establishment of a basis for waste treatment, potential recovery of valuable material, and the effect of discharged wastes on the receiving stream.

Sampling Procedures:

It would be rare if two industrial waste problems were alike in all details, and the approach to industrial waste sampling must deviate somewhat from the procedures for industrial water; each must be handled as an individual case. Sampling must be tailored to fit the operation of each manufacturing plant and the characteristics of the waste produced. Special procedures are necessary to handle problems in sampling wastes which vary considerably in composition, depending upon the type of industrial plant. Wastes discharged by industries are by nature of great variety, some being quite visible after discharge. Floating and emulsified oils from refinery operations, white water from pulp and paper mills, colored wastes from cleaning and dyeing establishments, silt and culm from mining operations can be readily seen. As a further example of the variation in the composition of industrial wastes, the combined discharge from an integrated steel mill may contain floating oil, mill scale, spent acid from pickling operations which may cause variations in pH and iron content, and dissolved gases. Thus suitable sampling locations must be decided upon as well as the frequency and type of sample to be collected. Examination of drawings showing underground sewers and manholes in manufacturing areas will help to locate appropriate points for sampling.

The degree of variation in rate of flow will determine the time interval for sampling. This interval must be short enough to provide a true representation of the flow. Although the rate of flow may vary only slightly, the concentration of waste products may range widely. Frequent sampling, that is, uniform 10-

or 15-min intervals, permits estimation of the average concentration during the sampling period. This is necessary if a representative sample is to be obtained.

Sampling Points:

Sampling points for waste waters are preferably located where flow conditions encourage a homogeneous mixture, such as the downstream side of a hydraulic jump, Parshall flume, or weir.

In sewers and deep narrow channels, samples should be removed from a point one third the water depth from the bottom. In wide channels, the point of collection should be rotated across the channel. In any event, velocity of flow at the sample point should be sufficient to prevent deposition of solids. Voluntary creation of turbulence during collection of samples may liberate dissolved gases and make the sample unrepresentative. A representative sample of a heterogeneous mixture of waste water, particularly one containing oil, is difficult to collect, but collection of a composite and analysis of an entire individual sample will give a fairly accurate estimate of the characteristics of the waste.

Recognized testing and precautionary measures[9] should be followed in taking samples from deep manholes to guard against accumulations of toxic and explosive gases and insufficiency of oxygen. Generally, a two-man testing crew is recommended for entering manholes to take samples.

Sampling Equipment:

Figure 11 shows a diagrammatic arrangement of a continuous sampler suitable for uniform flows of homogeneous waste water.[2]

Figures 12 and 13 show one type of

9 "How Sewer Manholes Are Checked for Toxic and Explosive Gases," *Public Works*, Vol. 85, p. 149, May, 1954; "Gaseous Fuels," Am. Gas Assn. Book, 1954, p. 334.

automatic sampling device and a diagrammatic arrangement of the installation, respectively. This kind of equipment would not be entirely practical for sampling industrial wastes water containing floating matter.

Sample Preservation:

Considerable research on the problem of preventing chemical, physical, and biological changes in waste water samples which might affect BOD, suspended solids, dissolved gases, cyanide, and phenol values has failed to perfect a

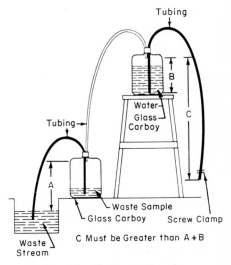

Fig. 11.—Continuous Sampler.

This simple jar-and-tube setup samples waste effectively when flow is nearly constant. As water drains from the upper carboy, the vacuum created siphons waste into the lower one. The rate of flow is regulated by the pinch clamp to fill the lower carboy during the sampling period.

universal treatment or method, or formulate a set of fixed rules applicable to samples of all types. Prompt analysis is undoubtedly the most positive assurance against error from sample deterioration.

Where it is imperative that stabilization and preservation be attempted, for example, when a 24-hr composite is

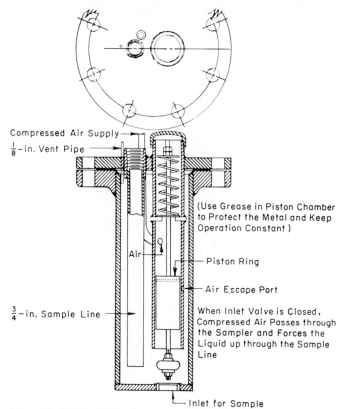

Compressed Air Supply

$\frac{1}{8}$-in. Vent Pipe

(Use Grease in Piston Chamber to Protect the Metal and Keep Operation Constant)

Air

Piston Ring

Air Escape Port

$\frac{3}{4}$-in. Sample Line

When Inlet Valve is Closed, Compressed Air Passes through the Sampler and Forces the Liquid up through the Sample Line

Inlet for Sample

FIG. 12.—Automatic Sampler. This air-lift automatic sampler takes samples from a sewer when a pump cannot be used.

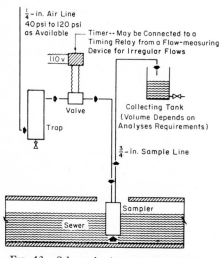

$\frac{1}{4}$-in. Air Line
40 psi to 120 psi
as Available

Timer-- May be Connected to a Timing Relay from a Flow-measuring Device for Irregular Flows

110 v

Valve

Trap

Collecting Tank
(Volume Depends on Analyses Requirements)

$\frac{3}{4}$-in. Sample Line

Sampler

Sewer

FIG. 13.—Schematic Arrangement of Automatic Sampler Shown in Fig. 12.

collected, it is recommended that the sample be refrigerated at 4 C.

Other methods applicable to many types of waste waters include chemical treatment, acidification, and alkalinization. Probable errors due to deterioration of the sample should be designated in reporting the analytical data.

SAMPLING PRECAUTIONS AND EQUIPMENT

The volume of water required for a sample depends on the number of determinations to be made. This is covered in detail in Methods D 510 and D 596.[8] Generally, a minimum of 2 to 3 liters should be collected. A volume of 4 liters is desirable for the determination of all mineral constituents. In any event, the quantity submitted to the laboratory should include a surplus for check analyses. If only a few sample determinations are required, the sample volume may be reduced correspondingly. When a sample has settleable solids, the container should be large enough to allow some air space to facilitate mixing in the laboratory.

There are certain minimum requirements for sampling equipment which should be observed. For example, the sample container must not change the sample composition. It must be clean and, if glass, should be of chemically resistant type. Wide-mouth glass-stoppered bottles are to be preferred for waste waters. Rubber stoppers are attacked by some solvents in wastes and thereby contaminate the sample. Hard rubber or plastic bottles with screw tops of the same material may be necessary. These are preferred for samples of condensed steam and other water in which the silica concentration is important.

Equipment for sampling purposes, cooling coils, degassers, steam sample nozzles, piping, and tubing intended for collecting acid waste water must be constructed of material resistant to the water being sampled. Such equipment must also withstand the temperature and pressure involved. Sampling equipment and piping for industrial water or steam not in continuous use must be flushed sufficiently to remove all stagnant water.

A new system must be flushed sufficiently to remove foreign material, such as rust, before placing it in service. The time required for cleansing depends on the piping and sampling equipment required. It is possible to be guided by the physical appearance of the effluent in most cases or by individual checking of samples. The sample outlet should discharge from the bottom of the sample container; this decreases the chance for atmospheric contamination. Overflowing the sample receiver also provides additional desirable flushing of the sample container. A volume of water equal to at least four to ten times the volume of the sample container should be overflowed to waste before taking the sample.

The rate of sample flow is highly important. If the rate of flow is too rapid, gas bubbles may form; if too slow, the sample may become contaminated. When samples are taken for determination of unstable constituents, unrepresentative or contaminated samples may provide highly misleading information. Continuous samplers for waste waters and steam require frequent inspection and cleaning to be reliable.

The foregoing discussion on sampling industrial water and waste water does not cover the multiplicity of situations that may be encountered. It offers partial direction for obtaining samples which accurately represent the mass to be sampled, and which meet laboratory needs for sample size. In all sampling procedures the sample collector must exercise good judgment in deciding whether the sample is representative and if laboratory examination will provide pertinent and useable data.

Flow Measurement

Flow measurement is an essential function in the study of industrial water as an engineering material. Since it involves principles of hydraulics and fluid mechanics that are applicable to all problems of flow measurement, a knowledge of the theory, methods, and types of equipment for measuring flow is essential. A simple measurement of the liquid depth in a standard container per unit of time serves conveniently for obtaining information on the amount of precipitation on the earth as rainfall. More complicated measurements involving rather intricate formulas and flow-measuring devices are necessary for determining the volume of surface runoff

45-60

and underground seepage collected in flowing streams, flows in distribution mains and piping, and flows in sewers and open channels used for the disposal of water as industrial waste.

Flow measurement is of inestimable value in the conservation of one of man's most valuable material assets. Economic considerations provide an outstanding reason for flow measurement of industrial water and waste water. Heavy costs are often involved to cover the material and labor for water-gathering systems and storage facilities, which include wells, dams, impounding reservoirs, tanks, pumps, and piping for transporting water. Installation and operating costs for treatment facilities are important factors in providing municipal and industrial water supplies. Flow measurement is an essential item in determining the cost of water delivered to consumers.

Flow measurement is important in the handling, treatment, and disposal of industrial waste water and domestic sewage, for control of discharge and making sewage service charges, and to provide records for state pollution control agencies authorized to enforce laws governing disposal of waste in state waters. Flow measurement is a necessary accessory to sampling techniques; without accurate measurement very little progress can be made with treatment methods or to establish the volume of waste that may be discharged without damage to the receiving waters.

Basic Requirements:

The network of piping, underground sewers, and open channels used to convey water and waste water in modern industrial plants presents many problems in flow measurement. There is no universal procedure because flows must be measured under a variety of conditions. The measurement methods must be applicable to specific conditions. The

type of flow device, its location, cost of installation, quality of flow data, and suitability for the service must be considered. This discussion covers briefly the kinds of flow-measuring devices, fundamentals of flow measurement, description and design of flow devices, and important points to consider in their selection. These should serve as a guide in choosing the equipment and method best suited to the purpose and in establishing a suitable location for obtaining data. The subject of hydraulics cannot be covered completely in this brief discussion, and it is suggested that references books[10] be reviewed to obtain basic fundamental concepts.

Points of Flow Measurement:

The points of flow measurement for industrial water may include the sources of supply, treatment processes, and distribution systems. Collection points at sewer inlets, sewer outfalls, treatment plants, open channels, and discharges to receiving waters are recommended for waste waters.

Devices and Methods for Flow Measurement:[11]

Devices used for flow measurement may fall into one of several classes: (1) head-area meters, (2) functional meters, (3) pumps, (4) displacement meters, (5) constant differential meters, and (6) inertial flowmeters. Other methods used frequently for flow measurement include surface floats, salt concentration, thermal techniques, and radioactive tracers.

Head-Area Meters.—Head-area meters are used only in open channel flow or

---

[10] H. W. King, "Handbook of Hydraulics;" G. E. Russell, "Textbook on Hydraulics;" H. W. King, C. O. Wisler, and J. G. Woodburn, "Hydraulics;" and A. H. Gibson, "Hydraulics and Its Applications."

[11] George E. Symons, "Flow Measurement," *Water & Sewage Works*, Vol. 101, p. 395, September, 1954.

partly filled pipes; they cannot be used on lines under pressure, but are useful to measure flow from reservoirs. These meters operate on the principle that a constriction or controlled barrier in the flow channel will back up the liquid and create a higher level (head) than the

FIG. 16.—Typical Installation of Head Area Meter for V-Notch Weir.

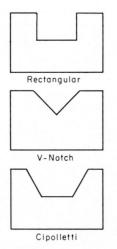

Rectangular

V-Notch

Cipolletti

FIG. 14.—Types of Weirs.

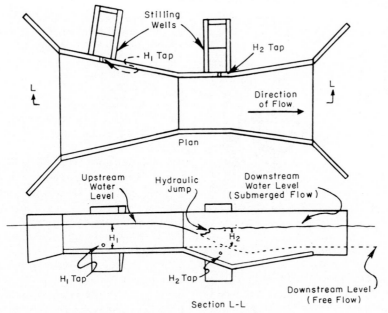

FIG. 15.—Basic Elements of Parshall Flume.

level below the barrier; that head will be a function of the velocity of flow and therefore of the flow rate. Head-area head-area meter and V-notch weir is shown in Fig. 16.

Functional Meters.—Functional meters

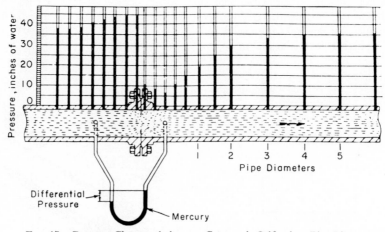

FIG. 17.—Pressure Characteristics at a Concentric Orifice in a Pipe Line.

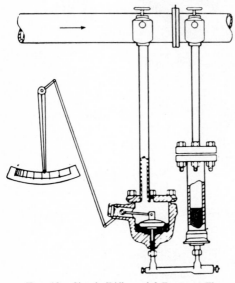

FIG. 18.—Simple Differential Pressure Flowmeter.

meters include weirs, measuring flumes, and open-end nozzles. Several types of weirs and the basic elements of a Parshall flume are shown in Figs. 14 and 15, respectively. A typical installation of

measure some function of fluid in movement and, with supplementary mechanical devices, convert that measurement into rate of flow or total flow. This principle is illustrated diagrammatically in Fig. 17. The components of a simple mechanical meter designed to function by differential pressure developed across an orifice installed in a pipe is shown in Fig. 18.

There are three types of functional meters:

(*a*) *Differential head devices* produce a difference in head between two points of the device, and this differential is a function of velocity. These devices include the venturi tube, Dall flow tube, insert nozzle, Gentile flow tube, and orifice. Typical examples of each are shown in Figs. 19 through 23. These devices are used in main-line metering and in metering flows at any point where water moves under pressure in a confined pipe.

(*b*) *Velocity meters* consist of a device by which a vane or propeller turns in direct ratio to the rate of flow past the propeller. These devices, similar to the one shown in Fig. 24, are used in main-line metering, pump discharges, etc.

(*c*) *Pitot tubes* consist of a vertical tube with a right-angled tip inserted in a flow,

Displacement Meters.—Displacement meters operate on the fill-and-draw principle. Fill-and-draw measurements of reservoirs and tanks can be made if

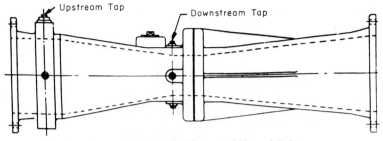

FIG. 19.—Schematic Diagram of Venturi Tube.

FIG. 20.—Dall Flow Tube.

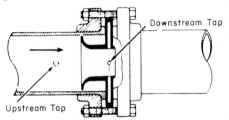

FIG. 21.—Schematic Diagram of Flow Nozzle.

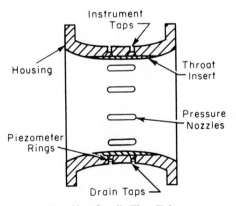

FIG. 22.—Gentile Flow Tube.

with the tip facing upstream. The height to which the fluid rises in the tube is a function of velocity and therefore of rate of flow.

Pumps.—Pumps can be used as measuring devices only if the number of repeat cycles can be determined. Controlled volume reciprocating pumps can be used easily for this purpose, but centrifugal pump discharges must be calibrated for each speed of operation, suction lift, or discharge head. Pumps are not generally used or recommended for flow measurement and should only be considered when other means prove to be impractical.

flows into and out of the tank do not occur simultaneously. When the fill-and-draw principle is applied to a closed device, a compartment is alternately filled and emptied.

Constant Differential Meters.—Constant differential meters, commonly

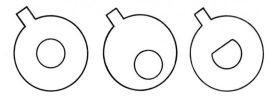

Fig. 23.—Orifice Plates—Concentric, Eccentric, and Segmental.

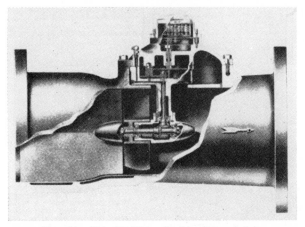

Fig. 24.—Velocity Meter (Builders' Propeloflo).

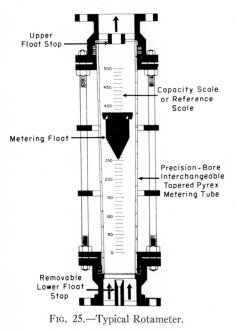

Upper Float Stop

Capacity Scale or Reference Scale

500
450
400

Metering Float

250
200
150
100
50
0

Precision-Bore Interchangeable Tapered Pyrex Metering Tube

Removable Lower Float Stop

Fig. 25.—Typical Rotameter.

called rotameters, consist of a tapered tube, smaller at the bottom than at the top, in which is confined a movable element termed a "float." The float rises or falls in the tube in proportion to changes in the rate of flow of the fluid. This device, which is illustrated diagrammatically in Fig. 25, is not used for measuring large flows; it has its greatest usefulness in measuring gas flows.

Inertial Flowmeters.—Inertial flowmeters measure mass rather than volume. They operate by indicating the inertial force of a moving mass of fluid.

Selection of Primary Units:

The device which actually measures the flow of a fluid is called a primary unit (weir, Parshall flume, open nozzle, venturi tube, Dall flow tube, orifice, etc.). The primary unit is only one of two parts of a metering device. Before discussing secondary units, it is desirable to comment on factors in the selection of primary units. Weirs are infrequently used in permanent installations for measuring industrial wastes. The following three sections are devoted to the other principal primary units.

Factors that have a bearing on the selection of the primary unit include type of service, engineering considerations, installation conditions, accessories, the measured data to the secondary unit; corrosion resistance required; cleanouts, inspection holes, and manholes; and construction costs as affected by pits for float tubes; forms for flumes, etc.

Installation factors cover the position of the device (vertical or horizontal), piping arrangements, vaults, and possible by-pass installations. Accessories required might consist of straightening vanes, flushing devices (intermittent or continuous), vents, vent cleaners, air

FIG. 26.—Types of Transmission: (a) Mechanical; (b) Electrical; and (c) Pneumatic.

comparative characteristics, and operator's convenience. Not all of the factors and items mentioned hereafter apply to all types of primary units; where they do apply, however, full consideration must be given to the evaluation of each factor.

Engineering considerations include such factors as allowable loss of head; throat size of the constriction; acceptable differential pressure; upstream and downstream flow conditions; type of fluid to be measured; laying-length of the unit (that is, length of pipe it will replace in the line); types of ends (flange, bell and spigot, concrete coupling); distance to secondary unit; type of unit to transmit

chambers, floats, float tubes, sediment traps, seals, etc.

Comparative characteristics of flow-measuring devices comprise accuracy, low cost, high capacity, range, permanent loss of head, life expectancy, suitability for solids-bearing liquids, freedom from field tapping, freedom from upstream disturbances, ability to handle high pressures, and ease of installation.

Secondary Instruments:

A secondary instrument or receiver is the device used to convert measurements sensed by, and transmitted from, the primary measuring unit, into observable information on flow. Liquid level and pressure also can be shown on secondary instruments.

Secondary instruments are classified in two ways: (*a*) according to type of information desired, and (*b*) according to method of transmission from primary to secondary unit.

Classes by Type of Information Desired. —These include:

Indicator: Shows rate of flow at moment of observation, in cfs, gpm, gph, mgd, etc.

Totalizer. Shows running total to time of observation, in cu ft, gal, mil gal, etc.

Recorder. Draws record on chart, showing rate of flow as a continuous record for each instant during a particular period (hour, day, week).

Combinations are available as indicator-recorder, totalizer-indicator, totalizer-recorder, and totalizer-indicator-recorder. Indicators have a single arm and dial. Indicator-recorders may have the indicator arm separate from the chart, or attached to the pen arm.

Classes by Type of Transmission.— These include mechanical, electrical, and pneumatic.

Mechanical transmission exists when the receiver is operated by cables directly connected to float wells which are in turn connected to the pressure take-offs (taps) of the primary device. Mechanical transmission also may be had by connecting the primary device pressure taps directly to mercury wells in the receiver unit.

Electrical transmission is used where the receiver cannot be located near the primary unit or where there is insufficient pressure for direct connection to the secondary unit. Electrical transmission is of the time-impulse type (Chronoflo Telemeter) whereby the length of time that the signal is transmitted is proportional to the magnitude of the function being measured (rate of flow, pressure, level, etc.). This signal can actuate a receiving instrument, or control pumps, chemical feeders or valves, or both. Electrical transmission is possible over any distance from feet to miles, over telephone circuits, private a-c or d-c lines, or multiservice wires. A sequencing unit (sequence unit transmitter) will transmit signals from several transmitters consecutively over the same pair of wires. Sequencing is useful in the operation and control of well-field pumps and booster pumping stations.

Pneumatic transmission is useful up to 1500 ft; it generally makes use of a varying controlled air pressure ranging from 3 to 15 psi. Principal features are absence of wiring, continuous output signal (pressure), extreme sensitivity to change in the variable being measured, and immediate response to change in variable. The three types of transmission are illustrated in Fig. 26.

CHAPTER VII
Analysis of Industrial Water and Industrial Waste Water

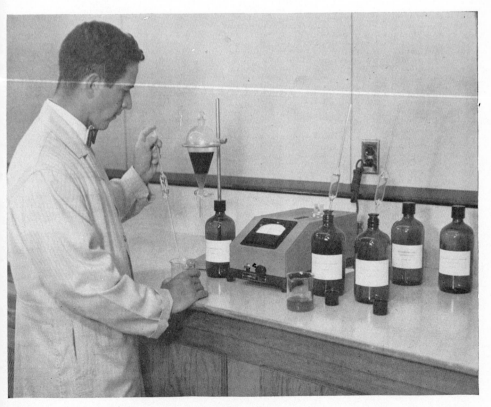

CHAPTER VII—ANALYSIS OF INDUSTRIAL WATER AND INDUSTRIAL WASTE WATER

Industrial water always contains impurities consisting of substances present in the supply water or added, intentionally or unintentionally, during its use. The character and quantity of the impurities depend on the environmental and service conditions to which the water is exposed.

Methods of analysis applicable to both industrial supply or process waters and to industrial waste waters are discussed in this chapter. The difference between the two types of waters is often only academic. In fact, waste water from one industrial process may become the supply water for another process. Industrial supply or process waters may contain higher concentrations of some constituents than some industrial waste waters. From the analytical standpoint, the same methods can often be used for both types of waters. Selection of constituents to be measured and methods of analysis for supply waters is based on the need for determining the suitability of the supply for a process use. Similarly, selection of constituents to be measured and the methods of analysis for waste water is based on determining the suitability of the water for re-use, disposal, or treatment prior to disposal.

Planning the Program of Analysis

Examination of industrial water for most routine uses will require relatively few tests of a comparatively simple nature. The accuracy sought will not be of the highest order, and tests will be performed to give the greatest economy of time and motion. In such work there is very little to be gained by preliminary qualitative testing, unless a rough determination is needed to bring the sample volume or concentration into the range of a particular procedure.

In contrast, complete analysis requires more elaborate planning, especially as it is often necessary to conserve the sample and to avoid repeating tedious operations. For example, some of the ASTM methods require preliminary removal of silica. When possible, such determinations should be made on aliquots of the portion on which silica has been determined gravimetrically.

Special Samples:

Preparation of the program of analysis should, if possible, precede sampling. Reasonable forethought will result in effective sampling. Even more important, special samples can be taken at nearly the same time as the principal sample and be representative of its quality. Examples of special samples are those for dissolved oxygen, for oil, and, in the case of high-purity water, for iron, copper, sodium, and silica.

Additional special samples, while not absolutely necesssary, are often very convenient. For example, they decrease the probability that errors will result due to loss of dissolved gases during the transfer of portions of the water for the several tests. Also, it is easier to refrigerate a separate sample to retard bacterial action, when necessary, than to do this for all samples or for a large sample.

111

Qualitative Tests:

Short qualitative or semiquantitative tests are very helpful in preparing the program of analysis. When practicable, such preliminary studies should precede the formal sampling since they provide valuable information on the number of special samples needed and on the total sample volume. Many elaborate and time-consuming operations can be avoided with nearly every sample when exploratory tests have disclosed the approximate concentration of each constituent present.

The abbreviated test procedures can be classified roughly as spectroscopic, microchemical, and macrochemical. The visible-arc spectroscopic detection of halogens and metallic ions[1] has proved to be very valuable for rapid and cheap assay of many of the constituents of an evaporated residue.

A more complete, but much less sensitive, qualitative examination can be made by a specially trained technician with a set of carefully selected chemical reagents and a good microscope.[2, 3] Somewhat similarly, selected reagents can be added to drops of the water sample on a spot plate or on filter paper and the results of the reaction used to estimate the concentration of the constituent sought.[4]

Macrochemical qualitative methods are described in standard texts, but the untrained chemist must use caution in the interpretation of the results, especially for the more sensitive tests. For example, benzidine reagent gives a good precipitate when the sulfate concentration is only 2 ppm, and the stannous

chloride - molybdate test will give a positive test with less than 0.1 ppm of phosphate ion.

Special Apparatus:

In general, the references in this chapter contain adequate descriptions of the special equipment required for the determinations discussed. Additional general information is available in the catalogs of chemical supply houses. Planning the program of analysis should include procurement of essential apparatus and its disposition in the laboratory, with due regard to space limitations and convenience.

Program of Analysis:

Method D 1256[5] covers a systematic scheme for examination of water samples, and gives an order of application of methods which permits the determination of existing constituents and properties in logical sequence. The scheme is intended to aid the water analyst to choose an analytical course that he can follow to determine one or all of the constituents or properties of industrial water.

Experience will quickly teach the analyst to connect the presence of one constituent with the necessary absence of another. For example, ferrous iron would not be expected in water that contains residual chlorine.

Many of the tests can be made while others are in progress. With some practice, the analyst will acquire a reliable sense of timing which will permit him to carry out the necessary operations with the greatest possible speed consistent with appropriate accuracy.

Calculating and Reporting:

In water analysis the sample is measured by volume, and it is often possible

[1] H. Jaffe, *American Mineralogist*, Vol. 34, p. 667 (1949)
[2] E. M. Chamot and C. W. Mason, "Handbook of Chemical Microscopy," Vol. II, John Wiley & Sons, Inc., New York, N. Y., 1940.
[3] See Method D 1245 in this Manual.
[4] F. Feigl, "Qualitative Analysis by Spot Tests," Nordemann Publishing Co., New York, N. Y., 1939.
[5] Appears in this publication.

TABLE I.—CONSTITUENTS AND PROPERTIES OF INDUSTRIAL WATERS.[a,b,c,d]

NOTE.—D and E numbers in parentheses refer to ASTM methods designated by these numbers in this publication.

Physical Tests (see pages 115 to 119 in text)	Chemical Tests				Biological or Other Tests (see pages 140 to 141 in text)
	Dissolved Gases (see pages 119 to 123 in text)	Cations (see pages 123 to 130 in text)	Anions (see pages 126 to 130 in text)	Miscellaneous (see pages 136 to 140 in text)	
Color	Ammonia (D 1426)	Aluminum (D 857)	Bromide and iodide (D 1246)	Acidity and basicity (alkalinity) (D 1067)	Biochemical oxygen demand
Electrical conductivity (D 1125)	Carbon dioxide (D 513)	Ammonium (D 1426)	Carbonate and bicarbonate (D 513)	Chemical oxygen demand (D 1252)	Immediate dissolved oxygen demand
Odor (D 1292)	Chlorine (D 1253 and D 1427)	Barium and strontium	Chloride (D 512)	Chlorine requirement (D 932)	Iron bacteria (D 932)
Oxidation-reduction potential (D 1498)	Hydrogen (D 1588)	Calcium and magnesium (D 511)	Chromate and dichromate	Chloroform-extractable matter (D 1291)	Microorganisms (D 1128)
Radioactivity (D 1690)	Hydrogen sulfide (D 1255)	Chromium (D 1687)	Cyanide	Hardness (D 1126)	Sulfate-reducing bacteria (D 993)
Specific gravity (D 1429)	Nitrogen	Copper (D 1688)	Fluoride (D 1179)	Nitrogen, Kjeldahl	Toxicity, acute, to fresh-water fishes (D 1345)
Surface tension (D 1590)	Oxygen (D 888 and D 1589)	Hydrazine (D 1385)	Hydroxide (D 514)	Nitrogen, organic	
Suspended and dissolved matter (D 1069)	Sulfur dioxide (includes SO₃, HSO₃, and free SO₂, if present)	Hydrogen ion (D 1293)	Nitrate (D 992)	Oily matter (D 1340)	
Turbidity		Iron (D 1068)	Nitrite (D 1254)	pH, colorimetric (D 1067)	
		Lead	Phosphate (D 515)	pH, electrometric (D 1293 and E 70)	
		Manganese (D 858)	Sulfate (D 516)	Phenol	
		Nickel	Sulfide (D 1255)	Silica (D 859 and D 1689)	
		Sodium and potassium (D 1127 and D 1428)	Sulfite (D 1339)		
		Zinc (D 1691)			

[a] Additional methods included in Part II of the Second Printing of the Second Edition are Methods D 1782 and D 1783.
[b] Additional methods included in Part II of the Third Printing of the Second Edition are Methods D 1884, D 1886, D 1888, D 1889, D 1890, D 1891, D 1941, D 1942, D 1943, and D 1944.
[c] Additional methods included in Part II of the Fourth Printing of the Second Edition are Methods D 2032, D 2033, D 2034, D 2035, D 2036, D 2037, D 2038, D 2039, D 2040, D 2184, D 2185, D 2186, and D 2187.
[d] Additional methods included in Part II of the Fifth Printing of the Second Edition are Methods D 2327, D 2328, D 2329, D 2330, D 2331, D 2332, D 2333, D 2334, and D 2335.
[e] Additional methods included in Part II of the Sixth Printing of the Second Edition are Methods D 2458, D 2459, D 2460, D 2461, D 2470, and D 2476.

to work on a quantity that fits in with the necessary calculations for constituent concentrations. It is most important, however, that all volumes be recorded when the operations are made.

Good records must be kept of all steps in each procedure. Calculations should be recorded in detail, so that they can readily be reviewed at some future date. Much valuable information is frequently obtained from such records.

Method D 596[5] includes a procedure for calculating percentage error in analysis based on balancing the totals of cations and anions found in a sample. This method also includes recommendations on the nature, extent, and form of reports of water analysis results.

SELECTING THE METHODS OF ANALYSIS

A variety of methods is generally available for each determination. In addition to the use to be made of the results, the choice of procedures is governed by the probable range of concentrations, the accuracy required, the presence of interfering substances, the skill of the analyst, and the apparatus that can be assembled. For example, the colorimetric procedure appropriate for detecting slight iron corrosion in a closed system would not be used normally for an acidic mine water in which the iron concentration is high. It would be foolish to require a boiler operator in a small low-pressure plant to analyze for boiler-water silica with the precise methods essential in high-pressure central stations. These examples show that the selection of the most practical methods for analyzing industrial water involves more than compiling a list containing a procedure for each constituent or property.

This chapter is intended as an aid in making the best compromise between speed on the one hand, and completeness and accuracy on the other. Therefore the discussion of each constituent indicates, in most cases, several available methods for determining that constituent and provides some basis for making choices in specific cases. Referee procedures, such as those included in this Manual as standard or tentative methods, are designed for the determination of individual constituents or properties and provide for minimizing the effects of interfering substances. Many of the ASTM methods include non-referee procedures which are usually shorter and give sufficiently accurate results for many purposes. References are made to these ASTM methods in this chapter and additional alternatives are often suggested.

The discussion of methods in this chapter is presented in alphabetical order by constituent or property in each of the following categories:

1. Physical Tests
2. Chemical Tests
    (a) Dissolved Gases
    (b) Cations
    (c) Anions
    (d) Miscellaneous
3. Biological or Other Tests

Table I provides a convenient index, both to ASTM methods and to this chapter. Reproduced in this volume are all ASTM methods current on the publication date. These methods should be consulted for further information on specific procedures mentioned. This is especially important in the second and subsequent printings of this edition of the Manual, because the methods are brought up to date for each printing, whereas the chapter contents will be changed only when a third edition is published.

This chapter mentions some of the sampling requirements for specific analyses, but reference should be made to Chapter VI and to the ASTM methods of sampling listed in the Index.

The Introduction to Laboratory Practices, which precedes the ASTM methods, presents a "philosophy" of laboratory operation and should be of value to the water analyst.

PHYSICAL TESTS

Properties of water not usually measured in the laboratory are not included in this listing. Of these, temperature is probably the most important.

Color:

Artificial color scales, using standards prepared from potassium chloroplatinate and cobaltous chloride solutions, are often used to measure natural color in water. Suspended matter must be removed by centrifuging before the comparisons are made. Addition of calcium chloride[6] to assist in centrifuging is desirable with some types of turbidity. Spectrophotometric and photometric methods have been developed,[7] some especially for industrial waste waters.[8]

Continuous measurement of color has been practiced to a very limited extent. Methods for measuring color, with particular emphasis on photometric methods which offer greatest promise for continuous analysis, are discussed by Staats.[9]

Electrical Conductivity:

Electrical conductivity has special significance because it is a quick and convenient method for measuring electrolyte concentration. The specific conductance of a dilute solution of an electrolyte is almost directly proportional to the ionic concentration of the electrolyte, and the total conductivity of a given water is equal to the sum of the several conductivities resulting from the electrolytes present. Because of the unusually high conductance per weight unit of hydrogen or hydroxide ion, samples frequently are neutralized before the electrical conductivity is measured.

The determination of conductivity can therefore be related to dissolved solids concentration. It is a useful guide to the purity of distilled water and is much used for evaluation of steam purity in the power industry. It is important to note, however, that dissolved gases (particularly carbon dioxide and ammonia) have an important effect on conductivity. When determining steam purity by this method, it is generally necessary to first reduce the concentration of these gases to very low levels and to correct for the amount remaining. (See also the discussion under *Suspended and Dissolved Matter* in this chapter.)

Conductivity measurements sometimes are required for special investigations of corrosion in water.

Method D 1125[5] describes the apparatus and procedure for determining electrical conductivity of industrial waters. Continuous measurement of conductivity of flowing samples is often used for monitoring process water.[10]

Odor:

As in the case of color, the odor of industrial supply and process waters is seldom measured quantitatively. The threshold odor number of water can be determined by using the sense of smell and a series of dilutions of the sample

[6] W. L. Lamar, *Analytical Chemistry*, Vol. 21, p. 276 (1949).

[7] A. T. Palin, *Water & Sewage Works*, Vol. 104, p. 492 (1957).

[8] "Standard Methods for the Examination of Water and Wastewater," Am. Public Health Assn., New York, N. Y., 11th Ed., p. 345 (1960).

[9] F. C. Staats, "Measurement of Color, Turbidity, Hardness, and Silica in Industrial Waters," Symposium on Continuous Analysis of Industrial Water and Industrial Waste Water, Am. Soc. Testing Mats., p. 33 (1952). (Issued as separate publication *ASTM STP No. 130*.)

[10] Robert Rosenthal, "Some Practical Aspects of the Measurement of pH, Electrical Conductivity, and Oxidation-Reduction Potential of Industrial Water," Symposium on Continuous Analysis of Industrial Water and Industrial Waste Water, Am. Soc. Testing Mats., p. 12 (1952). (Issued as separate publication *ASTM STP No. 130*.)

with odor-free water (Method D 1292[5]). The threshold number is obtained from a table which assigns an odor number to each sample dilution. The odor threshold of a sample is the number of volumes of dilution water required to yield a scarcely perceptible odor. Psychological influences are eliminated as much as possible by labeling the flasks in code and examining solutions in random order. Method D 1292 also includes a table for classifying odors by chemical types.

Oxidation-Reduction Potential:

Some of the applications of oxidation-reduction potential measurements in water have been summarized by Rosenthal.[10] In one stage of the sea-water bromine process, the concentration of free bromine in acidified sea water treated with chlorine is obtained by measuring the oxidation-reduction potential. A similar measurement on a plating plant waste is used as a gage of dichromate ion concentration for controlling the addition of a reducing agent. Continuous measurement of low chlorine concentrations is possible by this method. Empirical testing is necessary in adapting this method of measurement to specific ions in a particular application.

Method D 1498[5] describes a procedure for measuring oxidation-reduction potentials in water, using a calomel electrode - noble metal electrode and an appropriate meter. The measured value is corrected to express the oxidation-reduction potential referred to the normal hydrogen electrode. Results are reported in millivolts, and can be interpreted in terms of the concentration of specific ions only after empirical testing.

Radioactivity:

Radioactivity measurements are becoming increasingly important as the "nuclear age" progresses. Instrument methods are used which may indicate only the intensity of radiation for safety purposes, or which may provide information on the nature of the radiation, the intensity, and the half-life to permit quantitative determination of individual isotopic species.

These measurements may be important in industrial water analysis from two standpoints: (1) analysis for non-radioactive constituents by radioactivation methods, and (2) analysis to detect radioactive contamination of supply, process, or waste waters, or the concentration of radioactive isotopes that have been added as tracers. Trace quantities of some nonradioactive isotopes can be determined by the neutron radioactivation method.[11] The sample is exposed to neutron radiation in a nuclear reactor (or an accelerator) to produce a radioactive isotope of the element to be determined. Since this radioisotope has its own characteristic radiations and mode of decay, its concentration can be determined. Oak Ridge National Laboratory will perform this type of analysis on a fee basis. It is doubtful that this method will be widely used for water analysis because of the extensive facilities required, but it might find use in checking the accuracy of existing chemical methods of analysis for trace quantities of some elements.

The chapter on *Radioactive Nuclides in Water* should be consulted for further information on this subject. Method D 1690[5] gives procedures for measuring gamma radioactivity.

Specific Gravity:

Specific gravity is rarely an important property of an industrial supply or process water but may be significant in waste water analysis. It may be measured to the fourth decimal place with a bal-

[11] G. W. Leddicotte and S. A. Reynolds, *Nucleonics*, Vol. 8, No. 3, p. 62 (1951).

ance of the Westphal type which measures the buoyancy of the water on a totally immersed plummet. Method D 1429[5] referee procedure covers an accurate gravimetric determination using a specific-gravity bottle (pycnometer) in which a calibrated volume of the water is weighed at a known temperature. A reasonable approximation can be obtained quickly by weighing a pipeted sample and comparing it with the weight of the same volume of distilled or reagent water at the working temperature. Similar determinations can be made with a relatively rough platform balance using an Erlenmeyer flask, as described in Method D 1429 non-referee procedure.

Surface Tension:

Surface tension of a water sample is sometimes used to indicate contamination with surface-active material. This can be helpful, for example, in determining a possible cause of boiler water foaming. The ring tensiometer can be used to give a quantitative measurement of the force required to lift a standard wire ring from the surface of the sample. Method D 1590[5] is based on this principle.

A rough indication of surface tension can be obtained with a slender glass-stoppered glass tube which is filled to a standard mark with the sample. The tube is stoppered and placed in a horizontal position; and the length of the air bubble is compared with the length of the air bubble when distilled water is used in place of the sample. With samples of lowered surface tension, the bubble is longer than with distilled water. The tube is calibrated by filling to the standard mark with distilled water, stoppering, placing in a horizontal position, and marking the tube at the two ends of the air bubble.

Suspended and Dissolved Matter:

The amount of dissolved solids present in an industrial water is one of its more important properties since it is one of the factors that determine use and re-use of the water. The test also is useful in complete analysis because the result compared with the sum of the individual constituents can be used as a check on the analysis.

The suspended solids determination often is made on raw and process waters to show the load placed on clarifying and settling equipment. This determination also is used as a guide to the satisfactory operation of plant processes and to the final disposition of industrial wastes.

Methods for suspended and dissolved solids are grouped as Method D 1069.[5] Method A, intended primarily for high purity waters, requires equipment not available in most laboratories. It is possible to obtain an approximate measure of dissolved solids in this range (up to 5 ppm) by measuring the electrical conductivity of the water. (See discussion under *Electrical Conductivity.*) High-purity waters have low conductivities, however, and a considerable part of this conductivity may be due to dissolved gases such as carbon dioxide and ammonia. Corrections can be made when the concentrations of these gases are known.[12, 13] A good approximation can be made by boiling a sample down to less than half the original volume to drive off the dissolved gases, determining the conductivity of the cooled remainder, and correcting this value for

---

[12] E. P. Partridge, Discussion, *Proceedings,* Am. Soc. Testing Mats., Vol. 41, p. 1297 (1941).
[13] R. O. Parker and R. J. Ziobro, "Comments on Corrections to Steam Conductivity Measurements," Symposium on Steam Quality, Am. Soc. Testing Mats., p. 27 (1956). (Issued as separate publication *ASTM STP No. 192.*)

the reduction in volume.[14, 15] Special apparatus is available [16, 17] for removing the gases from the water before the conductivity determination is made. Even then, the results obtained cannot be related precisely to the dissolved solids content because some dissolved substances, such as silica and certain types of organic matter, contribute little or nothing to the conductivity.

Method B, applicable to waters with solids content of 25 ppm or more, involves weighing the dried residue after a known volume of water has been evaporated. If only concentration needs to be known, the quantity of sample selected should be sufficient to yield a minimum of 25 mg of residue. If the residue is to be analyzed, at least 100 mg of residue should be obtained. This method covers determination of (a) total suspended matter, (b) total dissolved matter, (c) total floating matter, (d) total settleable and nonsettleable matter and (e) total nonoily settleable matter, and (f) total nonsettleable matter. In addition, the portion of each of these totals that is either volatile or ignitible can be determined.

When specific gravity methods are used for determining dissolved solids, the accuracy of the determination depends almost entirely on calibration of the method with known solutions in which the dissolved substances have the same proportions as the sample. In a plant where there is comparatively little variation in the composition of a processed water, even the relatively rough hydrometer method furnishes a useful guide to concentration by evaporation during the process.

Turbidity:

Turbidity refers to the measurement of opacity or light-scattering resulting from suspended matter. It is reported in arbitrary numbers or units. Comparisons may be made in various ways,[18, 19] and the accuracy of the results will depend on the apparatus used.

Turbidity can be determined empirically with a Jackson candle turbidimeter. This consists of a graduated glass tube, a standard candle, and a support for the candle and tube. The water is poured into the tube until the image of the candle flame just disappears. The depth of water at this point is related to turbidity values by standardization of the apparatus; more usually it is converted directly into turbidity values by reference to tables supplied with the instrument. Waters of high turbidity, more than Jackson turbidity number 1000, are diluted before the test is made. When this method is used for samples with turbidity less than 25, determinations must be made by comparing the unknown with standard suspensions in a series of glass bottles or Nessler tubes.

When turbidity is lower than Jackson turbidity number 25, it is desirable to use a relative turbidity method such as nephelometry. This is based on the light-scattering properties (Tyndall effect) of the suspended solids. Nephelometers are available commercially, and the manufacturers' instructions should be followed in their use. Most of these instruments measure light scattered at approxi-

[14] P. B. Place, Discussion, *Proceedings*, Am. Soc. Testing Mats., Vol. 41, p. 1311 (1941).

[15] W. B. Gurney, "Measurement and Purification of Steam to 0.01 ppm Total Dissolved Solids," Symposium on Steam Quality, Am. Soc. Testing Mats., p. 3 (1956). (Issued as separate publication *ASTM STP No. 192*.)

[16] H. M. Rivers, W. H. Trautman and G. W. Gibble, *Transactions*, Am. Soc. Mechanical Engrs., Vol. 72, p. 511 (1950).

[17] A. B. Sisson, F. G Straub, and R. W. Lane, "Construction and Operation of Larson-Lane Steam Purity and Condensate Analyzers," Symposium on Steam Quality, Am. Soc. Testing Mats., p. 37 (1956) (Issued as separate publication *ASTM STP No. 192*.)

[18] J. R. Baylis, *Water & Sewage Works*, Vol. 80, p. 125 (1933).

[19] A. T. Palin, *Water & Sewage Works*, Vol. 104, p. 492 (1957).

mately 90 deg, or at 90 and 270 deg. Nephelos standards have been prepared by thoroughly mixing suitable amounts of finely divided titanium dioxide into partially polymerized polystyrene. Calibrated commercial standards in sealed tubes can be purchased. Results are reported in terms of nephelos units.

Neither of the preceding methods measures absolute turbidity. Instruments are commercially available for measuring absolute turbidity and are based on an integrating sphere which sums up most of the source light which has been scattered by the sample. Absolute turbidity is defined as the fractional decrease of incident monochromatic light intensity, due to scattering, in traversing 1 cm of fluid.

In some industrial research and control applications it is desirable to know the dissymmetry of the light-scattering at various angles in order to determine the average linear dimensions of the suspended particles. A goniophotometer can be used to obtain the geometric light-scattering pattern for this purpose.

DISSOLVED GASES

A special sample is generally taken for each dissolved gas determination. This is mandatory in the case of oxygen. Determination is usually made immediately after sampling because changes in dissolved gas content may occur rapidly when the sample is removed from its normal environment.

Ammonia:

Method D 1426[5] covers the determination of ammonia and ammonium ions. The referee procedure is applicable to all types of industrial waters. It involves buffering the sample with a mixture of phosphates to pH 7.4 to inhibit hydrolysis of organic nitrogen compounds, and distilling it into a boric acid solution. Ammonia nitrogen is measured in

the distillate by Nesslerization or by titrating with standard sulfuric acid. The non-referee procedure uses direct Nesslerization (without distillation) for rapid, routine determination of ammonia nitrogen. Interferences in both procedures are discussed in the method cited. Determinations should be carried out at room temperature (25 to 30 C).

Nessler reagent is a strongly alkaline solution containing a complex iodide of mercury which reacts with ammonia to form a brownish complex amine. The reaction is so sensitive that less than 0.1 ppm of ammonia can be measured easily. Color comparisons with standards can be made roughly in bottles, but more exactly in Nessler tubes. Color comparators or colorimeters are also used. Standards can be made from known concentrations of ammonia, or permanent standards may be prepared in Nessler tubes from solutions of potassium chloroplatinate and cobaltous chloride. Samples containing colored or turbidity-forming impurities frequently can be diluted with ammonia-free water until they no longer interfere with the determination. Barium, calcium, magnesium, and other metals that produce turbidity can first be precipitated in the water sample and the supernatant used for ammonia analysis. Cloudiness due to the formation of magnesium hydroxide and calcium carbonate can be prevented by using Rochelle salts or glassy polyphosphates to sequester the alkaline-earth ions.

The sodium phenolate method[20] is reportedly free from the annoyance caused by turbidity when determining low concentrations of ammonia colorimetrically. This procedure is based on photometric measurement of the intensity of the blue color formed when sodium hypochlorite is added to a sample containing a low concentration of ammonia plus sodium

---

[20] A. B. Crowther and R. S. Large, *Analyst*, Vol. 81, p. 64 (1956).

phenolate solution. It has been reported that presence of amines does not interfere with this method.

Carbon Dioxide:

Methods for carbon dioxide are given in Method D 513.[5] In the referee method all the carbon dioxide, whether present originally as carbonate, bicarbonate, or free CO_2, is separated from the sample and collected in standard barium hydroxide; the excess of the base is found by titration and calculated to carbon dioxide. In the non-referee method, the sample is treated to convert all carbon dioxide to strontium carbonate; the carbonate is then dissolved in hydrochloric acid and the excess is titrated and related to the original carbon dioxide content. Curves are included to enable estimation of the percentage composition of the sample in terms of carbonate, bicarbonate, and free carbon dioxide at all pH levels.

There are additional methods of somewhat more restricted applicability. Free carbon dioxide can be estimated very quickly by titrating a sample with sodium carbonate until only bicarbonate is present in the solution (phenolphthalein end point); this procedure is much used for carbon dioxide in well waters. Warder's method, in which the sample is titrated successively to phenolphthalein and methyl orange end points and the alkalinities so determined related to the several carbon dioxide species, is much used for lime-soda softener control. When used on boiler waters that contain constituents that interfere with the ready conversion of alkalinity to carbonate concentration, the method is less suitable because the accuracy of determining end points is decreased and corrections must be made for such ions as phosphate and sulfite. A variation of the method,[21] in

which the sample is titrated between definite pH limits before and after all carbon dioxide has been boiled off, avoids the principal titration errors and eliminates corrections by coupling them with the blank determination. Results are obtained as total carbon dioxide and are usually accurate to within 2 ppm. The method is less useful for colored waters and those containing much ferrous iron or volatile constituents such as ammonia, hydrogen sulfide, and sulfur dioxide.

Chlorine:

Samples to be analyzed for chlorine should be kept away from direct sunlight prior to analysis. The analysis should be made as soon as possible (not more than 5 min after sampling) because a chlorine residual may decrease with time as a result of any chlorine demand of the sample.

Determination of chlorine is important because an increasing proportion of industrial water is chlorinated. Among the many methods available, the most reliable results have been obtained amperometrically. The more commonly used procedures, however, are the orthotolidine and starch-iodide methods. The former depends on the intensity of the yellow color formed by the oxidation of the reagent by chlorine. In the latter, chlorine liberates iodine from a neutral iodide solution. The free iodine is then titrated with a standard reducing agent using starch as an indicator.

A rapid method for determining free chlorine residuals above 1.0 ppm in cooling waters involves titration of an acidified sample with a standard methyl orange solution. The method is not affected by low chromate concentrations.

Method D 1253[5] for industrial waters includes a referee and two non-referee procedures for determining total available chlorine residual. The referee

---

[21] D. S. McKinney and A. M. Amorosi, *Industrial and Engineering Chemistry, Analytical Edition*, Vol. 16, p. 315 (1944).

method and non-referee method A are both suitable for differentiating between free and combined residuals. The referee method is an amperometric titration with phenylarseneoxide. Non-referee method A is used for rapid control determinations of chlorine residuals up to 10 ppm, but is most sensitive below 1 ppm. Non-referee method B is applicable for chlorine residuals above 1.0 ppm and is particularly useful for measuring high residuals (10 to 300 ppm). Both non-referee methods are colorimetric procedures using orthotolidine to form the yellow color.

Method D 1427[5] permits determination of chlorine residual in the presence of most interfering constituents found in industrial waste water. Method A is a starch-iodide titration, and method B is an amperometric titration. Both cover total chlorine measurement, but only the latter is applicable to determination of free available chlorine.

Continuous recording of chlorine residual has passed from the experimental to the practical stage.[22]

Hydrogen:

Until fairly recently, hydrogen was not regarded as an important constituent of industrial water. It has now been recognized that the rate of corrosion reactions in expensive boiler systems can be followed by comparing hydrogen concentrations in the water and vapor in various parts of the system. The method used depends on elaborate instrumentation,[23, 24] since the concentration sought is of the order of parts per billion. Method D 1588[5] includes a referee procedure

based on separation of hydrogen and its measurement by thermal conductivity, and a non-referee procedure based on separation of hydrogen and its measurement volumetrically.

Analysis for dissolved hydrogen has become of interest in the nuclear power field due to the use of hydrogen as a suppressor of water dissociation in the primary systems of pressurized water nuclear power plants. The concentrations of interest are much higher than in the case of boiler systems, up to perhaps 10 ppm. A method often used employs a gas transfer apparatus for volumetric determination of the total dissolved gas evolved from a water sample under vacuum. A Blacet-Leighton apparatus is used to determine the proportion of hydrogen in a sample of the gas by measuring the reduction in gas sample volume after removing the hydrogen by exposure to heated copper oxide.

Hydrogen Sulfide:

Hydrogen sulfide is frequently determined in industrial waste waters, and sometimes in process waters, especially in connection with the presence of sulfate-reducing bacteria on well casings and in piping. Qualitatively, and semi-quantitatively, odors indicating hydrogen sulfide can be confirmed with lead acetate paper which is quickly darkened by exposure to the vapor from a slightly acidified sample. One quantitative method[25] depends on the reducing action of free sulfide on a standard iodine solution, the excess of which is determined by titration with standard sodium thiosulfate. It is best to analyze samples immediately. When this is not possible,

[22] A. E. Griffin, "Continuous Recording of Chlorine Residuals and Determination of Chlorine Demand," Symposium on Continuous Analysis of Industrial Water and Industrial Waste Water, Am. Soc. Testing Mats., p. 23 (1952). (Issued as separate publication *ASTM STP No. 130*.)

[23] "Power Station Chemistry," *Publication H-11*, Edison Electrical Inst., 1940.

[24] J. K. Rummel, "Continuous Measurement of Dissolved Gases in Water," Symposium on Continuous Analysis of Industrial Water and Industrial Waste Water, Am. Soc. Testing Mats., p. 42 (1952). (Issued as separate publication *ASTM STP No. 130*.)

[25] H. E. Johnson, *Sewage Works Journal*, Vol. 3, p. 205 (1931).

the sulfide content should be fixed by adding a suitable quantity of zinc acetate or cadmium chloride solution to precipitate zinc or cadmium sulfide.

Method D 1255[5] is a colorimetric method for sulfides. (See discussion of Sulfide later in this chapter under *Anions*.) The concentration of hydrogen sulfide is calculated from the concentration of dissolved sulfides and the pH of the sample.

Frequently it is necessary, because of the presence of sewage or interfering components, to separate hydrogen sulfide by evolution in a stream of inert gas and collect it in a zinc acetate or cadmium chloride solution before making either the iodimetric or the colorimetric determination. In the absence of suspended matter, isolation as zinc sulfide or cadmium sulfide can be made directly. Tests have shown that the segregation of hydrogen sulfide by inert gas transfer is not quantitative and the error is large when the concentration is low.

Nitrogen:

Dissolved nitrogen is not ordinarily of interest in industrial water. In pressurized water nuclear power reactors, the concentration of dissolved nitrogen in the primary water is sometimes important because of the possibility of radiation-induced reactions of nitrogen with dissolved oxygen to produce nitric acid, or with dissolved hydrogen to produce ammonia. These reactions can produce wide variations in the pH of the primary water. Nitrogen has been determined with the gas transfer and Blacet-Leighton apparatus. Dissolved oxygen and hydrogen are removed from the total gas, and the remainder reported as inert gas, most of which is nitrogen.

Oxygen:

Procedures in Method D 888[5] are applicable to industrial waters and have a wide range of usefulness. The basic method for oxygen depends on the quantitative oxidation of manganous hydroxide by dissolved oxygen and the subsequent quantitative release of iodine by the reaction of the resulting manganic compound with potassium iodide when the sample is acidified. Modifications have been developed to offset the action of interfering substances.

A special sample is taken for dissolved oxygen and analyzed immediately. Proper sampling is of utmost importance to the analysis. General information on sampling is given in ASTM Methods of Sampling D 510[5], D 860[5], and D 1066[5]. Detailed requirements for sampling for dissolved oxygen analysis are given in Method D 888.

A method[26] using only one reagent, an indigo-carmine dye, has been reported to be promising for measuring dissolved oxygen in low concentrations (less than 0.01 ppm). Instrumental methods[27] for continuous monitoring and recording of dissolved oxygen are available. The required equipment is relatively expensive, but can be justified where the need for continuous measurement is great and qualified personnel are available for maintenance of the equipment.

Method D 1589[5] includes four procedures for determining dissolved oxygen in industrial waste water. Included are the Altsterberg (azide), Rideal-Stewart (permanganate), Pomeroy-Kirschman - Alsterberg, and polarographic methods.

Sulfur Dioxide:

Total sulfur dioxide (including free SO_2, bisulfite, and sulfite ions) is classi-

---

[26] L. S. Buchoff, N. M. Ingber, and J. H. Brady, *Analytical Chemistry*, Vol. 27, p. 1401 (1955).

[27] Symposium on Determination of Dissolved Oxygen in Water, Am. Soc. Testing Mats. (1957). (Issued as separate publication *ASTM STP No. 219*.)

fied under dissolved gases because, like carbon dioxide, the relative concentrations of its ionic species are related to pH. A commonly used method[28] of analysis depends on the reaction of an excess of standard iodine with sulfite in acid solution. The excess iodine is titrated with sodium thiosulfate using starch as an internal indicator. The method is accurate if interferences such as sulfide are absent and if precautions are taken to avoid air oxidation of sulfite during the handling of the sample before the iodine reaction is complete. The sample should be added to the iodine solution, not the reverse. A fresh sample is required.

Method D 1339[5] is a more rapid, but less accurate, procedure employing a solution of potassium iodide and iodate (together equivalent to iodine monochloride when made acid with hydrochloric acid) for direct titration of sulfite. Starch solution is used to indicate the end point. A small quantity of organic or other oxidizable material is usually present in industrial waters, and high results must be expected. Nitrite, ferric hydroxide, and other oxidizing substances will cause low results. When the sulfite content is at least half the sulfate concentration, the iodate titer can be checked by determining sulfate on the titrated solution and subtracting the original sulfate content. Care must be taken to avoid contact of the sample with air which will convert part of the sulfite to sulfate.

CATIONS

Aluminum:

Method D 857[5] uses hematoxylin to develop a blue color with aluminum ion after interfering substances have been separated. The method is sensitive to 0.01 ppm aluminum and provides a technique whereby determination may be made of total aluminum and aluminum ion, the difference between the two being suspended aluminum.

The hematoxylin method is preferable to that using aluminon (aurintricarboxylic acid)[29] which produces a pink color suitable for colorimetric measurement. When aluminon is used, the interference of iron is frequently accepted, and the results obtained are corrected by subtracting 1 ppm of aluminum for every 2 ppm of ferric iron known to be present. In this sense it may be considered to be a rapid control test. Some analysts complex the iron to overcome its interference.

Another useful method,[30] involving special apparatus, depends on the fact that the chloroform solution of aluminum 8-hydroxyquinolinate gives an intense greenish-yellow fluorescence with ultraviolet light. The sensitivity of the method is reported to be approximately the same as that of the referee procedure and the results are said to be of comparable accuracy, especially at concentrations from 0.05 to 0.1 ppm. Also, the presence of iron does not cause interference.

Ammonium:

Concentrations of ammonium ion, as distinct from total ammonia content (see discussion of Ammonia under *Dissolved Gases* in this chapter) can be calculated readily from the latter value[31] if sufficient information is available. The total ammonium content is distributed among ammonium ion, free ammonia (ammonium hydroxide), and other un-ionized ammonium compounds. When the last can be neglected, the concentration of

[28] "Standard Methods for Examination of Water and Wastewater," Am. Public Health Assn., New York, N. Y., 11th Ed., p. 244 (1960).

[29] P. S. Roller, *Journal,* Am. Chemical Soc., Vol. 55, p. 2437 (1933).
[30] J. W. Tullo, W. J. Stringer, and G. A. F. Harrison, *Analyst,* Vol. 74, p. 296 (1949).
[31] D. S. McKinney, "Calculation of Equilibria in Dilute Water Solutions," *Proceedings,* Am. Soc. Testing Mats., Vol. 39, p. 1191 (1939).

ammonium ion at any given temperature depends on the pH of the water.

Generally speaking, the value is useful only for estimating the effect of small concentrations of ammonia on the conductivity of steam condensate. For this purpose, distribution may be obtained from a table[32] in which percentages of ionized and un-ionized ammonia are given for the pH range from 1 to 13. The difference between total ammonia and ammonium ion also has some significance in the prediction of losses of ammonia at vents.

Barium and Strontium:

Barium and strontium usually are negligible and unimportant. Small amounts of either barium or strontium in the absence of the other have been determined[33] with good accuracy by the colorimetric evaluation of the precipitated and redissolved chromate. Inasmuch as both are not often present in important concentrations in the same industrial water, this method may be generally useful. The sample should contain at least 10 mg of the constituent sought, and suitable precautions must be taken to effect its quantitative precipitation as the chromate.

Barium of the order of 50 ppm can be determined quickly by titration with sodium sulfate[34] in the presence of a suitable indicator. However, when special accuracy is required the gravimetric method, in which barium sulfate is precipitated and weighed, is recommended. A more rapid method would be the estimation of the turbidity resulting from the addition to the water of a small quantity of sulfuric acid, by comparison with similarly prepared standards.

For an accurate determination of strontium, it is essential that it be separated from calcium. When strontium is present, the standard gravimetric oxalate method determines calcium and strontium oxides together. The oxides are dissolved in nitric acid and the solution is evaporated to dryness. The residue is then heated to 160 C for 2 hr, cooled, and a mixture of equal parts of absolute alcohol and ether is added to dissolve calcium nitrate. Evaporation, heating, and extraction are repeated on the strontium nitrate residue until extraction of calcium nitrate is substantially complete (there is little or no residue when the extract is evaporated). Strontium then is converted to the sulfate, which is ignited and weighed. Quicker but considerably less reliable results can be obtained by using the control methods given for barium.

A flame photometric procedure developed as an accurate and relatively simple method for determining strontium in sea water[35] has been used also for industrial waters.

Calcium and Magnesium:

The standard method for calcium and magnesium, Method D 511,[5] employs conventional gravimetric procedures in which calcium is precipitated as the oxalate and magnesium as the phosphate. Weights of residues from ignition of the precipitates are converted to constituent concentrations.

Time-saving modifications have been used widely for routine testing. For example, the colorimetric titration for hardness discussed later in this chapter under *Miscellaneous Tests* can be used to determine calcium and magnesium sep-

[32] D. S. McKinney, "Calculation of Corrections to Conductivity Measurements for Dissolved Gases," *Proceedings*, Am. Soc. Testing Mats., Vol. 41, p. 1290 (1941).

[33] H. A. Freediani and B. J. Babler, *Industrial and Engineering Chemistry, Analytical Edition*, Vol. 11, p. 487 (1939).

[34] H. L. Kahler, *Industrial and Engineering Chemistry, Analytical Edition,* Vol. 12, p. 266 (1940).

[35] Tsaihwa J. Chow and Thomas G. Thompson, *Analytical Chemistry*, Vol. 27, p. 18 (1955).

arately in most industrial waters. The reprecipitation step in each gravimetric procedure may be omitted at a considerable sacrifice in accuracy, perhaps as much as 10 per cent of the value found. Finally, the calcium oxalate precipitate may be dissolved in sulfuric acid and the resulting oxalic acid titrated with standard potassium permanganate; the titer is directly related to the calcium content.

In comparison, the number of useful rapid methods for magnesium is relatively limited. The use of titan yellow as a reagent for rapid colorimetric determination of magnesium has been found to be unsatisfactory by many investigators. A variant called thiazole yellow is reported[36] to be a better reagent and provides a reproducible color that is not affected materially by iron, aluminum, manganese, phosphorus, or calcium. The optimum range is 1 to 6 ppm of magnesium, and the reported average accuracy is within 5 per cent. An Eriochrome Black T procedure[37] for direct determination of magnesium has been reported to be useful but it requires careful technique.

Chromium:

Chromium in water is of interest principally in the hexavalent form in connection with its use as a corrosion inhibitor. It is also a frequent component of industrial wastes in which it may be present in either the trivalent or hexavalent form, or both. A method for amounts of chromium in excess of 100 mg (in the absence of organic matter) involves oxidation of chromium to the hexavalent form with permanganate or silver nitrate and persulfate, destruction

of excess oxidant, and titration with standard ferrous sulfate solution. Excess ferrous sulfate may be used and back-titrated with dichromate, using *o*-phenanthroline, or with permanganate.

Graham[38] proposed a method which depends on the reaction of hexavalent chromium with diphenylcarbazide in acid solution to produce a reddish-violet color. The optimum range is up to 5 ppm chromium and the accuracy is about 4 per cent. Phosphoric acid has been shown to mask iron, the most important interfering element.[39] A similar method has been proposed for the determination of chromium in samples of polluted water, industrial wastes, or sewage.[40] Organic material is decomposed by fuming with strong acids, and other interfering metals are extracted. Chromium is oxidized to the hexavalent state with permanganate, the excess permanganate destroyed with azide, and the color developed with diphenylcarbazide. See Method D 1687[5] for similar procedures using either permanganate or hypobromite for oxidation. (Refer also to the discussion of Chromate and Dichromate under *Anions* in this chapter.)

Copper:

Copper has become increasingly important because of corrosion processes in which it is a factor.

One procedure[41] for copper depends on the yellow color produced with sodium diethyldithiocarbamate. This reagent is not specific for copper, but interfering

---

[36] N. Drosdoff and D. C. Nearpass, *Industrial and Engineering Chemistry, Analytical Edition*, Vol. 20, p. 673 (1948).

[37] "Methods for Collection and Analysis of Water Samples," U. S. Geological Survey Water Supply Paper No. 1454 (1959).

[38] D. W. Graham, *Journal*, Am. Water Works Assn., Vol. 35, p. 159 (1943).

[39] H. A. J. Pieters, W. J. Hanssen, and J. J. Geurts, *Analytica Chimica Acta*, Vol. 2, p. 382 (1948). (In English.)

[40] "Standard Methods for the Examination of Water and Wastewater," Am. Public Health Assn., New York, N. Y., 11th Ed., p. 370 (1960).

[41] L. Gerber, R. I. Classen, and C. S. Boruff, *Industrial and Engineering Chemistry, Analytical Edition*, Vol. 14, p. 364 (1942).

substances are seldom present in troublesome concentrations. Zinc and lead produce a white turbidity instead of the yellow color and must be removed. Iron interference can be reduced by precipitation with ammonia or by complexing with citrate, or by a variation of the procedure in which the colored copper complex is extracted with a suitable organic solvent for comparison with standards. Ammonium thioglycolate added during extraction will help remove interference from iron, nickel, manganese, and chromium. The method is sensitive, and direct determinations are made in the range between 0.1 and 1 ppm. Because of this high sensitivity, however, the reagents and the distilled water used for preparing standards must be selected carefully, since copper in small concentrations is a frequent contaminant. Another method[42, 43] using bis (2-hydroxyethyl) dithiocarbamate (cuprethol) instead of sodium diethyldithiocarbamate has been reported to be superior.

An adaptation of a method[44, 45, 46] used for determination of copper in steels and ferro-alloys has been used for determining very low copper content of high-purity water samples. It is a colorimetric method using neocuproine. This procedure is employed in Method D 1688.[5] Use of bathocuproine instead of neocuproine offers promise of being an improved method for copper.[47]

Low concentrations of copper are determined also by the potassium ferro-cyanide method.[48] Copper in a sample. from which lead has been removed as lead sulfate, is first concentrated by precipitation as copper sulfide. Any iron present is removed after the precipitate has been converted to nitrate, and potassium ferrocyanide is added to develop the reddish color which is then compared with standards.

The dithizone method proposed for copper (also used for zinc and other metals) depends upon formation of stable, colored metal dithizonates from extraction of aqueous solutions with dithizone in carbon tetrachloride or chloroform. By adjustment of pH, use of complexing agents and other techniques, separation of metal dithizonates is made. This method is time-consuming and it is less accurate than the cuprethol or cuproine methods.

A direct Zincon method described later under *Zinc* has also been adapted for determination of copper.

Another colorimetric method[49] depends on the greenish color produced with rubeanic acid (dithio-oxamide). An electrolytic method for copper has also been used. It involves deposition of copper metal on a platinum cathode and subsequent weighing of the electrode. This method is an excellent one for waters of high copper content, such as plating wastes. Method E 53[50] can be used for the electrolytic determination after first concentrating the sample.

Hydrazine:

Method D 1385[5] uses a colorimeter or photometer to measure the intensity of the specific, yellow reaction product of

[42] W. C. Woelfel, *The Analyst*, Vol. 20 p. 722 (1948).

[43] E. B. Sandell, "Colorimetric Determination of Traces of Metals," Interscience Publishers, New York, N. Y., 2nd Ed., 1950, p. 309.

[44] A. R. Gahler, *Analytical Chemistry*, Vol. 26, p. 577 (1954).

[45] Andrew J. Frank, Arthur B. Goulston, and Americo A. Deacutis, *Analytical Chemistry*, Vol. 29, p. 750 (1957).

[46] G. F. Smith and W. H. McCurdy, *Analytical Chemistry*, Vol. 24, p. 371 (1952).

[47] L. G. Borchardt and J. P. Butler, *Analytical Chemistry*, Vol. 29, p. 414 (1957).

[48] "Methods of Analysis," *Journal*, Assn. Official Agricultural Chemists, 6th Ed., 1945, p. 638.

[49] P. W. West and M. Compere, *Analytical Chemistry*, Vol. 21, p. 628 (1949).

[50] Method for Chemical Analysis of Copper (Electrolytic Determination of Copper) (E 53), 1964 Book of ASTM Standards, Part 32.

hydrazine and paradimethylaminobenz-aldehyde. The color intensity is proportional to the concentration of hydrazine. This method is not suitable for hydrazine concentrations above 2 ppm. The sample should be analyzed as soon as practicable after collecting, since hydrazine undergoes autoxidation as well as oxidation by oxidizing agents. Collecting the sample under acid will allow considerable delay in analysis without affecting results.

Other methods have been used, including one based on a potassium iodate-iodide titration similar to the control method for sulfite in Method D 1339.[5]

Hydrogen Ion:

Essentially, the hydrogen ion concentration is defined sufficiently when the pH of the sample has been determined by the methods discussed later in this chapter under *Miscellaneous Tests*. In industrial waters, the difference between the concentration of hydrogen ion and the activity value represented by pH is rarely important. It can be calculated[51] when a complete analysis of the water is available. Tables relating hydrogen ion concentration to pH are available[52] in many texts.

Iron:

Method D 1068[5] is based on the intensity of the orange-red color produced by the reaction of ferrous iron with orthophenanthroline. The reagent is specific for ferrous iron and, with special precautions, may be used for estimating the distribution of iron between the ferrous and ferric states. The proportions of soluble and suspended iron can be obtained by difference from determinations made on filtered and unfiltered samples. Method D 1068 was selected as a referee procedure because iron recovery was the most accurate for a large number of industrial waters enriched with small known amounts of iron. It was also least subject to interference. A modification using bathophenanthroline for extremely low iron concentrations has been developed.[53] This has been embodied in Method D 1068[5] for determining total iron concentrations up to 200 parts per billion in industrial water, particularly high-purity water and steam condensate.

Good results also have been obtained with bipyridyl and with mercaptoacetic acid. The principle of the bipyridyl method[54] is the formation of a pink complex with ferrous iron at a pH of 3 to 4. The reaction between mercaptoacetic acid and iron gives a relatively stable, reddish-purple color.[55]

A thiocyanate method[56] has also been used. Comparative results on samples of low iron concentration with the bathophenanthroline, orthophenanthroline, bipyridyl, and thiocyanate methods have been reported.[57] The bathophenanthroline method exhibited the greatest sensitivity.

When iron concentration is less than 0.1 ppm, it is necessary that the sample be collected under acid to assure full recovery of iron. It is often convenient to run both iron and copper on the acidified sample.

[51] D. S. McKinney, *Industrial and Engineering Chemistry, Analytical Edition*, Vol. 3, p. 192 (1931).
[52] H. T. S. Britton, "Hydrogen Ions," D. Van Nostrand Co., Inc., New York, N. Y., 4th Ed. (1955).
[53] G. F. Smith, W. H. McCurdy, and H. Diehl, *The Analyst*, Vol. 77, p. 418 (1952).
[54] M. L. Moss and M. G. Mellon, *Industrial and Engineering Chemistry, Analytical Edition*, Vol. 14, p. 862 (1942).
[55] H. W. Swank and M. G. Mellon, *Industrial and Engineering Chemistry, Analytical Edition*, Vol. 10, p. 7 (1938).
[56] J. T. Woods and M. G. Mellon, *Industrial and Engineering Chemistry, Analytical Edition*, Vol. 13, p. 551 (1941).
[57] R. F. Andres, *Proceedings*, 14th Annual Water Conference, Engineering Soc. of Western Pa., p. 106 (1953).

Lead:

Lead is not a common constituent of industrial water but its determination is sometimes desired, for example, in waters that have been in contact with piping or equipment lined with lead for corrosion-resistance.

Lead, especially in the small amounts found in natural waters, is usually determined with dithizone.[58] The red lead dithizonate precipitate is soluble in chloroform or carbon tetrachloride. Zinc in excess of 0.5 ppm and copper in excess of 0.2 ppm interfere by bleaching the purplish color but normal procedures eliminate such interferences by use of complexing and other agents. The range is approximately 0.01 to 0.2 ppm; careful application of the procedure provides results accurate to the lower limit of this range. An improvement in this general procedure was suggested by Snyder.[59]

Some chemists prefer a more tedious procedure,[60] also colorimetric, in which lead is successively converted to sulfide, sulfate, and finally back to the sulfide. Since the precipitated sulfides include any zinc, copper, and iron present, the lead is separated as the sulfate from a solution containing a high percentage of alcohol. The sulfate then is dissolved with ammonium acetate, converted to the sulfide, and in that form compared to color standards developed with known quantities of lead.

An electrolytic method is based on deposition of lead oxide on the anode with subsequent liberation of iodine from potassium iodide solution. The iodine is then titrated with thiosulfate. This method is especially useful for waste waters containing relatively large con-centrations of lead. With lower con-centrations, it is desirable to concentrate the lead by collecting it on a ferric hy-droxide precipitate.

Manganese:

Method D 858[5] depends on the use of periodate to oxidize manganese ions to permanganate; the manganese content is evaluated from the purple color produced. Periodate was selected as the oxidizing reagent after a study which included persulfates and bismuthate. In making the selection, consideration was limited to the range of manganese concentrations ordinarily present in industrial waters, that is, a maximum of 2 ppm.

A rapid method[61, 62] for manganese using tetrabase has been found useful by some laboratories.

Nickel:

Determination of nickel was not frequently required on samples of industrial supply or process waters in the past, but is becoming more important as more stainless steel is being used in water systems. Available methods include colorimetric determinations[63] using dimethylglyoxime, or heptoxime reagent in the presence of an oxidant.

Sodium and Potassium:

In Method D 1127,[63a] sodium and potassium are jointly isolated as chlorides; the former is then determined gravimetrically as sodium zinc uranyl acetate and the latter as potassium chloroplatinate. Inasmuch as almost all other cation constituents in industrial waters

[58] P. A. Clifford, *Journal*, Assn. Official Agricultural Chemists, Vol. 26, p. 26 (1943).

[59] L. J. Snyder, *Analytical Chemistry*, Vol. 19, p. 684 (1947).

[60] J. W. Hawley and W. Wilson, *The Analyst*, Vol. 62, p. 166 (1937).

[61] E. M. Gates and G. H. Ellis, *Journal of Biological Chemistry*, Vol. 168, p. 537 (1947).

[62] R. G. Harry, *Journal*, Soc. Chemical Industry, Vol. 50, p. 434T (1931).

[63] "Standard Methods for the Examination of Water and Wastewater," Am. Public Health Assn., New York, N. Y., 11th Ed., p. 386 (1960).

[63a] *1961 Book of ASTM Standards*, Part 10.

interfere by contaminating the precipitates, the initial separation as chlorides is essential for accuracy. Instead of weighing the precipitated complex acetate it is sometimes more convenient to dissolve it and establish the sodium equivalent by matching the colored solution against standards[64] prepared from known quantities. A tetraphenylborate method for potassium has been reported[65] to be more rapid and accurate than the chloroplatinate method.

The flame photometer (Method D 1428[5]) provides by far the simplest and most rapid method for potassium and sodium in low concentrations. Method A, using either direct-measuring or internal-standard flame photometers, is especially recommended for concentrations of sodium and potassium between 1 and 100 ppm. Method B covers the range of 0 to 1 ppm, using the direct-intensity method with either type of instrument. Method B is particularly useful in testing for "breakthrough" of demineralizers, steam purity, and contamination of condensate. Special precautions are required to avoid exposing the instrument to dust, drafts, and unclean air when working in these low concentrations. Method B is currently being taken out of Method D 1428 and will be published as a method for high-purity water under a separate ASTM serial designation.

Alkali chlorides in water supplies have also been estimated indirectly, but with considerable accuracy, by converting to oxides and sulfates.[66] The procedure involves controlled fuming with sulfuric acid. All the anions present in the weighed product are then determined by standard quantitative methods, and concentration of combined alkalies is obtained by simple calculation. Reported results indicate an accuracy of about 2 per cent for waters containing total solids of approximately 1000 ppm with a total alkali content of about 35 per cent. At lower concentrations, the alkali concentration was generally found to be 2 to 4 ppm low.

Zinc:

Zinc is found in small quantities in most industrial waters, resulting from corrosion of galvanized iron and brass in condensing, cooling, and distributing systems. A determination for zinc may be made as an indication of deterioration of particular equipment, for identification of the source of this constituent in water-formed deposits, to determine the concentration of zinc in systems using zinc salts as corrosion inhibitors, or to determine zinc as a pollutant in waste water.

The nephelometric procedure,[67] in which interfering substances are removed by hydrogen sulfide and turbidity is then developed with ferrocyanide, has been used successfully. The most suitable range for direct comparison with standards is 1 to 10 ppm. Since the zinc content is concentrated during the procedure, the lower limit in the original sample is about 0.05 ppm and the optimum comparison level about 0.2 ppm.

Zinc may be determined with diphenylthiocarbazone (dithizone). The reaction product is red in carbon tetrachloride. The reported lower limit of the method is 0.01 ppm[68] and the accuracy is within about 10 per cent.

[64] E. A. Arnold and A. R. Pray, *Industrial and Engineering Chemistry, Analytical Edition,* Vol. 15, p. 294 (1943).

[65] R. M. Engelbrecht and F. A. McCoy, *Analytical Chemistry,* Vol. 28, p. 1772 (1956).

[66] J. B. Romer, W. W. Cerna, and H. F. Hannum, "The Estimation of Sodium in Water Supplies by an Indirect Method," *Proceedings,* Am. Soc. Testing Mats., Vol. 38, p. 638 (1938).

[67] L. T. Fairhall and J. R. Richardson, *Journal,* Am. Chemical Soc., Vol. 52, p. 938 (1930).

[68] N. L. Allport and C. D. B. Moon, *The Analyst,* Vol. 64, p. 395 (1939).

A direct zincon method, in which heavy metals are complexed with cyanide, has been reported.[69, 70] The zinc is released with chloral hydrate and then reacted directly with zincon reagent. This procedure is the basis for Method D 1691.[5]

ANIONS

The designation "anion" or "negative ion" is more convenient than "nonmetallic radical."

Bromide and Iodide:

Method D 1246[5] determines iodide alone, and combined iodide and bromide. Iodide is determined by oxidizing the iodide to iodate with bromine in a buffered solution. The excess bromine is subsequently reduced by adding sodium formate. Iodine equivalent to the iodate is then liberated from added potassium iodide and titrated. Combined iodide and bromide are measured by oxidizing them to iodate and bromate with hypochlorite, the excess hypochlorite subsequently being reduced by adding sodium formate. Iodine equivalent to the combined iodate and bromate is then liberated from added potassium iodide and titrated. Bromide is calculated from the difference in the two titrations.

Methods are available for bromide in the absence of iodide. Good recovery of bromide ion in concentrations of 0.03 to 2.3 ppm is reported by a technique[71] in which bromine is first liberated by chlorine and then reacted with an iodide mixture to liberate iodine. Titration of the latter with standard thiosulfate solu-

tion completes the determination. A less accurate colorimetric method,[72] which depends on the bromination of phenol red, is available for the range of 1 to 4 ppm.

Variations of the method for iodide involve extraction procedures and use alternate oxidation techniques. The most simple and possibly the most used procedure is rated as an estimating test. Exactly 10 ml of sample is treated with 1 ml of carbon tetrachloride, 2 drops of concentrated sulfuric acid, and 4 drops of 2 per cent potassium nitrite solution. The color of the liberated iodine, concentrated in the carbon tetrachloride, is compared with standards prepared similarly. The lower sensitivity limit of about 0.5 ppm iodide can be extended by concentrating a large volume of sample by evaporation. Interferences in this method can be quite pronounced, and accuracy may vary over wide limits. A study of the procedure has shown excellent results in some cases, very erratic ones in others.

Carbonate and Bicarbonate:

The calculation of carbonate and bicarbonate concentrations from total carbon dioxide (discussed under *Dissolved Gases*) and pH is made in accordance with the directions in Method D 513.[5] For control purposes, approximations of reasonable accuracy can be made from alkalinity and pH determinations in accordance with nomographs.[73] This method is not applicable when the water contains appreciable concentrations of phosphates, silicates, sulfites, or certain kinds of organic matter.

A quick method for approximating carbonate in boiler water depends on the

[69] Richard M. Rush and John H. Yoe, *Analytical Chemistry*, Vol. 26, p. 1345 (1954).
[70] J. A. Platte and V. M. Marcy, paper presented at meeting of Division of Water, Sewage, and Sanitation Chemistry, Am. Chemical Soc., Chicago, Ill., Sept. 9, 1958.
[71] G. U. Houghton, *Journal*, Soc. Chemical Industry. Vol. 65, p. 277 (1946).

[72] V. A. Stenger and I. M. Kolthoff, *Journal*, Am. Chemical Soc., Vol. 57, p. 831 (1935).
[73] J. F. Dye, *Journal*, Am. Water Works Assn., Vol. 36, p. 895 (1944).

insolubility of barium carbonate and barium phosphate in alkaline solution. An aliquot of the sample is titrated to the phenolphthalein end point, and the titration is then repeated on a second aliquot to which barium chloride has been added. The difference between the two titers represents carbonate and phosphate alkalinity and may be calculated to carbonate if the phosphate concentration is known.

Chloride:

Method D 512[5] includes two referee procedures, the first a mercurometric titration applicable to high-purity industrial water and water relatively free of heavy metal ions, and the second a silver nitrate titration for use with low-purity industrial supply, process, and waste waters. In the first method, dilute mercuric nitrate solution is added to an acidified sample in the presence of mixed diphenylcarbazone - bromphenol blue indicator. The end point of the titration is the formation of the blue-violet mercury diphenylcarbazone complex. In the second method, the sample is adjusted to pH 8.3 and titrated with silver nitrate in the presence of potassium chromate indicator. The end point is indicated by persistence of the brick-red silver chromate color.

A mercury thiocyanate colorimetric method has also been used for extremely low concentrations.[74, 75, 76]

Titration methods using a small aliquot are normally employed when the chloride concentration is high. Concentrations above 1000 ppm can probably

be determined somewhat more accurately by a more cumbersome gravimetric procedure in which a slight excess of silver nitrate is used to precipitate silver chloride under a dim light. The precipitate is coagulated by digestion, filtered through a prepared porous crucible, washed free from silver nitrate (hot water), dried at 150 C, and weighed. A somewhat less accurate volumetric method for more concentrated chloride solutions involves titration to a light brown color in the presence of ferric alum indicator and thiocyanate ion. The limit of accuracy of this method is about 3 ppm on a 100-ml sample.

In these gravimetric and volumetric methods, corrections must be made for bromide and iodide if present.

Chromate and Dichromate:

A simple, direct colorimetric procedure is based on the yellow color of alkaline chromate. Chromate concentrations in excess of 10 ppm can be determined by a control test method involving titration with ferrous ammonium sulfate in sulfuric acid solution and using *o*-phenanthroline as the indicator.

Lower concentrations may be determined colorimetrically using the violet-red color developed by chromates with diphenylcarbazide in acid solution. This is sensitive to about 0.01 ppm. (Refer also to the preceding discussion on Chromium under *Cations*.)

Cyanide:

The concentration of cyanide in water is important because of its toxicity. The major problem in analyzing for cyanide is the removal of interfering substances from the sample because the analytical procedures available are not specific. Analysis should be made as soon as possible after the sample is collected because most cyanides are unstable.

[74] Satori Utsumi, *Journal*, Chemical Soc. Japan, Pure Chemistry Sect., Vol. 73, pp. 835, 838 (1952).

[75] Iwaji Iwasaki, Satori Utsumi, and Takejiro Ozawa, *Bulletin*, Chemical Soc. Japan, Vol. 25, p. 226 (1952).

[76] David M. Zall, Donald Fisher, and Mary Q. Garner, *Analytical Chemistry*, Vol. 28, p. 1665 (1956).

Published procedures[77, 78] are available for removing interfering substances and making the determination. Procedures for removal of sulfides, fatty acids, and oxidizing agents are outlined, and two alternate distillation procedures are given for removing most other interferences. After interferences are removed, cyanide is determined either by a modified Liebig titration method using *p*-dimethylaminobenzalrhodanine internal indicator, or by a colorimetric method using pyridine-pyrazolone.

Fluoride:

Method D 1179[5] provides three colorimetric procedures. The referee method and one of the non-referee methods involve bleaching by fluoride of the alizarin color produced in the presence of zirconium salts. The second non-referee method involves the bleaching by fluoride of the color from a zirconium-Eriochrome Cyanine R indicator. The referee method avoids interferences through isolation of fluoride ion by distillation. The non-referee methods include discussions of the interferences that affect the results and offer suggestions for making some limited corrections. When the effect of any substance present is unknown, or when the composition of the water is not known, prior isolation of the fluoride by distillation is required.

Hydroxide:

The standard method for hydroxide, Method D 514,[5] depends on the removal of carbonate and phosphate alkalinity before the hydroxide is titrated. The procedure uses strontium chloride under carefully controlled conditions. Some-

what less reliable results can be obtained more quickly with barium chloride, with which boiling to precipitate carbonate and phosphate ions is not necessary. The results are usually accurate to a few parts per million. The presence of silicate has been reported to produce high results with both methods.

The interpretation of titrations to phenolphthalein and methyl orange end points also is often used as a procedure for calculating hydroxide. The latter is estimated from the relationship that the phenolphthalein titration represents all the hydroxide and half the carbonate, and the complete titration to methyl orange represents all the hydroxide and all the carbonate. The interpretation becomes complicated when phosphate is present, although corrections are often made on the basis that one third of the phosphate is titrated to the phenolphthalein end point and a second third to the methyl orange end point. Other indicators, including mixed indicators,[79] have been substituted for methyl orange in this procedure. These alternate methods have doubtful accuracy unless the water is relatively free from organic matter, silicates, sulfites, and aluminates. Direct determination of hydroxide is generally much more reliable, and these alternate methods should be used only when an estimation of hydroxide will suffice, or after correlation between the alternate methods and the direct method has been established for a particular water.

A simplified procedure, based on Method D 514, is included in this Manual under *Abbreviated Methods for the Analysis of Water Supplies in the Evaporative Industry.*[5] It is intended for routine control purposes, such as boiler water testing.

[77] "Standard Methods for the Examination of Water and Wastewater," Am. Public Health Assn., New York, N. Y., 11th Ed., p. 350 (1960).

[78] "Procedures for Analyzing Metal-Finishing Wastes," Ohio River Valley Water Sanitation Commission, Cincinnati, Ohio (1954).

[79] S. S. Cooper, *Industrial and Engineering Chemistry, Analytical Edition*, Vol. 13, p. 466 (1941).

Nitrate:

Method D 992[5] is a rapid, simple, and precise colorimetric procedure. A yellow color is developed in the sample by the reaction of nitrate ion with concentrated sulfuric acid and a chloroform solution of brucine alkaloid. An accuracy of 0.5 ppm is obtainable in the range 0 to 50 ppm.

Another much-used colorimetric method,[80] in which a yellow color is developed with phenoldisulfonic acid, is very useful for many natural waters in which the chloride content is low. Errors as large as 50 per cent have been reported when the chloride content was 1000 ppm. Precipitation of the chloride with silver sulfate reduces the error, but special precautions must be taken to avoid loss of nitrate. The range is about the same as in Method D 992. For wastes containing color, it is necessary to clarify and decolorize[81] the samples before using this method. In addition, the method is not satisfactory for samples containing organic matter.

When the water sample is highly colored, the reduction method[82] is probably the best procedure available, especially if a Kjeldahl distillation system is at hand. The nitrate ion is reduced to ammonia, which is determined by evolution and titration. Any nitrite present will be determined with the nitrate. There is a persistent need for an accurate and dependable method for nitrate in such samples.

An abbreviated method for routine determination of nitrate ion in colorless boiler water is included in this Manual under *Abbreviated Methods for the Analysis of Water Supplies in the Evaporative Industry.*[5]

Nitrite:

Nitrite in natural water is generally regarded as evidence of pollution. The test is also made to check the possibility of nitrite interference with other determinations. Sodium nitrite has been used as a corrosion inhibitor. Sample bottles should be sterile, and nitrite ion should be run as soon as possible after sampling.

Most recommended procedures are colorimetric; they depend on the diazotization of an aromatic amine and subsequent coupling of the product with a second reagent to produce a dyestuff. Both reactions are stoichiometric under suitable conditions. The common reagents are sulfanilic acid and alphanaphthylamine, which are used in Method D 1254.[5] Precision is from 0.005 to 0.025 ppm and accuracy ±0.01 to 0.05 ppm when nitrite concentration is between 0.10 and 0.50 ppm. Method D 1254 includes a thorough discussion of the effects of interference on nitrite test results. Sulfanilamide and naphthyl ethylenediamine hydrochloride have also been used.[83]

An ASTM method is in preparation for determination of nitrite concentrations up to 1000 ppm or higher, which may be used for corrosion control. Originated by Lunge,[84] this method has been modified only slightly in the past 75 years. A modern procedure can be found in Scott.[85] The method is based upon oxidation of nitrite with a standard solution of permanganate in acid solution, addition of an excess of standard

[80] T. C. Hoppe, *Journal*, Am. Water Works Assn., Vol. 33, p. 1589 (1941).
[81] "Standard Methods for the Examination of Water and Wastewater," Am. Public Health Assn., New York, N. Y., 11th Ed., p. 300 (1960).
[82] W. C. Schroeder and A. A. Berk, *Bulletin*, U. S. Bureau of Mines, Vol 443, p. 83 (1941).

[83] M. B. Shinn, *Industrial and Engineering Chemistry*, Vol. 13, p. 33 (1941).
[84] Lunge, *Berichte*, Vol. 10, p. 1075 (1877).
[85] Scott, "Standard Methods of Chemical Analysis," Vol. I, 5th Ed., D. Van Nostrand & Co., New York, N. Y., 1939, p. 653.

oxalate, and back-titration of the excess with permanganate.

Phosphate:

Method D 515[5] includes four procedures for determining phosphates as follows:

1. The referee method is a gravimetric procedure which depends on successive precipitations of the phosphate ion as phosphomolybdate and magnesium ammonium phosphate. The latter is ignited to magnesium pyrophosphate and weighed. Heating in the presence of strong acids is included to convert most polyphosphates to the ortho form.

2. Non-referee method A is a volumetric procedure in which orthophosphate reacts with ammonium molybdate in a solution containing citric acid, nitric acid, and ammonium nitrate to form insoluble ammonium phosphomolybdate. The precipitate is washed free of acid and treated with sodium hydroxide. Excess sodium hydroxide is titrated with acid to an end point having a sharp color change at pH 7.5. This procedure also includes prior heating in the presence of strong acids to convert most of any polyphosphates present to orthophosphate. Results obtained by this method are often regarded as superior to referee results reported by the average analyst because of the simplicity of the procedure and the relatively few manipulations in which errors can be made. As a rough control test, the phosphate content is sometimes estimated from the volume of the yellow precipitate.

3. Non-referee method B is best suited to routine determination of orthophosphate in industrial water containing 2 to 25 ppm of phosphate ion as PO_4. Higher concentrations are diluted to this range. The method is based on the photometric measurement of the yellow color of phosphovanadomolybdic

acid developed in the sample. Highly colored water must be decolorized before testing.

4. Non-referee method C is a colorimetric procedure for orthophosphate for all industrial water except that which is highly polluted. It is intended primarily as a control test where high precision is not required. Comparisons are made directly in the 0.1 to 1.5 ppm range. Higher concentrations are measured by sample dilution. Measurement is made of the intensity of the color of the molybdate blue complex formed by reaction of orthophosphate with ammonium molybdate in the presence of a reducing agent. Stannous chloride is used as the reducing agent, but aminonaphtholsulfonic acid has also been used.[86] Matched Nessler tubes, commercial color comparators with permanent standards, or a photometer can be used for measuring the color intensity.

The third method listed above for phosphate does not provide for determining phosphorus that is present in the more complex phosphate species such as tripolyphosphate, the metaphosphates, and pyrophosphate. When it is essential that all of the phosphorus be determined, conversion of the complex phosphates to orthophosphate is made by boiling an acidified sample as described in the first two methods listed. A more rapid procedure for converting polyphosphates has been reported.[87] The difference between the orthophosphate concentration before and after such conversion is a measure of polyphosphate phosphorus.

Frequently it is desirable to estimate the concentration of a particular species.

---

[86] W. C. Schroeder and C. H. Fellows, *Transactions*, Am. Soc. Mechanical Engrs., Vol. 54, p. 213 (1932).

[87] R. Robertson, "Some New Developments in the Molybdenum Blue Method for Total and Ortho Phosphates in Water," presented at the 130th Meeting, Am. Chemical Soc., September, 1956.

Tripolyphosphate and pyrophosphoric acid may be determined by a combined titration and gravimetric determination of pyrophosphate.[88] Ortho- and metaphosphates do not interfere with this method. Both Bell and Jones[89] have reported methods for determination of metaphosphates in the presence of the other phosphate species.

An abbreviated method for orthophosphate for routine control use is included in this Manual under *Abbreviated Methods of Test for the Analysis of Water Supplies in the Evaporative Industry.*[5]

Sulfate:

Method D 516[5] referee procedure determines sulfate ion gravimetrically as barium sulfate. The method is simple and relatively free from pitfalls for the untrained analyst. When time is available for proper crystal growth in the precipitate and careful ignition of the residue, the referee method will be found to be less burdensome, though more time-consuming, than some of the control procedures, especially when the sulfate content is appreciable.

In the Method D 516 non-referee procedure, the sulfate is converted to barium sulfate turbidity for photometric comparison against standards. Originally used only when the sulfate concentration was relatively high, better instrumentation and more refined techniques have extended the usefulness of this procedure to very low concentrations.

In the benzidine procedure, an addition product of benzidine and sulfuric acid is precipitated from acid solution, washed free of mother liquor, redissolved in hot water, and titrated with standard sodium hydroxide. This method may not be highly accurate, but it is especially useful when differentiation from a relatively high sulfite concentration is required.

There are also a number of procedures involving titration of the sample with barium chloride in the presence of suitable indicators which change color in the presence of excess barium ion. One such indicator is tetrahydroxyquinone,[34] which gives best results when the sulfate concentration is at least 100 ppm; a special procedure is required when phosphate is present.

More recently a volumetric procedure[90, 91] using barium perchlorate solution as titrant and Thorin [2(2-hydroxy-3,6-disulfo-1-naphthylazo) benzenearsonic acid] as indicator has shown good results for very low concentrations. By suitable techniques many interferences found in other methods are eliminated. This procedure is used as the basis for a non-referee procedure in Method D 516.

Sulfide:

Total sulfides and dissolved sulfides can be determined in accordance with Method D 1255.[5] This is a colorimetric procedure based on the fact that p-amino dimethylaniline, ferric chloride, and sulfide ion react in acid solution to produce methylene blue. The concentration range of the method is 0.1 to 20 ppm of sulfide ion. Concentrations above 20 ppm can be determined by dilution. p-Amino dimethylaniline is poisonous and corrosive; it has been suggested that p-amino dimethylaniline sulfate, which is easier to handle, may be used instead.[92]

---

[88] R. N. Bell, *Analytical Chemistry*, Vol. 19, p. 97 (1947)

[89] L. T. Jones, *Industrial and Engineering Chemistry, Analytical Edition*, Vol. 14, p. 536 (1942).

[90] James S. Fritz, Stanley S. Yamamura, and Marlene J. Richard, *Analytical Chemistry*, Vol. 29, p. 158 (1957).

[91] James S. Fritz and Stanley S. Yamamura, *Analytical Chemistry*, Vol. 27, p. 1461 (1955).

[92] "Standard Methods for the Examination of Water and Wastewater," Am. Public Health Assn., New York, N. Y., 11th Ed., p. 333 (1960).

Hydrogen sulfide concentration can be calculated from the concentration of dissolved sulfides and pH. (See Hydrogen Sulfide under *Dissolved Gases* in this chapter.)

Sulfite:

Sulfite and bisulfite ion concentrations can be calculated[51] from total sulfur dioxide and pH. Equations can be set up parallel to those given for carbonates and carbon dioxide by using the appriate constants for sulfurous acid and sulfite ion.

Method D 1339[5] covers a potassium iodide-iodate method for the direct titration of sulfite for control purposes. (See Sulfur Dioxide under *Dissolved Gases* in this chapter.)

A similar method is included in this Manual under *Abbreviated Methods for the Analysis of Water Supplies in the Evaporative Industry.*[5]

MISCELLANEOUS CHEMICAL TESTS

Acidity and Basicity (Alkalinity):

Methods for determining acidity and alkalinity in industrial waters are grouped as Method D 1067.[5] Acidity and alkalinity are defined as capacities for neutralization, as distinct from pH which is an intensity factor.

The Method D 1067 referee procedure is applicable to industrial water and waste water containing organic or inorganic compounds. It involves electrometric titration with standard hydrochloric acid or sodium hydroxide either to specific pH end points, or by developing a titration curve for the sample and noting the pH values at the inflection points of the curve. The latter procedure is necessary for evaluation of the buffering capacity of water if the buffering salts are other than carbonates and bicarbonates.

Two non-referee procedures are included in Method D 1067. The first involves titration to a designated pH end point which is determined by comparison of the color developed by an added indicator with the color of a standard buffer solution containing the same added indicator. In the second method, designed for rapid measurements, the sample is titrated to a designated pH, the end point being determined by color change of certain indicators. Neither of these is applicable for waters highly polluted with industrial wastes, containing buffering materials at the end point, or containing materials that will interfere by reason of color, precipitation, or other factors.

Alkalinity or acidity in the intermediate range between pH 3.5 and pH 9 is arbitrarily regarded as resulting from the presence of weak bases or weak acids. Alkalinity above this range, or acidity below it, is considered to be due to the presence of relatively strong bases or strong acids, respectively.

Special procedures said to be sensitive and accurate to 0.05 ppm have been developed for measuring extremely low alkalinities.[93]

Chemical Oxygen Demand:

Chemical oxygen demand (COD) is defined as the amount of oxygen, expressed in parts per million, consumed under specified conditions in the oxidation of organic and oxidizable inorganic matter in waste water, corrected for the influence of chlorides. Method D 1252[5] uses a standard potassium dichromate solution in 50 per cent by volume sulfuric acid to oxidize organic and oxidizable inorganic material. The excess dichromate is then titrated with a standard ferrous ammonium sulfate solution, using ortho-phenanthroline ferrous complex as as internal indicator. This method is

---

[93] T. E. Larson and Laurel Henley, *Analytical Chemistry*, Vol. 27, p. 851 (1955).

recommended as a supplement to, but not as a substitute for, the biochemical oxygen demand (BOD) test which is the only test that indicates directly the quantity of oxygen that will be utilized by natural agencies in stabilizing organic matter. There is no inherent constant relationship between COD and BOD, but the COD test can be useful in evaluating the treatment and control of waste waters.

Methods for measuring biochemical oxygen demand and immediate dissolved oxygen demand are discussed later in this chapter.

Chlorine Requirement:

Often it is desirable to establish the quantity of chlorine required to achieve a specific objective in the treatment of a water by chlorination. This objective might be elimination of tastes and odors; reduction of biochemical oxygen demand by destroying or modifying decomposable organic substances; separation of grease in waste water; or destruction or modification of oxidizable constituents in waste water.

Method D 1291[5] provides a procedure for finding the chlorine requirement of process water and waste water. It involves adding a chlorine solution of known strength, in increasing increments of chlorine concentrations, to different portions of the sample water. The contact time and pH are maintained as specified for the particular object of chlorination. The chlorine requirement of the water is found by interpolation of a plotted curve of chlorine dosages against the results of chlorine residual tests or other tests which determine whether the specific object of the chlorination has been reached in the different sample portions. The chlorine requirement is the amount of chlorine, expressed in parts per million, required to achieve the objectives of chlorination.

Chloroform-Extractable Matter:

Matter extractable by chloroform from industrial waters (Method D 1178[5]) includes heavy oils and fats, many other types of organic matter, and small amounts of inorganic salts. The popular use of the word "oil" as synonymous with the more exact title is unfortunate.

This procedure depends upon the direct extraction of the sample with chloroform after special precautions have been taken to acidify the sample to pH 3 to 4 to free any saponifiable oil. The chloroform is then evaporated and the residue weighed. This method does not determine materials that are volatile under conditions of the test, nor does it determine specific oils, greases, or organic compounds.

Another procedure[94] fixes the extractable matter by occluding it on a bulky precipitate, such as ferric hydroxide, and subsequently extracting the material from the washed and dried floc. This procedure is said to reduce interference from inorganic salts, such as sodium sulfate and sodium chloride.

Variations of both procedures are used in which the extracting solvent is ether, petroleum ether, hexane, benzene, carbon tetrachloride, or ethyl acetate. Sometimes the acidified water is evaporated to dryness and the residue is extracted. Neither procedure provides a particularly accurate determination of oil.

It is important to use all of the special sample for one determination of extractable matter. Constituents like oil are not always homogeneously distributed through the water. Sometimes, particularly after several days of storage, much of the oil is adsorbed on the inner surface of the container. Every precaution should be taken to include this part of

---

[94] C. A. Noll and W. J. Tomlinson, *Industrial and Engineering Chemistry, Analytical Edition,* Vol. 15, p. 629 (1943).

the oil with the extract. Glass sample containers are essential. Polyethylene will adsorb the chloroform-extractable matter to a greater extent than glass.

Hardness:

Hardness is now generally accepted as representing the total concentration of calcium and magnesium ions. Originally hardness was understood to be the capacity of a water for precipitating soap. It was measured by the amount of soap required to produce a stable lather. Soap hardness has been expressed fundamentally in terms of the equivalents of metal ions capable of precipitating soap (including other polyvalent ions in addition to calcium and magnesium). It has commonly been reported in terms of the equivalent amount of calcium carbonate.

The soap hardness test is still used to some extent for determining the exhaustion point of domestic zeolite softeners and in some industrial applications, particularly when the soap-consuming power of the sample is the principal consideration. This method has been replaced to a large extent in recent years by a volumetric titration method in which a buffered water sample is titrated with an organic sequestering material which forms un-ionized complexes with calcium and magnesium. Titration is performed in the presence of an indicator dye which changes color sharply when the calcium and magnesium ions have been sequestered. By titrating a second aliquot of the sample in the presence of a different indicator and buffer, a separate determination can be made for calcium, thus differentiating between the calcium and magnesium components. This method is much more accurate than the soap method, particularly in very low hardness water.

Gravimetric methods are more dependable but more cumbersome than either of the two preceding methods with waters of unknown composition. Calcium

is determined by precipitation as the oxalate, which is then ignited to calcium oxide. Magnesium is determined by the precipitation of magnesium ammonium orthophosphate, which is then ignited to magnesium pyrophosphate. Total hardness is calculated from the sum of calcium and magnesium in the ignited residues.

Method D 1126[5] includes two of the procedures just described. The referee method is gravimetric; and the non-referee method is the volumetric titration procedure. In both the results are expressed in equivalents per million (epm).

An abbreviated version of the volumetric titration method is included under *Abbreviated Methods for the Analysis of Water Supplies in the Evaporative Industry.*[5] It is intended for routine testing for total hardness and calcium hardness of water for low pressure boilers.

Nitrogen, Total Kjeldahl:

The total Kjeldahl nitrogen includes both organic nitrogen and ammonia nitrogen, but not nitrate and nitrite nitrogen. The procedure[95] involves conversion of organic nitrogen to ammonium bisulfate by digestion in the presence of sulfuric acid and a catalyst. The ammonia is distilled from an alkaline medium and can be measured as given in the method cited or in Method D 1426 previously discussed under Ammonia in the section on *Dissolved Gases.* Nitrate and nitrite can be determined by the Kjeldahl method if these ions are first reduced to ammonia (see discussion of Nitrate in this chapter under *Anions).*

Nitrogen, Organic:

Organic nitrogen compounds are produced by biological processes. Hence an

[95] "Standard Methods for the Examination of Water and Wastewater," Am. Public Health Assn., New York, N. Y., 11th Ed., p. 307 (1960).

increase in organic nitrogen content of a water may indicate increased pollution. Organic nitrogen can be calculated by subtracting the ammonia nitrogen from the total Kjeldahl nitrogen. Organic nitrogen can be determined directly with the Kjeldahl method if the ammonia nitrogen is first removed by distilling a buffered sample.[95]

Oily Matter:

Oily matter is defined as hydrocarbons, hydrocarbon derivatives, and all liquid and unctuous substances that have boiling points of 90 C or above and are extractable from water at pH 5.0 or lower, using a suitable solvent.

Method D 1340[5] covers determination of volatile oily matter and extractable oily matter, with the total oily matter reported as the sum of the two quantities. Volatile oily matter is determined by refluxing the sample through a trap, and collecting and volumetrically measuring the volatile matter in the trap. The remaining sample is extracted and distilled to remove the solvent. The residue is cooled and weighed.

The procedure discussed earlier in this chapter for chloroform-extractable matter is similar to the "oily matter" procedure except that no provision is made for recovering and measuring the volatile fraction. There are also some differences in the extraction procedure.

pH:

Method D 1293[5] covers a procedure for electrometric measurement of the pH of industrial water and waste water with the glass electrode. It is intended for control and routine use. This method refers to Method E 70[5] for detailed information on equipment and procedures.

Careful sampling of the water is important, particularly in the case of distilled water and condensate. In fact, the true pH of nearly pure water in a closed system can be determined with accuracy only in flow cells. The water sample flows over the electrodes in such cells at the desired temperature of measurement without exposure to the atmosphere or to changes in pressure that would affect the dissolved gas content. The sample also must be shielded from entrainment of noncondensable gases which could dissolve as the temperature decreases.

In the non-referee procedures for acidity and basicity (alkalinity), Method D 1067,[5] indicator dyes are used to show the end points of the titrations to reference pH levels. The dyes are useful because they change color in various ranges of hydrogen ion concentrations.

There is a large number of weakly acidic (or basic) organic dye stuffs which undergo such color changes. The most suitable and accurate indicators are those which change color relatively sharply over a narrow range of pH. Such dyes provide a relatively rapid and inexpensive method for estimating pH where precise control is not absolutely essential. The pH of the prepared sample is read by matching colors with a graduated set of permanent standards mounted in a slide. Standards are prepared from buffer solutions, or they may be colored glass or solution.

In addition to personal errors that may arise due to differences in color perception, errors from temperature variations, differences in total-salts-concentration, chlorine, and specific indicator properties (buffer effect of the indicator) reduce the accuracy of the method.

Phenol:

Phenol and other phenolic compounds are determined by colorimetric methods and reported as phenol. Since other phenolic compounds, as a rule, are less sensitive than phenol to color development with the indicators used, the results represent the *minimum* concentration of phenolic compounds present.

Published procedures[96] include the Gibbs method using 2,6-dibromo-quinonechlorimide to develop the color, and the 4-aminoantipyrine method. The intensity of color developed in either test is measured with a spectrophotometer or a filter photometer. A modification of the 4-aminoantipyrine method is provided for samples containing more than 1 mg per liter of phenol and where extreme accuracy is not required. Smaller samples are used and extractions are not required. Screening procedures are necessary in all three methods when the sample contains organic or inorganic compounds which may interfere in color development with the reagents used.

Neither of the above methods measures *p*-cresol and certain other para-substituted phenols. A method for determining *p*-cresol has been reported.[97] It uses Gibbs reagent to couple with interfering phenols to form indophenols. *p*-Cresol is separated from the nonvolatile indophenols by steam distillation and measured by a diazo colorimetric method.

Silica:

Procedures for the determination of silica are included in Method D 859.[5] The referee method includes hydrochloric and perchloric acid procedures in which silica is separated and weighed as SiO_2. The methods differ only in the ease with which the dehydration of silica and its separation from impurities can be achieved. The perchloric acid method is superior in this respect but is not available to all analysts because of restrictions on the use of a material known to have caused serious fires and explosions.

In addition to the gravimetric methods which determine total silica, colorimetric methods are included for determining crystalloidal (noncolloidal) silica only.

In non-referee method A, color is developed in the water by a controlled reaction involving ammonium molybdate at a closely controlled pH (tannins interfere). For photometric determination of silica concentrations below 2 ppm, amino-naphthol-sulfonic acid is added to increase the sensitivity and eliminate tannin interference. Non-referee method B is similar but uses sodium sulfite as a reductant to prevent significant interference by tannin. In the colorimetric methods, silica concentrations above 2 ppm are usually compared with silica or chromate color standards, or measured photometrically. Below 2 ppm, photometric measurement is used.

Because of the importance attached to silica in boiler water in relation to turbine maintenance in high-pressure, high-temperature operation, special procedures such as the one outlined in Method D 1689[5] have been suggested for its determination in extremely dilute solutions. When silica concentrations are 0.1 ppm or less, special precaution[98] must be taken during sampling to avoid loss of silica to the sampling equipment. For example, in sampling steam, errors are said to result if the pressure on the steam is reduced ahead of the condenser.

BIOLOGICAL OR OTHER TESTS

Biochemical Oxygen Demand:

Biochemical oxygen demand (BOD) is the only test that indicates directly the quantity of oxygen that will be utilized by natural agencies in stabilizing organic matter. One method[99] involves diluting portions of the sample with oxygen-saturated water and analyzing for dissolved oxygen in the mixture after a

[96] *Ibid.*, pp. 197 and 403.
[97] George R. Tallon and Robert D. Hepner, *Analytical Chemistry*, Vol. 30, p. 1521 (1958).

[98] F. G. Straub, Bulletin 364, University of Illinois, Urbana, Ill., 1946.
[99] "Standard Methods for the Examination of Water and Wastewater," Am. Public Health Assn., New York, N. Y., 11th Ed., p. 318 (1960).

period of incubation (usually 5 days at 20 C). This is called the dilution method. Another method[100] is based on direct measurement of oxygen utilized by the sample under an air or oxygen atmosphere in a closed system with constant temperature and agitation. Oxygen utilization is determined by measuring the decrease in gas volume, or the change in pressure under constant volume conditions. This manometric method can be used at higher waste concentrations than those employed in the dilution method.

Immediate Dissolved Oxygen Demand:

It is sometimes desirable to differentiate between true biochemical oxygen demand and immediate dissolved oxygen demand (IDOD), for example, in waters containing sulfide, sulfite, or ferrous ions. The dilution method for measuring BOD is used to determine IDOD. The difference between the calculated dissolved oxygen concentration of the sample dilution and the observed dissolved oxygen after 15 min is the IDOD. The 15-min period has been arbitrarily selected as a standard.

Iron Bacteria:

Iron bacteria may clog water lines, reduce heat transfer, and cause staining. Method D 932[5] describes a procedure for the detection and identification of iron bacteria by examination under the microscope.

---

[100] Ibid., p. 396.

Microorganisms:

The chapter on *Treatment of Process Water and Waste Water* mentions the effects of, and treatment for, various microorganisms occurring in water. Method D 1128[5] covers the identification, by microscopic examination, of bacterial cells, mold filaments, algae, protozoa and other small animals, and such particles of inert material as may be found in process water and waste water.

Sulfate-Reducing Bacteria:

These bacteria cause corrosion and deposition problems in water systems. Method D 993[5] includes a referee procedure for identification and estimation of sulfate-reducing bacteria, based on iodometric determination of the hydrogen sulfide produced by the bacteria in a suitable medium under anaerobic conditions.

A non-referee procedure in Method D 993 provides for qualitative determination based on the use of lead acetate paper to detect hydrogen sulfide produced by the bacteria in a suitable medium.

Toxicity to Fresh-Water Fishes:

Method D 1345[5] is a bioassay procedure intended as a non-referee batch method for evaluating acute toxicity of wastes and of other pollutants to fresh-water fishes. Test animals are exposed to dilutions of the sample being evaluated for periods of 24 and 48 hr, and median tolerance limits are calculated.

CHAPTER VIII
Sampling and Identification of Water-Formed Deposits

CHAPTER VIII—SAMPLING AND IDENTIFICATION OF WATER-FORMED DEPOSITS

Pure water in an uncorrodible vessel would never leave a deposit. Although this ideal case has been very nearly reached in some instances, deposits are still found in most water or steam systems. The examination and analysis of these deposits provides the person responsible for water treatment with information about phenomena in the water system, and will frequently indicate to him the means for correcting the condition that caused the deposit.

This chapter covers the nature of water-formed deposits, the sampling of deposits for analysis, and methods for identification of the constituents of a deposit. Quantitative chemical analysis is dealt with in Chapter IX. Some of the instrumental methods discussed in this chapter are not at present widely used in the examination of water-formed deposits, but brief descriptions are included because there are instances where they can be used to advantage. Deposits may be divided into three general classes: inorganic, organic, and biological.

Inorganic deposits result from corrosion of containing surfaces; from precipitation by chemical reaction between two or more constituents of the water; or precipitation from physical causes, such as change in solubility with pressure or temperature, by evaporation to dryness, or by relief of supersaturation. Closely akin to these, but still somewhat distinct, is the sedimentation of suspended matter.

Organic deposits generally result from precipitation of organic materials nat- urally present in the water supply, contamination of condensate returns by process materials, or precipitation of certain organic treatment chemicals.

Biological deposits may occur as a result of precipitation, due to changing conditions, of biological matter present in the raw water supply, or they may be formed where they are found because of utilization of nutrients in the water and a favorable environment for biological growth.

The number of possible techniques available to the modern analyst is so large that only a bare outline can be given in this chapter. References in the chapter will suggest where more detailed information can be found.

SAMPLING OF DEPOSITS

Deposits are sampled at least twice before being submitted to chemical or physical tests. The field man first collects the gross sample from its point of formation, and the technician then prepares this sample for final examination. Deposits are not homogeneous but may differ in composition from one part of a system to another. It is therefore important that the field samples be taken from the point of occurrence without physical or chemical alteration.

Sampling Adherent Deposits:

The removal of a sample that adheres closely to the surface upon which it has been deposited is often extremely difficult. This is true of many deposits in boiler tubes, pipe lines, and condensers.

145

It is sometimes possible to remove a short section of a pipe or condenser tube, and then to dislodge the deposit by mechanical or thermal shock.

In most instances, a portion of the deposit must be removed without damage to the surface to which it adheres. Removal of a hard adherent deposit, such as analcite ($Na_2O \cdot Al_2O_3 \cdot 4SiO_2 \cdot 2H_2O$), anhydrite ($CaSO_4$), gehlenite ($3CaO \cdot Al_2O_3 \cdot 2SiO_2$), serpentine ($3MgO \cdot 2SiO_2 \cdot 2H_2O$), magnetite ($Fe_3O_4$), quartz ($SiO_2$), or magnesium hydroxide ($Mg(OH)_2$) will require the use of a chisel, a hammer, or an excellent steel scraper. The use of such tools to remove an extremely adherent deposit requires care. A representative sample should be obtained, but damage to the equipment must be avoided. It is often impossible to remove those samples of a deposit that would be most desirable for solving the problem of deposition. Any sample, in such cases, is better than none, even though it may not be the most desirable one.

Hard, adherent deposits are sometimes encountered on the buckets, nozzles, and diaphragms of steam turbines. A closely adherent deposit can be removed from the buckets of a steam turbine by peeling or scraping downward over the surface of the bucket with a sharp penknife, the cutting edge of the knife being used with the point down. A small envelope, with the sealing flap open and extending upward, is a very good receiving receptacle. Squeezing the edges of the envelope will make the sealing flap concave. By holding the top edge below the point of the knife in peeling, the loosened deposit drops conveniently into the open envelope. Similar deposits often found in heat exchangers or evaporators can be removed for sampling by cracking.

Loosely Adherent Deposits:

Deposits that adhere loosely to the surface upon which they have formed are readily removed. Many types of scrapers can be used: knife, spatula, spoon, a thin piece of wood, sheet metal, or even cardboard. Deposits of this kind are sludge in steam generators (boilers), cooling towers, cooling systems, air conditioning systems, feedwater heaters, water softeners, condensers, and heat exchangers, and also biological deposits in various water systems.

Thin Films:

Some deposits, particularly on rough or irregular surfaces, may be so thin that scraping does not remove much of the material. If the deposit is not too hard, a stiff bristle brush may be much more effective than scraping. If the deposit is tightly adherent, and the surface is smooth, thermal or mechanical shock will sometimes loosen it. Thermal shock may produce some alteration or decomposition of the deposit; note should be made in the information accompanying the sample when this method has been used.

Biological Slimes:

It is frequently impossible to identify a biological slime definitely if it is allowed to become dry before examination. If at all possible, therefore, the deposit should be kept in its environmental water. In some cases, where gas formation is active, as with sulfate-reducing bacteria, it may be necessary to refrigerate the sample during shipment, or to add a bactericide. The latter procedure of course kills the bacteria; it would make preparation of cultures impossible. The discretion of the sampler must be relied upon in such instances.

Selection of Samples:

The selection of a sample or samples is usually somewhat limited, but there are instances where a wide choice is possible. In cases where it is possible to select the samples of a deposit, such selection is best guided by a thorough consideration of the problem involved. Very often the removal of a number of samples will result in more informative analytical data than would be obtained from one composite representing the entire mass of deposit. A typical example is the sampling of deposits from a steam turbine. Samples from each stage are more desirable than a composite sample from all stages. Conversely, in the case of a tube failure in a steam generator, if inspection shows other sections of the boiler to be in satisfactory condition, a single sample from the affected area should suffice.

Deposits sometimes are encountered in layers. Usually it is possible in such cases to select several samples so that the individual layers may be examined in the laboratory, if desired.

Sample Quantity:

The most desirable amount of deposit to be submitted as a sample is not specific. The quantity of deposit that can be removed is often limited. In such instances it is better to submit a single mixed sample of half a gram or less than to collect no sample.

Five grams of deposit is desirable for an extensive X-ray diffraction study, although informative data may be obtained with as little as 0.1 g. A routine chemical analysis usually is possible with a sample of 10 g, but an elaborate laboratory investigation might require as much as 100 g.

Although there is a difference of opinion about the desired amount of deposit to be submitted as a sample, it is definitely best to provide considerably more sample than laboratory examination might require.

Labeling and Shipment of Samples:

After collection in the field, the sample must be properly protected to prevent change or contamination during shipment. A glass or plastic container is adequate for samples of deposit only, and a clean wooden box sealed against atmospheric moisture is suitable for samples that include the underlying surface. Biological deposits must be collected and kept in contact with the mother liquor, and be shipped in refrigerated containers.

The gross sample should always be accompanied by a detailed history. This includes the name and description of the equipment from which the sample was removed, the precise location, the appearance and extent of the deposit prior to removal, the exact method used in removing the sample, the temperature and pressure of the liquid or vapor phase from which the deposit was formed, the chemical analysis of the water, and an account of any abnormal or unusual conditions existing during formation of the deposit. Further details are given in Method D 887.[1]

Laboratory Sampling:

The final sampling is made by selecting a small representative portion from the gross sample for examination by special instruments. If the sample is received in contact with its original confining surface, the same precautions must be taken as described above in removing it from that surface. If it is possible to make a separation of heterogeneous layers, it may be advisable to do so, and to make separate examinations of these smaller select portions. The composition next to the confining surface may be different from that which was in contact with the water. Separation of these two different surfaces should be made to ascertain this possibility. After the final separations have been made, the handling of the sample for each type of instrument be

---

[1] Appears in this publication.

comes part of a specialized technique for that particular instrument. For example, portions on which index of refraction is required should be *crushed* to final size, whereas the portions should be *ground* for X-ray and spectrographic examination. Various other physical and chemical treatments may be given to portions of the sample undergoing identification.

Methods of Identification

The examination of any deposit begins with visual observation and the record-

odor as the sample is heated can be used to identify many types of organic material, such as carbohydrate, protein, amines, oil, coal, sulfur compounds other than sulfate, and a number of others. The suspicion of a given type of organic compound from the odor on heating may be verified by extracting the sample with a suitable solvent, and using the microscope, X-ray diffraction, or absorption spectroscopy to help confirm the initial suspicion. Table I indicates the various techniques applicable to the detection

TABLE I.—COMPARISON OF PRINCIPAL FIELDS OF APPLICATION AND LIMITATIONS OF THE METHODS USED FOR IDENTIFICATION.

Instrument	Principal Application	Limitations
Biological microscope..........	Identification of microorganisms in industrial water samples. Recognition of inorganic suspensions and differentiation from organic matter.	Number of organisms must be sufficiently great to be observable in the microscopic field.
Chemical (petrographic) microscope	Identification of individual crystals and amorphous clumps. Examination of microstructural details. Qualitative microchemical analysis.	Particle size must be not less than 10 μ. Crystals must be non-opaque. Sample must be insoluble in immersion medium.
X-ray diffraction..............	Identification of crystalline compounds.	Compounds must not be amorphous but particle size may be less than 0.01 μ.
Spectroscope.................	Qualitative detection of cationic constituents.	Sample must be low in volatile constituents.
Spectrograph.................	Quantitative estimation of minor cationic constituents.	Same as for spectroscope.

ing of the description in terms of size, shape, contour, color, odor, hardness, and magnetism. The choice of subsequent methods for identification is frequently suggested by the visual appearance. In the case of inorganic deposits the proper step, after visual examination, is to study it under magnification. This often reveals characteristics not visible to the unaided eye. The texture of various layers is more pronounced, and recognition of individual crystals may be possible.

After crushing or grinding, but before other tests are run, it is desirable to heat a small amount of the sample gently in a crucible and to note its behavior. A pronounced darkening of the sample is frequently indicative of organic matter. The

and identification of the types of material listed, and is intended as a reference to the instrumental descriptions that follow.

The identification of water-formed deposits is not a matter of using the proper single method, but of coordinating a number of methods to make each supplement the others. No single method tells all there is to be known about a sample. Each has a special field of application with its inherent advantages and disadvantages. The applications and limitations of commonly used methods of identification are discussed below so the proper instrument or combination of instruments may be applied to the investigation of these deposits.

The Biological Microscope:

The term "biological microscope" does not refer to a particular type of microscope but rather to the use to which the microscope is put, namely, the examination of biological matter. The essential requirement is to magnify the objects under observation so their distinctive form and features become readily recog-

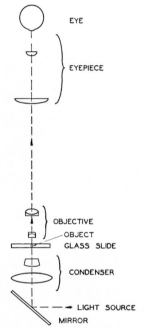

FIG. 1.—Functional Diagram of Biological Microscope.

nizable. The biological microscope operates functionally as illustrated in Fig. 1. Light from a source such as a lamp is reflected in a mirror located at the base of the instrument. The reflected beam is directed upward through a condenser and through the sample, which has been mounted on a glass slide and covered with a thin cover glass. The image of the microorganisms is magnified as the light continues upward through the lenses of the objective and the eyepiece. The magnified image is either observed directly at the eyepiece or photographed with a camera.

The living matter in biological deposits may consist of either single cell or multicell species performing the functions of growth, reproduction, and metabolism. Wide variations exist, however, in the conditions under which these functions are performed. Indeed the environmental conditions are often quite limited in this respect for any one kind of organism. For maintenance of life some organisms require iron, some sulfur, some carbon, all with or without oxygen, and they may be deprived of these essentials by changes in industrial operations. Thus, in addition to the living organisms, the sample may contain metabolic by-products and skeletons of dead organisms.

Observations of the material are made by enclosing a small drop of the sample-bearing liquid between a glass slide and a cover glass. The outlines of the objects under examination are observed under transmitted light. The various shapes may be described as similar to rods, filaments, chains, stalks, and capsules. Figure 2 shows some typical examples of magnified biological material.

Identification of the specific species is made by recognition of characteristic shapes and colors or by characteristic reaction to reagents. Some organisms will adsorb specific dyes and be recognizable by this property. Inorganic oxide sheaths may be dissolved from an organism by acids, thereby exposing features not recognizable with the sheath in place. If the sheath is iron oxide, the dissolved iron will color the liquid between the cover glass and the slide, suggesting an iron bacterium.

Recognition by shape is sometimes difficult and, for confirmatory information, the organisms may be inoculated into a culture medium. After a suitable incubation period the medium is tested for specific metabolic by-products of the

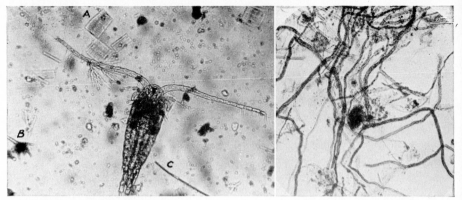

(a) (No. 10) Cyclops large organism. Also shows (A) Synedra, (B) Ceratium, and (C) Nastoe.

(b) Crenothrix with ferric oxide sheath in place.

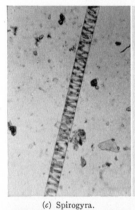
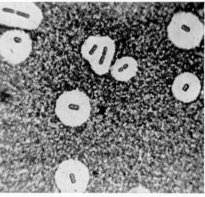

(c) Spirogyra.

(d) Anabena.

(e) Gram positive bacillus.

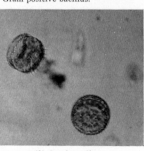

(f) Gram positive cocci.

(g) Asterionella.

(h) Stephanodiscus.

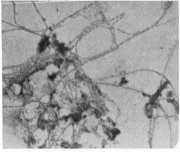

(i) Crenothrix with iron removed and stained with methylene blue.

(j) Ceratium.

FIG. 2.—Typical Biological Shapes.

150

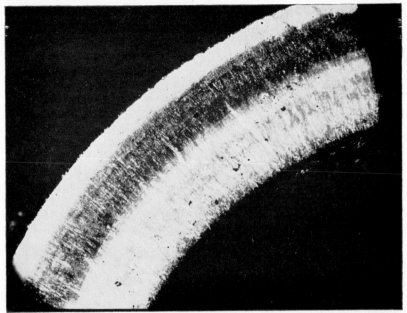

(a) Striated calcium sulfate scale.

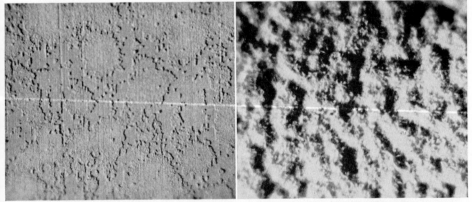

(b) Ferric oxide scale.

(c) Magnesium phosphate scale.

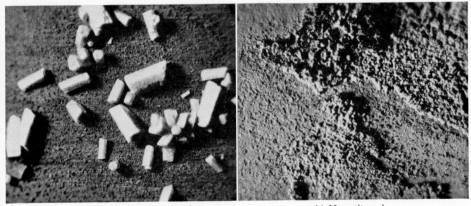

(d) Calcium sulfate lienic hydrate deposits.

(e) Magnetite scale.

FIG. 3.—Typical Water-Formed Deposits.

151

organism. For example, the formation of hydrogen sulfide in a sulfate culture medium is confirmatory evidence of the presence of sulfate-reducing bacteria.

Not all samples as received in the laboratory are suitable for biological examination. When the number of organisms is so small that a single drop of liquid might not contain any observable individuals of a suspected species, the sample may be centrifuged to concentrate the organisms and the observation made on the concentrate. On the other hand, samples may contain so much clay or other suspended matter as to greatly interfere with the examination. Such samples may be diluted to reduce the concentration of impurities, or separation of biological from inorganic material must be made before mounting the sample under the microscope.

The report of a microscopic examination usually indicates only those recognized microorganisms for which definite proof of presence was established. Quantitative values are assigned only when specific cultures can be made.

A microscope with three objectives (10×, 43×, and oil-immersion 97×), two eyepieces (5× and 10×), and an Abbé condenser can be purchased for about $350. A more adequate assembly, including an illuminator and a mechanical stage, can be bought for about $600.

Methods D 932,[1] D 993,[1] and D 1128[1] provide for identification of some bacteria and other microorganisms of industrial importance. There are other sources[2, 3, 4] of detailed information on the use of the biological microscope.

[2] D. H. Bergey, "Manual of Determinative Bacteriology," Williams and Wilkins Co., Baltimore, Md., 1938.
[3] "Manual of Methods for Pure Culture Study of Bacteria," Biotech Publications, Geneva, N. Y., 1946.
[4] F. W. Tanner, "The Microbiology of Foods," Garrard Press, Champaign, Ill., 2nd Ed., 1944.

The Chemical Microscope:

The chemical (or petrographic) microscope is so named because of the accessories and design which make it particularly suitable for the study of both optical properties and microchemical reactions. Rocklike deposits lend themselves most readily to direct examination by this microscope. Figure 3 illustrates the magnified structures of some typical water-formed deposits.

The functional operation illustrated by Fig. 4 is similar to that of the biological

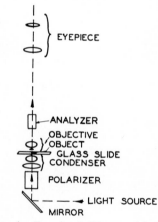

FIG. 4.—Functional Diagram of Chemical Microscope.

microscope with the addition of a polarizer and analyzer. Light from a source such as a lamp is reflected by the mirror and passes through the polarizer and condenser. The polarized light passes through the sample, which is supported by a glass slide mounted on a mechanical, graduated stage. The image of the object is magnified as the light passes upward through the objective, the analyzer, and the cross-hair eyepiece.

When ions in a solution react to form solid particles, the particles usually consist of repeating geometrical arrangements of the atoms in a three-dimensional network. This network of atoms or ions is called a crystal. If conditions were such that only one solid phase could precipitate from a solution, and the conditions of precipitation remained constant, the resulting solid product would consist of one or more crystals of the same substance. Ordinarily, however, it is possible for more than one substance to precipitate from a water at the same time, and the conditions of precipitation are seldom constant, so that we rarely have a single homogeneous deposit containing only one crystal phase. Also, variations in the composition of the water and changing conditions may give rise to a deposit consisting of layers of material of varying composition. Berry, Allen, and Snow[5] of the U. S. Steel Corp. have described a technique for examination of polished sections by reflected light, using a metallurgical microscope. While their studies were applied to refractories, the techniques are equally applicable to detailed study of the layering in a coherent scale of sufficient thickness. The edge of a deposit is ground approximately flat on a medium grit polishing paper, after which the piece is impregnated by immersion in a molten resin, such as glycol phthalate. The piece is removed while still hot, and allowed to cool in air. This resin is fairly hard at room temperature, and allows wet polishing of the surface of the scale without extensive tearing out of individual grains. Many of the epoxy resins, especially those of low viscosity, are also excellent impregnating materials. Many crystal phases can be recognized by their shape and brightness under reflected light, even though direct observation of optical properties cannot be made.

In some cases, it is possible to make thin sections of a scale, so that the structure may be examined by transmitted light under the microscope. Observation of birefringence and crystal orientation may suggest the compounds present in such a scale. Most boiler scales and sludges are not sufficiently coherent, however, nor do they consist of sufficiently large crystals for such techniques to be fruitful.

A crushed sample, preferably 100-mesh or finer, is suitable for two types of microscopic examination. Many crystals and compounds in deposits from water can be identified and their amounts estimated by examination of the powder under a chemical microscope equipped with polarized light, or with a petrographic microscope. Identification is accomplished by immersion of the powder in oils of various refractive indices; determination of the indices of the crystalline compounds is made by observing their relief against the oil of known refractive index.

Refractive indices are determined by crushing the sample to a size which will free from the agglomerate as many single crystals as possible without at the same time producing particles too small for clear resolution under the microscope. Sludge particles are often too small to provide optical data. Large-size particles are no deterrent because these can be crushed to sufficiently small size for measurements.

Amorphous material and glasses, as well as crystallized compounds, have optical characteristics that can be measured and may form a basis for identification. For examination of this type of material, optical microscopy is superior to X-ray diffraction.

Chemical microscopy is simply the technique of performing normal qualitative chemical tests on a microscope slide. The advantage of the microscope for this purpose is twofold. In the first place, observation of the crystals formed by these qualitative tests may permit distinction between several ions, all of

---

[5] T. F. Berry, W. C. Allen, and R. B. Snow, *Journal*, Am. Ceramic Soc., Vol. 33, p. 121 (1950).

which form precipitates with a given reagent. The second advantage is that the tests are quite rapid, and may be carried out with a very small volume of solution. This is of utmost importance where the size of the sample is limited. Chamot and Mason's "Handbook of Chemical Microscopy"[6] gives details for carrying out most of the common microchemical tests, and also gives illustrations of many of the crystals formed by these reactions. Tests for phosphate, ferrous and ferric iron, copper, zinc, nickel, calcium, magnesium, manganese, sodium, sulfate, chloride, and a number

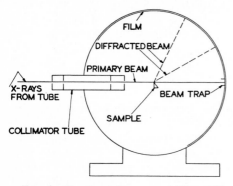

FIG. 5.—Functional Diagram of X-ray-Diffraction Unit.

of others can be readily made by this method.

The results from observations with the chemical microscope include a description of the appearance of the magnified gross structure, and a report of the presence of specific compounds and elements as determined from their refractive indices and reactions with spot-test reagents. The chemical microscope is a standard instrument and differs from the biological microscope in that it is equipped with a graduated rotating stage and polarizing prisms. Normal cost is between $500 and $1200. Detailed pro-

cedures for petrographic examination and tables of optical data are available in standard texts.[7, 8, 9, 10]

X-Ray Diffraction:

X-ray diffraction produces a pattern of lines on photographic film or peaks on a recorder chart. The position of the lines on the film or the peaks on the chart for any given type of X-radiation is determined by the distances between layers of atoms in the crystalline components of the sample. These interatomic distances can be calculated from the measured positions of the lines or peaks, and used to identify the crystalline compounds of a sample.

The essential functioning of the X-ray diffraction unit is illustrated in Fig. 5. X-rays pass through a collimator tube which restricts the beam to a very thin pencil of parallel rays. The collimating tube may be an integral part of the camera. The pencil of X-rays is intercepted by the sample located on the central axis of the camera. A large percentage of the beam penetrates the sample and is caught and dissipated in the beam trap. A small fraction of the primary beam is diffracted to the outer circumference of the camera and strikes the photographic film at definite positions depending upon the angles of diffraction. The magnitude of these angles of diffraction is determined by the atomic arrangement within the crystal compound producing the diffraction. After sufficient

[6] E. M. Chamot and C. W. Mason, "Handbook of Chemical Microscopy," John Wiley & Sons, New York, N. Y., 3rd Ed., 1958.

[7] E. S. Larsen and H. Berman, "The Microscopic Determination of the Non-Opaque Minerals," Bulletin 848, U.S. Geological Survey, 1934.

[8] A. N. Winchell, "The Microscopic Character of Artificial Inorganic Substances of Artificial Minerals," John Wiley & Sons, New York, N. Y., 1943.

[9] Ernest E. Walstrom, "Optical Crystallography," John Wiley & Sons, New York, N. Y., 1943.

[10] A. N. Winchell, "Elements of Optical Mineralogy," John Wiley & Sons, New York, N. Y., 1929, 1933, 1937.

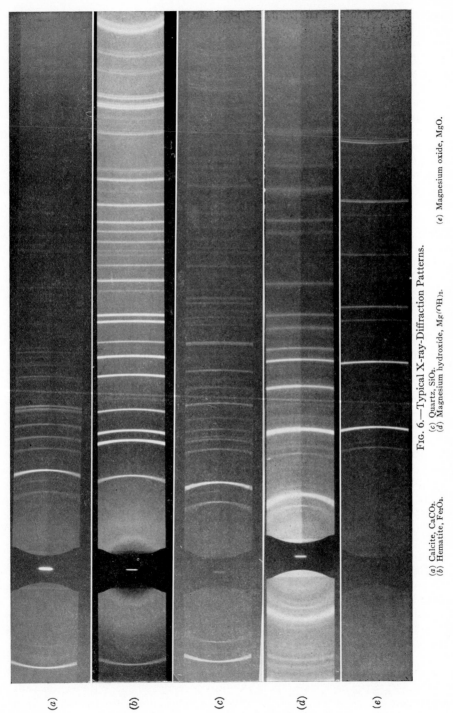

Fig. 6.—Typical X-ray-Diffraction Patterns.

(a) Calcite, CaCO₃.
(b) Hematite, Fe₂O₃.

(c) Quartz, SiO₂.
(d) Magnesium hydroxide, Mg(OH)₂.

(e) Magnesium oxide, MgO.

exposure, the photographic film is developed and patterns are produced, those shown in Fig. 6 being typical. These are compared with patterns or data produced by standard compounds. When the position and intensity of lines from the pattern of an unknown compound match those from the pattern of the standard, the unknown material is identical with that of the standard. Identification therefore requires a series of standards or a set of authenticated diffraction data. The best single source of crystal data is the "Card Index File of X-ray Diffraction Data for Chemical Analysis" available from ASTM. Details of procedure, with additional literature references, are given in Method D 934.[1]

The X-ray diffraction method of analysis is essentially one of identification of crystalline compounds present in a deposit. It is sometimes referred to as the "powder diffraction method," a name that indicates the most useful form in which samples are prepared for analysis. Most crystalline, water-formed deposits do not occur as powders but must be finely ground for proper mounting and for crystal distribution. Sludges usually are very finely divided but may cement or harden on drying and may also contain flakes or larger particles which are truly part of the sample. The only limitations on the type of sample that can be used for powder diffraction are that it be crystalline, that it be susceptible to grinding, and that a sufficient amount be available for manipulation.

Although the X-ray diffraction method is not usually considered to be a micro-method, with special care an analysis can be made with less than 10 mg of sample. Exposure of a sample to X-rays may require from 1 to 4 hr, and samples subject to change in the atmosphere in that length of time may be protected by enclosure in an airtight capsule during exposure.

In recent years, direct measurement techniques of X-ray diffraction have been introduced, employing counter tubes for detection of X-ray intensity. These instruments have distinct advantages. Ordinarily, they employ a somewhat larger sample, so that better integration of the over-all composition of a sample is possible. Secondly, although only one sample may be run at a time, they are considerably faster than photographic methods, because under most circumstances sufficient of the pattern can be run in a matter of 30 min to 1 hr. For detection of the presence or absence of a certain phase, it is necessary to scan only over an area where a line unique to the compound being sought is located. For instance, 2 or 3 min is sufficient to determine the presence of quartz in a turbine deposit. The pattern obtained is more nearly quantitative than that from film. Accurate quantitative analysis, however, must depend on careful consideration of the absorption characteristics of the sample, whether one is using the photographic or direct measurement technique. Because of the fact that a large, flat sample is used, direct measurement techniques are somewhat prone to preferred orientation unless the sample is prepared very carefully. This property is sometimes an advantage in qualitative analysis, as it may markedly increase the intensity of the strongest line, thus allowing detection of smaller amounts. A good example of this is anhydrite, which can be detected in a sludge in concentrations as low as 1 per cent because of this orientation, even though the anhydrite pattern is not exceptionally strong.

In the absence of substances in the sample that give high background, the sensitivity of the direct measurement technique is about the same as that of the photograph for those compounds which are well crystallized. With poorly crystalline substances, the advantage is decidedly with the direct measurement, or diffractometer, technique because broad peaks whose intensity is not greatly above background are much more easily detected by variation in the background level on a chart than gradual differences in blackening on a photographic film. Thus, the sensitivity for poorly crystallized magnesium silicate in a boiler sludge is frequently appreciably greater with a diffractometer than with photographic methods.

The method does not ordinarily detect low percentages of compounds in a deposit. The minimum amounts that can be detected may vary from 1 to 30 per cent, depending upon the efficiency of the compound as a diffractor and the absorption characteristics of other materials in the mixture. For example, 1 per cent copper can be detected in magnesium hydroxide, whereas from 5 to 10 per cent copper must be present for detection in an iron oxide sample. Copper is a good diffractor and magnesium hydroxide has low absorption compared with that of the iron oxides. Poorly crystallized compounds, such as frequently occur in the case of magnesium silicate, may escape detection when present in amounts as great as 30 per cent.

Solid solutions frequently can be detected if the solute has appreciably changed the lattice dimensions of the solvent phase. Solids of the solid solution type are common with such sodium salts as are deposited in superheaters and drypipes.

Crystal size or degree of crystallization may be determined qualitatively from the uniformity and breadth of the diffraction lines in a pattern. It is frequently possible to differentiate between the poorly crystallized and the well-crystallized species in a mixture.

In both of the above techniques, the diffractometer has a marked advantage over the photographic method. Photo-graphic film is not entirely dimensionally stable, and it is therefore sometimes difficult to detect very slight solid solution. Also, in a camera that will allow reasonable exposure, the lines on the film are relatively small, and it is not possible to detect very slight variation in line width.

By scanning over the area of interest at slow speed with the diffractometer, peaks of sharp lines can be located within 0.01 deg, thus permitting detection of extremely slight solid solution. Further, by employing narrow slits and fast time constants in the instrument, it is possible to achieve extremely high resolution, of an order that would be almost physically impossible on a photographic film. This allows at least partial separation of diffraction lines of well-crystallized substances which are so slightly separated that they might appear as a single line on a film. Of course, if the lines are exactly superimposed, they cannot be separated even by high resolution techniques.

There are, however, several distinct advantages to the photographic method. First, a pattern of high quality can be obtained on a very small amount of sample, such as 2 or 3 mg. Second, in a sample that gives a very complex pattern, such as one containing a large number of crystal phases, certain compounds found in deposits from water are prone to give somewhat spotty lines if they are not ground sufficiently fine. These spotty lines stand out quite well on the film, and permit separation of the pattern into two distinct types of lines, which frequently aids identification. Quartz, calcium sulfate, calcium carbonate, and analcite are compounds that often develop rather large crystals and are particularly likely to give spotty lines. The third advantage for film lies in the ease with which a number of X-ray patterns may be compared by placing the films edge to edge on a viewing box. This is done much more easily with films than with charts.

Because of its ability to give useful patterns with samples consisting of very small crystals or of crystals that are opaque to light, the X-ray method is generally more widely applicable to deposits than the petrographic microscope. The microscope, however, can give useful information about the state of aggregation, can detect amorphous materials which contribute little or nothing to the X-ray pattern, and permits identification of a single crystal on a whole slide of material, thus providing a sensitivity much greater than that of the X-ray method, provided the crystal is of sufficient size. Where both instruments are available, it is generally advisable to run the X-ray diffraction pattern first, thus giving a good average composition of the sample, and to use the petrographic microscope to detect glasses and amorphous materials, those substances present in too small amounts for X-ray detection, and information about the state of agglomeration of the sample.

The report of an X-ray diffraction analysis should give the name and formula for the crystalline species identified, together with an estimate of the relative amounts of the identified phases present, and any remarks regarding crystal size, solid solution, or other pertinent information that may have been obtained.

The equipment used in the photographic method consists essentially of a source of constant high-voltage electrical current, an X-ray diffraction tube in an appropriate mount, and a cylindrical camera. Suitable commercial units are manufactured at a cost of $3500 or more.

The diffractometer is considerably more complex, and consists of a source of highly stabilized high voltage electrical current, the X-ray tube, a counter tube, an amplifier, ratemeter and recording circuits, and an adjustable goniometer for mounting the counter tube and the sample and providing for rotation of the counter tube about a focusing circle, on which are the X-ray tube, the sample, and the counter tube. Such equipment is available as commercial units starting at about $10,000.

X-Ray Spectroscopy:

Secondary X-rays are generated when X-rays of sufficiently short wavelength are absorbed by matter. These secondary rays are characteristic of the elements present in the irradiated material. The X-ray spectrograph is an instrument for separating the X-radiations from the various elements of the absorbing material, and for detecting and recording their wavelengths and relative intensities. The apparatus used for such detection is not greatly different from the X-ray diffractometer, and most of the components of one instrument are used for the other.

The chief difference lies in the fact that the sample is the source of the X-radiation in X-ray spectroscopy, rather than the X-ray tube, as in diffraction. A single crystal, cut parallel to one of the principal planes, takes the place of the powdered sample in the diffractometer technique, and diffracts the various wavelengths of X-rays at different angles, thus allowing each wavelength to be separately detected by the counter tube.

X-ray spectra are very simple, consisting at the most of about 15 lines, not all of which are of significant intensity. These lines as a group vary in wavelength in a regular manner with the atomic number of the element. Complete X-ray spectra are therefore known for all elements. The wavelengths have been precisely calculated, and most of them have been very carefully checked experimentally.

The smaller the atomic number of the element, the longer the wavelength of the corresponding lines of the X-ray spectra. "L" series spectra are used in analysis for the heavy elements, that is to say, those heavier than barium, and the "K" series for the lighter elements. Elements of atomic number smaller than titanium give rise to radiation of sufficiently long wavelengths that their absorption in air is too great for good sensitivity. A helium atmosphere is therefore maintained from the sample, past the analyzing crystal, to the window of the counter tube. This has allowed detection of elements as light as sulfur. Softer radiation than this is absorbed strongly in the window of sealed counter tubes, and counting losses are consequently high. This has been solved recently by the use of a flow counter tube employing a thin organic film such as Mylar or Formvar as a window in the tube, and, since this tube is not gas tight, allowing the counting gas to flow continuously through the tube. Elements as light as sodium have been detected by such counters, and quite useful intensities have been obtained for aluminum, silicon, phosphorus and, except for quite low concentrations, for magnesium. This method is useful over a very wide range of concentrations, from as low as a few parts per million in favorable cases up to 100 per cent. Some elements influence the excitation of others in a manner that would be predicted from a knowledge of the laws of absorption of X-rays and the periodic table of the elements

Optical Spectroscopy:

Emission spectroscopy is a method of analysis for elements that depends on the fact that when atoms are excited by either thermal or electrical means, light is given off as discrete wavelengths as the atoms return to their normal state. If this light is defined by a slit, separated into its various wavelengths by a prism or diffraction grating, brought to a focus by a lens system and viewed with an eyepiece, recorded on film, or measured by photoelectric means, the elements that have given rise to the spectral lines can be identified by locating the characteristic wavelengths in published tables of spectra.

The common sources of excitation for spectrographic analysis are flame, d-c arc, a-c arc, and high-voltage spark. Each has special uses and the advantage and limitations of each one will be discussed briefly.

The flame of a bunsen or Meker burner is at a sufficiently high temperature to excite the atoms of only the alkali and alkaline earth metals and a few others, if the concentration is sufficiently high. Propane-air, propane-oxygen, acetylene-air, oxygen-acetylene, and oxygen-hydrogen flames produce successively higher temperatures. The atoms of about 43 elements can be excited with acetylene-oxygen or hydrogen-oxygen flames. The sensitivity for many of these elements is not very high. The flame is a highly reproducible source, however, if fuel and air or oxygen pressures are carefully controlled; it is quite satisfactory for the analysis of solutions, which represent ideally homogeneous samples. The flame spectrophotometer is actually a small direct-reading spectrograph.

The d-c arc, which is operated at a voltage from 50 to about 250, is an extremely sensitive source because it is capable of producing very high temperatures. The detection of a number of elements in parts per million concentrations in a solid sample is quite possible with this energy source. The reproducibility of this source is somewhat limited because of the tendency of the arc to wander. It is therefore considered highly satisfactory for qualitative analysis because of its sensitivity, but it is probably not the best one for quantitative analysis.

The high voltage a-c arc, using a voltage of 1000 or more, is a steadier and more reproducible source than the d-c arc and, except for extreme cases, has adequate sensitivity for most of the elements. The chief drawback to this source is the dangerously high voltage, which requires safety interlocks and careful shielding for protection of the operator.

The high-voltage spark is a very reproducible source, using 10,000 to 50,000 v across the two electrodes, and a synchronous interrupter to extinguish the spark and prevent it from becoming an arc. The discharge is predominantly electrical in nature, rather than thermal, and in many cases it is cool enough that one can handle the electrodes immediately after exposure. A condenser and inductor are usually added to this circuit to produce some heating effect. Although the reproducibility of the discharge is quite high, because of the low temperature comparatively little material is consumed, and sampling problems are sometimes major. The spark source, however, is readily adapted to the analysis of solutions, where a completely homogeneous sample is possible.

The simplest type of dispersing instrument is the visual spectroscope, commonly called the Bunsen spectroscope. It consists of a focusing lens, a slit, a prism, and a telescope on a movable arm for viewing the spectra produced. In addition, a wavelength scale is usually sent through the prism from a side tube, and brought to focus in the telescope just above the spectrum of the sample to be studied. The spectroscope is limited to the elements that have lines in the visible part of spectrum, and is generally considered to be a qualitative instrument, although some estimate of amounts can usually be made. The instrument is simple and it has many potential uses, but it has the drawback of poor dispersion, which makes it difficult to resolve some lines which are normally close together. In addition, simultaneous observation of all parts of the spectrum is not possible.

The spectrograph employs either a prism or a diffraction grating as the dispersing device and, for general use, photographic film as the recording medium. For routine production control, where the same elements are normally being determined, it is entirely practical to replace the photographic film with a photoelectric device for recording the relative light intensities of the various elements to be analyzed for. Generally, however, problems in industrial water treatment are sufficiently varied that the direct reading spectrograph would be of limited use.

Metals, which conduct electricity, can be used as their own electrodes, but most of the materials encountered in industrial water treatment are nonconductors. Therefore the sample is usually placed in a small core in a carbon or graphite electrode, which is generally made the lower electrode. The upper electrode is usually a plain carbon or graphite rod, ground to a blunt point. The cavity in the lower electrode may be formed with a center post, to decrease wandering of the arc, and may also be undercut, the narrow neck tending to increase the arc temperature by decreasing the conduction of heat down the electrode. Metal electrodes are occasionally used for special cases, but graphite is quite satisfactory for general work.

Very satisfactory electrodes can be made for the a-c arc and high-voltage spark by thoroughly mixing the powdered sample with graphite, often with a buffer also, and pressing into a pellet under high pressure. The pellet is placed in a metal holder, the other electrode being a tipped carbon rod. This technique is not wholly satisfactory for use with the d-c arc, because of the high temperature.

45-83

Fineness of the powdered sample is important. Since the sample usually melts in the d-c arc, a 200-mesh sample is adequately fine. For the a-c arc and high-voltage spark, however, where relatively little material is consumed, the sample should be at least 325-mesh, or should be fused with a flux to insure uniformity. Alkali metal borates are satisfactory fluxes for most samples. Solutions are atomized into the flame or spark. In the latter case, a rotating graphite disk which dips into a container of the solution can be used; the spark is generated at the side of the disk opposite the solution container. One great advantage for the solution method is the ease with which synthetic standards are prepared, and the simplicity of the addition of an internal standard to the unknown sample to serve as a reference. This procedure increases accuracy by allowing the determination of concentration ratios rather than absolute values of concentration.

ASTM Committee E-2 on Emission Spectroscopy publishes a number of methods in a single volume for determination of impurities in various materials. Most of these, however, are not applicable to deposits from water because of the lack of a uniform matrix. Possible methods have been published elsewhere, and are currently being submitted to Committee E-2 for inclusion in future publications. These so-called "Universal Methods" are generally of somewhat lower accuracy than those for determining impurities in rather pure materials, but are of much wider applicability. It seems probable that many of these will be adaptable for use in deposits from water.

A complete spectroscope, with an adequate d-c arc source and various accessory materials, can be purchased for slightly under a thousand dollars. Spectrographic units, which include microphotometers for measuring the photographic film or plate, start in the neighborhood of $10,000, and may run as high as $35,000, depending upon the complexity of the equipment desired.

The microphotometer is actually a dual instrument. It normally consists of equipment for projecting a reference film, on which the location of the sensitive lines of the various elements are indicated, beside that of the unknown spectrum for qualitative analysis. In addition, a densitometer portion permits determination of the photographic blackness, expressed as per cent transmittance, for any given line. A comparison of photographic blackness with known samples is used to plot working curves for the various elements to be determined quantitatively, and the transmissions of the lines on the unknowns are converted to concentrations from these curves. The results of spectrographic analysis are recorded as elements, without indication of the state of combination. A number of standard reference books are available for all operations dealing with the spectrograph.

Electron Microscope:

Many particles of sludge, as well as certain corrosion products, are too finely divided to be studied with an optical microscope. These small particles can often be profitably studied by electron microscopy. The electron microscope is similar to the optical microscope in many ways, but the entire optical path is in high vacuum. Electrons are generated by a hot filament, and are driven from the filament by a focusing cap at high negative potential, located immediately behind the filament. The electron beam is further focused by a series of electrostatic or electromagnetic lenses, corresponding to the condenser in an optical microscope. The crystals, or other matter making up the sample, absorb electrons according to their thickness and the ab-

45-83

sorbing power of the atoms, and the shadow thus formed is viewed on a fluorescent screen, or photographed. The resolving power of the electron beam is very high, and magnification of the photographic plate may be used to bring out more detail.

The sample for examination should be dispersed as much as possible, as agglomerates of a large number of particles cannot be studied except at the edges. A thin film of a resin such as Formvar or collodion is prepared by placing a drop of solution of the resin on water and allowing the solvent to evaporate. The film is then picked up on a platinum screen, and the sample deposited on the film and allowed to dry.

A second technique that may be applicable is the replica technique, normally used to study metal surfaces. In this method, the resin is applied to the surface to be studied, allowed to dry and then stripped off, usually by immersion in water. The film retains the contours of the surface to which it was applied; thus it is thinner where there were elevations, and thicker where there were depressions. The film is removed from the surface of the water on the platinum screen, as above, and viewed with the microscope. The replica may be shadowed with chromium metal evaporated on the surface to improve contrast.

Much can be learned about the crystal shapes and the sizes of sludge particles, the type of material which acts to bind them together, and tendencies to twin, or branch, by study of electron micrographs. Most of these phenomena occur in crystals that are under 1 micron in size, and this makes study with the optical microscope nearly impossible. Because certain unique properties of a crystalline substance, such as refractive index, cannot be measured with the electron microscope, this instrument should not be considered a means of identifying a completely unknown substance. Rather, identification of the phases should be completed prior to the electron microscope study.

Absorption Spectroscopy:

The identification of organic substances usually presents some problems not common in the inorganic field. Most of the substances occurring in water-formed deposits are either not crystalline, or they are sufficiently complex mixtures that the crystal phases would not be identifiable by an X-ray diffraction pattern. Many are soluble in the oils used for refractive index determination, which limits the use of the microscope. Although methods such as melting and boiling points, refractive index, elemental analysis, and similar techniques can be used in some cases to identify pure compounds, none of these is generally applicable to deposits, which usually are not pure.

Most organic compounds, and many inorganic as well, show sharp absorption bands in the infrared region of the spectrum. These absorption bands have their source in different modes of vibration and rotation within a molecule. The most useful analytical wavelength range is from about 2 to 15 μ, or slightly longer in the case of the halogens. The following types of linkage give bands in specific regions, which can be used to characterize the particular group: C—H (aliphatic), C—H (aromatic), N—H, O—H (phenolic), S—H, C—O, C=O (aldehyde), C=O (acid), C—C, C=C, C≡C, C≡N, C—Cl, C—Br, C—I. Each specific absorption band will shift somewhat, due to changes in adjoining groups, but the band will still be within the same general region.

The source of infrared radiation may be a lamp whose filament operates at a low temperature, thus giving more infrared and less visible light, or it may be a Globar element. The temperature of the source must be carefully controlled to prevent change in the distribution of spectral intensity.

The light from the source is passed through the sample, then broken up into its various wavelengths by a prism, usually of quartz or rock salt. Alternatively, a diffraction grating may be used, but care to prevent interference from overlapping orders must be taken. In the 2- to 15-μ range commonly used for survey work, a rock salt prism is generally employed, as the transmission of quartz drops off sharply beyond 3.5 μ. Rock salt is also the usual cell window for nonaqueous solution techniques.

After isolation of the desired wavelength band by a variable slit, the radiation falls on a detecting and measuring device, most commonly a thermocouple. Lead sulfide photocells are more sensitive detectors for wavelengths up to about 5 μ.

Scanning of the absorption spectrum is accomplished by rotation of the prism rather than by movement of the slit. The output of the detecting device is amplified and fed to a recorder.

A most useful survey device for completely unknown nonvolatile solid samples is the potassium bromide pellet technique. The sample is ground briefly with powdered potassium bromide and the mixture placed in an evacuable die. A mechanical vacuum pump removes the entrapped air, and the mixture is then pressed at about 15,000 psi. The absence of air results in a solid pellet free of bubbles, which is used as the absorber. This technique is not fully quantitative, but does tell where the absorption bands lie.

More quantitative results are obtained by selecting solvents that do not absorb in the region of interest and running the spectrum in these solvents. Concentra-

tions employed are of the order of 1 to 10 per cent.

Gases also usually give characteristic infrared absorption bands, and these

TABLE II.—TYPICAL REPORT FORM FOR RESULTS BY DIFFERENT METHODS OF IDENTIFICATION FOR TWO DIFFERENT SAMPLES.

Sample A	Sample B
CHEMICAL ANALYSIS	
SiO_2................ 19.7	SiO_2................ 17.9
Fe_2O_3............... 26.6	Fe_2O_3............... 2.6
CaO.............. 10.8	CaO.............. 30.8
MgO.............. 16.2	MgO.............. 17.9
SO_3............... 0.1	SO_3............... 0.1
P_2O_5............... 12.3	CO_2............... 24.2
Cu................ 5.4	Loss on ignition...... 30.5
Loss on ignition...... 8.5	
MICROSCOPIC ANALYSIS	
Considerable amount of iron oxide present in colored bands. Some hydroxyapatite and considerable amount of poorly crystallized compound, probably magnesium silicate. Small quantities of dendrites of metallic copper.	Large amount of highly birefringent calcite present. Magnesium silicate also present. Iron oxides present as a minor constituent.
X-RAY DIFFRACTION ANALYSIS	
Hematite, serpentine, hydroxyapatite, and metallic copper all identified with probable percentages in the order named. Particle size for the serpentine and the hydroxyapatite very small.	Calcite and serpentine present in about equal amounts. Serpentine present in extremely small particle size while the calcite was present in two forms, one in crystals of quite large size and the other in crystals of very small size.
SPECTROSCOPIC ANALYSIS	
Constituents over 5 per cent: Si, Fe, Ca, and Mg Constituents 0.5 to 5 per cent: Cu Constituents 0.05 to 0.5 per cent: Mn and Cr	Constituents over 5 per cent: Si, Ca, and Mg Constituents 0.5 to 5 per cent: Fe Constituents 0.05 to 0.5 per cent: Zn, Al, and Mn
SPECTROGRAPHIC ANALYSIS	
Mn................ 0.13	Zn................ 0.43
Cr................ 0.07	Al................ 0.17
Ni................ 0.01	Mn................ 0.08
Cu................ 5.29	Pb................ 0.02

bands are the basis for continuous monitoring of gas streams.

A few typical applications to water-formed deposits are the detection of oil in turbine deposits and classification as to type, determination of the type and degree of degradation of amines, and possible identification of the source of stream pollutants.

The above descriptive material is intended to suggest some uses of instrumental methods to aid in the identification of water-formed deposits. Some of these methods are described in detail in various ASTM Methods. Others are described more fully in the references listed in Appendix III.

SUMMARY

The primary object of all sampling procedures is to bring the original specimen to the place of observation or analysis without alteration of composition, structure, or physical properties. Methods of microscopy, diffraction, and spectroscopy provide means for determining facts about the chemical and physical nature of the sample which are not available by other means. According to the type of information desired about the sample, there is a choice of methods, each of which is highly specific. The fields of principal application and limitations are compared in Table I.

To indicate further the kind of information each method provides, a typical analysis report for each method is given in Table II on twc samples of water-formed deposits.

A typical report from the examination of water by the biological microscope is as follows:

Sample A.—Organisms of the short rod-shaped variety were observed in clusters of 1 to 10 surrounded by a mucoid capsule. Considerable quantities of rust-brown hydrous ferric oxide surround the capsules. The organism is identified as an iron bacterium of the genus *Siderocapsa*.

Sample B.—Sample contained a number of protozoa which moved quite rapidly across the field of vision of the microscope. Living diatoms of characteristic shape were present along with other isotropic, suspended, inorganic materials. Algae of both the green filamentous and the unicellular variety were present.

CHAPTER IX
Analysis of Water-Formed Deposits

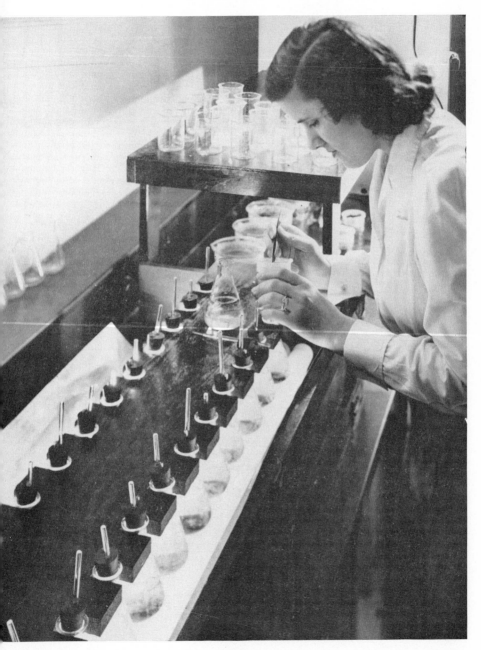

CHAPTER IX—ANALYSIS OF WATER-FORMED DEPOSITS

Many of the difficulties that arise during the industrial use of water are closely related to water-formed sludges, scales, and corrosion products. The composition of such deposits can be interpreted to provide a guide for practical preventive treatment of either the water or its environment. In the proper hands, complete and detailed information concerning water-formed deposits can be useful; unless this information is accurate, however, it can be misleading. Accordingly, reliable methods should be available for the analysis of carefully selected samples.

The chemical analysis of water-formed deposits presents a challenge to the analyst's skill and causes him to muster all the knowledge of his profession. The usual quantitative analysis will yield the elemental composition of the major constituents of such deposits, but other tools must be used to determine accurately the combinations of these elements. These include the spectrograph, biological and petrographic microscopes, and X-ray diffraction equipment described in Chapter VIII.

It is often possible to determine the source or cause of water-formed deposits from the results of chemical and physical analyses. The treatment for removal or prevention of such deposits can thus be accomplished scientifically instead of by trial and error.

Frequently the analyst must know the composition of the water involved if he is to make an accurate diagnosis of industrial water deposit problems. In addition, information on the type and composition of equipment through which the water passes, the type of water treatment used, and temperatures and pressure existing in the system, can be useful. With this information and the results of his own analysis, the chemist usually is able to suggest a cause and cure for the water-formed deposit when he reports its chemical composition.

Care must be exercised in selecting a representative sample for analysis, since the value of an analysis is related to the sampling technique employed. Sampling practice is dealt with in Chapter VIII and Method D 887.[1]

PRELIMINARY EXAMINATION OF DEPOSITS

The method of preparing a sample for analysis depends to a great extent on the type of water-formed deposit: scale, sludge, corrosion product, or biological deposit.

Immediately after removing the deposit from the container, its characteristics should be recorded for later comparison with observations made during the field sampling. Photographs are a very good form of record. Pertinent information includes quantity, color, dimensions, hardness, magnetism, odor, contour, structure, and consistency. It is especially important to note whether the sample was received in place on its confining surface. In removing deposits from

---

[1] Appears in this publication.

167

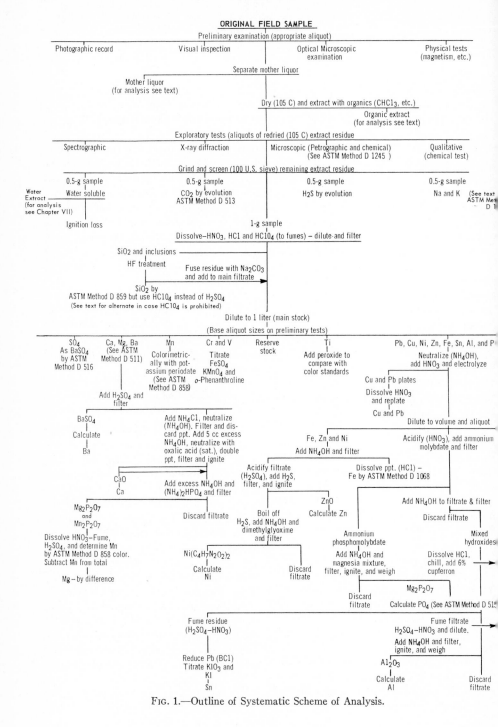

FIG. 1.—Outline of Systematic Scheme of Analysis.

confining surfaces, great care must be exercised to avoid contaminating the sample with particles of the surface.

The entire sample or a representative portion should be freed from water and oil so that it may be properly pulverized. If the material is very wet, it is best to decant off the excess liquid (mother liquor) and first to air-dry the sample or to dry it at a low temperature such as 35 C to prevent loss by spattering. Following this, the sample should be dried at 105 C, extracted with organic solvents, such as chloroform, and redried at 105 C. Drying at 105 C and organic extraction constitute the first treatments if mother liquor is absent. The dried material finally should be ground in a mortar and quartered down to a sample of 10 or 15 g. This sample should be further ground to pass a 100-mesh U.S. sieve and then should be bottled and tumbled to insure thorough mixing. The bottle should be labeled with all information necessary to identify its contents completely.

When significant differences in deposit structure are visible, such as laminations or colored bands, it may be desirable to divide these portions and analyze them separately. Separations can be made with a sharp blade, preferably under a low power microscope. A separate bottle should be used for each portion.

Preliminary tests on the sample will often reveal sufficient information for the analyst to make a direct approach to the analysis rather than to follow the systematic scheme discussed later. A spectrograph may be used for a quick determination of the elemental composition. X-ray diffraction equipment operated by skilled personnel can be extremely useful for identifying compounds. Such equipment is not always accessible and, as a substitute, the petrographic microscope is very useful for the initial examination. A simpler microscope, although limited in its ap-

plicability, is useful if a petrographic model is not available.

If sufficient information accompanied the sample of water-formed deposit, shrewd guesses can be made about its likely composition. Preliminary tests for these suspected constituents may be accomplished by means of spot tests[2] and by simple qualitative tests. For example, carbonates will react with acid to liberate carbon dioxide; iron can be dissolved in acid and precipitated with ammonium hydroxide; sulfide can be detected by heating with acid and noting the odor of hydrogen sulfide; and oil can be detected by extracting with chloroform, evaporating, and examining the residue. Standard analytical tests will include complete lists of such qualitative tests

SYSTEMATIC ANALYSIS OF DEPOSITS

Any analytical scheme can be only a guide, and the analyst must use his skill and ingenuity in carrying out or modifying such a scheme. It is impossible to draw a blueprint that will fit rigidly all water-formed deposits that may confront the analyst. As one instance, it will be noted that the accompanying scheme (Fig. 1) requires the use of four $\frac{1}{2}$-g samples plus a 1-g sample for a total of 3 g. Duplicate tests would require more. If a smaller sample is received, it may not be possible to make all the determinations, or it may be necessary to carry them out on much smaller quantities. On the other hand, preliminary examination of the deposit may show that a small sample is adequate for the accurate determination of all important constituents.

The systematic analysis is shown graphically in Fig. 1, and the separate steps are discussed in the following paragraphs.

[2] Fritz Feigl, "Qualitative Analysis by Spot Tests," 3rd Ed., Elsevier Publishing Co., New York, N. Y., 1946.

Treatment of Extracts

Mother liquor separated from a field sample frequently will include solids which led to formation of the deposit. Soluble constituents such as chloride, sulfate, nitrate, and metal ions can be detected by standard analytical procedures such as the ASTM methods in this Manual.

Extracted organic matter sometimes can be identified as lubricant, fuel oil, rust preventive, or paint residue. However, heat and pressure associated with deposit formation often will decompose the original organic matter and yield decomposition products that cannot be traced back to it. Such tests as saponification number, iodine number, viscosity, and additive identification sometimes are useful in fixing the original source of organic contamination.

Treatment of the Half-Gram Samples (Fig. 1)

Water-Soluble Matter:

This test should be made immediately ahead of the ignition-loss test, and on the same sample, to remove hydrates and certain other components that might confuse the ignition-loss value. If appreciable water-soluble matter is present, it should be examined for the usual water-soluble ions: chlorides, bromides, fluorides, sulfides, sulfates, phosphates, nitrates, silicates, and metal ions. If any are found in significant amounts they should be determined quantitatively. Normally the water-soluble content of a water-side deposit will be low, but certain deposits, like calcium hydroxide, can cause difficulty even though they are reasonably soluble.

Ignition Loss:

Ignition loss will include such items as organic matter, carbon, sulfur (sulfite and sulfide), carbon dioxide from carbonates, and, on rare occasions, nitrogen oxides or ammonia. Certain hydrates not removed by the water solubility test also may be decomposed. The results of the ignition-loss test are difficult to interpret, for while some constituents are being driven away, others are being oxidized to higher weight values. For example, reduced forms of iron oxide and copper can increase in weight on ignition.

The principal merit of ignition is in helping to confirm the presence of constituents indicated by other tests. If a large amount of free copper is found in preliminary inspection, a proportionate increase in weight on ignition will be expected. On the other hand, if a large amount of organic is observed in the extraction test, then a large loss of weight on ignition would be expected.

Often, heating to a lower temperature than usual 900 to 1000 C will provide useful information. Carbonaceous samples, for example, should be heated to a maximum temperature of 500 C. The report of analysis should give the ignition temperature and length of ignition time.

H₂S by Evolution:

A qualitative test for hydrogen sulfide, using sulfuric acid and lead-acetate test paper, should be made first. If this test is positive, a standard evolution method[3] should be followed.

CO₂ by Evolution:

A qualitative test for carbon dioxide should be made first by adding mineral acid and passing any evolved gas into a solution of either calcium hydroxide or barium hydroxide. If this test is positive (cloud produced), the quantitative determination can be made either gravimetrically,[4] using the standard Ascarite

---

[3] W. W. Scott, "Standard Methods of Chemical Analysis," Vol. I, 5th Ed., D. Van Nostrand Co., New York, N. Y., 1939, p. 911.
[4] *Ibid.*, p. 235.

absorption tower, or volumetrically,[5] using modifications of a method originally developed for carbon dioxide in industrial waters. The modifications permitting determinations to be made on solid samples are only minor, and the method is more rapid than the gravimetric method.

Sodium and Potassium:

Sodium and potassium salts usually will be found with the water-soluble portions (mother liquor or water extract), but in some cases they may occur in complexes which remain behind in the silica residue and return to the master solution with the fusion thereof. In the latter case, the analysis will depend on the competence of the operator and the equipment at his disposal. The tedious J. Lawrence Smith Method[6] often may be the most appropriate for the purpose, but newer techniques using the flame photometer may be more convenient for those having such equipment.

SYSTEMATIC TREATMENT OF THE MAIN ANALYTICAL SAMPLE (1 g)

Solution of water-formed deposits is generally best effected with a mixture of mineral acids, including hydrochloric, nitric, and perchloric. Complete solution of certain silicate complexes may be impossible by this means, but these will be broken down by treatment of the silicate residue with hydrofluoric acid and subsequent treatment with sodium carbonate. If laboratory regulations prohibit use of perchloric acid, initial solution can be brought about with nitric and hydrochloric acid or with nitric-sulfuric acid. In the first instance, repeated dehydration may be required to

---

[5] F. E. Clarke, *Industrial and Engineering Chemistry, Analytical Edition*, Vol. 19, p. 889 (1947).
[6] Scott, *op. cit.*, p. 882.

separate the silica. In the second case, analysis for certain constituents will be affected by the sulfuric acid. For example, it will add sulfate ion and precipitate barium. Separate samples must be used for such constituents when this method of solution is used.

If a large amount of phosphate is present in the original sample subjected to fuming with nitric, hydrochloric, and perchloric acids, considerable phosphate will be separated with the silica and some of it may be lost as phosphoric acid if too much sulfuric or perchloric acid is used in the hydrofluoric acid treatment of the silica residue. The silica residue may also include barium sulfate and tin, as well as sodium and potassium from silica complexes. These will be returned to the original sample, however, with the sodium carbonate fusion.

The final filtrate from the silica determination is divided into six aliquots, as shown in Fig. 1. The size of these aliquots should be based on preliminary exploratory tests so as to yield the best volume for each determination. It will be noted that perchloric acid is recommended in place of sulfuric acid in the hydrofluoric acid treatment. This eliminates introduction of sulfate ion.

The analyses of the several aliquots of the analytical scheme are discussed below in the order of their occurrence in Fig. 1.

Sulfate:

Sulfate is determined by precipitation as barium sulfate. If the iron content is high, preliminary precipitation and filtration to remove excess iron will reduce to a minimum the contamination of the barium sulfate precipitate.

Calcium, Magnesium, and Barium:

Calcium and magnesium are determined in series, after removing iron and aluminum, by adding ammonium chloride and neutralizing with ammonium hydroxide. Other metals need not be removed because the double precipitation of calcium will reduce occlusions to insignificant proportions, while the phosphates of such ions as copper, nickel, and zinc are largely soluble in ammoniacal solution, though they are insoluble in neutral solution.

The calcium is precipitated as calcium oxalate. This can be ignited and determined as calcium oxide or dissolved in sulfuric acid and titrated with standard permanganate.

Magnesium is precipitated as magnesium ammonia phosphate and ignited to magnesium pyrophosphate. This residue will also include manganese pyrophosphate as well as traces of heavy metals. The presence of manganese accounts for treatment of the residue and determination of magnesium by difference. It also is practicable to calculate the manganese pyrophosphate from the manganese determination. If extreme accuracy in the magnesium determinations is desired, or if the original deposit contains very large amounts of copper, nickel, zinc, and lead, the analyst may wish to remove these interferences by treating the solution with hydrogen sulfide, filtering off the sulfide precipitate, and boiling the filtrate to remove hydrogen sulfide before following the scheme shown in Fig. 1. Alternatively, the heavy metals usually present in water-formed deposits may be separated by the mercury cathode.

Manganese:

Since the primary solution is a perchloric acid medium, manganese can be determined colorimetrically by the standard potassium periodate method described in various texts.

Chromium and Vanadium:

An experienced technician can do these two determinations simultaneously by the indicated scheme. The chromate and vanadate ions oxidize a part of the ferrous ion and the excess ferrous ion is titrated with potassium permanganate to disappearance of the red o-phenanthroline color. The vanadium is then oxidized by the permanganate. Titration is complete when the pink color from 1 drop of permanganate persists for 30 sec. The permanganate consumed in the latter part of the titration is equivalent to the vanadium. The chromium is determined by difference from the residual ferrous ion titration after subtracting the ferrous ion calculated to have been used to reduce the vanadium.

If the vanadium content is relatively high, greater than 0.5 per cent, the o-phenanthroline end point is difficult to determine. In this case it is more practical to titrate the chromium and vanadium completely with permanganate in the same manner than to reduce the vanadium with ferrous sulfate, oxidize the residual ferrous sulfate (but not the vanadium) with ammonium persulfate, and finally titrate the vanadium with permanganate. It also is possible to determine vanadium by electrometric titration with ferrous sulfate.

Fortunately vanadium is a rather unusual water-side deposit so that precise analyses for it generally are not required.

Titanium:

The standard method of oxidation with peroxide and determining titanium by comparison with color standards is satisfactory for most boiler deposit work. Vanadium produces a similar color and will yield essentially a quantitative error. If the vanadium content is known it can be subtracted. Again, the absence of vanadium from most water-formed deposits makes this error relatively unimportant.

Lead, Copper, Nickel, Zinc, Iron, Tin, Aluminum, and Phosphate:

This large group of constituents is handled together because primary removal of copper and lead, followed by removal of phosphate, eliminate pertinent interferences from the schemes for the remaining constituents.

Plating copper and lead from perchloric acid solution generally results in a dark copper plate containing traces of lead. This can be overcome by dissolving the plated metals in nitric acid and redepositing them.

It is practical, but unnecessary, to separate copper and lead with hydrogen sulfide and then to dissolve the precipitate in nitric acid and plate the metals in the same manner. This method also separates tin as a sulfide but it will remain dissolved in the acid electrolyte after plating. The hydrogen sulfide must be driven off by heating before completing the scheme.

Zinc may be determined gravimetrically as the oxide or colorimetrically by the use of Zincon.

The nickel dimethylglyoxime residue can be measured either gravimetrically or colorimetrically by standard procedures.

The phosphorus is removed early in the sequence to prevent interference. It can be determined gravimetrically or volumetrically as ammonium phosphomolybdate or gravimetrically as magnesium pyrophosphate. All are standard analytical procedures.

The cupferron reagent used to separate iron and tin from the mixed hydroxides decomposes slowly and should be freshly prepared for use. Stability of cupferron is sometimes enhanced by adding 50 mg of acetophenelidide per liter of 6 per cent aqueous solution. If a small bag containing ammonium carbonate is suspended in a bottle containing the dry cupferron reagent, its quality can be maintained for a longer period.

Iron cupferron precipitate is only slowly attacked in the cold by $2N$ hydrochloric acid (used to wash the precipitate prior to washing with ammonium hydroxide), but hot acid decomposes it. For this reason the precipitation must be done in the cold. Nitric acid should be absent when cupferron is used as a precipitant. For this reason the mixed hydroxides are dissolved in hydrochloric acid.

It is also practical to determine iron and titanium as mixed oxides by ashing the cupferron precipitate. If the precipitate is bulky it should be wet-oxidized with nitric and sulfuric acids and then reprecipitated with ammonium hydroxide. Direct ignition is satisfactory for small precipitates. The iron oxide can be corrected for the titanium oxide determined earlier. Iron may also be determined colorimetrically by *o*-phenanthroline, with which titanium does not interfere.

Precautions must be taken in determining aluminum as an oxide, since aluminum oxide is a desiccant and will increase in weight if not kept in the proper atmosphere. Large amounts of aluminum may be determined by sodium fluoride - sulfuric acid titration, using phenolphthalein or a pH meter as indicator.

CONCLUSIONS

The preceding information on analysis of deposits is not intended to be exhaustive. The discussion and tables of compounds likely to be found in water-formed deposits (Chapter IV) should be used as a guide to the analyst in determining his course of procedure. There may be occasions when preliminary qualitative tests indicate the presence of elements not included in the scheme discussed herein. In such cases, the analyst will perforce have to use his ingenuity and modify the procedures to effect the necessary separations and choose methods which will adequately determine the elements so indicated. Many of the methods discussed in Chapter VII for the analysis of industrial waters may be applicable to the determination of certain constituents of water-formed deposits, and the analyst is advised to study that chapter carefully.

CHAPTER X
Radioactive Nuclides in Water

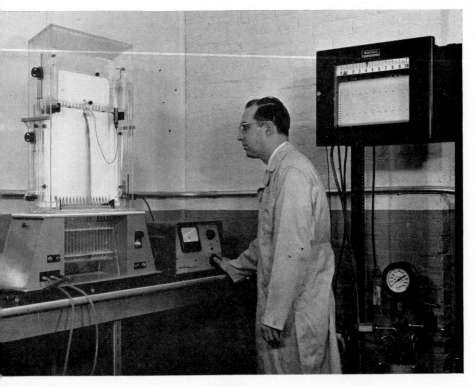

CHAPTER X—RADIOACTIVE NUCLIDES IN WATER

Before the summer of 1945 it could be fairly stated that the problem of radioactive contamination of water did not exist. True, some radioactive springs were known, but these aroused little interest, except for possible use of the supposed healing properties of the water. The successful testing of an atomic bomb in the New Mexico desert on July 16, 1945, changed this situation. Fogging of some packages of photographic film was traced to radioactive débris from this bomb. The radionuclides had got into the process water and then into the wrapping paper. This is the first known damage to a commercial product from radioactively contaminated water.

Radioactivity may be defined as the spontaneous emission of penetrating energetic radiation from certain atomic nuclei. The early workers in the field soon classified the radiation into three types, called alpha (α), beta (β), and gamma (γ) rays, on the basis of their ability to penetrate matter. They were also able to establish their nature, finding that alpha and beta rays were high-speed particles, while gamma rays were electromagnetic waves similar to X-rays. The results of these early studies can be tabulated as shown in Table I.

The emission of these radiations is associated with a nuclear disintegration, which is the rearrangement of the constituents of the nucleus into a more stable configuration with an associated release of energy. The rate of emission is characteristic of the radioactive material (also called radionuclide), and is described by the time required for half of the unstable nuclei to complete their rearrangements and emissions: the half-life. After the lapse of one half-life, since the number of unstable nuclei has been reduced to one-half the original number, the emission rate (or activity) is also reduced to one-half of its initial value. The quantity of radioactive material is measured by the rate of disintegration; that amount of a nuclide in which 3.7×10^{10} atoms disintegrate per second is defined as a curie. Ordinarily, subdivisions of this unit, milli-, micro-, or even micromicrocuries, are used. These are 10^{-3}, 10^{-6}, and 10^{-12} curies respectively. The term picocurie is occasionally used as a synonym for micromicrocurie.

The energy released in a nuclear disintegration is large, usually of the order of a million times as much as is involved in ordinary chemical changes. When alpha particles or gamma rays are emitted, these carry off substantially all the energy released. In beta emission, however, the available energy is divided between the beta particle and a neutrino, which is not ordinarily observable. The division of the energy varies in individual disintegrations, so that a particular beta particle may have an energy from zero up to the maximum available, the average being about one third of the total energy released. Consequently, beta radiation has a continuous energy spectrum, while alpha and gamma radiations are characterized by line spectra.

The unit of energy most used in radioactivity is the electron volt, the energy gained by an electron in passing through a potential difference of 1 v. It is equal to

177

1.6 × 10^{-12} ergs. Alpha particles have energies of a few million electron volts (Mev); beta and gamma radiations may have energies from zero up to a few Mev.

The three types of radiations interact with matter in somewhat different ways. Both the charged particles (alpha and beta) react primarily by electrostatic interaction with the electrons of the ma-

no definite range, but is statistically reduced in quantity as it passes through matter. This gamma interaction has been compared to the process of firing machine gun bullets at random into a forest, in which each bullet is unaffected until it strikes a tree, when it loses all or part (if it ricochets) of its energy. The extent of the interaction of the three types of

TABLE I.—TYPES OF RADIATION: NATURE AND PENETRATION ABILITY.

Type	Penetration		Nature
	Air	Solids	
Alpha.........	few centimeters	few microns	fast-moving helium nuclei
Beta...........	meters	several millimeters	very rapid electrons (+ and −)[a]
Gamma.........	many meters	several centimeters	electromagnetic radiations of very high energy

All the beta radiation from naturally occurring materials consists of negative electrons; the emission of positive electrons (positrons) by certain man-made materials was discovered in the 1930's

TABLE II.—INTERACTION OF RADIATION WITH MATTER.

Radiation; Energy, Mev	Range, cm		Energy Transfer, Mev per cm		Tenth-thickness,[a] cm	
	Air	Aluminum	Air	Aluminum	Lead	Aluminum
Alpha, 5................	3.5	0.0018	1.43	2800	...	...
Alpha, 7................	5.9	0.0033	1.19	2100	...	...
Beta, 0.5................	125	0.06	0.0040	8.3	...	...
Beta, 3.0................	1320	0.64	0.0023	4.7	...	...
Gamma, 0.1.............	...	...	...	...	0.037	5.1
Gamma, 1.0.............	...	...	...	...	2.9	13.8

[a] Thickness needed to reduce intensity to 10 per cent of incident intensity.

terial, transferring energy to each electron that they approach sufficiently closely. Quantitatively, the actions differ considerably, with the heavier, slower-moving alpha particle interacting with many more electrons per unit path length. The interaction of gamma radiation with matter is essentially statistical in nature, with each individual gamma photon transferring no energy until it interacts, usually with an electron, whereupon it transfers all or a large part of its energy. The gamma radiation has

radiation with matter is illustrated in Table II.

The primary effect of the interaction of any one of the three types of radiation with matter is the transfer of energy to electrons, resulting in the production of ions or of excited molecules. Secondary changes in matter include such phenomena as the darkening of photographic film, the initiation of chemical changes, and biological effects. The extent of such effects is dependent on the dose, or amount of energy absorbed by the ma-

TABLE III.—NATURAL RADIOACTIVE SERIES.

Atomic Number	Element	Atomic Weight	Historical Name	Radiation, Half-Life		Remarks
			URANIUM-RADIUM SERIES			
92....	Uranium.........	238	uranium I	α	4.5×10^9 yr	
90....	Thorium.........	234	uranium X-1	β	24 days	
91....	Protactinium.....	234m	uranium X-2	β	1.2 min	
91....	Protactinium^a.....	234	uranium Z	β	6.7 hr	
92....	Uranium.........	234	uranium II	α	3×10^5 yr	
90....	Thorium.........	230	ionium	α	8×10^4 yr	
88....	Radium..........	226	radium	α	1620 yr	
86....	Radon...........	222	radon	α	3.8 days	
84....	Polonium........	218	radium A	$\alpha(\beta)$ 3 min		β 0.03 per cent
82....	Lead.............	214	radium B	β	27 min	
85....	Astatine^a........	218		α	2 sec	
83....	Bismuth.........	214	radium C	$\beta(\alpha)$ 20 min		α 0.04 per cent
84....	Polonium........	214	radium C$'$	α	$<10^{-6}$ sec	
81....	Thallium^a........	210	radium C$''$	β	1.5 min	
82....	Lead.............	210	radium D	β	$\sim$20 yr	
83....	Bismuth.........	210	radium E	$\beta(\alpha)$ 5 days		$\alpha \sim 10^{-5}$ per cent
84....	Polonium........	210	radium F	α	138 days	
81....	Thallium^a........	206		β	4 min	
82....	Lead.............	206	radium G	stable		
			THORIUM SERIES			
90....	Thorium.........	232	thorium	α	1.4×10^{10} yr	
88....	Radium..........	228	mesothorium 1	β	6.7 yr	
89....	Actinium........	228	mesothorium 2	β	6.1 hr	
90....	Thorium.........	228	radiothorium	α	1.9 yr	
88....	Radium..........	224	thorium X	α	3.6 days	
86 ...	Radon...........	220	thoron	α	1 min	
84....	Polonium........	216	thorium A	$\alpha(\beta)$ 0.16 sec		β 0.01 per cent
82....	Lead.............	212	thorium B	β	10.6 hr	
85....	Astatine^a........	216		α	3×10^{-4} sec	
83....	Bismuth.........	212	thorium C	$\beta(\alpha)$ 60 min		α 33.7 per cent
84....	Polonium........	212	thorium C$'$	α	3×10^{-7} sec	
81....	Thallium^b........	208	thorium C$''$	β	3 min	
82....	Lead.............	208	thorium D	stable		
			URANIUM-ACTINIUM SERIES			
92....	Uranium.........	235	actino-uranium	α	7×10^8 yr	
90....	Thorium.........	231	uranium Y	β	26 hr	
91....	Protactinium.....	231	protactinium	α	3×10^4 yr	
89....	Actinium........	227	actinium	$\beta(\alpha)$ 22 yr		α 1.2 per cent
90....	Thorium.........	227	radioactinium	α	19 days	
87....	Francium^c........	223	actinium K	β	21 min	
88....	Radium..........	223	actinium X	α	12 days	
86....	Radon...........	219	actinon	α	4 sec	
84....	Polonium........	215	actinium A	$\alpha(\beta)$ 2×10^{-3} sec		$\beta < 10^{-3}$ per cent
82....	Lead.............	211	actinium B	β	36 min	
85....	Astatine^a........	215		α	10^{-4} sec	
83....	Bismuth.........	211	actinium C	$\alpha(\beta)$ 2 min		β 0.32 per cent
81....	Thallium........	207	actinium C$''$	β	5 min	
84....	Polonium^a.......	211	actinium C$'$	α	25 sec	
82....	Lead.............	207	actinium D	stable		

^{a} Minor component, <1 per cent.
^{b} Minor component, 33.7 per cent.
^{c} Minor component, 1.2 per cent.

terial. The unit of energy absorption is the rad, which is equivalent to the absorption of 100 ergs per gram of material.

Biological systems in particular are affected by radiation. Destruction of cells by large doses is the basis for radiation therapy for cancer. The effects of excessive exposure in man vary from skin burns through nausea, anemia, loss of resistance to infection, and even death. Smaller radiation doses may cause more subtle damage, leading to cancer and to genetic mutations. While information about the potential damage from low levels of radiation is unfortunately inexact, "acceptable risk" levels are established by the International Commission on Radiological Protection (ICRP) and the National Committee on Radiation Protection and Measurements (NCRP). The present values are set at 5 rems per yr for radiation workers and 0.5 rems per yr for the general population. (A rem is an amount of radiation dose biologically equivalent to 1 rad of beta or gamma radiation.)

Because of their ionizing, photographic, and especially biological effects, the quantities of radioactive materials in commercial products, in air, in water, and in foods, must be rigidly controlled. For each radionuclide, a concentration may be determined, based on its physical, chemical, and metabolic characteristics, such that no organ of the body will receive more than the "acceptable risk" exposure given above. The ICRP and NCRP also establish these maximum permissible concentrations.

NATURALLY OCCURRING RADIONUCLIDES

The Heavy Element Series:

Although radioactive contamination has been a problem for only a short time, radioactive materials have always been part of the environment. The major sources of natural radioactivity are uranium and thorium ores. These contain a great variety of radionuclides, differing in chemical nature, half-life, and type and energy of radiations, but linked genetically into three series, each stemming from an element of very long half-life. The three series are listed in Table III.

Some of these elements can be dissolved, in ratios depending on their individual solubilities, whenever water runs through formations containing them. In addition, since element 86 (radon) is an inert gas, it can move through the soil and so reach water not in contact with the radioactive formation. Because of its relatively long half-life, radon-222 can move through the ground for much greater distances than radon-220 or radon-219. In radioactive springs, radon-222 and its immediate daughters, radium A through radium C', are usually the most conspicuous components. The radium-226 content of ordinary surface or ground waters will generally be less than 0.5 micromicrocuries per liter, while the radon-222 content of the same water may be as high as 100 micromicrocuries per liter. In some spring waters, radon contents may be in the range of microcuries per liter, with radium levels as high as thousands of micromicrocuries per liter.

Each of the foregoing radioactive series owes its occurrence in nature to the existence of a long-lived parent, uranium-238, thorium-232, and uranium-235, respectively. All the other elements in the series have short half-lives, geologically speaking, and would no longer be present except for continual formation.

Other Long-Lived Materials:

Radioactive series do not occur in other parts of the periodic system, and the only radionuclides existing are those few species of geologically long half-life. The most important of these is potassium-40, which comprises 0.012 per cent of natural potassium, and thus contributes radioactivity to all potassium-containing systems. For each milligram of potassium, there will be almost two radioactive disintegrations per minute (dpm). Water itself will therefore be radioactive in proportion to its potassium content, plus a contribution from biological material. The second most important natural activity of this type in water is rubidium-

production by cosmic-ray bombardment of the atmosphere. These nuclides are also listed in Table IV. The most important of these are carbon-14 and hydrogen-3 (tritium). Carbon-14 is formed by the action of cosmic-ray neutrons on atmospheric nitrogen, while tritium is formed directly in the splitting of atoms struck by the high-energy cosmic ray particles. Both of these are oxidized, to carbon dioxide and water, and enter the biosphere and hydrosphere. None of the other ra-

TABLE IV.—OTHER NATURALLY OCCURRING RADIONUCLIDES.

Nuclide	Half-life, years	Abundance, per cent	Specific Activity, dpm per g element	Total in Sea, megacuries[a]
Hydrogen-3	12	varies	varies	200
Beryllium-7	53 days	varies	varies	
Carbon-14	5600	varies	0 to 15	270
Potassium-40	$\sim 10^9$	0.012	1800	460 000
Vanadium-50	4×10^{14}	0.25	0.1	
Rubidium-87	5×10^{10}	27.85	50 000	8400
Indium-115	6×10^{14}	95.7	11	
Lanthanum-138	1×10^{11}	0.09	52	
Cerium-142	5×10^{15}	11.07	0.12	
Neodymium-144	5×10^{15}	23.87	0.26	
Samarium-147	1×10^{11}	15.1	8200	
Lutetium-176	$\sim 10^{10}$	2.6	$\sim 12\ 000$	
Rhenium-187	$\sim 10^{10}$	62.9	$\sim 270\ 000$	
Platinum-190	6×10^{11}	0.012	0.8	
Platinum-192	$\sim 10^{15}$	0.78	~ 0.03	
Bismuth-209	over 10^{18}	100	< 0.004	

[a] One megacurie = 10^6 curies.

87, which forms almost 28 per cent of all natural rubidium. Because of the low abundance of rubidium in the earth's crust, as compared to potassium, rubidium activity is relatively unimportant in fresh waters. Both potassium and rubidium contribute significantly to the radioactivity of sea water, as shown in Table IV. Additional minor radioactive elements of long half-life are included in Table IV.

Cosmic-Ray-Produced Nuclides:

A few radioactive materials of short half-life exist in nature from continuous

dioactive nuclides formed by cosmic-ray bombardment exists in large enough quantities to be of any real importance.

RADIONUCLIDES IN REACTOR COOLANTS AND MODERATORS

In addition to the naturally occurring radioactive species discussed in the preceding section, a large number of artificially produced radionuclides are known. Most of these originate in the fission of heavy atoms or as a result of the bombardment of stable materials by nuclear particles, especially neutrons ("activation"). Since a nuclear reactor functions by the fission of uranium or plutonium and is an extremely strong source of neutrons, radioactive isotopes are formed in large quantities.

In most reactors, the fission chain reaction is principally propagated by neutrons of low (thermal) energies. The primary high-energy fission neutrons are slowed to thermal energies (moderated) by repeated interactions with light elements, of which hydrogen is the most effective. Water, the cheapest hydrogenous material, is a very common moderator. Water also is frequently used for heat-transfer in reactors.

Natural Water:

Water itself, when exposed to a neutron flux, does not yield any important radioactivities. There is a rather intense radiation from nitrogen-16, a product of the interaction of neutrons with oxygen-16, but this material has such a short half-life (7 sec), that any system suitable for containing the reactor will be adequate to protect against it. But many materials present in natural waters will yield radionuclides of relatively long half-life under neutron irradiation. The potential hazard from these materials must be considered in plant operations, and, if discharged, their concentrations must be kept below values at which they might be detrimental to the environment.

The largest American installation using natural water as coolant is the reactor complex at Hanford, Wash. The effect of the reactor operations on the Columbia River has been studied extensively, including the radionuclide content of the water, and of fish and other biological forms in the river. Although a large number of radionuclides are formed in the water during its passage through the reactors, most of these have such short half-lives that they very soon become insignificant. Radioactive forms of manganese arsenic, copper, sodium, phos-

phorus, zinc, chromium, and iron are prominent in the reactor cooling water, and many others are formed in lesser amounts.

In addition to the radionuclides formed by neutron irradiation of stable elements in the water, there is always the possibility of fission product leakage from the fuel elements into the cooling water. While careful design and painstaking workmanship confine such leakage to trivial amounts, some fission products can be identified in the water. The most important of these are iodine, strontium, barium, and the rare earths. Generally speaking, fission products are of greater biological significance than the induced activities, and very elaborate instrumentation is provided to detect leakage before it becomes a problem.

A rather special case of potential formation of radionuclides in a natural water is the operation of nuclear powered vessels. Here, although the coolant moderator is usually very carefully purified water in a closed system, the designer must consider the possibility of reactor neutrons passing through the hull to activate sodium and other elements in the water in which the ship floats. Sufficient neutron shielding to prevent this is therefore included in the reactor plant.

Treated Waters:

In most water-moderated or water-cooled reactors, extremely pure demineralized water is used. This may be ordinary (light) water or deuterium oxide (heavy water). In many systems the water is continuously purified by ion-exchange demineralizers.

There are several reasons for using such rigorously purified water in reactors. One advantage of pure water is that only a small amount of radioactivity is formed in it. In absolutely pure water, only the unimportant 7-sec isotope nitrogen-16 would be formed. In practice, this ideal is unattainable, but the purer the water, the closer it can be approached. Another advantage is neutron economy. Not only is every radioactive atom in the water a nuisance, but its formation has required one neutron. Such unproductive consumption of neutrons is expensive in reactor technology.

In spite of extreme purity and the use of highly corrosion-resistant alloys, a minute amount of corrosion occurs in every system. Continuous bombardment by the large neutron flux inside the reactor core induces very significant activity even in these tiny amounts of corrosion products. The nature of the alloys involved determines the character of the induced activities. The most important induced radionuclides in stainless steel systems include isotopes of chromium, manganese, iron, cobalt, and nickel.

A second source of radionuclides is material specifically added for corrosion control. Practically all the common materials of this type, such as chromate, phosphate, and silicate, become radioactive in the reactor. A special case is the production of tritium by neutron bombardment of lithium, the lithium being added as hydroxide for pH control. Tritium, a pure beta emitter of low biological effect, is considered a less serious problem than the radioactive sodium or potassium that would result if hydroxides of these elements were used.

Just as in natural water systems, there could be some minute leakage of fission products from the fuel elements into the treated coolant water. Here also, the fission products are more hazardous than the induced activities and their concentration in the water must be rigidly controlled.

Treated water systems, because of the high cost of the water, are invariably closed, recirculating systems. Although the contaminated primary coolant is retained within the shielded enclosure, some bleed-off and makeup is usually necessary. Uncontrolled discharge of the radioactive waste water to the environment is not permissible; therefore, waste tanks are usually provided in which the water (a) is stored for decay, (b) is monitored before discharge, and (c) is fed into the environment at a controlled rate so that permissible levels are not exceeded.

Canal Coolants:

In addition to reactor coolant and moderator, water is used in the "canals" in which fuel elements are stored prior to processing. These fuel elements, containing an enormous quantity of radioisotopes, require considerable cooling to dissipate the residual heat of the radioactive decay. The gamma radiation from these elements is very intense, so that they must be heavily shielded to permit plant personnel to work in the vicinity. Water about 25 ft deep serves both these purposes satisfactorily. The fuel elements, after a sufficient cooling period, are removed by remote-control tools.

Canal waters become contaminated by transfer of the radioactive primary coolant adhering to the fuel element when it is removed from the reactor; in the case of a leaking element, there is also some contamination from fission products. The total contamination from both of these sources is ordinarily minor, but provision must be made for draining any contaminated canal water to waste tanks and replacing it with fresh water.

RADIONUCLIDES FROM CHEMICAL PROCESSING OF ORES, REACTOR FUELS, AND BLANKET MATERIALS

Ores:

The primary natural materials useful in nuclear energy are uranium and thorium. Uranium-235 is the only natural fissionable material; uranium-238 and thorium-232 are the raw materials for manufacture of artificial fissionable materials. The first steps in nuclear technology are thus the mining and refining of these materials. Uranium and thorium are each the progenitor of long series of radioactive elements, any or all of which may be present in the ores.

Of all the daughter elements, those of relatively long half-life include thorium-

persist much longer than any conceivable control measures and their treatment must be absolutely foolproof. The more soluble materials, of course, may eventually reach and contaminate waters. Of all the nuclides listed in the preceding paragraph, radium-226 is the most harmful in a water environment by reason of its biochemical properties, its long half-life, and the energetic radiations of it and its immediate daughter products. The present maximum permissible concentra-

TABLE V.—NUCLIDES IN REACTOR TECHNOLOGY.

Nuclide	Type	Maximum Permissible Concentration (Occupational)			
		Water		Air	
		μc per ml^a	μg per liter	μc per ml^a	μg per liter
Strontium-89............	fission product	7×10^{-5}	3×10^{-6}	2×10^{-8}	7×10^{-10}
Strontium-90............	fission product	8×10^{-7}	4×10^{-6}	2×10^{-10}	1×10^{-9}
Ruthenium-106..........	fission product	1×10^{-4}	3×10^{-5}	2×10^{-8}	6×10^{-9}
Iodine-131..............	fission product	6×10^{-5}	5×10^{-7}	6×10^{-9}	5×10^{-11}
Cerium-144.............	fission product	1×10^{-4}	3×10^{-5}	2×10^{-9}	6×10^{-10}
Radium-226.............	natural	4×10^{-8}	4×10^{-5}	8×10^{-12}	8×10^{-9}
Thorium (natural)........	natural	5×10^{-7}	5000	3×10^{-11}	0.3
Thorium-234.............	natural	2×10^{-4}	9×10^{-6}	1×10^{-8}	4×10^{-10}
Uranium (natural)........	natural	2×10^{-6}	3000	3×10^{-11}	0.05
Uranium-233.............	artificial heavy	3×10^{-6}	0.3	3×10^{-11}	3×10^{-9}
Plutonium-239...........	artificial heavy	3×10^{-6}	0.05	2×10^{-12}	3×10^{-8}
Americium-241..........	artificial heavy	3×10^{-6}	9×10^{-4}	4×10^{-11}	1×10^{-8}

^{a} International Committee on Radiological Protection, *British Journal of Radiology*, Suppl. No. 6, Table C. VIII, December, 1954.

230 (ionium), radium-226, and lead-210 (radium D) in the uranium-radium series, and radium-228 (mesothorium 1) and thorium-228 (radiothorium) in the thorium series. The long-lived protactinium-231 and actinium-227 occur in uranium, but since they are derived from relatively scarce uranium-235 (0.71 per cent) they are less important. In removing the desired uranium or thorium from ore, the other radioactive elements present will be left behind. Depending upon the process, these elements may occur in various chemical forms with different solubilities. Those of long half-life will

tion of this material in uncontrolled waters is only 4×10^{-9} microcuries per ml, (about 9 disintegrations per min per liter), or 4×10^{-12} g per liter. Obviously extreme precautions are necessary to limit losses to this small amount.

Reactor Fuel and Blanket Materials:

A wide variety of radionuclides are liberated from fuel elements when these elements are processed chemically. Conventional processing at the present time involves complete dissolution of the elements, separation and purification of the heavy metals, especially uranium and plutonium, and discharge of the waste to storage. The radioactive elements present in fuel elements include both fission products and neutron-activated elements.

Fission products of the heavy metals include all the elements from about atomic number 30 (zinc) to about atomic number 64 (gadolinium). The elements as first formed have excess neutrons and rapidly change by radioactive decay into more stable elements emitting beta and gamma radiation. After a reactor has been operating for some time, it will contain a large variety of radionuclides of both short and long half-lives. If a fuel element is then removed from the reactor and stored, the short-lived materials will change into either stable or longer-lived isotopes, so that most of the radioactivity will then be in the form of materials of long half-life. Some of the more important of these materials are listed in Table V.

All reactor fuels, and especially all reactor blanket materials (materials placed around the reactor core to form additional fissionable material from neutrons that would otherwise escape), will contain a number of artificial heavy elements, also listed in Table V.

On dissolution of a fuel element, all these fission products and heavy elements are free from confinement, and pass into the liquid. The volatile materials, such as inert gases and halogens, pass off as vapors. If released to the atmosphere, they can settle out or be washed into surface waters by rain, thereby becoming potential contaminants of the water environment. The fission products remaining after processing constitute an intensely radioactive aqueous waste, which at present is stored indefinitely. The product phase, chiefly heavy metals, is also strongly radioactive; it requires special methods of handling to avoid contamination of the environment. Partly because of the hazard, and partly because of the very high value of the products, control is normally so thorough that only negligible quantities of product are lost as wastes.

The extraordinary precautions necessary in handling these materials may be judged from the quantities considered permissible in an industrial environment (Table V); if discharged to an uncontrolled area, these values should be reduced by a factor of 10.

RADIONUCLIDES FROM FALL-OUT

Fission Products:

The most widespread type of radioactive contamination at present is fall-out from nuclear weapons testing. These tests have produced a considerable atmospheric content of fission products of intermediate and long half-lives, which gradually settle to the earth. In addition to settling under their own weight and as a result of atmospheric currents, larger quantities of these materials are brought down by rain and snow.

In the United States during October, 1958, it was unusual to find a rain or a surface water that contained no detectable fission-product activity. Levels of activity in rain may range from a few to thousands of micromicrocuries per liter, while in surface waters they will generally be of the order of tens of micromicrocuries per liter. In the period during and shortly after a weapons test series, rain activity may reach the order of hundreds of thousands and surface water activities hundreds of micromicrocuries per liter. These increases are primarily due to fission products of short half-life, which do not persist in the atmosphere. Levels in ground waters are ordinarily much lower than these, depending largely on the speed with which the ground water is replenished by rain and surface water.

When rain containing fission product activity falls on the ground, much of the activity is transferred to the soil, mostly by adsorption on soil particles or on atmospheric particulates washed down with the rain. As a result, the fraction of radioactive material reaching streams or other bodies of water is relatively small, except where large water areas are exposed to direct rainout. Although water contamination is less than it would be if these mechanisms were not operative, this cannot be counted as a clear gain since much of the radioactivity remaining

TABLE VI.—RADIONUCLIDES FOUND IN FALL-OUT.

Long-Lived Fission Products:

Strontium-89	Ruthenium-106
Strontium-90	Cesium-137
Yttrium-91	Cerium-141
Zirconium-95	Cerium-144
Niobium-95	Promethium-147
Ruthenium-103	Samarium-151

Short-Lived Fission Products:

Molybdenum-99	Iodine-133
Technetium-99m	Iodine-135
Tellurium-132	Barium-140
Iodine-131	Praseodymium-143
Iodine-132	Neodymium-147

Induced Activities:

Carbon-14	Cobalt-57
Calcium-45	Cobalt-58
Manganese-54	Cobalt-60
Iron-55	Zinc-65
Iron-59	

in the soil becomes available to plants, and so enters the food chain with the possibility of eventual ingestion by humans. Where rainfall is collected in cisterns for drinking water, much of the radioactivity is removed by adsorption on the collection surfaces, and by settling out and adsorption on the walls of the cistern.

The fission products cover a wide range of chemical elements. Consequently their behavior in water is characterized by large variations. Some, such as zirconium, being very insoluble in most aquatic environments, settle out more or less rapidly with particulate material, thus becoming concentrated in silts and

sludges. Others remain in solution for a much longer time and hence can be carried much farther in streams. Still others enter into the biological cycle and become distributed in a manner depending upon the biota present in each stream.

As a result of the processes described in the preceding paragraph, combined with normal radioactive decay, the total activity of a body of water may decrease rapidly after contamination. This decrease, however, does not necessarily imply a proportionate decrease in the biological hazard of this water, which depends strongly upon the radionuclide composition of the contamination. Removal of even large amounts of a relatively nonhazardous component does not have much effect on the potential biological damage.

Induced Activities:

In addition to the fission products which are formed in fairly definite proportions in the actual nuclear explosion, radioactive materials are formed by irradiation with the neutrons produced in the explosion. The nature and quantity of these induced radioactive nuclides depends on the exact circumstances of the explosion, which determine the exposure to neutron fluxes. Thus, in a high-altitude burst, only those materials present in the bomb and in the air could be irradiated, while in a burst close to the ground, all the elements present in the soil would be potential sources of induced activity. In a subsurface explosion at sea, such materials as the sodium in the water would become radioactive under the resultant neutron bombardment.

The amount of fission product radioactivity formed during an explosion is so large that normally the induced activity would not be noticeable in the early stages; however, as the fission products of short half-life disappear, those induced activities of longer half-life would become relatively more prominent. A number of these induced radionuclides are concentrated by biological systems and in many cases they have been detected in fish or other specimens taken from the water.

Table VI lists some of the more important fission products and induced radioisotopes that have been found in fall-out.

RADIOTRACERS IN WATER

The number of potential applications of radiotracer studies in aqueous systems staggers the imagination; only a few can be selected as examples. For the sake of simplicity, tracer studies in which the water itself is the subject will be chosen.

Selection of Tracer Materials:

The prime requirement of any tracer is that it shall actually trace the process under investigation. To illustrate, marbles are entirely unsatisfactory in tracing stream flow, oranges are reasonably satisfactory (at least so far as surface flow is concerned), fluorescein dye in solution is usually suitable. The same principles apply with radiotracers. In flow studies, presumably the best radiotracer for water would be tritiated water; reasonably good results could be expected with tracers which react with the stream environment to a very small degree, while tracers that tend to precipitate out, enter into the biology of the stream, or be removed by ion-exchange properties of the silts, would give poorer, less conclusive results.

After it has been established that one (or several) tracers are suitable, a number of other characteristics of the radioactive material become important. These characteristics include ease of detection and measurement, suitable half-life (long enough for the experiment but not so long as to interfere with subsequent experiments or use of the water), low ra-

diological hazard, availability, and low (or at least reasonable) cost.

Hydraulic Tracing:

A fairly large number of radionuclides have been used in tracing flow. Tritium would be ideal except for the difficulty of measuring its extremely soft beta radiation. Excellent results have been obtained with bromine-82, but there is the objection that the material has a half-life of only 36 hr. It is therefore most useful in studying small artificial systems, such as settling basins and the like. Another halogen that has been used successfully in such applications is iodine-131.

In longer studies, a nuclide of greater half-life usually is needed. Iodine-131 is sufficiently long-lived for many experiments, but the maximum permissible concentration of this material in public waters is so low that its use is thereby restricted. One of the best nuclides for flow tracing in nature is rubidium-86, which has a half-life of 19 days, emits readily detectable beta and gamma radiation, and is relatively insensitive to precipitation or other sedimentation. Scandium-46 has also been used under conditions such that it would remain in solution or at least form fine, essentially nonsettling particles. In following the movement of silts, scandium-46 and gold-198 have proved suitable.

Biological Tracing:

The discussion here will be confined to studies of the movement of radioisotopes in the biota of a stream. This is particularly important in understanding the fate of radionuclides introduced into a stream. The outstanding opportunity for this type of study has been in the Columbia River, where use of the river water as reactor coolant has resulted in the presence of a wide spectrum of irradiated radioelements in the stream. Many of these materials are concentrated strongly by algae and other plankton; much of this concentration appears to be a surface or adsorption phenomenon. As one examines other forms higher in the food chain, the number of elements concentrated (and often the degree of concentration) becomes less, partly because of rejection of these elements in the diet or in digestion, partly by disappearance of nuclides of short half-life. Thus, in the Columbia River, the nuclides most generally present in fish are phosphorus-32 and strontium-89, in contrast to the reactor effluent activities which consist largely of arsenic, manganese, and copper.

Some laboratory experiments have been performed on the uptake of certain nuclides by fish and other aquatic forms. Most of the work has been concentrated on fission products, particularly strontium and cesium. The results of these studies, oversimplified, may be summarized by saying that many elements are taken up by the more primitive feeders, such as algae and mollusks. Forms feeding upon these primitive forms generally take up less of the insoluble elements, except in the contents of the digestive tract. A number of non-fission-product nuclides, particularly zinc, cobalt, and iron isotopes, are taken up by mollusks, and surprisingly large quantities of zinc have been found in fish.

DISPOSAL OF WATER CONTAINING RADIOACTIVE NUCLIDES

Low-Activity Wastes:

It is difficult to make hard-and-fast statements about the disposal of water containing radioactive materials. As is the case with other wastes, disposal varies with the nature and quantity of the material, and with the ability of the environment to accommodate the waste. Since the term "radioactive material"

covers such a wide variety of nuclides of different physical, chemical, and biological properties, the disposal of wastes will inevitably be a matter of individual determination in each case.

A large majority of users of radionuclides can dispose of their wastes with only the most elementary precautions. The Atomic Energy Commission has established regulations for the sewer disposal of radionuclides by its licensees. The average research user of isotopes need only measure the activity of his waste to make sure that its concentration when discharged will be acceptable. Beyond this, he must only make sure that the activity is prevented from depositing on plumbing, where it might become a hazard.

Even where an isotope user must dispose of quantities too large for direct discharge, simple treatment methods often suffice, for example, storage of materials of short half-life. In this case the waste is retained until radioactive decay reduces the activity to a level that will permit safe discharge. Where storage would be impractical, as in the case of high activity or long half-life, the radionuclide may often be removed from the waste water by coagulation, precipitation, or ion-exchange techniques. The concentrated nuclide in solid form can then be stored if convenient, or disposed of by burial. The decontaminated water, after its radioactivity has been shown to be at a safe level, can be discharged.

Waste water containing radionuclides at somewhat higher levels, say of the order of a few millicuries per gallon, is rather common in the nuclear industry. Here it is considered "low-level" even though its activity may be much higher than would be considered "low" outside the industry. Such wastes often originate in laboratory or decontamination operations, or in operations involving the draining of a small volume of highly radioactive material. Normally such wastes require treatment prior to discharge. The treatment may be impoundment for decay, coagulation or precipitation, or ion exchange. A somewhat more stringent treatment, suitable for use with higher concentrations of radionuclides, is concentration by evaporation, suitable precautions being taken to minimize carryover of spray in the condensate. This converts the waste into two parts, a condensate ready for monitoring and discharge, and "bottoms" of high-level waste. Electrodialysis with ion exchange membranes, which has been suggested as an alternate treatment to evaporation, must still be considered an experimental method although theory and preliminary investigations have been somewhat promising. Since these treatments will not affect all nuclides to the same extent, the discharge of the treated water must be regulated in accordance with its nuclide composition as well as its total radioactivity content.

Wastes may be discharged to the environment only after necessary treatment, when required, and after monitoring to make sure that the radioactivity actually is at an acceptable level. Discharge may be through sewer systems, when convenient, or directly into streams or other bodies of water. Discharge into the ground is often practiced in controlled areas. In this case the ion-exchange capacity of the soil often provides a form of storage so that somewhat higher levels of activity can be discharged than would be acceptable for direct stream discharge. Adequate monitoring is required where ground disposal is used, to insure that the ground water will not be adversely affected.

High-Activity Wastes:

High-activity wastes may be defined as those containing radionuclides at a concentration of the order of curies per gallon. Most of these wastes originate in the chemical processing of irradiated reactor fuels. Their treatment is made difficult by their chemical properties (acidity, salt content, and so on) as well as by their radioactivity. Generally speaking, these wastes cannot be discharged. They must be stored, and treatment and disposal is only a way of making the storage as inexpensive as possible. The wastes may be stored in tanks, or disposal may be concealed as in discharge to the ocean or into geological formations, or they may be converted into a solid, nonleachable form. In all these cases, however, there is reliance on the material staying where it is put, and not being allowed to leak into the environment.

The only reliable, tested method for large quantities of high-level wastes is permanent tank storage. The waste is usually concentrated by evaporation to the greatest extent possible, the condensate being discharged as a low-level waste. The concentrated bottoms are then transferred to special tanks. These tanks must be corrosion-resistant and must provide for removal of the heat produced by radioactive disintegration. Although storage is stated to be "permanent," this cannot yet be considered definitely established, because the nuclear industry is less than twenty years old and retention for centuries is required. It is definitely established, however, that this treatment is expensive.

A treatment successfully used on small quantities of highly radioactive wastes is conversion into a solid such as concrete. One way of doing this is to add enough cement to the waste that it will set. The cement is usually allowed to set in drums, which are then buried either in the ground or in the deep sea. A modification of this method which offers much promise, and which has been tested on a small scale, is conversion of the waste into a glassy or ceramic material. The waste is calcined to alumina or zirconia and leached. The leached radionuclides may be taken up on clay by adsorption or ion exchange, and the clay is then fired to change its crystal structure in such a way that the radionuclides cannot be desorbed or leached. The ceramic pellets could presumably be stored much more cheaply than tank storage, because of the two factors of reduced volume and noncorrosive nature.

Another form of treatment that has been proved in the laboratory involves separation of the long-lived nuclides strontium-90 and cesium-137 on barium sulfate and potassium alum, respectively. These two nuclides may then be stored rather cheaply because the volume has been markedly reduced. An aqueous phase suitable for discharge is obtained by solvent extraction of the residual fission products from the waste water. These fission products present a much simpler storage problem because of their shorter half-lives.

Ultimate Disposal:

The term "disposal at sea" really has two meanings. In one, it is contemplated that the material remain sealed indefinitely out of contact with the sea water; in the other, the material is introduced into the deep sea but is not sealed from it, and reliance is placed on the slowness of mixing in the sea to limit the spread of radioactivity into the human environment. Unfortunately, our present knowledge of the sea is not adequate to permit full confidence in slow mixing. Rates of transport, and especially of biological transport, are still very uncertain. Therefore all present disposal at sea is actually sealed storage. Sealed containers, usually concrete-filled steel drums, designed to withstand the pressures and corrosion of the sea, are discharged into depths of 1000 fathoms or more. Presumably the drum and eventu-

ally the concrete will be corroded away, but it is hoped that this process will be slow enough that even the longer-lived dangerous nuclides will have decayed to insignificant levels.

Because of the cost of tank storage and of transportation for burial at sea, there is much interest in underground disposal. This is different from discharge into the soil as utilized for low-level wastes. The concept with high-activity wastes is utilization of sealed geological formations as permanent storage. A number of types of geological formations have been considered; at present the most promising appear to be salt domes.

SAMPLING AND MEASUREMENT OF RADIOACTIVE WATER

Sampling:

In sampling water for determination of its radioactivity, whether this be for gross or for radionuclide assay, the normal principles of sampling apply. Since no analysis is better than the sample, it is necessary to make certain that the sample drawn is actually representative of what is needed, both in space and time. The possibility that the analyst may require a continuously composited sample, even one composited proportionally to flow rate, should not be disregarded. Where adequate mixing is not assured, a number of samples from different points and various depths may be taken, either for individual analysis or for compositing. The principles involved in this aspect of sampling will not be mentioned further, because they have been covered in detail in Chapter VI.

Sampling for radioactivity determinations, however, does have one requirement not commonly found in other sampling. This is the need to prevent loss of the radioactive material to the sampler or container. When, as is often the case, the amount of nuclide is only of the order of 10^{-12} g, or even less, normal adsorptive losses on container walls may amount to an important percentage of the activity. Glass or plastic materials appear to give somewhat less difficulty of this kind than do metals. Where necessary, addition of carrier materials or chelating agents or acidification may be employed to minimize adsorptive losses.

Often no adsorptive losses are found in sampling streams or other natural waters. It appears that in such waters the easily adsorbable materials are already on the surfaces of whatever suspended solids may be present. Therefore treatment to prevent adsorption may result in undesired transfer of radionuclides from the suspended to the dissolved phase.

Measurement:

Only the most general survey of the problems of measurement of radioactivity in water is in order here. Specific details are the subject of numerous articles and books. As it is often necessary to measure extremely small amounts of radioactive material in water, the problem of sensitivity or detectability becomes paramount.

Detectability is limited by the random nature of the radioactive disintegration process. The result is a statistical uncertainty in the number of counts observed, setting an inherent lower limit to the precision of the determination. At low enough levels, there is a question of whether there actually were any counts in a given period beyond what might be due to the background, that is, the counts caused by cosmic rays and by naturally occurring radionuclides in and around the instrument. Three techniques are available to get enough counts to permit a definite answer to this question: start with a large sample, detect as many of the radiations as possible, and suppress the background. It is not often convenient to collect or process samples larger than a liter or so, and sample size is often further restricted by solids content. This will be further considered in the discussion of methods of sample preparation.

High efficiency of detection is chiefly a function of the instrument type, although it is also affected by sample preparation. As far as the instrument is concerned, three factors are paramount. First is geometry, or fraction of radiation emitted toward the detector. This is primarily determined by sample and detector size, and by the distance between them. Next comes absorption, which refers to failure of part of the radiation to penetrate the sample solids, the air or other material between the sample and detector, or the wall of the detector itself. Third is the actual detector efficiency, or the fraction of radiations entering the detector which causes a response. Highest over-all efficiency occurs when a sample is placed inside a detector able to respond to each disintegration. Such 100 per cent efficiency is customarily attained only with gaseous samples, although it can be approached with solid samples in special 4-pi counters.

Background suppression is most commonly attained by surrounding the detector with lead or other heavy shielding to block gamma radiation from reaching it. Lead is used in thicknesses up to about 4 in.; iron up to 8 in. Even such quantities of shielding will not block cosmic rays; these can only be eliminated by adding additional detectors which inactivate the counter momentarily when a cosmic ray passes through them. For lowest background levels, careful choice of the materials of the detectors and shielding is important. Thus iron normally contains less radioactive material than lead, and so is more suited for critical shielding applications.

Instrumentation Types:

Three principles of detection are used in measurement: gas ionization, scintillation, and photographic darkening. The last is omitted as not strictly an instrumental technique, although it is very widely used in such applications as personnel monitoring by film badges and in autoradiography. Each of the other two techniques may be used to provide an average, pointer-type indication, or to count individual events.

A second classification of instruments is by the type of radiation they are designed to measure. Since alpha particles are characterized by small penetrating power and high energy dissipation, alpha detectors must be made with extremely thin windows for the entrance of the radiation, or (more usual) with provision for the sample to be introduced into the detector. Only moderate amplification is provided to take advantage of the high energy dissipation, permitting low response for other types of radiation, including cosmic rays. In scintillation alpha detectors, discrimination against other radiations is provided by using a very thin zinc sulfide scintillating screen which gives only very small light pulses with beta and gamma radiation.

In the detection of beta particles, window requirements are less stringent than for alpha particles. The ordinary Geiger-Müller tubes may have glass or metal walls with a thickness of 30 mg per sq cm, or mica windows from 1 to 4 mg per sq cm thick. For the highest efficiency, the sample may be introduced into the detector, as for alpha particles. In fact, the same instrument may be used to detect alpha particles or beta (plus alpha) particles merely by changing the voltage so as to provide higher or lower amplification. Scintillation beta detectors commonly have an organic scintillator, such as an anthracene crystal. The scintillator molecules may be dispersed in plastic to make detectors of varying sizes and shapes.

Gamma rays are characterized by large penetration through matter, therefore the detectors should have as much mass as possible. High atomic number increases the response. Ionization chambers may contain gas under high pressure while gamma Geiger tubes usually have cathodes of silver, bismuth, or other heavy metal. Windows may be made heavy (300 mg per sq cm or more) to reduce response to beta particles. The detection of gamma radiation by scintillation counters has reached a high state of development. Most detectors use sodium iodide crystals (thallium-activated). The heavy salt provides a large mass, and gamma absorption is enhanced by the large percentage of iodine, with its high atomic number.

Some less common instruments of more specialized type may be mentioned briefly. The 4-pi counter is designed to permit detection, with 100 per cent efficiency, of alpha or beta particles. Sample preparation requirements are so stringent that they limit use of the instrument to calibration, rather than to routine work. In liquid scintillation counters, the sample is dissolved in an organic solution of a scintillator, so that all the radiations can produce scintillations. This instrument has been especially developed for the special cases of measuring the very weak radiations from carbon-14 (0.15 Mev) and from tritium (0.018 Mev).

Sample Preparation:

Sample preparation techniques are intimately connected with the type of radiation and with the instrumentation available. Alpha particles travel only a few microns in water and beta particles only a few millimeters; thus any detector measuring these in unprocessed water will be observing only a very thin film

39–81

immediately surrounding it. Such an instrument will therefore respond only to relatively high radionuclide contents. Gamma rays, on the other hand, have a much larger range in water, and large unprocessed samples can be used. Even in this case, the material at large distances from the detector will have poorer geometrical efficiency.

For alpha and beta measurements, and for many gamma measurements, separation of the radioactive material from the water is required. The most common technique for this is evaporation of the water and transfer of the residual solids to a dish or planchet suitable for the counter being used. Removal of the water does not completely eliminate self-absorption loss. Even with a sample as thin as 5 mg per sq cm, an appreciable part of the beta radiation and as much as 50 per cent of the alpha radiation is lost.

Chemical separation is required where a specific radionuclide must be determined in a mixture. This technique must also be used if the solids content of the water is so high that simple evaporation is inapplicable.

HAZARDS

This section will be limited to hazards to those working with water containing radioactive nuclides, whether these be deliberately added tracers or incidental to a nuclear operation. The generalized hazards from discharge of water containing nuclides have been implicit in the preceding sections.

The present thinking on radiological hazards is best summarized by the National Committee on Radiation Protection and Measurements in the National Bureau of Standards Handbook 59, as amended April 15, 1957. The most important points are that the total accumulated radiation dose should be kept as low as possible, and in any case shall not

exceed 5 rems for each year beyond age 18, nor shall the dose in any 13-week period exceed 3 rems. Where exposure is restricted to skin, extremities, bone or thyroid, somewhat higher doses are permitted.

Hazards to workers with radioactive materials may be external and internal. External hazards arise as a result of the worker being close to a source of ionizing radiation. Measurement of radiation levels in the vicinity of radioactive material is relatively simple in most cases. The primary concern in this situation is with the highly penetrating gamma rays, since it is a simple matter to shield out the beta particles. Alpha emitters are of no concern as external sources, since this type of radiation is unable to penetrate the nonliving exterior layer of the skin.

Several kinds of measuring devices are in general use as monitors of radiation levels. One of the most useful is the film badge, routinely worn during working hours. This is simply a holder for X-ray film. At the end of a predetermined period, which may be a week or more, the films are removed from the badge, developed, and the accumulated radiation dose determined by comparison with films exposed to known doses. The film badge is widely used because of its simplicity, reliability, and permanence as a record. The film badge usually includes devices to permit identification of the type of radiation; by varying the thickness and nature of the covering of the film it is possible to distinguish beta particles, soft gamma rays, harder gamma rays, and neutrons.

Survey meters are commonly used for more rapid indication of radiation levels. One type (ionization chamber) indicates the radiation level by measuring the ion current in a gas space between two electrodes. This current is proportional to the ionization produced by the radiation. A second type employs a Geiger tube and gives an indication proportional to the counting rate. This type, while considerably more sensitive, is less directly related to dose rate and is not operable in high radiation fields. Both types may come with shutters thick enough to stop beta particles and thus differentiate between beta and gamma radiation.

Two special forms of these instruments deserve special mention. One is the dosimeter, which is a small ionization chamber that can be carried in a pocket. Before use, the electrodes are charged to a definite voltage, and the total accumulated dose can be read at any time by measuring the decline in voltage. The other form is the alpha survey meter, usually an ionization chamber or proportional chamber equipped with a very thin window through which alpha particles can pass. The primary function of this instrument is the measurement of alpha contamination of surfaces.

Three factors are paramount in the control of external radiation hazard: shielding, distance, and time. Storage in suitable shields reduces radiation from sources to an acceptable level. Well-designed shielding during actual work with nuclides can minimize the radiation dosage. The radiation level decreases as the square of the distance from a point source, and many operations can be carried out safely by remaining at a sufficient distance from the source. Re-

mote handling tools, simple or complicated, are important in such cases. When it is impossible to reduce the radiation level in an operation to a low level the duration of exposure may be controlled, either by performing the operation rapidly, or by using several sets of workers to complete it.

Internal hazard through ingestion or inhalation of radioactive material is more subtle. The most important factors in its prevention are good working habits, particularly careful planning, and good housekeeping practices. Not only should the quantities of nuclides used in an experiment be kept as small as possible, but nuclides of low physiological hazard should be used whenever there is a choice. All operations that may produce air-borne radionuclides should be carried out in an adequate hood. Good housekeeping practices include working in trays, regular monitoring and clean-up of surfaces, careful washing when leaving the laboratory, and prohibition of eating, drinking, or smoking in the laboratory.

Monitoring of workers for internal contamination is most often done by analysis of urine, or less often of feces. If a worker is aware that he has ingested radioactive material, he should induce vomiting. Treatment beyond this is strictly the function of the physician, who should be called immediately.

SOURCES OF INFORMATION

Because of the novelty of the subject of radioactivity to many of the readers of this Manual, information on the literature of this field may be useful. It is not possible to make an exhaustive compilation of sources; accordingly, the following materials have been listed in the belief that they form a useful survey. Very possibly equally good materials have been omitted through lack of acquaintance with them.

Books:

For the novice in the field, books undoubtedly give the best introduction to a subject. The first

three books listed are excellent surveys of radioactivity and atomic energy, at a level comprehensible to the nonspecialist:

G. Friedlander and J. W. Kennedy, "Nuclear and Radiochemistry," John Wiley and Sons, Inc., New York, N. Y., 1955.

R. E. Lapp and H. L. Andrews, "Nuclear Radiation Physics," 2nd Ed., Prentice-Hall, Inc., New York, N. Y., 1954.

S. Glasstone, "Sourcebook on Atomic Energy," 2nd Ed., D. Van Nostrand Co., Inc., Princeton, N. J., 1958.

The next book can be recommended as a

classic in the field, although somewhat old. It is particularly strong with respect to naturally occurring radionuclides:

E. R. Rutherford, J. Chadwick, and C. E. Ellis, "Radiations from Radioactive Substances," Cambridge University Press, 1951.

The next group includes somewhat less general texts, each good in its field, which is generally indicated by the title:

R. L. Murray, "Introduction to Nuclear Engineering," Prentice-Hall, Inc., New York, N. Y., 1954.

S. Glasstone, "Principles of Nuclear Reactor Engineering," D. Van Nostrand Co., Inc., Princeton, N. J., 1955.

C. R. McCullough, "Safety Aspects of Nuclear Reactors," D. Van Nostrand Co., Inc., Princeton, N. J., 1957.

J. Sharpe, "Nuclear Radiation Detectors," Methuen, London, England, and John Wiley and Sons, New York, N. Y., 1955.

D. Taylor, "The Measurement of Radioisotopes," Methuen, London, England, and John Wiley and Sons, New York, N, Y., 1951.

H. D. Smyth, "A General Account of the Development of Methods of Using Atomic Energy for Military Purpose Under the Auspices of the United States Government (1940–1945)," U. S. Govt. Printing Office, Washington, D. C., 1945 (better known as the "Smyth Report").

S. Glasstone (Editor), "The Effects of Nuclear Weapons," U. S. Govt. Printing Office, Washington, D. C., 1957 (much information on fall-out).

C. D. Coryell and N. Sugarman (Editors), "Radiochemical Studies: The Fission Products," McGraw-Hill Book Co., Inc., New York, N. Y., 1951.

A. C. Wahl and N. A. Bonner, "Radioactivity Applied to Chemistry," John Wiley and Sons, Inc., New York, N. Y., 1951.

Compendia:

Intermediate between books and the periodical literature are reports of conferences, groups of papers, and similar compendia. A few of these may be listed:

National Nuclear Energy Series—a record and summary of Manhattan District and early Atomic Energy Commission research. McGraw-Hill Book Co., Inc., New York, N. Y.

"Proceedings of the International Conference on the Peaceful Uses of Atomic Energy," the record of the 1955 Geneva Conference, 16 Vols., United Nations, New York, N. Y., 1956.

"Proceedings of the Second International Conference on the Peaceful Uses of Atomic Energy," the record of the 1958 Geneva Conference, 34 Vols., United Nations, New York, N. Y., 1959. (An edited series of 12 volumes is available from Pergamon Press, New York, N. Y.)

"Progress in Nuclear Energy," nine series each covering a specific area. Probably will appear annually. Pergamon Press, New York, N. Y.

A further group of useful publications of this general type include:

Semi-Annual Reports to Congress, U. S. Atomic Energy Commission, U. S. Govt. Printing Office, Washington, D. C. Each of the later reports is subtitled according to its principal subject. These include:

Sixth Semi-Annual Report, "Atomic Energy and the Life Sciences."

Eighth Semi-Annual Report, "Control of Radiation Hazards in the Atomic Energy Program."

Thirteenth Semi-Annual Report, "Assuring Public Safety in Continental Weapons Tests."

Twenty-first Semi-Annual Report, "Radiation Safety and Major Activities in the Atomic Energy Programs."

Twenty-fifth Semi-Annual Report, "Atomic Industrial Progress and Second World Conference."

Annual Reports, United Kingdom Atomic Energy Authority, H. M. Stationery Office, London, England.

"The Nature of Radioactive Fallout and Its Effects on Man," hearings before the Special Subcommittee on Radiation of the Joint Committee on Atomic Energy, 85th Congress. U. S. Govt. Printing Office, 1957.

"Industrial Radioactive Waste Disposal," hearings before the Special Radiation Subcommittee of the Joint Committee on Atomic Energy, 86th Congress. U. S. Govt. Printing Office, 1959.

Reports of the National Academy of Sciences—National Research Council, Washington, D. C.:

"The Biological Effects of Atomic Radiation"

"The Disposal of Radioactive Waste on Land"

Symposium on Radioactivity in Industrial Water and Industrial Waste Water," Am. Soc. Testing Mats. (1959). (Issued as separate publication *ASTM STP No. 235.*)

Recommendations of the National Committee on Radiation Protection and Measurements (NCRP), published as Handbooks of the National Bureau of Standards. U. S. Govt. Printing Office, Washington, D. C. The handbooks include:

Handbook 49, "Recommendations for Waste Disposal of Phosphorus-32 and Iodine-131 for Medical Users," Nov., 1951.

Handbook 51, "Radiological Monitoring Methods and Instruments," April, 1952.

Handbook 52,ⁱ "Maximum Permissible Amounts of Radioisotopes in the Human Body and Maximum Permissible Concentrations in Air and Water," March, 1953.

Handbook 53, "Recommendations for the Disposal of Carbon-14 Wastes," Oct., 1953.

Handbook 54, "Protection Against Radiations from Radium, Cobalt-60, and Cesium-137," Sept., 1954.

Handbook 58, "Radioactive Waste Disposal in the Ocean," Aug., 1954.

Handbook 59, "Permissible Dose from External Sources of Ionizing Radiation," Sept., 1954.

Handbook 69, "Maximum Permissible Body Burdens and Maximum Permissible Concentrations of Radionuclides in Air and Water for Occupational Exposure," June, 1959.

S. Kinsman, et al, "Radiological Health Handbook," Office of Technical Services, U. S. Dept. of Commerce, Washington, D. C.

"Glossary of Terms in Nuclear Science and Technology," American Standard ASA N1.1–1957, Am. Soc. Mechanical Engrs., 29 W. 29th Street, New York, N. Y., 1957.

Periodical Literature:

The periodical literature in nuclear energy is so voluminous that only a brief glimpse into the field can be given. In addition to the usual journal publications, a vast number of government reports (including U. S. Atomic Energy Commission, U. K. Atomic Energy Authority, and similar groups) are available. For this reason the abstract literature in this field is especially important. Fortunately, the first journal listed below does an outstanding job of covering the report literature, in addition to providing adequate coverage of the journals. The other abstract coverage listed is generally somewhat more specialized than Nuclear Science Abstracts.

Abstracts, Reviews, and Bibliographies:

Nuclear Science Abstracts
Public Health Engineering Abstracts
Journal, Am. Water Works Assn., Abstract Section
Chemical Abstracts (outstanding coverage of journal literature)

Sewage and Industrial Wastes: Annual Review of Literature on Radioactive Wastes

Analytical Chemistry: Reviews (usually each April)

Water Pollution Abstracts

TID Bibliographies, U.S. AEC, especially:
TID-4563, "Special Sources of Information on Isotopes"
TID-3511, "Bibliography on Uses of Radioactive and Stable Isotopes in Industry"
TID-3050, "Bibliography of Selected AEC Reports of Interest to Industry"

AERE Bibliographies, United Kingdom Atomic Energy Authority, especially:
AERE-Lib (L1) "Sources of Information in Atomic Energy."
AERE-Inf/Bib 96 "A List of Reports and Published Papers by AERE Staff" (with Supplements).

"Publications on Atomic Energy," H. M. Stationery Office, London, England, 1956.

"Selected Readings on Atomic Energy," U. S. Govt. Printing Office, Washington, D. C., 1955.

Journals:

General:
Nucleonics (particularly valuable for nuclear news)
International Journal of Applied Radiation and Isotopes (applications of radionuclides in industry, medicine, and science; radiation techniques; radiochemistry)
Science (contains technical articles of general interest)
Nature (generally similar to *Science*)

Analytical Techniques, Including Instrumentation:
Analytical Chemistry
Analytica Chimica Acta
Analyst
Reviews of Scientific Instruments

Water Journals:
Journal, Am. Water Works Assn.
Sewage and Industrial Wastes
Water Pollution Research

Miscellaneous:
Transactions, Am. Geophysical Union (hydrology; meteorology; natural activity)
Radiation Research
Industrial and Engineering Chemistry (especially radiation waste treatment)
Health Physics

PART II

ASTM STANDARDS ON INDUSTRIAL WATER AND INDUSTRIAL WASTE WATER

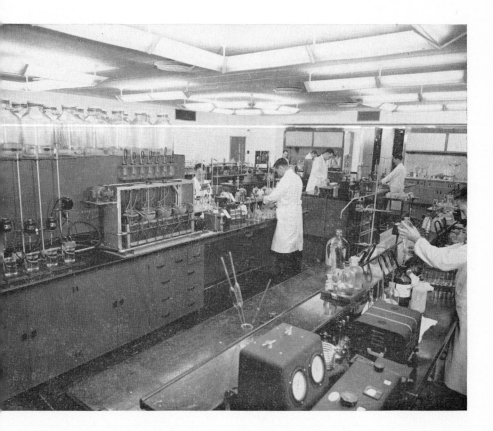

INTRODUCTION TO LABORATORY PRACTICES

Any compilation of knowledge represents a compromise, and the Manual on Industrial Water and Waste Water is no exception. It was prepared for maximum usefulness to the broadest segment of water analysts and to provide industrial management with background information. The technical ability and experience of analysts vary greatly. Success in using the methods will depend not only on detailed compliance with specified procedures but on proper preparation, general practices, and interpretation. Unfortunately, it is not possible to provide complete technical guidance with the methods. Consequently the "philosophy" of laboratory operation is an individualistic responsibility.

Analytical methods may represent sound scientific principles and years of development, but if they are misused or misinterpreted the effort is wasted. Similarly, the most modern facilities and equipment do not insure analytical success if improperly used. Individual samples require individual selection of a sampling procedure, preservation and preparation, analytical methodology, operator skill, and the like. A review of some of these factors should be helpful to both the novice and the professional. Frequently there will be several choices of analytical methods. Should referee or non-referee methods be used? Referee methods generally are more exact, highly accurate, more complicated, time-consuming; require greater operator skill and more costly equipment; take greater preparation; cover a narrower range; and usually take longer to repeat. Non-referee methods may not be as precise, but they offer means for rapid estimation of constituents under many circumstances. They are shorter and less complicated, and they take less operator skill and simpler equipment. Unfortunately, it is impossible to anticipate all considerations, and the analyst must select the best method for his purpose. To do this he must have all the available facts, and he must understand the role of the analyses in the problem to be solved.

The analyst should not cease to quest for new methods once he has found a satisfactory one. He is expected to contribute more than cookbook application of analytical schemes. Methods offering greater specificity and reliability are continually being developed. He should be aware of these, and evaluate and introduce them if they are improvements.

The number and kind of tests to be made often constitute a problem. A review of appropriate chapters in the Manual will usually guide the analyst to a proper conclusion.

Sample and reagent containers should be selected with care. Choice of clear or colored, soft or Pyrex glass; plastic or carbon containers; or stopper material can influence accuracy. Transfer lines in analytical equipment should be selected with similar care. These should be of the shortest possible length and chosen to avoid absorption or dissolution of constituents or contamination. For example, phenols and hydrocarbons are readily absorbed by rubber tubing. Sulfur dioxide and some other compounds tend to react with the plasticizers used in various synthetic plastic formulations.

199

In water analyses[1] which include chemical and biological evaluations, the cleanliness of the glassware is of utmost importance. Since concentrations of some constituents may be reported in parts per billion, even slight traces of extraneous material can cause appreciable errors. For example, many cleaners leave detergent and phosphate residues on glassware unless it has been thoroughly rinsed. If adventitious substances are present and are either a required part of the analysis or happen to interfere with the method, errors are inevitable.

Glassware may be segregated for specific uses, but it is better to treat the entire lot for the severest case. Spot checks on reagent water blanks carried through an analytical scheme would be highly illuminating in some laboratories.[2]

There should be occasional checks on known samples to establish relative accuracies between laboratories and among analysts in a laboratory. It is also desirable to establish day-to-day variations. Wherever statistical aid is available it should be used. At least two separate duplicates should be analyzed in every determination, with additional replication in special cases. Of course, too many replicates are a waste of time and material and do not in themselves insure accuracy.

Other sources of error are infrequent calibration or standardization of analytical equipment such as spectrophotometers, pH meters, and other instruments. Calibration curves should be checked periodically. New dye lots should always be checked because batch-to-batch variations may shift calibration curves. Thermometers should not be assumed to be correct but should be compared with one known to read true.

Laboratory safety may seem unrelated to analytical accuracy but this is not the case. It has a bearing on the performance of analyst and equipment. There are many subtle dangers associated with handling chemicals. The analyst must be prepared to recognize these. This might be illustrated by the use of an azide in an analysis. If heavy-metal ions are present there is danger of forming highly unstable metal azides; these azides are explosive when dry. Some solvents have a cumulative effect and adequate ventilation is essential. Some laboratories use automatic burets to transfer all acids. This eliminates unnecessary handling and the possibility of rapid addition to water, which might cause a corrosive fluid to spatter. Many other examples might be given but it is sufficient to note that awareness of safety and toxicology should be required of every analyst.

The most careful analysis is useless if the sample was not representative. Changes might be occurring even while a sample is taken. Provision should be made in advance for proper sampling equipment and procedure. Special problems are presented by mixtures that tend to stratify. Concentrations of oil and dissolved oxygen often vary with depth; an adequate number of samples from a series of depths should be composited to get a representative sample. If hydrocarbons that are partly or wholly immiscible are involved, then separate samples should be taken. The total contents of the sample containers should be extracted for each analysis (Method D 1340). Other compounds such as hydrogen sulfide require separate sampling and immediate preservation. ASTM methods on sampling provide further details and precautions.[3]

The analyst must exercise care and

---

[1] Scheme for Analysis of Industrial Water and Industrial Waste Water (D 1256).
[2] Specifications for Reagent Water (D 1193).

[3] Specifications for Equipment for Sampling Industrial Water and Steam (D 1192); Method of Sampling Water from Boilers (D 860); Methods of Sampling Industrial Water (D 510); Method of Sampling Steam (D 1066); Method of Field Sampling of Water-Formed Deposits (D 887); Methods of Sampling Homogeneous Industrial Waste Water (D 1496).

judgment in reporting results.[4] Explanatory references are necessary to insure completeness, to detail the meaning of quantitative data, and to facilitate comparison of the results of one experimenter or laboratory with another. For example, odor thresholds should be accompanied by a record of the temperature of analysis, and biochemical oxygen demand (BOD) should be reported with both time of incubation and temperature. Any departures in analytical procedure must be recorded and reported. If some of the constituents were not measured directly, this should be noted, for example, dissolved solids (by difference). A description of the material before and after sampling and the method of sampling must be given in special terms of the standards.

Analytical results must be reported in a manner that will not imply a fictitious significance. If numerical values are improperly reported they may lead to serious misinterpretation. The reported value should contain but one digital value that is not absolutely precise. This digit is the last one to the right. A weight of 4.7165 g implies a precise measurement accurate to $\pm 0.000n$, whereas 4.7 g would be the reported value for weighing the same object on a single-beam balance accurate to $\pm 0.n$ g. The value n is used to designate the least significant figure. The plus-or-minus sign describes a variance inherent in the measuring process. The usual way of describing this variability is by the root-mean-square of the variance, known as the standard deviation.

In making calculations the result will not have significance greater than the least significant value used in the computation. For example, 6.250 times 1.1 equals 6.8750, but must be rounded to 6.9. The method of rounding dictates that if values of 5 or greater are dropped, the preceding digit is raised by one. Values of 4 or less are dropped without any change in the preceding digit, for example, 1.008 times 4.3 equals 4.3344 which is rounded to 4.3 in practical application.

Zeros are never added to values to the right of the decimal point if the precision is not warranted. A temptation often exists to balance the columns of numbers in tabulating results. For example, assume a water analysis:

pH. 6.83
Aluminum as Al, ppm. 0.25
Nitrate as NO$_3$, ppm. 6.5

These values tell the reader something about the methods that were used. The pH reading of 6.83 indicates the use of a precise potentiometric technique. A less precise instrument would give a result reported as 6.8, while a color comparison procedure would probably be estimated as 7. The accuracy of the aluminum and nitrate methods are 0.01 and 0.5, respectively. Adding a zero to 6.5 to show 6.50 would be improper. Other examples will occur to the laboratory investigator. No attempt is made here to discuss relative errors but references[5, 6] exist which present the mathematical aspects.

It would be improper to neglect a statement concerning training, for it is proper training of the analyst that guarantees accuracy and precision in his work and confidence in the results obtained. This means not only technological, but housekeeping and safety, training. A well-informed analyst who understands the importance and objectives of his work is the chief asset of any laboratory.

---

[4] Method of Reporting Results of Analysis of Industrial Water and Industrial Waste Water (D 596); Method of Reporting Results of Examination and Analysis of Water-Formed Deposits (D 933); Definitions of Terms Relating to Industrial Water and Industrial Waste Water (D 1129).

[5] Kaiser S. Kunz, "Numerical Analysis," McGraw-Hill Book Co., New York, N. Y., 1957, p. 362.

[6] Proposed Procedure for Determination of Precision of Committee D-19 Methods, which appears in this publication.

PROPOSED PROCEDURE FOR DETERMINATION OF PRECISION OF COMMITTEE D-19 METHODS[1,2]

This proposed procedure is published as information only. Comments are solicited and should be addressed to the American Society for Testing and Materials, 1916 Race St., Philadelphia 3, Pa.

Precision[3]

11. (a) Each method of analysis, determination, or measurement requires a statement of the precision attainable by the method. For Committee D-19 methods this statement must conform with the definition of precision in the Definitions of Terms Relating to Industrial Water and Industrial Waste Water (ASTM Designation: D 1129).[4] This means that the task group proposing a new or revised method must carry out suitable planned trials from which the precision (over-all and single-operator estimated standard deviations) of the method can be calculated. This method provides general guidance to task groups in planning and conducting such a determination of precision. Distribution of identical, stable samples is essential for this general plan; suggestions for methods for which such samples are impossible are also given.

Considerable pilot work on a method must precede the determination of its precision. This pilot work should explore such variables as reaction time and temperature, concentration of reagents, interferences, calibration, and sample size. All potentially significant factors must be prescribed and controlled closely in advance because cooperative identification and definition of them can be expensive. Disregard of such factors may introduce so much variation among cooperators that results are misleading or inconclusive. Only after a proposed method has been tried, proved and reduced to unequivocal written form should a determination of its precision be attempted.

(b) It is desired to develop a statement of precision of a test method that indicates the contribution to over-all variation of selected causes such as concentration, laboratory, operators, apparatus, and others that may or have been shown to have strong effects on the results. Since any method can be tried in only a limited number of applications, the standard deviation calculated from the results of any planned program can be only an estimate of the universe standard deviation. For this reason the symbol s (sample standard deviation) is used here. The total standard deviation, s_T,

---

[1] This proposed procedure is under the jurisdiction of the ASTM Committee D-19 on Industrial Water. A list of members may be found in the ASTM Year Book.

[2] Published as information, December 1962. This procedure is part of a new edition of the "Guide for the Administration and Operation of ASTM Committee D-19."

[3] For further information see the Report of Committee E-11 on Statistical Methods Preprint No. 65, and the Report of Committee E-15 on Analysis and Testing of Industrial Chemicals, Preprint No. 67, Sixty-fourth Annual Meeting, Am. Soc. Testing Mats., June 25–30, 1961; and A. J. Duncan, "Quality Control and Industrial Statistics," Rev. Ed., Richard D. Irwin, Inc., Holmwood, Ill. (1959).

[4] Appears in this publication.

of the planned sample is the result of many sources of variation—both recognized and unknown. The mathematical relationship is:

$$s_T^2 = s_A^2 + s_C^2 + s_O^2 + s_L^2 \cdots + s_Y^2 \dots\dots\dots\dots\dots\dots\dots\dots (1)$$

where the subscripts have the following significance: T = total, A = apparatus, C = cooperating laboratory, O = operator, L = level of material, and Y = unknown.

A determination of precision requires that data be provided to assess the relative effects of important sources of variation. This is most economically accomplished by following the principles of statistical design, which can also be applied so as to permit estimation of the magnitude of the effect of these sources of variances.

(c) Four variables must be included in virtually every planned determination of precision: *apparatus, laboratory, operator,* and *level,* because these items cannot be identical for all users of a method. Definition of *apparatus* and *laboratory* is superfluous. If the apparatus required is unique or of such a kind that no laboratory could be expected to have more than one, *laboratory* and *apparatus* variables cannot be separated but must be pooled in the *laboratory* variable. *Operator* designates the individual analysts who participate in the program in the several cooperating laboratories. *Level* of material refers to the amount or concentration measured by the method, since it is important to know whether precision is constant throughout the range of applicability or if it is related to level. Any other variables which pilot work has shown cannot be controlled closely enough to be insignificant must be added to the above basic ones. Time or day of reaction and quality of atmosphere are variables that may be significant.

When the variables to be explored have been defined, decisions must be made as to the number of each variable to be employed. Each must be employed at least in duplicate. Larger numbers, while statistically desirable, increase the labor and expense of the project. All alternate *apparatus* in each laboratory must be used in the evaluation of a method. If only usual laboratory apparatus (glassware, oven, balance, etc.) is required, at least two such arrays should be segregated in each cooperating laboratory and each employed by each operator for a series of determinations. (This may seem extreme, but it is a sensible precaution against unsuspected error from a familiar source.) A minimum of three *laboratories* should be selected; more are desirable. While there is no theoretical upper limit, the practicalities of sample distribution and of collection and analysis of results suggest that additional returns rapidly diminish above about eight cooperating laboratories. However, the use of a larger number of laboratories and single operators will provide a better estimate of the universal standard deviation of the method. The necessity for the same number of *operators* in each laboratory may set a limit of two. If operator skill and experience with the method are significant a larger number should be provided. If pilot work suggests that precision is linear with level, at least three levels of material should be included; more levels should be analyzed if precision was shown or is expectd to be other than constant or linear. Generally, *day* will be a random variable and should be treated as such in the planning of tests and in the statistical analysis of the data. However, readings within each laboratory at two quite different times or days are preferable. If time or day has been shown to influence the measurements, close control over the date and time of analysis will be essential. Similar decisions on numbers of other agreed-upon variables must be made by the task group.

After the variables and number of each have been determined, the number of determinations to be made under each set of conditions can be calculated. This number, called the number of *replicates*, must satisfy the following inequality:

$$r > 1 + \frac{30}{P} \quad\dots\dots\dots\dots\dots\dots\dots\dots\dots\dots\dots\dots (2)$$

in which r is the number of replicates and P is the product of the number of the several variables. For example, with duplicate *apparatus* and *operators*, five *laboratories*, and three *levels*:

$$P = 2 \times 2 \times 5 \times 3 = 60$$

$$r > 1 + 30/60$$

Thus, two replicates must be tested by the method under each condition of the program. If *apparatus* and *laboratory* variables were pooled, or if only two laboratories were participating, the formula would require triplicate determinations by each operator. The formula prescribes a *minimum* number of replicates (never less than duplicate) and a larger number is statistically desirable, subject only to the practical limitations of cost and time mentioned above.

(*d*) A copy of the method under investigation, written instructions for carrying out his part of the program, and the necessary samples for test should be supplied to each operator. No supplementary instructions or explanations, such as by telephone or from a task group member within a cooperating laboratory, should be supplied to one participant if not to all. Distribution should be made from, and operator's reports should be submitted to, one place—preferably the same one. Sample containers should be clearly marked with a code, informative to the distributors but not informative to the operator. Samples should be sized to supply only the predetermined number of replicates (with reasonable allowance for pipetting, rinsing, etc.), as a precaution against trial runs or post-selection of reported data by operators. There should be a separate set of samples for each operator so that operators within a laboratory do not draw from a common supply nor consult effectively with one another concerning results. Sample concentrations should not be near limits of sensitivity or easily surmized values (1, 5, etc.). The above are requirements for statistical independence of results and are not intended to asperse the professional integrity or morals of operators.

(*e*) *All* results must be reported and the data tabulated for review by the task group. A relatively rapid and efficient method of review is to prepare control charts for each of the variables included in the program. Alternatively, the contribution of the several variables can be estimated by calculating the standard deviations of each: s_A, s_L, s_O, etc. A more efficient and informative method is an analysis of variance performed by calculating the mean sum of squares for the variables. Regardless of the method used absolutely no data should be discarded and none disregarded unless the control charts or other valid statistical criteria show them clearly to be erroneous or aberrant. Control charts and variance analyses may be misleading in some cases. Statistical references[5] provide valid criteria for excluding data from precision evaluations.

---

[5] W. J. Dixon, "Processing Data, etc.," *Biometrics*, Vol. 9, pp. 74–89 (1953), and the Recommended Practice for Dealing with Outlying Observations (ASTM Designation: E 178), 1967 Book of ASTM Standards, Part 30.

The standard deviation of the entire array of reviewed and acceptable data is calculated to provide the value to be stated as the *precision* of the method. Several equations are available for calculation of the standard deviation, the root mean square of all deviations from the arithmetic mean. A convenient one is:

$$s_T = \sqrt{\frac{\sum\limits_{i=1}^{n} (X_i - \bar{X})^2}{n - 1}}$$

or, the more convenient form for an automatic desk calculator:

$$s_T = \sqrt{\frac{\sum X_i^2 - \dfrac{(\sum X_i)^2}{n}}{n - 1}} \dotfill (3)$$

where X_i = individual n values whose average is $\bar{X}$.

If statistical tests show that precision varies significantly with *level* of material, an over-all standard deviation may be a misleading index of precision. In such a case the mean, $\bar{X}_L$, and standard deviation, s_L, should be calculated for each reported level. A plot of s_L versus $\bar{X}_L$ will indicate quickly any significant relationship. Unless the several plotted points fit a smooth curve of considerable slope, there is no significant relationship requiring mention. If s_L increases linearly with $\bar{X}_L$, it may be possible to transform the data so that the precision statement can be made in percentage of the amount determined. If the relationship is inverse or curvilinear, it would be better to make a precision statement such as:

The precision of the method varies with the quantity being determined, as expressed by the following equation (or as shown in Fig. *Y*).

Figure *Y* then would be the smooth curve of standard deviation versus the mean level, possibly on semilogarithmic paper if the range of applicability is wide but without data points. The use of an equation is the preferred method of expressing variation of precision with level when the relationship is other than constant or a percentage of the level.

The results of a single operator, s_O, should agree more closely than those between operators or laboratories. If the variation contributed by a single operator is relatively small compared to that contributed by other sources, this fact will be helpful to users of the method and must be conveyed to them. Having only s_T as a guide, such a user might be satisfied with a degree of agreement among his own results that would be mediocre or suspicious were s_O but a small fraction of s_T or when $s_O < s_T/2$. If the precision of a single operator is important, a suggested wording of the statement is:

The precision of this method is Z (rounded value of s_T in ppm, per cent, or other unit). The results of a single operator may be expected to have a precision of Z' (rounded value of s_O in the same units).

To determine s_O, the mean and standard deviation should be calculated for all of the results reported by each operator for each level. The individual operator standard deviations then should be squared and summed, the sum of squares divided by the number of operators, and the square root of the quotient extracted. Unless the resulting value for s_O is half, or less, that for s_T, the difference scarcely is worth mention in the method.

As stated in the first paragraph, when distribution of identical, stable samples is impossible, the round-robin method of determining the over-all standard deviation cannot be used. Devices such as calculating a time-dependent regression curve or distribution of samples in sealed ampoules might be employed. However, such strata-

TABLE I.—ROUND-ROBIN TEST DATA.
(Partial Data for Determination of Phosphate in Industrial Water and Industrial Waste Water)

LABORATORY 1

Sample	Operator 1				Operator 2			
	Day 1		Day 2		Day 1		Day 2	
	Run 1	Run 2	Run 1	Run 2	Run 1	Run 2	Run 1	Run 2
	X_1	X_2	X_3	X_4	X_5	X_6	X_7	X_8
1..........	1.18	1.23	1.19	1.22	1.24	1.23	1.24	1.24
2..........	0.416	0.419	0.425	0.416	0.407	0.407	0.417	0.407
3..........	0.097	0.097	0.103	0.103	0.117	0.117	0.127	0.117

LABORATORY 2

Sample	Operator 1				Operator 2			
	Day 1		Day 2		Day 1		Day 2	
	Run 1	Run 2	Run 1	Run 2	Run 1	Run 2	Run 1	Run 2
	X_9	X_{10}	X_{11}	X_{12}	X_{13}	X_{14}	X_{15}	X_{16}
1..........	1.12	1.12	1.12	1.13	1.20	1.22	1.19	1.17
2..........	0.35	0.37	0.37	0.37	0.41	0.42	0.41	0.40
3..........	0.12	0.10	0.10	0.10	0.11	0.10	0.11	0.10

LABORATORY 3

Sample	Operator 1				Operator 2			
	Day 1		Day 2		Day 1		Day 2	
	Run 1	Run 2	Run 1	Run 2	Run 1	Run 2	Run 1	Run 2
	X_{17}	X_{18}	X_{19}	X_{20}	X_{21}	X_{22}	X_{23}	X_{24}
1..........	1.17	1.19	1.16	1.16	1.18	1.18	1.15	1.17
2..........	0.40	0.41	0.38	0.40	0.39	0.38	0.39	0.39
3..........	0.10	0.11	0.10	0.10	0.13	0.12	0.11	0.12

gems are bound to introduce uncertainty where assurance is being sought, so that it is probably more effective to approach the desired end from the opposite direction.

Referring again to Eq 1, the total variance is the sum of that contributed by each of several factors or variables, known and unknown. When the total cannot be estimated over-all, as by a round-robin program, the factor of next greatest practical importance is the *operator* or *laboratory* precision. A reasonably reliable estimate of s_o can be obtained by several cooperating laboratories carrying out a prescribed series of determinations upon samples locally prepared in accordance with task-group instructions. The individual operator standard deviations can be combined as described above to obtain s_O. This plan can also be used for preliminary single-laboratory studies of separate effects of temperature, chemical interferences, and instrument variation when inclusion of multiple variables in a comprehensive round-robin test is likely to complicate seriously the data collection and evaluation. The resulting precision statement would be something like the following:

The results obtained by a single analyst using this method should have a precision of Z' (rounded value of s_O). The over-all precision of the method is not this good, but it cannot be stated exactly.

Variance attributable to apparatus, level, and similar sources also could be estimated by such a cooperative effort. However, s_C and s_T are unattainable this way,

TABLE II.—TABULATION OF SUMS.

Sample	True ppm	ΣX_i	ΣX_i^2	n
1 (L_1)...............	1.2	28.400	33.6414	24
2 (L_2)...............	0.4	9.554	3.812	24
3 (L_3)...............	0.1	2.608	0.285732	24

$$s_{L_1} = \sqrt{\frac{\Sigma(X_i^2) - \frac{(\Sigma X_i)^2}{n}}{n-1}}$$

$$s_{L_1} = \sqrt{\frac{33.6414 - \frac{(28.4)^2}{24}}{23}} = 0.039 \text{ ppm}$$

$$s_{L_2} = \sqrt{\frac{3.812 - \frac{(9.554)^2}{24}}{23}} = 0.0196 \text{ ppm}$$

$$s_{L_3} = \sqrt{\frac{0.2857 - \frac{(2.608)^2}{24}}{23}} = 0.0075 \text{ ppm}$$

so that the task group must decide how much labor is appropriate to achieve a fuller answer which cannot be complete.

Where instability of water components and properties make cooperative testing impracticable, use the following wording:

The precision and accuracy of this method was not universally tested. The transient nature of the equilibria involved and the pronounced variation in the characteristics of different waters preclude interlaboratory tests for precision and accuracy.

(f) Make the statistical evaluations in the manner illustrated by the following examples:

Sample Precision Calculation Using Partial Data from Interlaboratory Round-Robin Test (Phosphate Determination)

Background Information:

The purpose of this data analysis is to determine the extent to which interlaboratory agreement was affected by level of phosphate concentration, random day-to-day variations of test conditions, operator-sample interactions, and test equipment factors.

An analysis of variance is included for information. This is a summary technique which separates the total observed variation into component variations assignable to the various sources mentioned above.

Sample Data:

The data (in parts per million of phosphate) for three samples in three laboratories, each with two operators and two days of testing are given in Table I.

Calculation of Precision or Standard Deviation (s):

The examples are intended to show the rudimentary techniques of determining the order of precision attainable when a standard method is applied universally or individually and do not explore the many facets of a complete statistical analysis. If the 72 pieces of data in Table I had been obtained on a single sample (one concentration of phosphate), it would be desirable to treat them as a single series $(X_1$ to X_{72} in determining s_T by Eq 3.

Where several samples of different concentrations make up the series, as in this case, it is more informative to determine s_L^2 for each concentration (each sample) and then to determine s_L for each level or s_T from the average s_L^2 value if precision does not vary with level. For this reason the data of Table I were treated as three series of 24 items each for the calculations given in Table II.

The basic equation, Eq 3, is applied after calculating the sum and the sum of the squares of the individual items for each series as shown in Table II.

Since precision is not constant or proportional to the level of material, an equation for the linear function should be calculated as suggested in Section 11(e). When the precision is constant for all levels tested the over-all standard deviation is the average standard deviation calculated by pooling the sums of squares as follows:

$$s_T = \sqrt{\frac{(n_{L_1} \times s_{L_1}^2) + (n_{L_2} \times s_{L_2}^2) + (n_{L_3} \times s_{L_3}^2)}{n_{L_1} + n_{L_2} + n_{L_3}}} \quad\dots\dots\dots\dots\dots (4)$$

Operator Precision:

The operator precision is calculated in the same manner by pooling the sums of squares obtained from single operators, s_O^2 , for each level.

Single-Laboratory Precision:[6]

The single-laboratory precision, s_C , is a useful tool where round-robin testing is impracticable, to evaluate a method prior to round-robin testing or to compare the precision of two methods. The conditions of test generally involve only one operator, one laboratory, and one apparatus with repeated runs of aliquots from one large sample or from several samples if the effect of concentration is to be determined. The precision is calculated using Eq 3, except that s_C is found instead of s_T .

All quantities computed from a small collection of data are only estimates of the properties of the system which was the source of the data. Consequently, a limited number of data will not approach the true standard deviation, σ, as closely as a larger number of tests, and the information must be used accordingly.

---

[6] For further information see Table I of the Recommended Practice for Interlaboratory Testing of Textile Materials (ASTM Designation: D 990), 1966 Book of ASTM Standards, Part 24, and standard text books on statistical methods.

Probability Level or Confidence in Sample Averages:

NOTE 1.—This determination is useful but not essential.

A probability level of P per cent refers to the expectation that the μ value does not differ by more than some stated amount from the estimate made from the data. The $\bar{X}$ and s values are only estimates of the μ and σ which would be approached as $n \to \infty$. The average or arithmetic mean $\bar{X}$ is obtained by dividing the sum of the observations by the number of observations. It is an estimate of μ, a quantity to which the average will converge as the number of measurements increases. The

TABLE III.—DEGREES OF FREEDOM AND EXPECTED MEAN SQUARE.
(For Data in Table I)

Source of Variance	Degrees of Freedom, DF	Expected Mean Square, $E(MS)$
Laboratories (3)	$3 - 1 = 2$	$\sigma_r^2 + 2\sigma_D^2 + 2(2)\sigma_O^2 + 2(2)(2)\sigma_C^2$
Operators (2 per laboratory)	$3(2 - 1) = 3$	$\sigma_r^2 + 2\sigma_D^2 + 2(2)\sigma_O^2$
Days (2 per operator)	$3(2)(2 - 1) = 6$	$\sigma_r^2 + 2\sigma_D^2$
Runs (2 per day)	$3(2)(2)(2 - 1) = 12$	σ_r^2
Total	$3(2)(2)(2) - 1 = 23$	

TABLE IV.—SUMMATION.

Item	Laboratory 1				Laboratory 2				Laboratory 3			
	Operator 1		Operator 2		Operator 1		Operator 2		Operator 1		Operator 2	
	Day 1	Day 2	Day 1	Day 2	Day 1	Day 2	Day 1	Day 2	Day 1	Day 2	Day 1	Day 2
Run 1	1.18	1.19	1.24	1.24	1.12	1.12	1.20	1.19	1.17	1.16	1.18	1.15
Run 2	1.23	1.22	1.23	1.24	1.12	1.13	1.22	1.17	1.19	1.16	1.18	1.17
Sums for days	2.41	2.41	2.47	2.48	2.24	2.25	2.42	2.36	2.36	2.32	2.36	2.32
Sums for operators	4.82		4.95		4.49		4.78		4.68		4.68	
Sums for labs	9.77				9.27				9.36			
Over-all sum	28.40											

quantity μ may or may not be the true value. This depends on the presence or absence of systematic errors or bias. The standard deviation, s, is a measure of the variability of a set of results. The true standard deviation, σ, is a parameter of the whole population. Once the standard deviation of an experimental setup is found, the precision can be stated and confidence limits applied to an average value.

It is informative to place limits about the quantity $\bar{X}$ to include the unknown quantity μ. A probability level may be selected such that in P per cent of the cases μ would be included in the limits placed about $\bar{X}$. The confidence limits are calculated by adding to and subtracting from $\bar{X}$ the quantity $ts/\sqrt{n}$. The t values are taken from t-tables available in any statistical text. The value $s/\sqrt{n}$ is called the standard deviation of the mean $\bar{X}$ and is identified as $s_{\bar{X}}$. It is, in effect, the standard deviation of the distribution of the sample means. Sample means tend to be normally distributed.

$$\text{Confidence interval} = \bar{X} \pm ts_{\bar{x}} = \bar{X} \pm \frac{ts}{\sqrt{n}}.$$

ANALYSIS OF VARIANCE

This analysis is presented as information for those interested in determining the relative effects of all recognized sources of variation. However, this powerful tool which can point to the source of weakness in an analytical method, need not be invoked. Only the data for Sample 1 in Table I is used in the following example since Sample 2 and 3 data would be subjected to the same statistical treatment. The nested classification of the data and no interaction effects make for simple computational and interpretive procedures. In this analysis the degree of freedom, DF, the sums of squares, SS, the mean square, MS, and the F-ratio are calculated for each source of variance.

TABLE V.—ANALYSIS OF VARIANCE OF SAMPLE 1 ROUND-ROBIN TEST DATA
(Data From Table I)

Source of Variance	Sum of Squares, SS	Degrees of Freedom, DF	Mean Square, MS	F-Ratio	F-Value at 95 Per Cent Confidence Level	
Laboratory...............	0.0177	2	0.0088	2.1	9.55	NS[a]
Operators...............	0.0126	3	0.0042	17.5	3.16	HS[b]
Days...................	0.0018	6	0.00030	1.36	3.00	NS[a]
Runs..................	0.0026	12	0.00022			
Total................	0.0347	23				

[a] NS = not significant.
[b] HS = highly significant.

(1) The degree of freedom for each source of variance generally is one less than the number of factors involved therein. However, this may not necessarily be true for each case and consulting a statistical reference is recommended. For Sample 1 data of Table I the calculations of the degrees of freedom are as shown in Table III.

For most analytical methods the time or day-to-day effects are not due to calendar days on which the analyses are performed, but rather to time effects which are random in nature. The model for the expected mean square, E(MS), of an infinite population where time is a random effect and a nested classification prevails, is shown in Table III, where σ_r^2 = residual mean square, σ_D^2 = day mean square, σ_O^2 = operator mean square, and σ_C^2 = laboratory mean square. The actual use of the expected mean square will be evident later on in the example. The subsequent sequence of events should be followed to obtain information for the analysis of variance.

(2) First determine the computational sums of squares by summing the items contributory to each source of variance as shown in Table IV.

(3) Use the information in Table IV to calculate the sum of squares, SS, for each source of variance as follows:

(a) Square the sum for each of the three laboratories, add, divide by the number of items, n, for each laboratory and subtract the square of the over-all sum divided by the total number of items:

$$\text{Laboratory SS} = \frac{(9.77)^2 + (9.27)^2 + (9.36)^2}{8} - \frac{(28.40)^2}{24}$$

$$= 33.6244 - 33.6067 = 0.0177$$

(*b*) Square the sum for each operator, add, divide by the number of items, and subtract the sum of the squares for each laboratory divided by the number of items:

$$\text{Operator SS} = \frac{(4.82)^2 + (4.95)^2 + \cdots + (4.68)^2}{4} - \frac{(9.77)^2 + (9.27)^2 + (9.36)^2}{8}$$

$$= 33.6370 - 33.6244 = 0.0126$$

(*c*) Sum the squares for each day, divide by the number of items, and subtract the quotient from the sum of the squares for each operator divided by the number of items:

$$\text{Day SS} = \frac{(2.41)^2 + (2.41)^2 + \cdots + (2.32)^2}{2} - \frac{(4.82)^2 + (4.95)^2 + \cdots + (4.68)^2}{4}$$

$$= 33.6388 - 33.6370 = 0.0018$$

(*d*) Sum the squares for each run, divide by the number of items, and subtract the quotient from the sum of squares for each day divided by the number of items:

$$\text{Run SS} = \frac{(1.18)^2 + (1.23)^2 + \cdots + (1.17)^2}{1} - \frac{(2.41)^2 + (2.41)^2 + \cdots + (2.32)^2}{2}$$

$$= 33.6414 - 33.6388 = 0.0026$$

(*e*) Calculate the total sum of squares by summing the squares of the sums for each run and subtracting the number obtained by dividing the square of the over-all sum by the total number of items:

$$\text{Total SS} = 33.6414 - 33.6067 = 0.0347$$

(*4*) Obtain the mean square, MS, for each variance by dividing the sum of squares by the degrees of freedom for each as calculated in Table III. Table V shows the values from these calculations.

(*5*) After recording the F-values obtained from tables available in any quality control or statistical handbook, compare the F-ratio obtained from the data to the F-value for the particular confidence level selected. If the calculated F-ratio exceeds the F-value there is a significant difference for that source of variance tested. The magnitude of significance is indicated by the amount which the F-ratio exceeds the F-value. Calculate the F-ratios and compare as follows:

$$\frac{\text{MS (days)}}{\text{MS (residual)}} = \frac{0.00030}{0.00022} = 1.36$$

which is less than $F_{0.95}(6, 12) = 3.00$ and there was no significant variance between days. Since there was no significant difference, the Day SS and Run SS (residual) can be pooled to test operator difference.

$$\text{Residual MS} = \frac{0.0018 + 0.0026}{6 + 12} = 0.00024$$

and

$$\frac{\text{MS (operators)}}{\text{MS (residual)}} = \frac{0.0042}{0.00024} = 17.5$$

which is larger than $F_{0.95}$ (3, 18) = 3.16 and the variance between operators is shown to be highly significant. Since a significant difference exists between operators, use the mean square for operators to test for laboratory variance instead of pooling the variances for runs, days, and operators.

$$\frac{\text{MS (laboratories)}}{\text{MS (operators)}} = \frac{0.0088}{0.0042} = 2.1$$

which is less than the 95th percentile value of F with 2 and 3 degrees of freedom which is $F_{0.95}$ (2, 3) = 9.55 and the variance between laboratories was not significant.

Also the analysis of variance for the data of Sample 1, Table I, shows that for a fixed sample size the minimum variance of $\bar{X}$ will be obtained when the determinations are distributed over as many operators (or laboratories if only one operator per laboratory) as possible and will not be significantly lowered by increasing the number of replicates that each operator analyses. Although the analysis of variance indicated that there was no significant difference between laboratories, the few degrees of freedom, 3, add uncertainty to the conclusion that there is no significant difference between laboratories. Primarily, the analysis proved that the hypothesis holds only for this particular case. This uncertainty caused by a minimal number of laboratories participating is a good argument for maximizing the number of cooperating laboratories in any round-robin test of a method.

(*g*) The Results Adviser is available for consultation on all phases of planning cooperative tests, statistical treatment of test data, and expression of precision and accuracy of methods. However, as his title indicates, he is an adviser and as such is not responsible for actual design of experiment or reduction of raw data to usable form. These primary steps must be performed by the task group with the help of the Guide.

(*h*) In seeking advice or approval of proposed round-robin test plans, submit information on the following to the Results Adviser:

(*1*) Number of participating laboratories,

(*2*) Number of operators involved,

(*3*) Number of samples,

(*4*) Number of determinations per sample and per operator,

(*5*) Number of levels (concentrations, etc.) to be tested, and

(*6*) Variety of test equipment expected, if considered pertinent.

(*i*) In seeking approval of supporting data and precision and accuracy calculations, provide the Results Adviser with:

(*1*) All test data resulting from the cooperative tests,

(*2*) All statistical calculations, and

(*3*) Any background information that may have influenced the results.

NOTE 2.—For other suggestions on reporting test data, reference may be made to the ASTM Manual on Quality Control of Materials.[7] This manual gives, in addition to a brief discussion of the theoretical aspects of the measurement of precision, useful examples and convenient short-cut methods of calculation. See also the Recommended Practices for Designating Significant Places in Specified Limiting Values (ASTM Designation: E 29).[8]

---

[7] *ASTM STP No. 15-c*, January, 1951, available as a separate publication.
[8] 1967 Book of ASTM Standards, Part 30.

Standard Classification of

WATER USED IN MILLING OF PORCELAIN ENAMEL[1]

ASTM Designation: C 375 – 58

ADOPTED, 1958

This Standard of the American Society for Testing and Materials is issued under the fixed designation C 375; the final number indicates the year of original adoption as standard or, in the case of revision, the year of last revision.

Scope

1. This classification covers water used in the milling of porcelain enamel frit.

Classification

2. Three classes of water are covered, based on the maximum impurity analyses as defined in Table I. For porcelain enamel frits, Class A water should cause no difficulties in the production of a high quality finish. Class B water may be used by slight compensations in processing.

Mill addition water falling into Class C should be treated before use in order to preclude faulty enamel production.

Methods of Analysis

3. The elements and properties listed in Table I shall be determined in accordance with the following methods:

TABLE I.—CLASSIFICATION OF WATER FOR USE IN MILLING PORCELAIN ENAMEL.

Class	Maximum Concentrations, ppm									pH
	Calcium	Magnesium	Iron	Manganese	Sulfate	Chloride	Hardness	Total Solids	Bicarbonate	
A.................	31	7.5	0.30	0.005	25	13	38.5	147	117	7.6
B.................	43	10.0	0.62	1.05	102	18	53.0	198	86	7.5
C	53	18.0	0.43	...	105	18	71.0	284	78	7.3

(a) *Sampling.*—Methods of Sampling Industrial Water (ASTM Designation: D 510).[2]

(b) *Bicarbonate.*—Methods of Test for Total Carbon Dioxide and Calculation of the Carbonate and Bicarbonate Ions

[1] Under the standardization procedure of the Society, this classification is under the jurisdiction of the ASTM Committee C-22 on Porcelain Enamel. A list of members may be found in the ASTM Year Book.

[2] Appears in this publication.

in Industrial Water (ASTM Designation: D 513).[2]

(c) *Calcium and Magnesium.*—Method of Test for Calcium Ion and Magnesium Ion in Industrial Water (ASTM Designation: D 511).[2]

(d) *Chloride.*—Methods of Test for Chloride Ion in Industrial Water and Industrial Waste Water (ASTM Designation: D 512).[2]

(e) *Hardness.*—Methods of Test for Hardness in Industrial Water (ASTM Designation: D 1126).[2]

(f) *Iron.*—Method of Test for Iron in Industrial Water and Industrial Waste Water (ASTM Designation: D 1068).[2]

(g) *Manganese.*—Method of Test for Manganese in Industrial Water and Industrial Waste Water (ASTM Designation: D 858).[2]

(h) *pH.*—Method of Test for pH of Industrial Water and Industrial Waste Water (ASTM Designation: D 1293).[2]

(i) *Sulfate.*—Methods of Test for Sulfate Ion in Industrial Water and Industrial Waste Water (ASTM Designation: D 516).[2]

(j) *Total Solids.*—Methods of Test for Suspended and Dissolved Solids in Industrial Water (ASTM Designation: D 1888).[2]

APPROVED AS
USA STANDARD Z111.1-1964 (2nd ed.)
BY USA STANDARDS INSTITUTE
UDC628.17:628.515

Tentative Methods of
SAMPLING INDUSTRIAL WATER[1]

ASTM Designation: D 510 – 64 T

ISSUED, 1952; REVISED, 1954, 1955, 1962, 1964

These Tentative Methods have been approved by the sponsoring committee and accepted by the Society in accordance with established procedures, for use pending adoption as standard. Suggestions for revisions should be addressed to the Society at 1916 Race St., Philadelphia 3, Pa.

Scope

1. (*a*) These methods cover the sampling of industrial water and industrial waste water.[2, 3] The following methods are included:

	Sections
Sampling for Chemical or Physical Tests	4 to 16
Sampling for Biological Tests	17 to 31
Sampling for Radioactivity Determinations	32 to 41

(*b*) Normal variations in processes and in equipment from plant to plant preclude the possibility of specifying standard methods of sampling that are applicable in all cases. Definite principles have, however, been established as a basis for the formulation of procedures for sampling which are applicable in general and probably applicable in most specific cases. Where modifications of these procedures are necessary, they may be made by the exercise of trained judgment in each individual case.

(*c*) Changes which may be necessary in these procedures under specific circumstances may be made in any particular case by mutual agreement of the parties concerned.

Summary of Methods

2. The following general rules are applicable to all sampling methods:

(*a*) The samples must represent the conditions existing at the point taken.

(*b*) The samples must be of sufficient volume and must be taken frequently enough to permit reproducibility of testing requisite for the desired objective, as

---

[1] Under the standardization procedure of the Society, these methods are under the jurisdiction of the ASTM Committee D-19 on Industrial Water. A list of members may be found in the ASTM Year Book.

[2] Directions for sampling water intended for sanitary and domestic use may be found in "Standard Methods for the Examination of Water and Wastewater," Am. Public Health Assn., New York, N. Y., current edition.

[3] "Methods for the Collection and Analysis of Water Samples," Geological Survey Water Supply Paper 1454, U. S. Government Printing Office (1960).

215

TABLE I.—VOLUME OF SAMPLE REQUIRED FOR DETERMINATION OF THE VARIOUS CONSTITUENTS OF INDUSTRIAL WATER.

PHYSICAL TESTS

Volume of Sample,[a] ml

*Color and Odor	100 to 500
*Corrosivity	flowing sample
*Electrical conductivity	100
*pH, electrometric	100
Radioactivity	100 to 1000
*Specific gravity	100
*Temperature	flowing sample
*Toxicity	1000 to 20 000
*Turbidity	100 to 1000

CHEMICAL TESTS

Dissolved Gases:

†Ammonia, NH_3	500
†Carbon dioxide, free CO_2	200
†Chlorine, free Cl_2	200
†Hydrogen, H_2	1000
†Hydrogen sulfide, H_2S	500
†Oxygen, O_2	500 to 1000
†Sulfur dioxide, free SO_2	100

Miscellaneous:

Acidity and alkalinity	100
Bacteria, iron	500
Bacteria, sulfate-reducing	100
Biochemical oxygen demand	100 to 500
Carbon dioxide, total CO_2 (including CO_3^{--}, HCO_3^-, and free)	200
Chemical oxygen demand (dichromate)	50 to 100
Chlorine requirement	2000 to 4000
Chlorine, total residual Cl_2 (including OCl^-, $HOCl$, NH_2Cl, $NHCl_2$, and free)	200
Chloroform - extractable matter	1000
Detergents	100 to 200
Hardness	50 to 100
Hydrazine	50 to 100
Microorganisms	100 to 200
Volatile and filming amines	500 to 1000
Oily matter	3000 to 5000
Organic nitrogen	500 to 1000
Phenolic compounds	800 to 4000
pH, colorimetric	10 to 20
Polyphosphates	100 to 200

Volume of Sample,[a] ml

Miscellaneous:

Silica	50 to 1000
Solids, dissolved	100 to 20 000
Solids, suspended	50 to 1000
Tannin and lignin	100 to 200

Cations:

Aluminum, Al^{+++}	100 to 1000
†Ammonium, NH_4^+	500
Antimony, Sb^{+++} to Sb^{+++++}	100 to 1000
Arsenic, As $^{+++}$ to As^{+++++}	100 to 1000
Barium, Ba^{++}	100 to 1000
Cadmium, Cd^{++}	100 to 1000
Calcium, Ca^{++}	100 to 1000
Chromium, Cr^{+++} to Cr^{++++++}	100 to 1000
Copper, Cu^{++}	200 to 4000
†Iron, Fe^{++} and Fe^{+++}	100 to 1000
Lead, Pb^{++}	100 to 4000
Magnesium, Mg^{++}	100 to 1000
Manganese, Mn^{++} to $Mn^{+++++++}$	100 to 1000
Mercury, Hg^+ and Hg^{++}	100 to 1000
Potassium, K^+	100 to 1000
Nickel, Ni^{++}	100 to 1000
Silver, Ag^+	100 to 1000
Sodium, Na^+	100 to 1000
Strontium, Sr^{++}	100 to 1000
Tin, Sn^{++} and Sn^{++++}	100 to 1000
Zinc, Zn^{++}	100 to 1000

Anions:

Bicarbonate, HCO_3	100 to 200
Bromide, Br^-	100
Carbonate, CO_3^{--}	100 to 200
Chloride, Cl^-	25 to 100
Cyanide, Cn^-	25 to 100
Fluoride, Fl^-	200
Hydroxide, OH^-	50 to 100
Iodide, I^-	100
Nitrate, NO_3^-	10 to 100
Nitrite, NO_2^-	50 to 100
Phosphate, ortho, PO_4^{---}, HPO_4^{--}, $H_2PO_4^-$	50 to 100
Sulfate, SO_4^{--}, HSO_4^-	100 to 1000
Sulfide, S^{--}, HS^-	100 to 500
Sulfite, SO_3^{--}, HSO_3^-	50 to 100

[a] Volumes specified in this table should be considered as a guide for the approximate quantity of sample necessary for the particular analysis. The exact quantity used should be consistent with the volume prescribed in the standard method of analysis, whenever the volume is specified.

* Aliquot may be used for other determinations.

† Samples for unstable constituents must be obtained in separate containers, preserved as prescribed, completely filled and sealed against all exposure.

conditioned by the methods of analysis to be employed.

(c) The samples must be collected, packed, shipped, and manipulated prior to analysis in a manner that safeguards against change in the particular constituents or properties to be examined.

Definitions

3. (a) The terms "industrial water," "biological tests," and "sterile" in these methods are defined in accordance with the Definitions of Terms Relating to Industrial Water and Industrial Waste Water (ASTM Designation: D 1129),[4] as follows:

Industrial Water.—Water (including its impurities) used directly or indirectly in industrial processes.

Biological Tests.—Examination for the purpose of determining the presence, identity, numbers, or effects of the presence of any organism in industrial water.

Sterile.—Free from any viable organism, either active or dormant.

(b) For definitions of other terms used in these methods, refer to Definitions D 1129.

SAMPLING FOR CHEMICAL OR PHYSICAL TESTS

Application

4. This method is applicable to sampling industrial water supplies from sources such as wells, rivers, streams, lakes, oceans, reservoirs, pipe lines and conduits, processing tanks and vats, spray ponds, towers, and filters, at atmospheric or higher pressures for chemical or physical tests. Certain supplies or test methods require special handling of samples. For additional information refer to sampling methods governing such supplies or test methods.[2]

---

[4] Appears in this publication.

Apparatus

5. (a) For apparatus required for sampling such as lines, valves and fittings, coolers or condensers, degassers, containers, special collecting devices and shipping containers, refer to the Specifications for Equipment for Sampling Industrial Water and Steam (ASTM Designation: D 1192).[4]

(b) Refer to the apparatus description in the applicable test method if special apparatus is required for any particular test.

(c) When contact with the air causes a change in the concentration of a constituent to be determined, such as dissolved oxygen, carbon dioxide, or other constituent listed as "unstable" in Table I, use the applicable apparatus specified in Paragraph (a) (Note 1).

NOTE 1.—The apparatus described in the Methods of Test for Dissolved Oxygen in Industrial Water (ASTM Designation: D 888)[4] is frequently convenient for this purpose.

Frequency and Duration of Sampling

6. A reasonably accurate estimate of the composition of a raw water piped from a large body of water, such as the Great Lakes, far enough from the shoreline to avoid variation from inflowing tributaries and sewage contamination, may be made by taking individual samples at infrequent intervals, such as biweekly or monthly, sufficient to cover seasonal changes. If samples are taken from near the shoreline of such a body of water or from a river, take them at shorter intervals, for instance daily, to provide more exact knowledge of the variations in composition where these are of importance in the use to which the water is to be put. Where greater variations occur or closer control in plant intake water is required, collect more frequent samples, for example at hourly intervals.

Composite Samples

7. (a) Composite samples may be made by mutual agreement of the interested parties by combining individual samples taken at frequent intervals or by means of an automatic sampler. In either case, indicate whether the volume of sample is proportional to the rate of flow. At the end of a definite period, mix the composite sample thoroughly so that determinations on a portion of the composite sample will represent the average for the stable constituents.

(b) Variations of unstable constituents, for which individual samples are specified in Table I, may be determined by analysis on the individual samples.

(c) In sampling process-effluent waters, collect composite samples covering periods of 12 hr or less, in at least one 24-hr period. Collect increments for composite samples at regular intervals from 15 min to 1 hr, and in proportion to the rate of flow of the effluent water. This may be conveniently done by taking a simple multiple in milliliters of the flow in gallons per minute or other unit of flow. Choose a suitable factor to give the proper volume (about 4 liters) for the composite sample.

(d) When samples are taken from a stream, composite samples for analysis normally consist of equal quantities of daily samples for a suitable number of consecutive days; for example, seven days.

Temperature Adjustment of Samples

8. Where samples of water are taken at other than ambient temperature, use coils as described in Section 5(a) to adjust the sample approximately to the ambient temperature (Note 2).

Note 2.—Some test methods require adjustment of sample to other than ambient temperatures. Carry out such temperature adjustment as required.

Suspended Solids

9. (a) Normally, samples are secured without separation of suspended solids. Where constituents are present in colloidal and flocculent suspension, take the sample so that they are present in representative proportion (Note 3).

Note 3.—Samples containing such materials are not normally affected by exposure to air, but on long standing sedimentation may occur.

(b) If it is desired to secure samples free of suspended solids from water at an elevated temperature, incorporate a filter in a by-pass line to the cooling coil, and take the sample through this filter (Note 4).

Note 4.—The reason for filtering the sample hot is to separate the suspended material on the filter before crystallization of dissolved material or re-solution of suspended material occurs due to the drop in temperature.

Volume of Sample

10. (a) Furnish a minimum volume of water of 2 liters (Note 5) in the sample for analysis.

Note 5.—A sample of 4 liters is preferable; and, in some cases, a sample as large as 20 liters may be necessary. The number of tests to be made and the amount required for each test by the procedure employed determines the size of the sample above the minimum specified. It is always desirable to have some of the sample left over for checking analyses or for further analysis at a later date.

(b) The estimates in Table I cover the volume of sample required for the usual determinations that are made on a water sample as well as for several tests that are made for special purposes.

Point of Sampling

11. (a) Choose the point of sampling with extreme care so that a representative sample of the water to be tested is obtained.

(b) Because of a wide variety of conditions found in streams, lakes, reservoirs, and other bodies of water, it is not possible to prescribe the exact point of sampling. Where the water in a stream is mixed so as to approach uniformity, a sample taken at any point in the cross-section is satisfactory. For large rivers or for streams not likely to be uniformly mixed, three or more samples are desirable and are usually taken at the midpoint of equal cross-sectional areas. Ordinarily samples are taken at these points and then combined to obtain an integrated sample of such a stream of water.

(c) Choose the location of the sampling point with respect to the information desired and in conformity to local conditions. Allow sufficient distance downstream with respect to stream flow at the time of sampling from a tributary or source of industrial or sewage pollution to permit thorough mixing. If this is not possible, it is better to sample the stream above the tributary or source of pollution and in addition to sample the tributary or source of pollution. In general, a distance of one to three miles below the tributary is sufficient.

(d) Collect samples at least one half mile below dams or waterfalls to allow time for the escape of entrained air. Where lakes, reservoirs, or other bodies of water are sampled, sufficient distance must be allowed to eliminate the influence of local conditions.

(e) It is desirable to take a series of samples from any source of water to determine whether differences in composition are likely to exist, before final selection of the sampling point.

(f) Choose sampling points in pipelines, conduits, tanks, vats, filters, zeolite and chemical water softeners, deionizing processes, surface condensers, evaporators, or condensate return lines with respect to the characteristics of the individual piece of equipment containing the water to be tested, the character and changes occurring between the inlet and outlet water, and rate of passage through the equipment. Again take care a representative sample is ensured by allowing mixing to take place. Avoid taking the sample along the wall of the pipe or conduit but take it within the stream.

(g) Insert nozzles to sampling cocks into the pipe line or piece of equipment to such a depth as to prevent pipe surface sampling. Choose a point along the length of the pipe where there will be a minimum disturbance of flow due to fittings.

(h) In the absence of any other sampling connections, take samples from water-level or gage-glass drain lines or petcocks. Such samples are not representative of the average composition of the water in the vessel and are not to be used in case of controversy.

Preparation of Sample Bottles

12. Prepare and clean sample containers according to the procedures specified in Section 5. Then rinse with reagent water conforming to the Specifications for Reagent Water (ASTM Designation: D 1193)[4] and dry by draining.

Taking the Sample

13. (a) Regulate the rate of flow to not more than 500 ml per min, after first flushing the sample line at a rate high enough to remove all sediment and gas pockets. In special cases where dissolved gases are released from solution by the drop in pressure, note this on the label.

(b) When sampling water from cocks or valves, insert the sample line, or a thoroughly washed glass or sulfur-free rubber tube extension of the sample line, into the sampling bottle so that it touches the bottom. Allow a volume of water equal to at least ten times the volume of the sample container to flow into and overflow from the container before the sample is taken.

52–44

FIG. 1.—Depth-Integrating Samplers.

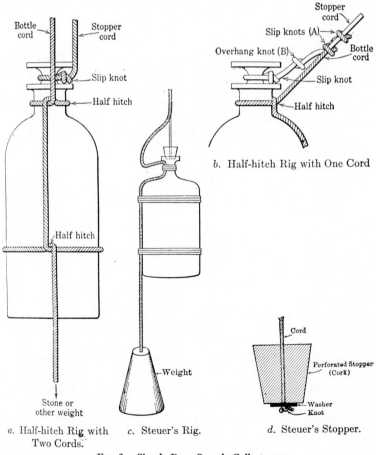

a. Half-hitch Rig with Two Cords.

b. Half-hitch Rig with One Cord

c. Steuer's Rig.

d. Steuer's Stopper.

FIG. 2.—Simple Deep Sample Collectors.

220

(c) Where contact with air would cause a change in the concentration of a constituent to be determined, take the sample out of contact with air and completely fill the container (Notes 6 and 7).

NOTE 6.—When the apparatus referred to in Note 1 is applicable, take the sample out of contact with air by one of the procedures described therein.

reservoirs, and other bodies of water, depth-integrating samplers or point samplers are used. When collection of water is for the determination of non-volatile constituents and constituents unaffected by aeration, the depth-integrating samplers may consist only of a mechanism for holding and submerging the container. When the bottle is low-

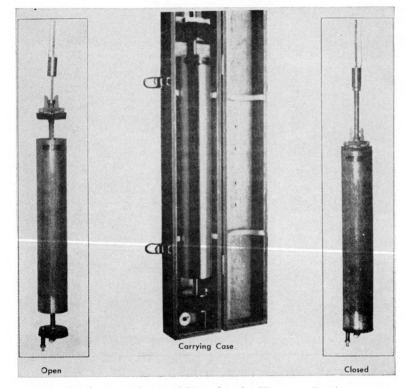

FIG. 3.—Foerst Improved Water Sampler (Kemmerer Type).

NOTE 7.—The following constituents require the above precautions:

Oxygen	Hardness
Total carbon dioxide	Hydrogen
Total ammonia	Sulfur dioxide
Hydrogen sulfide	Ammonium
Free chlorine	Iron
pH	Acidity and alkalinity

(d) For sampling of unconfined waters throughout the vertical profile and at any specific depth in streams, lakes,

ered at a uniform rate, water is admitted throughout the vertical profile. The simplest deep sampling device consists of a weighted glass bottle (Fig. 1) that is lowered by nylon rope or plastic-covered wire. When the bottle has filled, air bubbles will cease to rise to the surface, indicating that the bottle can be raised with the representative sample.

Point samplers are used to collect

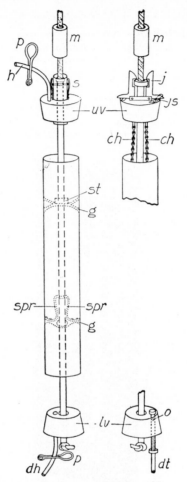

ch—chain which anchors upper valve to upper interior guide.
dh—rubber drain tube.
dt—brass drain tube.
g—interior guide fastened to inner surface of sampler.
h—rubber tube.
j—jaw of release.
js—jaw spring.
lv—lower valve.
m—messenger.
o—opening interior of drain tube.
p—pinch cock.
s—upper release spring operating on horizontal pin, one end of which fits into groove on central rod.
spr—spring fastened to lower internal guide and operating in groove on central rod to provide lower release.
st—stop on central rod.
uv—upper valve.
Left.—View of complete sampler with valves open.
Top right.—Another type of construction of upper valve and tripping device.
Bottom right.—Another type of construction of lower valve and drain tube.

      FIG. 4.—Diagram Showing Structural Features of Modified Kemmerer Sampler.[5]

---

[5] P. S. Welch, *Limnological Methods*, p. 200, Fig. 59.

water at a specific depth below the water surface and may be simple or complex. Simple deep sample collectors are shown in Fig. 2. These may be lowered to any desired depth before the stoppers are removed. One type of device of more complex design is the Foerst[6] modified Kemmerer-type water sampler shown in Figs. 3 and 4. The sampler is lowered to the desired depth in the open position; then the messenger weight which trips the closing mechanism is run down the suspension line. The messenger weight must meet the triggering device on the top of the sampler squarely. Hence, a set of messenger weights drilled to accommodate suspension lines of different diameters permits the use of the sampler with a wide variety of ropes and cables. The Foerst sampler is available in brass construction and thus resists corrosion. However, fabrication from stainless steel may be desirable to prevent contamination of the water sample with metals from the copper bearing alloys.

Detachable weights are useful with practically all samplers, since appreciable weight is necessary in excess of that required to submerge the bottle. In moving water, inadequately weighted samplers drift with the current and tend to ride on the water surface at the end of the suspension line. Added weight also decreases the angle between the suspension line and the vertical, thereby increasing the accuracy of depth measurement.

The collection and handling of samples for the determination of dissolved gas content and constituents affected by aeration require special equipment and careful technique. The sampler assembly for collecting samples for the determination of dissolved oxygen content and biochemical-oxygen demand described

by the American Public Health Association[7] and others, or a modification thereof, is generally accepted as standard apparatus for sampling open water. This sampler provides for a threefold displacement of water in the sample container without aeration. A non-aerated sample collected in a Foerst sampler can be transferred by means of a tube connected to the outlet valve projecting into the bottom of a sample bottle. A minimum of three displacements of water in the bottle is required,

(e) When samples are to be shipped do not fill the bottle entirely, in order to allow some room for expansion when subjected to a change in temperature (Note 8).

NOTE 8.—An air space of 10 to 25 ml usually suffices for this purpose, although this does not protect against bursting of the container due to freezing.

Preservation of Samples

14. Add chemical preservatives to samples only as specified in specific test methods.

Time Interval Between Collection and Analysis of Samples

15. (a) In general allow as short a time as possible to elapse between the collection of a sample and its analysis. Under some conditions, analysis in the field is necessary to secure reliable results. The actual time which may be allowed to intervene between the collection and analysis of a sample varies with the type of examination to be conducted, the character of the sample, and the time interval allowable for applying corrective treatment.

(b) On the statement of an analysis, specify the length of time elapsed be-

---

[6] Developed by Dr. G. L. Kemmerer of the United States Bureau of Fisheries and modified by Foerst Mechanical Specialties Co., Chicago, Ill.

[7] For a description of this sampler see "Standard Methods for the Examination of Water and Waste Water," Am. Public Health Assn., New York, N. Y., 11th Ed. (1960), p. 308, Fig. 21.

tween collection and analysis of the sample.

(c) Make the determination of dissolved gases, for instance, oxygen, hydrogen sulfide, and carbon dioxide, at the source; except that in some cases such constituents may be fixed and determined later as specified in the specific test methods.

Labeling and Transportation of Samples

16. Refer to Section 15 and to the Specifications for Equipment for Sampling Industrial Water and Steam (ASTM Designation: D 1192).[4]

SAMPLING FOR BIOLOGICAL TESTS

Application

17. This method is applicable to sampling industrial water supplies from sources such as wells, rivers, streams, lakes, oceans, reservoirs, pipe lines and conduits, processing tanks and vats, spray ponds, towers, and filters at atmospheric or higher pressures for biological tests.[2] Certain supplies or test methods require special handling of samples. For additional information refer to sampling methods covering such supplies or test methods.

Apparatus

18. (a) For apparatus required for sampling, such as valves, sample lines, etc., refer to Specifications D 1192.

NOTE 9.—It is preferable to avoid special sample lines which may tend to allow organism growth during standing periods, and to use constantly flowing pipes or frequently used outlets.

NOTE 10.—Any sample line installed must be permanent in nature and not contain rubber or plastic joints. Heat as much of the line as possible after installation with a torch or other suitable heat source to at least 100 C, and flush it thoroughly for at least 15 min before taking the first sample.

(b) Sterilizer.—Provide a dry hot-air sterilizer capable of sterilizing sample

bottles at a uniform temperature throughout the sterilizer of not less than 170 C for 1 hr.

(c) Sample Bottles.—Provide four wide-mouth sample bottles of at least 300-ml capacity with ground-glass stoppers. Metal or plastic, wide-mouth, screw caps may also be used on sample bottles. Such caps and their liners must be capable of withstanding sterilization temperatures. They must produce no compounds by volatilization during sterilizing, and they must impart no toxic or bacteriostatic compounds to the water sample.

Reagents and Materials

19. (a) Purity of Reagents.—Reagent grade chemicals shall be used in all tests. Unless otherwise indicated, it is intended that all reagents shall conform to the specifications of the Committee on Analytical Reagents of the American Chemical Society, where such specifications are available.[8] Other grades may be used, provided it is first ascertained that the reagent is of sufficiently high purity to permit its use without lessening the accuracy of the determination.

(b) Purity of Water.—Unless otherwise indicated, references to water shall be understood to mean reagent water conforming to the Specifications for Reagent Water (ASTM Designation: D 1193).[4]

(c) Cleaning Solution, Acid Dichromate.[9]—Prepare a saturated water solution of sodium dichromate ($Na_2Cr_2O_7$). To 32 ml of this solution add 1 liter of concentrated sulfuric acid (H_2SO_4, sp gr 1.84) (Note 11).

[8] "Reagent Chemicals, American Chemical Society Specifications," Am. Chemical Soc., Washington, D. C. For suggestions on the testing of reagents not listed by the American Chemical Society, see "Reagent Chemicals and Standards," by Joseph Rosin, D. Van Nostrand Co., Inc., New York, N. Y. and the "United States Pharmacopeia."

[9] This reagent is used only for preparation of apparatus.

NOTE 11.—Always add the acid to the solution carefully. Never add the solution to the acid, as spattering may result.

(d) *Nitric Acid Solution* (1:4).—Mix 1 volume of concentrated nitric acid (HNO_3, sp gr 1.42) with 4 volumes of water.

(e) *Sodium Thiosulfate* ($Na_2S_2O_3$), powdered.

Frequency and Duration of Sampling

20. See Section 6.

Composite Samples

21. It is preferable not to take composite samples for industrial biological examination, since this delays the analysis of the samples and increases risk of contamination which are both undesirable. If it is agreed by all parties to take a composite sample, pour the individual samples into a clean sterile bottle, maintained at 0 C to 10 C. The composite sample must be examined within 12 hr of the time the first sample was introduced.

Temperature Adjustment of Samples

22. See Section 8.

Suspended Solids

23. See Section 9(a).

Volume of Sample

24. Ordinarily two 300-ml sample bottles are sufficient for biological tests. Some special tests may dictate larger samples. Take such samples in larger sterile bottles according to this procedure.

Point of Sampling

25. See Section 11.

Preparation of Sample Bottles

26. (a) Clean the sample bottles with hot cleaning solution, preceded by soap washing if necessary (Note 12). Rinse out residual cleaning solution with reagent water and then rinse bottles thoroughly with dilute nitric acid to remove any possible heavy metal contamination or residual chromate. Finally, rinse the bottles thoroughly with water and dry by draining.

NOTE 12.—Cleaning solution is extremely corrosive and should not contact flesh or clothing.

(b) Add 0.02 to 0.05 g of $Na_2S_2O_3$, if the samples to be taken contain free chlorine, unless thiosulfate interfers with the subsequent examination, in which case omit this addition.

(c) Stopper and cover the bottle tops and necks with metal foil dust covers to protect from contamination. Sterilize the bottles in a dry hot-air sterilizer at a minimum of 170 C for at least 1 hr.

Taking Sample from Sample Line or Tap

27. (a) Allow the water to run from the sample line or tap for at least 5 min or long enough to flush, with six to ten times its volume, the entire part of the system that has been stagnant for 2 hr or more.

(b) Turn off the sample outlet and empty it of water without touching the inside. Flame the outside of the outlet until well heated (Note 13). Turn on the sample outlet.

NOTE 13.—Flame the outlet with a suitable torch, wad of cotton soaked in alcohol, or other device that will avoid the deposition of soot, which is undesirable. This flaming procedure may be omitted if the outlet is carefully cleaned by use of a swab of cotton or other suitable material thoroughly saturated with denatured ethyl alcohol (70 per cent).

(c) Choose a sample bottle containing sodium thiosulfate if the water being sampled contains free chlorine, has been chlorinated, or contains any free or combined available oxidizing agent intended to sterilize it. If such sterilizing agents are not present, the thiosulfate may be omitted. In cases where thiosulfate interferes with subsequent examination, such as examination for sulfate reducing bacteria, etc., omit the use of thiosulfate in the sample bottle even if such sterilizing agents are present. In this case, if such sterilizing agents are present the examination must be performed as soon as possible.

(*d*) Remove the stopper from the

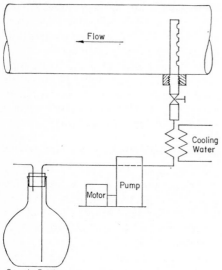

Fig. 5.—Arrangement for Extraction of Water Sample at Low and Subatmospheric Pressure.

sample bottle. Grasp the stopper by the dust cover so as not to contaminate it by touching it; do not lay it down. Hold the bottle by the bottom to avoid touching the neck. Quickly hold the bottle under the flowing water to be sampled until it is about three fourths full. Replace the stopper and promptly crimp the metal dust cover in place over the neck of the bottle (Note 14).

Note 14.—Take care that the stopper and bottle neck are not touched during this operation and that no dust blows into the bottle, in so far as possible.

(*e*) When the water to be sampled is confined at low or subatmospheric pressure, special means must be provided to extract the sample. The simplest arrangement, where physical conditions permit, is the installation of a barometric leg. Equipment for removal of a sample from a line or system operating under vacuum is shown in Fig. 5. A satisfactory arrangement consists of a small positive displacement-type pump arranged to discharge into the sampling container at atmospheric pressure. The pump[10] should be of such material and construction that the sample will not be contaminated. The sample receiver may also be located between the pump and the sampling point. With this arrangement, the receiver must be valved off, equalized to atmospheric pressure, and drained into a container.

Taking Sample from Unconfined Waters, Open Vats, or Tanks

28. (*a*) Choose the sample bottle as directed in Section 27(*c*).

(*b*) Remove the stopper from the sample bottle. Grasp the stopper by the dust cover and the bottle by the bottom to avoid contamination.

(*c*) Holding the stopper by the dust cover in one hand, invert the bottle in the other hand. Quickly plunge the inverted bottle beneath the surface of the water in a sweeping motion to about elbow depth. Carry the bottle by the sweeping motion rapidly in and out of the water. During the sweeping motion, direct the mouth of the bottle in the direction of motion at the bottom of the sweep so that it emerges right side up full of water. If the water being sampled is flowing, direct the sweeping motion against the current (Notes 15 and 16). Immediately flip water out of the sample

[10] Two commercially available pumps that appear to be suitable for this service are the "Sigma Motor" and the "Vanton."

bottle until it is approximately three-fourths full. Close the sample bottle as directed in Section 27(d).

NOTE 15.—The sweeping motion, against the current, if any, avoids the entry into the sample bottle of any of the bacteria abundantly present on the skin of the arm or hand.

NOTE 16.—Take care in this plunging procedure to avoid the entry of any obvious or undue floating dust, other floating material, or very top surface water into the bottle. Exclude from the bottle, in so far as possible, any sediment on the bottom of the body of water.

Refrigeration and Storage of Samples Prior to Examination

29. (a) If the sample is examined within 2 hr of collection, store it in a cool place without icing.

(b) If the sample is held more than 2 hr before examination, store it in a refrigerator or ice chest at a temperature of not more than 10 C. The interval between collection and examination of the sample must in no case be more than 12 hr, or 6 hr if the sample is suspected to contain large numbers of organisms.

(c) If the sample is transported, ship it in an insulated, iced container so as to maintain the temperature between 0 and 10 C and so as to allow it to be examined within 12 hr of collection (Note 17).

NOTE 17.—In some cases, it is impossible to refrigerate samples during shipment or to examine them within 12 hr of collection. Such samples must be viewed with suspicion and judged accordingly, since organisms in such samples may be multiplied or reduced considerably. Delay of the examination should be noted on the examination report. Examination in the field, if possible, is preferred in this case.

Preservatives in Samples

30. Do not add preservatives to the sample, except for sodium thiosulfate to destroy chlorine residuals or except as specified under specific methods of examination.

Labeling Samples

31. For instructions on labeling samples, see the Specifications for Equipment for Sampling Industrial Water and Steam (ASTM Designation: D 1192).[4]

SAMPLING OF RADIOACTIVE WATER

Application

32. This method is applicable to sampling radioactive industrial water from sources such as wells, rivers, streams, lakes, oceans, reservoirs, pipe lines and conduits, processing tanks and vats, spray ponds, towers, and filters, including nuclear reactor cooling water, at atmospheric or higher pressures. Because of the radioactive substances in the water, certain supplies may require handling precautions or other special handling. Such handling will depend on the amount of radioactive substances contained in the water and whether determination is to be made for gross radioactivity, for a specific radionuclide or radionuclides, or for nonradioactive constituents by established chemical or physical tests.[11]

Handling Precautions

33. (a) Because of the potential hazards related to working with water containing radioactive nuclides, special handling of radioactive samples may be required. Information on radiological hazards and recommendations on radiation protection have been published by the National Committee on Radiation Protection[12, 13] and the Federal

---

[11] A discussion of radionuclides in water may be found on p. 177.

[12] "Permissible Dose from External Sources of Ionizing Radiation," *Handbook No. 59*, Nat. Bureau Standards (1954); also addendum to *Handbook No. 59* (April 15, 1958).

[13] "Maximum Permissible Body Burdens and Maximum Permissible Concentrations of Radionuclides in Air and in Water for Occupational Exposure," *Handbook No. 69*, Nat. Bureau Standards (June 5, 1959).

Radiation Council.[14] The recommendations of the Federal Radiation Council on radiation protection guides have been adopted by all federal agencies by executive order of the President.[15] The existing standards for protection against radiation are set forth in the Code of Federal Regulations.[16] Special methods and precautionary measures for handling radioactive samples are described in the literature.[17, 18]

(b) When sampling process waters where radioactivity levels may be high, such as nuclear reactor cooling waters, applicable health physics regulations shall be followed. In such cases, the use of suitable protective clothing may be required. Personnel monitoring devices may be necessary where external radiation levels present a potential hazard. Where the level of radioactivity in the sampling area is sufficiently great to introduce a radiation hazard, shielding for sample lines, coolers, and collection devices may be required to minimize exposure to radiation. Precautionary measures should be exercised to prevent contamination and spread of radioactivity by spillage of samples or by leakage or breakage of sampling lines, valves, containers, etc. In addition, precautions should be taken to prevent release of gaseous or airborne radioactive substances, thereby preventing a hazard to the individual collecting the sample.

(c) If sample containers are to be shipped, they should be shielded and packed to comply with regulations for shipping radioactive materials.[19]

Apparatus

34. For apparatus required for sampling, such as valves, sample lines, sample coolers, sample containers and shipping containers, refer to the Specification for Equipment for Sampling Industrial Water and Steam (ASTM Designation: D 1192).[4] The choice of sample container will depend to a large extent on the type of sample involved and its level of radioactivity. Plastic containers usually are preferable when sampling for radioactivity determinations. As indicated in Section 33, consideration must be given to the level of radioactivity in the sampling area and of the sample itself. Special apparatus may be required for shielding sample lines, sample containers, and shipping containers.

Frequency and Duration of Sampling

35. The frequency and duration of sampling will depend primarily on the intended application of the analytical results. In general, the recommendations given in Section 6 should be followed. For specific cases, and when sampling for radioactivity determinations, refer to appropriate texts.[17, 20, 21] The duration of sampling should be adequate to ensure collection of a representative sample.

Composite Samples

36. The procedure for compositing samples should, in general, be as de-

[14] "Background Material for the Development of Radiation Protection Standards," Federal Radiation Council Staff Report No. 1 (May 13, 1960), U. S. Government Printing Office, Washington 25, D. C.

[15] Federal Register, May 18, 1960, p. 4402.

[16] Code of Federal Regulations, Title 10-Atomic Energy, Part 20, Standards for Protection Against Radiation.

[17] G. Friedlander and J. W. Kennedy, "Nuclear and Radiochemistry," John Wiley and Sons, Inc., New York, N. Y. (1955).

[18] R. T. Overman and H. M. Clark, "Radioisotope Techniques," McGraw-Hill Book Co., Inc., New York, N. Y. (1960).

[19] U. S. Atomic Energy Commission Handbook of Federal Regulations Applying to Transportation of Radioactive Materials (May, 1958).

[20] W. J. Price, "Nuclear Radiation Detection," McGraw-Hill Book Co., Inc., New York, N. Y. (1958).

[21] H. Etherington, Nuclear Engineering Handbook, McGraw-Hill Book Co., Inc., New York, N. Y. (1958).

scribed in Section 7. To estimate radioactive decay, the time of collection and the quantity of each sample comprising the composite should be noted.

Suspended Solids

37. (a) When determining radioactivity in water, it generally is desirable to determine to what extent the activity is distributed between dissolved and suspended matter. If the distribution of radioactivity between dissolved and suspended solids is to be determined, filtration of a known volume of the sample will be required. The volume of sample needed will be a function of the activity level, and a general requirement, applicable to all cases, cannot be established. For methods of determining suspended and dissolved solids refer to the Methods of Test for Particulate and Dissolved Matter in Industrial Water (ASTM Designation: D 1888).[4]

NOTE 18.—Radioactive substances often are present in water in microgram quantities or less. Loss of activity from solution may occur during filtration due to adsorption of the radioactive materials on the filtering media.

(b) Filtration normally is performed at room temperature using a filter material compatible with the water sample under study. If it is desired to secure samples free of suspended solids from water at an elevated temperature, the recommendations of Section 9(b) should be followed. Filter materials for use with radioactive water samples include sintered-metal types (stainless steel, nickel, platinum) for water at elevated temperature, or cellulose ester membrane, cellulose paper, or fritted glass filters for water at room temperature. The sample should be filtered as soon as possible after collection.

NOTE 19: Caution.—Suspended solids that are dried on the filter may present an airborne ingestion hazard; thus, care should be exercised in handling the residue on the filter.

Point of Sampling

38. Sampling points should be chosen as described in Section 11.

Preparation of Sample Containers

39. Prepare and clean sample containers as directed in Sections 5 and 12. When sampling for radioactivity determinations, precautions should be taken to reduce the magnitude of activity adsorbed on the container walls. Plastic materials or wax-coated containers give less difficulty in this respect than do glass or metals. Treatment to minimize adsorption losses will depend on the subsequent analysis. Adsorption of radioactive materials on container walls often can be minimized by addition of a suitable acid or complexing agent. The addition of liquids such as acids, however, may change the distribution of radioactivity between the dissolved and suspended constituents. The addition of stable isotopes as carrier material may also be employed if determinations are to be made for specific radionuclides.

Taking the Sample

40. (a) Procedures for collecting the sample should, in general, follow those described in Section 13.

(b) When the water sampled is under pressure and contains gaseous radioactive substances, the container employed should be designed to prevent any disproportionate loss of the gases during sampling.

(c) Suitable measures should be employed to minimize adsorptive losses of radioactivity, if not already accomplished during preparation of the sample container.

NOTE 20.—When sampling streams or other natural waters, easily adsorbable materials may already be on the surfaces of whatever suspended solids are present. In such cases, treatment to prevent adsorption may result in undesired transfer of radionuclides from the suspended to the dissolved phase.

Time Interval Between Collection and Analysis of Samples

41. (*a*) Refer to Section 15.

(*b*) When sampling for radioactivity determinations, the exact time of sample collection should be noted. If short-lived activity is of interest, analysis should be made as rapidly as practical to minimize loss of activity by radioactive decay. If only long-lived activity is of interest, measurement of the radioactivity sometimes can be simplified by allowing sufficient time before analysis for the decay of the short-lived radionuclides.

Standard Method of Test for

CALCIUM ION AND MAGNESIUM ION IN INDUSTRIAL WATER[1]

ASTM Designation: D 511 – 52 (1965)

ADOPTED, 1942; REVISED, 1952; REAPPROVED, 1965

This Standard of the American Society for Testing and Materials is issued under the fixed designation D 511; the number immediately following the designation indicates the year of original adoption or, in the case of revision, the year of last revision. A number in parentheses indicates the year of last reapproval.

NOTE.—This method was editorially revised and rearranged in March, 1955.

Scope and Application

1. This method covers the gravimetric determination of calcium ion and magnesium ion after removal of silica, phosphates, iron, aluminum, and manganese, when necessary. The method is applicable to industrial water.

Principle of Method

2. After removing common interferences, calcium is precipitated twice as calcium oxalate, which finally is ignited and weighed as calcium oxide. Magnesium is determined on the calcium filtrate by double precipitation as magnesium ammonium phosphate and ignition to magnesium pyrophosphate.

Definitions

3. For definitions of terms used in this method, refer to the Definitions of Terms Relating to Industrial Water and Industrial Waste Water (ASTM Designation: D 1129).[2]

Purity of Reagents

4. (a) Reagent grade chemicals shall be used in all tests. Unless otherwise indicated, it is intended that all reagents shall conform to the specifications of the Committee on Analytical Reagents of the American Chemical Society, where such specifications are available.[3] Other grades may be used, provided it is first ascertained that the reagent is of sufficiently high purity to permit its use

---

[1] Under the standardization procedure of the Society, this method is under the jurisdiction of the ASTM Committee D-19 on Industrial Water. A list of members may be found in the ASTM Year Book.

[2] Appears in this publication.

[3] "Reagent Chemicals, American Chemical Society Specifications," Am. Chem. Soc., Washington, D. C. For suggestions on the testing of reagents not listed by the American Chemical Society, see "Reagent Chemicals and Standards," by Joseph Rosin, D. Van Nostrand Co., Inc., New York, N. Y., and the "United States Pharmacopeia."

without lessening the accuracy of the determination.

(b) Unless otherwise indicated, references to water shall be understood to mean reagent water conforming to the Specifications for Reagent Water (ASTM Designation: D 1193).[2]

Reagents

5. (a) *Ammonium Chloride Solution* (*20 g NH₄Cl per liter*).—Dissolve 20 g of NH_4Cl in water and dilute to 1 liter.

(b) *Ammonium Hydroxide* (*sp gr 0.90*).

(c) *Ammonium Hydroxide* (*1:19*).— Mix 1 volume of NH_4OH (sp gr 0.90) with 19 volumes of water.

(d) *Ammonium Oxalate Solution.*— Prepare a solution, saturated at room temperature, of ammonium oxalate in water.

(e) *Ammonium Persulfate.*

(f) *Ferric Chloride.*

(g) *Hydrochloric Acid* (*sp gr 1.19*).

(h) *Hydrochloric Acid* (*1:1*).—Mix 1 volume of HCl (sp gr 1.19) with 1 volume of water.

(i) *Methyl Red Indicator.*—Dissolve 0.01 g of water-soluble methyl red in 100 ml of water.

(j) *Nitric Acid* (*sp gr 1.42*).

(k) *Sodium Ammonium Hydrogen Orthophosphate Solution.*—Prepare a solution, saturated at room temperature, of sodium ammonium hydrogen orthophosphate (microcosmic salt) in water.

Sampling

6. Collect the sample in accordance with the applicable method of the American Society for Testing and Materials, as follows:

D 510—Sampling Industrial Water,[2]
D 860—Sampling Water from Boilers,[2]
D 1066—Sampling Steam.[2]

Procedure

7. (a) If possible, select a volume of sample sufficient to contain 10 to 100 mg of calcium.

(b) Acidify the sample with HCl (sp gr 1.19), adding 2 ml in excess, and then evaporate it to dryness (Note 1).

Note 1.—During evaporation the walls of the container should be moistened to avoid retention of silica.

(c) To the dry residue add 2 ml of HCl (1:1); dilute the solution to approximately 75 ml with water, and heat to boiling. Filter the silica residue and wash on the filter paper with at least two successive additions of hot HCl (1:1) and then with at least three successive additions of hot water, adding the washings to the filtrate.

(d) *Removal of Phosphates, Iron, Aluminum, and Manganese.*—In all cases when the special removal of manganese is unnecessary, follow the regular procedure as described in Paragraph (f). If the amount of manganese present in the water is known to be significantly large with respect to the magnesium, or if possible error in the magnesium determination due to manganese is to be avoided, follow the special procedure as described in Paragraph (g).

(e) *Removal of Phosphates.*—If phosphates are shown by preliminary test to be present, add sufficient FeCl₃ to the combined filtrate and washings from Paragraph (c) to produce a red-brown precipitate, after which follow the procedure described in Paragraph (f) or (g).

(f) *Regular Removal of Iron and Aluminum.*—Heat the combined filtrate and washings procured under Paragraph (c) or (e) to boiling and add a few drops of HNO₃. Cool the solution, add a few drops of methyl red indicator, then add NH₄OH (sp gr 0.90) until the solution has turned distinctly yellow. Boil the solution for 2 min, then filter off the precipitated iron and aluminum hydroxides. Wash the precipitate on the filter with three successive additions of hot water.

(g) *Special Removal of Manganese with Iron and Aluminum.*—To the combined filtrate and washings procured under Paragraph (c) or (e) add 1 g of $(NH_4)_2S_2O_8$, and then NH_4OH (1:19) until the solution is definitely ammoniacal. Boil the solution for at least 15 min, with frequent additions of NH_4OH (1:19), to maintain a slight excess alkalinity. Allow to cool 10 to 15 min. Filter off the precipitate, and wash twice with NH_4Cl solution and at least three times with hot water.

(h) *Precipitation of Calcium Oxalate.*— To the filtrate procured under Paragraph (f) or (g), add approximately 10 ml of NH_4OH (sp gr 0.90) and heat the solution to the boiling point, but do not allow to boil. Add to the solution at the boiling point, drop by drop, saturated ammonium oxalate solution in excess. Hold the solution at the boiling point for several minutes, and then maintain at 80 to 90 C for at least 2 hr before filtration. Filter off the precipitate of calcium oxalate and wash on the filter with at least three successive additions of NH_4OH (1:19). Reserve the combined filtrate and washings if magnesium is to be determined.

(i) *Reprecipitation of Calcium Oxalate.* —Dissolve the precipitate and wash into the original beaker in which it was precipitated, by the addition of a few milliliters of HCl (1:1) to the filter. Wash the paper sparingly with at least three successive additions of hot water. Add a few drops of methyl red indicator. Then add NH_4OH (sp gr 0.90) until the solution has turned distinctly yellow, and heat the solution to the boiling point. Repeat the operations of precipitating, filtering, and

washing calcium oxalate as given in Paragraph (h). If magnesium is to be determined, add the combined filtrate and washings to that previously reserved from Paragraph (h).

(j) *Ignition of Calcium Precipitate.*— Ignite the filter paper and its contents to constant weight in a platinum crucible at a temperature between 1100 and 1200 C (Notes 2, 3, and 4).

Note 2.—The absorption of sulfur oxide from the flames of gas high in sulfur impinging on the crucible during ignition must be avoided.

Note 3.—The crucible should be cooled after ignition in a desiccator containing concentrated H_2SO_4.

Note 4.—The hygroscopic nature of CaO should be kept in mind during weighing.

(k) *Precipitation of Magnesium Ammonium Orthophosphate.*—Acidify the combined filtrates and washings procured under Paragraph (i) with HCl (sp gr 1.19). Add an excess of sodium ammonium hydrogen orthophosphate solution, and evaporate the solution slowly until a precipitate begins to crystallize (Note 5). Add NH_4OH (sp gr 0.90) to the hot solution, drop by drop, with constant stirring, until approximately 5 ml more than the amount required to make the solution definitely ammoniacal is present. Continue stirring for several minutes until precipitation is complete, and allow the precipitate to stand for at least 4 hr at room temperature. Filter off the precipitate and wash ten times on the filter paper with NH_4OH (1:19).

Note 5.—Diammonium hydrogen orthophosphate may be used as a precipitant in place of sodium ammonium hydrogen orthophosphate, if preferred.

(l) *Reprecipitation of Magnesium Ammonium Orthophosphate.*—Wash the precipitate back into the original beaker with cold water, and dissolve with hot HCl (1:1). Repeat the operations of precipitating, filtering, and washing the magnesium ammonium orthophosphate, as given in Paragraph (k), using 1 to 2 ml of sodium ammonium hydrogen orthophosphate solution (Note 5) and washing finally with NH₄OH (1:19).

(m) *Ignition of Magnesium Precipitate.*—Place the filter paper and contents in a weighed crucible and dry thoroughly, after which slowly char and consume the paper without inflaming. Ignite the residue to constant weight (Note 6).

Note 6.—Unless ignition of paper and precipitate is done slowly and at a low temperature until carbon is consumed, the carbon becomes partially "fireproofed" and cannot be burned out.

Calculation

8. Calculate the concentrations of calcium ion and of magnesium ion, in parts per million, as follows:

$$\text{Calcium, ppm} = W_c \times \frac{714,600}{S}$$

$$\text{Magnesium, ppm} = W_m \times \frac{218,400}{S}$$

where:

W_c = grams of CaO,
W_m = grams of $Mg_2P_2O_7$, and
S = milliliters of sample.

Precision and Accuracy

9. Precision is determined primarily by balance reproducibility and ranges from about 0.1 per cent to about 2 per cent of the weight of precipitate, depending on the relationship of balance reproducibility to amount of precipitate weighed. Since double precipitation removes virtually all interferences, accuracy should equal precision.

Tentative Methods of Test for
CHLORIDE ION IN INDUSTRIAL WATER AND INDUSTRIAL WASTE WATER[1]

ASTM Designation: D 512 – 62 T

ISSUED, 1955; REVISED, 1962

(Includes Former Method D 1885)

These Tentative Methods have been approved by the sponsoring committee and accepted by the Society in accordance with established procedures, for use pending adoption as standard. Suggestions for revisions should be addressed to the Society at 1916 Race St., Philadelphia 3, Pa.

Scope

1. (*a*) These methods cover the determination of chloride ion in industrial water and industrial waste water. The following three methods are included:

	Sections
Referee Method A (Mercurimetric Titration)	5 to 12
Referee Method B (Silver Nitrate Titration)	13 to 19
Referee Method C (Colorimetric Method)	20 to 29

(*b*) Referee Method A is applicable to industrial water relatively low in solids and relatively free of heavy metal ions. Referee Method B is applicable to more mineralized industrial water and industrial waste water. Referee Method C covers the colorimetric determination of low concentrations of chloride ion in industrial waters having very low solids contents.

Definitions

2. For definitions of terms used in these methods, refer to the Definitions of Terms Relating to Industrial Water and Industrial Waste Water (ASTM Designation: D 1129).[2]

Purity of Reagents

3. (*a*) Reagent grade chemicals shall be used in all tests. Unless otherwise indicated, it is intended that all reagents shall conform to the specifications of the Committee on Analytical Reagents of the American Chemical Society, where such specifications are available.[3] Other grades may be used, provided it is first ascertained that the reagent is of sufficiently high purity to permit its use

---

[1] Under the standardization procedure of the Society, these methods are under the jurisdiction of the ASTM Committee D-19 on Industrial Water. A list of members may be found in the ASTM Year Book.

[2] Appears in this publication.

[3] "Reagent Chemicals, American Chemical Society Specifications," Am. Chemical Soc., Washington, D. C. For suggestions on the testing of reagents not listed by the American Chemical Society, see "Reagent Chemicals and Standards," by Joseph Rosin, D. Van Nostrand Co., Inc., New York, N. Y., and the "United States Pharmacopeia."

without lessening the accuracy of the determination.

(b) Unless otherwise indicated, references to water shall be understood to mean reagent water conforming to the Specifications for Reagent Water (ASTM Designation: D 1193).[2] In addition, reagent water shall be free of halide ion.

Sampling

4. Collect the sample in accordance with the applicable method of the American Society for Testing and Materials, as follows:

D 510—Sampling Industrial Water,[2]
D 860—Sampling Water from Boilers,[2]
D 1066—Sampling Steam.[2]
D 1496—Sampling Homogeneous Industrial Waste Water.[2]

REFEREE METHOD A

(Mercurimetric Titration)[4]

Application

5. This method can be used to determine all concentrations of chloride ion in industrial water, provided intolerable interferences are absent. It is particularly useful for analysis of boiler water, boiler feedwater, distillate, condensate, and other relatively pure industrial waters where low chloride concentrations must be determined accurately.

Summary of Method

6. Dilute mercuric nitrate solution is added to an acidified sample in the presence of mixed diphenylcarbazone—bromophenol blue indicator. The end point of the titration is the formation of the blue-violet mercury diphenylcarbazone complex.

___

[4] For information of interest in connection with this method, and supporting data, reference may be made to F. E. Clarke, "Determination of Chloride in Water," *Analytical Chemistry,* Vol. 22, April, 1950, pp. 553–555, and Vol. 22, Nov., 1950, p. 1458.

Interferences

7. The anions and cations generally found in industrial water offer no interference. Zinc, lead, nickel, and ferrous and chromous ions affect solution and end-point colors, but do not reduce the accuracy of the titration when present in concentrations up to 100 ppm. Copper is tolerable up to 50 ppm. Titration in the presence of chromate ion requires indicator with extra background color (alphazurine) and prior reduction for concentrations above 100 ppm. Ferric ion above 10 ppm must be reduced before titration, and sulfite ion must be oxidized. A part of bromide ion and fluoride ion will be titrated with the chloride. Quaternary ammonium salts also interfere if present in significant amounts (1 to 2 ppm). Deep color also may interfere.

Apparatus

8. *Microburet,* 1-ml or 5-ml, with 0.01-ml graduation intervals.

Reagents

9. (a) *Hydrogen Peroxide (30 per cent)* (H_2O_2).

(b) *Hydroquinone Solution (10 g per liter).*—Dissolve 1 g of purified hydroquinone in water and dilute to 100 ml.

(c) *Mercuric Nitrate, Standard Solution (0.025 N).*—Dissolve 4.2830 g of mercuric nitrate ($Hg(NO_3)_2 \cdot H_2O$) in 50 ml of water acidified with 0.5 ml of concentrated nitric acid (HNO_3, sp gr 1.42). Dilute the acidified $Hg(NO_3)_2$ solution with water to 1 liter. Filter if necessary, and standardize against the standard sodium chloride (NaCl) solution, using the procedure described in Section 10 (Note 1).

(d) *Mercuric Nitrate, Standard Solution (0.0141 N).*—Dissolve 2.4200 g of $Hg(NO_3)_2 \cdot H_2O$ in 25 ml of water acidified with 0.25 ml of concentrated HNO_3 (sp gr 1.42). Dilute the acidified $Hg(NO_3)_2$ solution with water to 1 liter. Filter if necessary, and standardize against the standard NaCl solution, using the procedure described in Section 10 (Note 1).

Note 1: *Sharpness of End Point.*—The end point, while sharp, can be improved somewhat for certain types of water by adding to the titration sample several drops of an 0.05-g per liter solution of xylene cyanole FF or alphazurine blue green dye (color index 714). These chemicals can be mixed with the indicator in the same proportions.

(*e*) *Mixed Indicator.*—Dissolve 0.5 g of crystalline diphenylcarbazone[5] and 0.05 g of bromophenol blue powder in 75 ml of ethyl alcohol (95 per cent), and dilute to 100 ml with the alcohol (Note 2). Store in a brown bottle and discard after 6 months (Note 3).

Note 2.—Denatured alcohol is not suitable. Methanol or isopropanol may be used if pure ethyl alcohol is not available.

Note 3.—Liquid indicator generally deteriorates to the point that it yields no endpoint color after 12 to 18 months of storage. High temperature (above 100 F) and exposure to bright light may shorten storage life. A dry powder mixture of the two indicator ingredients is stable for much longer periods. Both the powder mixture (capsule form) and the liquid indicator are available commercially.

(*f*) *Nitric Acid (3:997).*—Mix 3 volumes of concentrated nitric acid (HNO_3, sp gr 1.42) with 997 volumes of water.

(*g*) *pH Indicating Paper.*—Long-range type, covering a pH range 1 to 11.[6]

(*h*) *Sodium Chloride, Standard Solution (0.025 N).*—Dry several grams of sodium chloride (NaCl) for 1 hr at 600 C.

[5] Eastman Kodak No. 4459S diphenylcarbazone and No. 752 tetrabromophenolsulfonephthalein (bromophenol blue) have been found satisfactory for this purpose. This diphenylcarbazone 1-bromophenol blue indicator is covered by U. S. Patent No. 2,784,064. By publication of this method the American Society for Testing and Materials does not undertake to insure anyone utilizing the method against liability for infringement of Letters Patent nor assume any such liability and such publication should not be construed as a recommendation of any patented or proprietary reagents or procedure that may be involved.
[6] pH Hydrion Paper A-B has been found satisfactory for this purpose.

Dissolve 1.4613 ± 0.0002 g of the dry salt in water, and dilute to 1 liter at 20 C in a volumetric flask (Note 4).

Note 4.—Drying for 2 hr at 105 C is adequate for practically all analytical work. If ultimate accuracy of standardization is desired, fuse NaCl and cool it in a desiccator.

(*i*) *Sodium Hydroxide Solution (10 g per liter).*—Dissolve 10 g of sodium hydroxide (NaOH) in water and dilute to 1 liter.

Procedure

10. (*a*) Use a volume of sample such that it will contain not more than 20 mg of chloride ion, diluting the sample with water to approximately 50-ml volume if necessary. If the volume of sample contains less than 2.5 mg of chloride ion, make the final titration as described in Paragraph (*b*), with 0.0141 N $Hg(NO_3)_2$ solution, using a 1 or 5-ml microburet. In this latter case, determine an indicator blank on 50 ml of chloride-free water, applying the same procedure followed for the sample. If the sample contains less than 0.1 ppm chloride, concentrate an appropriate volume of sample to 50 ml.

(*b*) Add 5 to 10 drops of mixed indicator, and shake or swirl the flask. If a blue-violet or red color develops, add HNO_3 (3:997) dropwise until the color changes to yellow. Add 1 ml of excess acid. If a yellow or orange color forms immediately on addition of the mixed indicator, add NaOH solution (10 g NaOH per liter) dropwise until the color changes to blue-violet; then add HNO_3 (3:997) dropwise until the color changes to yellow and further add 1 ml excess of acid (Note 5).

Note 5.—The prescribed acidification provides a satisfactory pH range of 3.0 to 3.5. Acidified samples on which electrometric pH measurements have been made shall not be used for chloride determinations, because the use of the calomel reference electrode may introduce error due to chloride contamination. Instrumental pH measurement may be made on an aliquot of the sample, the chloride content determined on the balance of the sample being corrected accordingly.

(c) Titrate the solution with 0.025 N Hg(NO$_3$)$_2$ solution until a blue-violet color, as viewed by transmitted light, persists throughout the solution (Note 6). Record the milliliters of Hg(NO$_3$)$_2$ solution added.

(d) If chromate ion is present in the absence of iron and in concentration less than 100 ppm, use the alphazurine modified mixed indicator (Note 1) and acidify the sample as described in Paragraph (a), but to pH 3 as indicated by pH indicating paper. Titrate the solution as described in Paragraph (b), but to an olive-purple end point (Note 6).

NOTE 6.—The use of indicator modifications and the presence of heavy metal ions can change solution colors without affecting accuracy of the determination. For example, solutions containing alphazurine may be bright blue when neutral, grayish purple when basic, blue-green when acidic, and blue-violet at the chloride end point. Solutions containing about 100 ppm nickel ion and normal mixed indicator are purple when neutral, green when acid, and gray at the chloride end point. When applying this method to samples that contain colored ions or that require modified indicator, it is recommended that the operator familiarize himself with the specific color changes involved by experimenting with solutions prepared as standards for comparison of color effects.

(e) If chromate ion is present in the absence of iron and in concentration greater than 100 ppm, add 2 ml of fresh hydroquinone solution and proceed as described in Paragraph (c).

(f) If ferric ion is present in the absence or presence of chromate ion, use a sample of such volume as to contain no more than 2.5 mg of ferric ion or of ferric ion plus chromate ion. Add 2 ml of fresh hydroquinone solution, and proceed as described in Paragraphs (a) and (b).

(g) If sulfite ion is present, add 0.5 ml of H$_2$O$_2$ to 50 ml of the sample in the Erlenmeyer flask and mix for 1 min. Then proceed as described in Paragraphs (a) and (b).

Calculation

11. Calculate the chloride ion concentration, in parts per million, in the original sample as follows:

$$\text{Chloride, ppm} = \frac{(V_1 - V_2) \times N \times 35\ 500}{S}$$

where:
V_1 = milliliters of standard Hg(NO$_3$)$_2$ solution required for titration of the sample,
V_2 = milliliters of standard Hg(NO$_3$)$_2$ solution required for titration of the blank,
N = normality of the Hg(NO$_3$)$_2$ solution, and
S = milliliters of sample used.

Precision

12. The precision of this method is 0.1 ppm or 2 per cent of the chloride ion content, whichever is greater.

REFEREE METHOD B
(Silver Nitrate Titration)

Application

13. This method is intended primarily for industrial water and industrial waste water where the chloride content is 5 ppm or more, and where interferences such as color or high concentrations of heavy metal ions render Referee Method A impracticable.

Summary of Method

14. Water adjusted to pH 8.3 is titrated with silver nitrate solution in the presence of potassium chromate indicator. The end point is indicated by persistence of the brick-red silver chromate color.

Interferences

15. Bromide, iodide, and sulfide are titrated along with the chloride. Ortho-

phosphate and polyphosphate interfere if present in concentrations greater than 250 and 25 ppm, respectively. Sulfite and objectionable color or turbidity must be eliminated. Compounds which precipitate at pH 8.3 (certain hydroxides) may cause error by occlusion.

Reagents

16. (a) *Hydrogen Peroxide (30 per cent) (H_2O_2).*

(b) *Phenolphthalein Indicator (5.0 g per liter).*—Dissolve 0.5 g of phenolphthalein in 50 ml of ethyl alcohol (95 per cent) (Note 7). Dilute to 100 ml with water.

NOTE 7.—Specially denatured ethyl alcohol conforming to Formula No. 3A or 30 of the U.S. Bureau of Internal Revenue may be substituted for ethyl alcohol (95 per cent).

(c) *Potassium Chromate Indicator.*—Dissolve 50 g of potassium chromate (K_2CrO_4) in 100 ml of water, and add silver nitrate ($AgNO_3$) until a slight red precipitate is produced. Allow the solution to stand, protected from light, for at least 24 hr after the addition of $AgNO_3$. Then filter the solution to remove the precipitate, and dilute to 1 liter with water.

(d) *Silver Nitrate, Standard Solution (0.025 N).*—Crush approximately 5 g of silver nitrate ($AgNO_3$) crystals and dry to constant weight at 40 C. Dissolve 4.2473 ± 0.0002 g of the crushed, dried crystals in water and dilute to 1 liter. Standardize against the standard NaCl solution, using the procedure given in Section 17.

(e) *Sodium Chloride, Standard Solution (0.025 N).*—Prepare as described in Section 9(h).

(f) *Sodium Hydroxide Solution (10 g per liter.)*—Prepare as described in Section 9(i).

(g) *Sulfuric Acid (1:19).*—Carefully add 1 volume of concentrated sulfuric acid (H_2SO_4, sp gr 1.84) to 19 volumes of water, while mixing.

Procedure

17. (a) Pour 50 ml, or less, of the sample, containing not more than 20 nor less than 0.25 mg of chloride ion, into a casserole. Dilute to approximately 50 ml with water, if necessary. Adjust the pH to the phenolphthalein end point (pH 8.3), using H_2SO_4 (1:19) or NaOH solution (10 g per liter).

(b) Add approximately 1.0 ml of K_2CrO_4 indicator and mix. Add standard $AgNO_3$ solution dropwise from a 25-ml buret until the brick-red (or pink) color persists throughout the sample when illuminated with a yellow light or viewed with yellow goggles.

(c) Repeat the procedure described in Paragraphs (a) and (b), using exactly one half as much original sample, diluted to 50 ml with halide-free water.

(d) If sulfite ion is present, add 0.5 ml of H_2O_2 to the samples described in Paragraphs (a) and (c), and mix for 1 min. Adjust the pH, then proceed as described in Paragraphs (b) and (c).

Calculation

18. Calculate the chloride ion concentration in the original sample, in parts per million, as follows:

$$\text{Chloride, ppm} = \frac{(V_1 - V_2) \times N \times 71\ 000}{S}$$

where:
V_1 = milliliters of standard $AgNO_3$ solution added in titrating the sample prepared in Section 17(a),
V_2 = milliliters of standard $AgNO_3$ solution added in titrating the sample prepared in Section 17(c),
N = normality of standard $AgNO_3$ solution, and
S = milliliters of original sample in the 50-ml test sample prepared in Section 17(a).

52-48

Precision

19. The precision of this method was not universally tested.

REFEREE METHOD C

(Colorimetric Method)

Application

20. This method[7] may be applied to waters containing chloride ion in concentrations from 0.02 to 10 ppm. It is

TABLE I.—CONCENTRATION RANGES FOR COLOR MEASUREMENT.

Method of Color Measurement	Optimum Range, mg of chloride ion per 25-ml water sample
Nessler tubes, 300 mm	0.005 to 0.25
Filter photometer, blue filter, 425 mμ, 2.3-cm cell	0.003 to 0.25
Spectrophotometer, 463 mμ:	
1.0-cm cell	0.005 to 0.25
10-cm cell	0.0005 to 0.05

particularly useful for analysis of boiler water, boiler feedwaters, distillate, condensate, and other relatively pure industrial waters where low chloride concentrations must be determined accurately.

Summary of Method

21. Solutions of ferric ammonium sulfate and mercuric thiocyanate are added to the sample. The chloride ion reacts with the mercuric thiocyanate to produce

---

[7] For further information on this method, the following references may be of interest:

Iwasaki, Utsumi, and Ozawa, "New Colorimetric Determination of Chloride Using Mercuric Thiocyanate and Ferric Ion." *Bulletin, Chemical Soc. Japan,* Vol. 25, p. 226 (1952).

J. S. Swain, "Absorptiometric Determination of Low Concentrations of Chlorides," *Chemistry and Industry,* Society of Chemical Industry, Great Britain, No. 20, p. 418 (1956).

D. M. Zall, D. Fisher, and M. Q. Garner, "Photometric Determination of Chlorides in Water," *Analytical Chemistry,* Vol. 28, No. 11, p. 1655 (1956).

---

thiocyanate ion which in turn combines with ferric ion to form red ferric thiocyanate. The intensity of the color, which is proportional to the concentration of the chloride ion, is measured photometrically at a wavelength of 463 mμ, or by visual comparison with standard solutions.

Interferences

22. Bromides, iodides, cyanides, thiosulfates, and nitrites interfere in this method. Color, if present in the sample, will interfere with visual comparison and depending upon its spectral absorbance may interfere with the photometric measurement.

Apparatus

23. The apparatus for measurement of the color developed shall consist of Nessler tubes or a photometer suitable for measurements at a wavelength of 463 mμ (Note 8). Table I indicates the optimum range of concentration for some typical methods of color measurement.

NOTE 8.—Photometers and photometric practice prescribed in this method shall conform to the Recommended Practice for Photometric Methods for Chemical Analysis of Metals (ASTM Designation: E 60).[8]

Reagents

24. (a) *Ferric Alum Solution.*—Dissolve 5.0 g of ferrous ammonium sulfate ($Fe(NH_4)_2(SO_4)_2 \cdot 6H_2O$) in 20 ml of water. Add 38 ml of concentrated nitric acid (HNO_3, sp gr 1.42) and boil to oxidize the iron and remove the oxides of nitrogen. Dilute to 100 ml with halide-free water.

(b) *Mercuric Thiocyanate, Methanol Solution (3 g per liter).*—Dissolve 0.30 g of mercuric thiocyanate ($Hg(CNS)_2$) in

---

[8] 1967 Book of ASTM Standards, Part 32.

100 ml of methanol. Store in amber bottles. Allow to stand for at least 24 hr before using. (**Caution,** see Note 9). Do not use if more than four weeks old (Note 10).

Note 9: **Caution**—Mercuric salts are very poisonous. Due precautions should be observed when using this material.

Note 10.—A slight precipitate may form and settle out after the 24 hr. Care must be taken so that this precipitate is not resuspended when using the reagent. Only the clear, supernatant liquid must be used.

(c) *Sodium Chloride, Standard Solution* (*10 mg Cl⁻ per liter*).—Dry sodium chloride (NaCl) to constant weight at 105 C. Prepare a stock solution by dissolving exactly 1.649 of the dry salt in water and dilute to 1 liter. Prepare the standard solution as needed by diluting 10 ml of the stock solution to 1 liter with halide-free water. The resulting standard contains 10 mg of chloride ion per liter.

Sampling

25. Since chloride ion is a very common contaminant, extreme care must be exercised in the collection and processing of the sample (Note 11).

Note 11.—Soak all new glassware in ho nitric acid (HNO₃, 1:20) for several hours. To be certain that new glassware is conditioned for the test, run a chloride determination on halide-free water. After the run rinse the glassware thoroughly. Soak the glassware in halide-free water between tests. Discard all glassware that appears etched or scratched.

Calibration

26. (a) Prepare a series of reference standards by diluting suitable volumes of the standard chloride solution with halide-free water. The series should cover the optimum range of the selected method of color measurement described

in Table I. The temperature of the solutions used for calibration must be the same as that of the sample to be tested.

(b) Treat each reference standard as described in Section 27.

(c) Prepare a calibration curve by plotting the readings on the photometer versus the concentration of chlorides. When the scale of the photometer reads directly in absorbance, plot the curve on rectilinear paper. When the scale reads in transmittance, it is convenient to plot the results on semilog paper, using the single cycle log axis to plot transmittance and the linear axis to plot the concentrations.

Procedure

27. (a) Transfer 25 ml of sample to a glass-stoppered cylinder and add successively 5 ml of ferric alum solution and 2.5 ml of mercuric thiocyanate solution. Mix thoroughly and allow to stand for 10 min.

(b) Measure the intensity of the color formed either by comparison with suitable reference standards in Nessler tubes or by a photometer chosen to cover the desired range as indicated in Table I. Adjust the zero setting of the photometer by using 25 ml of halide-free water, tested in accordance with Paragraph (a), instead of the sample.

Calculation

28. Determine the number of milligrams of chloride ion in the sample either by direct visual comparison with reference standards or by use of a suitable calibration curve.

$$\text{Chloride, ppm} = 40\,A$$

where A = milligrams of chloride ion in the sample.

Precision[9]

29. The precision of the method, or over-all standard of deviation of error from the average error, varies with the quantity of chloride (Cl⁻) being determined. The precision can best be expressed as follows:

$$S_T = 0.011 + 0.094\ X$$

where S_T is the precision in parts per million at the concentration X (ppm).

---

[9] Supporting data giving results of cooperative tests have been filed at ASTM Headquarters.

Standard Methods of Test for

TOTAL CARBON DIOXIDE AND CALCULATION OF THE CARBONATE AND BICARBONATE IONS IN INDUSTRIAL WATER[1]

ASTM Designation: D 513 – 57 (1965)

ADOPTED, 1957; REAPPROVED, 1965

This Standard of the American Society for Testing and Materials is issued under the fixed designation D 513; the number immediately following the designation indicates the year of original adoption or, in the case of revision, the year of last revision. A number in parentheses indicates the year of last reapproval.

Scope

1. (a) These methods cover the determination of total carbon dioxide, both dissolved and chemically combined, in industrial water. The methods also cover the calculation of the concentrations of carbonic acid, bicarbonate ion, and carbonate ion. Two methods are given, as follows:

	Sections
Referee Method	5 to 12
Non-Referee Method	13 to 20

(b) The referee method provides the maximum accuracy and freedom from interference. The non-referee method requires less apparatus, but is less precise and more liable to interference problems.

Definitions

2. For definitions of terms used in these methods, refer to the Standard Definitions of Terms Relating to Industrial Water and Industrial Waste Water (ASTM Designation: D 1129).[2]

Purity of Reagents

3. (a) Reagent grade chemicals shall be used in all tests. Unless otherwise indicated, it is intended that all reagents shall conform to the specifications of the Committee on Analytical Reagents of the American Chemical Society, where such specifications are available.[3] Other grades may be used, provided it is first ascertained that the reagent is of sufficiently high purity to permit its use without lessening the accuracy of the determination.

(b) Unless otherwise indicated, refer-

---

[1] Under the standardization procedure of the Society, these methods are under the jurisdiction of the ASTM Committee D-19 on Industrial Water. A list of members may be found in the ASTM Year Book.

[2] Appears in this publication.

[3] "Reagent Chemicals, American Chemical Society Specifications," Am. Chem. Soc., Washington, D. C. For suggestions on the testing of reagents not listed by the American Chemical Society, see "Reagent Chemicals and Standards," by Joseph Rosin, D. Van Nostrand Co, Inc., New York, N. Y., and the "United States Pharmacopoeia."

ences to water shall be understood to mean reagent water conforming to the Specifications for Reagent Water (ASTM Designation: D 1193).[2]

Sampling

4. Collect the sample in accordance with the applicable method of the American Society for Testing and Materials, as follows:

D 510—Sampling Industrial Water,[2]
D 860—Sampling Water from Boilers,[2]
D 1066—Sampling Steam.[2]

REFEREE METHOD[4]

Application

5. All concentrations of carbon dioxide, carbonate ion, and bicarbonate ion in industrial water may be accurately determined by use of this method without interference by color, turbidity, and common contaminants.

Principle of Method

6. Carbon dioxide is liberated by acidifying and heating the sample in a closed system, which includes a condenser, a gas scrubber, a carbon dioxide absorber, an expansion bladder, and a circulating pump. The carbon dioxide combines with barium hydroxide in the absorber, and the excess hydroxide is titrated with standard acid.

Interferences

7. Any volatile acid, base, or barium precipitant not removed by the chromic acid scrubbing solution will interfere with the test. Hydrogen sulfide is a common water contaminant of this type, but provision is made for its removal.

---

[4] For information and supporting data in connection with this method, reference may be made to F. E. Clarke, "Determination of Carbon Dioxide in Water," *Analytical Chemistry*, Vol. **19**, November, 1947, p. 889.

Apparatus

8. The basic apparatus for the determination shall consist of an evolution flask, an absorption flask, and a pump connected into a closed system so that the contained air can be circulated continuously through both flasks. The recommended arrangement of apparatus and accessories is shown in Fig. 1. Details of a suitable condenser are shown in Fig. 2.

Reagents

9. (a) *Sulfuric Acid (7:993).*—Dilute 7 ml of H_2SO_4 (sp gr 1.84) to 1 liter with water.

(b) *Standard Hydrochloric Acid (0.04 N).*—Dilute 3.42 ml of HCl (sp gr 1.19) to 1 liter and standardize.

(c) *Barium Hydroxide Solution (2.7 g $Ba(OH)_2$ per liter).*—Dissolve 5.0 g of $Ba(OH)_2 \cdot 8H_2O$ in 1 liter of freshly boiled water. Store in a bottle fitted with an automatic-zero buret, and protect the air inlet of the bottle and the vent of the buret with soda-asbestos (Ascarite) or soda-lime tubes.

(d) *Phenolphthalein Indicator Solution.*—Dissolve 5 g of phenolphthalein in 1 liter of a 50 per cent solution of ethyl alcohol in water.

(e) *Scrubbing Solution.*—Prepare a saturated solution of $K_2Cr_2O_7$ in H_2SO_4 (sp gr 1.84) (Note 1).

Note 1.—This scrubbing solution will absorb interfering substances normally present, including NH_3 and SO_2, but not H_2S. The latter can be removed by a supplementary scrubber containing iodine solution (25.4 g I_2 per liter), placed between the $K_2Cr_2O_7$ - H_2SO_4 trap and the condenser.

Procedure

10. (a) *Blank Determination.*—Acidify 400 ml of water to the methyl orange end point (approximately pH 4) with H_2SO_4 (7:993) and boil vigorously in an Erlenmeyer flask for at least 15 min to remove dissolved CO_2, for

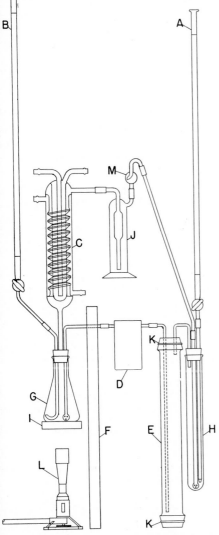

A—50-ml buret for HCl.
B—50-ml buret for H₂SO₄
C—Double Friedrichs condenser.[5]
D—Circulating pump.[6] Fully closed, bellows or diaphragm type, capable of circulating at least 1 liter of air per minute against the static water head of the system (approximately 3 ft).
E—Expansion bladder. Sufficient length of rubber, Gooch crucible tubing to contain the air displaced from the top of the evolution flask (*G*) without creating significant back pressure. A 20-in. length of 2-in. tubing with No. 11 rubber-stopper terminals generally is adequate.
F—Heat barrier, 1-in. Transite board.
G—Evolution flask, 300-ml Erlenmeyer.
H—Absorption flask, 3 by 30-cm test tube.
I—Ring support.
J—Purifying jar Fleming type, containing 10 to 25 ml of scrubbing solution. The jar should be cleaned and the scrubbing solution replaced whenever the solution becomes cloudy, diluted, or discolored, but not less frequently than monthly.
K—Rubber band for securing bladder.
L—Burner.
M—Kjeldahl connecting bulb.

Note.—This assembly of apparatus can be supported from two ring stands. For portable installation, an inverted U made from ½-in. rod of suitable length, with the open end welded to a heavy base, provides a compact and stable support.

Fɪɢ. 1.—Apparatus Assembly for Determination of Total Carbon Dioxide by the Evolution Method.

the purpose of making a blank determination.

(*1*) Add 0.2 ml of phenolphthalein indicator to the clean absorption flask, *H*, measure into it 50.00 ml of Ba(OH)₂ solution, and place the flask securely on the stopper, as shown in Fig. 1. Pour approximately 200 ml of the freshly boiled water into the evolution flask,

G, and add 15 ml of H₂SO₄ (7:993) from the buret, *B*. Turn on the cooling water

---

[5] Order from glassware manufacturer according to details given in Fig. 2.
[6] The air-vacuum "Dynapump," available from laboratory supply houses, and the Model 500 Autopulse electric fuel pump, available from automobile accessory suppliers, have been found satisfactory for this purpose.

to the condenser, *C*, light the burner, *L*, and heat the contents of the evolution flask rapidly to boiling. When boiling begins, start air circulation with the pump, *D*, reduce the burner flame to maintain boiling, without excessive refluxing, and continue boiling and air

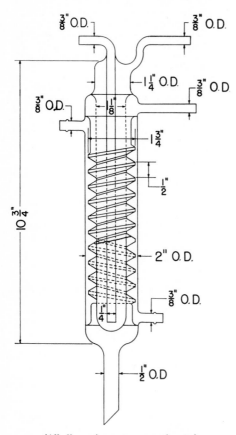

(All dimensions are approximate.)

FIG. 2.—Condenser for Carbon Dioxide Apparatus.

circulation for 5 min. Starting and stopping the pump several times in rapid succession, at the beginning of the circulation, will prevent priming while equalizing pressures. Without shutting off either pump or burner, titrate the $Ba(OH)_2$ in the absorption flask with 0.04 *N* HCl from the buret, *A*. The end point of the titration must be approached

slowly for accurate results or it will be either overrun or the pink color of phenolphthalein will reappear. Record the milliliters of HCl used in the titration as "*B*."

(2) Make one or more such blank determinations before each series of CO_2 determinations. If the apparatus and reagents have been unused for several days, a series of blank determinations may be required. Continue the series until three consecutive values check within 0.1 ml of 0.04 *N* HCl.

(*b*) *Carbon Dioxide Determination.*— Repeat the procedure described in Paragraph (*a*)(*1*) on a 200-ml portion of the clear sample (Notes 2 and 3). Record the milliliters of HCl added as "*S*."

NOTE 2.—If the carbon dioxide content of the sample exceeds 150 ppm, a proportionately smaller sample should be taken, followed by appropriate adjustment in the calculations in Section 10. If the carbon dioxide content is below 1 ppm, use a proportionately larger evolution flask and sample. In cases of unusual sample sizes, either the volume of air above the sample in the evolution flask must be kept the same, or the air bladder volume must be increased appropriately to prevent pressure build-up.

NOTE 3.—Where extremely accurate measurement of free CO_2 is required, special sample handling techniques are necessary. A satisfactory scheme is to evacuate the generating flask and introduce the sample at reduced pressure. Fig. 3 shows a suitable arrangement of the apparatus for this purpose.

(*c*) *pH Determination.*—Determine the pH of the clear sample (Note 4) by the Tentative Method for Determination of pH of Aqueous Solutions with the Glass Electrode (ASTM Designation: E 70).[2]

NOTE 4.—If the temperature of the sample at the time of the test is different from its temperature at the time of collection, a different CO_2 - HCO_3 - CO_3 equilibrium and a different pH will result. This may be partially overcome by cooling the sample to the collection temperature and shaking it thoroughly before opening it for CO_2 and pH tests.

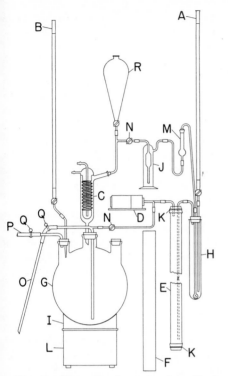

A—50-ml buret for HCl.
B—50-ml buret for H₂SO₄.
C—Double Friedrichs condenser.[5]
D—Circulating pump.[6] Fully closed, bellows or diaphragm type, capable of circulating at least 1 liter of air per minute against the static water head of the system (approximately 3 ft).
E—Expansion bladder. Sufficient length of rubber, Gooch crucible tubing to contain the air displaced from the top of the evolution flask (G) without creating significant back pressure. A 60-in. length of 2-in. tubing with No. 11 rubber-stopper terminals generally is adequate.
F—Heat barrier, 1-in. Transite board.
G—Evolution flask, 3-liter, 3-neck distillation flask.
H—Absorption flask, 3 by 30-cm test tube.
I—Ring or ceramic support.
J—Dry trap, Fleming purifying jar, 38 by 190 mm.
K—Rubber band for securing bladder.
L—Heater, 2-kw hot plate.
M—Mist trap, calcium chloride tube filled with glass wool.
N—Stopcocks, 6-mm tubing size.
O—Sample inlet, 12-mm glass tube.
P—Evacuation tube, 12-mm.
Q—Pinch clamps.
R—Carbon dioxide trap, 250-ml separatory funnel with soda lime.

Fɪɢ. 3.—Alternative Apparatus Assembly for Determination of Total Carbon Dioxide by the Evolution Method (Introduction of Sample at Reduced Pressure).

Calculations

11. (a) Calculate the total concentration of carbon dioxide, as follows:

Total carbon dioxide, ppm = 110 N ($B - S$)

where:

N = normality of HCl,
B = milliliters of HCl required for titration of 50 ml of Ba(OH)₂ solution (Section 10 (a)), and
S = milliliters of HCl required for titration of residual Ba(OH)₂ after absorption of the CO₂ evolved from the sample (Section 10 (b)).

(b) Estimate the concentrations in parts per million of carbonic acid, carbonate ion, and bicarbonate ion by means of the curves in Fig. 4 (Notes 5 and 6). These curves express the respective fractions of the total carbon dioxide that are present as undissociated carbonic acid (H₂CO₃), bicarbonate ion (HCO₃), and

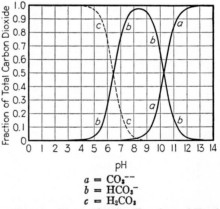

a = CO₃⁻⁻
b = HCO₃⁻
c = H₂CO₃

Fɪɢ. 4.—Curves Showing Fractions of Total Carbon Dioxide Present as the Respective Ions at Various Hydrogen Ion Concentrations.

carbonate ion (CO₃) at all pH levels. Using the pH of the original sample (Section 10 (c)) as the abscissa, read the corresponding ordinates of the three curves of Fig. 4 (Note 7) and record the three values (whose sum should equal 1.0) as *a*, *b*, and *c*, respectively. Calculate the several acid and ion concentrations in parts per million as follows:

$$CO_2 = 150\ Na\ (B - S)$$
$$HCO_3 = 152.5\ Nb\ (B - S)$$
$$H_2CO_3 = 155\ Nc\ (B - S)$$

Note 5.—Concentrations in parts per million can be converted to equivalents per million by the factors given in the Standard Method of Reporting Results of Analysis of Industrial Water and Industrial Waste Water (ASTM Designation: D 596).[2]

Note 6.—Since this method of estimating ion concentrations is based on data for the ionization of carbonic acid at 25 C, the values obtained hold for this temperature only. At any other temperature the ion concentrations will have other values, which may be calculated if the dissociation constants of carbonic acid at this temperature are known. The values for the ion concentrations obtained in this manner are first approximations based upon the assumption that the activity coefficient of each ion is unity.

Note 7.—For greater accuracy in reading,

TABLE 1—pH VALUES BASED ON DISSOCIATION CONSTANTS.

pH	Fraction of Total Carbon Dioxide[a] Present as		
	H_2CO_3	HCO_3^-	CO_3^{--}
2.0............	1.0000	....	....
2.5............	0.9999	0.0001	....
3.0............	0.9996	0.0004	....
3.5............	0.9986	0.0014	....
4.0............	0.9957	0.0043	....
4.5............	0.9866	0.0134	....
5.0............	0.9587	0.0413	....
5.5............	0.8800	0.1200	....
6.0............	0.6988	0.3012	0.0000
6.5............	0.4232	0.5767	0.0001
7.0............	0.1883	0.8113	0.0004
7.5............	0.0683	0.9303	0.0014
8.0............	0.0226	0.9728	0.0046
8.5............	0.0072	0.9783	0.0145
9.0............	0.0022	0.9530	0.0448
9.5............	0.0006	0.8701	0.1293
10.0............	0.0002	0.6801	0.3197
10.5............	0.0000	0.4022	0.5978
11.0............	....	0.1754	0.8246
11.5............	....	0.0630	0.9370
12.0............	....	0.0208	0.9792
12.5............	....	0.0067	0.9933
13.0............	....	0.0021	0.9979

[a] These values have been calculated from dissociation constants given in W. M. Latimer's "Oxidation Potentials," Prentice Hall, Inc., 1938, New York, N. Y.

the curves in Fig. 4 may be reproduced on a large scale from the data given in Table 1.

Precision and Accuracy

12. Total carbon dioxide in concentrations between 1 ppm and 50 ppm can be determined on a 200-ml sample with a precision of 0.25 ppm, and in concentrations above 50 ppm, with a precision of 0.5 ppm. Precision is correspondingly better when large samples are used for low concentrations. The accuracy of the determination is essentially the same as the precision. The precision of division of total carbon dioxide into the concentrations of coexisting ions depends on the accuracy with which the scale of Fig. 4 can be read and the accuracy with which temperature corrections are made.

Non-Referee Method

Application

13. This method is applicable to the determination of total carbon dioxide in waters when the amounts of silicates, phosphates, magnesium, iron, aluminum, or ammonia do not exceed the amounts shown under "Interferences." It is not applicable when iron and phosphate are present together, and special care must be taken when magnesium is present (Note 8).

Principle of Method

14. The carbon dioxide and bicarbonate ion are fixed with sodium hydroxide and precipitated as strontium carbonate. The solution is then neutralized, the carbon dioxide is removed by aeration in the presence of excess acid, and the quantity removed is determined by back-titration of the acid.

Interferences[7]

15. The following substances will not interfere, provided their concentrations are less than the values shown: 200 ppm

[7] Data on the effect of interferences on this method are given in Appendix I to the Report of Committee D-19, see *Proceedings*, Am. Soc. Testing Mats., Vol. 54 (1954).

phosphate; 50 ppm of iron, silica, or aluminum, and 25 ppm NH_4^-. Magnesium interferes with the end point of the first titration, which must be done slowly until a stable color forms. About 10 min titrating time is required for 25 ppm magnesium.

Apparatus

16. The apparatus shall consist of the following items, arranged as shown in Fig. 5:

(a) *Erlenmeyer Flask*, 500-ml, widemouth, fitted with a three-hole rubber stopper containing a Folin aeration inlet

0.1 g of $Ba(OH)_2$, and dilute to 1 liter with distilled water. Store in a paraffin-coated, chemically resistant glass bottle or a plastic bottle fitted with an automatic-zero buret, and protect both the air inlet of the bottle and the vent of the buret with soda-lime or Ascarite tubes. Allow the carbonate to settle and standardize against the 0.04 N HCl.

(d) *Strontium Chloride Solution* (*100 g $SrCl_2$ per liter*).—Dissolve 100 g of $SrCl_2$ in water and dilute to 1 liter.

Procedure

18. (a) Place 50 ml of 0.04 N NaOH

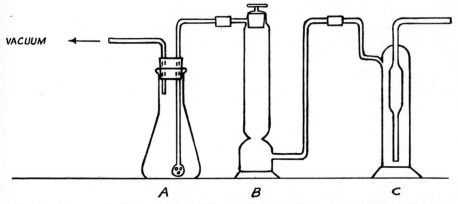

FIG. 5.—Apparatus for Determination of Total Carbon Dioxide by the Non-Referee Method.

tube, an outlet tube, and a removable glass-rod plug.

(b) *Two-Compartment Purifying Jar*, with the lower compartment filled with glass wool and the upper compartment filled with soda-asbestos (Ascarite).

(c) *Fleming Purifying Jar*, one-third full of H_2SO_4 (sp gr 1.84).

Reagents

17. (a) *Standard Hydrochloric Acid* (*0.04 N*).—See Section 9(b).

(b) *Phenolphthalein Indicator*.—See Section 9(d).

(c) *Standard Sodium Hydroxide Solution* (*0.04 N*).—Dissolve 1.7 g of NaOH in approximately 100 ml of water, add

solution and 0.2 ml of phenolphthalein indicator in a 500-ml wide-mouth Erlenmeyer flask and add 200 ml of sample and a strip each of pH 10–12 and pH 12–14 indicator papers. If the solution is below pH 12, start again with a smaller sample. Stopper and let the solution stand for a few minutes. Add 10 ml of $SrCl_2$ solution, insert the three-hole stopper containing inlet and outlet tubes and glass rod, and shake thoroughly until the $SrCO_3$ appears to be completely precipitated. Then let stand at least 5 min.

(b) Remove the glass rod. Through the opening in the stopper add slowly from a buret, with constant agitation, sufficient 0.04 N HCl to make the solution just colorless and keep it so for 1 min; then add 50.0 ml of 0.04 N HCl and replace the glass rod. Attach the inlet tube to the purification train and the outlet tube to a source of vacuum (see Fig. 5). Draw air through the aspirator at the rate of approximately 1 liter per min for 5 min.

(c) Remove the flask, take out the glass rod, and slowly titrate to a persistent pink color with 0.04 N NaOH solution. Record the volume, in milliliters, of NaOH solution added as "S."

(d) Repeat the operations described in Paragraphs (a) to (c) except to add, in place of the measured volume of sample, the same volume of freshly boiled water (Note 8). Record the volume, in milliliters, of 0.04 N NaOH solution required as "B."

Note 8.—If magnesium, ammonium, or aluminum ions are present in the water to be tested, a standard carbonate solution should be made to contain the suspected concentrations of the constituents, so that the character of the end point can be studied and taken into account in titration of the sample.

Calculations

19. Calculate the total concentration of carbon dioxide, and estimate the concentration of carbonic acid and carbonate and bicarbonate ions as described in Section 11(a) and (b).

Precision and Accuracy

20. Total carbon dioxide in concentrations below 50 ppm can be determined with a precision of ±1 ppm, and in concentrations above 50 ppm, with a precision of ±2 ppm. Accuracy approaches precision if interfering substances are absent. In other cases, it must be established by use of the Referee Method (Sections 5 to 12).

Standard Method of Test for

HYDROXIDE ION IN INDUSTRIAL WATER AND INDUSTRIAL WASTE WATER[1]

ASTM Designation: D 514 – 47 (1965)

ADOPTED, 1941; REVISED, 1947; REAPPROVED, 1965

This Standard of the American Society for Testing and Materials is issued under the fixed designation D 514; the number immediately following the designation indicates the year of original adoption or, in the case of revision, the year of last revision. A number in parentheses indicates the year of last reapproval.

NOTE.—This method was editorially revised and rearranged in March, 1955.

Scope and Application

1. This method covers the volumetric, differential titration of hydroxide ion. It is intended primarily for alkaline industrial waters, like boiler feedwaters and boiler waters, but is also applicable to industrial waste waters where interferences are not excessive.

Principle of Method

2. Hydroxide ion is titrated to the phenolphthalein end point with acid after strontium chloride is added to precipitate carbonate and phosphate ions.

Definitions

3. For definitions of terms used in this method, refer to the Definitions of Terms Relating to Industrial Water and Indus-

trial Waste Water (ASTM Designation: D 1129).[2]

Interferences

4. There is no known method of chemical analysis by which the exact concentration of hydroxide ion may be determined when other acid-consuming components are present. Aluminates, silicates, chromates, and organic matter affect the titration to some extent. If their combined concentrations are very low as compared with that of hydroxide ion (10 per cent or less), interference should be tolerable.

Purity of Reagents

5. (*a*) Reagent grade chemicals shall be used in all tests. Unless otherwise indicated, it is intended that all reagents shall conform to the specifications of the Committee on Analytical Reagents of

[1] Under the standardization procedure of the Society, this method is under the jurisdiction of the ASTM Committee D-19 on Industrial Water. A list of members may be found in the ASTM Year Book.

[2] Appears in this publication.

17–89

the American Chemical Society, where such specifications are available.[3] Other grades may be used, provided it is first ascertained that the reagent is of sufficiently high purity to permit its use without lessening the accuracy of the determination.

(b) Unless otherwise indicated, references to water shall be understood to mean reagent water conforming to the Specifications for Reagent Water (ASTM Designation: D 1193).[2]

Reagents

6. (a) *Standard Acid (0.02 N).*—Mix 1.71 ml of HCl (sp gr 1.19) or 0.56 ml of H_2SO_4 (sp gr 1.84) with 700 ml of water, dilute to 1 liter with water, and standardize.

(b) *Phenolphthalein Indicator.*—Dissolve 0.5 g of phenolphthalein in 100 ml of a 50 per cent solution of ethyl alcohol in water.

(c) *Strontium Chloride Solution (2.68 g SrCl₂ per liter).*—Dissolve 4.5 g of $SrCl_2 \cdot 6H_2O$ in water and dilute to 1 liter.

Sampling

7. Collect the sample in accordance with the applicable method of the American Society for Testing and Materials, as follows:

D 510—Sampling Industrial Water,[2]
D 860—Sampling Water from Boilers,[2]
D 1066—Sampling Steam.[2]

[3] "Reagent Chemicals, American Chemical Society Specifications," Am. Chem. Soc., Washington, D. C. For suggestions on the testing of reagents not listed by the American Chemical Society, see "Reagent Chemicals and Standards," by Joseph Rosin, D. Van Nostrand Co., Inc., New York, N. Y., and the "United States Pharmacopeia."

Procedure

8. (a) Pour into a 250-ml Erlenmeyer flask 100 ml, or less, of sample containing not more than 15 mg of hydroxide ion. Dilute to 100 ml, if necessary.

(b) Add quickly, while stirring, 1 ml of SrCl₂ solution for each milligram of either carbonate ion or orthophosphate ion present, plus a 4-ml excess (Note).

Note.—If the concentrations of carbonate and phosphate are not known, sufficient SrCl₂ should be added to cover the highest probable concentration. The excess reagent used will not interfere, but may produce turbidity by precipitating $SrSO_4$.

(c) Stopper the flask loosely to minimize CO_2 absorption, boil the solution for a few seconds, and then cool with the stopper in place.

(d) Remove the stopper, add 0.2 ml of phenolphthalein indicator (approximately 4 drops) and quickly titrate the sample to the phenolphthalein end point (pink to colorless) with standard acid. Swirl the sample continuously during titration to prevent solution of the precipitate.

Calculation

9. Calculate the concentration of hydroxide ion, in parts per million, as follows:

$$\text{Hydroxide ion, ppm} = \frac{17000 \times N \times V}{S}$$

where:
N = normality of standard acid,
V = milliliters of standard acid used, and
S = milliliters of original sample.

Tentative Methods of Test for
PHOSPHATE IN INDUSTRIAL WATER[1]

ASTM Designation: D 515 - 66 T

Issued, 1955; Last Revised, 1966

These Tentative Methods have been approved by the sponsoring committee and accepted by the Society in accordance with established procedures, for use pending adoption as standard. Suggestions for revisions should be addressed to the Society at 1916 Race St., Philadelphia, Pa. 19103.

1. Scope

1.1 These methods cover the determination of dissolved phosphates in industrial water. The following four methods are included:

	Sections
Referee Method (Gravimetric Method)	5 to 11
Non-Referee Method A (Colorimetric Amino Reduction Method)	12 to 20
Non-Referee Method B (Colorimetric Vanadomolybdate Method)	21 to 29
Non-Referee Method C (Colorimetric Stannous Chloride Reduction Method)	30 to 38

1.2 All of the methods are based on reactions that are specific for the orthophosphate ion. Preliminary treatment is provided for removal of color and turbidity. Heating in the presence of strong acids is included in three methods to convert most polyphosphates to the ortho form. As described, the gravimetric method is used to determine all phosphates that can be dissolved and con-verted to the ortho form by the prescribed treatment. Non-Referee Method B covers the determination of only orthophosphate, whereas Non-Referee Methods A and C cover the determination of both ortho and total phosphate. Selection of the method to use for a specific water depends on its expected phosphate content and possible interfering ions in the water.

2. Definitions

2.1 For definitions of terms used in these methods, refer to ASTM Definitions D 1129, Terms Relating to Industrial Water and Industrial Waste Water.[2]

3. Purity of Reagents

3.1 Reagent grade chemicals, or equivalent, as specified in ASTM Methods E 200, Preparation, Standardization, and Storage of Standard Solutions for Chemical Analysis[2] shall be used in all tests.

3.2 Unless otherwise indicated, references to water shall be understood to

[1] Under the standardization procedure of the Society, these methods are under the jurisdiction of the ASTM Committee D-19 on Industrial Water. A list of members may be found in the ASTM Year Book.

[2] Appears in this publication.

mean reagent water conforming to ASTM Specifications D 1193, for Reagent Water.[2] Either grade of water may be used in these methods.

4. Sampling

4.1 Collect the sample in accordance with the applicable method of the American Society for Testing and Materials, as follows:

D 510—Sampling Industrial Water,[2]
D 860—Sampling Water from Boilers,[2] and
D 1066—Sampling Steam.[2]

REFEREE METHOD

(Gravimetric Method)

5. Application

5.1 This method is applicable to all industrial water, but is best performed when the sample aliquot contains 10 mg or more of PO_4.

6. Summary of Method

6.1 Two successive separations of orthophosphate ion are made, first as ammonium phosphomolybdate and then as magnesium ammonium phosphate. The latter is ignited to magnesium pyrophosphate and weighed.

7. Interferences

7.1 Phosphite interferes by conversion to orthophosphate. Arsenic and vanadium compounds are precipitated along with phosphate, and must be removed. Precipitation of the ammonium phosphomolybdate is retarded by hydrochloric, sulfuric, or hydrofluoric acids and their ammonium salts, hence their use in samples prior to the determination of phosphate should be kept to a minimum.

8. Reagents

8.1 *Ammonium Hydroxide (sp gr 0.90)*—Concentrated ammonium hydroxide (NH_4OH).

8.2 *Ammonium Hydroxide (1:1)*—Mix 1 volume of concentrated NH_4OH (sp gr 0.90) with 1 volume of water.

8.3 *Ammonium Hydroxide (1:19)*—Mix 1 volume of concentrated NH_4OH (sp gr 0.90) with 19 volumes of water.

8.4 *Ammonium Nitrate Solution (20 g/liter)*—Dissolve 2 g of ammonium nitrate (NH_4NO_3) in water and dilute to 100 ml.

8.5 *Hydrochloric Acid (sp gr 1.19)*—Concentrated hydrochloric acid (HCl).

8.6 *Magnesia Mixture*—Dissolve 50 g of magnesium chloride ($MgCl_2 \cdot 6H_2O$) and 100 g of ammonium chloride (NH_4Cl) in 500 ml of water. Add concentrated NH_4OH (sp gr 0.90) in slight excess, using litmus paper as the indicator, and allow the solution to stand overnight. If a precipitate develops, filter using fine textured paper before diluting to 1 liter with water.

8.7 *Methyl Orange Indicator (0.5 g/liter)*—Dissolve 0.05 g of methyl orange in water and dilute to 100 ml.

8.8 *Molybdate Solution*—Dissolve 118 g of molybdic acid (85 per cent MoO_3) in a mixture of 400 ml of water and 80 ml of concentrated NH_4OH (sp gr 0.90). Prepare a second solution containing 400 ml of concentrated nitric acid (HNO_3, sp gr 1.42) and 600 ml of water. While vigorously stirring the HNO_3, slowly add the molybdate solution. Let the mixture stand for 24 to 48 hr; then filter through a sintered-glass funnel.

8.9 *Nitric Acid (sp gr 1.42)*—Concentrated nitric acid (HNO_3).

8.10 *Potassium Nitrate* (KNO_3).

8.11 *Silver Nitrate Solution (100 g/liter)*—Dissolve 10 g of silver nitrate ($AgNO_3$) in water and dilute to 100 ml.

8.12 *Wetting Agent*—Add 1 ml of a 100 per cent active nonionic liquid wetting agent to 1 liter of water and mix.

9. Procedure

9.1 *Preparation of Sample*—Measure

into a beaker a quantity of sample containing phosphates equivalent to not less than 10 nor more than 50 mg of PO_4. Concentrate, or dilute with water, if necessary, to approximately 100 ml (Notes 1 and 2). Add 4 g of KNO_3 and boil for 1 min. Allow to stand for several minutes to settle the coagulated material (Note 3). Filter through a very retentive filter paper into a 400-ml beaker. Wash the residue twice with a minimum volume of water, allowing the funnel to drain completely after each washing.

Note 1—If boiling is required to concentrate the sample, the pH of the resulting solution should be adjusted to approximately the same value as that of the original sample; otherwise, some dissolved phosphate may precipitate or precipitated phosphate may dissolve. Use a 10 per cent by weight solution of NaOH or HNO_3 for the adjustment.

Note 2—Omit the coagulation step described in 9.1 and proceed to 9.2 if a measure of both precipitated and dissolved phosphate is desired. In this case take a representative, well-mixed sample.

Note 3—A clear aliquot can normally be expected after coagulation. However, in some samples, for example, tannin- or lignin-treated boiler water, precipitated phosphate removal may not be complete. In such cases add 2 to 4 ml of sodium hypochlorite solution (5 per cent available chlorine, phosphate-free), and boil the sample for 1 additional minute.

9.2 *Conversion of Polyphosphates to Orthophosphate*—To the filtrate and washings add 3 or 4 drops of methyl orange indicator. Add 15 ml of HNO_3 in excess of that required to neutralize the sample. Cover the beaker and boil the acidified solution for at least 30 min (Note 4). The volume after boiling should be between 25 and 50 ml. Cool, and dilute to approximately 100 ml with water. Neutralize the sample with concentrated NH_4OH (sp gr 0.90) and add 5 ml of HNO_3. Filter the solution if turbid.

Note 4—If the sample is known to contain only orthophosphates, the solution need not be boiled. On the other hand, certain complex phosphates may require a 6 to 12-hr digestion period for complete conversion.

9.3 *Precipitation as Ammonium Phosphomolybdate*—Heat the solution to 80 to 85 C and slowly add 15 ml of molybdate solution, swirling the beaker while adding the reagent. Continue the agitation until the precipitate starts to form. Allow the beaker to stand quietly for 1 hr at a temperature of 40 to 60 C, agitate again by swirling, then set aside at room temperature for not less than 12 hr. Add one drop of wetting agent to the sample and separate the precipitate by filtration through a sintered-glass crucible (with suction) or through a medium retentive filter paper (Note 5); wash the filter five times with NH_4NO_3 solution. Discard the filtrate and washings.

Note 5—A stream of NH_4NO_3 solution from a wash bottle should be used for transferring the precipitate from the beaker to the filter. Complete transfer is readily effected in this manner. The use of stirring rods and policemen should be avoided, since they cause the precipitate to smear and make its removal difficult.

9.4 *Precipitation as Magnesium Ammonium Phosphate*—Dissolve the ammonium phosphomolybdate on the filter with a fine stream of warm NH_4OH (1:1), collecting the solution in a 400-ml beaker. Adjust the volume of the solution to 100 to 150 ml with water, add three or four drops of methyl orange indicator, then add HCl to neutralize the NH_4OH. A yellow precipitate forms during acidification but redissolves when sufficient acid has been added. Continue adding acid dropwise beyond the methyl orange end point until the precipitate disappears. To the acidified solution add dropwise, with constant stirring, 15 ml of magnesia mixture. Continue to stir and neutralize the acidity by very slow addition of NH_4OH (1:1). Add 10 ml excess NH_4OH (1:1) for each 100 ml of solution. Agitate well and set aside for not less than 4 hr. Collect the precipitate on very retentive, ashless filter paper and wash it with NH_4OH (1:19) until free of chlorides, as indicated by lack of turbidity on addition of $AgNO_3$ solution to the last portion of washings. Transfer the paper and contents to a weighed platinum or porcelain crucible.

9.5 *Ignition*—Char the paper at low temperature, burn off the carbon at a temperature below 900 C, and then ignite to constant weight at 1050 to to 1100 C. Cool in a desiccator and weigh the residue as magnesium pyrophosphate ($Mg_2P_2O_7$).

10. Calculation

10.1 Calculate the PO_4 equivalent of the dissolved phosphate (Note 6) in the sample, in parts per million, as follows:

$$\text{Phosphate, ppm } PO_4 = \frac{W \times 853,400}{S}$$

where:
W = grams of precipitate, and
S = milliliters of sample used.

Note 6—Both particulate and dissolved phosphates are measured if the coagulation filtration step in 9.1 is omitted. In that event it shall be so indicated when reporting results.

11. Precision

11.1 The precision of this method may be expressed as follows:

$$S_T = \frac{5a + 250}{S}$$

where:
S_T = over-all precision, ppm,
a = concentration of phosphate in the sample tested, ppm, and
S = milliliters of sample used.

Non-Referee Method A

(Colorimetric Amino Reduction Method)

12. Application

12.1 This method is applicable to the routine determination of either orthophosphate or total phosphate (orthophosphate plus polyphosphate) in industrial waters containing 0.5 to 10 ppm PO_4. This method, modified by the addition of bismuth salt[3] to the acid reagent, is applicable to industrial waters containing 0.1 to 2.5 ppm PO_4. The ranges, which can be extended upward by diluting a smaller aliquot to the prescribed volume, are for photometric measurements in a 20-mm cell.

13. Summary of Method

13.1 Orthophosphate reacts with ammonium molybdate in an acid medium to form a phosphomolybdate which in turn is reduced to a molybdenum blue complex with amino-naphthol-sulfonic acid. The color is proportional in intensity to the phosphate concentration. When bismuth salt is added to the sulfuric acid reagent, the intensity of the blue color developed in the test is increased fourfold.

13.2 Only orthophosphate forms a blue color in the test. Such polyphosphates as pyro-, meta-, and tripolyphosphate, however, can be made to react in the test if hydrolyzed to the ortho form by boiling the acidified sample. Thus, the polyphosphate content of a water can be calculated by subtracting the orthophosphate found in an unboiled sample from the total phosphate found in an acidified, boiled sample. Certain organic phosphates are partially or totally hydrolyzed to the reactive ortho form and are measured in the total phosphate determination.

14. Interferences

14.1 Up to 40 ppm iron, 75 ppm chromate and 50,000 ppm chloride will not

---

[3] Use of bismuth salt in the test is based on the article by R. S. Robertson, "Rapid Method for Estimation of Total Phosphate in Water," *Journal*, Am. Water Works Assn., Vol. 52, p. 483 (1960).

interfere with the test. If more than 75 ppm chromate are present in the sample, the reference solution for the photometric measurement should not be water; instead it must be the sample treated with all reagents except the molybdate solution. No more than 1500 ppm chloride should be present in the sample when the bismuth modification is followed. Interference from nitrite can be overcome by adding 0.1 g of sulfamic acid to the sample before adding the molybdate. A silica concentration fifty times larger than that of the phosphate will cause an error of less than 2 per cent.

14.2 When sulfide is present in concentrations higher than several parts per million, a blue color forms after adding the molybdate. This interference can be eliminated by adding sufficient saturated potassium permanganate solution to the sample to produce a permanent, weak pink color before adding the molybdate. If a sample, such as a boiler water, contains a dispersing agent, filtration may not remove precipitated phosphates completely. To floc the precipitated phosphates, in this case, the sample should be heated in the presence of potassium nitrate and sodium hypochlorite before filtering, as given in 9.1 and Note 3. To prevent formation of calcium sulfate precipitate, 7 ml of concentrated hydrochloric acid (HCl, sp gr 1.19) should be used in place of the sulfuric acid solution when calcium in the sample is greater than 200 ppm.

14.3 Rapidity of the blue color development depends on temperature. The temperature of the sample and reagents should be between 70 and 95 F (21 and 35 C).

15. Apparatus

15.1 *Photometer*—A spectrophotometer or filter photometer suitable for measurements at 650 mμ. Filter photometers and photometric practices pre-scribed in this method shall conform to ASTM Recommended Practice E 60, Photometric Methods for Chemical Analysis of Metals,[4] and spectrophotometers to ASTM Recommended Practice E 275, Describing and Measuring Performance of Spectrophotometers.[5] The range specified in 12.1 is applicable to test solutions measured in a 20-mm cell.

16. Reagents

16.1 *Amino Solution*—Dissolve in 100 ml of water the following chemicals in the given order: 3.7 g of sodium sulfite (Na_2SO_3), 0.100 g of 1-amino-2-naphthol-4-sulfonic acid,[6] and 6.2 g of sodium metabisulfite ($Na_2S_2O_5$). Store the solution in an amber bottle and make up fresh every two weeks.

16.2 *Ammonium Molybdate Solution (48 g/liter)*—Dissolve 48 g of ammonium molybdate [$(NH_4)_6Mo_7O_{24}\cdot4H_2O$] in about 800 ml of water. Add 2.5 ml of concentrated ammonium hydroxide (NH_4OH, sp gr 0.90) and dilute to 1 liter with water.

16.3 *Phosphate, Standard Solution (1 ml = 0.01 mg PO$_4$)*—Prepare a standard phosphate solution containing 0.1 mg of PO_4/ml by dissolving 0.1433 g of oven-dried potassium dihydrogen phosphate (KH_2PO_4) in water and diluting to 1 liter. Dilute 100 ml of this solution to 1 liter with water.

16.4 *Sulfuric Acid Solution*—Add 370 ml of concentrated sulfuric acid (H_2SO_4, sp gr 1.84) slowly to about 600 ml of water. Cool and dilute the solution to 1 liter with water.

16.5 *Sulfuric Acid Solution (Bi added)*—Dissolve 1.200 g of bismuth nitrate [$Bi(NO_3)_3\cdot5H_2O$] in 250 ml of the H_2SO_4 solution while still warm.

---

[4] *1967 Book of ASTM Standards*, Part 32.
[5] *1967 Book of ASTM Standards*, Part 30.
[6] Eastman Kodak No. 360 chemical has been found satisfactory for this purpose.

17. Calibration

17.1 *For Range 0.5 to 10 ppm:*

17.1.1 Prepare a series of standard phosphate solutions to cover the range from 0 to 10 ppm. Make up the standards by diluting suitable volumes of phosphate solution (1 ml = 0.01 mg PO_4) to 100 ml with water. One milliliter of phosphate solution diluted to 100 ml produces a standard containing 0.1 ppm PO_4.

17.1.2 Develop color in the series of standards as directed in 18.1. Measure the color absorbance of each standard at 650 mμ using water as the reference solution for the initial photometer setting to zero. Plot the absorbance values as ordinates and the corresponding phosphate concentrations as abscissas (Note 7).

Note 7—A separate calibration curve must be made for each photometer. Each curve must be checked periodically to ensure reproducibility.

17.2 *For Range 0.1 to 2.5 ppm:*

17.2.1 Prepare a series of standard phosphate solutions to cover the range from 0 to 2.5 ppm. Make up the standards by diluting suitable volumes of phosphate solution (1 ml = 0.01 mg PO_4) to 100 ml with water. One milliliter of phosphate solution diluted to 100 ml produces a standard containing 0.1 ppm PO_4.

17.2.2 Develop color in the series of standards as directed in 18.3. Measure the color absorbance at 650 mμ of each standard, using water as the reference solution for the initial photometer setting to zero. Plot the absorbance values as ordinates and the corresponding phosphate concentrations as abscissas (Note 7).

18. Procedure

18.1 *Orthophosphate, Range 0.5 to 10 ppm:*

18.1.1 Transfer 100 ml of the clear sample containing 10 ppm PO_4 or less into a 250-ml Erlenmeyer flask. For higher concentrations, use a smaller sample and dilute to 100 ml with water. Filter the sample if turbid. If the sample contains a dispersive, treat with potassium nitrate (KNO_3) and sodium hypochlorite (NaOCl) as described in 9.1 and Note 3 before filtering. Limit filtrate washing to avoid a volume greater than 100 ml.

18.1.2 Add the following reagents in the given order to the sample, mixing after each addition: 5 ml of H_2SO_4 solution, 5 ml of ammonium molybdate solution, and 5 ml of amino solution. Allow 10 min for color development.

18.1.3 Measure color absorbance of the test sample at 650 mμ, employing water as the reference solution. See 14.1 when chromate is higher than 75 ppm in the sample analyzed. Record the orthophosphate concentration indicated by the calibration curve established in 17.1.

18.2 *Total Phosphate, Range 0.5 to 10 ppm:*

18.2.1 Proceed as described in 18.1.1.

18.2.2 Add 5 ml of H_2SO_4 solution to the sample. Use 7 ml of concentrated hydrochloric acid (HCl, sp gr 1.19) instead of 5 ml of H_2SO_4 solution if the calcium in the sample is more than 200 ppm. Boil the solution for at least 30 min on a hot plate, adding water to keep the volume between 25 and 100 ml. Alternatively, heat the solution for 10 min in an autoclave or pressure cooker at 15 to 20 psig. Cool the solution to about 75 F (24 C). Do not overchill the solution. Dilute the solution to 105 ml with water by means of a plastic graduated cylinder having a mark made at the 105-ml level.

18.2.3 Add 5 ml of ammonium molybdate solution and 5 ml of amino solution, mixing after each addition. Allow 10.0 min for color development.

18.2.4 Proceed as described in 18.1.3 to obtain total phosphate.

18.3 *Orthophosphate, Range 0.1 to 2.5 ppm:*

18.3.1 Proceed as described in 18.1 using 5 ml of the H_2SO_4 solution containing bismuth in place of the 5 ml of H_2SO_4 solution.

18.4 *Total Phosphate, Range 0.1 to 2.5 ppm:*

18.4.1 Proceed as described in 18.2 using 5 ml of the H_2SO_4 solution containing bismuth in place of the 5 ml of H_2SO_4 solution.

19. Calculation

19.1 Calculate the concentration of the PO_4 equivalent of the ortho (or total) phosphate, in parts per million as follows:

Ortho (or total) phosphate, ppm PO_4

$$= C \times \frac{100}{S}$$

where:

C = parts per million PO_4 indicated by the calibration curve, and

S = milliliters of sample used.

Polyphosphate = total phosphate
                 − orthophosphate

20. Precision

20.1 The results obtained by a single analyst using this method have the following precision:

$$S_o = \frac{0.6a + 0.3}{S}$$

where:

S_o = single operator precision, ppm,

a = concentration of phosphate, ppm, and

S = milliliters of sample used.

Non-Referee Method B

(Colorimetric Vanadomolybdate Method)

21. Application

21.1 This method is applicable to the routine determination of orthophosphate in industrial water. It is best suited to boiler feedwater and boiler water containing 2 to 25 ppm PO_4. The range can be extended upward by diluting the sample.

22. Summary of Method

22.1 This method is based on the photometric measurement of the yellow color of phosphovanadomolybdic acid developed in the sample. This color intensity is proportional to the orthophosphate concentration of the sample.

23. Interferences

23.1 This method is not suitable for highly colored water, such as tannin-treated boiler water, unless the color is first removed (Note 3). High concentrations of ferric ions interfere with this test, but generally are not present in the water for which the method is intended.

24. Apparatus

24.1 *Photometer*—See 15.1, except that measurements shall be made at a wavelength of 400 to 420 mμ. The range of the test depends on the light path length of the solution being measured. The range specified in 21.1 is applicable to test solutions measured in a 20-mm cell.

25. Reagents

25.1 *Ammonium Vanadomolybdate Solution*—Dissolve 40 g of ammonium molybdate $[(NH_4)_6Mo_7O_{24} \cdot 4H_2O]$ in 400 ml of water. Dissolve 1.0 g of ammonium metavanadate (NH_4VO_3) in a mixture of 300 ml of water and 200 ml of concentrated nitric acid $(HNO_3$, sp gr 1.42).

Add the first solution to the second solution, mix, and dilute to 1 liter with water.

25.2 *Phosphate, Standard Solution (1 ml = 0.1 mg PO₄)*—Dissolve 0.1433 g of oven-dried potassium dihydrogen phosphate (KH_2PO_4) in water and dilute to 1 liter in a volumetric flask.

26. Calibration and Standardization

26.1 Prepare a series of standard phosphate solutions to cover the range from 0 to 25 ppm. Prepare the standards by diluting suitable volumes of phosphate solution (1 ml = 0.1 mg PO_4) to 50 ml with water. One milliliter of phosphate solution diluted to 50 ml produces a standard containing 2.0 ppm of phosphate.

26.2 Develop color in the series of standards as prescribed in 27.1.

26.3 Measure the absorbance at 400 to 420 mμ with a filter photometer or at 400 mμ with a spectrophotometer, using water as the reference solution. Plot the absorbance values obtained as ordinates, and the corresponding phosphate concentrations as abscissas (Note 7).

27. Procedure

27.1 Transfer 50 ml of a clear sample (filter with suction if suspended matter is present) into an Erlenmeyer flask. If the sample contains more than 25 ppm PO_4, use a correspondingly smaller sample. Add 25 ml of ammonium vanadomolybdate solution to the sample and mix well. Allow 2 min for color development. Measure the color absorbance at 400 to 420 mμ with the filter photometer or at 400 mμ with the spectrophotometer, using water as the reference sample. Record the phosphate concentration indicated by the calibration curve prepared in accordance with 26. Calibration and Standardization.

28. Calculation

28.1 Calculate the concentration of phosphate, in parts per million, as follows:

$$\text{Phosphate, ppm } PO_4 = C \times \frac{50}{S}$$

where:

C = parts per million PO_4 indicated by the calibration curve for the determined color absorbance, and

S = milliliters of sample used.

29. Precision

29.1 The precision of the method may be expressed as follows:

$$S_T = 0.019a + 0.19, \text{ and}$$
$$S_O = 0.011a + 0.05$$

where:

S_T = over-all precision, ppm

S_O = single operator precision, ppm, and

a = concentration of phosphate, ppm.

Non-Referee Method C

(Colorimetric Stannous Chloride Reduction Method)

30. Application

30.1 This method is intended primarily as a control test for waters containing 0.1 to 1.5 ppm PO_4. The range, which can be extended upward by diluting the sample, is for photometric measurements in a 20-mm cell. The range can also be varied by measuring the color in cells having optical depths greater or less than 20 mm. The method covers the determination of either orthophosphate alone or total phosphate (orthophosphate plus polyphosphate).

31. Summary of Method

31.1 Orthophosphate reacts with ammonium molybdate in an acid medium to form a phosphomolybdate which in turn is reduced to a molybdenum blue complex with stannous chloride. The color is proportional in intensity to the phosphate concentration.

31.2 Only orthophosphate forms a blue color in the test. Such polyphosphates as pyro-, meta-, and tripolyphosphate, however, can be made to react in the test if they are hydrolyzed to the ortho form by boiling the acidified sample. Thus, the polyphosphate content of a water can be calculated by subtracting the orthophosphate found in the unboiled sample from the total phosphate found in the acidified, boiled sample. Certain organic phosphates are partially or totally hydrolyzed to the reactive ortho form and are measured in the total phosphate determination.

32. Interferences

32.1 Up to 0.5 ppm iron, 25 ppm silica, and 1000 ppm chloride will not interfere with the test. Oxidizing agents such as chromate, peroxide, and nitrate will bleach the blue color. Interference from nitrite can be overcome by adding 0.1 g of sulfamic acid to the sample before adding the molybdate solution.

32.2 Rapidity of the blue color development depends on temperature. The temperature of the sample and reagents should be between 70 and 95 F (21 and 35 C). Organic phosphate produces high polyphosphate results if hydrolyzed to the ortho form in the total phosphate test.

33. Apparatus

33.1 *Photometer*—See 15.1.

34. Reagents

34.1 *Ammonium Molybdate Solution (48 g/liter)*—See 16.2.

34.2 *Phosphate, Standard Solution (1 ml = 0.01 mg PO₄)*—See 16.3.

34.3 *Stannous Chloride Solution (25 g/liter)*—Dissolve 2.5 g of a fresh supply of stannous chloride ($SnCl_2 \cdot 2H_2O$) in 100 ml of glycerin. Heat with stirring in a water bath to hasten solution. The reagent is stable and does not require

special storage or the addition of preservatives.

34.4 *Sulfuric Acid Solution*—See 16.4.

35. Calibration and Standardization

35.1 Prepare a series of standard phosphate solutions to cover the range from 0 to 1.5 ppm. Make up the standards by diluting suitable volumes of phosphate solution (1 ml = 0.01 mg PO₄) to 100 ml with water. One milliliter of phosphate solution diluted to 100 ml produces a standard containing 0.1 ppm PO₄.

35.2 Develop color in the series of standards as directed in 36.1. Measure the color absorbance of each standard at 650 mμ with a photometer using water as the reference solution. Plot the absorbance values as ordinates and the corresponding phosphate concentrations as abscissas (Note 7).

36. Procedure

36.1 *Orthophosphate:*

36.1.1 To determine orthophosphate, pour 100 ml of the clear sample containing 1.5 ppm PO₄ or less into a 250-ml Erlenmeyer flask. For higher concentrations, use a smaller sample and dilute to 100 ml with water. Filter the sample if turbid.

36.1.2 Add the following reagents in the given order to the sample, mixing after each addition: 4 ml of H_2SO_4 solution, 2 ml of ammonium molybdate solution, and 15 drops (0.7 ml) of $SnCl_2$ solution. Allow 10 min for color development.

36.1.3 Determine the color absorbance of the test sample at 650 mμ, employing water as the reference solution (Note 8). Record the phosphate concentration indicated by the calibration curve prepared as described in 35. Calibration and Standardization.

Note 8—If a commercial color comparator is to be used, treat the clear sample as directed in the instructions supplied by the manufacturer

12–10

of the comparator, using the reagents provided with the comparator. Make color comparisons between the sample solution and the permanent standards with which the comparator is equipped. Record the phosphate concentration as directed by the manufacturer of the comparator.

36.2 Total Phosphate:

36.2.1 Pour 100 ml of the clear sample as prepared in 36.1.1 into a flask. Add 4 ml of H_2SO_4 solution to the sample and boil for at least 30 min on a hot plate, adding water to keep the volume between 25 and 100 ml. Alternatively, heat the solution for 10 min in an autoclave or pressure cooker at 15 to 20 psig. Cool the solution to about 75 F (24 C). Do not overchill the solution. Dilute the solution to 104 ml with water and continue as described in 36.1.2, beginning with the addition of ammonium molybdate solution, and continue as described in 36.1.3.

37. Calculation

37.1 Calculate the concentration of the PO_4 equivalent of the ortho (or total) phosphate, in parts per million as follows:

Ortho (or total) phosphate, ppm PO_4

$$= C \times \frac{100}{S}$$

where:

C = parts per million PO_4 indicated by the matching standard or by the calibration curve, and

S = milliliters of sample used.

Polyphosphate = total phosphate
          − orthophosphate

38. Precision

38.1 The precision of the method varies with the quantity of phosphate being determined and may be expressed as follows:

$$S_T = \frac{10.7a + 1.6}{S}$$

$$S_O = \frac{0.8a + 0.4}{S}$$

where:

S_T = over-all precision, ppm,

S_O = single operator precision, ppm,

a = concentration of phosphate in the sample tested, ppm, and

S = milliliters of sample taken for the test.

Tentative Methods of Test for

SULFATE ION IN INDUSTRIAL WATER AND INDUSTRIAL WASTE WATER[1]

ASTM Designation: D 516 – 63 T

ISSUED, 1955; REVISED, 1959, 1963.[2]

These Tentative Methods have been approved by the sponsoring committee and accepted by the Society in accordance with established procedures, for use pending adoption as standard. Suggestions for revisions should be addressed to the Society at 1916 Race St., Philadelphia 3, Pa.

Scope

1. (a) These methods cover the determination of sulfate ion in industrial water and industrial waste water. Three methods are given as follows:

	Sections
Referee Method (Gravimetric Method)	5 to 11
Non-Referee Method A (Turbidimetric Method)	12 to 20
Non-Referee Method B (Volumetric Method)	21 to 31

(b) The Referee method is a primary measure of sulfate ion in all industrial water. The Non-referee methods are less time-consuming but often more liable to interference than the Referee method. They are particularly useful in the lower sulfate range, below 20 ppm SO_4^{--}.

Definitions

2. For definitions of terms used in these methods, refer to the Definitions of Terms Relating to Industrial Water and Industrial Waste Water (ASTM Designation: D 1129).[3]

Purity of Reagents

3. (a) Reagent grade chemicals shall be used in all tests. Unless otherwise indicated, it is intended that all reagents shall conform to the specifications of the Committee on Analytical Reagents of

---

[1] Under the standardization procedure of the Society, these methods are under the jurisdiction of the ASTM Committee D-19 on Industrial Water. A list of members may be found in the ASTM Year Book.

[2] Latest revision accepted by the Society at the Annual Meeting, June, 1963.

Prior to their present publication as tentative, these methods were published as tentative from 1938 to 1942, being revised in 1940. They were adopted as standard in 1942, and published as standard from 1942 to 1955, being revised in 1949. They were revised and reverted to tentative in 1955.

[3] Appears in this publication.

[4] "Reagent Chemicals, American Chemical Society Specifications," Am. Chem. Soc., Washington, D. C. For suggestions on the testing of reagents not listed by the American Chemical Society, see "Reagent Chemicals and Standards," by Joseph Rosin, D. Van Nostrand Co.. Inc., New York, N. Y., and the "United States Pharmacopeia."

the American Chemical Society, where such specifications are available.[4] Other grades may be used, provided it is first ascertained that the reagent is of sufficiently high purity to permit its use without lessening the accuracy of the determination.

(b) Unless otherwise indicated, references to water shall be understood to mean reagent water conforming to the Specifications for Reagent Water (ASTM Designation: D 1193).[3] In addition, reagent water used for these methods shall be sulfate-free.

Sampling

4. Collect the sample in accordance with the applicable method of the American Society for Testing Materials, as follows:

D 510—Sampling Industrial Water,[3]
D 860—Sampling Water from Boilers,[3]
D 1066—Sampling Steam,[3]
D 1496—Sampling Homogeneous Industrial Waste Water.[3]

REFEREE METHOD

(Gravimetric Method)

Application

5. This method is applicable to all types of industrial water and industrial waste water. It is directly applicable to samples containing approximately 20 to 100 ppm of sulfate ion (SO_4^{--}). It can be extended to higher or lower ranges by adjusting the sample size.

Summary of Method

6. Sulfate ion is precipitated and weighed as barium sulfate after removal of silica and other insoluble matter.

Interferences

7. (a) Sulfites and sulfides may oxidize and precipitate with the sulfate. Turbidity caused by silica or other insoluble material would interfere if allowed to be present, but removal of such interference is provided in this method.

(b) Other substances tend to be occluded or adsorbed on the barium sulfate, but these do not significantly affect the precision and accuracy of the method.

Reagents

8. (a) *Ammonium Hydroxide* (*sp gr 0.90*).—Concentrated ammonium hydroxide (NH₄OH).

(b) *Barium Chloride Solution* (*118 g per liter*).—Dissolve 118 g of barium chloride ($BaCl_2 \cdot 2H_2O$) in water and dilute to 1 liter.

(c) *Hydrochloric Acid* (*1:9*).—Mix 1 volume of hydrochloric acid (HCl, sp gr 1.19) with 9 volumes of water.

(d) *Hydrofluoric Acid* (*48 to 51 per cent*).—Concentrated hydrofluoric acid (HF).

(e) *Methyl Orange Indicator* (*0.5 g per liter*).—Dissolve 0.05 g of methyl orange in water and dilute to 100 ml.

(f) *Nitric Acid* (*sp gr 1.42*).—Concentrated nitric acid (HNO₃).

(g) *Picric Acid* (*saturated aqueous solution*).

(h) *Silver Nitrate Solution* (*100 g per liter*).—Dissolve 10 g of silver nitrate (AgNO₃) in water and dilute to 100 ml.

(i) *Sulfuric Acid* (*sp gr 1.84*).—Concentrated sulfuric acid (H₂SO₄).

Procedure

9. (a) Filter the sample if it is turbid, using a fine, ashless paper (Note 1). Wash the beaker and the filter thoroughly with hot water.

NOTE 1.—Silica may be removed before applying this method by dehydration with HCl or perchloric acid (HClO₄) in accordance with the respective procedures in the Methods of Test for Silica in Industrial Water and Industrial Waste Water (ASTM Designation: D 859).[3] In this case, the ignition described in Paragraph (e) need not be done in a platinum crucible.

(b) Measure into the beaker a quantity of the clear sample containing sulfate ion equivalent to 10 to 50 mg of barium sulfate ($BaSO_4$). Adjust the volume by evaporation or dilution with water to approximately 200 ml. Adjust the acidity of the sample to the methyl orange end point and add 10 ml excess of HCl (1:9).

(c) Heat the acidified solution to boiling and slowly add to it 5 ml of hot $BaCl_2$ solution (Note 2). Stir the sample vigorously while adding the $BaCl_2$ solution. Keep the temperature just below boiling until the liquid has become clear and the precipitate has settled out completely. In no case shall this settling period be less than 2 hr.

NOTE 2.—Faster precipitation and a coarser precipitate can be obtained by adding 10 ml of saturated picric acid solution and boiling the sample 5 min before adding $BaCl_2$.

(d) Filter the suspension of $BaSO_4$ on a fine, ashless filter paper, and wash the precipitate with hot water until the washings are substantially free of chlorides, as indicated by testing the last portion of the washings with $AgNO_3$ solution (Note 3). Avoid excessive washing. If any $BaSO_4$ passes through the filter, pour the filtrate through the paper a second time (Note 4).

NOTE 3.—Do not attempt to obtain a completely negative test for chloride. Discontinue washing when no more than a faint opalescence is produced in the test.

NOTE 4.—If the filtrate is poured through the paper a second time, $AgNO_3$ must not be present in the filtrate.

(e) Place the filter paper and contents in a weighed platinum crucible (Note 1), and char and consume the paper slowly without flaming. Ignite the residue at approximately 800 C for 1 hr, or until it is apparent that all carbon has been consumed.

(f) Add a drop of H_2SO_4 and a few drops of HF, and evaporate under a hood to expel silica as silicon tetrafluoride (SiF_4). Reignite at about 800 C, cool in a desiccator, and weigh the $BaSO_4$.

Calculation

10. Calculate the concentration of sulfate ion (SO_4^{--}) in parts per million, as follows:

$$\text{Sulfate, ppm} = \frac{W \times 411,500}{S}$$

where:

W = grams of $BaSO_4$, and
S = milliliters of sample.

Precision and Accuracy

11. Results by this method are precise to 1.0 per cent of the amount of sulfate ion present.

NON-REFEREE METHOD A
(Turbidimetric Method)

Application

12. This method is intended for rapid routine or control tests for sulfate ion in industrial water where extreme accuracy and precision are not required. It is directly applicable over the range of 10 to 100 ppm of sulfate ion (SO_4^{--}).

Summary of Method

13. Sulfate ion is converted to a barium sulfate suspension under controlled conditions. Glycerin solution and a sodium chloride solution are added to stabilize the suspension and minimize interferences. The resulting turbidity is determined by a photoelectric colorimeter or spectrophotometer and compared to a curve prepared from standard sulfate solutions.

Interferences

14. (a) Insoluble suspended matter in the sample must be removed. Dark colors that can not be compensated for in the procedure interfere with the measure-

ment of suspended barium sulfate (BaSO$_4$).

(b) Although other ions normally found in water do not appear to interfere, the formation of the barium sulfate suspension is very critical. This method is more suitable as a control procedure where concentration and type of impurities present in the water are relatively constant. Determinations that are in doubt should be checked by the Referee Method in some cases, or by the procedure suggested in Note 7.

Apparatus

15. *Photometer.*—A filter photometer or spectrophotometer suitable for measurements between 350 and 425 mμ, the preferable wave-length range being 380 to 400 mμ. The cell for the instrument should have a light path through the sample of approximately 40 mm, and should hold about 50 ml of sample.

Reagents and Materials

16. (a) *Barium Chloride.*—Crystals of barium chloride (BaCl$_2 \cdot$2H$_2$O) screened to 20 to 30-mesh.

(b) *Glycerol Solution (1:1).*—Mix 1 volume of glycerol with 1 volume of water (Note 5).

NOTE 5.—A stabilizing solution containing sodium carboxymethylcellulose (10 g per liter) may be used instead of the glycerol solution.[5]

(c) *Sodium Chloride Solution (240 g per liter).*—Dissolve 240 g of sodium chloride (NaCl) in water containing 20 ml of concentrated hydrochloric acid (HCl, sp gr 1.19), and dilute to 1 liter with water. Filter the solution if turbid.

(d) *Sulfate, Standard Solution (1 ml = 0.100 mg SO$_4{}^{--}$).*—Dissolve 0.1479 g of

---

[5] The following commercial reagents also have been found suitable: Colloresine LV, obtainable from the General Aniline and Film Corp., New York, N. Y.; or from the Irwin Dyestuff Corp., Ltd., Montreal, Canada; or Hercules CMC-70 Premium Low, obtainable from the Hercules Powder Co., Wilmington, Del.

anhydrous sodium sulfate (Na$_2$SO$_4$) in water, and dilute with water to 1 liter in a volumetric flask. Standardize by the procedure prescribed in Section 9.

Calibration

17. Follow the procedure given in Section 18, using appropriate amounts of the standard sulfate solution prepared in accordance with Section 16 (d), and prepare a calibration curve showing sulfate ion content in parts per million plotted against the corresponding photometer readings (Note 6). Prepare standards by diluting with water 0.0, 2.0, 5.0, 10.0, 15.0, 20.0, 30.0, 40.0, and 50.0 ml of standard sulfate solution to 50-ml volumes in volumetric flasks. These solutions will have sulfate ion concentrations of 0.0, 4.0, 10.0, 20.0, 30.0, 40.0, 60.0, 80.0 and 100.0 ppm, respectively.

NOTE 6.—A separate calibration curve must be prepared for each photometer and a new curve must be prepared if it is necessary to change the cell, lamp, or filter, or if any other alterations of instrument or reagents are made. Check the curve with each series of tests by running two or more solutions of known sulfate concentrations.

Procedure

18. (a) Filter the sample if it is turbid, and adjust the temperature to between 15 and 30 C.

(b) Pipet into a 200-ml beaker 50 ml or less of the clear sample containing between 0.5 and 5 mg of sulfate ion (Note 7). Dilute to 50 ml with water if required, and add 10.0 ml of glycerol solution (Note 5) and 5.0 ml of NaCl solution.

NOTE 7.—The solubility of BaSO$_4$ is such that difficulty may be experienced in the determination of sulfate concentrations below about 10 ppm. This can be overcome by concentrating the sample or by adding 5 ml of standard sulfate solution (1 ml = 0.100 mg SO$_4{}^{--}$) to the sample before diluting to 50 ml. This will add 0.5 mg SO$_4$ to the sample, which must be subtracted from the final result.

(c) Fill a 40-mm sample cell with sample solution, wipe it with a clean, dry cloth, and place it in the cell compartment. Set the colorimeter to zero absorbance (100 per cent transmission) for a blank. This compensates for any acid-insoluble matter that has not been filtered out, or for color present, or for both.

(d) Pour the sample solution from the cell back into the beaker and add, with stirring, 0.3 g of $BaCl_2 \cdot 2H_2O$ crystals (Note 8). Continue gently stirring the solution for 1 min. Let it stand for 4 min, and stir again for 15 sec. Fill the sample cell as before, and immediately make a reading with the photometer.

Note 8.—The stirring should be at a constant rate in all determinations. The use of a magnetic stirrer has been found satisfactory for this purpose.

(e) If interferences are suspected, dilute the sample with an equal volume of water, and determine the sulfate concentration again. If the value so determined is one-half that in the undiluted sample, interferences may be assumed to be absent.

Calculation

19. Convert the photometer readings obtained with the sample to ppm sulfate ion (SO_4^{--}) by use of the calibration curve described in Section 17.

Precision

20. The precision of this method depends on the interferences present, and the skill of the analyst. When no interfering substances are present, a careful analyst can obtain a precision of 5 per cent of the SO_4^{--} or 2 ppm, whichever is greater.

Non-Referee Method B[6]

(Volumetric Method)

Application

21. This method is intended for the rapid volumetric determination of a wide range of sulfate ion concentrations in industrial water. It can be used directly for routine or control tests for sulfate ion (SO_4^{--}) in certain industrial waters and, when extended by the use of ion-exchange and micro technique, for the accurate determination of SO_4^{--} over the range 5 to 1000 ppm.

Summary of Method

22. Sulfate ion is titrated in an alcoholic solution under controlled acid conditions with a standard barium chloride solution using thorin as the indicator. Under controlled conditions of titration, the end point is relatively sharp, the indicator changing from a yellow to a stable pink color.

Interferences

23. (a) Both cations and anions may cause coprecipitation errors with barium sulfate precipitate. Potassium, iron, aluminum, phosphate, fluoride, and nitrate are the worst offenders. Most metallic ions also interfere seriously by forming colored complexes with the thorin indicator, especially in alcohol - water mixtures.

(b) Interference by cations is eliminated by removal by ion exchange. However, chromium and zirconium may form varying quantities of anion complexes with sulfate ion under certain conditions.

(c) Fluorides and nitrates cause no serious interference up to concentrations of 2 and 50 ppm respectively.

(d) Ortho and metaphosphates interfere when present in excess of about 2 ppm. In industrial water, such as boiler water, the orthophosphate is removed by precipitation with magnesium carbonate and filtration in the cold.

[6] For additional information on this method, see James S. Fritz and Stanley S. Yamamura, "Rapid Microtitration of Sulfate," *Analytical Chemistry*, Vol. 27, No. 9, Sept., 1955, p. 1461.

(e) Sulfite interference is eliminated by determining the sulfate equivalent of the sulfite and subtraction of this sulfate from the determined sulfate content. Sulfides also interfere but can usually be removed by precipitation as zinc sulfide.

(f) Chlorides obscure the pink end point if present in concentrations greater than 1000 ppm when the sulfate present is low (about 5 ppm). The noninterfering concentration of chloride increases with increasing sulfate content.

(g) Chromium present as chromates and dichromates is converted by treatment with hydrogen peroxide to the cation, Cr^{+++}, which is then removed by ion exchange.

Apparatus

24. (a) *Titration Assembly.*—For high accuracy and determination of low SO_4^{--} concentration, a microburet reading to 0.01 ml is necessary. Efficient magnetic stirring improves the speed and convenience of titration.

(b) *Ion Exchange Column.*—A suitable continuous flow column may be prepared by pouring 30 cm of a washed, wet resin, 20 to 25-mesh size into a glass column of 9 to 10-mm ID and 50 ± 0.5 cm in length, the top of which widens to a reservoir of 50 to 55-mm ID and 10 ± 0.5 cm in length.

The resin is held on a suitable screen or filter plug and the flow is controlled by a length of 2-mm bore capillary tubing joined to the bottom of the column. This tubing is bent into a U shape and rises to about 13 mm above the resin bed and then makes a U bend downward for about 5 to 7 cm.

Other designs of exchange columns are suitable such as a small glass column, using only 25 mm of washed resin, 100- to 200-mesh size, 65- to 70-mm total length and 15-mm ID widening to a reservoir cup 50 to 55 mm in length and 30- to 35-mm ID. This column is useful for very small samples which must be washed through the bed with water. Correction must be made for the amount of wash water used.

(c) The exchange columns shall be regenerated when about two thirds exhausted. Regeneration shall be carried out by passing HCl (1:4) through the resin column and thorough washing with water. If the resin column shows no visual change as exhaustion proceeds, it is advisable to regenerate after one or two samples have passed through it.

Reagents and Materials

25. (a) *Alcohol.*[7]—Ethyl alcohol (95 per cent), isopropyl alcohol, or methyl alcohol.

(b) *Ammonium Hydroxide (1:99).*—Mix 1 volume of ammonium hydroxide (NH_4OH, sp gr 0.90) with 99 volumes of water.

(c) *Barium Chloride, Standard Solution (1 ml = 0.500 mg SO_4^{--}).*—Dissolve 1.221 g of barium chloride ($BaCl_2 \cdot 2H_2O$) in 1 liter of water that has been adjusted to pH 3.8 to 4.0 with dilute HCl. Standardize in accordance with Section 26 (a) and (b), against standard sodium sulfate solutions that have been passed through the ion-exchange resin.

(d) *Hydrochloric Acid (1:4).*—Mix 1 volume of concentrated hydrochloric acid HCl, (sp gr 1.19) with 4 volumes of water.

(e) *Hydrochloric Acid (1:99).*—Mix 1 volume of HCl (sp gr 1.19) with 99 volumes of water.

(f) *Hydrogen Peroxide (30 per cent).*—Concentrated hydrogen peroxide (H_2O_2).

(g) *Iodine, Standard Solution (1 ml = 0.480 mg SO_4^{--}).*—Dissolve 10 g of KI in 100 ml of water, add 1.27 g of iodine crystals, and stir until solution is complete. Dilute to 1 liter with water and

---

[7] Specially denatured ethyl alcohol conforming to Formula No. 3A or 30 of the U. S. Bureau of Internal Revenue may be substituted for 95 per cent ethyl alcohol.

store in a dark bottle. Standardize against 0.01 N $Na_2S_2O_3$ solution.

(h) *Ion-Exchange Resin.*[8]—A cationic exchange resin, 20- to 25-mesh or 100 to 200-mesh.

(i) *Magnesium Carbonate* ($MgCO_3$).

(j) *Phenolphthalein Indicator Solution (5.0 g per liter).*—Dissolve 0.5 g of phenolphthalein in 50 ml of 95 per cent ethyl alcohol.[7] Dilute to 100 ml with water.

(k) *Potassium Dichromate.*[9]—Heat potassium dichromate ($K_2Cr_2O_7$) in a platinum crucible to a temperature just above its fusion point (396 C), taking care to exclude all dust and organic matter. After cooling, crush the fused salt to a powder in an agate mortar and preserve in a glass-stoppered bottle.

(l) *Potassium Iodide.*[9]—This should not yield a blue color when 1 g is dissolved in freshly boiled reagent-grade deaerated water treated with 5 drops (0.25 ml) of 1 N sulfuric acid (H_2SO_4) and 1 ml of freshly prepared starch solution.

(m) *Sodium Bicarbonate*[9] ($NaHCO_3$).

(n) *Sodium Carbonate,*[9] anhydrous (Na_2CO_3).

(o) *Sodium Thiosulfate, Standard Solution (0.01 N).*[10]—Using a 1000-ml volumetric flask, dissolve 2.482 g of sodium thiosulfate ($Na_2S_2O_3 \cdot 5H_2O$) in approximately 800 ml of water that has just been boiled and cooled and invert the flask at regular short intervals until the solid is dissolved. Stabilize the solution by dissolving in it in the same manner 1 g of sodium carbonate (Na_2CO_3) and dilute to 1 liter with the boiled water. Standardize against potassium dichromate ($K_2Cr_2O_7$) as follows:

Dissolve 2 g of potassium iodide (KI) and 2 g of sodium bicarbonate ($NaHCO_3$)

in 300 ml of water in a 500-ml Erlenmeyer flask and add concentrated hydrochloric acid (HCl, sp gr 1.19) slowly, while swirling the flask, until carbon dioxide gas evolution ceases. Add 10 ml excess of HCl, mix, and then dissolve 0.010 g of dried potassium dichromate ($K_2Cr_2O_7$) in the solution. Wash down the inside of the flask with a small amount of water without agitating the flask, and allow to stand for 10 min. Titrate with the $Na_2S_2O_3$ solution, using starch solution as the indicator, until the color just changes from blue to the green color of the chromic salt.

Calculate as follows:

Normality of thiosulfate

$$= \frac{\text{g of } K_2Cr_2O_7 \times 1000}{\text{Equiv. Wt of } K_2Cr_2O_7 \ (49.04) \times S}$$

where S = ml of $Na_2S_2O_3$ required.

(p) *Starch Indicator.*[9]—Make a paste of 1 g of arrowroot starch or soluble iodometric starch with cold water. Pour the paste into 100 ml of boiling water and boil for several minutes. Store in a glass-stoppered bottle in a cool place. Starch solution prepared in this manner will remain chemically stable for two or three days.

(q) *Sulfate, Standard Solution (1 ml = 0.100 mg SO_4^{--}).*—See Section 16(d).

(r) *Sulfuric Acid (sp gr 1.84).*[9] Concentrated sulfuric acid (H_2SO_4).

(s) *Thorin Solution (20 g per liter).*—Dissolve 0.2 g of thorin (2(2-hydroxy-3,6-disulfo-1-naphthylazo) benzene arsonic acid) in 100 ml of water.

Standardization of Barium Chloride Solution

26. (a) Prepare a series of standard sulfate solutions by diluting with water 0.0, 2.0, 5.0, 10.0, 15.0, 25.0, 35.0, and 50.0 ml of the standard sulfate solution (1 ml = 0.100 mg SO_4^{--}) to 50 ml in volumetric flasks. These solutions will

---

[8] Commercial resins Dowex 50 x 8 and Amberlite IR-120 have been found satisfactory for this purpose.

[9] Reagent used for standardization only.

have sulfate ion concentrations of 0.0, 4.0, 10.0, 20.0, 30.0, 50.0, 70.0, and 100.0 ppm respectively.

(b) Determine the blank and sulfate equivalent of the barium chloride solution (Note 9) in accordance with Section 27(c), (d), and (e).

NOTE 9.—A solution of known sulfate concentration should be run with each series of tests or new reagents to check the standardization curve. The blank used to determine sulfate content is preferably that determined from the standardization curve extrapolated to zero.

Procedure in the Presence of Sulfite, Phosphate, and Chromium

27. (a) In the presence of sulfite and phosphate interference, as in boiler water, pipet 25.0 ml of filtered sample containing 10 to 500 ppm SO_4^{--} into a 100-ml beaker. Add 0.5 ml of starch indicator and titrate the sulfite with iodine solution (1 ml = 0.480 mg SO_4^{--}) (Note 10). Record the volume of standard iodine solution required to obtain a blue color.

NOTE 10.—A separate sample may be used to determine the sulfite by the Method of Test for Sulfite Ion in Industrial water (ASTM Designation: D 1339).[3]

(b) Add 2 to 3 drops of phenolphthalein indicator solution and adjust pH to about 8.3 with HCl (1:99) or NH_4OH (1:99). Add 0.3 to 0.5 g $MgCO_3$ and boil gently for 5 min, using a cover glass to minimize evaporation loss. Cool to 10 C (Note 11). Filter through acid-washed, open-texture, rapid filter paper into a 50-ml volumetric flask. Wash the precipitate with three 5-ml portions of water at 10 C. If chromium is present or suspected, add, with shaking, a few drops of H_2O_2. Adjust the volume to 50 ml with water.

NOTE 11.—Phosphate ion is almost completely precipitated at or below 10 C, but solubility increases with increasing temperature.

(c) Pass the solution through the ion-exchange column and discard the first 25 to 30 ml of effluent. Pipet 10.0 ml of the next effluent into a small white porcelain dish (100- to 125-ml capacity). (Note 12.)

NOTE 12.—When the amount of sample is limited, the sample may be passed through the small ion exchange column described in Section 24 (b) and rinsed through with four or five times its volume of water, so that the final elutriate is 50.0 ml. Concentrate this elutriate to 10.0 ml, or take a 10.0-ml aliquot.

(d) Add 40 ml of alcohol and 2 drops of thorin indicator. Adjust the pH to 3.8 to 4.0 by carefully adding dropwise NH_4OH (1:99) until the solution just turns pink (Note 13). Then add HCl (1:99) dropwise until the pink color disappears.

NOTE 13.—If the NH_4OH is added too fast, it is possible to overrun the color change from yellow to pink and the sample continues to be yellow. It is then impossible to develop the pink color by addition of NH_4OH.

(e) Prepare a blank using water and reagents described in Section 27 (a) to (d), and record the iodine solution used for the sulfite correction of the blank. Titrate the sample with $BaCl_2$ solution (1 ml = 0.500 mg SO_4^{--}), using the untitrated yellow blank as a color reference, to a stable pink color which deepens to a reddish pink on overtitration. Then titrate the blank to the same color reached in the sample. Allow a time lapse of 3 to 5 sec between additions of the last few increments of $BaCl_2$ solution (Notes 14 and 15).

NOTE 14.—The color change may best be seen with constant stirring and a daylight fluorescent light. If such a light is not available, the use of blue tinted glasses, such as American Optical No. F-9247, is helpful.

NOTE 15.—For very low sulfate concentrations a less concentrated $BaCl_2$ solution (1 ml = 0.200 mg SO_4^{--}) is advised. A standard sodium sulfate solution may be added to the sample to raise the total sulfate concentration to 10 to 15 ppm SO_4^{--}. This added sulfate must be subtracted from the final result.

Procedure in the Absence of Sulfite, Phosphate, and Chromium

28. Pass 50 ml of the filtered sample directly through the ion exchange column (Note 11). Collect 10.0 ml of effluent and proceed in accordance with Section 27(c), (d), and (e), using the extrapolated blank.

Procedure in the Presence of Negligible Interferences

29. If interfering cations are low and high accuracy is not required, as in certain control tests, directly titrate 10.0 ml of the filtered sample in accordance with the procedure described in Section 27 (d) and (e).

Calculation

30. Calculate the sulfate ion (SO_4^{--}) concentration in the original sample, in parts per million, as follows:

$$\text{Sulfate, ppm} = \frac{(V_1 - B_1) \times 500}{S_1}$$
$$- \frac{(V_2 - B_2) \times 480}{S_2}$$

where:

$V_1 =$ milliliters of $BaCl_2$ solution required for titration of the sample,

$V_2 =$ milliliters of iodine solution required for titration of the sample for sulfite correction,

$B_1 =$ milliliters of $BaCl_2$ solution required for titration of the blank,

$B_2 =$ milliliters of iodine solution required for titration of the blank for sulfite correction,

$S_1 =$ milliliters of original sample titrated, consideration being given to any dilution when passing through the ion exchange column, and

$S_2 =$ milliliters of original sample titrated for the sulfite correction.

Precision and Accuracy[10]

31. Titration of SO_4^{--} in the range 5 to 100 ppm, after ion-exchange treatment, is accurate to 1.5 ppm. The precision of this method up to 100 ppm (excluding laboratory differences) is 0.7 ppm. Single operator precision may be expected to be 0.5 ppm.

---

[10] Supporting data giving results of cooperative tests have been filed at ASTM Headquarters

Standard Method of

REPORTING RESULTS OF ANALYSIS OF INDUSTRIAL WATER AND INDUSTRIAL WASTE WATER[1]

ASTM Designation: D 596 – 64

ADOPTED, 1955; REVISED, 1958, 1963, 1964

This Standard of the American Society for Testing and Materials is issued under the fixed designation D 596; the final number indicates the year of original adoption as standard or, in the case of revision, the year of last revision.

Scope and Application

1. This method[2] presents recommendations as to the nature, extent, and form in which the results of analysis of industrial water and industrial waste water should be presented. All analyses are to be made in accordance with the methods of test of the American Society for Testing and Materials, unless otherwise specified.

NOTE 1.—While various other methods of reporting the analysis of industrial water and industrial waste water are in use, this method is intended as a rational and comprehensive practice for general application. For use in specific industries or individual cases, hypothetical combinations of certain ions may be useful and desirable.

Definitions

2. (a) The terms "part per million,"

"equivalent per million," and "part per billion" in this method are defined in accordance with the Definitions of Terms Relating to Industrial Water and Industrial Waste Water (ASTM Designation: D 1129),[3] as follows:

Part per Million.—A measure of proportion by weight, equivalent to a unit weight of solute per million unit weights of solution.

NOTE 2.—A part per million is generally considered equivalent to a milligram per liter, but this is not precise. A part per million is equivalent to a milligram of solute per kilogram of solution.

Equivalent per Million.—A unit chemical equivalent weight of solute per million unit weights of solution. Concentration in equivalents per million is calculated by dividing concentration in parts per million by the chemical combining weight of the substance or ion

NOTE 3.—This unit also has been called "milliequivalents per liter" and "milligram equivalents per kilogram." The latter term is

---

[1] Under the standardization procedure of the Society, this method is under the jurisdiction of the ASTM Committee D-19 on Industrial Water. A list of members may be found in the ASTM Year Book.

[2] This method has been reviewed by the Joint Committee on Uniformity of Methods of Water Examination and conforms to that committee's recommendations.

[3] Appears in this publication.

precise, but the former will be in error if the specific gravity of the solution is not exactly 1.0.

Part per Billion.—A measure of proportion by weight, equivalent to a unit weight of solute per billion (10^9) unit weights of solution.

NOTE 4.—A part per billion is generally considered equivalent to one millionth of a gram per liter, but this is not precise. A part per billion is equivalent to a milligram of solute per 1000 kilograms of solution.

(*b*) For definitions of other terms used in this method, refer to Definitions D 1129.

History of Sample

3. Information regarding the source and history of the sample to be included in the report of analysis should be as follows:

Name of company supplying sample,
Name and location of plant,
Date and time of sampling,
Number of sample,
Source of sample or name and other designation of equipment sampled,
Point of sampling,
Pressure,
Temperature and rate of flow of the liquid in equipment from which the sample is taken,
Temperature of sample,
Results of field tests made on the sample, and
Signature of sampler.

Cation - Anion Balance

4. (*a*) A scheme for examination and analysis of industrial water is given in the Scheme for Analysis of Industrial Water and Industrial Waste Water (ASTM Designation: 1256).[3]

(*b*) The deviation from a perfect balance between cations and anions determined in solids or dissolved gases may be appraised by totalling separately the determined concentrations in equivalents

per million of anions and cations. The error in analysis, either positive or negative, may be calculated from the following empirical formula:[4]

$$\text{Percentage error} = \frac{\text{cations} - \text{anions}}{\text{cations} + \text{anions}} \times 100$$

NOTE 5.—With careful work, the percentage error may be 2 per cent for a water containing 100 ppm of dissolved salts, 1 per cent for a much more concentrated water, and 5 per cent for a water containing only 25 ppm of dissolved salts.[5]

Hydrogen Ion Concentration

5. (*a*) Report the hydrogen ion concentration of the sample as pH at 25 C. If determined at another temperature, report this temperature.

(*b*) State the method by which the pH was determined. If an electrometric method was employed, specify the type of electrode used. If determined colorimetrically, report the indicator used as well as whether a colorimeter or comparator was employed.

Suspended Matter (Suspended Solids)

6. (*a*) Report the concentration of undissolved or suspended matter (undissolved or suspended solids) in parts per million.

(*b*) Report the concentration of colloidally dispersed matter (solids) in parts per million.

(*c*) Report the concentration of such individual insoluble salts as are determined in parts per million.

Dissolved Matter (Dissolved Solids)

7. (*a*) Express the concentration of dissolved matter (dissolved solids) (by evaporation) in parts per million. Report the temperature at which the residue was

---

[4] Adapted from H. Stabler, "The Mineral Analysis of Water for Industrial Use," *Water Supply Paper No. 274*, U. S. Geological Survey, p. 168 (1911).

[5] W. D. Collins, "Notes on Practical Water Analysis," *Water Supply Paper No. 596-H*, U. S. Geological Survey, pp. 254–255 (1928).

heated for the determination of dissolved matter.

(b) Report the concentration of dissolved salts simultaneously in parts per million and in equivalents per million of the individually determined ions. For convenience, the anions should be arranged in one group and the cations in another.

(c) Report two or more ions of similar properties, whose joint effect is measured by a single determination, only in equivalents per million. For example: soap hardness, acidity, alkalinity.

(d) Report the concentration of dissolved organic matter only in parts per million.

(e) The concentration of the total of dissolved salts (by calculation) may be expressed either in parts per million or in equivalents per million, or both.

Dissolved Gases

8. Report the concentration of individual gases dissolved in water in parts per million.

NOTE 6.—The concentration of each gas when combined in water may be calculated to its respective ionic concentrations either in parts per million or in equivalents per million or both.

Odor

9. (a) A procedure for examination of industrial water for odor is given in the Method of Test for Odor in Industrial Water and Industrial Waste Water (ASTM Designation: D 1292).[3]

(b) Report the odor intensity as odor intensity index calculated as follows:

$$\text{Odor intensity index} = 3.3 \log \left(\frac{200}{A}\right) + 3D$$

where:

A = milliliters of sample or milliliters of aliquot of the primary dilution used, and

D = number of 25:175 primary dilutions required to reach the determinable magnitude of odor intensity.

(c) The odor intensity may be calculated as threshold odor number if desired by the procedure described in Method D 1292, Appendix II.

Acidity and Alkalinity

10. (a) Referee procedures for examination of industrial water and industrial waste water for acidity and alkalinity are given in the Methods of Test for Acidity and Alkalinity of Industrial Water (ASTM Designation: D 1884)[3] and the Methods of Test for Acidity or Basicity of Industrial Waste Water (ASTM Designation: D 1067).[3]

(b) Calculate the acidity or alkalinity in equivalents per million as follows:

$$\text{Acidity (or alkalinity), epm} = AN \times 10$$

where:

A = milliliters of standard acid or alkali required for the titration, and

N = normality of the standard solution.

(c) Report the results of titrations to specific end points as follows: The acidity (or alkalinity) to pH ——————— is ——————— epm.

Hardness

11. (a) A referee procedure for examination of industrial water for hardness is given in the Methods of Test for Hardness in Industrial Water (ASTM Designation: D 1126).[3]

(b) Calculate the total hardness in the sample from the calcium and magnesium content as follows:

$$\text{Total hardness, epm} = \frac{A}{20.04} + \frac{B}{12.16}$$

where:

A = calcium ion, in parts per million present in the sample, and

B = magnesium ion, in parts per million, present in the sample.

(c) To convert hardness in equivalents per million to equivalent CaCO₃ in parts per million, multiply by 50.

Special Consideration for Industrial Waste Water

12. (a) The following system is suggested for reporting test data on industrial waste water:

Concentration	Report
In parts per billion (ppb)[a]	from 0 to 1,000
In parts per million (ppm)	from 1 to 10,000
Per cent by weight	10,000 ppm and over

---

[a] "Billion" is understood to be 10^9.

In reporting per cent by weight, so specify, and state the specific gravity of the liquid if it differs from 1.0.

(b) For determinations of "residue on evaporation" of dissolved matter, report the temperature at which the constant weight was obtained.

(c) Report volatile matter by volume or by weight, stating the basis selected. If on the basis of volume, also state the temperature and pressure at which measurements were made.

(d) Report settleable matter by the Imhoff cone method in terms of milliliters per liter.

(e) Report hydrogen ion concentration as pH, and state the temperature of observation.

Conversion Factors

13. (a) The following table lists factors for interconversion between the units recommended in this method and other units in common use:

To Convert	Into	Multiply By
ml (or cc) of dissolved oxygen per liter	ppm	1.429[a]
Grains per U. S. gallon	ppm	17.12[a]
Grains per Imperial gallon	ppm	14.25[a]
Parts per 100,000	ppm	10.0
Grams per liter	ppm	1000[a]
Normality	epm	1000[a]
Per cent of normal	epm	10.0[a]
ppm as CaCO₃	epm	0.02
Grains per U. S. gallon as CaCO₃	epm	0.3424[a]
Grains per Imperial gallon as CaCO₃	epm	0.285[a]
ppm	ml (or cc) of dissolved oxygen per liter	0.7[a]
ppm	grains per U. S. gallon	0.058[a]
ppm	grains per Imperial gallon	0.071[a]
ppm	parts per 100,000	0.1
ppm	grams per liter	0.001[a]
epm	normality	0.001[a]
epm	per cent of normal	0.1[a]
epm	ppm as CaCO₃	50.0
epm	grains per U. S. gallon as CaCO₃	2.92[a]
epm	grains per Imperial gallon as CaCO₃	3.51[a]

---

[a] Factors based on weight per volume are approximate unless the specific gravity of the sample is unity. When the specific gravity is not one, apply a correction by dividing the conversion to epm and ppm by the specific gravity, and by multiplying the conversion from epm and ppm by the specific gravity.

(b) The following table lists factors for interconversion of parts per million and equivalents per million of the common ions:[6]

[6] Based on International Atomic Weights (1961), published in *Chemical and Engineering News*, Nov. 20, 1961, p. 43.

Ion	Multiplier	
	ppm to epm	epm to ppm
Ca^{++}	0.04990	20.04
Mg^{++}	0.08226	12.156
Ba^{++}	0.01456	68.67
Sr^{++}	0.02283	43.81
Zn^{++}	0.03060	32.68
Cu^{++}	0.03148	31.77
Pb^{++}	0.00965	103.60
Na^+	0.04350	22.9898
K^+	0.02557	39.102
NH_4^+	0.05544	18.0386
H^+	0.99209	1.00797
Fe^{++}	0.03581	27.924
Fe^{+++}	0.05372	18.616
Al^{+++}	0.11119	8.9938
Mn^{++}	0.03641	27.4690
Mn^{++++}	0.07281	13.7345
HCO_3^-	0.01639	61.0173
CO_3^{--}	0.03333	30.0047
OH^-	0.05880	17.0074
$H_2PO_4^-$	0.01031	96.9873
HPO_4^{--}	0.02084	47.9897
PO_4^{---}	0.03159	31.6571
SiO_3^{--}	0.02629	38.0421
CN^-	0.03844	26.0179
SO_4^{--}	0.02082	48.031
HSO_4^-	0.01030	97.070
SO_3^{--}	0.02498	40.031
HSO_3^-	0.01234	81.070
S^{--}	0.06238	16.032
HS^-	0.03024	33.072
Cl^-	0.02821	35.453
Br^-	0.01251	79.909
I^-	0.00788	126.9044
F^-	0.05264	18.9984
NO_3^-	0.01613	62.0049
NO_2^-	0.02174	46.0055
Cr^{+++}	0.05770	17.332
Cr^{++++++}	0.11539	8.666
CrO_4^{--}	0.01724	57.997

APPROVED AS
USA STANDARD Z111.6-1964
BY USA STANDARDS INSTITUTE
UDC 663.61:620.193

Standard Method of

CORROSIVITY TEST OF INDUSTRIAL WATER (USBM* EMBRITTLEMENT DETECTOR METHOD)[1]

ASTM Designation: D 807 – 52 (1965)

ADOPTED, 1949; REVISED, 1952; REAPPROVED, 1965

This Standard of the American Society for Testing and Materials is issued under the fixed designation D 807; the number immediately following the designation indicates the year of original adoption or, in the case of revision, the year of last revision. A number in parentheses indicates the year of last reapproval.

NOTE—Former Note 5 was deleted editorially in August, 1963.

1. Scope

1.1 This method,[2] known as the embrittlement-detector test, covers the apparatus and procedure for determining the embrittling or nonembrittling characteristics of the water in an operating boiler. The interpretation of the results shall be restricted to the limits set forth in 11. Interpretation of Results.

NOTE 1—The embrittlement detector was designed to reproduce closely the conditions existing in an actual boiler seam. It is considered probable that the individual conditions of leakage, concentration, and stress in the boiler seam can equal those in the detector. The essential difference between the detector and the boiler is that the former is so constructed and operated that these three major factors act simultaneously, continuously, and under the most favorable circumstances to produce cracking; whereas, in the boiler the three factors are brought together only

under unique circumstances. Furthermore, in the detector any cracking is produced in a small test surface that can be inspected thoroughly, while the susceptible areas in a boiler are large and can be inspected only with difficulty. In these respects the embrittlement detector provides an accelerated test of the fourth condition necessary

[2] This method was developed during an investigation conducted under a cooperative agreement between the Joint Research Committee on Boiler Feedwater Studies and the United States Bureau of Mines.

For information on the development of this method reference may be made to the following:

W. C. Schroeder and A. A. Berk, "Intercrystalline Cracking of Boiler Steel and Its Prevention," *Bulletin 443*, U. S. Bureau of Mines, 1941.

W. C. Schroeder, A. A. Berk, and C. K. Stoddard, "Embrittlement Detector Testing on Boilers," *Power Plant Engineering*, Vol. 45, August, 1941, pp. 76–69.

"Embrittlement Symposium," *Transactions*, Am. Soc. Mech. Engrs., Vol. 64, pp. 393–444, 1942.

S. F. Whirl and T. E. Purcell, "Protection Against Caustic Embrittlement by Coordinated Phosphate-pH Control," *Proceedings*, Third Annual Water Conference, Engrs. Soc. of Western Penna., pp. 45–60, 1942.

A. A. Berk and W. C. Schroeder, "A Practical Way to Prevent Embrittlement Cracking," *Transactions*, Am. Soc. Mech. Engrs., Vol. 65, pp. 701–711 (1943).

* United States Bureau of Mines.

[1] Under the standardization procedure of the Society, this method is under the jurisdiction of the ASTM Committee D-19 on Industrial Water. A list of members may be found in the ASTM Year Book.

277

for embrittlement, the embrittling nature of the boiler water.

Note 2—Cracks in a specimen after being subjected to this test indicate that the boiler water can cause embrittlement cracking, but not that the boiler in question necessarily has cracked or will crack.

1.2 The effectiveness of treatment to prevent cracking, as well as an indication of whether an unsafe condition exists, are shown by this test. Such treatments are evaluated in terms of test specimen resistance to failure.

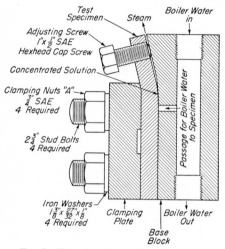

FIG. 1—Cross-Section of Embrittlement Detector.

1.3 The method may be applied to embrittlement resistance testing of steels other than boiler plate, provided that a duplicate, unexposed specimen does not crack when bent 90 deg on a 2-in radius.

2. Summary of Method

2.1 For embrittlement cracking of the boiler metal to be possible, the boiler water must concentrate a thousand times or more in contact with the metal under high residual or applied tensile stress. In a boiler such concentration may take place in riveted seams or in annular spaces at tube ends, and the steel at such locations may be highly stressed when the boiler is constructed or may become highly stressed when it is operated. If the chemicals in the boiler water concentrate in the seams to develop an embrittling solution, cracking may occur.

2.2 In the embrittlement detector (Fig. 1), the conditions of concentration and stress are provided by the design of the unit. Boiler water is permitted to seep slowly from the small hole through the restricted space between the contact

FIG. 2—Embrittlement Detector Installed.

surfaces of the test specimen and the groove in the block. As this extremely slow flow takes place toward atmospheric pressure, the heat in the metal and in the liquid causes progressive evaporation to produce an increasingly concentrated solution. When the detector is properly adjusted, concentrated boiler water is in contact with the stressed test surface of the specimen, thus providing the necessary factor to determine whether the boiler water can cause embrittlement cracking.

3. Definitions

3.1 The term "embrittlement cracking" in this method is defined in accord-

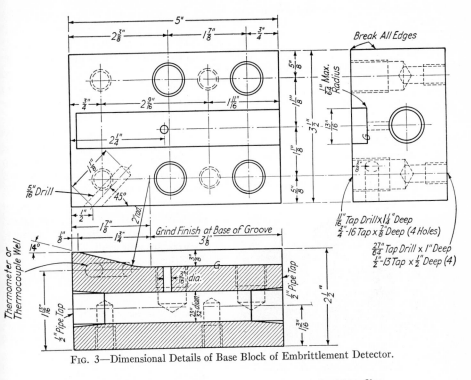

FIG. 3—Dimensional Details of Base Block of Embrittlement Detector.

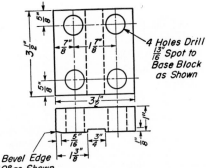

FIG. 4—Dimensional Details of Clamping Plate of Embrittlement Detector.

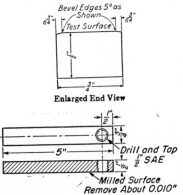

FIG. 5—Dimensional Details of Test Specimen

ance with ASTM Definitions D 1129, Terms Relating to Industrial Water and Industrial Waste Water[3] as follows:

3.1.1 *Embrittlement Cracking*—A form of metal failure that occurs in steam boilers at riveted joints and at tube ends,

the cracking being predominantly inter-crystalline.

NOTE 3—This form of cracking, which has been known as "caustic embrittlement," is believed to result from the action of certain constituents of concentrated boiler water upon steel under stress.

NOTE 4—For a detailed discussion as to what

[3] Appears in this publication.

cracking should be considered significant for the purpose of this test, see 10. Inspection, of this Method D 807.

3.2 For definitions of other terms used in this method, refer to Definitions D 1129.

4. Apparatus

4.1 *Embrittlement Detector*—The embrittlement detector shall consist of the unit, complete with steel specimen, as shown assembled in cross section in Fig. 1 and as the installed unit in Fig. 2. The

Rectangular Bars of 1-in. Cold-Rolled Plate Held Together by 1-in. Bolts. Distance Between Bars $3\frac{1}{4}$ in. Pressure Transmitted by a $1\frac{1}{2}$ in. Round Bar.

Fig. 6—Jig for Bending Specimen After Test.

principal parts consist of a rectangular block base through which the water circulates and in which a groove has been machined to receive the test specimen, a test specimen, and a clamping plate which fits over four stud bolts in the block. When the nuts on the stud bolts are tightened, the pressure of the clamping plate molds the test specimen to the contour of the groove, thus stressing in tension the surface of the specimen. Working drawings (Note 4) showing the dimensions of all the machined parts are shown in Figs. 3 to 5. Accurate machining of the groove with respect to the small hole through which the boiler water is brought to the test surface of the specimen is especially important.

4.2 *Wrenches*—An extra-heavy box-type wrench of $1\frac{1}{16}$-in. opening is recommended for assembling and adjusting the unit. A lighter box-type wrench of $\frac{3}{4}$-in. opening is recommended for the hexagonal head of the adjusting screw in the end of the specimen.

4.3 *Jig for Bending Specimen*—A jig as shown in Fig. 6, or its equivalent, is recommended for bending the specimen with a hydraulic press at the end of the test to reveal cracks that may have been formed but are too fine to be visible without additional stressing of the steel surface. Other devices may be substituted to effect the same purpose of bending the specimen uniformly in the proper place without injuring the surface to be studied (Note 5). A vise and sledge hammer shall not be used.

NOTE 5—The surface to be studied is the stressed area, which starts $\frac{1}{4}$ in. above the spot corresponding to the opening in the test block and extends about 1 in. toward the adjusting screw.

5. Test Specimens

5.1 Cut test specimens $\frac{1}{2}$ by $\frac{3}{4}$ by 5 in. from $\frac{1}{2}$ by $\frac{3}{4}$-in. cold-finished bar stock (Notes 6 and 7) conforming to grade 1020 of ASTM Specifications A 108, for Cold-Finished Carbon Steel Bars and Shafting.[4]

NOTE 6—Where specimens of cold-rolled steel have been cracked, similar specimens machined from boiler plate conforming to ASTM Specification A 515, for Carbon Steel Plates of Intermediate Tensile Strength for Pressure Vessels for Intermediate and Higher Temperature Service[5] or hot-rolled steel of comparable composition may be tested to determine the severity of the embrittling condition. Hot-rolled steel has proved less susceptible to cracking than cold-rolled steel.

NOTE 7—Alloy steels are often more susceptible for cracking than the standard cold-rolled steel specified for test specimens. Where the water tested is used in alloy-steel boilers, it is desirable that the test specimen be prepared

---

[4] *1967 Book of ASTM Standards*, Part 3.
[5] *1967 Book of ASTM Standards*, Part 4.

from the same material or from bars of similar composition and physical properties.

5.2 Finish the test surface of the specimen by either grinding with a surface grinder to a finish comparable to that produced by No. 2 metallographic polishing paper, or milling to remove surface imperfections and smoothing with No. 2 metallographic paper to remove the cutter marks. Grind and polish along the length of the specimen. If the specimen surface still shows visible flaws, such as holes, oxide, or rolling marks, after 0.01 in. has been removed, discard the specimen and prepare another one.

5.3 Bevel the edges of the test surface 5 deg, as shown in Fig. 5.

5.4 Center the threaded hole in the specimen for the adjusting screw and tap as specified in Fig. 5 so that the cap screw is perpendicular to the surface. The adjusting screw shall be sufficiently free so that it can be turned easily with the fingers.

NOTE 8—Specimens that have been prepared in accordance with the directions given in 5. Test Specimens, may be obtained from the major water-treating companies.

6. Assembly of Specimen and Detector

6.1 When a new specimen is to be installed in the detector (Note 9), clean the block, especially the surface of the groove, with hot water to dissolve soluble solids, and scrape lightly to remove less soluble incrustations. Polish the groove with fine emery cloth. Finally open the inlet valve for an instant to make sure that the small leakage hole is cleaned out, then wipe the groove clean. Treat the stud threads with graphite suspended in oil (Note 10).

NOTE 9—When received from the manufacturer the detector is already assembled with the specimen in position and should be steam tight. It is recommended that the specimen not be removed from the detector until after the first test is completed.

NOTE 10—A little graphite suspended in oil applied to the threads of the studs and the adjusting screw will minimize seizing. Use kerosine instead of oil if the pressure is greater than 500 psi.

6.2 To assemble the specimen and the detector, center the specimen with the smoothed surface facing the groove of the block so that the end with the adjusting screw hole is flush with the end of the block not grooved. Place the clamping plate over the studs, with the beveled edge inward and toward the end of the specimen containing the adjusting screw. Place the washers and nuts on the studs. Tighten alternately and evenly first the nuts on the top pair of studs (Note 10) in the center of the detector block thus forcing the surface of the test specimen to conform to the curvature of the groove. Then tighten the nuts on the bottom pair of studs. Finally tighten the nuts on the top pair of studs to bring the surfaces close enough together so that the small hole in the detector block groove is sealed (Note 11).

NOTE 11—There shall be no leakage from the detector when the valves are opened and water at full boiler pressure flows through the block.

6.3 Insert the adjusting screw in the specimen and turn it down with the fingers until it just touches the block.

7. Installation of Detector

7.1 Connect the assembled detector to the operating boiler so that boiler water will circulate through the block (Note 12). Flush clean the inlet line to the detector before the detector is attached.

NOTE 12—The detector may be installed in a bypass to a continuous blow-down line or in a recirculating line if one is available. The effluent from the detector may be returned to the boiler or discharged to waste.

7.2 Maintain the temperature and pressure of the water circulating through the detector block substantially the same as the temperature (Note 13) and pressure of the water in the boiler. Determine the temperature by means of a thermocouple or thermometer inserted in a small hole provided for it in the block.

NOTE 13—It will usually be found necessary to insulate the inlet line to prevent heat losses.

7.3 Mount the detector so that the specimen is vertical, with the adjusting screw at the top (Figs. 1 and 2). Fasten it to a rigid frame by bolts, the holes for which are provided in the back of the detector block. Considerable force is exerted on the stud bolts when a specimen is inserted and when adjustments are made, so that it is necessary for the detector to be solidly fastened. There should be a free space in front and to the sides of the detector to permit inspection and adjustments.

7.4 Provide the $\frac{1}{2}$-in. inlet and outlet lines with valves so that the specimen may be removed and a new specimen inserted while the boiler is in operation.

7.5 If the boiler pressure is especially high and the plant operator objects to threaded joints, attach the detector to the inlet and outlet lines by means of a standard welding procedure such as that specified in Section IX of the ASME Boiler Construction Code, Standard Qualification for Welding Procedure and Welding Operator.

8. Procedure

8.1 Inspect the detector for correct assembly and installation. Back off the adjusting screw so that it does not touch the block. The clamping nuts must be drawn down tightly so that no leakage occurs when full boiler pressure is applied to the unit. If this precaution is not followed, the test may be ruined.

8.2 Open the valves to start circulation of the boiler water through the detector block. Where throttling is necessary, as in a waste-water line, throttle only on the outlet side.

8.3 When the unit is very close to boiler temperature, start the test by backing off the two upper clamping nuts equally and cautiously by tapping the end of the applied wrench lightly with a hammer.

8.4 Diffusion of boiler water between the contact surfaces is properly adjusted when a mist of condensed vapor, issuing from between the specimen and the block, is just barely visible on a cold piece of glass or polished metal held above the upper end of the specimen.

8.5 Restore the stress in the specimen by turning down the adjusting screw until it just bears on the detector block.

8.6 Maintain the proper rate of leakage of boiler water between the test surface and the block by adjustment not more often than once each day; and only after inspection results in a negative test on the cold, condensing surface.

NOTE 14—Do not adjust more than once each day, even when the mist of condensed vapor can be detected only for a short time after each daily adjustment.

NOTE 15—The personal factor in the operation of the embrittlement detector can result in test conditions whereby an embrittling water will not cause cracking of the test specimens. The reverse is not true. When an adjustment of the leakage rate results in even momentary excess leakage, the probability of a poor test is increased.

8.7 If adjustment is necessary, first turn down the adjusting screw one sixth of a turn. If this does not cause the haze to appear on the condenser surface, repeat the operations described in 8.3, 8.4, and 8.5.

NOTE 16—The one sixth of a turn of the adjusting screw is a maximum. Approach it cautiously and do not repeat if the haze does not appear.

NOTE 17—Exercise caution to prevent water from bubbling up under the specimen, for this indicates so high a rate of seepage that concentrated solution formed between the contact surfaces will be washed out. Caution should also be taken to prevent steam from shooting from the sides of the specimen.

8.8 Do not remove the test specimen or wash down the detector during the test.

8.9 At the completion of the test period, close the valves to and from the detector and remove the specimen for inspection.

8.10 Replace the specimen as described in 6. Assembly of Specimen and Detector.

8.11 Keep a log showing the dates when the unit was inspected, dates when adjustment was required, dates when water bubbled from the unit, and any departures from standard procedure.

NOTE 18—Boiler water analysis and log data may increase the usefulness of the records when results are compared.

9. Test Interval

9.1 Continue the first test for 30 operating days. Do not stop the test over week ends or holidays because of the absence of personnel responsible for inspection or adjustment of the detector. The test may be continued if the boiler is banked but up to pressure. If the boiler pressure is to be lowered, close the valves controlling the detector before the boiler is shut down and do not open until the boiler is up to pressure. It is not necessary that the 30 operating days be consecutive, but they should be as closely consecutive as possible.

9.2 If no cracking in the specimen is found from the first test of 30 days, make a second test for 60 operating days.

9.3 If no cracking in the test specimen is found from the second test, make a third test for 90 operating days.

NOTE 19—Additional tests for periods of 90 operating days or longer may be made as a continuing check upon boiler-water conditions.

10. Inspection

10.1 Inspect the specimen as removed from the detector for evidence of having been properly exposed and for color of test surface. This color will be usually dark gray or black (Note 20). Excessive solids indicate the possibility that the rate of diffusion of boiler water was too rapid and that the concentrated solution was formed in the vicinity of the adjusting screw where the specimen is not stressed rather than on the stressed area. There should be a sharply defined spot corresponding to the hole in the groove of the detector block.

NOTE 20—If the boiler water contains nitrate ions in appreciable amount, the test surface may appear red rather than dark gray or black.

10.2 Only the specimen inspector should remove any solid deposits from the specimen. Wash the specimen in hot water after removal of such deposits.

NOTE 21—Watch the test surface as it dries in air. Fine cracks are often revealed momentarily as the film of moisture recedes, and the depth of the crack can sometimes be determined similarly on the sides of the specimen.

10.3 Examine the surface of the specimen with a magnifying glass. If no cracks are visible, remove the adjusting screw and place the specimen in a jig, as shown in Fig. 6. Carefully apply pressure with a hydraulic press, or the equivalent, to bend the steel in the stressed area, effecting a vertical displacement of about $\frac{1}{2}$ in. Again carefully inspect the stressed area for cracks (Note 22). Oxide coatings on specimens subjected to this test may become heavy enough to fracture when the metal is bent, and as a result the metal may become slightly fissured. Also, pits often become elongated fissures when the metal is bent. Do not confuse such fissures, check marks, and similar surface imperfections with cracks due to embrittlement.

NOTE 22—The bending may distort the steel so much that the intercrystalline path of the crack is obscured and becomes more difficult to find on metallographic examination. When this examination is to be made, the jig may still be used to reveal the existence and position of cracks, but the bar should be bent as little as possible.

10.4 The crack may be examined metallographically (Note 23) for evidence of intercrystalline cracking (Note 24), which constitutes positive proof of embrittlement.

NOTE 23—For recommended procedures for metallographic examination, refer to ASTM Methods E 2, Preparation of Micrographs of Metals and Alloys[6] and ASTM Methods E 3, Preparation of Metallographic Specimens.[6]

NOTE 24—Embrittlement cracks in alloy steels often tend to be intracrystalline, following slip planes rather than grain boundaries.

11. Interpretation of Results

11.1 The presence of cracks in a specimen tested in accordance with this method shall be attributed to embrittlement caused by the boiler water. Failure of the specimen may be differentiated for comparison purposes as "bad cracking," "cracking," or "slight cracking."

11.2 A boiler water may be considered

---

[6] *1967 Book of ASTM Standards*, Part 31.

to have had no embrittling tendencies during the period of the tests when successive 30-, 60-, and 90-day tests each have shown no cracking of the test specimens.

12. Precision and Accuracy

12.1 Since the character of a boiler water may change with variation in the water supply or the chemical treatment of the water, any conclusions based upon the condition of the test specimens are strictly valid only with respect to the actual periods of exposure.

12.2 Inasmuch as a personal element is involved in the operation of the detector, there is an uncertainty factor in a test that results in no cracking. Correlation of more than 800 tests made by average plant personnel indicates that the probable chance of error is no more than 5 per cent after 30-, 60-, and 90-day tests have been completed.

NOTE 25—Reports of additional tests for future correlation will be welcomed and should be addressed to ASTM Headquarters, 1916 Race St., Philadelphia, Pa. 19103.

Tentative Methods of Test for

ALUMINUM IN INDUSTRIAL WATER AND INDUSTRIAL WASTE WATER[1]

ASTM Designation: D 857 – 66 T

Issued, 1966

These Tentative Methods have been approved by the sponsoring committee and accepted by the Society in accordance with established procedures, for use pending adoption as standard. Suggestions for revisions should be addressed to the Society at 1916 Race St., Philadelphia, Pa. 19103.

1. Scope

1.1 These methods cover the determination of aluminum in industrial water and industrial waste water. Three methods are given as follows:

	Sections
Referee Method A (Fluorometric).	5 to 13
Referee Method B (Spectrophotometric).....................	14 to 23
Non-Referee Method C (Spectrophotometric)................	24 to 32

1.2 Referee Method A is applicable to water relatively low in solids and containing up to 5 ppb of soluble aluminum. Referee Method B is applicable to water relatively high in interfering cations and containing from 0.00 to 0.50 ppm of total aluminum. Non-Referee Method C is applicable to water relatively free of interfering ions and containing from 0.00 to 2.00 ppm of soluble aluminum.

2. Definitions

2.1 For definitions of terms used in these methods, refer to ASTM Definitions D 1129, Terms Relating to Industrial Water and Industrial Waste Water.[2]

3. Purity of Reagents

3.1 Reagent grade chemicals or equivalent, as specified in ASTM Methods E 200, Preparation, Standardization, and Storage of Standard Solutions for Chemical Analysis,[2] shall be used in all tests.

3.2 Unless otherwise indicated, references to water shall be understood to mean reagent water conforming to ASTM Specifications D 1193, for Reagent Water,[2] Referee Grade.

4. Sampling

4.1 Collect the sample in accordance with the applicable method of the American Society for Testing and Materials, as follows:

---

[1] Under the standardization procedure of the Society, these methods are under the jurisdiction of the ASTM Committee D-19 on Industrial Water. A list of members may be found in the ASTM Year Book.

[2] Appears in this publication.

D 510—Sampling Industrial Water,[2]
D 860—Sampling Water from Boilers,[2]
D 1066—Sampling Steam,[2]
D 1192—Sampling Industrial Water and Steam, Spec. for Equipment for,[2] and
D 1496—Sampling Homogeneous Industrial Waste Water.[2]

4.2 For methods used to condition sample containers, see 8.2.

REFEREE METHOD A

5. Application

5.1 This method[3] is applicable to the determination of soluble aluminum in

TABLE 1—LIMITING CONCENTRATION OF INTERFERING IONS.

Ion	Limiting Concentration, ppb
Ca++	>1000
Co++	>1000
Cr+++	30
Cu++	20
F-	5
Fe+++	100
Mg++	200
NH4+	500
Ni++	>1000
Pb++	1000
PO4---	3
SiO3--	>1000
SO4--	>1000
Zn++	1000
Morpholine	100

industrial water in concentrations below 5 ppb. The water must be of relatively high purity. Heavy metal ions of the order of 20 ppb produce interferences.

6. Summary of Method

6.1 The fluorescence of an aluminum-morin complex formed at a pH of 3 is measured and referred to a previously prepared calibration curve to determine the aluminum concentration.

7. Interferences

7.1 The limiting concentration of interfering ions in a solution of 2 ppb of aluminum is given in Table 1.

8. Apparatus

8.1 *Fluorometer*, equipped with a mercury arc source, a 440-mμ excitation filter, and a 525-mμ fluorescence filter.

9. Reagent

9.1 *Acetic Acid (1:1)*—Mix one volume of glacial acetic acid (sp gr 1.05) with one volume of water.

9.2 *Aluminum, Standard Solution (1 ml = 0.010 mg Al)*—Dissolve 1.769 g of aluminum potassium sulfate ($AlK(SO_4)_2 \cdot 12H_2O$) in water. Add 10 ml of concentrated hydrochloric acid (HCl, sp gr 1.19). Dilute to 1 liter and mix. Dilute 100 ml of the above solution to 1 liter.

9.3 *Morin Solution*—Dissolve 0.1 g of morin[4] in 100 ml of Formula 30 alcohol (86 per cent ethanol, 9 per cent methanol, 5 per cent water).

9.4 *Quinine Sulfate Solution (0.010 g/ liter)*—Dissolve 10 mg of quinine sulfate in 1 liter of sulfuric acid (H_2SO_4, 1:70). This solution is stable indefinitely.

10. Preparation of Apparatus

10.1 Soak all glassware (for both sampling and testing) in hot HCl (1:1) for 2 hr. Drain and rinse at least five times with water. Drain and flush with methyl alcohol, ethyl alcohol, or isopropyl alcohol.

11. Calibration

11.1 Prepare a solution containing 100 ppb of aluminum by diluting 10 ml of the aluminum stock solution (see 9.2) to 1 liter.

11.2 One milliliter of the 100-ppb

---

[3] F. Will, III; "Fluorometric Determination of Aluminum in the Parts Per Billion Range," *Analytical Chemistry*, Vol. 33, 1961, pp. 1360–2.

[4] A satisfactory grade of morin may be obtained from K and K Laboratories, Inc., 121 Express St. (Engineer's Hill), Plainview, N. Y. 11803.

aluminum solution diluted to 100 ml gives a 1-ppb concentration. To a triplicate series of 100-ml volumetric flasks, add respectively 0, 1, 2, 3, 4 and 5 ml of aluminum solution from 11.1. Make up each standard to volume with water.

11.3 From these standards make a calibration curve in the range 0 to 5 ppb. Refer to 12.1 through 12.4 for the development of fluorescence.

11.4 Plot the fluorometer readings from the standards against the respective parts per billion of aluminum.

12. Procedure

12.1 Transfer to a 100-ml volumetric flask, 1 ml of acetic acid (1:1). Add the sample up to the 100-ml mark. Similarly prepare a 5-ppb standard to serve as a reference.

12.2 To a separate flask or beaker add 5 ml of morin solution and dilute with the 100-ml acidified sample from 12.1. Allow to stand at room temperature for 20 min.

12.3 Transfer portions of each solution to like photometric cells. Set the fluorometer to 100 with the developed 5-ppb standard and the quinine sulfate solution according to the manufacturer's manual.

12.4 Measure the fluorescence of the samples and refer to the calibration curve to convert fluorometer readings to parts per billion of aluminum.

13. Precision

13.1 The precision[5] of the method may be expressed as follows:

$$S_c = \frac{7.9 - 1.1X}{V}$$

where:
S_c = single laboratory precision, ppb of aluminum,

---

[5] Supporting data giving the results of cooperative tests have been filed at ASTM Headquarters.

X = concentration of aluminum, ppb, and
V = milliliters of sample taken for test.

REFEREE METHOD B

14. Application

14.1 This method[6] is applicable to the determination of total aluminum in industrial water in the range of 0.00 to 0.50 ppm as Al^{+++} (based on a 100-ml sample). The range of the test may be extended by taking a suitable aliquot.

TABLE 2—LIMITING CONCENTRATION OF INTERFERING IONS.

Ion	Limiting Concentration, mg/sample aliquot
Cu^{++}	0.10
Mn^{++}	0.01
PO_4^{---}	0.50
Polyphosphate (PO_4^{---})	0.50
F^-	0.50
Fe^{+++}	0.10
Mg^{++}	0.50
Ca^{++}	3.20

15. Summary of Method

15.1 The aluminum is complexed with sodium fluoride to prevent its reaction with 8-quinolinol while interfering ions are removed by a weak cationic ion exchange resin and an 8-quinolinol-chloroform extraction. The aluminum is then made reactive to the 8-quinolinol by pH adjustment and its chloroform-extracted 8-quinolinate is measured spectrophotometrically.

16. Interferences

16.1 Table 2 shows the milligrams of extraneous ions which do not interfere in the determination of up to 0.04 mg of aluminum in a sample.

---

[6] C. A. Noll and L. J. Stafanelli, "Fluorometric and Spectrophotometric Determination of Aluminum in Industrial Water," *Analytical Chemistry*, Vol. 35, 1963, 1914–16.

17. Apparatus

17.1 *Spectrophotometer*, suitable for measurement at a wave-length of 380 mμ and having sample cells of 10-mm light path. Photometers and photometric practices prescribed in this method shall conform to ASTM Recommended Practice E 60, Photometric Methods for the Chemical Analysis of Metals.[7] The spectrophotometer shall conform to the ASTM Recommended Practice E 275, for Describing and Measuring Performance of Spectrophotometers.[8]

17.2 *Specific Conductance Equipment*, suitable for measuring the specific conductance of water up to 3000 micromhos. The apparatus and practices related to its use shall conform to ASTM Methods D 1125, Test for Electrical Conductivity of Industrial Water and Industrial Waste Water.[2]

17.3 *Shaker*, reciprocating, adjusted for shaking at the rate of about 2 strokes per sec with a horizontal stroke of about 1 in.

18. Reagents and Materials

18.1 *Aluminum Stock Solution (1 ml = 0.010 mg Al)*—See 9.2.

18.2 *Buffer Solution (pH 4.4 to 4.9)*—Add 238 ml of concentrated ammonium hydroxide (NH_4OH, sp gr 0.90) to 500 ml of water. Slowly add 111 ml of glacial acetic acid (sp gr 1.05); mix, and dilute to 1 liter.

18.3 *Chloroform ($CHCl_3$)*.

18.4 *8-Quinolinol Solution (2 per cent)* —Dissolve 2 g of 8-hydroxyquinoline (melting point 74 to 76 C) in 6 ml of glacial acetic acid and dilute to 100 ml with water.

18.5 *Hydrochloric Acid (sp gr 1.19)*— Concentrated hydrochloric acid (HCl).

18.6 *Hydrochloric acid (1:124)*—Mix 1 volume of concentrated HCl (sp gr 1.19) with 124 volumes of water.

18.7 *Ion-Exchange Resin,*[9] (20 to 30 mesh) regenerated with hydrochloric acid. Before using the ion-exchange beads, backwash them in a column until the effluent water is free from visible turbidity and chloride. Check for chloride by adding 2 drops of 1.0 per cent silver nitrate ($AgNO_3$) to 10 ml of effluent water. This should not produce any visible turbidity.

18.8 *Nitric Acid (sp gr 1.42)*—Concentrated nitric acid (HNO_3).

18.9 *Silver Nitrate Solution (10 g/ liter)*—Dissolve 1 g of silver nitrate ($AgNO_3$) in water and dilute to 100 ml. Store in a brown bottle.

18.10 *Sodium Fluoride Solution (2 g/ liter)*—Dissolve 2 g of sodium fluoride (NaF) in water and dilute to 1 liter. Store in a polyethylene bottle.

18.11 *Sodium Sulfate (Na_2SO_4)*, anhydrous.

19. Preparation of Apparatus

19.1 Clean all glassware as described in 10.1.

20. Calibration

20.1 Prepare in triplicate a series of five standards covering the range of 0 to 0.5 ppm aluminum. One milliliter of aluminum standard solution (see 9.2) diluted to 100 ml gives a solution of 0.1 ppm aluminum.

20.2 Treat each reference standard as described in 21.1 starting with 21.1.2.

20.3 Prepare a calibration curve in parts per million by plotting absorbance of the standard solutions against concentration of aluminum.

21. Procedure

21.1 *Total Aluminum:*

21.1.1 *Sample Size*—Normally use a 100-ml sample. The sample size may be

---

[7] *1967 Book of ASTM Standards*, Part 32.
[8] *1967 Book of ASTM Standards*, Part 30.

[9] IRC-50 resin available from Rohm & Haas Co., Independence Mall West, Phila., Pa., or equivalent, has been found satisfactory for this purpose.

increased or reduced but the aluminum content must not exceed 0.05 mg. The specific conductance of the original water should be less than $250,000/V$ micromhos, where V = volume of sample taken for analysis.

21.1.2 Shake the sample and immediately pipet an aliquot into a 250-ml borosilicate glass beaker. Add 5 ml of concentrated HCl (sp gr 1.19) and evaporate to 5 to 10 ml. Add 5 ml of HNO_3 (sp gr 1.42) and continue evaporation to dryness on a steam bath or equivalent. *DO NOT BAKE RESIDUE.*

21.1.3 Remove from steam bath and wet the residue with 2 ml of HCl (1:124). Add 80 ml of water and mix thoroughly. At this point all of the residue must be completely solubilized. Add 4 ml of NaF solution and mix.

21.1.4 Add 15 g of moist IRC-50 ion exchange resin beads to an 8-oz wide-mouth bottle with cover. Transfer the sample from 21.1.3 to the wide-mouth bottle, rinse the beaker with 5 ml of water, and add to the sample. Then add 0.5 ml of buffer solution (pH 4.4 to 4.9), cap, and place the bottle on the shaker.

21.1.5 Adjust the shaker for 2 strokes per sec and shake the sample for 20 ± 3 min.

21.1.6 Filter the sample into a 250-ml separatory funnel. Add 2 ml of 8-quinolinol solution to the sample, hand shake for 15 sec, and let stand for 2 min.

21.1.7 Add 25 ml of chloroform to the sample in the separatory funnel, hand shake for 1 min, and allow to stand until separation of the two liquids occurs; this separation usually requires 10 min. Discard the chloroform and repeat the extraction with 10 ml of chloroform and again discard the chloroform.

21.1.8 Add 10 ml of buffer solution (pH 4.4 to 4.9) to the sample remaining in the separatory funnel from 21.1.7 and thoroughly mix. Add 2 ml of 8-quinolinol solution, mix for 15 sec and let stand for 3 min. Add 25 ml of chloroform and hand shake for 1 min. Allow to stand until the two liquids completely separate.

21.1.9 Line a glass funnel with a very retentive, dense-textured filter paper (9 cm), and fill the funnel to approximately one third its depth with anhydrous Na_2SO_4. Wash the funnel thoroughly with chloroform.

21.1.10 Filter the chloroform layer from 21.1.8 through the funnel described in 21.1.9 and collect the filtrate in a 50-ml volumetric flask. Repeat the chloroform extraction using 10 ml and hand shake for 1 min. Allow to stand until the two liquids completely separate. Filter the chloroform layer through the funnel into the 50-ml volumetric flask. Rinse the funnel with chloroform but be careful not to exceed the 50-ml mark on the flask.

21.1.11 Dilute the solution to 50 ml with chloroform, mix, and read the developed color in the spectrophotometer at a wavelength of 380 mμ.

21.1.12 Refer to the calibration curve to convert spectrophotometer readings to parts per million of aluminum.

21.2 *Soluble Aluminum:*

21.2.1 Filter the sample and then proceed as described in 21.1.

22. Calculation

22.1 Calculate the concentration of aluminum in parts per million as follows:

Aluminum (total or dissolved), ppm

$$= \frac{C \times 100}{V}$$

where:

C = parts per million from the calibration curve, and

V = milliliters of sample taken for test.

23. Precision

23.1 The precision of this method may be expressed as follows:

49–67

$$S_O = \frac{0.9}{V}$$

where:

S_O = single operator precision in parts per million of aluminum, and

V = milliliters of sample taken for the test.

NON-REFEREE METHOD C

24. Application

24.1 This method[10] is applicable to industrial water and industrial waste water relatively free of interfering substances. The procedure is simple and

TABLE 3—INTERFERENCE EFFECTS.

Constituent	Parts Per Million	Aluminum Found, ppm
Mg............ {	40	1.04
	80	1.09
Zn..............	5	1.05
Mn........... {	5	1.17
	10	1.28
F.............. {	1	0.94
	2	0.90
	5	0.80

rapid, but only soluble aluminum is determined.

25. Summary of the Method

25.1 Ferron (8-hydroxy-7-iodo-5-quinoline sulfonic acid) reacts with aluminum to form a soluble complex that absorbs ultraviolet light. The absorbance of the complex is proportional to the soluble aluminum and is measured by a spectrophotometer at a wavelength of 370 mμ.

25.2 A significant interference from iron is greatly minimized by adding orthophenanthroline. This has the additional advantage that iron may be simul-

---

[10] U. S. Geological Survey Water Supply *Paper 1454.*

taneously determined, but at a wavelength of 520 mμ.

26. Interferences

26.1 Iron is most frequently associated with aluminum in water and each part per million of iron increases the aluminum reading about 0.01 ppm. In this method the iron interference is determined and corrections are subtracted.

26.2 Several other metals and anions cause interference, but only manganese, lead, cobalt, and fluoride show sufficiently pronounced effects to require correction. Beryllium minimizes the interference of fluoride. The relative interference effects of certain constituents are indicated by the results obtained in solutions containing 1.00 ppm of aluminum and given in Table 3. Orthophosphate up to 5 ppm and residual chlorine up to 5 ppm do not interfere. Natural color and turbidity interfere in the aluminum determination, and a correction is usually required.

27. Apparatus

27.1 *Spectrophotometer*, using sample cells of 10-mm light path and providing light sources at wavelengths of 370 and 520 mμ (see 17.1).

28. Reagents

28.1 *Aluminum, Standard Solution (1 ml = 0.010 mg Al)*—See 9.2.

28.2 *Ferron-Orthophenanthroline Reagent*—Add 0.5 g of ferron and 1.0 g of orthophenanthroline to approximately 1 liter of water. Stir, preferably mechanically, for at least 2 hr until the maximum solution is obtained. If any solids settle out, decant the clear supernatant liquid for use.

28.3 *Hydroxylamine Hydrochloride Solution (100 g/liter)*—Dissolve 100 g of hydroxylamine hydrochloride ($NH_2OH \cdot HCl$) in water. Add 40 ml of concentrated hydrochloric acid (HCl, sp gr 1.19). Add

1 g of beryllium sulfate (BeSO$_4$·4H$_2$O) and dissolve. Dilute to approximately 1 liter with water.

NOTE: **Caution**—Beryllium compounds should be handled with extreme care to avoid inhalation. Use of a properly designed fume hood or a respirator designed for toxic materials is recommended for the weighing step. Any spillage should be promptly handled with the same degree of caution.[11]

28.4 *Iron, Standard Solution (1 ml = 0.010 mg Fe)*—Dissolve 0.7022 g of ferrous ammonium sulfate (FeSO$_4$·(NH$_4$)$_2$SO$_4$·6H$_2$O) in 50 ml of water and 20 ml of concentrated sulfuric acid (H$_2$SO$_4$, sp gr 1.84). Dilute with water to 1 liter and mix. Dilute 100 ml of the above solution to 1 liter and mix.

28.5 *Sodium Acetate (275 g/liter)*—Dissolve 275 g of sodium acetate trihydrate (NaC$_2$H$_3$O$_2$·3H$_2$O) in water and dilute to 1 liter.

29. Calibration

29.1 *Aluminum Curve:*

29.1.1 To eleven 100-ml volumetric flasks, add respectively 0.0, 2.0, 4.0, 6.0, 8.0, 10.0, 12.0, 14.0, 16.0, 18.0 and 20.0 ml of aluminum standard; each milliliter diluted to 100 ml gives a solution of 0.10 ppm aluminum.

29.1.2 Using the procedure described in 30, develop the color and measure the absorbance of each standard at a wavelength of 370 mμ.

29.1.3 Make a calibration curve plotting the absorbance against concentration.

29.2 *Iron Correction Curve:*

29.2.1 To nine 100-ml volumetric flasks, add respectively 0.0, 5.0, 10.0, 15.0, 20.0, 25.0, 30.0, 35.0 and 40.0 ml of iron standard. Dilute to 100 ml. Each milliliter diluted to this volume gives a solution of 0.10 ppm of iron.

29.2.2 Using the procedure described in 30, develop the color and measure the absorbance at two wavelengths, 370 and 520 mμ.

29.2.3 Make curves plotting absorbance against concentration of iron at the two specified wavelengths.

30. Procedure

30.1 Pipet a 25-ml sample into a beaker or flask.

30.2 Add 2 ml of hydroxylamine hydrochloride solution and let stand for about 30 min to permit complete reduction of ferric iron.

30.3 Add 5 ml of ferron-orthophenanthroline solution and mix.

30.4 Add 2 ml of sodium acetate solution and let stand at least 10 min but not more than 30 min.

30.5 Transfer the test solution to a spectrophotometer and measure the absorbance at 370 and 520 mμ.

31. Calculations

31.1 Designate the absorbance measurement at 370 mμ as A.

31.2 Using the iron correction curve locate the absorbance value measured at 520 mμ. At the same iron concentration read the corresponding absorbance at 370 mμ. Designate this value as B.

31.3 A minus B is the corrected absorbance. Using the aluminum calibration curve, find the aluminum concentration corresponding to the corrected absorbance.

32. Precision

32.1 The precision of this method may be expressed as follows:

$$S_O = 0.035 \text{ ppm}$$

where:
S_O = single operator precision in parts per million of aluminum.

---

[11] For further information see "The Metal Beryllium," Editors D. W. White and J. E. Burke, American Society for Metals, 1955.

Standard Method of Test for
MANGANESE IN INDUSTRIAL WATER AND INDUSTRIAL WASTE WATER[1]

ASTM Designation: D 858 – 65

ADOPTED, 1965

This Standard of the American Society for Testing and Materials is issued under the fixed designation D 858; the final number indicates the year of original adoption as standard or, in the case of revision, the year of last revision.

Scope

1. (a) This method covers the determination of manganese in industrial water and industrial waste water and includes both soluble and insoluble manganese. It does not cover determination of the valence state of manganese in the sample.

(b) The method covers the range 0.025 to 15 ppm of manganese as Mn, but the range may be extended by dilution of the sample.

Summary of Method

2. Insoluble manganese is solubilized by digestion with hydrochloric acid and the soluble manganese is oxidized to permanganate with ammonium persulfate in the presence of silver nitrate. The resulting color is compared with standards either visually or instrumentally.

Definitions

3. For definitions of terms in these methods, refer to the Definitions of Terms Relating to Industrial Water and Industrial Waste Water (ASTM Designation: D 1129).[2]

Interferences

4. Constituents, other than manganese, that produce colors in the range of 525 mμ under the conditions of the test interfere, but a partial correction for such interferences is provided in the present method. Cobalt compounds fall into this class. Organic matter, halogens, and material capable of producing turbidity interfere, but the procedure herein described eliminates their effect.

Apparatus

5. (a) *Photometer.* — Spectrophotometer or filter photometer suitable for use in the range of 525 mμ. The filter photometers and photometric practice prescribed in this method shall conform to the Recommended Practice for Pho-

[1] Under the standardization procedure of the Society, this method is under the jurisdiction of the ASTM Committee D-19 on Industrial Water. A list of members may be found in the ASTM Year Book.

[2] Appears in this publication.

tometric Methods for Chemical Analysis of Metals (ASTM Designation: E 60).[3] The spectrophotometers shall conform to the Recommended Practice for Describing and Measuring Performance of Spectrophotometers (ASTM Designation: E 275).[4]

(b) *Nessler Color Comparison Tubes*, 50-ml capacity, matched and colorless.

Reagents

6. (a) *Purity of Reagents.*—Reagent grade chemicals shall be used in all tests. Unless otherwise indicated, it is intended that all reagents shall conform to the specifications of the Committee on Analytical Reagents of the American Chemical Society, where such specifications are available.[5] Other grades may be used, provided it is first ascertained that the reagent is of sufficiently high purity to permit its use without lessening the accuracy of the determination.

(b) *Purity of Water.*—Unless otherwise indicated, references to water shall be understood to mean reagent water conforming to the Specifications for Reagent Water (ASTM Designation: D 1193).[2]

(c) *Ammonium Persulfate* $((NH_4)_2S_2O_8)$, crystals.

(d) *Hydrochloric Acid (sp gr 1.19).*—Concentrated hydrochloric acid (HCl).

(e) *Manganese, Standard Solution (1 ml = 0.10 mg Mn).*—Dissolve 3.20 g of potassium permanganate $(KMnO_4)$ in 1 liter of boiling water in a Florence flask. Cover with a beaker and simmer ½ hr. Cool to room temperature and filter twice through fritted glass into a dark colored, glass-stoppered bottle. Standardize as follows: weigh duplicate

[3] *1967 Book of ASTM Standards*, Part 32.
[4] *1967 Book of ASTM Standards*, Part 30.
[5] "Reagent Chemicals, American Chemical Society Specifications," Am. Chemical Soc., Washington, D. C. For suggestions on the testing of reagents not listed by the American Chemical Society, see "Reagent Chemicals and Standards," by Joseph Rosin, D. Van Nostrand Co., Inc., New York, N. Y., and the "United States Pharmacopeia."

0.2500 g National Bureau of Standards oxidimetric grade sodium oxalate $(Na_2C_2O_4)$ or equivalent into 400-ml beakers. Add 200 ml of water to each beaker and heat to 90 C. Add 10 ml of sulfuric acid $(H_2SO_4, 1:1)$ to each beaker. Titrate with the $KMnO_4$ solution to a faint pink end point, persistent for 1 min. Calculate the normality of the $KMnO_4$ solution and the volume required to produce 1 liter of solution containing 0.10 mg Mn per ml. Measure this volume into a 500-ml Erlenmeyer flask and add 10 ml of H_2SO_4 (1:1). Reduce by adding 0.6 g of sodium bisulfite $(NaHSO_3)$ and heat to almost boiling. If traces of manganese dioxide (MnO_2) remain, add increments of about 0.05 g of $NaHSO_3$ until the solution entirely clear of sulfur dioxide (SO_2) is evident. Boil off the SO_2. Cool, transfer to a 1-liter volumetric flask, dilute to the mark with water, and mix.

(f) *Preventive Solution.*—Dissolve 75 g of mercuric sulfate $(HgSO_4)$ in 400 ml of concentrated nitric acid $(HNO_3,$ sp gr 1.42) and 200 ml of water. Add 200 ml of concentrated phosphoric acid $(H_3PO_4,$ 85 per cent) and 0.035 g of silver nitrate $(AgNO_3)$, and dilute, after cooling, to 1 liter.

(g) *Sodium Bisulfite* $(NaHSO_3),$[6] granular.

(h) *Sodium Nitrite Solution (20 g per liter).*—Dissolve 2.0 g of sodium nitrite $(NaNO_2)$ in water and dilute to 100 ml.

(i) *Sodium Oxalate.*[6]—National Bureau of Standards oxidimetric grade sodium oxalate $(Na_2C_2O_4)$, dried 1 hr at 105 C and cooled in a desiccator.

(j) *Sulfuric Acid (sp gr 1.84).*—Concentrated sulfuric acid (H_2SO_4).

(k) *Sulfuric Acid (1:1).*—Carefully mix 1 volume of H_2SO_4 (sp gr 1.84) with 1 volume of water.

(l) *Sulfuric Acid (1:19).*—Carefully

[6] Reagent used for standardization purposes only.

mix 1 volume of H_2SO_4 (sp gr 1.84) with 19 volumes of water.

Sampling

7. (a) Collect the sample in accordance with the applicable method of the American Society for Testing and Materials, as follows:

D 510—Sampling Industrial Water,[2]
D 860—Sampling Water from Boilers,[2]
D 1066—Sampling Steam,[2]
D 1496—Sampling Homogeneous Industrial Waste Water.[2]

(b) While manganese may exist in a soluble form when a sample, as from a deep well, is first collected, it oxidizes to higher oxidation states and precipitates from solution. Hence, unless a sample is analyzed immediately after collection, it should be stabilized by acidifying with H_2SO_4 to a pH of approximately 2.0 (1 ml of H_2SO_4 (1:19) added to 200 ml). This precaution may simplify the analytical procedure needed.

Calibration and Standardization

8. (a) Prepare an appropriate series of standard manganese dilutions, including the approximate concentration expected in the sample, by diluting increments of the standard manganese solution, prepared in accordance with Section 6(e), plus 1 ml of H_2SO_4 (1:19), to 1 liter with water.

(b) Pipet 100-ml portions of the standard manganese solutions into 250-ml Erlenmeyer flasks and proceed as described in Section 9(d) and (g). Plot absorbance against the manganese concentrations.

(c) Preparation of a calibration curve is required only for photometric determinations. A separate calibration curve must be made for each photometer or spectrophotometer. This curve must be checked periodically to ensure reproducibility.

Procedure

9. (a) Pipet into a 250-ml Erlenmeyer

flask 100 ml of sample and proceed in accordance with Paragraph (d) except that if the presence of insoluble manganese, excessive amounts of organic matter, halogens, or turbidity-producing materials, or all three is suspected, proceed in accordance with Paragraph (c). If a blank has not been run on the reagents, also carry through the analysis on 100 ml of water using the appropriate procedure.

If the sample has been taken without stabilization with H_2SO_4 and there is evidence in the sample container of an adhering deposit that might include manganese, dissolve it in a minimum of H_2SO_4 and add it to the sample. Taking the original sample directly in a small container with H_2SO_4 and using the entire sample for the determination of total manganese avoids this problem.

Usually 100 ml is a satisfactory sample size. However, if the manganese content is less than 0.2 ppm, use 200 ml and if the manganese content is high, use an appropriately smaller volume. In either case apply proper factors to the manganese concentrations calculated in Section 10.

(b) If visual comparison is to be made, prepare 0.05-ppm incremental standard manganese dilutions in accordance with Section 8(a), to cover a concentration range bracketing the anticipated manganese concentration of the sample. Pipet 100 ml of each standard solution thus prepared into individual 250-ml Erlenmeyer flasks, and treat them as described in Paragraph (d).

(c) Add 5 ml of HCl (sp gr 1.19) and evaporate to about 25 ml. Digest at the boiling point until inorganic insoluble matter dissolves. Carefully evaporate to just dryness. Cool. Add 5 ml of H_2SO_4 (sp gr 1.84), and 10 ml of HNO_3 (sp gr 1.42). Mix and evaporate to dense white fumes. Cool. Add 10 ml of HNO_3 (sp gr 1.42) and evaporate to dense white fumes a second time. Cool

Add 40 ml of water, warm, and filter through fiber-glass filter paper or equivalent. Rinse the flask and wash the filter three times with 10-ml portions of hot water. Transfer the filtrate to the original Erlenmeyer flask, rinsing the filter flask with four 5-ml portions of water.

(d) Add 5 ml of preventive solution and adjust to about 90 ml by either boiling or dilution. Add 1 g of $(NH_4)_2S_2O_8$. Place the flask on a hot plate and bring to a boil in 2 min. Cool in air 1 min and then rapidly under a cold water tap to room temperature. Transfer to a 100-ml volumetric flask, dilute with water to the mark, and mix.

(e) If visual comparison is to be made, transfer 50 ml of the oxidized sample solution to a Nessler tube and compare the color of the solution with the color of the series of standard manganese dilutions prepared in accordance with Paragraphs (b) and (d) and contained in similar Nessler tubes. Record the concentration of the standard solution in parts per million of manganese, that matches the sample solution in color. Add 1 drop of $NaNO_2$ solution to the Nessler tube and mix. After the color fades, record the concentration of standard dilution in parts per million of manganese, that matches the bleached sample solution in color. Subtract the bleached reading from the unbleached reading and record as gross parts per million of manganese.

(f) Transfer 50 ml of the blank to a Nessler tube and compare the color with the series of standard manganese dilutions. Record the blank as parts per million of manganese. Then,

Net Mn = gross Mn − blank
(all as ppm Mn)

(g) If photometric measurement is to be made, transfer a portion of the sample solution to a sample cell. Measure the absorbance at 525 mμ in a photometer,

setting the instrument for zero absorbance with water. Add 1 drop of $NaNO_2$ solution to the sample cell, and mix. After the color fades, read the absorbance at 525 mμ. Subtract the absorbance of the bleached solution from the absorbance of the unbleached solution and record as gross absorbance.

(h) Measure the absorbance of the blank at 525 mμ. Subtract the blank absorbance from the gross absorbance obtained in Paragraph (g) and record as the net absorbance. Convert the net absorbance to net parts per million of manganese using the curve prepared in accordance with Section 8.

Calculation

10. The net concentration determined in accordance with Section 9(f) or (h) represents the concentration, in parts per million of manganese, if the sample volume is 100 ml. If the sample volume varies, calculate the parts per million of manganese in the sample as follows:

$$ \text{Mn, ppm} = \frac{A}{B} \times 100 $$

where:

A = net parts per million of manganese, and
B = milliliters of sample used.

Precision[7]

11. The precision of the method varies with the quantity of manganese (Mn) being determined. When color measurement is made instrumentally, precision is expressed as follows:

$$ S_T = 0.029x + 0.01 $$

where:
S_T = precision, in parts per million, and
x = concentration, in parts per million.

---

[7] Supporting data provided by the Steel Industry Action Committee have been filed at ASTM Headquarters.

Tentative Methods of Test for

SILICA IN INDUSTRIAL WATER AND INDUSTRIAL WASTE WATER[1]

ASTM Designation: D 859 – 64 T

Issued, 1945; Revised, 1947, 1950, 1955, 1964

These Tentative Methods have been approved by the sponsoring committee and accepted by the Society in accordance with established procedures for use pending adoption as standard. Suggestions for revisions should be addressed to the Society at 1916 Race St., Philadelphia 3, Pa.

Scope

1. (a) These methods[2] cover the determination of silica in industrial water and industrial waste water. The following four methods are included:

	Sections
Referee Method A (Gravimetric Method)	5 to 11
Referee Method B (Colorimetric Method)	12 to 20
Non-Referee Method C (Colorimetric Method)	21 to 29
Non-Referee Method D (Colorimetric Method)	30 to 38

(b) Referee Method A covers gravimetric, acid-dehydration procedures; it is independent of interferences, and is a primary measure of total silica in water.

Referee Method B covers the photometric determination of soluble silica in industrial waters where the silica content is in the range of 0 to 1000 ppb. Non-Referee Methods C and D are colorimetric determinations, and are secondary measures of crystalloidal (noncolloidal) silica in that they must be standardized against Referee Method A or primary silica standards.

Definitions

2. For definitions of terms used in these methods, refer to the Definitions of Terms Relating to Industrial Water and Industrial Waste Water (ASTM Designation: D 1129).[3]

Purity of Reagents

3. (a) Reagent grade chemicals shall be used in all tests. Unless otherwise indicated, it is intended that all reagents shall conform to the specifications of the Committee on Analytical Reagents of the American Chemical Society, where such

---

[1] Under the standardization procedure of the Society, these methods are under the jurisdiction of the ASTM Committee D-19 on Industrial Water. A list of members may be found in the ASTM Year Book.

[2] These methods are a combination of the Methods of Test for Silica in Industrial Water and Industrial Waste Water (ASTM Designation: D 859), Referee Method A and Non-Referee Methods C and D, and the Method of Test for Silica in High-Purity Water (ASTM Designation: D 1689), Referee Method B.

[3] Appears in this publication.

specifications are available.[4] Other grades may be used, provided it is first ascertained that the reagent is of sufficiently high purity to permit its use without lessening the accuracy of the determination.

(b) Unless otherwise indicated, references to water shall be understood to mean reagent water conforming to the Specifications for Reagent Water (ASTM Designation: D 1193).[3] In addition, the water shall be made silica-free by distillation or demineralization (Note 1) and determined as such in accordance with the method of test being used.

Note 1.—The collecting apparatus and storage containers for the reagent water must be polyethylene or other suitable plastic.

Sampling

4. (a) Collect the sample in accordance with the applicable method of the American Society for Testing and Materials, as follows:

D 510—Sampling Industrial Water,[3]
D 860—Sampling Water from Boilers,[3]
D 1066—Sampling Steam,[3] and
D 1496—Sampling Homogeneous Industrial Waste Water.[3]

(b) In addition, cool the samples to 35 C or below, and collect them in plastic, or stainless steel bottles, provided with rubber or plastic stoppers. Samples containing more than 1 ppm of silica may be collected in chemically-resistant glass bottles without significant error, provided that the water is neutral or slightly acidic and the silica determination is made in less than 24 hr.

---

[4] "Reagent Chemicals, American Chemical Society Specifications," Am. Chemical Soc., Washington, D. C. For suggestions on the testing of reagents not listed by the American Chemical Society, see "Reagent Chemicals and Standards," by Joseph Rosin, D. Van Nostrand Co., Inc., New York, N. Y. and the "United States Pharmacopeia."

Referee Method A

(Gravimetric Method)

Scope and Application

5. The gravimetric procedures covered by Referee Method A are applicable to the determination of total silica present in all industrial water and industrial waste water. Silica as low as 1 ppm can be determined accurately by concentrating the sample.

Summary of Method

6. Silicon compounds dissolved or suspended in the water are concentrated and precipitated as partially dehydrated silica by evaporation with either perchloric acid or hydrochloric acid (**Caution,** see Note 2). Dehydration is completed by ignition, and the silica is volatilized as silicon tetrafluoride. Complete silicate residues that do not yield to this treatment are dissolved by alkali fusion and dehydrated with perchloric acid.

Note 2: **Caution.**—Hydrochloric acid should be used when perchloric acid is prohibited. Warm perchloric acid solutions react explosively with organic matter such as oil, paper, starch, wood, etc., the explosive force being directly proportional to the exposed surface area of the organic matter. The presence of nitric acid prevents this spontaneous reaction, and is positive insurance against explosion during evaporation of water samples with perchloric acid, even if they contain organic matter.[5] The preboil with aqua regia will remove most organic matter; however, if the original sample contains large quantities of organic matter, such as oil films, chunks of wood, or coal dust, the organic matter should be removed by a suitable method before analysis.

Interferences

7. The anions and cations generally found in industrial water and industrial waste water offer no interference.

---

[5] Precautions for the use of perchloric acid are available in "Chemical Safety Data Sheet SD 11," published by the Manufacturing Chemists' Association of the United States.

Reagents

8. (*a*) *Hydrochloric Acid* (*sp gr 1.19*). —Concentrated hydrochloric acid (HCl).

(*b*) *Hydrochloric Acid* (*1:49*).—Mix 1 volume of concentrated hydrochloric acid (HCl, sp gr 1.19) with 49 volumes of water.

(*c*) *Hydrofluoric Acid* (*48 to 51 per cent*).—Concentrated hydrofluoric acid (HF).

(*d*) *Methyl Orange Indicator* (*0.5 g. per liter*).—Dissolve 0.05 g of methyl orange in water and dilute to 100 ml with water.

(*e*) *Nitric Acid* (*sp gr 1.42*).—Concentrated nitric acid (HNO_3).

(*f*) *Perchloric Acid* (*70 per cent*).— Concentrated perchloric acid ($HClO_4$).

(*g*) *Sodium Carbonate* (Na_2CO_3), anhydrous powder.

(*h*) *Sulfuric Acid* (*sp gr 1.84*).—Concentrated sulfuric acid (H_2SO_4).

Procedure

9. (*a*) If the water is alkaline to methyl orange, add to a volume of sample containing silicon compounds equivalent to not less than 5 mg of SiO_2, sufficient concentrated HCl (sp gr 1.19) to neutralize it and provide a 5-ml excess. If the water is originally acid to methyl orange, add the 5-ml excess of HCl immediately without neutralization of the sample. Evaporate the acidified sample to a volume of approximately 100 ml in a 400-ml, scratch-free, low-form, chemically-resistant glass beaker (Note 3) on a water bath or hot plate under a fume hood. If the silica content is so low that a very large quantity of water must be evaporated, do not increase the size of the evaporating beaker, but provide a means for preventing contamination of the sample with atmospheric dust, and periodically replenish the evaporating liquid with increments from the acidified sample reservoir. An infrared lamp is a convenient means of simultaneously shielding and evaporating the sample.

If the use of $HClO_4$ is permissible, continue in accordance with Paragraphs (*b*) to (*g*). Where use of $HClO_4$ is considered to be undesirable, the determination may be completed in accordance with Paragraphs (*h*) to (*k*).

Note 3.—A glass evaporator has been specified instead of platinum because glass yields equivalent accuracy and is not affected by the reagents. Platinum will be attacked if significant quantities of nitrate ions and chloride ions are present simultaneously. If it is necessary or desirable to use platinum for any reason, this deficiency can be overcome by making the initial acidification with HNO_3 instead of HCl, provided the sample does not contain large quantities of chloride (sea water, etc.) or constituents that are insoluble in HNO_3 solution.

Perchloric Acid Dehydration

(*b*) Add 30 ml of concentrated HCl (sp gr 1.19) and 10 ml of HNO_3 and continue evaporation to a volume of approximately 20 ml. Add 20 ml of HNO_3 and 10 ml of $HClO_4$ (**Caution,** see Note 2) to the sample, and again evaporate on a hot plate under a fume hood until the dense white fumes of $HClO_4$ appear and the concentrated liquid is boiling. Continue to boil the concentrate for 10 min.

(*c*) Cool the concentrate and add 50 ml of water. Boil this diluted solution for several minutes and filter it through an ashless, medium-texture paper. Wash the residue on the paper with at least 15 increments of hot HCl (1:49) to remove the $HClO_4$. It is important to wash the entire paper, including the extreme upper edge, to prevent sparking during ignition of the residue.

(*d*) Place the filter paper with its dehydrated residue in a weighed platinum crucible, dry and char the paper without flaming it, and then ignite the charred residue for 30 min at 1000 to 1200 C Cool in a desiccator and weigh. Repeat the ignition until a constant weight is obtained.

(*e*) Add several drops of H_2SO_4 and about 5 ml of HF to the weighed residue in the crucible and evaporate to dryness on a low-temperature hot plate or water bath under a fume hood. Re-ignite the residue at 1000 to 1200 C and weigh. Repeat the ignition until a constant weight is obtained.

(f) If complex silicates are known to be present, fuse the final ignition residue with Na_2CO_3, dissolve the fusion in HCl (1:49), and repeat the acid dehydration (Paragraphs (b) to (e)) on the resulting solution.

(g) Determine a reagent blank by making an identical silica determination on the quantity of water required for the washing and diluting described in Paragraphs (c) and (f).

Hydrochloric Acid Dehydration

(Alternate Method)

(h) If the use of $HClO_4$ is considered to be undesirable, add 5 ml of concentrated HCl (sp gr 1.19) to the sample that has been acidified and evaporated in accordance with Paragraph (a). Continue to evaporate the sample to dryness on a water bath, with periodic additions of three more 5-ml increments of HCl. Dry the evaporated residue in an oven at 110 C for 1 hr.

(i) Add 5 ml of concentrated HCl (sp gr 1.19) and then 50 ml of water to the dried residue in the beaker, warm the beaker and its contents, and stir the mixture with a rubber policeman to dissolve or suspend all of the residue. Filter the warm solution through an ashless, medium-texture paper. Wash the residue on the paper 15 times with HCl (1:49) and then with several small increments of water. Cover the funnel containing the paper and its residue with a clean watch glass, and reserve it for later ignition.

(j) Return the filtrate obtained in accordance with Paragraph (i) to the original evaporating beaker, and evaporate to dryness on a water bath with periodic addition of two 5-ml increments of con-

centrated HCl (sp gr 1.19). Dry and repeat the filtration and washing described in Paragraphs (h) and (i), using a second funnel and filter paper.

(k) Proceed as directed in Paragraphs (d) to (g), igniting both filter papers in the same crucible.

Calculation

10. Calculate the concentration of silica, in parts per million as follows:

$$SiO_2, ppm = \frac{(W_1 - W_2) - (W_3 - W_4)}{V}$$

where:

W_1 = weight of crucible and sample residue, in milligrams, after first ignition,

W_2 = weight of crucible and sample residue, in milligrams, after treatment with HF and re-ignition,

W_3 = weight of crucible and blank residue, in milligrams, after first ignition,

W_4 = weight of crucible and blank residue, in milligrams, after treatment with HF and re-ignition, and

V = liters of sample used.

Precision

11. (a) For $HClO_4$ dehydration, precision is limited by balance reproducibility and the volume of sample used. If it is assumed that the analytical balance is reproducible to 0.1 mg, the total of four weighings required for the reagent blank and the sample can cause a maximum variation in precision of the order of 0.4 mg (0.4 ppm for a 1-liter sample).

(b) For HCl dehydration, precision is estimated from analytical data[6] to be approximately equivalent to that attainable with the $HClO_4$ dehydration. However, the silica values are consistently low.

---

[6] Supporting data for this method appear in the Report of Committee D-19, *Proceedings*, Am. Soc. Testing Mats., Vol. 50, p. 399 (1950).

Referee Method B
(Colorimetric Method)

Scope and Application

12. This method covers the photometric determination of soluble silica in industrial water, such as steam condensate, effluent from silica-removing ion-exchange beds, or any other industrial water whose silica content does not exceed 1000 ppb. Samples containing more than 1000 ppb should be analyzed in accordance with Referee Method A or by using the nonreferee methods.

Summary of Method

13. This method is based on the reaction of the soluble silica with molybdate ion to form a greenish-yellow complex which in turn is converted to a blue complex by reduction with 1-amino-2-naphthol-4-sulfonic acid. Phosphate interference is eliminated by the use of oxalic acid.

Interferences

14. The types of samples prescribed in Section 12 normally do not contain a significant concentration of interfering substances.

Apparatus

15. (a) *Spectrophotometer or Filter Photometer* (*Note 4*).—To obtain maximum sensitivity and reproducibility, absorbance readings should be made at 815 mμ. However, if the instrument is not capable of measuring absorbance at 815 mμ, measurements may be made in the range of 640 to 700 mμ with sacrifice in precision.

Note 4.—A discussion of photometers and photometric practice is given in the Recommended Practice for Photometric Methods for Chemical Analysis of Metals (ASTM Designation: E 60).[7] Spectrophotometers shall conform to the Recommended Practice for Describing and Measuring Performance of Spectrophotometers (ASTM Designation: E 275).[8]

[7] *1967 Book of ASTM Standards*, Part 32.
[8] *1967 Book of ASTM Standards*, Part 30.

(b) *Sample Cells.*—The cell size to be used depends on the range covered and the particular instrument used. Table I is intended as a guide in selecting proper cell size.

Reagents

Note 5.—Store all reagents to be used in this method in polyethylene or other suitable plastic bottles.

16. (a) *Amino-Naphthol-Sulfonic Acid Solution.*—Dissolve 0.5 g of 1-amino-2-naphthol-4-sulfonic acid in 50 ml of a solution containing 1 g of sodium sulfite (Na$_2$SO$_3$). After dissolving, add the solution to 100 ml of a solution containing 30

TABLE I.—APPLICATION RANGES OF APPARATUS FOR MEASUREMENT OF COLOR.

Apparatus for Color Measurement	Range Covered, ppb
Spectrophotometer:	
10-mm cell..............	50 to 1000
100-mm cell..............	2 to 200
Filter photometer:	
23-mm cell..............	20 to 1000
50-mm cell..............	10 to 1000

g of sodium hydrogen sulfite (NaHSO$_3$). Make up to 200 ml and store in a dark, plastic bottle. Prepare a fresh solution every 2 weeks.

(b) *Ammonium Molybdate Solution* (*100 g per liter*).—Dissolve 10 g of ammonium paramolybdate ((NH$_4$)$_6$Mo$_7$O$_{24}$·4H$_2$O) in 100 ml of water.

(c) *Hydrochloric Acid* (*1:1*).—Mix 1 volume of concentrated hydrochloric acid (HCl, sp gr 1.19) with 1 volume of water.

(d) *Oxalic Acid Solution* (*100 g per liter*).—Dissolve 10 g of oxalic acid (H$_2$C$_2$O$_4$·2H$_2$O) in 100 ml of water.

(e) *Silica, Standard Solution* (*1 ml = 1 mg SiO$_2$*).—Dissolve 4.732 g of sodium metasilicate (Na$_2$SiO$_3$·9H$_2$O) in water and dilute to 1 liter with water. Check the concentration of this solution in accordance with Referee Method A.

Calibration and Standardization

17. (a) Prepare a series of standards covering a concentration range up to 1000 ppb SiO₂ by proper dilution of the standard silica solution. Treat 50-ml aliquots of the standards as described in Section 18(a), (b), and (c).

(b) Using a 50-ml aliquot of silica-free water, treated as described in Section 18(a), (b), and (c), set the spectrophotometer at zero absorbance at 815 mμ (see Section 15) and read the absorbance of each of the standards.

(c) Prepare a calibration curve, plotting absorbance against parts per billion of silica as SiO₂.

Procedure

18. (a) Transfer quantitatively 50.0 ml of the sample to a polyethylene or other suitable plastic container and add, in quick succession, 1 ml of HCl (1:1) and 2 ml of the ammonium molybdate solution. Mix well.

(b) After exactly 5 min, add 1.5 ml of oxalic acid and again mix well.

(c) After 1 min, add 2 ml of amino-naphthol-sulfonic acid. Mix well and allow to stand for 10 min.

(d) Treat a 50-ml aliquot of silica-free water as described in Paragraphs (a), (b), and (c). Using this as a reference solution, set the spectrophotometer at zero absorbance at 815 mμ (see Section 15) and measure the absorbance of the sample.

Calculation

19. Calculation is not required. Silica concentration, in parts per billion, may be read directly from the calibration curve prepared in accordance with Section 17.

Precision

20. The over-all and single operator precision may be expressed as follows:

$$S_0 = 0.005 \ X + 0.7$$

$$S_T = 0.03 \ X + 1.3$$

where:

S_0 = single operator precision,
S_T = over-all precision, and
X = concentration of silica determined in ppb.

Non-Referee Method C

(Colorimetric Method)

Application

21. This method is applicable to the determination of crystalloidal (noncolloidal) silica in industrial water and industrial waste water that does not have excessive color or turbidity interferences, but it cannot be used to determine total silica. The method is particularly applicable to rapid control analysis of crystalloidal silica below 10 ppm. When used in conjunction with Referee Method A, it is useful in differentiating between colloidal and crystalloidal silica.

Summary of Method

22. Crystalloidal silica reacts with molybdate ion in acidic solution (optimum pH 1.2 to 1.5) to form a greenish-yellow color complex. This is approximately proportional to the silica concentration of the water, but does not follow Beer's law perfectly. The sensitivity of the test is increased by addition of amino-naphthol-sulfonic acid, which produces a blue color. The color complexes are evaluated by comparison with standard colors, by means of a filter photometer, or by means of a spectrophotometer.

Interferences

23. Turbidity, color (tannin, copper ion, etc.), and chromate ion interfere. Tannin interference is eliminated in the determination of silica concentrations less than 2 ppm.

Apparatus

24. Use one of the following means for color evaluation:

(a) *Matched Nessler Tubes*, 100-ml capacity,

(b) *Duboscq-Type Color Comparator*,

(c) *Photoelectric Filter Photometer* (see Note 4), or

(d) *Spectrophotometer*.

Reagents (See Note 5)

25. (a) *Amino-Naphthol-Sulfonic Acid Solution*. See Section 16(a).

(b) *Ammonium Molybdate Solution (100 g per liter).*—See Section 16(b).

(c) *Buffer Solution (10 g per liter)*.— Dissolve 10 g of sodium tetraborate ($Na_2B_4O_7 \cdot 10H_2O$) in water and dilute to 1 liter.

(d) *Hydrochloric Acid (sp gr 1.19)*.— Concentrated hydrochloric acid (HCl).

(e) *Oxalic Acid Solution (100 g per liter)*.—See Section 16(d).

(f) *Potassium Chromate Color Standard Solution (0.63 g per liter)*.—Dissolve 0.63 g of potassium chromate (K_2CrO_4) in water and dilute to 1 liter with water in a volumetric flask.

(g) *Silica, Standard Solution (1 ml = 1 mg SiO_2)*.—See Section 16(e).

Calibration and Standardization

26. (a) *Silica Standards*.—One milliliter of standard silica solution (1 ml = 1 mg SiO_2) diluted to 1 liter with water results in a solution of 1 ppm SiO_2 concentration. Prepare a series of standards so that the concentrations of SiO_2 will bracket the anticipated concentration of SiO_2 in the sample.

(b) *Chromate Color Standards*.—One milliliter of K_2CrO_4 color standard solution diluted and buffered as described herein results in a solution having the same color as a sample containing 2 ppm SiO_2, after being treated as described in Section 28. Prepare a series of color standards so that their indicated con-

centrations of SiO_2 will bracket the anticipated concentration of SiO_2 in the sample. Add 25 ml of buffer solution to the appropriate volume of K_2CrO_4 color standard solution, and dilute the buffered solution to 54.5 ml with water. Agitate the mixture to provide a uniform color.

(c) *Calibration of the Photometer*.—Develop color in the appropriate series of silica standards prepared in accordance with Paragraph (a) by application of the procedure given in Section 27(b) or (e). Prepare a graph, plotting absorbances against parts per million of concentrations of SiO_2. Use a 410-mμ wavelength or, if amino-naphthol-sulfonic acid is added, use an 815-mμ wavelength. However, acceptable absorbance measurements can be made up to 440 mμ or down to 615 mμ, respectively, with instruments providing only wide energy bands (see Note 4).

Procedure

27. (a) Use the color development and measurement technique given for the concentration of silica and available means of color evaluation, as follows:

	Paragraph
Concentrations greater than 2 ppm SiO_2 :	
Visual comparison with silica standards	(b)
Visual comparison with chromate color standards	(c)
Photometric measurement	(d)
Concentrations less than 2 ppm SiO_2 :	
Photometric measurement	(e)

(b) To 50-ml aliquots of the sample and of each of the silica standards prepared in accordance with Section 26(a), add in quick succession 0.5 ml of concentrated HCl (sp gr 1.19), and 2 ml of ammonium molybdate solution, and mix. Allow to stand for 5 min and then add 1.5 ml of oxalic acid solution. Transfer equal volumes of the colored sample solution and silica standards to separate Nessler tubes or Duboscq color comparator tubes and determine the silica concentration of the sample by visually comparing its color with that of each of the silica standards against a uniform source of daylight or artificial light. Record the indicated SiO$_2$ concentration of the standard most nearly matching the treated sample in color.

(c) If the visual comparison is to be made against the chromate color standards prepared in accordance with Section 26(b) instead of the silica standards, proceed as described in Paragraph (b) of this section, but substitute the chromate color standards.

(d) If photometric measurement is to be made for SiO$_2$ concentrations greater than 2 ppm, develop the color of the sample in accordance with Paragraph (b), and determine its absorbance by means of the filter photometer or spectrophotometer at 410 to 440 mμ (Section 26(c)), against a silica-free water blank treated in the same manner, and using the same length of light path through the sample as that used in calibration. Record the concentration of SiO$_2$ in the sample indicated by the calibration curve prepared in accordance with Section 26(c).

(e) If photometric measurement is to be made for SiO$_2$ concentrations less than 2 ppm, develop the color of the sample in accordance with Paragraph (b), except to add 2 ml of amino-naphthol-sulfonic acid solution 1 min after the addition of the oxalic acid solution, and allow the color to develop for an additional 5 min. Determine the absorbance of the sample solution by means of a filter photometer at 615 mμ or by means of a spectrophotometer at 815 mμ (Note 6). Make all absorbance readings against a silica-free blank treated in the same manner as the sample, using the same length of light path through the sample as that used in calibration. Record the concentration of silica in the sample indicated by the calibration curve prepared in accordance with Section 26(c).

NOTE 6.—Measurements made at 815 mμ provide maximum sensitivity and reproducibility, but cannot be made with filter photometers or spectrophotometers limited to the visual range.

Calculation

28. Calculation is not required. Silica concentration, in parts per million, is indicated directly by the matched standard or from the calibration curve.

Precision

29. For visual comparison in the range of 2 to 20 ppm, silica standards or chromate color standards should be at least 1 ppm apart for proper definition, so that precision becomes 1.0 ppm. For visual comparisons in the range of 20 to 50 ppm, the standards should be 2 ppm apart and the precision will be 2 ppm. Photometric evaluations by the amino-naphthol-sulfonic acid procedure (Section 27(e)) have an estimated precision of 0.10 ppm in the range of 0 to 2 ppm. Photometric evaluations of the silico-molybdate color in the range of 2 ppm to 50 ppm have an estimated precision of approximately 4 per cent of the quantity of silica measured.

NON-REFEREE METHOD D

(Colorimetric Method)

Scope and Application

30. The applicability of this method is similar to that of Non-Referee Method C, except that this method also is applicable to industrial water and industrial waste water colored with tannin.

Summary of Method

31. In the presence of a reducing agent such as sodium sulfite, crystalloidal silica reacts with molybdate ion to form a blue color complex that is not affected significantly by either phosphate ion or tannin.

Interferences

32. Except for tannin, the interferences given in Section 23 also interfere in this method.

Apparatus

33. See Section 24.

Reagents (See Note 5)

34. (a) *Ammonium Molybdate Solution.*—See Section 16(b).

(b) *Hydrochloric Acid* (*1:49*).—See Section 8(b).

(c) *Silica, Standard Solution* (*1 ml = 1 mg SiO₂*).—See Section 16(e).

(d) *Sodium Sulfite Solution* (*170 g per liter*).—Dissolve 170 g of sodium sulfite (Na₂SO₃) in water and dilute to 1 liter with water.

Calibration and Standardization

35. Prepare silica standards as described in Section 26(a). If a photometer is used, develop the color of the standards in accordance with Section 36, and construct a calibration curve at 815 mμ, or between 615 and 815 mμ as described in Section 26(c).

Procedure

36. To 10-ml portions of the sample and of each silica standard add, with thorough mixing, 5 ml of HCl (1:49) and 5 ml of ammonium molybdate solution. Allow to stand 1 min, then add 10 ml of Na₂SO₃ solution, and mix. Allow the mixture to stand for 5 min, and then determine the SiO₂ concentration by visual comparison of the color of the sample with the color of the silica standards, as directed in Section 27(b), or by the photometric procedure given in Section 27(e), excluding the addition of amino-naphthol-sulfonic acid solution. The temperature of the sample must be within 3 C of the temperature of the silica standards used when preparing the calibration curve.

Calculation

37. See Section 28.

Precision

38. The precision of this method for the range of 2 to 50 ppm will be the same as that indicated in Section 29 for Non-Referee Method C.

APPROVED AS
USA STANDARD Z111.7-1964
BY USA STANDARDS INSTITUTE
UDC 663.61:543

Standard Method of

SAMPLING WATER FROM BOILERS[1]

ASTM Designation: D 860 – 54 (1965)

ADOPTED, 1954; REAPPROVED, 1965

This Standard of the American Society for Testing and Materials is issued under the fixed designation D 860; the number immediately following the designation indicates the year of original adoption or, in the case of revision, the year of last revision. A number in parentheses indicates the year of last reapproval.

1. Scope

1.1 This method covers the basic requirements for the sampling of boiler water from steam generators for analysis of boiler water constituents and control, and for special investigations.

1.2 This method applies only to the sampling of boiler water. It does not provide details, such as tests to be made, quantity of sample required, time interval between collection and analysis of sample, etc. For such information, refer to ASTM Methods D 510, Sampling Industrial Water.[2]

2. Summary of Method

2.1 The essential sampling apparatus required, point of sampling, and procedure, with and without separation of suspended solids, are described. However, specific details of sampling applicable to all boilers are not provided because of the variety of design in old and

new boilers and the diversity of purposes for which boiler water may be sampled.

3. Definitions

3.1 The terms "boiler water" and "control analysis" in these methods are defined in accordance with ASTM Definitions D 1129, Terms Relating to Industrial Water and Industrial Waste Water,[2] as follows:

3.1.1 *Boiler Water*—A term construed to mean a representative sample of the circulating boiler water, after the generated steam has been separated, and before the incoming feed water or added chemical becomes mixed with it so that its composition is affected.

3.1.2 *Control Analysis*—The determination of specific ions or properties used as criteria of proper boiler operation.

3.2 For definitions of other terms used in this method, refer to Definitions D 1129.

4. Apparatus

4.1 *Sampling Tube or Nozzle*—A sampling tube or nozzle of such design and so located that the collected sample

---

[1] Under the standardization procedure of the Society, this method is under the jurisdiction of the ASTM Committee D-19 on Industrial Water. A list of members may be found in the ASTM Year Book.

[2] Appears in this publication.

satisfies the purpose for which it was taken.

4.2 *Sampling Line* conforming to ASTM Specifications D 1192, Equipment for Sampling Industrial Water and steam.[2]

4.3 *Cooling Coil*—A sample cooler of such size that the sample may be cooled to less than 100 F when a flow rate of not less than 500 ml (approximately 1 pt or 1 lb)/min is established. For details of construction, refer to Specifications D 1192.

4.4 *Pressure-Type Filter*—A filter for securing clarified boiler water samples at operating temperature, of such material (Note 1) that the composition of the sample will not be affected significantly by reaction between the filter and hot, usually alkaline, boiler water.

NOTE 1—Stainless steel filters are satisfactory for this purpose.

4.5 *Sample Containers* conforming to Specifications D 1192.

5. Point of Sampling

5.1 Select the point of sampling so as to obtain the desired boiler water sample, as defined in 3.1. The exact point of sampling depends on boiler design, location of chemical and water feed lines, and other local conditions. Take samples from the continuous blowdown line at the boiler, unless a special sampling nozzle is available. In all cases, take samples only when the water is at normal operating level. In the absence of any sampling connections take the samples from the water column drain lines, or other convenient outlet below the water level. Such samples are not representative of the average boiler water and are not to be used in case of controversy. Significant variation in the composition of water may exist throughout the boiler. For this reason, samples taken from several locations simultaneously may be desirable.

5.2 A special sampling nozzle is the most desirable method for taking a sample; however, a properly located, continuous blowdown line may serve as a satisfactory substitute. Locate nozzles or sampling tubes at points remote from confining surfaces and in a submerged position. In selecting the location for nozzles and sampling lines, avoid the possibility of unseparated steam inclusion, excessive amounts of suspended matter, incoming feed water, and added chemicals.

6. Procedure

6.1 Before collecting the sample, purge the sample lines of stagnant water and sediment by means of a hot free blow, or by a cooled and regulated flow of water for sufficient time to complete its purpose. Take precautions to avoid dilution by condensed steam or concentration due to "flashing."

6.2 Before taking the sample, establish a continuous flow of not less than 500 ml (approximately 1 pt or 1 lb)/min, cooled to less than 100 F. If the sample is to be collected for special constituents, the sampling method for the specific test should be used. Recommended minimum purging periods for different sizes of sampling lines are as follows:

Pipe Size, in.	Purging Period per Foot of Line, sec
1/8	5
1/4	10
3/8	15
1/2	25
3/4	40
1	60

6.3 Before taking the sample, rinse the sample container at least three times by filling it to one fourth of its capacity with boiler water, shaking, then emptying.

6.4 Collect the boiler water sample by upward displacement through a tube extending to the bottom of the container. Allow the container to overflow at least five volumes, then stopper the container

(Note 2) with a stopper previously rinsed with the sample water.

Note 2—If analysis cannot be made immediately, the containers should be tightly stoppered to prevent atmospheric contamination.

6.5 Since boiler water concentrations vary at different water levels, or boiler ratings, and are influenced by the amount of water in the boiler, take all samples when the boiler water is at normal operating level, unless there is a specific reason for sampling under other conditions. For comparative testing under abnormal conditions, take samples at similar ratings and similar water levels to avoid dilution or concentration due to changes in the amount of water in the boiler.

6.6 If the chemical equilibrium in the water at the boiler operating conditions is desired, filter the water sample at the operating temperature and pressure of the boiler. This refinement requires a pressure-type filter between the boiler and cooling coil to permit the hot samples to be filtered as they leave the boiler.

6.7 Immediately upon taking each sample, mark it according to Specifications D 1192.

6.8 If the samples are to be transported or shipped any appreciable distance, pack the sample containers in shipping containers conforming to Specifications D 1192. Label the shipping containers as described in Specifications D 1192.

APPROVED AS
USA STANDARD Z111.8-1964
BY USA STANDARDS INSTITUTE
UDC663.61:620.11

Standard Method of
FIELD SAMPLING OF WATER-FORMED DEPOSITS[1]

ASTM Designation: D 887 – 49 (1965)

ADOPTED, 1949; REAPPROVED, 1965

This Standard of the American Society for Testing and Materials is issued under the fixed designation D 887; the number immediately following the designation indicates the year of original adoption or, in the case of revision, the year of last revision. A number in parentheses indicates the year of last reapproval.

NOTE—Editorial changes were made in Section 2 and Note 23 in June, 1961.

Scope

1. This method covers the selection, removal, storage, and description of any samples of deposit formed on surfaces in contact with water in any of its phases. It also defines the various types of deposits.

Definitions

2. (a) *Water-Formed Deposits*—A water-formed deposit is any accumulation of insoluble material derived from water or formed by the reaction of water upon surfaces in contact with the water.

NOTE 1—Deposits formed from or by water in all its phases may be further classified as scale, sludge, corrosion products, or biological deposit.

NOTE 2—The over-all composition of a deposit of some part of a deposit may be determined by chemical or spectrographic analysis; the constituents actually present as chemical

substances may be identified by microscope or X-ray diffraction studies. Organisms may be identified by microscopic or biological methods.

(b) *Scale*—Scale is a deposit formed from solution directly in place upon a confining surface.

NOTE 3—Scale is a deposit that usually will retain its physical shape when mechanical means are used to remove it from the surface on which it is deposited. Scale, which may or may not adhere to the underlying surface, is usually crystalline and dense, frequently laminated, and occasionally columnar in structure.

NOTE 4—Mill scale, formed on iron or steel heated in an atmosphere containing oxygen, consists chiefly of magnetic iron oxide, Fe_3O_4.

(c) *Sludge*—Sludge is a water-formed sedimentary deposit.

NOTE 5—The water-formed sedimentary deposit may include all suspended solids carried by the water.

NOTE 6—Sludge usually does not cohere sufficiently to retain its physical shape when mechanical means are used to remove it from the surface on which it deposits, but it may be baked in place and be hard and adherent.

[1] Under the standardization procedure of the Society, this method is under the jurisdiction of the ASTM Committee D-19 on Industrial Water. A list of members may be found in the ASTM Year Book.

(*d*) *Corrosion Products*—The corrosion product is a result of chemical or electrochemical reaction between a metal and its environment.

NOTE 7—A corrosion product resulting from the action of water, such as rust, usually consists of insoluble material deposited on or near the corroded area; corrosion products may, however, be deposited a considerable distance from the point at which the metal is undergoing attack.

(*e*) *Biological Deposits*—Biological deposits are water-formed deposits of organisms or the products of their life processes.

NOTE 8—The biological deposits may be composed of microscopic organisms, as in slimes, or of macroscopic types such as barnacles or mussels. Slimes are usually composed of deposits of a gelatinous or filamentous nature.

(*f*) For definitions of other terms used in this method, refer to ASTM Definitions D 1129, Terms Relating to Industrial Water and Industrial Waste Water.[2]

Selection of Samples

3. The selection of samples necessarily depends on the experience and judgment of the investigator. The intended use of the sample and the accessibility of the deposit will influence the selection of a sampling method. Preferred and alternate methods are as follows:

Preferred Method—Select one or more separate samples (primary samples) from the area of failure, heaviest deposition, or principal concern and additional separate samples from any adjacent or related areas that might contain deposits significantly different from the primary samples (Note 9).

NOTE 9—In applying this method to a scale-ruptured boiler tube, samples would be selected from the bulged or ruptured area and from representative areas in the unfailed portion of the tube and in other tubes of the failed and adjacent rows.

---

[2] Appears in this publication.

Alternate Method A—Select one or more separate samples from the area of failure, heaviest deposition, or principal concern and an additional composite sample from adjacent or closely related areas (Note 10).

NOTE 10—In the sample discussed in Note 9, this would be the preferred method if only the damaged tube could be removed for *spot* sampling.

Alternate Method B—Select one or more separate samples from the area of failure, heaviest deposition, or principal concern (Note 11).

NOTE 11—This method shall be used when it is impracticable to sample adjacent or related areas or when it is improbable that the information gained by such sampling will justify the additional work involved.

Alternate Method C—Select a composite sample from the smallest surface that will include the area of failure, heaviest deposition, or principal concern and that will provide an adequate sample (Note 12).

NOTE 12—This method shall be resorted to only when the area of principal concern is not available for *spot* sampling as when a heavily scaled boiler tube cannot be removed.

General Requirements for Removal of Deposits

4. Deposits shall be removed in such a manner that they remain as nearly as possible in their original states (Note 13). Samples shall contain fragments sufficiently large to allow examination and analysis of the individual layers and particles if the deposit is not uniform. Frequently it is necessary or desirable to obtain a sample of the underlying surface with the deposit intact (Notes 14 and 15). Because of the variety of surfaces that are subject to water-formed deposits, it is impossible to prescribe a standard method of removal and frequently is impracticable to collect the ideal type of sample discussed above. Preferred and

alternate methods for removing water-formed deposits from various common types of surfaces that may be encountered are described in Sections 5 to 9. The investigator must resort to his individual experience and judgment in applying these methods to his specific problem and in devising new methods of removal when these methods are inapplicable. In every case, the method employed shall provide a sample that is adequate for test purposes. The quantity of sample required for a complete test will vary from about 10 to 100 g depending on the proportion of water and other volatile constituents and on the nature of the deposit. Microscopic, X-ray diffraction, and spectrographic tests can be made on very limited samples when large quantities of deposit are not available. Samples for biological tests shall be collected in sterile containers, using sterile instruments.

Note 13—Photographs of a deposit in its original state and in different stages of removal provide a valuable record of its appearance. Photomicrographs frequently offer clues to the source of a deposit.

Note 14—Unavoidable fragments of the underlying surface shall be left in the sample for removal at the laboratory.

Note 15—Samples of underlying surfaces, such as tube sections, shall be permanently marked (as with dies) to show the exact position occupied in service.

Removal of Deposits from Concave Surfaces of Small Cylinders (Small Pipes, Tubes from Economizers, Water-Tube Boilers, and Super-heaters, etc.)

5. (a) *Preferred Method*—Remove from each tube or pipe (or portion thereof) to be sampled, a cylindrical section that contains adequate deposits for a single test sample (10 to 100 g) (Note 16). Split the section longitudinally with a shaper or dry saw (no oil) and dislodge the deposit by squeezing the freshly cut, open edges of the two resulting hemicylindrical

sections in a vise. Care shall be taken not to contaminate the sample with deposits from the exterior (convex) surface of the section. If opposite walls of the section might contain different types of deposits, as in a fire-row boiler tube, the longitudinal split shall be made so as to separate the dissimilar portions. When the deposit cannot be dislodged by squeezing the tube or when the underlying metal is required for metallurgical tests, separate the sample by a suitable mechanical means that will not score the tube metal intolerably or otherwise contaminate the sample. Soft, elastic sludges, slimes, or other wet deposits generally can be spaded off with a laboratory spatula or other blunt instrument. Adherent corrosion-cores usually can be knocked out with a hammer and chisel-like instrument.

Note 16—It generally is preferable to forward the sample sections to the laboratory for removal of the deposit and examination of the underlying surface.

(b) *Alternate Method*—When it is not permissible to destroy the pipe or tube by sectioning (Note 17), remove superficial deposits by brushing the interior surface and then dislodge the principal deposit with a turbine, vibrating head, or rotary cutter. The action of the cutter shall be vigorous enough to remove the deposit, instead of simply polishing it, but shall not be so severe that it causes excessive abrasion of the underlying surface. Wet deposits that cannot be removed satisfactorily in this fashion shall be scraped out with a suitable implement (Note 18).

Note 17—A by-pass line provides a convenient means of evaluating pipe-line deposits without disrupting the main line. Access to main-line deposits frequently can be obtained by removing a valve, coupling, or union.

Note 18—This method may yield a large quantity of nonhomogeneous deposit. In such instances, a relatively large sample (1 qt or more) shall be selected, taking care to include adequate representative portions of the principal constituents.

Removal of Deposits from Convex Surfaces of Small Cylinders (Fire Tubes, Evaporator Tubes, Heating Coils, etc.)

6. (a) *Preferred Method*—When removal of the affected tube is permissible, collect a suitable sample by the method in Section 5(a), taking care to avoid contamination of the sample with deposits from the concave surface of the specimen.

(b) *Alternate Method A*—If it is impracticable to remove the tube concerned, dislodge the external deposit by means of thermal or mechanical shock. In thermal shocking (cracking), which is particularly applicable to evaporator tubes, the deposit is dried and heated to approximately 200 F with internal steam. The steam is then released and the deposit is immediately chilled with a spray of cold water. Because of its relatively high temperature, the deposit will not be affected appreciably by this procedure if a limited quantity of water is used. Any other procedure that will effect sudden temperature change without damaging the deposit or the equipment concerned will be equally satisfactory. Mechanical shock is effected simply by beating the tube with an implement that will not damage it, such as a hammer or chains. This procedure is useful only in removing deposits that are brittle and relatively nonadherent. Whatever method of shock is employed, provision shall be made for collecting the deposit as it falls from the tube so that contamination will not result (Note 19).

NOTE 19—This method generally yields a relatively large quantity of deposit which shall be sampled as indicated in Note 18.

(c) *Alternate Method B*—If the tube cannot be removed and shocking is ineffective, separate the deposit by scraping, spading, or chiseling with a suitable implement. Whenever possible, insert the implement between the deposit and the underlying surface and flake off large fragments. Care shall be taken to avoid excess scoring of the underlying surface.

Removal of Deposits from Concave Surfaces of Large Cylinders (Drums, Tanks, Large Conduits, Deaerator Shells, etc.)

7. (a) *Preferred Method*—Dislodge sample deposits by shocking whenever possible to preserve stratification and prevent contamination by the underlying surface. Striking the deposit with a chipping hammer or the outside of the cylinder with a maul frequently will dislodge brittle, mildly adherent deposits. The thermal shock method described in Section 6(b) may be used when practicable.

(b) *Alternate Method*—Remove the deposit by the method described in Section 6(c) (Note 20).

NOTE 20—This method is applicable to tightly adherent scales and elastic sludges that cannot be removed by shocking.

Removal of Deposits from Flat and Curved (Noncylindrical) Solid Surfaces (Rectangular Tanks, Ponds, Settling Basins, Turbine Blades, etc.)

8. (a) *Preferred Method*—Remove the deposit by the method described in Section 6(b) whenever such treatment will effect a satisfactory separation without damaging the deposit or the underlying surface intolerably. This method is not applicable to ponds, settling basins, and similar equipment.

(b) *Alternate Method*—Remove the deposit by the method described in Section (6c) (Note 21).

NOTE 21—Thin, adherent turbine-blade deposits frequently can be stripped satisfactorily by running the point of a pocketknife across the surface at right angles to the edges of the buckets.

Removal of Deposits from Granular Surfaces (Sand Filters, Ion-Exchange Beds, etc.)

9. *Preferred Method*—Spade or scrape the intake surface and other pertinent strata of the filter or exchanger bed to a sufficient depth to provide a 1- to 5-lb sample (Note 22) of the filter or exchange material from each sampled zone. Where large bed size makes it impracticable to remove a layer from the entire surface, remove a layer 1 or 2 in. in depth from an area sufficient to provide the desired sample. In beds that contain multiple, parallel, well-defined strata, sample the strata in succession, starting with the uppermost, and excavate each as necessary to expose an adequate area of the underlying stratum. Beds that do not contain definite strata shall be sampled at several uniformly separated depths at least 6 in. apart.

NOTE 22—The relatively large sample specified in this instance is necessitated by the fact that only a part of the sample represents the deposit being investigated.

Storage of Samples

10. Place each sample, as soon as possible after removal from the surface, in a container that will protect it from contamination or chemical change (Note 23). Corrodible metal containers shall not be used for wet samples. Samples of slime or other biological deposit shall be refrigerated during storage and shipment (Note 24), taking care not to subject them to freezing conditions.

NOTE 23—A wide-mouth glass bottle, plastic vial, or noncorrodible metal container will provide adequate protection for samples of deposits.

NOTE 24—A clean wooden box sealed against atmospheric moisture is satisfactory for storage and shipment of sample surfaces such as tube sections.

Description of Samples

11. Immediately upon placing each sample in its container, affix a label or a cardboard or linen tag (preferably a label) to the container. Note the following information on the label or tag as soon as it becomes available. If this information is too voluminous for inclusion on the label or tag, forward it in a separate letter or report, properly identified with the samples concerned.

(*1*) Name of company supplying sample,

(*2*) Name and location of plant,

(*3*) Date and time of sampling,

(*4*) Number of sample,

(*5*) Name and other designation of equipment from which sample was removed,

(*6*) Precise location from which sample was removed (for example, exactly what turbine blade),

(*7*) Appearance and extent of deposit prior to removal,

(*8*) Type of deposit—whether scale, sludge, biological deposit or corrosion product as defined in Section 2.

(*9*) Exact method that was used in removing the sample and notes concerning any contamination that might have occurred during the process,

(*10*) Operating temperature and pressure of liquid or vapor in the equipment that contained the deposit,

(*11*) Type of treatment applied to the water that formed the deposit or to the water that furnished steam to the affected zone,

(*12*) An account of discrepancies in operating condition that may have contributed to deposition (for example, water starving),

(*13*) Results of field tests made on the sample or related equipment, and

(*14*) Signature of sampler.

Standard Methods of Test for
DISSOLVED OXYGEN IN INDUSTRIAL WATER[1]

ASTM Designation: D 888 – 66
ADOPTED, 1966

This Standard of the American Society for Testing and Materials is issued under the fixed designation D 888; the number immediately following the designation indicates the year of original adoption or, in the case of revision, the year of last revision. A number in parentheses indicates the year of last reapproval.

Scope

1. (*a*) These methods cover the determination of dissolved oxygen in industrial water. Five methods are given, as follows:

	Sections
Referee Method A (Colorimetric-Indigo Carmine)	5 to 13
Referee Method B (Dead Stop End Point)	14 to 21
Referee Method C (Potentiometric End Point)	22 to 29
Non-Referee Method D (Thiosulfate Titration)	30 to 37
Non-Referee Method E (Thiosulfate Titration-Starch Indicator)	38 to 45

(*b*) The referee methods provide the most precise and accurate procedure for the determination of dissolved oxygen in industrial waters and are especially designed for those having concentrations below 1 ppm. Method A is particularly suited for waters in the range below 0.05 ppm. The non-referee methods have greater simplicity and generally less precision with corresponding limitations in application.

Definitions

2. For definitions of terms used in these methods, refer to the Definitions of Terms Relating to Industrial Water and Industrial Waste Water (ASTM Designation: D 1129).[2]

Purity of Reagents

3. (*a*) Reagent grade chemicals, or their equivalent, as defined in accordance with ASTM Methods E 200, for Preparation, Standardization, and Storage of Standard Solutions for Chemical Analysis,[2] shall be used in all tests.

[1] Under the standardization procedure of the Society, these methods are under the jurisdiction of the ASTM Committee D-19 on Industrial Water. A list of members may be found in the ASTM Year Book.

By publication of these methods the American Society for Testing and Materials does not undertake to insure anyone using these methods, against liability for infringement of Letters Patent nor assume such liability, and such publication should not be construed as a recommendation of any patented proprietary reagents or procedure that may be involved.

[2] Appears in this publication.

313

(b) Unless otherwise indicated, reference to water shall be understood to mean reagent water conforming to ASTM Specifications D 1193, for Reagent Water.[2] Referee-grade water shall preferably be used in the preparation of reagents for all referee methods.

Sampling

4. (a) If possible, use stainless steel tubing for the sample line. The sample line shall contain a suitable cooling coil if the water being sampled is above room temperature, in which case cool the sample to 60 to 65 F (16 to 18 C). When a cooling coil is used, the valve for cooling water adjustment shall be at the inlet to the cooling coil and the overflow shall be to a point of lower elevation. The valve for adjusting the flow of sample shall be at the outlet from the cooling coil. The sample flow shall be adjusted to a rate that will fill the sampling vessel or vessels in 40 to 60 sec and flow long enough to provide a minimum of ten changes of water in the sample vessels. If the sampling line is used intermittently, allow sufficient time to flush adequately the sample line and cooling coil before using.

(b) Further requirements for sampling are given in the individual procedures. For general information on sampling, reference shall be made to the applicable method of the American Society for Testing and Materials, as follows:

D 510—Sampling Industrial Water,[2]
D 860—Sampling Water from Boilers,[2]
D 1066—Sampling Steam,[2] and
D 1192—Equipment for Sampling Industrial Water and Steam.[2]

REFEREE METHOD A (COLORIMETRIC INDIGO CARMINE)[3]

Application

5. This method is applicable to water containing less than 0.06 ppm of dissolved oxygen, such as steam condensate and deaerated boiler feedwater.

Summary of Method

6. Dissolved oxygen reacts under alkaline conditions with the indigo carmine solution to produce a progressive color change from yellow-green through red to blue and blue-green. The result of each test can be determined by comparison of color developed in the sample with color standards made up to represent different concentrations of dissolved oxygen.

Interferences

7. Tannin, hydrazine, and sulfite do not interfere in concentrations up to 1 ppm. Ferric iron, cyclohexylamine, and morpholine in concentrations up to 4 ppm can be tolerated. Ferrous iron will produce low results and copper will cause high results. In samples where ferrous iron and copper are present, their combined interference is frequently zero.

Apparatus

8. (a) Buret.—A 25 or 50-ml buret.

(b) Sampling Bucket, with an overflow at least 1 in. above the top of the sampling vessel.

(c) Sampling Vessels.—Nessler-type 60-ml tubes or 300-ml BOD bottles having a raised lip around the neck and glass stoppers ground to a conical lower tip.

Reagents

9. (a) Color Standards, Stock Solutions, as follows:

(1) Red Color Standard, No. CS-A. —Dissolve 59.29 g of cobaltous chloride hexahydrate ($CoCl_2 \cdot 6H_2O$) in sufficient HCl (1:99) to make 1 liter.

(2) Yellow Color Standard, No. CS-B. —Dissolve 45.05 g of ferric chloride

---

[3] This method involves the use of an indigo carmine indicator solution covered by U. S. Patent 2,967,092.

hexahydrate ($FeCl_3 \cdot 6H_2O$) in sufficient HCl (1:99) to make 1 liter.

(3) *Blue Color Standard, No. CS-C.*—Dissolve 62.45 g of cupric sulfate pentahydrate ($CuSO_4 \cdot 5H_2O$) in sufficient HCl (1:99) to make 1 liter.

Store all stock solutions in dark-colored bottles to prevent fading.

(b) *Hydrochloric Acid (sp gr 1.19).*—Concentrated hydrochloric acid (HCl).

(c) *Hydrochloric Acid (1:99).*—Mix 1 volume of concentrated HCl (sp gr 1.19) with 99 volumes of water.

(d) *Indigo Carmine Solution.*—Dissolve 0.18 g of 100 per cent indigo carmine and 2.0 g of dextrose (or glucose) in 50 ml of water. *Allowance must be made for the purity of the indigo carmine when the assay is less than 100 per cent.* Add 750 ml of glycerin and mix thoroughly. The solution is usable for at least 30 days if stored in a refrigerator. The stock solution deteriorates rapidly if allowed to stand in a lighted room at ambient temperature in an ordinary reagent bottle. Smaller quantities of the indigo carmine solution may be prepared by proportionately reducing the quantity of reagents. The indigo carmine and dextrose may be weighed, mixed, and stored in capsules or vials for great lengths of time as long as the mixture remains dry.

(e) *Indigo Carmine-Potassium Hydroxide Reagent.*—In a small bottle mix four parts by volume of indigo carmine solution with one part of the potassium hydroxide (KOH) solution. Stopper and invert several times until mixture is complete. Allow the reagent to stand undisturbed until the initial red color changes to lemon yellow. Keep in a dark cool place. Prepare a fresh solution daily.

(f) *Potassium Hydroxide Solution (530 g per liter).*—Dissolve 530 g of potassium hydroxide (KOH) in water and dilute to 1 liter.

Sampling

10. Place the sampling vessel in the sampling bucket and collect the sample under water using stainless steel or glass tubing and short pieces of neoprene tubing for connections where required. Do not use copper tubing or long sections of rubber tubing. Adjust the sample flow between 500 and 1000 ml per min maintaining sample temperature below 70 F (21 C) and below room temperature. Reduce the sample flow to 100 to 200

TABLE I.—STOCK SOLUTIONS.

Equivalent Dissolved Oxygen, ppm	Milliliters of Color Standards		
	CS-A	CS-B	CS-C
0.000	0.75	35.0	...
0.005	5.0	20.0	...
0.010	6.25	12.5	...
0.015	9.4	10.0	...
0.020	(13.0)	(6.4)	...
0.025	14.4	3.8	...
0.030	(14.6)	(3.3)	(0.2)[a]
0.035	(15.1)	(2.9)	(1.1)
0.040	(15.5)	(2.4)	(2.2)
0.045	(16.1)	(2.0)	(2.8)
0.050	(18.3)	(1.7)	(8.1)
0.055	(21.7)	(1.4)	(13.1)
0.060	(25.0)	(1.0)	(18.0)

[a] Figures in parentheses are estimated from original data which are not in parentheses.

ml per min when using 60-ml sample tubes. Introduce the flowing sample into the bottom of a scrupulously clean sample vessel with a small tube. Spin the sample vessel several times to dislodge air bubbles or film adhering to the glass wall. Allow the sample to continue overflowing from the vessel for several more minutes.

Calibration

11. Prepare a series of color standards as listed in Table I. Place the amounts of stock solutions listed in Table I in 300-ml borosilicate glass-stoppered reagent bottles. Add 2.3 ml of HCl (sp gr 1.19) to each and dilute to the neck of the

bottle with water. Stopper with plastic or lightly lubricated glass stoppers and mix by inversion. Store in a dark place to minimize fading of colors.

Procedure

12. (a) Mount the buret directly above the sampling vessel neck so that the buret tip dips into the overflowing sample to a depth of about $\frac{1}{2}$ in. Fill the buret with indigo carmine-potassium hydroxide reagent to about 1 ml above the zero mark. Drain the buret to the zero mark into the overflowing sample, and allow the sample to flush for 1 min longer. Remove the sample tubing gently from the sampling vessel so as not to introduce air bubbles. Do not remove the sample bottle or tube from the sample bucket. Quickly introduce 0.8 ml of indigo carmine-potassium hydroxide reagent from the buret into the sample if a 60-ml Nessler-type tube is used. If a BOD bottle is used add 4 ml of the reagent. Raise the buret above the sample vessel and immediately stopper the vessel firmly with a rinsed glass stopper, being careful to exclude air bubbles. Invert the vessel several times to mix. A color indicative of the dissolved oxygen concentration will develop. Place the sample vessel on a white surface and match its color with the previously prepared standards by viewing them at a 45-deg angle using a "cool" white fluorescent lamp for illumination. A better color match may be obtained by using a 3-lamp fixture containing two "deluxe white" and one "daylite" fluorescent lamps with an opal glass beneath the sample tubes or bottles. Colors should be matched as soon as possible after mixing the reagent and sample, since the colors are not stable for more than 30 min and air leakage may cause a change in color.

(b) The method used should be stated when reporting results.

Precision[4]

13. The precision of this method may be expressed as follows:

$$S_O = 0.052X + 0.7$$

where:

S_O = single operator precision, and
X = concentration of dissolved oxygen determined in parts per billion.

REFEREE METHOD B

(Dead-Stop End Point)

Application

14. This method is applicable primarily to industrial water having dissolved oxygen concentrations below 1 ppm. It is particularly suitable for oxygen determinations in steam condensate and boiler feedwater.

Summary of Method

15. The sample is collected in a tube of special design. Free iodine is liberated in an amount equivalent to the oxygen originally dissolved in the sample. The iodine is titrated by adding an excess of thiosulfate and back titrating with potassium iodate using a special apparatus with a cathode ray tube for end point detection.

Interferences

16. Reducing interferences are minimized by the careful preparation of the iodized alkaline iodide reagent.

Apparatus

17. (a) Beaker.—An 800-ml Griffin low-form beaker.

(b) Burets.—Three 10 or 25-ml burets, having a stopcock bore not greater than 2 mm and a maximum tip diameter not exceeding 3 mm; two 10-ml burets with 0.01-ml divisions.

---

[4] Supporting data for the precision statement have been filed at ASTM Headquarters.

(c) *Graduated Cylinder.*—A 10-ml graduated cylinder with 0.1-ml divisions.

(d) *Electrometric Dead-Stop Indicating Apparatus,* equipped with 5-in. platinum electrodes, such that the assembly is sensitive to the addition of 0.05 ml of 0.005 N KIO_3 to 500 ml of water at the end point.[5]

(e) *Sample Tubes.*—Two glass sample tubes as shown in Fig. 1, having a nominal capacity of 500 ml. The two tubes should not vary from each other by more than 10 ml, and the capacity of each tube shall be determined to the nearest 1 ml.[6]

(f) *Stirrer.*—A variable-speed, motor-

tion stand to support the stirrer and electrodes so that the beaker containing the sample can be removed easily, permitting the rinsing of the electrodes and stirrer.

Reagents (Note 1)

18. (a) *Iodine, Standard Solution (0.1 N).*—Dissolve 6.346 g of resublimed iodine in a solution of 75 g of KI in 60 ml of water and dilute with water to 500 ml in a volumetric flask. Store in a dark, stoppered bottle.

(b) *Manganous Sulfate Solution (364 g per liter).*—Dissolve 364 g of manganous sulfate ($MnSO_4 \cdot H_2O$) in water, filter,

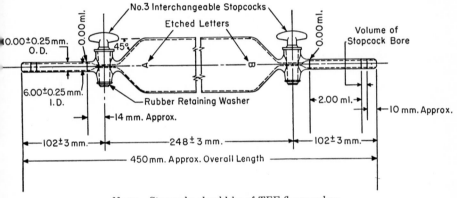

NOTE.—Stopcocks should be of TFE-fluorocarbon.
FIG. 1.—500-ml Sample Tube for Dissolved Oxygen Determination.[6]

driven stirrer with a TFE-fluorocarbon-coated stirrer bar.

(g) *Titration Stand.*—A suitable titra-

[5] R. G. Ulmer, J. M. Reynar, and J. M. Decker, "Applicability of the Schwartz-Gurney Method for Determining Dissolved Oxygen in Boiler Feedwater and Modification of the Method to Make it Especially Applicable in the Presence of Such Impurities as are Encountered in Power Plants," *Proceedings,* Am. Soc. Testing Mats., Vol. 43, p. 1258 (1943).

[6] McLean sampling tube as modified by the Engineering Experiment Station, U. S. Navy, and by the Heat Exchange Institute. This figure was editorially revised in February, 1951. For information on the modification of the sampling tube and test procedure developed by the Heat Exchange Institute, see the paper by J. F. Sebald, "An Evaluation of Test Methods for the Determination of Dissolved Oxygen in De-aerated Boiler Feedwater," *Proceedings,* Am. Soc. Testing Mats. Vol. 47, p. 1121 (1947).

and dilute to 1 liter. No more than a trace of iodine should be liberated when the solution is added to an acidified potassium iodide (KI) solution.

(c) *Potassium Iodate, Standard Solution (0.1 N).*—Dissolve 3.5670 g of potassium iodate (KIO_3) in 800 ml of water, add 0.5 g of sodium bicarbonate (Na·HCO_3) and then dilute to 1 liter.

(d) *Potassium Iodate, Standard Solution (0.005 N).*—With a calibrated pipet transfer 25 ml of 0.1 N KIO_3 solution to a 500-ml volumetric flask. Dilute to the mark with water and mix completely.

(e) *Potassium Iodide, Alkaline Solution (150 g KI per liter).*—Dissolve 700 g of potassium hydroxide (KOH) in sufficient water to make approximately 700 ml of solution in a 1-liter volumetric flask and cool to room temperature. Dissolve 150 g of iodate-free potassium iodide (KI), in 200 ml of water and mix with the KOH solution in the volumetric flask. Dilute to 1 liter with water, mix, and store in a dark, rubber-stoppered bottle.

(f) *Potassium Iodide, Iodized Alkaline Solution.*—Half fill a 250-ml volumetric flask with the alkaline KI solution. Add an accurately measured, small amount of 0.1 N iodine solution, sufficient to react with all reducing interference in the water to be analyzed when the procedure described in Section 19 or 27 is followed. Dilute to the mark with the alkaline KI solution.

While the iodized alkaline iodide solution must be used for accurate determinations, the minimum sufficient quantity of 0.1 N iodine required to yield detectable iodine in the blank should be used because the precision of the results decreases with increase in iodine concentration. As a trial, use 10 ml of 0.1 N iodine in preparing the iodized alkaline iodide solution and use on a test run. Prepare a second solution, if necessary, using more or less 0.1 N iodine, depending on the results of the test run.

(g) *Sodium Thiosulfate, Standard Solution (0.1 N).*—Prepare and standardize in accordance with Methods E 200.

(h) *Sodium Thiosulfate, Standard Solution (0.005 N).*—With a calibrated pipet transfer 12.50 ml of 0.1 N $Na_2S_2O_3$ solution to a 250-ml volumetric flask. Dilute to the mark with water and mix completely. This solution should be prepared not more than 12 to 15 hr before using.

(i) *Starch Solution.*

(j) *Sulfuric Acid (3:1).*—Pour carefully 750 ml of concentrated sulfuric acid (H_2SO_4, sp gr 1.84) into 250 ml of water in a beaker. Cool to room temperature, transfer to a 1-liter volumetric flask, and dilute to the mark with water.

Procedure

19. (a) *Adjustment of the Electrometric Dead-Stop Indicating Apparatus.*—Turn on the apparatus 15 min before a titration is to be made. Add 500 ml of water to a clean 800-ml beaker and place the beaker on the titrating stand. Immerse the lower portion of both electrodes in the water. Start the stirrer and adjust its speed to mix the sample rapidly without drawing air into the sample. Add 2 ml of H_2SO_4 (3:1) to the beaker, then 1 ml of iodized alkaline iodide, and finally 1 ml of $MnSO_4$ solution. From the 0.01-ml graduated 10-ml buret add 0.5 ml of 0.005 N $Na_2S_2O_3$. Using the coarse and fine adjustments on the indicating apparatus, adjust the "eye" so that it is approximately 80 per cent open. Keep the electrodes submerged in this solution until the sample is collected and fixed.

(b) *Sampling.*—Arrange the two sample tubes in a support so that they are vertical, with their upper outlets free of hose connections and at a higher level than the valve for adjustment of sample flow. Connect the lower ends to the sampling line by means of neoprene rubber tubing and a Y-tube. The length of the tubing should be as short as possible to prevent oxygen diffusion into the sample. If possible, use stainless steel tubing with short lengths of rubber tubing as connectors. After the sample flow has continued long enough to provide at least ten changes of water in the sampling tubes, close the upper stopcocks of the two tubes simultaneously and immediately close the two lower stopcocks. Remove the tubing connections.

If the line being sampled is under such high pressure that the sampling tubes or connecting tubing may burst with the water hammer when the stopcocks are closed, the sample flow may be throttled with the control valve just before the sample is removed, but the sample flow should not be shut off completely. Invert and examine both tubes to ensure the absence of any gas bubble. If any bubble is discovered, discard both samples and collect new ones.

(c) *Fixing.*—Fill the three burets with the iodized alkaline iodide solution, MnSO₄ solution, and H₂SO₄ (3:1), respectively. Designate the larger one of the duplicate tubes as the sample and the other as the blank. Flick the water from the upper nipple of the sample flask and fill the nipple to the upper calibration mark with the iodized alkaline iodide solution. Any bubble entrapped in the nipple within or below the reagent can be removed by probing with a clean copper wire until it rises to the surface. Open one stopcock and admit the reagent by control with the other until the meniscus in the nipple coincides with the lower calibration mark. Precisely the same point on the meniscus at the upper and lower calibration must be used. Close both stopcocks and rinse both nipples of the sampling tube with a fine stream of water. Flick out the excess water, invert the tube, and fill the nipple now on top to the 2.0-ml calibration mark with the MnSO₄ solution and introduce it into the sample as described for the addition of the iodized alkaline iodide solution. Again rinse both nipples of the sampling tube, shake or rotate the tube to mix the sample thoroughly, and lay it aside. Following precisely the directions given above for adding the reagents to the sample, add to the blank the indicated amount of iodized alkaline iodide solution through the upper nipple and stopcock, and add the same amount, first of H₂SO₄ (3:1) and then of the MnSO₄ solution, through the lower nipple. Rinse both nipples between additions, as directed above, and mix the blank between the second and final addition. Finally, mix the sample thoroughly, as directed above, to resuspend the precipitate. A significant error is introduced if the

precipitate is allowed to settle so that more than a proportional amount is removed with the volume withdrawn to permit the addition of the H₂SO₄ (3:1). Add to the sample an amount of H₂SO₄ (3:1) to fill the nipple to the upper calibration point, rinse both ends of the flask, and again mix thoroughly. Fixing should be completed within 15 min after sampling.

(d) *Titration of the Blank.*—Drain the blank into a clean 800-ml beaker by opening both stopcocks. Place the beaker on the titrating stand with both electrodes immersed approximately 2 in. in the sample and start the stirrer. Add 0.5 ml of 0.005 N Na₂S₂O₃ to the blank. If the "eye" does not open approximately 80 per cent, readjust with the apparatus adjustments as described in Paragraph (a). Using a buret with 0.01-ml subdivisions, titrate with 0.005 N KIO₃ until a permanent reduction in the opening of the "eye" is obtained. Record the milliliters of thiosulfate and iodate required for the titration.

(e) *Titration of the Sample.*—Discard the blank sample and drain the beaker carefully. Drain the contents of the sample tube into the beaker used for the blank titration and place it on the titration stand as described in Paragraph (d). Start the stirrer and then add 0.005 N Na₂S₂O₃ in 0.5-ml increments until the "eye" opens 80 per cent. Titrate with 0.005 N KIO₃ until a permanent reduction in the opening of the eye is obtained. Record the milliliters of thiosulfate and iodate required for the titration.

Calculation

20. (a) Calculate the dissolved oxygen content of the sample, in parts per million, as follows:

Dissolved oxygen, ppm O₂

$$= \left(\frac{16,000[\,(ns - me) - (nb - mf)\,]}{Vs + Vb} \right) - 0.0104$$

where:

n = normality of the $Na_2S_2O_3$ solution,

s = milliliters of $Na_2S_2O_3$ solution required for titration of the sample,

m = normality of the KIO_3 solution,

e = milliliters of KIO_3 solution required for titration of the sample,

b = milliliters of $Na_2S_2O_3$ solution required for titration of the blank,

f = milliliters of KIO_3 solution required for titration of the blank,

Vs = volume of sample, in milliliters,

Vb = volume of blank in milliliters, and

0.0104 = correction for oxygen introduced with the reagents (Note 1).

Note 1.—The reagents must be prepared several days prior to use and allowed to come to equilibrium with the oxygen in the air.[7]

(b) The method used should be stated when reporting results.

Precision

21. The precision of the method is 0.004 ppm of oxygen.

Referee Method C

(Potentiometric End Point)

Application

22. This method is applicable to the determination of dissolved oxygen in steam condensate, boiler feedwater, and industrial water having oxygen concentrations below 1 ppm. Titration is somewhat more involved than in Referee Method B, but can be done with conventional laboratory equipment.

Summary of Method

23. The sample is collected in a tube of special design. Free iodine is liberated in an amount equivalent to the oxygen originally dissolved in the sample. The iodine is titrated potentiometrically with thiosulfate, the end point being the maximum change in voltage per unit of thiosulfate added.

Interferences

24. Careful preparation of the iodized alkaline iodide reagent minimizes reducing interferences.[8]

Apparatus

25. (a) *Beaker.*—See Section 17(a).

(b) *Burets.*—See Section 17(b).

(c) *Graduated Cylinder.*—See Section 17(c).

(d) *Calomel Electrode.*—Any calomel reference electrode of either the glass sleeve or asbestos fiber wick type of satisfactory size is suitable. The 5-in. pencil type is a convenient form.

(e) *Platinum Electrodes.*—Any commercial platinum electrode of suitable size can be used. The 5-in. pencil type is a convenient form.

(f) *Potentiometer.*—A potentiometer having a limit of error not greater than ±0.003 v and a total range of the order of 1 v. A galvanometer for use with this potentiometer should have an external critical damping resistance of the order of 10,000 ohms and a sensitivity of the order of 0.125 μa per millimeter scale division. The potentiometer may be of the type employing either a self-contained galvanometer or an external

---

[7] For further information, see A. H. White, C. H. Leland, and D. W. Button, "Determination of Dissolved Oxygen in Boiler Feedwater," *Proceedings*, Am. Soc. Testing Mats., Vol. 36, Part II, p. 697 (1936).

[8] For further information on interferences, see R. C. Adams, R. E. Barnett, and D. E. Keller, Jr., "Field and Laboratory Determination of Dissolved Oxygen," *Proceedings*, Am. Soc. Testing Mats., Vol. 43, p. 1240 (1943)

galvanometer, as desired. A glass electrode pH meter having the proper voltage range may be used.

(g) *Sample Tubes.*—See Section 17(e).

Reagents

26. (a) *Iodine, Standard Solution (0.1 N).*—See Section 18(a).

(b) *Manganous Sulfate Solution (364 g per liter).*—See Section 18(b).

(c) *Potassium Iodide, Alkaline Solution (150 g KI per liter).*—See Section 18(e).

(d) *Potassium Iodide, Iodized Alkaline Solution.*—See Section 18(f).

(e) *Sodium Thiosulfate, Standard Solution (0.1 N).*—See Section 18(g).

(f) *Sodium Thiosulfate, Standard Solution (0.005 N).*—See Section 18(h).

(g) *Starch Indicator.*

(h) *Sulfuric Acid (3:1).*—See Section 18(i).

Procedure

27. (a) *Sampling.*—Select two clean sampling tubes of approximately equal capacities and obtain samples as described in Section 19(b).

(b) *Fixing.*—See Section 19(c).

(c) *Titration of Blank.*—Invert the sample tube and drain out a sufficient volume of sample to equalize the volume of "sample" and "blank" into a 10-ml graduated cylinder. Record the volume withdrawn and discard it. Drain the blank into the clean 800-ml beaker by opening both stopcocks. Do not rinse or blow through the sampling tube, but shake the last drops from the lower nipple into the beaker. Rinse both electrodes with water, and readjust the sleeve on the calomel electrode to provide a fresh junction. Place the beaker on the titrating stand with both electrodes immersed in the sample, start the stirrer, and adjust its speed to mix the sample rapidly without causing a vortex suffi-

cient to draw bubbles of air into the liquid. Read and record the emf between the electrodes. Fill a 10-ml buret (0.01-ml subdivisions) with 0.005 N Na₂S₂O₃, and adjust exactly to the zero mark. Proceed with the titration, rinsing the tip of the pipet in the sample after each addition. Record the cumulative amounts of thiosulfate and the emf after each addition, and make progressively smaller additions as the end point is approached and passed, allowing a sufficient interval between additions to enable electrodes and solution to come to equilibrium. Titration should be completed within 30 min after sampling. In a third column, parallel to those used for recording the milliliters of thiosulfate and emf, record the quotient $(\Delta \text{ emf})/(\Delta \text{ thiosulfate})$ for each addition. The maximum numerical value of this quotient, without regard to sign, occurs at the end point of the titration. The end point can be identified by inspection of the values in the third column, so that plotting of the data is unnecessary.

(d) *Titration of Sample.*—Empty the beaker, rinse it and the electrodes with water, prepare a fresh junction with the sleeve of the calomel electrode, and drain the sample into the beaker. Titrate the sample as described for the blank in Paragraph (c).

Calculation

28. (a) Calculate the dissolved oxygen content of the sample, in parts per million, as follows (Note 2):

Dissolved oxygen, ppm

$$= \left(\frac{16,000n(S - B)}{Vs + Vb} \right) - 0.0104$$

where:

n = normality of the Na₂S₂O₃ solution (nominally 0.005),

S = milliliters of $Na_2S_2O_3$ solution required for titration of the sample,

Vs = volume of sample in milliliters (volume of sample tube minus volume of portion discarded immediately before titration (Section 27 (c)),

B = milliliters of $Na_2S_2O_3$ solution required for titration of the blank,

Vb = volume of blank in milliliters, and

0.0104 = correction for oxygen introduced with the reagents (Note 1).

Note 2.—Inaccuracy of the results calculated by the method increases with difference in capacities of the two sampling tubes, the amount of oxygen dissolved in the water samples, and the concentration of redox impurities in the water.

(b) The method used should be stated when reporting results.

Precision

29. A skilled operator using this method can obtain results with a precision of 0.002 ppm of oxygen.

Non-Referee Method D

Application

30. This method is applicable to industrial water having a dissolved oxygen concentration greater than 0.005 ppm.

Summary of Method

31. The sample is collected in a tube of special design shown in Fig. 1. The free iodine liberated in an amount equivalent to the oxygen in the sample is titrated with thiosulfate using starch indicator.

Interferences

32. The use of the proper amount of iodized alkaline iodide will minimize error from reducing interferences.

Apparatus

33. (a) *Casserole.*—A 1-liter glazed porcelain casserole, clear white in color.

(b) *Miscellaneous.*—Sample tubes, and 10-ml burets with 0.01-ml divisions described in Section 17. The motor-stirrer described in Section 17(f), if available, is of great convenience.

Reagents

34. See Section 18(a), (b), (e), (f), (h), (i) and (j).

Procedure

35. (a) *Sampling.*—Collect the samples as described in Section 19(b). If the temperature of the cooling water is too high to attain a sample temperature of 60 to 65 F (16 to 18 C), a supplementary cooler, such as a coiled length of stainless steel tubing in a bath of cracked ice or ice water, shall be used. Do not attempt to cool the sample after collection.

(b) *Fixing.*—Fix the sample and blank as described in Section 19(c).

(c) *Titration of Blank.*—Drain the blank, which shall be at a temperature not above 70 F, into the clean casserole and add 10 drops of starch indicator solution. Fill the buret in accordance with the volume required for the titration, with $0.005N$ $Na_2S_2O_3$. Start the motor stirrer, if available; otherwise, stir constantly with a clean glass rod. Titrate to the disappearance of the blue, starch iodine color, rinsing the tip of the buret in the sample after each addition as the end point approaches.

(d) *Titration of Sample.*—Empty and rinse the casserole and rain the sample into it. Titrate as described in Paragraph (c).

Calculation

36. Calculate the dissolved oxygen content of the sample, in parts per million, by the rapid method described in

Section 28. The procedure used should be stated when reporting results.

Precision

37. An experienced analyst using this method can obtain results with a precision of 0.004 ppm of oxygen.

NON-REFEREE METHOD E

Application

38. This method is applicable to industrial water containing more than 0.05 ppm of oxygen and having low concentrations of reducing and oxidizing materials.

Summary of Method

39. The sample is collected in a BOD bottle. The free iodine liberated in an amount equivalent to the oxygen in the sample is titrated with thiosulfate using starch as an indicator.

Interferences

40. Reducing and oxidizing materials in the sample will interfere in this method. The former leads to low results and the latter to high results.

Apparatus

41. (a) *Sample Bottle.*—One 300-ml BOD bottle having a raised lip around the neck and a glass stopper ground to a conical lower tip. The capacity of the bottle must be measured to the nearest milliliter and the stopper should be tied to the neck of the bottle with a loop of cord.

(b) *Pipets and Casserole.*—Three 2-ml transfer pipets, a casserole (Section 33(a)), and serological pipets of 1.00 and 5.00-ml capacities, graduated in 0.01 and 0.10-ml divisions, respectively.

Reagents

42. See Section 18(b), (e), (g), (i), and (j).

Procedure

43. (a) *Sampling.*—Collect the sample in a 300-ml BOD bottle as described in Section 10. Connect the source of the sample to a length of glass tubing slightly longer than the depth of the bottle. Put the glass tubing into the bottle and allow the bottle to fill and overflow, with the water entering at the bottom, until there have been at least ten changes of the contents. Wet the stopper and then slowly withdraw the glass tube while the sample continues to flow through it. As soon as the tip of the tube clears the liquid surface, ease the stopper into the neck and let it float down into its seat. Twist the stopper in tight, invert the bottle, and inspect for air bubbles. If any can be seen, discard the sample and collect another.

(b) *Fixing.*—Fill a 2-ml transfer pipet with alkaline potassium iodide solution, and with the pipet filled to the tip so that no bubble of air will be forced into the sample, ease the bottle stopper out of its seat and simultaneously thrust the pipet tip past it and into the neck of the bottle. Allow the contents of the pipet to drain into the bottle and, as the level in the pipet approaches that in the bottle, raise the pipet out of the bottle and let the stopper fall back into its seat. Fill another 2-ml pipet with $MnSO_4$ solution and add this to the sample in the same way. Seat the stopper tightly, and shake or rotate the bottle to mix the contents thoroughly. Allow the bottle to stand and, when the precipitate has settled below the shoulder of the bottle, add 2 ml of H_2SO_4 (3:1) in the same way. Stopper and shake until all precipitate is dissolved. Fixing should be completed within 15 min after sampling.

(c) *Titration.*—Empty the cup around the stopper of the bottle and wash it with water. If the temperature of the sample is above 70 F (21 C), cool it by immersing the bottle in a bath of cracked ice. Remove the stopper, drain the contents of the bottle into the casserole, and titrate with 0.1 N Na$_2$S$_2$O$_3$ as described in Section 35(c). Titration should be completed within 30 min after sampling.

Calculation

44. (a) Calculate the dissolved oxygen content of the sample, in parts per million, as follows:

$$\text{Dissolved oxygen, ppm} = \frac{8000nS}{v}$$

where:

n = normality of the Na$_2$S$_2$O$_3$ solution (nominally 0.1),

S = milliliters of Na$_2$S$_2$O$_3$ solution required for titration, and

v = milliliters of sample used.

(b) The method used should be stated when reporting results.

Precision

45. Where this method is applicable, an experienced analyst can obtain results with a precision of 0.03 ppm of oxygen.

Standard Method of Test for
IRON BACTERIA IN INDUSTRIAL WATER AND WATER-FORMED DEPOSITS[1]

ASTM Designation: D 932 – 58 (1965)

ADOPTED, 1951; REVISED, 1958; REAPPROVED, 1965

This Standard of the American Society for Testing and Materials is issued under the fixed designation D 932; the final number indicates the year of original adoption as standard or, in the case of revision, the year of last revision.

> NOTE.—An editorial change was made in Section 8(c) in June, 1959.

Scope and Application

1. This method describes the procedure for the detection of iron bacteria by examination under the microscope. The method provides for the identification of the following genera of bacteria found in industrial water and water formed deposits: *Siderocapsa*, *Gallionella* (*Didymohelix*), *Sphaerotilus*, *Crenothrix*, *Leptothrix*, and *Clonothrix*.

Principle of Method

2. The iron bacteria are generally filamentous, algae-like forms, typically found in water, and frequently surrounded by a sheath which is usually encrusted with iron (1, 2).[2] However, Starkey (3) reports another type which is classified among the true bacteria. Detection and identification is accomplished by microscopic examination of sediment from the sample. Table I and Figs. 1 to 10 (3) may be used to differentiate the various types.

Definitions

3. For definitions of terms used in this method, refer to the Definitions of Terms Relating to Industrial Water and Industrial Waste Water (ASTM Designation: D 1129).[3]

Apparatus

4. The apparatus shall consist of the following:

(a) *Centrifuge*, complete with conical tubes.

(b) *Filter Paper or Blotter.*

(c) *Microscope* that provides a magnification of 400X to 1000X and is complete with a suitable light source. A dark-field condenser is useful.

(d) *Pipets.*—10-ml Mohr-type pipets, with an opening 3 to 4 mm in width, for thick samples; and 1-ml Mohr-type pipets for thin samples.

(e) *Slides*, standard type, 1 by 3-in., with either plain or frosted end.

(f) *Cover Glasses*, round or square type, $\frac{3}{4}$ in. in diameter.

(g) *Spatula*, small and narrow, for handling thick samples.

---

[1] Under the standardization procedure of the Society, this method is under the jurisdiction of the ASTM Committee D-19 on Industrial Water. A list of members may be found in the ASTM Year Book.

[2] The boldface numbers in parentheses refer to the list of references appended to this method.

---

[3] Appears in this publication.

Purity of Reagents

5. (*a*) Reagent grade chemicals shall be used in all tests. Unless otherwise indicated, it is intended that all reagents shall conform to the specifications of the may be used, provided it is first ascertained that the reagent is of sufficiently high purity to permit its use without lessening the accuracy of the determination.

TABLE I.—KEY FOR IDENTIFICATION OF BACTERIA.

I. TRUE BACTERIA:

Capsulated coccoid or short rods

Genus: *Siderocapsa* (Fig. 1)

The organisms are coccoid or short rods, occurring in groups of 1 to 30 but generally less than 10, surrounded by a mucoid capsule. The deposit surrounding the capsule is rust-brown due to the presence of hydrous ferric oxide.

II. STALKED BACTERIA:

Twisted or straight bands resembling a ribbon or a row of beads. Bacteria are rod-shaped and borne at the top of the stalk.

Genus: *Gallionella* (*Didymohelix*) (Figs. 2 and 3)

The stalks are slender (1 to 3 microns), dichotomously branched, composed of colloidal hydrous ferric oxide. The bacteria are frequently overlooked and the stalk considered as the bacterium.

III. FILAMENTOUS BACTERIA:

A. Not encrusted with iron:

Genus: *Sphaerotilus* (Fig. 4)

The filaments are attached, colorless, may show false branching. The cells are rod-shaped or oval, 1.5 to 4 microns in diameter, surrounded by a firm sheath which is entirely organic and not impregnated with iron.

B Encrusted with iron:

(*1*) Not branched:

Genus: *Crenothrix* (Figs. 5, 6, and 10)

The filaments are usually attached to a firm substrate, and are differentiated into a base and a tip. The sheath is plainly visible and is thin and colorless at the tip, becoming thick and encrusted with iron oxide at the base. The cells vary from cylindrical to spherical, the diameter being between 2 and 9 microns. Spherical, nonmotile reproductive bodies are formed. False branching may occur due to germination of spores within the sheath.
(*2*) May be branched:
    (*a*) Cells from 0.5 to 1 micron in diameter

Genus: *Leptothrix* (Figs. 7 and 8)

The filaments contain colorless, cylindrical cells which first have a thin colorless sheath that later becomes encrusted with iron oxide.
(*b*) Cells 2 microns or more in diameter

Genus: *Clonothrix* (Fig. 9)

Filaments attached, show false branching. The sheaths are organic and encrusted with iron hydroxide or manganese, are broader at the base, and taper to the tip, varying from 7 to 2 microns. The cells are colorless, cylindrical, 2 by 10 microns. The filaments are colorless when young, becoming dark, yellowish-brown with age. Forms spherical reproductive cells on the short branches of the younger portions of the filaments.

Committee on Analytical Reagents of the American Chemical Society, where such specifications are available.[4] Other grades

[4] "Reagent Chemicals, American Chemical Society Specifications," Am. Chem. Soc., Washington, D. C. For suggestions on the testing of reagents not listed by the American Chemical Society, see "Reagent Chemicals and Standards," by Joseph Rosin, D. Van Nostrand Co., Inc., New York, N. Y., and the "United States Pharmacopeia."

(*b*) Unless otherwise indicated, references to water shall be understood to mean reagent water conforming to the Specifications for Reagent Water (ASTM Designation: D 1193).[3]

Reagents

6. (*a*) *Hydrochloric Acid (1:4)*.—Mix one volume of HCl (sp gr 1.19) with four volumes of water.

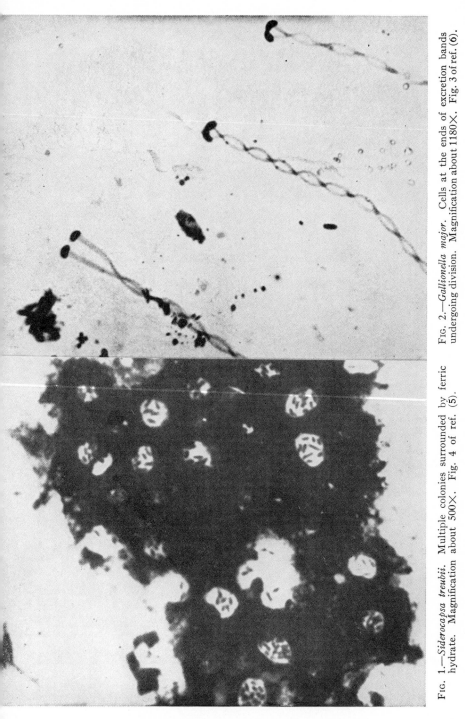

Fig. 1.—*Siderocapsa treubii.* Multiple colonies surrounded by ferric hydrate. Magnification about 500×. Fig. 4 of ref. (5).

Fig. 2.—*Gallionella major.* Cells at the ends of excretion bands undergoing division. Magnification about 1180×. Fig. 3 of ref. (6).

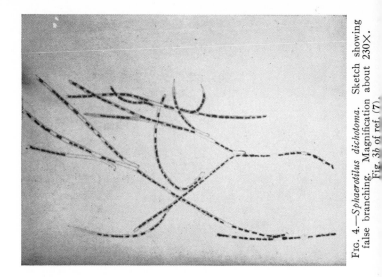

Fig. 4.—*Sphaerotilus dichotoma.* Sketch showing false branching. Magnification about 230×. Fig. 3b of ref. (7).

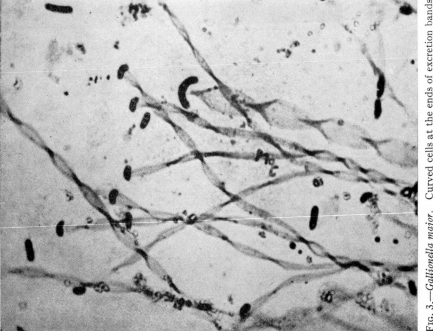

Fig. 3.—*Gallionella major.* Curved cells at the ends of excretion bands. Magnification about 1120×. Fig. 6 of ref. (6).

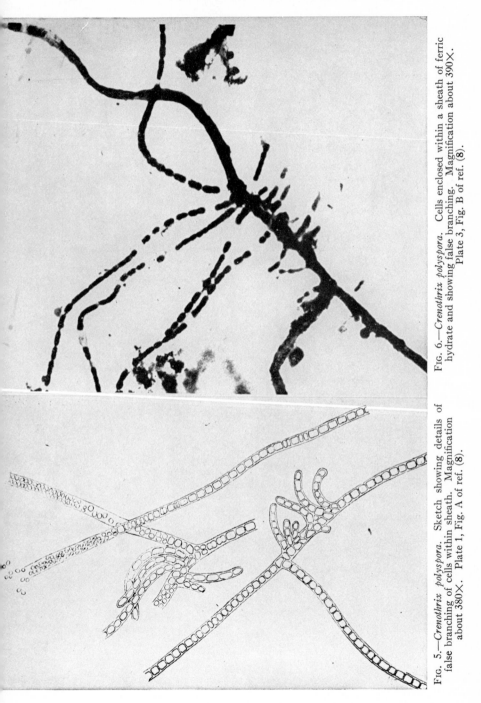

Fig. 6.—*Crenothrix polyspora.* Cells enclosed within a sheath of ferric hydrate and showing false branching. Magnification about 390X. Plate 3, Fig. B of ref. (8).

Fig. 5.—*Crenothrix polyspora.* Sketch showing details of false branching of cells within sheath. Magnification about 380X. Plate 1, Fig. A of ref. (8).

FIG. 7.—*Leptothrix ochracea.* Cells coming out of their   FIG. 8.—*Leptothrix ochracea.* Sheaths from an accumulation of

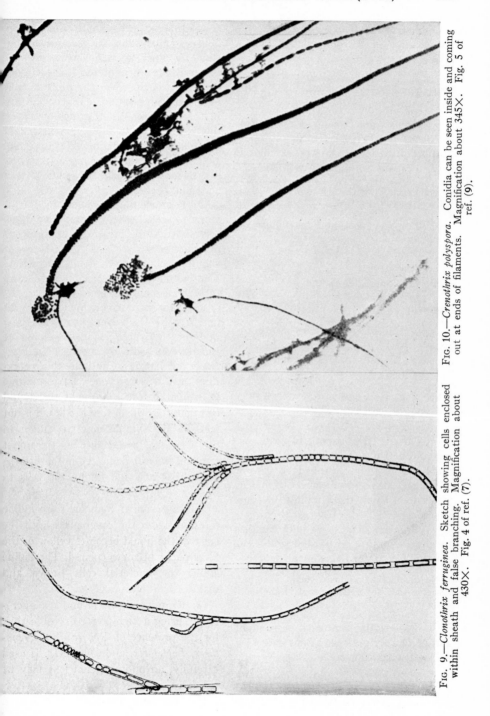

FIG. 10.—*Crenothrix polyspora.* Conidia can be seen inside and coming out at ends of filaments. Magnification about 345×. Fig. 5 of ref. (9).

FIG. 9.—*Clonothrix ferruginea.* Sketch showing cells enclosed within sheath and false branching. Magnification about 430×. Fig. 4 of ref. (7).

(*b*) *Iodine Solution.*—Prepare Gram's modification of Lugol's solution (4) as follows:

Iodine...............................	1.0 g
Potassium iodide....................	2.0 g
Water............................	300 ml

(*c*) *Ammonium Oxalate - Crystal Violet Solution.*—Prepare Hucker's modification of the Gram stain (4) as follows:

(*1*) Prepare Solution A as follows:

Crystal violet (90 per cent dye content).	2.0 g
Ethyl alcohol (95 per cent)...........	20 ml

(*2*) Prepare Solution B as follows:

Ammonium oxalate..................	0.8 g
Water............................	80 ml

(*3*) Mix Solutions A and B.

Sampling

7. (*a*) Collect the samples in accordance with the applicable method of the American Society for Testing and Materials, as follows:

D 510—Sampling Industrial Water,[3]
D 887—Field Sampling of Water-Formed Deposits.[3]

(*b*) Obtain a 1-pt sample of water, using a sterile 1-qt bottle. The bottle should not be more than half-filled because of the oxygen demand of suspended matter which may cause the sample to become anaerobic.

(*c*) Transfer deposit or mud samples to a wide-mouth bottle and add clear chlorine-free water to cover the deposit.

NOTE.—In mud samples, viable organisms, when present, are usually found at the mud-water interface.

(*d*) Protect the samples from sunlight and preferably preserve at not over 75 F during transportation.

Procedure

8. (*a*) Place a portion of the sample on the slide and apply a cover glass

A spatula or wide-mouth pipet is of help in transferring the sample to the slide. A pipet is useful when flocs of material are encountered, as the flocs settle to the tip when the pipet is held in a vertical position, and concentrate in the first drop. In the case of a very dilute or a water sample, concentrate the filaments by centrifuging, pour off the supernatant liquid, and repeat if necessary. Transfer some of the sediment to a slide and proceed.

(*b*) Examine the slide under the microscope to see whether encrusted or colorless sheaths are present. The presence of the twisted stalks of *Gallionella* should be noted at this point, since treatment with acid as described in Paragraph (*c*) will dissolve the delicate stalks.

(*c*) Place hydrochloric acid (1:4) at one side of the cover glass and draw underneath by absorbing the liquid at the opposite side by means of a filter paper or blotter. Continue this procedure until no more yellow ferric chloride is evident in the solution. Care should be taken that the flow of the liquid is not fast, or the sample may be drawn to the absorbent material. This treatment removes the iron deposited in the sheaths of the bacteria and allows the cells to be seen.

(*d*) In a similar manner, rinse iodine solution under the cover glass until the color of the liquid becomes yellow or the filter paper becomes colored. The iodine stains the bacterial cells brown and makes them more easily visible.

(*e*) Examine the slide under a microscope, using a high-power dry objective, for the presence of *Sphaerotilus, Crenothrix, Leptothrix,* and *Clonothrix.* If used carefully, an oil-immersion lens may be helpful.

(*f*) Prepare a new slide by placing a drop of the sample on a clean slide and allow it to air-dry. Then stain for 1 min with ammonium oxalate - crystal violet solution, wash with water, and allow to dry. Examine under an oil-immersion lens for the presence of *Siderocapsa*, which will appear violet colored.

Precision and Accuracy

9. The report should state "Present" or "Not found, probably absent." A statement should be made as to the relative abundance of organisms present. A negative report should be made only after examination of several slides.

REFERENCES

(1) D. H. Bergy, "Manual of Determinative Bacteriology," pp. 881–889, Williams & Wilkins Co., Baltimore 2, Md. (1938).
(2) A. J. Salle, "Fundamental Principles of Bacteriology," pp. 516–519, McGraw-Hill Book Co., Inc., New York, N. Y. (1943).
(3) Robert L. Starkey, "Transformation of Iron by Bacteria in Water," *Journal*, Am. Water Works Assn., Vol. 37, pp. 963–984 (1945).
(4) "Manual of Methods for Pure Culture Study of Bacteria," p. IV 46–8, Biotech Publications, Geneva, N. Y. (1946).
(5) Yvette Hardman and A. T. Henrici, "Studies of Fresh Water Bacteria V. Distribution of *Siderocapsa treubii* in some Lakes and Streams," *Journal of Bacteriology*, Vol. 37, p. 97 (1939).
(6) N. Cholodny, "Planta," Vol. 8 (1929).
(7) H. Molisch, "Die Eisenbakterien," Gustav Fischer, Jena, p. 83 (1910).
(8) E. C. Harder, "Iron-Depositing Bacteria and Their Geologic Relationship," U. S. Geological Survey, Professional Paper 113, p. 89 (1919).
(9) N. Cholodny, "Die Eisenbakterien," Gustav Fischer, Jena (1926).

Standard Method of

REPORTING RESULTS OF EXAMINATION AND ANALYSiS OF WATER-FORMED DEPOSITS[1]

ASTM Designation: D 933 – 50 (1965)

ADOPTED, 1949; REVISED, 1950; REAPPROVED, 1965

This Standard of the American Society for Testing and Materials is issued under the fixed designation D 933; the number immediately following the designation indicates the year of original adoption or, in the case of revision, the year of last revision. A number in parentheses indicates the year of last reapproval.

Scope

1. This method describes the manner in which the results of examination and analysis for inorganic constituents of deposits formed from industrial waters are to be reported.

NOTE 1.—All analyses are to be made in accordance with the methods of test of the American Society for Testing Materials, unless otherwise specified.

NOTE 2.—While various other methods of reporting the analysis of water-formed deposits are in use, this method is intended as a rational and comprehensive practice for general application. For use in specific industries or individual cases, molecular combinations may be useful and desirable.

Definitions

2. For definitions of terms used in this method, reference should be made to the Definitions of Terms Relating to Industrial Water and Industrial Waste Water (ASTM Designation: D 1129).[2]

History of Sample

3. Information regarding the source and history of the sample shall be included in the report of the analysis. This information should be that specified in the Method of Field Sampling of Water-Formed Deposits (ASTM Designation: D 887),[2] as follows:

(1) Name of company supplying sample,

(2) Name and location of plant,

(3) Date and time of sampling,

(4) Number of sample,

(5) Name and other designation of equipment from which sample was removed,

(6) Precise location from which sample was removed (for example, exactly what turbine blade),

[1] Under the standardization procedure of the Society, this method is under the jurisdiction of the ASTM Committee D-19 on Industrial Water. A list of members may be found in the ASTM Year Book.

[2] Appears in this publication.

(7) Appearance and extent of deposit prior to removal,

(8) Type of deposit—whether scale, sludge, biological deposit, or corrosion product as defined in Method D 887,

(9) Exact method that was used in removing the sample and notes concerning any contamination that might have occurred during the process,

(13) Results of field tests made on the sample or related equipment, and

(14) Signature of sampler.

Physical Characteristics

4. The report shall include a description of the physical characteristics of the sample, including any peculiarities

TABLE I.—CONSTITUENTS OF WATER-FORMED DEPOSITS TO BE REPORTED.

Oxides:[a]

Iron oxide,[b] Fe_2O_3
Alumina,[c] Al_2O_3
Calcium oxide, CaO
Magnesium oxide, MgO
Sodium oxide,[d] Na_2O
Potassium oxide,[d] K_2O
Copper oxide, CuO
Zinc oxide, ZnO
Lead oxide, PbO
Titanium oxide, TiO_2
Nickel oxide, NiO
Chromium oxide, Cr_2O_3
Tin oxide, SnO_2

Acid Anhydrides:[e]

Carbonate, CO_2
Chloride, Cl
Nitrate, N_2O_5
Sulfate, SO_3
Sulfite, SO_2
Sulfide,[f] S
Phosphate, P_2O_5
Silica, SiO_2

Miscellaneous:

Ammonia (reported as NH_3)
Water-soluble matter
Ether-extractable matter (oil)
Carbonaceous matter[g]
Combined water
Moisture
Total weight of sample (where significant)

[a] Expression of analytical results in terms of oxides is an arbitrary procedure sanctionede by long usage and general convenience. Adherence to this convention does not imply th ι any of the oxides necessarily are present in the sample as such, although this may actually be the case with respect to such items as iron oxide and silica A metal oxide shall be reported in the form listed in Table I unless the form present has been otherwise identified. Any metal definitely identified to be present in the sample in the metallic form shall be reported as such.

[b] When iron oxides other than Fe_2O_3 are known to be present (Fe_3O_4 and FeO), but determination of the separate oxide forms is considered not to be essential, report as "Iron oxides as Fe_2O_3."

[c] If alumina is not separated from iron oxide in the analytical procedure, report as "Iron and aluminum oxides as Fe_2O_3."

[d] If sodium and potassium are not separated, report as "Sodium and potassium oxides as Na_2O.'

[e] Organic acid radicals of soaps shall be reported as the anhydride of oleic acid ($C_{13}H_{33}O_2$), unless the specific acid has been identified.

[f] Elementary sulfur shall be reported as S.

[g] Graphite or other forms of carbon shall be reported as C.

(10) Operating temperature and pressure of liquid or vapor in the equipment that contained the deposit,

(11) Type of treatment applied to the water that formed the deposit or to the water that furnished steam to the affected zone,

(12) An account of discrepancies in operating condition that may have contributed to deposition (for example, water starving),

that may be pertinent in its further examination (Note 3).

NOTE 3.—Characteristics such as the following may be recorded: color, form, (scaly, slimy, drusy, etc.), texture (oily, smooth, friable, gritty, etc.), hardness, magnetic properties (as determined by test with magnet), and structure (amorphous, crystalline, columnar crystals).

Completeness and Accuracy of Analysis

5. (a) The determinations to be reported in a complete analysis shall be those listed in Table I. For many prac-

tical purposes, a less complete analysis will suffice. In other instances the location or nature of the deposit or a knowledge of the composition of the equipment affected will suggest the need for determinations in addition to those listed.

(b) The completeness and accuracy of the analysis should be carefully appraised before reporting. In a complete analysis, the summation of all determinations under oxides, acid radicals, ether-extractable matter, carbonaceous matter, and combined water shall total 100 ± 2 per cent (Note 4).

NOTE 4.—A summation in excess of 102 per cent indicates a positive error in one or more of the determinations (or the calculation of a metal or element as an oxide, or the calculation of a lower oxide as a higher oxide). The converse may be indicated when the summation is below 98 per cent, or it may be due to the presence of a substance not identified and not determined.

Reporting of Chemical Analysis

6. (a) All data, except water, shall be reported as percentage by weight of the dry sample. Water shall be reported on the as-received basis.

(b) For convenience in calculation, values for oxides, acid anhydrides, and combined water may also be expressed on a basis of chemical equivalents. Values for relative equivalents are obtained by dividing each value of percentage by weight by the equivalent weight of the respective oxide, acid radical, or water.

(c) Quantitative determinations shall be reported to the nearest 0.1 per cent (Note 5). When a quantitative determination is made and a negative result is obtained, it shall be reported as "0.0" with a notation as to the amount of sample used and the method of determination. When a determination has been omitted, but the heading of the determination is carried in a tabulation with determinations of other samples, the absence of a determination for any other specific sample shall be indicated by an entry "no determination" or by a dash.

The terms "nil," "none," and "trace" shall not be used. If the qualitative determination shows presence, and a quantitative determination shows absence, the item shall be reported as "less than 0.1" with a notation that this is a qualitative estimation.

NOTE 5.—In so far as applicable, the Recommended Practices for Designating Significant Places in Specified Limiting Values (ASTM Designation: E 29),[3] shall be followed in expressing numerical results.

Reporting Results of X-ray Diffraction and Petrographic Examination

7. All constituents identified by X-ray diffraction or petrographic examination shall be reported according to the following rules (Notes 6 to 9):

(1) *Silicon Compounds:*—Report all compounds containing silicon, except the simple alkali silicates, by their trivial name and combined-oxide formula. Example: acmite, $Na_2O \cdot Fe_2O_3 \cdot 4SiO_2$.

(2) *Polymorphous Compounds:*—Report compounds having more than one crystal form by their trivial name and chemical formula. Examples: calcite, $\beta CaCO_3$ and aragonite, $\gamma CaCO_3$.

(3) *Multiple Salts:*—Report multiple salts by their trivial name and combined-compound formula. Examples: burkeite, $Na_2CO_3 \cdot 2Na_2SO_4$, and malachite, $CuCO_3 \cdot Cu(OH)_2$.

(4) *Other Compounds:*—Report compounds not covered by the above rules by their chemical name and chemical formula. Example: sodium chloride, NaCl.

(5) *Controversial Compounds:*—Report compounds whose nomenclature is in controversy in accordance with the latest revision of the ASTM Card Index File of X-ray Diffraction Data,[4] subject to conformance with rules (1) to (4).

---

[3] 1967 Book of ASTM Standards, Part 30.
[4] This Card Index File may be purchased from the American Society for Testing and Materials, 1916 Race St., Philadelphia 3, Pa.

NOTE 6.—If a compound can be reported by several rules, the rule first listed which covers that compound shall prevail.

NOTE 7.—Free elements shall be considered as compounds in applying the above rules.

NOTE 8.—If the compound does not have a trivial name and the rule calls for a trivial name, the chemical name shall be used.

NOTE 9.—The Greek letter and Roman numeral conventions already adopted in the literature shall be accepted as standard.

Reporting Results of Spectrochemical Analysis

8. Results of spectrochemical analysis shall be reported in terms of elements present (Note 10).

NOTE 10.—The elements may be grouped as major, minor, and trace constituents, with due regard for variation in the sensitivity of the method for the various elements reported. A satisfactory grouping in terms of percentage of the element present is as follows:

	Amount of Element Present, per cent
Major	over 5
Minor	0.5 to 5
Trace	under 0.5

While the indentification of elements is positive quantitative measurements are only approximations.

Standard Method for

IDENTIFICATION OF CRYSTALLINE COMPOUNDS IN WATER-FORMED DEPOSITS BY X-RAY DIFFRACTION[1]

ASTM Designation: D 934 – 52 (1965)

ADOPTED, 1952; REAPPROVED, 1965

This Standard of the American Society for Testing and Materials is issued under the fixed designation D 934; the number immediately following the designation indicates the year of original adoption or, in the case of revision, the year of last revision. A number in parentheses indicates the year of last reapproval.

Scope

1. This method describes equipment and a procedure for the identification by X-ray diffraction of crystalline compounds (1, 2, 3, 4)[2] in deposits formed from or by water during its industrial use. The procedure is basically that of Hull (5) with the contributions of Hanawalt, Rinn, and Frevel (6). This method yields positive identification of the crystalline components of water-formed solids for which X-ray diffraction data are available or can be obtained. Without special treatment, amorphous phases cannot be identified. The sensitivity for a given component varies with a combination of such factors as the density, degree of crystallization, particle size, coincidence of strong lines of components, and the kind and arrangement of the atoms of the component. Minimum percentages for identification may therefore vary between the ranges of 5 to 40 per cent.

NOTE 1.—The practice and theory of X-ray diffraction have been described in available reference works (7, 8, 9, 10, 11, 12).

Definitions

2. Definitions of the terms employed in this method shall be in accordance with the Definitions of Terms Relating to Industrial Water and Industrial Waste Water (ASTM Designation D 1129).[3]

Apparatus

3. (a) *Radiation.*—The radiation shall be the characteristic K_α emission from a chromium, iron, cobalt, copper, or molybdenum target X-ray tube (Note

---

[1] Under the standardization procedure of the Society, this method is under the jurisdiction of the ASTM Committee D-19 on Industrial Water. A list of members may be found in the ASTM Year Book.

[2] The boldface numbers in parentheses refer to the references listed at the end of this method.

[3] Appears in this publication.

). The K_α radiation shall be purified by removing the K_β radiation with a filter. These filters are as follows:

X-Ray Target Material	Filter Element
Chromium	Vanadium
Iron	Manganese
Cobalt	Iron
Copper	Nickel
Molybdenum	Zirconium

The filter, either as the free metal or metal oxide, shall be of a thickness sufficient to reduce the intensity of the K_β radiation to $\frac{1}{200}$ of that of the K_α radiation and shall be located in the path of the beam before, but not at, the last aperture of the collimating system or between the test specimen and the film, preferably at least $\frac{1}{4}$ in. from the film.

NOTE 2.—Copper radiation is not as satisfactory as the other recommended radiations for specimens containing considerable iron or iron-bearing compounds because of excessive fluorescence, which will produce marked fogging on the film.

(b) *Cameras.*—The camera shall conform to the following requirements:

(1) The design shall be of the circular Hull-Debye-Scherrer type,

(2) The dimensions shall permit recording of spacings up to 15 Angström units (Å),

(3) A means for rotation or oscillation of the test specimen shall be provided,

(4) The design shall permit some of the diffraction lines to be recorded on both sides of the undeviated beam, and

(5) The collimating system shall permit the resolution of diffraction lines 0.02 Å apart in the range 2.80 to 3.00 Å, when using a substance or mixture of substances that gives the sharpest possible diffraction lines.

(c) *Film.*—The X-ray film shall be the screenless type (Note 3). The film shall be handled and processed according to the recommendations of the film manufacturer.

NOTE 3.—With molybdenum radiation a screen-type film with the fluorazure type intensifying screen may be used.

Standard Patterns

4. Prepare standard X-ray diffraction patterns, using pure compounds likely to occur in water-formed deposits, on the same or exactly similar camera and with the same radiation as will be used for the identification. When samples of such compounds are not available for preparing standard patterns, use published authenticated data of interplanar spacings and relative intensities (Notes 4 and 5).

NOTE 4.—Much of this published data has been compiled in a Card Index File under the joint auspices of the American Society for Testing and Materials, the American Crystallographic Association, and the British Institute of Physics. The Card Index File may be purchased from the American Society for Testing and Materials, 1916 Race St., Philadelphia 3, Pa.

NOTE 5.—A method of indexing the standard patterns is described by Hanawalt, Rinn, and Frevel (6).

Method of Sampling

5. Take samples in accordance with the Standard Method of Field Sampling of Water-Formed Deposits (ASTM Designation: D 887).[3] Samples taken from specific locations and kept as nearly as possible in their original condition are most suitable for X-ray diffraction analysis. Air-dry moist samples before grinding. When samples contain oil, prepare a chloroform-insoluble fraction by drying the specimen for 1 hr at 105 C and then extracting for 2 hr, using chloroform in a Soxhlet extractor. Air-dry to remove solvent from the specimen. Proceed in accordance with either of the following Paragraphs (a) or (b),

depending on the type of analysis desired.

(*a*) *Composite Analysis.*—For a composite analysis, grind about 20 g of the deposit to pass a No. 30 (595-micron) sieve. Reduce the sample to about 5 g and grind to pass a No. 100 (149-micron) sieve.

(*b*) *Layer or Flake Analysis.*—For analysis of layers or flakes of a nonuniform deposit, remove approximately 0.1 g of the desired portion using a tweezers, knife, sharp pick, or small grinding tool.

Chemical Treatment of Samples

6. Depending on the contents of the sample, it may or may not be necessary to concentrate insoluble components by chemical treatments (Note 6). If this is not necessary, disregard any chemical treatment and grind and mount the test specimen in accordance with Section 7. When it is necessary to concentrate insoluble components, as by selective leaching, use one or more of the chemical treatments described in the following Paragraphs (*a*) to (*f*). After treatment grind and mount the insoluble component as described in Section 7.

Note 6.—These treatments are used when a component is present in too small an amount to give the number of lines required for identification (Section 9(*a*)).

(*a*) Prepare a hydrochloric acid-insoluble fraction by adding cold 5 per cent hydrochloric acid solution (1 volume of concentrated HCl (sp gr 1.19) to 6 volumes of water) to the powdered specimen in the ratio of 200 ml of acid per gram of sample. After 30 min filter, wash, and air-dry the residue (Note 7).

Note 7.—Many silicates and other acid insoluble components of a sample may be concentrated by this treatment by the removal of such components as carbonates, phosphates and hydroxides. Acid leaching will also partially decompose some of the silicates (13) such as serpentine, xonotlite, and analcite.

(*b*) Prepare a nitric acid-insoluble fraction by adding 5 per cent nitric acid (1 part of concentrated HNO_3 (sp gr 1.42) to 13 parts of water) to the powdered specimen in the ratio of 200 ml of acid per gram of sample. After 30 min filter, wash, and air-dry the residue (Note 8).

Note 8.—In addition to carbonates, hydroxides, etc., metallic copper and most copper compounds may be removed by this treatment.

(*c*) Prepare a fraction insoluble in an anhydrous diethyl ether - hydrochloric acid mixture by adding diethyl ether saturated with HCl (Note 9) to the powdered specimen in the ratio of 200 ml of solution per gram of sample. After 30 min filter and air-dry the residue (Note 10).

Note 9.—Prepare the solution by bubbling dry gaseous HCl into anhydrous diethyl ether. Isopropyl ether may also be used.

Note 10.—Hematite, magnetite, and other iron-containing compounds may be removed by this treatment.

(*d*) Prepare an acetic acid-insoluble fraction by adding a 25 per cent solution of acetic acid (1 part of glacial acetic acid to 3 parts of water) to the powdered specimen in the ratio of 200 ml of acid per gram of sample. After 30 min filter wash, and air-dry the residue (Note 11).

Note 11.—Some components that are soluble in mineral acids may be concentrated by this treatment.

(*e*) Prepare a water-insoluble fraction by adding water to the powdered specimen in the ratio of 200 ml of water per gram of sample. After 1 hr filter, wash and air-dry the residue.

(*f*) Prepare an ammonium chloride-insoluble fraction by adding a 10 per cent ammonium chloride solution (100 g NH_4Cl per liter) to the powdered specimen in the ratio of 200 ml of solution per gram of sample. After 1 hr filter, wash, and air-dry the residue (Note 12).

NOTE 12.—Calcium and magnesium hydroxdes may be removed by this treatment.

Preparation of Test Specimen

7. (a) *Grinding Test Specimen.*—Grind a 0.1 to 0.5-g portion of the sample from Section 5 or 6 in a mullite or similar mortar with a mullite or similar pestle until it is fine enough to pass a 200-mesh cloth or a No. 200 (74-micron) sieve (Notes 13 and 14).

NOTE 13.—Samples ground until grittiness has disappeared and until the sample has a tendency to smear under the pestle will normally be ground fine enough.

NOTE 14.—Metallic samples on which powder patterns are desired may be sufficiently subdivided by using a fine file or fine jeweler's saw to remove the necessary amount from the original sample. The file must be very clean and harder than the metal being filed. The pressure applied when using the tool should be no greater than necessary.

(b) *Mounting Powdered Specimen.*—Mount the powdered test specimen in such shape or form as required by the camera used so that the diffracted beam emerges from the specimen at the axial center of the camera (Notes 15 and 16).

NOTE 15.—Sample holders or containers that intercept the diffracted beam must be highly transparent to X-radiation.

NOTE 16.—When using the wedge-type specimen mount, it is advantageous to have a cellophane-covered wedge (14) for specimens that undergo structural change during the exposure.

Procedure for Taking Patterns

8. Load the film and mount the test specimen as recommended by the apparatus manufacturer. Mount the camera before the window of the X-ray tube in such a manner as to produce a strong uniform beam through the collimating system. Shield the tube windows so as to provide adequate protection to the operator and prevent stray radiation from fogging the film during exposure. Apply to the tube the proper potential and milliamperage as specified by the manufacturer. Check the position of the test specimen with respect to the beam to ensure that no displacement has taken place during the mounting of the camera. Process the film after the proper exposure (Note 17).

NOTE 17.—The exposure and development time of the film shall be such that maximum contrast is obtained between pattern lines and film background when using a good diffractor such as sodium chloride.

Identification of Patterns

9. (a) Place the pattern of the test specimen beside that of a standard on a viewing light so that the corresponding edges of the patterns come together and the centers of diffraction (Note 18) lie on the same vertical line. Visually scan the specimen pattern for the strong lines occurring in the standard pattern. Find by repeated trial the standard pattern whose strong lines match strong lines of the specimen pattern when compared in the above manner. The substance represented by the standard pattern shall be considered to be a component of the test specimen if at least the six strongest lines (Notes 19 and 20) of the standard pattern occur in the specimen pattern in the corresponding positions and with the correct relative intensities. When making this comparison, due regard must be given to the possibility of increased intensity of certain lines because of the superposition of lines of more than one component. Considering those lines of the specimen pattern not accounted for by the above match, including those of greater than normal intensity, repeat the matching with standard patterns until all the lines of the specimen pattern are accounted for.

(b) When there are lines in the test specimen pattern that cannot be matched by the available standard patterns, determine their interplanar spacings (Note 21) and relative intensities (Note 22) by film measurement. Compare these values with published data, in the manner described in Paragraph (*a*), until a match is found, using the same criteria as prescribed in Paragraph (*a*).

NOTE 18.—The center of diffraction of the undeviated beam is found by locating the midpoint between corresponding lines on either side of the central spot.

NOTE 19.—When other evidence, such as chemical analysis, spectrographic analysis, or petrographic examination, supports the finding of a component in a specimen, fewer lines may be considered to constitute an identification.

NOTE 20.—In the case of some simple substances, when fewer than six lines occur, supporting evidence such as mentioned in Note 19 is required.

NOTE 21.—The interplanar spacings, *d*, may be determined by calculation from the following formula:

$$d = \frac{\lambda}{2 \sin \frac{180l}{2\pi r}}$$

where:

d = interplanar spacing in Angström units,

λ = wave length in Angström units of the X-rays employed.

l = distance on film in centimeters from center of diffraction to the line being measured and

r = radius of the camera in centimeters.

They may also be determined by measuring directly using a scale ruled in Angströms for the camera – radiation combination used.

NOTE 22.—The line intensities are estimated by comparison against a set of lines prepared by exposure with constant radiation at multiples of the time required to produce a barely visible mark on the film.

Report

10. Results of this test shall be reported in accordance with the Method of Reporting Results of Examination and Analysis of Water-Formed Deposits (ASTM Designation: D 933).[3]

REFERENCES

(1) T. C. Alcock, L. M. Clark, and E. F. Thurston, "The Sealing of Boilers. Part V. Identification of Some of the Combinations of Silica and of Magnesia in Boiler Scales," *Journal of the Chemical Society* (London), Vol. 63, p. 292 (1944).

(2) C. E. Imhoff and L. A. Burkardt, "X-ray Diffraction Methods in the Study of Power Plant Deposits," *Industrial and Engineering Chemistry*, Vol. 35, p. 873 (1943); *Proceedings*, Am. Soc. Testing Mats., Vol. 43, p. 1276 (1943).

(3) E. P. Partridge, R. K. Scott, and P. H. Morrison, "Diagnosis of Water Problems at Limbo Station," *Proceedings*, Am. Soc. Testing Mats., Vol. 43, p. 1289 (1943).

(4) H. W. Rinn, Discussion of reference (3), *Proceedings*, Am. Soc. Testing Mats., Vol. 43, p. 1308 (1943).

(5) A. W. Hull, "A New Method of X-Ray Crystal Analysis," *Physical Revue*, Vol. 10, p. 661 (1917).

(6) J. D. Hanawalt, H. W. Rinn, and L. K. Frevel, "Chemical Analysis by X-Ray Diffraction," *Industrial and Engineering Chem-*

istry, Analytical Edition, Vol. 10, p. 457 (1938).

(7) C. S. Barrett, "Structure of Metals," McGraw-Hill Book Co., Inc. (1943).

(8) C. W. Bunn, "Chemical Crystallography," Oxford University Press (1946).

(9) G. L. Clark, "Applied X-rays," Third Edition, McGraw-Hill Book Co., Inc. (1940).

(10) W. P. Davey, "A Study of Crystal Structure and Its Application," McGraw-Hill Book Co., Inc. (1934).

(11) W. T. Sproull, "X-Ray in Practice," McGraw-Hill Book Co., Inc. (1946).

(12) A. F. Wells, "Structural Inorganic Chemistry," Oxford University Press (1945).

(13) K. J. Nurata, "Internal Structure of Silicate Minerals that Gelatinize with Acid," *American Mineralogist*, Vol. 28, p. 545 (1943).

(14) C. L. Christ and E. F. Champayne, "Sealed Sample Holder for X-Ray Diffraction Powder Work," *The Review of Scientific Instruments*, Vol. 19, No. 2, p. 117 (1948).

APPROVED AS
USA STANDARD Z111.9-1966
BY USA STANDARDS INSTITUTE
UDC 663.61:620.1

Standard Method of

CORROSIVITY TEST OF INDUSTRIAL WATER (NDHA* METHOD)[1]

ASTM Designation: D 935 – 66

ADOPTED, 1949; REVISED, 1966

This Standard of the American Society for Testing and Materials is issued under the fixed designation D 935; the number immediately following the designation indicates the year of original adoption or, in the case of revision, the year of last revision. A number in parentheses indicates the year of last reapproval.

Scope

1. This method covers a procedure, known as the NDHA* method, for studying the corrosivity of waters. It is particularly applicable to waters relatively free of suspended materials at temperatures below 200 C and at flow rates below 5 ft per sec, and has had extensive use for determining corrosion by steam condensate.

NOTE 1.—This method conforms to the general requirements for conducting plant tests given in the Recommended Practice for Conducting Plant Corrosion Tests (ASTM Designation: A 224).[2]

NOTE 2.—The prime purpose of the test is to investigate the corrosive characteristics of waters in the equipment in which the test is made. It may fail to indicate the corrosive characteristics of the same water in different equipment. Results may be used also to indicate the ability of the materials tested to withstand corrosion by the water.

---

* National District Heating Association.
[1] Under the standardization procedure of the Society, this method is under the jurisdiction of the ASTM Committee D-19 on Industrial Water. A list of members may be found in the ASTM Year Book.
[2] 1967 Book of ASTM Standards, Part 3.

Apparatus

2. (*a*) The apparatus consists of a train of three helical wire coils mounted in a supporting frame and electrically insulated from the frame and from each other. A detailed drawing of the tester is shown in Fig. 1.

(*b*) The helical coils are the test specimens. Standard coils shall be formed by winding on a $\frac{1}{8}$-in. mandrel 7 to 10 turns of 0.050 ± 0.001-in. diameter wire conforming to SAE 1010 (Note 3). The finished coil and ends shall be adjusted to the dimensions shown in Fig. 1.

NOTE 3.—For special purposes, wire of other composition may be used.

(*c*) The supporting frame shall be fabricated to the dimensions given in Fig. 1 from the same material as the coils. The frame may be used for the measurement of pitting. In this measurement it should be noted that the bends at the ends of the frame produce strains at these points.

(*d*) A clamp, supporting base, or tack weld is required for holding the assembly in a fixed position during the test. For

343

tests in piping systems, a pipe plug prepared as shown in Fig. 1 may be conveniently used for insertion of the holder into one side of a pipe tee.

oughly degreased by immersion in a suitable solvent such as ethyl ether or carbon tetrachloride. Upon removal they shall be placed in a drying oven

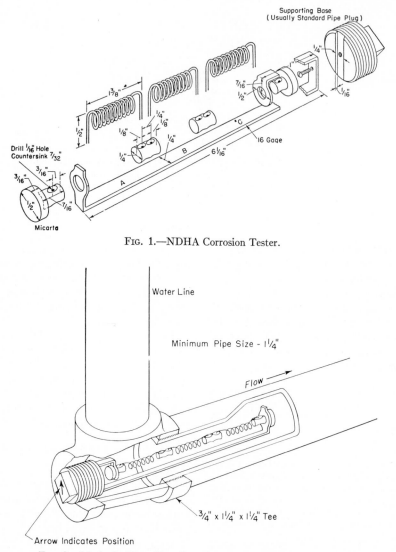

FIG. 1.—NDHA Corrosion Tester.

FIG. 2.—Method of Installing Corrosion Tester in Small Diameter Pipe.

Procedure

3. (a) *Preparation of Testers.*—Before a tester is assembled, the supporting frame and helical coils shall be thor-

held at 105 C for about 1 hr, then removed and stored in a desiccator. After cooling, the helical wire coils shall be weighed on an analytical balance to the nearest 0.001 g. This weight, together with the position the coil will occupy in the assembled unit, shall be recorded.

(b) *Installation of Tester.*—A tester may be installed in a pipe line (Note 4), whenever it does not unduly obstruct the flow of water or create undesirable turbulence. A satisfactory arrangement is illustrated in Fig. 2. A tester may also be installed in any practicable location in tanks and other large equipment.

NOTE 4.—When a tester is to be installed in a pipe line, the internal diameter of the pipe should be not less than $1\frac{1}{4}$ in. The use of the tester in pipe lines is described in several articles.[3]

(c) *Recording of Data.*—All available information on the physical and chemical characteristics of the environment in which the test is made shall be recorded and included in the report of the test.

(d) *Duration of Test.*—The minimum recommended test period is 30 days or that period of time in which the wire coils lose approximately 10 per cent of their initial weight.

(e) *Cleaning of Specimens after Testing.*—After removal from the corroding environment, the surfaces of the frame and coils shall be thoroughly cleaned (Note 5) of all corrosion products.

NOTE 5.—Washing in a stream of hot water, while brushing vigorously with a bristle brush, may be used to remove less adherent deposits. Inhibited acid solutions, electrolytic pickling, alkaline salt solutions, or some other chemical cleaning method must usually be used for complete removal of corrosion products.

The criterion of suitability of any cleaning method is its ability to remove corrosion products with as little loss of metal as possible.

[3] J. H. Walker, "A Method of Measuring Corrosiveness," *Proceedings*, Am. Soc. Testing Materials, Vol. 40, p. 1342 (1940).

L. F. Collins and E. L. Henderson, "Corrosion in Steam Heating Systems," *Heating, Piping and Air Conditioning*, Vol. 11, September, p. 593, October, p. 620, November, p. 675, December, p. 735 (1939).

L. F. Collins, "Corrosion in Condensate Piping," *Power Plant Engineering*, Vol. 48, March, 1944, p. 88.

(f) *Pitting.*—If either the frame or coils have suffered pitting, the depth of pits may be measured by any suitable procedure and the results expressed as depth of such pits in inches for the time of exposure (Note 6).

NOTE 6.—It is common practice to measure the ten deepest pits and report the average depth of these, as well as that of the deepest pit.

Calculations

4. (a) Rates of corrosion may be expressed either as weight loss per unit of area per unit of time or the equivalent rate of penetration. The most commonly employed units are milligrams per square decimeter per day (24 hr), (abbreviated mdd) for the one, and inches penetration per year (abbreviated ipy) or centimeters penetration per year (abbreviated cmpy) for the other. The penetration in inches per year (ipy) may be calculated as follows:

$$\text{Penetration, ipy} = \frac{D}{2T} \times \frac{W_1 - W_2}{W_1 + \sqrt{W_1 W_2}}$$

where:
D = initial diameter of wire in inches,
T = time of exposure in years,
W_1 = initial weight of wire in grams, and
W_2 = final weight of wire in grams.

(b) The relationship between corrosion rate in milligrams per square decimeter per day (mdd) and penetration in inches per year (ipy) is based on the following equation:

$$\text{ipy} = \text{mdd} \times \frac{0.001437}{d}$$

where:
d = density of the metal in grams per cubic centimeter.

(c) The relationship between corrosion rate in milligrams per square decimeter per day (mdd) and penetration in centimeters per year (cmpy) is based on the following equation:

TABLE I.—RELATIONSHIP BETWEEN CORROSION RATE IN MILLIGRAMS PER SQUARE DECIMETER PER DAY (MDD) AND PENETRATION IN INCHES PER YEAR (IPY) AND PENETRATION IN CENTIMETERS PER YEAR (CMPY).

Material	Density, g per cu cm	Penetration Equivalent to a Corrosion Rate of 1 mdd in	
		ipy	cmpy
Aluminum	2.72	0.000528	0.001346
Brass (admiralty)	8.54	0.000168	0.000427
Brass (red)	8.75	0.000164	0.000416
Brass (yellow)	8.47	0.000170	0.000432
Bronze (phosphorus, 5 per cent tin)	8.86	0.000162	0.000412
Bronze (silicon)	8.54	0.000168	0.000427
Bronze (cast) (85-5-5-5)	8.70	0.000165	0.000419
Cast iron	7.20	0.000200	0.000508
Copper	8.92	0.000161	0.000409
Copper-nickel alloy (70-30)	8.95	0.000161	0.000409
Inconel	8.51	0.000169	0.000429
Lead (chemical)	11.35	0.000127	0.000323
Monel	8.84	0.000163	0.000414
Nickel	8.89	0.000162	0.000412
Ni-resist	7.48	0.000192	0.000488
Silver	10.50	0.000137	0.000348
Stainless steel (type 304)	7.92	0.000181	0.000462
Stainless steel (type 430)	7.61	0.000189	0.000480
Steel (mild)	7.86	0.000183	0.000465
Tin	7.29	0.000197	0.000500
Zinc	7.15	0.000201	0.000510

$$cmpy = mdd \times \frac{0.00365}{d}$$

where:

d = density of the metal in grams per cubic centimeter.

(d) For the more common metals and alloys, the multipliers listed in Table I may be used to convert values in milligrams per square decimeter per day (mdd) into either inches penetration per year (ipy) or centimeters penetration per year (cmpy).

Interpretation of Data

5. Caution is suggested in the application of the data to predict the life of the equipment. The significance of the test may be enhanced by securing as complete data as possible on those characteristics of the water that are likely to influence corrosion. These include composition, pH value, temperature, rate of flow, and the like.

Report

6. The report of the test shall include the items mentioned in Section 3(c) to (f) and Section 5.

Standard Method of Test for

NITRATE ION IN INDUSTRIAL WATER[1]

ASTM Designation: D 992 - 52 (1965)

ADOPTED, 1952; REAPPROVED, 1965

This Standard of the American Society for Testing and Materials is issued under the fixed designation D 992; the number immediately following the designation indicates the year of original adoption or, in the case of revision, the year of last revision. A number in parentheses indicates the year of last reapproval.

NOTE.—An editorial change in Section 7 was made in June, 1958. Footnote 5 was added editorially in May, 1959, and further revised in November, 1959.

Scope

1. This method covers the colorimetric determination of nitrate ion in industrial water, particularly in water intended for use in steam boilers.

Principle of Method

2. A chloroform solution of brucine alkaloid and sulfuric acid added to the sample to be tested produces a yellow color, the intensity of which is proportional to the amount of nitrate ion present in the water. The intensity of the color is measured at 470 mμ by means of a photoelectric photometer.

Interfering Substances

3. (a) Nitrite ion interferes with the nitrate ion determination in proportion to its concentration in the sample.

NOTE 1.—In most industrial waters, nitrite ion is present to the extent of only 1 ppm. or less, which is considered negligible and without significant influence on the test.

(b) Table I shows amounts of various inorganic substances that have been found to be present without causing interference in tests for nitrate ion.

TABLE I.—CONCENTRATIONS OF ADDED SUBSTANCES THAT DO NOT CAUSE INTERFERENCE.

ON (FORM ADDED)[a]	CONCENTRATION, PPM
Fe^{++}	250
Fe^{+++}	250
OH^- (NaOH)	85
NH_4^+	65
Ca^{++}	100
Mg^{++}	60
Cl^- (NaCl)	1000
SO_3^{--} (Na_2SO_3)	50
PO_4^{---}	200
PO_3^- ($NaPO_3$ glass)	40
SiO_2	200

[a] The figures listed do not represent the maximum amounts of impurities that can be present before interference with the nitrate determination is experienced. They merely represent amounts of each impurity that have been found to have no effect on the nitrate determination.

(c) Organic matter in the form of tannin extract interferes to a varying extent with the nitrate determination, depending on the type of photometer used and the means provided for adjusting the zero reference point.

NOTE 2.—Satisfactory results have been obtained in the presence of 100 ppm. of organic matter as quebracho tannin.

[1] Under the standardization procedure of the Society, this method is under the jurisdiction of the ASTM Committee D-19 on Industrial Water. A list of members may be found in the ASTM Year Book.

347

Application

4. This method may be used for the analysis of industrial waters that are essentially colorless.

Apparatus

5. The apparatus shall consist of the following:

(a) *Photometer.*—Any commercial photoelectric filter photometer or spectrophotometer suitable for measurements at 470 mμ.

(b) *Beakers.*—Two 50-ml. beakers.

(c) *Pipets.*—5-ml. and 10-ml. pipets.

(d) *Burets.*—10-ml. and 50-ml. burets, both graduated in 0.1-ml. divisions.

Purity of Reagents

6. (a) *Reagents.*—Reagent grade chemicals shall be used in all tests. Unless otherwise indicated, it is intended that all reagents shall conform to the specifications of the Committee on Analytical Reagents of the American Chemical Society, where such specifications are available.[2] Other grades may be used, provided it is first ascertained that the reagent is of sufficiently high purity to permit its use without lessening the accuracy of the determination.

(b) *Water.*—Unless otherwise indicated, references to water shall be understood to mean water conforming to the requirements for reagent water in the Specifications for Reagent Water (ASTM Designation: D 1193).[3]

[2] "Reagent Chemicals, American Chemical Society Specifications," Am. Chem. Soc., Washington, D. C. For suggestions on the testing of reagents not listed by the American Chemical Society, see "Reagent Chemicals and Standards," by Joseph Rosin, D. Van Nostrand Co., Inc., New York, N. Y., and the "United States Pharmacopeia."

[3] Appears in this publication.

[4] Prepared brucine alkaloid solution available from the W. A. Taylor Co., Baltimore, Md., has been found satisfactory for this purpose. Brucine sulfate, available from the Fisher Scientific Co., Pittsburgh, Pa., has been found satisfactory for use in preparation of the brucine solution.

Reagents

7. (a) *Brucine Alkaloid Solution.*[4]—Dissolve 5 g. of pure brucine alkaloid crystals (**Caution,** see Note 3) in approximately 20 ml. of chloroform and dilute to 100 ml. with chloroform.

Note 3: **Caution**—Brucine is a very poisonous alkaloid and care should be taken in handling it.

(b) *Potassium Nitrate, Standard Solution.*—Dry KNO_3 in an oven at 105 ± 1 C. (220 ± 2 F.) for 24 hr. Weigh out 1.631 g., dissolve in approximately 20 ml. of reagent water, and dilute to 1 liter with reagent water in a volumetric flask. One milliliter of this solution is equivalent to 1 mg. of nitrate ion.

(c) *Sulfuric Acid (sp. gr. 1.84).*

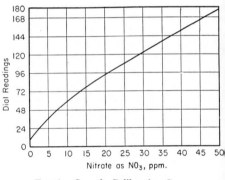

FIG. 1.—Sample Calibration Curve.

Sampling

8. Samples shall be collected in accordance with the applicable method of the American Society for Testing and Materials, as follows:

	A.S.T.M. Designations[a]
Plant or confined waters	D 510
Boiler water	D 860
Steam	D 1066

[a] These designations refer to the following methods: Methods of Sampling Industrial Water (ASTM Designation: D 510).[3]
Method of Sampling Water from Boilers (ASTM Designation: D 860).[3]
Method of Sampling Steam (ASTM Designation: D 1066).[3]

Preparation of Calibration Curve

9. Following the procedure given in

Section 10 and using varied amounts of the KNO₃ solution prepared in accordance with Section 7(a), prepare a calibration curve showing nitrate ion content in parts per million and the corresponding photometer readings. It is suggested that samples be prepared by diluting 0, 5, 10, 15, 20, 30, 40, and 50 ml. portions of KNO₃ solution to 1 liter with reagent water in volumetric flasks. These solutions will have nitrate ion concentrations of 0, 5, 10, 15, 20, 30, 40, and 50 ppm., respectively. A sample calibration curve is shown in Fig. 1.

NOTE 4.—The calibration curve must be prepared independently for each photometer and checked from time to time. Curves prepared with one photometer may not be used with a different instrument.

Procedure

10. (a) Pipet 5.0-ml. portions of the sample free of suspended matter into each of two clean, dry 50-ml. beakers. To one beaker first add from a buret 0.2 ml. of brucine alkaloid solution and then to each beaker add 10 ml. of H₂SO₄ (sp. gr. 1.84) from a second buret. Add the H₂SO₄ slowly to avoid spattering and mix thoroughly.

(b) To the sample not treated with brucine, add with a pipet 10 ml. of reagent water. Swirl to mix, cool to room temperature, and transfer a portion of the sample to the photometer cell. Place the cell in the instrument and set the photometer to the zero reference point, using the 470 mμ filter.

(c) When the brucine-treated sample has stood for at least 3 min., but not over 10 min., add 10 ml. of reagent water, mix, and cool to room temperature. Transfer to the photometer cell as above and determine the photometer reading. Read the nitrate ion content equivalent to the photometer reading from the calibration curve.

Accuracy

11. In the range of nitrate concentrations from 0 to 50 ppm. as NO₃, and in the absence of interfering substances, an accuracy of 0.5 ppm. can be obtained.

NOTE 5.—This method gives greatest accuracy on samples having up to about 20 ppm. of nitrate as NO₃. Above about 50 ppm., the change in transmittance with concentration decreases so that reasonable accuracy is not obtainable. Samples having a nitrate content above 50 ppm., and preferably those above 20 ppm., should be diluted with reagent water. The result obtained should be multiplied by the proper factor to obtain the nitrate content of the original sample.

Standard Methods of Test for

SULFATE-REDUCING BACTERIA IN INDUSTRIAL WATER AND WATER-FORMED DEPOSITS[1]

ASTM Designation: D 993 – 58 (1965)

ADOPTED, 1951; REVISED, 1958; REAPPROVED, 1965

This Standard of the American Society for Testing and Materials is issued under the fixed designation D 993; the number immediately following the designation indicates the year of original adoption or, in the case of revision, the year of last revision. A number in parentheses indicates the year of last reapproval.

Scope

1. (*a*) These methods are intended for the detection of the presence of sulfate-reducing bacteria when present in deposits or industrial water samples and for estimation of the number of bacteria present. Two methods are given, as follows:

	Sections
Referee Method	5 to 10
Non-Referee Method	11 to 16

(*b*) The referee method covers the preferred procedure for the detection and estimation of sulfate-reducing bacteria in industrial water samples. The non-referee method covers a procedure of greater simplicity and lesser precision than the referee method.

Definitions

2. For definitions of terms used in this method, refer to the Definitions of Terms Relating to Industrial Water and Industrial Waste Water (ASTM Designation: D 1129).[2]

Purity of Reagents

3. (*a*) Reagent grade chemicals shall be used in all tests. Unless otherwise indicated, it is intended that all reagents shall conform to the specifications of the Committee on Analytical Reagents of the American Chemical Society, where such specifications are available.[3] Other grades may be used, provided it is first ascertained that the reagent is of sufficiently high purity to permit its use without lessening the accuracy of the determination. The suitability of the chemicals shall be checked by incorporating them in a culture medium and test-

---

[1] Under the standardization procedure of the Society, these methods are under the jurisdiction of the ASTM Committee D-19 on Industrial Water A list of members may be found in the ASTM Year Book.

[2] Appears in this publication.

[3] "Reagent Chemicals, American Chemical Society Specifications," Am. Chem. Soc., Washington, D. C. For suggestions on the testing of reagents not listed by the American Chemical Society, see "Reagent Chemicals and Standards," by Joseph Rosin, D. Van Nostrand Co., Inc., New York, N. Y., and the "United States Pharmacopeia."

ing for typical growth of a known culture of sulfate-reducing bacteria.

(b) Unless otherwise indicated, references to water shall be understood to mean reagent water conforming to the Specifications for Reagent Water (ASTM Designation: D 1193).[2]

Sampling

4. (a) Secure water samples in bottles, preferably sterile, which shall be completely filled to exclude oxygen. Collect the samples in accordance with the Tentative Methods of Sampling Industrial Water (ASTM Designation: D 510).[2]

(b) Collect samples of corrosion products in a bottle, preferably sterile, and completely fill the bottle with mother liquor. If mother liquor is not available, tap water may be substituted. For general information on sampling of corrosion products, refer to the Standard Method of Field Sampling of Water-Formed Deposits (ASTM Designation: D 887).[2]

REFEREE METHOD

Application

5. This method is intended for the detection and estimation of sulfate-reducing bacteria that can grow anaerobically on a limited source of organic nutrient.

Principle of Method

6. The test for sulfate-reducing bacteria by this method is based upon the iodimetric determination of the hydrogen sulfide produced by sulfate-reducing bacteria in a suitable culture medium.

Apparatus

7. The apparatus shall consist of the following:

(a) Bottles with Screw Caps, 8-oz, square-section, for water blanks.

(b) Bottles with Solid Glass Stoppers.—30- or 60-ml bottles, of chemically resistant borosilicate glass, with standard-taper stoppers.

(c) Cotton, nonabsorbent.

(d) Cover Glasses, round or square type.

(e) Flask, 1.5- or 2-liter, chemically resistant borosilicate glass.

(f) Microscope.—A microscope that will provide a magnification of 500X to 1500X and is complete with a suitable light source. Par-focal lenses, a mechanical stage, and a dark-field condenser simplify examination.

(g) Pipets.—A 10-ml Mohr-type pipet with an opening of 3 to 4 mm, and a 1-ml Mohr or serological type pipet graduated in 0.1-ml divisions.

(h) Slides, standard or hanging-drop type.

(i) Spatula, small and narrow, for handling thick samples.

Reagents

8. (a) Dipotassium Acid Phosphate.—K_2HPO_4.

(b) Ammonium Chloride.—NH_4Cl.

(c) Asparagin.

(d) Magnesium Sulfate.— $MgSO_4 \cdot 7H_2O$.

(e) Sodium Lactate Solution, U.S.P. (62 to 65 per cent).

(f) Ferrous Ammonium Sulfate.—$Fe(NH_4)_2(SO_4)_2 \cdot 6H_2O$.

(g) Calcium Chloride.—$CaCl_2 \cdot 2H_2O$.

(h) Iodine, Standard Solution (0.01 N).—Dissolve 0.6346 g of resublimed iodine in a solution of 7.5 g of potassium iodide (KI) and 6 ml of water and dilute to 500 ml in a volumetric flask. Store in dark, glass-stoppered bottle. Standardize against 0.01 N $Na_2S_2O_3$ solution (Paragraph (j)).

(i) India Ink.

(j) Sodium Thiosulfate, Standard Solution (0.01 N).—Dissolve 2.484 g of sodium thiosulfate ($Na_2S_2O_3 \cdot 5H_2O$) in

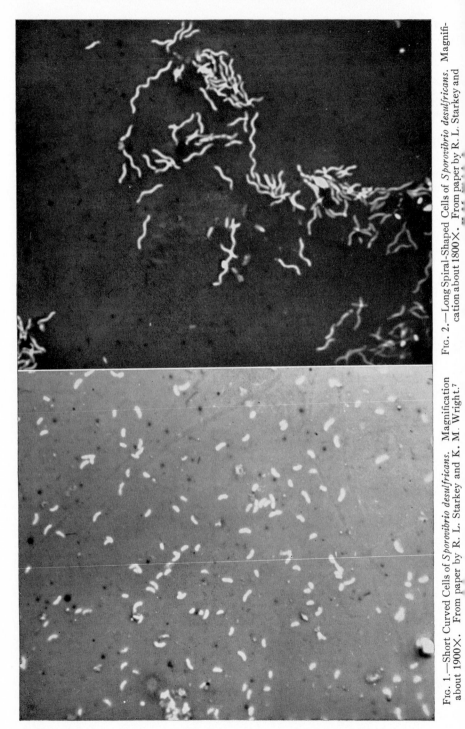

FIG. 2.—Long Spiral-Shaped Cells of *Sporovibrio desulfricans*. Magnification about 1800×. From paper by R. L. Starkey and

FIG. 1.—Short Curved Cells of *Sporovibrio desulfricans*. Magnification about 1900×. From paper by R. L. Starkey and K. M. Wright.[7]

water and dilute to 1 liter in a volumetric flask. Determine the exact normality by titration against a weighed amount of potassium dichromate ($K_2Cr_2O_7$) (Note 1).

NOTE 1.—If frequent restandardization of this solution is to be avoided, it must be stabilized with an inhibitor. One per cent of potassium furoate will limit the decrease in normality to less than 2 per cent in one year, over half of this decrease occurring in the first month. Four tenths per cent of borax has been used for the same purpose.

(k) *Starch Indicator.*—Make a paste of 1 g of arrowroot starch or soluble iodometric starch in cold water. Pour the paste into 100 ml of boiling water and boil for several minutes. Store in a glass-stoppered bottle in a cool place. Starch solution prepared in this manner will remain chemically stable for two or three days.

Procedure

9. (a) *Preparation of Culture Medium.* —A modification of Beckwith's formula[4] is satisfactory to determine the reduction of inorganic sulfates. Prepare this culture medium as follows:

K_2HPO_4	0.5 g
NH_4Cl or asparagin	1.0 g
$MgSO_4 \cdot 7H_2O$	2.5 g
Sodium lactate solution	6.0 g
$Fe(NH_4)_2(SO_4)_2 \cdot 6H_2O$	0.1 g
$CaCl_2 \cdot 2H_2O$	0.1 g
Tap water	to make a total volume of 1000 ml

Prepare the medium in a cotton-stoppered flask. Insert a small piece of paper between the ground-glass surfaces of each glass-stoppered bottle so that the stopper will not stick. Cover the top of each bottle with foil or paper hoods to prevent any possible contamination. Sterilize the medium and bottles in an autoclave at 15 psi and 121 C for 15 min.

(b) *Inoculation.*—Quickly cool the me-dium in the flask and fill the sterilized bottles about one-half full. Add the sample in various amounts by means of a pipet, observing aseptic technique. A commonly used range of dilutions is from 10 to 0.1 ml per bottle, and duplicate bottles of each dilution are desirable. In the case of a thick deposit, transfer an estimated amount to the bottle by means of a spatula that has been sterilized in a flame. If a sample is suspected of containing a large number of organisms, prepare suitable dilutions in sterile reagent water by placing 1.0 or 0.1 ml of the original sample in a 99-ml blank, shaking, and transferring aliquots to the bottles. After the portions of sample have been added, completely fill the bottles with culture medium and firmly insert the stoppers. Include one uninoculated bottle as a sterility control for the medium.

(c) *Incubation.*—Incubate all bottles at 30 C, except that if the sample was collected at an elevated temperature, a temperature of 55 C may be used.

(d) *Observation of Growth.*—Growth may occur in 2 or 3 days, but incubation should be continued for a month in the case of negative bottles. Positive bottles will have a black to gray flocculent precipitate and the sides of the bottle may have a dark film. When the material that is added is quite dark, the film on the sides may be the only macroscopic sign of growth. In the case of slight or no apparent growth, chemical analysis should be used. If desired, a microscopic examination may be made for the presence of *Sporovibrio desulfuricans* as described by Starkey.[5] These bacteria vary from short, curved rods to long spirals and may be observed by means of a wet mount with dark-field lighting or an India ink smear with bright-field lighting (Figs. 1 and 2).

---

[4] T. H. Beckwith, "The Bacterial Corrosion of Iron and Steel," *Journal*, Am. Water Works Assn., Vol. 33, pp. 147–167 (1941).

[5] R. L. Starkey and K. M. Wright, "Anaerobic Corrosion of Iron in Soil," Am. Gas Assn., Technical Department Distributing Committee (1945).

(e) *Determination of Hydrogen Sulfide.* —To a flask or bottle, add a greater amount of 0.01 N iodine solution than is needed to combine with the H_2S contained in the incubated sample being tested; about 25 ml usually is sufficient. To this iodine solution, add 5 ml of acetic acid (1:9) and 5.0 ml of the incubated sample. Shake, and back-titrate the excess iodine with 0.01 N $Na_2S_2O_3$ solution, using starch as an indicator. Titrate the uninoculated bottle as well as the culture bottles.

Calculation and Report

10. (a) Calculate the amount of H_2S formed in each culture bottle tested, as follows:

Hydrogen sulfide, ppm $= (AB - CD) \times 341$

where:

A = milliliters of iodine solution added,
B = normality of the iodine solution,
C = milliliters of $Na_2S_2O_3$ solution required for back-titration, and
D = normality of the $Na_2S_2O_3$ solution.

(b) Report sulfate-reducing bacteria as absent if less than 50 ppm of H_2S, or the same amount as in the control bottle, is found. Report sulfate-reducing bacteria as present if more than 50 ppm of H_2S, or more than the amount in the control bottle, is found.

NOTE 2.—Heavy growth may give as high as 350 ppm of H_2S.

NON-REFEREE METHOD

Application

11. This method is intended for the determination of sulfate-reducing bacteria when the highest precision is not required and when only test tubes are available for cultivation.

Principle of Method

12. The test for sulfate-reducing bacteria by this method is based upon the qualitative determination by lead acetate paper of the hydrogen sulfide produced by sulfate-reducing bacteria in a suitable culture medium.

Apparatus

13. The apparatus shall consist of the following:

(a) *Sealing Material.* —Paraffin or "vaspar" (50 per cent petroleum jelly and 50 per cent paraffin).

(b) *Test Tubes.* —Bacteriological tubes, $\frac{3}{4}$ by 6-in. (18 by 150-mm), of chemically resistant borosilicate glass, are satisfactory, although other types and sizes may be used.

(c) *Miscellaneous.* —Bottles, cotton, pipets, and spatula, as described in Section 7 (a), (c), (g), and (i).

Reagents

14. (a) *Agar, Bacteriological or U.S.P.*
(b) *Hydrochloric Acid (sp gr 1.19).*
(c) *Lead Acetate Paper.*
(d) For descriptions of other reagents that are required, see Section 8 (a) to (g).

Procedure

15. (a) *Preparation of Culture Medium.* —Prepare the culture medium as described in Section 9(a). Dispense in test tubes to a depth of about 3 in. or a volume of 15 ml. Plug the tubes with cotton, and sterilize the tubes and sealing material at 15 psi and 121 C for 15 min in the autoclave. The medium will have a flocculent precipitate. When separate colonies are desired, a solid medium may be prepared by adding 2 per cent by weight of agar to the solution.

(b) *Inoculation.* —Cool the test tubes to about 50 C if agar is included in the formula; if no agar is present, cool the tubes quickly. Discard the cotton plugs. Pipet various amounts of the liquid sample (Note 3) into a series of test tubes, observing aseptic technique. (See Section 9(b) for further dilution details.)

Include one tube that has not been inoculated as a sterility control for the medium. Seal the tubes immediately with sterile paraffin or "vaspar" and allow the seals to harden.

NOTE 3.—If the sample contains a considerable amount of H_2S, sufficient may be transferred with the sample to give a false positive test. The use of small amounts of sample reduces this possibility.

(c) *Incubation.*—Incubate all tubes at 30 C.

(d) *Observation.*—Observe growth as described in Section 9(d). Test doubtful tubes by removing the seal and seeking the odor of H_2S. A trace may be detected by removing the seal, adding a few drops of HCl (sp gr 1.19), heating with lead acetate paper over the mouth of the tube, and noting any dark or dis-

colored area on the paper as an indication of H_2S (Note 4).

NOTE 4.—A negative tube indicates that no growth occurred under these conditions. In the majority of cases such a tube indicates the absence of bacteria, but it is possible that a few organisms were present that could not grow under the conditions of cultivation.

Report

16. (a) Report sulfate-reducing bacteria as absent if no H_2S can be identified, and report the bacteria as present if H_2S is identified.

(b) The results may be qualified by stating the greatest dilution in which growth takes place, thus giving an approximation of the bacteria present. The number of bacteria may be reported if the medium is solidified with agar and the colonies can be counted.

Tentative Method of

SAMPLING STEAM[1]

ASTM Designation: D 1066 – 65 T

ISSUED, 1949; LAST REVISED, 1965

This Tentative Method has been approved by the sponsoring committee and accepted by the Society in accordance with established procedures, for use pending adoption as standard. Suggestions for revisions should be addressed to the Society at 1916 Race St., Philadelphia, Pa. 19103.

1. Scope

1.1 This method covers the sampling of saturated and superheated steam. It is applicable to steam flowing through boiler drum leads or in a pipeline at pressures sufficiently above atmospheric to establish the required rate of sample flow; it also is applicable to steam at lower and subatmospheric pressures for which means must be provided to establish the required rate of flow and to deliver the sample to a container at atmospheric pressure.

2. Description of Terms and Definitions

2.1 *Sampling*—The term sampling in this method shall mean the withdrawal of a representative portion of the steam flowing in the boiler drum lead or pipeline by means of a single-port or multiport-type sampling nozzle, and the de-livery of this portion of steam in vapor form to an apparatus for analysis, or condensed to a container in which the liquefied sample may be preserved for subsequent analysis.

2.2 For definitions of terms used in these methods, refer to ASTM Definitions D 1129, Terms Relating to Industrial Water and Industrial Waste Water.[2]

3. General Principles

3.1 *Types of Impurities*—The impurities in steam may be solid, liquid, or gaseous. Solid impurities consist of alkalies and sodium salts of chloride, sulfate, phosphate, sulfite, and silicate present in the boiler water. Superheated steam may also contain iron and copper oxides and free silica. Gaseous impurities, including ammonia, carbon dioxide, nitrogen, hydrogen, oxygen, and volatile amines, may be introduced into the boiler with the feed water or may be generated within the boiler; sulfur dioxide, hydrogen sulfide, and hydrazine have also been reported. Gaseous impurities may also include the

[1] Under the standardization procedure of the Society, this method is under the jurisdiction of the ASTM Committee D-19 on Industrial Water. A list of members may be found in the ASTM Year Book.

[2] Appears in this publication.

356

vapor phase of certain solid boiler water constituents, particularly silica; these are molecularly dispersed in high-density steam.

3.2 *Sampling Nozzle Location*—Solid and liquid impurities consist of dusts and mists that are mechanically entrained in the steam. Since they are of higher density than the steam and may not be uniformly dispersed, special consideration is required and an attempt should be made to sample before impurities can segregate. In drum or header-type boilers this generally can be done by inserting a single-

purities. This is especially important if flow through the nozzle is vertically upward.

3.4 *Superheated Steam*—Since the impurities in high-pressure superheated steam occur as vapor or as extremely fine dust, withdrawing a representative sample may be much less a problem than prevention of the depositing of steam-borne impurities on the surface of the sampling line downstream from the sampling nozzle. Such deposition can be avoided by injecting into the sampling nozzle sufficient water to remove all

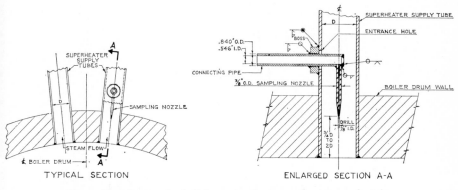

NOTE—Sampling nozzle shall be centered on superheater supply tube.
FIG. 1—Steam Sampling Nozzle, Single-Port Type.

port sampling nozzle in the steam offtake connections. In cases where steam is sampled from a pipeline, a multiport-type sampling nozzle extending across the pipe diameter must ordinarily be used to approach representative sampling.

3.3 *Rate of Sampling*—One important requirement in the sampling of fluid streams carrying particles in suspension is isokinetic sampling, wherein the velocity entering the port or ports of the sampling nozzles shall be the same as the velocity in the stream being sampled. A second requirement is velocity of sample flow within the sampling nozzle. Beyond the inlet port, the velocity should be kept high to minimize the loss of im-

superheat from the steam sample and to provide a small amount of moisture. The injected water is preferably a portion of the condensed and cooled steam sample.

4. Apparatus[3]

4.1 The necessary apparatus for the sampling of steam consists of the sampling nozzle, tubing, necessary valves and fittings and, when required, a sample condenser and cooler, as prescribed in 5. Saturated Steam Sampling Nozzles, to 7. Valves, Pipe, and Fittings.

---

[3] See ASTM Specifications D 1192, for Equipment for Sampling Industrial Water and Steam, which appear in this publication.

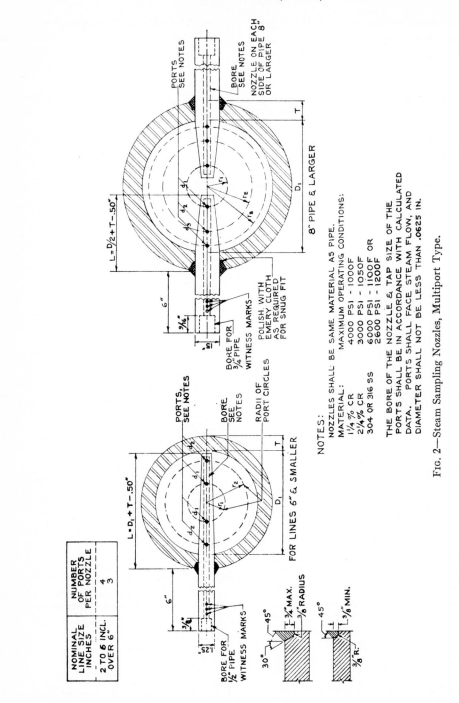

FIG. 2—Steam Sampling Nozzles, Multiport Type.

5. Saturated Steam Sampling Nozzles

5.1 The recommended form of single port nozzle for sampling saturated steam in tubes at an offtake connection close to the boiler drum or a header is shown in Fig. 1. This nozzle consists of a piece of pipe inserted through the tube wall with the port centered and opposing the di-

Nominal pipe size	_____	in.
D_0 = Pipe OD	_____	in.
D_1 = Pipe ID	_____	in.
T = Pipe wall thickness	_____	in.
N = Total number of ports	_____	
Radii of port circles:		
$r_1 = \sqrt{0.5A/\pi N}$	_____	in.
$r_2 = \sqrt{3A/\pi N}$	_____	in.
$r_3 = \sqrt{5A/\pi N}$	_____	in.
$r_4 = \sqrt{7A/\pi N}$	_____	in.
F = Flow rate of fluid through pipe	_____	lb/hr
f = Flow rate of total sample extracted	_____	lb/hr
A = Traverse area of pipe $= 0.7854 D_1{}^2$	_____	in.²
a = Total port area $= Af/F$	_____	in.²
d = Diameter of ports $= \sqrt{a/0.7854N}$	Use_____drill	in.*
b = Diameter of nozzle bore $= \sqrt{3a/1.5708}$	Use_____drill	in.

* Port diameter shall be not less than 0.0625 in. To increase the port diameter, increase the flow rate of sample extracted.

FIG. 3—Calculations for Steam Sampling Nozzles for Lines 6 in. and Larger, Equal Size Ports, Unequally Spaced.

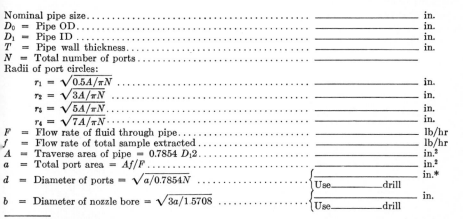

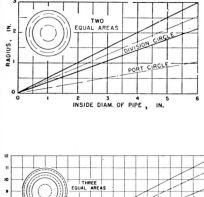

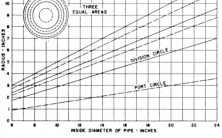

FIG. 4—Radii of Circles for Dividing a Circular Pipe into Annuli of Equal Areas.

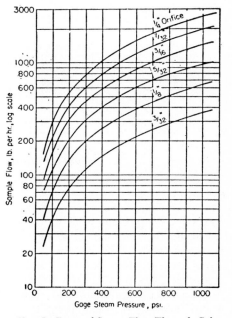

FIG. 5—Rates of Steam Flow Through Calorimeter Orifices at Different Pressures.

rection of flow. A typical nozzle designed for installation in a 3-in. tube (2.6-in. ID) with tube area of 5.31 in.² carrying 20,000 lb/hr of steam at 1500 psi, would have a sampling port area of 0.0123 in.² (one port 0.125 in. in diameter). The sampling rate should be 46 lb/hr.

5.2 The recommended form of multiport-type nozzle for sampling saturated

section (Note 2). The number of sampling ports shall be selected according to the internal diameter of the pipe or tube as follows:

Actual Inside Diameter, in.	Number of Ports Per Nozzle
2 to 6	4
Over 6	3 (in each section)

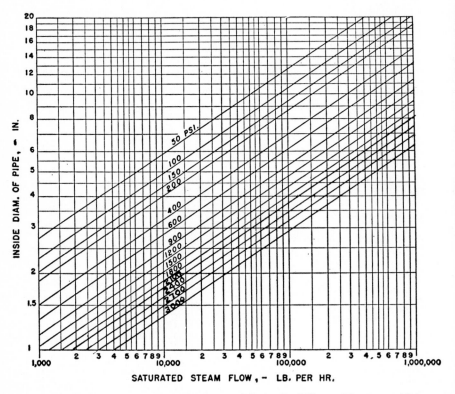

FIG. 6—Approximate Rates of Flow for Saturated Steam for Different Pipe Internal Diameters at Different Pressures.

steam in large pipelines is shown in Fig. 2. This nozzle, of special design and proportioned for a specific condition, is inserted through the pipe wall (Note 1) extending across the pipe on a diameter. The nozzle shall be provided with cleanly drilled holes or sampling ports facing upstream in the pipe and so spaced that each port represents an equal area of pipe

NOTE 1—In steam lines over 6 in. in diameter, and particularly in the case of steam at high pressure and high velocity, it is essential that the nozzle be designed for sufficient strength to eliminate the possibility of failure through vibration or wear.

NOTE 2—As a guide in the determination of the proportions of the multiport sampling nozzle, reference may be made to Figs. 2 through 4. In the pipelines 8 in. and larger, two nozzles may be used as equivalent to a full length nozzle. The portion of the nozzle exposed within the pipe is tapered so that it may be inserted easily through the hole in the pipe and to reduce abrasive wear. The tapered design also makes for greater stiffness.

sampling ports may be correctly installed facing upstream.

5.3 Each port of a multiport sampling nozzle shall withdraw a portion of the

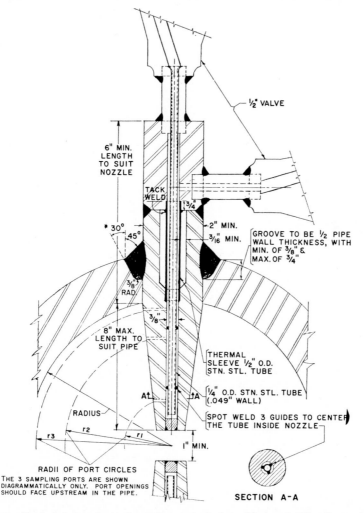

NOTE—Typical design shown for 12-in. nominal pipe with two half-length nozzles.

FIG. 7—Modified Design of Multiport Nozzle for Sampling Superheated Steam.

The sample ports shall be drilled cleanly, using a drill of the proper size. The entrance end shall not be chamfered. The bore of the sampler should be reamed after the ports are drilled to ensure that any burrs are removed.

A witness mark should be placed on the external extension of the sampling nozzle so that

main stream equivalent to the area of the portion of the pipe in which it is located. This requires, for ports of equal size, that the spacing shall be such that the ports withdraw equal portions of the sample from equal areas of pipe section. Ideally,

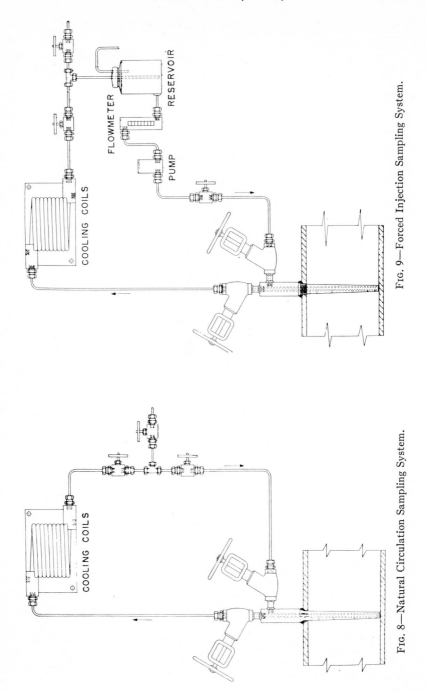

FIG. 9—Forced Injection Sampling System.

FIG. 8—Natural Circulation Sampling System.

equal pressure drop should occur across each sampling port. To promote this condition, the total area of sampling ports should be less than two thirds of the inside cross sectional area of the nozzle.

5.4 The ratio of total port area to the pipe area should be equal to the ratio of the rate of sample flow to the rate of steam flow (Notes 2 and 3). Under this condition, the velocity of steam entering the sampling ports will be that of the steam flowing in the pipe and will represent isokinetic flow (Notes 3 and 4).

Note 3—When the sample is analyzed for moisture content by throttling or separating calorimeters, the rate of sample flow in the pipe from which the sample is taken is fixed by the characteristics of the calorimeter. The sampling nozzle can be designed for only one rate of flow. See Fig. 5 for the sampling rate for the particular calorimeter orifice at the given steam pressure and Fig. 6 for the steam flow rate in the pipe.

Note 4—When the sample is condensed or cooled for analysis, the sampling nozzle may be designed for maximum rate of steam flow and the rate of sample flow may be adjusted for lower rates of steam flow. For the given pipe diameter, determine steam flow at the operating pressure using Fig. 6. Assume a convenient maximum sample rate consistent with the steam flow and with the equipment provided for condensation and cooling.

5.5 The sampling rate is determined as follows:

$$f = (a/A)F$$

where:

f and F = sample flow rate and steam flow rate, respectively, and

a/A = ratio of total port area to pipe area.

5.6 The material selected for the sampling nozzle and the weld material used to install the nozzle shall be compatible with the steam piping material. The design of the welded joint and the welding and inspection procedures used shall comply with all applicable codes to ensure an adequate, reliable joint. The material for all the sampling nozzles shall also be selected so that the steam sample is not contaminated by the material.

6. Superheated Steam Sampling Nozzles

6.1 For superheated steam sampling, a modified multiport-type nozzle is recommended similar to that used for saturated steam in large pipelines except that a small tube shall be inserted into the sampling nozzle to be used as described in 6.5 for injecting water to remove superheat and provide a small amount of moisture. The end of the tube shall extend beyond the last port of the nozzle and separate external connections shall be provided for the internal tube and for the annulus surrounding it. An example of this arrangement is shown in Fig. 7.

6.2 When the modified nozzle is installed vertically through the top of a horizontal steam line or horizontally in a vertical steam line with downward flow (Note 5), water is injected through the annulus and the sample is withdrawn through the internal tube. When installed vertically through the bottom of a horizontal steam line, water is injected through the internal tube and the sample is withdrawn through the annulus.

Note 5—The modified nozzle should not be used in a vertical steam line with upward flow, because the injected water may drain from the nozzle through the sampling ports.

6.3 If the temperature of the superheated steam exceeds the saturation temperature by 50 F or more, the sampling nozzle shall be attached to the steam line by a thermal sleeve or by a similar means designed to prevent large temperature gradients and resultant excessive thermal stresses in the sampling nozzle or steam line.

6.4 The sampling system shall be either a natural or forced circulation system as shown in Figs. 8 and 9. The natural circulation system requires a standing leg of water at the injection point so that the cooling coil must be located at a reasonable height above the sampling nozzle to develop a sufficient water leg below to promote circulation. The forced circulation system is positive and more readily controlled and is, therefore, preferable to the natural circulation system.

6.5 To assure satisfactory operation of either a natural or forced circulation system, sufficient water must be injected into the sampling nozzle to remove all superheat from the steam. A flowmeter shall be provided to measure the rate of water injection. An indicating thermometer may be used to measure the temperature of the effluent from the sampling nozzle to determine that no superheat remains.

6.6 All piping and fittings shall be fabricated of a material sufficiently corrosion-resistant to avoid contamination of the sample.

7. Valves, Pipe and Fittings

7.1 The shortest possible connection (Note 6) shall be used between the sampling nozzle and the calorimeter or cooling coil.

NOTE 6—In the sampling of saturated steam, it should be kept in mind that the steam and condensate will dissolve to some degree any substance contacted. For this reason, the area of surfaces exposed to the sample[3] and the time that the sample is in contact with these surfaces should be kept at a minimum.

7.2 For use with a calorimeter,[4] the valves, connecting piping, and fittings shall be of carbon steel of suitable schedule as specified in the American Standard Code for Pressure Piping.[5]

7.3 When the sample is to be condensed or cooled, all connecting piping and fittings between the sampling nozzle and condenser shall be of stainless steel

at least as resistant to reaction with steam as 18 per cent chromium, 8 per cent nickel steel.[6]

8. Condensing and Cooling Coil

8.1 When the sample is to be condensed and cooled, a tubular heat exchanger of one of several available types may be used. The common requirements of such condensers are as follows:

8.1.1 The tube through which the sample flows shall be made of stainless steel at least as resistant to reaction with the steam as 18 per cent chromium, 8 per cent nickel steel.[6]

8.1.2 The tube shall be continuous and shall extend through the cooling jacket so that there will be no danger of contamination of the sample by the cooling water.

8.1.3 The tube shall be of sufficient strength to withstand the full pressure of the steam being sampled.

8.1.4 The tube diameter shall be small enough so that storage within the coil is low and the time lag of sample through the condenser will be at a minimum.

9. Point of Sampling

9.1 When sampling saturated steam from a boiler drum or header arranged with multiple tubular connections to a superheater header, samples shall be taken from selected tubes at regularly spaced points. A single-port sampling nozzle installed in individual tubes (Fig. 1) is preferable to the multiport nozzle.

9.2 The inlet to the sampling nozzle should be located in the area between $\frac{3}{4}$ D and 2D positions (Fig. 1). In this region, pressure, mass flow, and moisture level have little effect on performance. Sample rate versus efficiency characteristics are fairly uniform. Beyond this point the

---

[4] Refer to ASME Power Test Code, "Part 11 —Determination of Quality of Steam" (1959).
[5] USA Standard Code for Pressure Piping (USASI No. B31.1–1955).

[6] A suitable steel for this purpose is Type 316, of ASTM Specifications A 312, for Seamless and Welded Austenitic Stainless Steel Pipe, *1967 Book of ASTM Standards*, Part 1. Alternative materials are Type 304 or 347 stainless steel.

sample will be affected to some degree by the steam flow rate.

9.3 In a pipeline, the multiport-type sampling nozzle is preferable to a single port nozzle. Locations upstream from the first pipe bend, in the order of their preference, are as follows:

9.3.1 Vertical pipe, downward flow,

pheric pressure to provide an adequate sample flow rate, the extraction of the sample presents no problem. At low and subatmospheric pressures, special means must be provided to establish sample flow and to deliver a flowing or batch sample to a container at atmospheric or subatmospheric pressure, respectively. Several

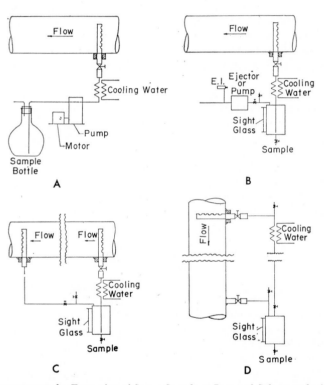

FIG. 10—Arrangements for Extraction of Steam Sample at Low and Subatmospheric Pressure.

9.3.2 Vertical pipe, upward flow,

9.3.3 Horizontal pipe, vertical insertion, and

9.3.4 Horizontal pipe, horizontal insertion.

9.3.5 The sampling nozzle shall not be located immediately after a pipe bend or a valve (unless the valve aperture is concentric with the pipe).

10. Extraction of Sample

10.1 When the steam to be sampled is at a pressure high enough above atmos-

methods of providing sample flow may be employed as follows:

10.1.1 A barometric leg may be used where sufficient height is available. From the bottom of such a leg the sample may flow to atmospheric pressure through a conductivity cell chamber or to a container. It is not advisable when sampling steam to elevate the line from the sampling nozzle to obtain height for a barometric leg because of condensation and reverse drip in the upwardly extended line.

10.1.2 A small condensate pump may be used to extract the sample from the condenser outlet and deliver a continuous flow to a container such as is shown in Fig. 10A. This pump should be of a design and material that will not result in contamination of the sample.

10.1.3 A vacuum pump of either a mechanical or fluid jet type may be used to establish the necessary differential to obtain batch samples. The pump suction may be connected to a sample receiver either of glass or other material, in which case it should be equipped with a sight glass (Fig. 10B). If local conditions permit, a connection to a plant condenser or other point of low pressure could be used in place of the pump or ejector.

10.1.4 If points of sufficient pressure difference can be located in accessible parts of the conduit through which the steam being sampled flows, the sampling system could be connected between these points. Any such differential could be increased by arranging the sampling nozzle with the sampling ports facing upstream (standard for steam sampling), so that it would serve as an impact nozzle. The downstream tap could be a reversed nozzle to increase further the differential. The downstream connection should be provided with a throttle valve to control the rate of flow through the sampling system. A sampling collecting chamber, appropriately valved, should be connected to the sampling line at the outlet end of the condenser cooler (Fig. 10C).

10.1.5 If a vertical section of a pipe or conduit is available, a batch sample may be collected as shown in Fig. 10D. This has an advantage over the arrangement shown in Fig. 10C in that a greater differential pressure will be provided by the water leg below the condenser.

10.2 In the methods described in 10.1, it is assumed that a bulk sample is required for laboratory analysis. The sample receiver should be of sufficient size for the required volume of sample. The rate of sample flow may be determined by rate of level rise in the container. With the methods described in 10.1.1 and 10.1.2, the sample is delivered into a container at atmospheric pressure. With the methods described in 10.1.3, 10.1.4, and 10.1.5, the sample receiver should be valved off from the collecting system, equalized to atmospheric pressure through a protective train, and drained into a suitable receiver. Initial fillings should be discarded until there is assurance that the collecting system is clean.

10.3 When conductometric methods of analysis only are required, a continuous flow through an electrode chamber may be provided, the drips being returned to the point of low pressure or discarded to waste by the pump or ejector. The rate of sample flow may be determined by the rate of flow of the cooling water and its temperature rise.

11. Procedure

11.1 When a new sample line is being put into service, flow steam and condensate through it for 24 hr before samples are collected.

11.2 Before a sampling period, blow steam through the sample line to remove any material that may have deposited in it. Adjust the flow rate to that desired during sampling and flow the sample at this rate for 1 hr or longer before electric conductivity measurements are recorded or before a sample is collected for other methods of analysis.

11.3 When samples of condensate are collected for evaporative analysis, the flasks or other types of containers should be meticulously cleaned before using. Borosilicate glass is a satisfactory material for such containers but they should be aged by allowing them to stand for several days full of distilled water. This aging of borosilicate glass may be hastened by a preliminary treatment with dilute caustic soda (10 g/liter). Containers fabricated from suitable metals or plastics may also be used.[7]

11.4 Samples should be analyzed as soon as possible after collection. After use, the flasks should be rinsed with hydrochloric acid (HCl, 1:1). These flasks should be reserved and used for no other purpose than steam samples.

11.5 When the condensed sample is to be analyzed by the electrical conductance method, cool it to 25 C.

11.6 When dissolved gases are to be determined, cool the sample to 20 C or lower.[8]

[7] See ASTM Method D 1069, Test for Suspended and Dissolved Matter (Suspended and Dissolved Solids) in Industrial Waste Water, which appears in this publication.

[8] See ASTM Methods D 888, Test for Dissolved Oxygen in Industrial Water, which appear in this publication.

Standard Methods of Test for
ACIDITY OR BASICITY OF INDUSTRIAL WASTE WATER[1]

ASTM Designation: D 1067 – 64
ADOPTED, 1964.[2]

This Standard of the American Society for Testing and Materials is issued under the fixed designation D 1067; the final number indicates the year of original adoption as standard or, in the case of revision, the year of last revision.

Scope

1. (*a*) These methods cover the determination of the acidity or basicity of industrial waste water. Three methods are included, as follows:

	Sections
Referee Method (Electrometric Titration)	5 to 13
Non-Referee Method A (Color Change Titration)	14 to 21
Non-Referee Method B (Color Change Titration - Interference Control)	22 to 29

(*b*) In all of the methods the hydrogen or hydroxyl ions present in water by virtue of the dissociation or hydrolysis of its solutes, or both, are neutralized by titration with standard alkali (acidity)

or acid (basicity). The referee method is used to develop an electrometric titration curve (sometimes referred to as a pH curve), which curve defines the acidity or basicity of the sample, and from which the acidity or basicity can be determined relative to a particular pH end point. The non-referee methods are used to determine acidity or basicity relative to a predesignated end point based on the change in color of an internal indicator or equivalent end point measured by a pH meter. They are suitable for routine control purposes.

(*c*) When titrating to selected datum points, the choice of end points will be determined primarily by the applicable process controls for the water. The choice must be such, however, that significant errors in titration due to inflection points on a typical titration curve are avoided. In some instances the titration end point may be at a pH beyond that at which the constituents of the water cease to react with the acid or alkali. Conversely, the desired end point may be such that only a part of the neutralizing capacity is measured.

[1] Under the standardization procedure of the Society, these methods are under the jurisdiction of the ASTM Committee D-19 on Industrial Water. A list of members may be found in the ASTM Year Book.

[2] Adopted as standard August 31, 1964, by action of the Society at the Annual Meeting and confirming letter ballot.
Prior to their present adoption as standard, these methods were published as tentative from 1949 to 1960, being revised in 1951, 1955, and 1957. They were discontinued in 1961, at which time the Methods of Test for Acidity and Alkalinity of Industrial Water were issued under designation D 1884. They were again published as tentative from 1962 to 1964.

368

Definitions

2. (*a*) The terms "acidity" and "basicity" in these methods are defined in accordance with the Definitions of Terms Relating to Industrial Water and Industrial Waste Water (ASTM Designation: D 1129)[3] as follows:

Acidity.—The quantitative capacity of aqueous media to react with hydroxyl ions.

Basicity.—The quantitative capacity of aqueous media to react with hydrogen ions.

(*b*) For definitions of other terms used in these methods, refer to Definitions D 1129.

Purity of Reagents

3. (*a*) Reagent grade chemicals shall be used in all tests. Unless otherwise indicated, it is intended that all reagents shall conform to the specifications of the Committee on Analytical Reagents of the American Chemical Society, where such specifications are available.[4] Other grades may be used, provided it is first ascertained that the reagent is of sufficiently high purity to permit its use without lessening the accuracy of the determination.

(*b*) Unless otherwise indicated, references to water shall be understood to mean reagent water conforming to the Specifications for Reagent Water (ASTM Designation: D 1193).[3] In addition, reagent water for this test shall be free of carbon dioxide (CO_2) and shall have a pH between 6.2 and 7.2 at 25 C.

---

[3] Appears in this publication.

[4] "Reagent Chemicals, American Chemical Society Specifications," Am. Chemical Soc., Washington, D. C. For suggestions on the testing of reagents not listed by the American Chemical Society, see "Reagent Chemicals and Standards," by Joseph Rosin, D. Van Nostrand Co., Inc., New York, N. Y. and the "United States Pharmacopeia."

Sampling

4. Collect the sample in accordance with the Methods of Sampling Industrial Water (ASTM Designation: D 510).[3]

REFEREE METHOD

(Electrometric Titration)

Application

5. This method is applicable to the determination of acidity or basicity of all industrial waste waters. It is used for the development of a titration curve that will define acidity or basicity of industrial waste water.

Summary of Method

6. A sample aliquot is titrated directly with standard acid or alkali. When developing a titration curve to define acidity or basicity, a pH reading is taken after each small addition of the standard solution.

Interferences

7. Although oily matter, soaps, suspended solids, and other waste materials may interfere with the pH measurement, these materials may not be removed to increase precision, because some are an important component of the acid or alkali-consuming property of the sample. Similarly, the development of a precipitate during titration may make the glass electrode sluggish and cause erratic results.

Apparatus

8. (*a*) *Electrometric pH Measurement Apparatus*, conforming to the requirements given in the Methods of Test for pH of Industrial Water and Industrial Waste Water (ASTM Designation: D 1293).[3]

(*b*) *Burets*, 50-ml, graduated in 0.1-ml divisions.

Reagents

9. (*a*) *Hydrochloric Acid, Standard (0.02 N) (Note 1).*—Add 1.70 ml of

concentrated hydrochloric acid (HCl, sp gr 1.19) to 100 ml of water, dilute to 1 liter, and mix well. Standardize electrometrically against sodium carbonate (Na_2CO_3) prepared by heating sodium bicarbonate ($NaHCO_3$) for 2 hr at 270 C. The inflection point corresponding to the complete titration of the carbonic acid salts will be very close to pH 3.9.

NOTE 1.—Sulfuric acid having a normality of 0.02 N may be used instead of hydrochloric acid. Prepare and standardize in like manner, using 0.56 ml of concentrated sulfuric acid (H_2SO_4, sp gr 1.84) for 1 liter of 0.02 N acid.

(b) *Sodium Hydroxide, Standard Solution (0.02 N).*—Dilute a calculated quantity of settled sodium hydroxide (NaOH) solution (1:1 by weight) to 1 liter with water and mix well. Store in a polyethylene or heavily waxed bottle. Protect the solution by providing a soda-asbestos or soda-lime bulb at the air inlet. Standardize electrometrically against National Bureau of Standards certified potassium acid phthalate ($KHC_8H_4O_4$). The inflection point corresponding to the complete titration of phthalic acid will be very close to pH 8.6.

Procedure

10. (a) Mount the glass and reference electrodes in two of the holes of a clean, three-hole rubber stopper chosen to fit a 300-ml, tall-form, Berzelius beaker without a spout. Place the electrodes in the beaker and standardize the pH meter. Rinse the electrodes first with water, then with a portion of the sample. Following the final rinse, drain the beaker completely.

(b) Pipet a 100-ml aliquot of the sample into the beaker through the third hole in the stopper. Hold the tip of the pipet near the bottom of the beaker while discharging the sample.

(c) Measure the pH of the sample in accordance with the Method of Test for pH of Industrial Water and Industrial Waste Water (ASTM Designation: D 1293).[3]

(d) Add the applicable 0.02 N standard solution in increments of 0.5 ml or less. After each addition mix the solution thoroughly. Determine the pH when the mixture has reached equilibrium as indicated by a constant pH reading (Note 2). Mechanical stirring, preferably of the magnetic type, is required for this operation. Mixing by means of a gas stream is not permitted. Continue the titration until the necessary data have been obtained. If the titration requires appreciably more than 25 ml of standard solution, use a 0.1 N solution prepared and standardized in the same manner.

NOTE 2.—The equilibrium time will vary with different waters as the reaction rate constants of different chemical equilibrium systems vary. When developing a titration curve it is particularly important that equilibrium conditions be obtained before adding each succeeding increment of titrant. In some instances the reaction time may be an interval of seconds while other slower, more complex reactions may require intervals of many minutes to come to complete equilibrium. For example, hydrolyzable salts such as iron and aluminum sulfates, or both, in the sample may cause severely delayed equilibrium.

(e) To develop a titration curve (Note 3), plot the cumulative milliliters of standard solution added to the sample aliquot against the observed pH values.

NOTE 3.—An electrometric titration curve is smooth, with the pH changing progressively in a single direction if equilibrium is achieved after each incremental addition of titrant, and may contain one or more inflection points. Ragged or irregular curves may indicate that equilibrium was not attained before adding succeeding increments of titrant.

Calculation

11. Calculate the acidity or basicity

of a particular pH point in equivalents per million, as follows:

Acidity (or basicity), epm $= AN \times 10$

where:

A = milliliters of standard acid or alkali required for the titration, and

N = normality of the standard solution.

Report

12. (a) Report the results of titrations to specific end points as follows: "The acidity (or basicity) to pH — is — epm."

acidity or basicity of industrial waters that contain no materials that buffer at the end point or other materials that interfere with the titration by reason of color, precipitation, etc.

Summary of Method

15. The sample is titrated with standard acid or alkali to a designated pH, the end point being determined by the color change of an internal indicator or equivalent end point measured by a pH meter (Note 4).

NOTE 4.— Table I giving equivalent pH end points may be used to select the proper pH point equivalent to a particular internal color

TABLE I.—pH END POINTS EQUIVALENT TO COLOR CHANGE INDICATOR.

Indicator	Range		End Point	
	pH	Color	pH	Color
Phenolphthalein..............	8.0 to 10	colorless-red	8.2	pink
Methyl orange...............	3.2 to 4.4	pink-yellow	3.2	pink-orange
Methyl purple[5]..............	4.8 to 5.4	purple-green	4.9	grey-purple
Methyl red.................	4.2 to 6.2	pink-yellow	5.5	orange
Bromcresol green............	4.0 to 5.4	yellow-blue	4.5	green
Bromphenol blue............	3.0 to 4.6	yellow-blue	3.7	green

(b) Appropriate factors for converting epm to other units are given in the Method of Reporting Results of Analysis of Industrial Water and Industrial Waste Water (ASTM Designation: D 596).[3]

Precision

13. The precision of this method has not been universally tested. The transient nature of the equilibria involved and the pronounced variation in the characteristics of different waters preclude tests for precision.

NON-REFEREE METHOD A

(Color-Change Titration)

Application

14. This method is useful for the rapid, routine control measurement of

change indicator. Electrometric pH measuring apparatus (See Section 8) may be used alternatively to indicate the pH end point in place of an internal color change indicator.

Interferences

16. Appreciable natural color or the formation of a precipitate during titration of the sample may mask the color change. Materials present in some industrial waste waters may interfere chemically with the titration by destroying the indicator. Variable results may be experienced with waters containing oxidizing or reducing substances, depending on the equilibrium conditions and the manner in which the sample is handled.

Reagents

17. (a) Bromcresol Green Indicator (1

g per liter).—Dissolve 0.1 g of bromcresol green in 2.9 ml of 0.02 *N* NaOH. Dilute to 100 ml with water.

(*b*) *Hydrochloric Acid, Standard Solution (0.02 N) (Note 1).*—See Section 9(*a*), except that the acid may be standardized by colorimetric titration using bromcresol green indicator.

(*c*) *Methyl Orange Indicator (0.5 g per liter).*—Dissolve 0.05 g of methyl orange in water and dilute to 100 ml.

(*d*) *Methyl Purple Indicator.*—Proprietary compound.[5]

(*e*) *Methyl Red Indicator (1 g per liter).*—Dissolve 0.1 g of water-soluble methyl red in water and dilute to 100 ml.

(*f*) *Phenolphthalein Indicator (5.0 g per liter).*—Dissolve 0.5 g of phenolphthalein in 50 ml of ethyl alcohol (95 per cent) (Note 5) and dilute to 100 ml with water.

NOTE 5.—Specially denatured ethyl alcohol conforming to Formula No. 3A or 30 of the U. S. Bureau of Internal Revenue may be substituted for 95 per cent ethyl alcohol.

(*g*) *Sodium Hydroxide, Standard Solution (0.02 N).*—See Section 9(*b*), except that the alkali may be standardized by colorimetric titration, using phenolphthalein indicator.

Procedure

18. (*a*) Pipet 100 ml of the sample into a 250-ml narrow-mouth Erlenmeyer flask. Place the pipet tip at the bottom of the flask while discharging the sample.

(*b*) Add 0.2 ml of the appropriate indicator (Note 6) and titrate with 0.02 *N* HCl (for basicity) or 0.02 *N* NaOH solution (for acidity) until a persistent color change is noted (Note 4). Add the standard solution in small increments, swirling the flask vigorously or using mechanical stirring after each

---

[5] Available as a prepared reagent from most chemical supply houses.

addition. As the end point is approached, a momentary change in color will be noted in that portion of the sample with which the reagent first mixes. From that point on, make the additions dropwise. If the titration requires appreciably more than 25 ml of HCl or NaOH, use an 0.1 *N* solution prepared and standardized in the same manner.

NOTE 6.—After some practice, slightly more or less indicator may be preferred. The analyst must use the same quantity of phenolphthalein at all times, however, since at a given pH the intensity of one-color indicators depends upon the quantity.

Calculation

19. Calculate the acidity or basicity in equivalents per million as follows:

$$\text{Acidity (or basicity), epm} = \frac{AN}{B} \times 1000$$

where:
A = milliliters of HCl or NaOH solution required for the titration,
N = normality of the HCl or NaOH solution, and
B = milliliters of sample used.

Report

20. Report the results of titrations as follows: "The acidity (or basicity) to — is — epm," indicating the name of the indicator used, for example, "The acidity to methyl orange is — epm."

Precision

21. See Section 13.

NON-REFEREE METHOD B

(Color Change Titration – Interference Control)

Application

22. This method covers the rapid, routine control measurement of acidity or basicity of industrial waste waters that contain oxidizing, reducing, or

hydrolyzable materials. It is particularly applicable to mine drainage, industrial waste waters carrying waste acids, and similar waters. Volatile compounds contributing to acidity or basicity may be evolved during the boiling procedure of this method.

Summary of Method

23. The sample is boiled to accelerate chemical reaction to equilibrium, cooled, and titrated with standard acid or alkali to a designated pH, the end point being determined by the color change of an internal indicator or equivalent pH end point measured by a pH meter.

Interferences

24. Appreciable natural color or the formation of a precipitate while titrating the sample may mask the color change. Materials present in some industrial waste waters may interfere chemically with the titration by destroying the indicator.

Reagents

25. (a) *Hydrochloric Acid Standard Solution (0.02 N) (See Note 1).*—See Section 9(a), except that the acid may be standardized by colorimetric titration, using bromcresol green indicator.

(b) *Sodium Hydroxide, Standard Solution (0.02 N).*—See Section 9(b).

Procedure

26. (a) Pipet 100 ml of the sample into a 250-ml narrow-mouth Erlenmeyer flask. Place the pipet tip at the bottom of the flask while discharging the sample.

(b) Heat the sample to boiling and continue boiling for 2 min. Cool to room temperature out of contact with the atmosphere.

(c) Add 0.2 ml of the appropriate indicator (Note 6) and titrate with 0.02 N NaOH solution until a permanent color change is noted (Note 4). Add the NaOH in small increments, swirling the flask vigorously after each addition. As the end point is approached, a momentary change in color will be noted in that portion of the sample with which the reagent first mixes. From that point on, make the additions dropwise. If the titration requires appreciably more than 25 ml of NaOH, use a 0.1 N solution prepared and standardized in the same manner.

(d) If the sample is alkaline to the indicator after boiling, add 0.1 N hydrochloric acid (HCl) (Note 1) in 10-ml increments to the sample and boil as described in Paragraph (b) until the sample is acid to the indicator. Then proceed as described in Paragraph (c).

Calculation

27. Calculate the acidity or basicity in equivalents per million as follows:

$$\text{Acidity (boiled), epm} = \frac{BN_b}{S} \times 1000$$

$$\text{Basicity (boiled), epm} = \frac{AN_a - BN_b}{S} \times 1000$$

where:

A = milliliters of HCl added to the sample,

B = milliliters of NaOH required for titration of the sample,

N_a = normality of the HCl,

N_b = normality of the NaOH, and

S = milliliters of sample used.

Report

28. Report the results of titrations as follows: "The acidity (or basicity) (boiled) to — is — epm, indicating the name of the indicator used, for example, "The acidity (boiled) to methyl orange is — epm."

Precision

29. See Section 13.

Tentative Methods of Test for
IRON IN INDUSTRIAL WATER AND INDUSTRIAL WASTE WATER[1]

ASTM Designation: D 1068 – 62 T

Issued, 1949; Last Revised, 1962

(Includes Former Method D 1497)

These Tentative Methods have been approved by the sponsoring committee and accepted by the Society in accordance with established procedures, for use pending adoption as standard. Suggestions for revisions should be addressed to the Society at 1916 Race St., Philadelphia 3, Pa.

Scope

1. These methods[2,3] cover the determination of iron in industrial water and in industrial waste water. Procedures are given for determining total iron, dissolved iron, and ferrous iron. Suspended iron may be calculated from the total iron and soluble iron determinations. Three methods are given as follows:

	Sections
Referee Method A	5 to 15
Referee Method B	16 to 25
Non-Referee Method C	26 to 35

---

[1] Under the standardization procedure of the Society, these methods are under the jurisdiction of the ASTM Committee D-19 on Industrial Water. A list of members may be found in the ASTM Year Book.

[2] For further information on these methods, the following references may be of interest:

W. B. Fortune and M. G. Mellon, "Determination of Iron with o-Phenanthroline, a Spectrophotometric Study," *Industrial and Engineering Chemistry*, Analytical Edition, Vol. 10, p. 60 (1938).

L. G. Saywell and B. B. Cunningham, "Determination of Iron, Colorimetric o-Phenanthroline Method," *Industrial and Engineering Chemistry*, Analytical Edition, Vol. 10, No. 2, p. 67 (1938).

Definitions

2. For definitions of terms used in these methods, refer to the Definitions of Terms Relating to Industrial Water and Industrial Waste Water (ASTM Designation: D 1129).[4]

Purity of Reagents

3. (a) Reagent grade chemicals shall be used in all tests. Unless otherwise indicated, it is intended that all reagents shall conform to the specifications of the Committee on Analytical Reagents of the American Chemical Society, where such specifications are available.[5] Other grades may be used, provided it is first ascertained that the reagent is of sufficiently high purity to permit its use

---

[3] These methods conform essentially to the recommendations made by the Joint Committee on Uniformity of Methods of Water Examination in Nov., 1959.

[4] Appears in this publication.

[5] "Reagent Chemicals, American Chemical Society Specifications," Am. Chemical Soc., Washington, D. C. For suggestions on the testing of reagents not listed by the American Chemical Society, see "Reagent Chemicals and Standards," by Joseph Rosin, D. Van Nostrand Co., Inc., New York, N. Y., and the "United States Pharmacopeia."

without lessening the accuracy of the determination. The purity of the reagents shall be checked by determining a blank as described in Sections 11(e) and 22(c).

(b) Unless otherwise indicated, references to water shall be understood to mean reagent water conforming to the Specifications for Reagent Water (ASTM Designation: D 1193).[4] In addition, water shall be iron-free, and water used for preparing solutions for the determination of ferrous iron shall be freshly boiled and essentially oxygen-free.

Sampling

4. Collect the sample in accordance with the applicable methods of the American Society for Testing and Materials, as follows:

D 510—Sampling Industrial Water,[4]
D 860—Sampling Water from Boilers,[4]
D 1066—Sampling Steam,[4] and
D 1496—Sampling Homogeneous Industrial Waste Water.[4]

REFEREE METHOD A

Application

5. This method is applicable to industrial water and industrial waste water having iron concentrations above 0.05 ppm. For accurate determinations of iron below this concentration, Referee Method B should be used. Before application to industrial waste water, the presence of possible interfering constituents must be considered, their effects studied and, if necessary, the interferences eliminated by suitable means.

Summary of Method[6]

6. (a) Insoluble iron and iron oxides are put into solution by treatment with acids; or, if the iron is not readily soluble in acids, fusion techniques are applied. Under some conditions, this method prescribes the use of perchloric acid (**Caution,** Note 1).

NOTE 1: **Caution.**—Warm perchloric acid

solutions react explosively with organic matter. The use of nitric acid with perchloric acid prevents this spontaneous reaction and is positive insurance against explosion during evaporations of water samples with perchloric acid.[7]

(b) The iron is determined colorimetrically with 1,10-phenanthroline (o-phenanthroline), which forms an orange-red complex with ferrous iron. The intensity of the color produced is proportional to the amount of ferrous iron in the water. Hydroxylamine hydrochloride is added to reduce ferric iron to the ferrous state when determining total and dissolved iron.

(c) This method follows Beer's Law for the ranges given in Section 8. Maximum absorption occurs at about 510 mμ, the wavelength recommended for photometric measurement of the color intensity.

Interferences

7. (a) In comparison with other reagents for iron, o-phenanthroline is relatively free from interferences. Interference may be caused by copper, cobalt, chromium, or zinc if these metals are

[6] For further information on this method and interferences, the following references are of particular interest:

W. B. Fortune and M. G. Mellon, "Determination of Iron with o-Phenanthroline, a Spectrophotometric Study," *Industrial and Engineering Chemistry*, Analytical Edition, Vol. 10, p. 60 (1938).

E. B. Sandell, "Colorimetric Determination of Traces of Metals," Interscience Publishers, Inc., Second Edition (1950).

M. G. Mellon, "Analytical Absorption Spectroscopy," John Wiley and Sons, Inc. (1950).

W. W. Brandt, "Chelate Complexes of 1,10-Phenanthroline and Related Compounds," *Chemical Review*, Vol. 54, p. 959 (1954).

S. L. Bandemer and P. J. Schaible, "Determination of Iron—A Study of the o-Phenanthroline Method," *Industrial and Engineering Chemistry*, Analytical Edition, Vol. 16, p. 317 (1944).

L. K. Reitz, A. S. O'Brien and T. L. Davis, "Evaluation of Three Iron Methods," *Analytical Chemistry*, Vol. 22, p. 1470 (1950).

[7] Precautions for the use of perchloric acid are available in "Chemical Safety Data Sheet SD 11," published by the Manufacturing Chemists' Association of the United States.

present in concentrations exceeding ten times that of iron. Nickel interferes when present in excess of 2 ppm. Bismuth and silver give precipitates with *o*-phenanthroline, and must be completely absent. Cadmium and mercuric ions also form precipitates, but with small amounts of these ions it is possible to prevent appreciable interference by adding excess *o*-phenanthroline. Molybdenum will give a milky solution, but the interference may be overcome by adjusting the pH to above 5.5. Cyanides interfere if present. Aluminum is added to displace iron from complexes with certain other anions such as phosphate, in which form it would be slow to react. Large amounts of phosphate also interfere.

(*b*) It is beyond the scope of these methods to describe means for overcoming all of the possible interferences that may be encountered in the methods, particularly with highly contaminated water and industrial waste water. The methods used must be tailored to meet the specific requirements. General suggestions and detailed information are given in Note 2. Interferences may also be eliminated by extracting the iron with diisopropyl ether from an acid solution and then extracting the ether with water to obtain an interference-free water solution.

Note 2.—With samples that are highly colored or contain large amounts of organic material, a suitable ash treatment should first be applied. Wet-ashing with concentrated sulfuric acid (H_2SO_4, sp gr 1.84) and concentrated nitric acid (HNO_3, sp gr 1.42) or dry-ashing at temperatures not exceeding 700 C is satisfactory. The use of silica dishes instead of platinum dishes is recommended for ashing samples that contain high concentrations of sodium hydroxide (NaOH) or potassium hydroxide (KOH). Platinum dishes may be used if the sample is first neutralized with H_2SO_4.

If it is suspected that a portion of the iron is insoluble in acid, the ash should be fused with potassium bisulfate ($KHSO_4$) and then dissolved in the usual manner.

The use of perchloric acid ($HClO_4$, 60 or 70 per cent) is sometimes helpful in dissolving suspended iron and iron oxides. After addition of concentrated hydrochloric acid (HCl, sp gr 1.19) to the sample and evaporation to a small volume (15 to 20 ml), add 3 ml of $HClO_4$ (60 or 70 per cent) and 3 ml of H_2SO_4. Evaporate to fumes of sulfur trioxide (SO_3) to remove all the $HClO_4$, cool, dissolve, and treat the sample in the usual manner.

Caution.—If organic matter is present or suspected, 3 ml of HNO_3 must be added with the $HClO_4$ and H_2SO_4 to prevent possible spontaneous combustion of the organic matter. In this case, evaporate to dense white fumes, cool the beaker, wash the inside of the beaker carefully with a few milliliters of water, add a few drops of formic acid, fume again to remove the last traces of HNO_3, and then proceed as directed.

Blank determinations should be made with all reagents used in any of the above steps in order to correct for any iron contamination. After such treatments, the procedure for determination of ferrous iron (Sections 12 and 33) will no longer apply, since the relative quantities of ferrous and ferric iron in the samples will be altered.

Apparatus

8. Use one of the following means of color evaluation. The right-hand column indicates the optimum range for each.

Method of Color Measurement	Range covered, mg of iron per 100 ml of final solution
Nessler tubes, 100-ml	0.01 to 0.3
Filter photometer (510 mμ):[a]	
2.5-cm cell	0.01 to 0.4
10-cm cell	0.002 to 0.05
Spectrophotometer (510 mμ):[a]	
1-cm cell	0.01 to 0.5
10-cm cell	0.001 to 0.05

[a] A discussion of photometers and photometric practice is given in the Recommended Practice for Photometric Methods for Chemical Analysis of Metals (ASTM Designation E 60).[8]

Reagents and Materials

9. (*a*) *Aluminum Nitrate Solution* (*222 g per liter*).—Dissolve 222 g of aluminum nitrate ($Al(NO_3)_3 \cdot 9H_2O$) in 200 ml of water. Add 20 ml of ammonium thiocyanate (NH_4CNS) solution (200 g NH_4CNS per liter) and stir well. Extract

—————
[8] 1967 Book of ASTM Standards, Part 32.

the red color with three 75-ml portions of a mixture of a 71.5 per cent isoamyl alcohol and 28.5 per cent ethyl ether by volume, using a separatory funnel. Transfer the colorless solution after extraction to a 800-ml beaker, add 200 ml of concentrated nitric acid (HNO_3, sp gr 1.42), and boil to decompose excess NH_4CNS. The solution after boiling for about 2 hr should be clear; if not, continue boiling until all yellow color is removed. Cool and dilute to 1 liter with water.

NOTE 3: **Caution.**—Decomposition of the NH_4CNS must be done in a hood, due to the poisonous nature of the decomposition products.

(b) *Ammonium Acetate Solution (100 g per liter).*—Dissolve 100 g of ammonium acetate ($NH_4C_2H_3O_2$) in 100 ml of water. Add 200 ml of acetic acid, dilute to 1 liter with water, and mix.

(c) *Ammonium Hydroxide (1:1).*—Mix 1 volume of concentrated ammonium hydroxide (NH_4OH, sp gr 0.90) with 1 volume of water.

(d) *Congo Red Paper.*

(e) *Diisopropyl Ether.*—Alcohol free, boiling point 67 to 69 C.

(f) *Hydrochloric Acid (sp gr 1.19).*—Concentrated hydrochloric acid (HCl).

(g) *Hydroxylamine Hydrochloride Solution (100 g per liter).*—Dissolve 10 g of hydroxylamine hydrochloride ($NH_2OH \cdot HCl$) in water and dilute to 100 ml with water.

(h) *Iron, Standard Solution (1 ml = 0.1 mg Fe).*—Dissolve 0.7022 g of ferrous ammonium sulfate ($FeSO_4(NH_4)_2SO_4 \cdot 6H_2O$) in 50 ml of water and 20 ml of concentrated sulfuric acid (H_2SO_4, sp gr 1.84). Dilute with water to 1 liter in a volumetric flask and mix. The standard solution (1 ml = 0.1 mg Fe) may also be prepared by dissolving 0.1000 g of clean electrolytic iron wire in 15 ml of H_2SO_4 (1:4) and diluting to 1 liter in a volumetric flask. In either case, the solu-

tion may be further diluted for convenience and accuracy in the preparation of the calibration standards; however, in such a case, the above-indicated strength is altered and the changes in concentration should be noted.

(i) *o-Phenanthroline Solution (1 g per liter).*—Dissolve 0.1 g of 1,10-phenanthroline monohydrate in 10 ml of iron-free ethanol[9] and dilute to 100 ml with water.

(j) *Sulfuric Acid (1:4).*—Carefully mix 1 volume of concentrated sulfuric acid (H_2SO_4, sp gr 1.84) with 4 volumes of water.

Calibration

10. (a) Prepare a series of standards to cover the expected range of iron concentrations by adding the reagents as described in Section 11(c) to measured volumes of standard iron solution and diluting to 100 ml with water. Carry a blank containing no added iron through all the steps in the procedure in order to correct for any iron in the reagents.

(b) For photometer comparisons, prepare a calibration curve by plotting the absorbances of the standard solutions against the milligrams of iron per 100 ml of solution (Note 4).

NOTE 4.—A separate calibration curve must be made for each photometer or spectrophotometer. Each curve must be checked periodically to ensure reproducibility.

Procedure for Total Iron

11. (a) Mix the original sample thoroughly and transfer a portion that will contain approximately 0.005 to 0.4 mg of iron to a beaker or an Erlenmeyer flask. If there is evidence of a deposit, which may contain iron, adhering to the sample container, dissolve it and add the solution to the sample (Note 2). Taking the sample directly in a

---

[9] Specially denatured alcohol conforming to Formula No. 30 of the U. S. Bureau of Internal Revenue, has been found satisfactory for this purpose.

small container and using the entire sample for the determination of total iron is advantageous in such cases.

(*b*) If necessary, dilute the sample to about a 50-ml volume with iron-free water. Add 2 ml of HCl (sp gr 1.19) and 1 ml of hydroxylamine hydrochloride solution, and boil to a 10-ml volume to dissolve any suspended iron (Note 5). Some samples may require more acid and longer boiling to effect complete solution of all the iron. Residual turbidity after boiling may be removed by filtering through fine-texture, ashless filter paper and washing the insoluble material with water. Adjust the volume of the clear solution to about 75 ml (Note 6).

NOTE 5.—Omit the hydroxylamine hydrochloride solution if interferences are to be removed by the use of diisopropyl ether. The iron must be in the ferric state.

NOTE 6.—The volume should be kept at 10 ml if diisopropyl ether is used to remove interferences as follows: Transfer the sample to a 125-ml separatory funnel and add 14 ml of HCl (sp gr 1.19). Cool the solution and make three extractions with 25, 10, and 10 ml of diisopropyl ether, respectively. Extract the combined ether solutions with 25 and 10 ml of iron-free water. Determine the iron content of the combined aqueous extracts in accordance with Paragraphs (*c*) and (*d*).

(*c*) Add the following reagents in order, mixing after addition of each: 1 ml of hydroxylamine hydrochloride solution, 5 ml of $Al(NO_3)_3$ solution, 5 ml of *o*-phenanthroline solution, and NH_4OH (1:1) as required to bring the pH to 3.5 to 4.0. This may be done electrometrically with a pH meter, with congo red paper (made just alkaline to the paper), or by making just alkaline to the first indication of a precipitate of aluminum hydroxide. Then add 5 ml of ammonium acetate solution. Transfer the mixture to a 100-ml volumetric flask, dilute to the mark with water, and mix thoroughly.

(*d*) Measure the color by means of any applicable apparatus listed in Section 8. Although the color complex is extremely stable, it is preferable to read colors from 2 to 5 min after mixing (Note 7). Make photometric measurements at approximately 510 mμ.

NOTE 7.—In the presence of large amounts of phosphates, the procedure must be altered to include the addition of citrate and hydroquinone, and a standing time of 30 min as described by S. L. Bandemer and P. J. Schaible.[6]

(*e*) In photometric work, with samples showing no appreciable color, carry a blank containing no added iron through all steps of the procedure in order to correct for iron contamination in the reagents and optical effects involved in adjusting the photometer. This blank solution should be colorless. In the case of colored samples, use an additional blank prepared by using the sample and adding all reagents except the *o*-phenanthroline to compensate for the color of the water provided.

(*f*) For visual comparison in Nessler tubes, or when using a Duboscq-type colorimeter, develop the color of the reference standards at the same time as that of the sample under examination.

Procedure for Dissolved Iron

12. Allow the sample to settle (Note 8), then decant a portion through a suitable filter (such as fine-texture, ashless filter paper) to remove suspended iron. After rejecting the first 25 ml of filtrate, collect a suitable, measured portion of the filtrate, add 1 ml HCl, dilute to 75 ml, and proceed in accordance with Section 11(*c*).

NOTE 8.—Because of the tendency of dissolved ferrous iron to oxidize and precipitate on standing, the determination of dissolved iron or ferrous iron should be made as soon as possible after collecting the sample. In the case of an extremely unstable sample, where iron precipitation occurs soon after collection of the sample, the dissolved iron must be determined immediately or it will be possible to determine only the total iron. Where suspended iron is present in such cases, an approximate measure of the dissolved iron may be obtained by filtering a portion of the sample immediately after its collection and later making a determination of the total iron present in the filtered sample.

Procedure for Ferrous Iron

13. (*a*) Proceed in accordance with Section 11, but omit the addition of hydroxylamine hydrochloride solution. Blanket the sample with nitrogen during all steps and use freshly boiled water

11(*d*). Make the appropriate correction for dilution of sample with reagents.

Calculation

14. (*a*) Calculate total iron, dissolved iron, and ferrous iron, in parts per million, as follows:

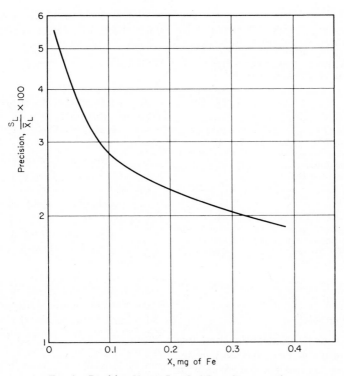

FIG. 1.—Precision Versus Level of Iron Concentration.

for making the dilution after developing the color. Avoid any exposure of the sample to air prior to color development.

(*b*) To determine ferrous iron at the time of the collection of the sample, place 5 ml of the ammonium acetate-acetic acid solution and 5 ml of *o*-phenanthroline solution in a 100-ml stoppered bottle. Fill the bottle to the top with water sample and stopper the bottle. In the laboratory, dilute if necessary and read the color as described in Section

Iron (total, dissolved, or ferrous), ppm

$$= \frac{W}{S} \times 1000$$

where:

W = milligrams of iron found in accordance with Section 11, 12 or 13, and

S = milliliters of original sample present in 100 ml of final solution.

(*b*) Calculate the suspended iron, in parts per million, as follows:

Suspended iron, ppm
= total iron − dissolved iron

Precision[10]

15. The precision of the method varies with the quantity being determined as shown in Fig. 1.

REFEREE METHOD B

Scope and Application

16. This method is specifically applicable to the determination of low concen-

TABLE I.—METHODS OF
COLOR MEASUREMENT.

	Range Covered, in ppb
Nessler tube, 300-mm..........	20 to 200
Filter photometer (green filter, 533 mμ[a]	
5- to 10-cm cell..............	10 to 60
Spectrophotometer (533 mμ)[a]	
5-cm cell....................	5 to 60
10-cm cell...................	2 to 30

[a] A discussion of photometers and photometric practice is given in the Recommended Practice for Photometric Methods for Chemical Analysis of Metals (ASTM Designation: E 60).[8]

trations of iron (200 ppb and under) in industrial water.

Summary of Method

17. (a) Total iron is determined by this method. Insoluble iron and iron oxides are put into solution by treatment with acid.

(b) The iron is reduced with hydroxylamine hydrochloride and then reacted with 4,7-diphenyl-1,10-phenanthroline (bathophenanthroline). The red ferrous complex is extracted from the aqueous solution with *n*-hexyl or isoamyl alcohol and the intensity of its color measured. Maximum absorption of the complex occurs at 533 mμ, and Beer's law is valid.

---

[10] Supporting data and literature references pertinent to this method are given in Appendix I to the report of Committee D-19, *Proceedings*, Am. Soc. Testing Mats., Vol. 55 (1955).

Interferences[11]

18. If the pH is between 3.3 and 3.7, a 1-ppm concentration of the following ions does not interfere with the test: copper, manganese, aluminum, zinc, magnesium, sodium, silica, nitrate, and orthophosphate.

Apparatus

19. Use one of the means of color evaluation shown in Table I. The right-hand column shows the optimum range for each.

Reagents

20. (a) *Alcohol, n-Hexyl (preferred)* or *Isoamyl (alternate)*.

(b) *Alcohol, Methyl, Ethyl, or Isopropyl*.

(c) *Ammonium Hydroxide (sp gr 0.90)* —Concentrated ammonium hydroxide (NH_4OH).

(d) *Ammonium Hydroxide (1:1).*—See Section 9(c).

(e) *Bathophenanthroline Solution (0.835 g per liter).*—Dissolve 0.0835 g of 4,7-diphenyl-1,10-phenanthroline in 100 ml of ethyl alcohol (95 per cent).

(f) *Hydrochloric Acid (sp gr 1.19).*—Concentrated hydrochloric acid (HCl). When necessary, distill the acid to remove the iron. If this treatment does not remove the iron, determine the iron content by using various volumes in the procedure and extrapolating.

(g) *Hydroxylamine Hydrochloride Solution (100 g per liter).*—Dissolve 10 g of hydroxylamine hydrochloride ($NH_2OH \cdot HCl$) (Note 9) in water and dilute to 100 ml.

NOTE 9.—The $NH_4OH \cdot HCl$ frequently contains some iron as an impurity. This impurity

---

[11] For further information on interferences, the following reference is of particular interest:
G. F. Smith, et al, "The Colorimetric Determination of Iron in Raw and Treated Municipal Water Supplies by Use of 4:7-Diphenyl-1:10-Phenanthroline," *Analyst*, Vol. 77, p. 418 (1952).

may be removed by treating the solution with bathophenanthroline and extracting with n-hexyl or isoamyl alcohol. Repeat the addition of bathophenanthroline and extraction with n-hexyl or isoamyl alcohol until the alcohol extract is free of color.

(h) *Iron Standard Solution* (1 ml = 0.1 mg Fe).—See Section 9(h).

Sampling

21. Since iron may plate on the sample container, collect the sample in a temperature-resistant glass bottle (not a plastic bottle) and acidify it to pH 3.3 to 3.7 with HCl (Note 10).

NOTE 10.—Soak all new glassware (for both sampling and testing) in hot HCl (1:1) for 2 hr. Drain and rinse at least five times with demineralized iron free water. Before use, and after use (before again using) clean all glassware by making an iron extraction in each piece (without separating the alcohol - water layers). Drain and flush with iron-free methyl alcohol, ethyl alcohol, or isopropyl alcohol.

Calibration

22. (a) Prepare a series of standards to cover the expected range of iron concentrations by diluting the standard iron solution (Section 20(h)). Make up each standard to a volume of 50 ml with demineralized water and acidify each to pH 3.3 to 3.7.

(b) Add 2.0 ml of $NH_2OH \cdot HCl$ solution to each standard and transfer to a separatory funnel. Extract and proceed as described in Section 23(b), (c), and (d).

(c) Simultaneously carry out a blank determination using 50 ml of water and all reagents, except for the standard iron solution. Correct the readings of the standards for this blank value. For photometer comparisons, prepare a calibration curve by plotting the absorbances of the standards against the iron contents of the standards.

Procedure

23. (a) Transfer a sample containing 0.00025 to 0.003 mg of iron (Note 11) to

a clean beaker (Note 10). Dilute to 50 ml with water and add 5.0 ml of HCl and 2.0 ml of $NH_2OH \cdot HCl$ solution. Heat the solution for 30 to 60 min at 60 C. The 60-min time usually is preferable. Cool to room temperature (not over 34 C). Add 4.0 ml of NH_4OH (sp gr 0.90) and adjust the pH to 3.3 to 3.7 with NH_4OH (1:1) (Note 12).

NOTE 11.—A 50-ml sample ordinarily is used. Depending upon the instrument used in the color measurement and the sample's iron content, more or less sample is used. If less sample is used, dilute to 50 ml with demineralized, iron-free water. The amounts of n-hexyl or isoamyl alcohol used will be determined by the color-measuring instrument. In no case shall it be less than 10 ml, and if the iron in the sample volume taken for analysis exceeds 0.003 mg not less than 15 ml of n-hexyl or isoamyl alcohol shall be used. The calibration curve must be made with alcohol volumes equal to those used in the analysis.

NOTE 12.—No internal indicators should be used to adjust the pH. If sufficient sample is available, a trial run can be made to note the amount of NH_4OH needed for proper pH adjustment. Otherwise, an external indicator such as pH paper (range 1.0 to 5.5) may be used, taking care not to contaminate the sample.

(b) Transfer the solution to a 125-ml separatory funnel (Note 13). Add 3.0 ml of the bathophenanthroline solution, shake vigorously for 30 sec, and allow to stand 5 min for color development. Add 10.0 ml of n-hexyl or isoamyl alcohol. (Note 11) and shake vigorously for 1 min.

NOTE 13.—Use either silicone stopcock grease on the stopcock or a funnel with a TFE-fluorocarbon stopcock.

(c) Allow at least 5 min for complete separation of the water and alcohol layers; then drain the water layer from the funnel and discard. Shake out of the stem as much water as practical; then drain the alcohol layer into a suitable container. Add 5 ml of methyl, ethyl, or isopropyl alcohol to the funnel and wash the internal surfaces by rolling and tumbling the funnel. Drain this alcohol into the previously drained alcohol extract (Note 14).

Note 14.—The purpose of the methyl, ethyl, or isopropyl alcohol addition is to rinse the funnel of an adsorbed layer of iron-rich alcohol and to solubilize the water that is present and thus prevent turbidity in the *n*-hexyl or isoamyl alcohol. With proper technique, 5 ml of these water-soluble alcohols is sufficient.

(*d*) Measure the color of the alcohol solution by means of any applicable apparatus listed in Section 19. When using Nessler tubes, dilute the solution to the mark on the tube with more alcohol and mix. When using a photometer, adjust the instrument to zero absorbance reading with a reference solution consisting of the alcohol mixture used for the extraction of the color and make the determination on the test solution diluted to appropriate volume with alcohol.

(*e*) Carry out a blank determination on 50 ml of water, with all reagents, heating, and extracting in the same manner as for the sample. Correct the reading on the sample for this blank.

Calculation

24. Calculate the concentration of iron in parts per billion as follows:

$$\text{Iron, ppb} = \frac{W \times 1,000,000}{S}$$

where:
W = milligrams of iron read from calibration curve or present in matching standard in Nessler tube, and
S = milliliters of sample used.

Precision

25. Precision varies with the concentration of iron being measured and the method of measurement. Duplicate determinations should agree within 1 ppb.

Non-Referee Method C

Application

26. This method is applicable to industrial water and to industrial waste

water having iron concentrations above 0.05 ppm. For accurate determinations of iron below this concentration Referee Method B should be used.

Summary of Method

27. This method is similar to referee method A, except that certain reagents are combined for convenient usage, and purification of the aluminum nitrate is obviated by the addition of a sequestering agent.

Apparatus

28. See Section 8.

Reagents and Materials

29. (*a*) *Ammonium Hydroxide (1:1).*—See Section 9(*c*).

(*b*) *Congo Red Paper.*

(*c*) *Ferrous Iron Reagent.*—Dissolve 200 g of sodium acetate in water and to it add 200 g of aluminum nitrate $(Al(NO_3)_3 \cdot 9H_2O)$ that previously has been dissolved in 150 ml of water. Add 4 g of disodium dihydrogen ethylenediamine tetraacetate dihydrate that previously has been dissolved in 50 ml of water. Mix and dilute to 1 liter with water.

(*d*) *Hydrochloric Acid (sp gr 1.19).*—Concentrated hydrochloric acid (HCl).

(*e*) *Iron, Standard Solution (1 ml = 0.1 mg Fe).*—See Section 9(*h*).

(*f*) *o-Phenanthroline Solution (1 g per liter).*—See Section 9(*i*).

(*g*) *Total Iron Reagent.*—Dissolve 100 g of hydroxylamine hydrochloride $(NH_2OH \cdot HCl)$ in 200 ml of water. Neutralize to pH 8.0 with sodium hydroxide solution (NaOH, 200 g per liter), and dilute to 600 ml. Add 100 ml of glacial acetic acid and 200 g of $Al(NO_3)_3 \cdot 9H_2O$ that previously have been dissolved in 150 ml of water. Add 4 g of disodium dihydrogen ethylenediamine tetraacetate dihydrate that previously have been dissolved in 50 ml of water. Mix and dilute to 1 liter with water.

Calibration

30. (*a*) Prepare a series of standards to cover the expected range of iron concentrations by adding the reagents as described in Section 31(*b*) to measured volumes of standard iron solution diluted as necessary.

(*b*) For photometer comparisons, prepare a calibration curve in parts per million by plotting the absorbances of the standard solutions against the milligrams of iron per 50 ml of solution, multiplied by 20 (Note 4).

Procedure for Total Iron

31. (*a*) Mix the original sample thoroughly and transfer to a beaker a portion that will contain approximately 0.005 to 0.4 mg of iron, diluting or concentrating if necessary. If there is evidence of a deposit, which may contain iron, adhering to the sample container, dissolve it and add the solution to the sample (Note 2). Taking the sample directly in a small container and using the entire sample for the determination of total iron is advantageous.

(*b*) Add 2 ml of HCl (sp gr 1.19) and boil to approximately one half the original volume. Add NH_4OH (1:1) to make the solution just alkaline to congo red paper or to pH 3.0 to 3.5 using a pH meter. Dilute to 50 ml with water. Residual turbidity after boiling may be removed by filtration. Transfer a 10-ml portion of the solution to a beaker. Add 1 ml of the total iron reagent, then 1 ml of the *o*-phenanthroline solution and mix thoroughly.

(*c*) Measure the color in accordance with Section 11(*d*) to (*f*).

Procedure for Dissolved Iron

32. Repeat the procedure described in Section 31 on the filtrate of an aliquot filtered through a fine-texture, ashless filter paper.

Procedure for Ferrous Iron

33. Proceed in accordance with Section 31 (Note 8), but substitute the ferrous iron reagent for the total iron reagent. Use freshly boiled (oxygen-free) water for making any necessary dilutions. Avoid unnecessary exposure of the sample to air.

Calculation

34. (*a*) Calculate total iron, dissolved iron, and ferrous iron, in parts per million, as follows:

$$\text{Iron (total, dissolved, or ferrous), ppm} = \frac{W}{S} \times 50$$

where:

W = parts per million of iron found by comparison or read from the calibration curve, and

S = milliliters of original sample represented in the 50 ml of final solution.

(*b*) Calculate the suspended iron, in parts per million, as follows:

Suspended iron, ppm
$$= \text{total iron} - \text{dissolved iron}$$

Precision

35. The precision of this method was not universally tested.

Standard Methods of Test for
PARTICULATE AND DISSOLVED MATTER IN INDUSTRIAL WASTE WATER[1]

ASTM Designation: D 1069 – 66
ADOPTED, 1966

This Standard of the American Society for Testing and Materials is issued under the fixed designation D 1069; the number immediately following the designation indicates the year of original adoption or, in the case of revision, the year of last revision. A number in parentheses indicates the year of last reapproval.

Scope

1. These methods cover the determination of particulate and dissolved matter, free of extractable material removed with solvent, in industrial waste water. The methods are applicable to the determination and differentiation of particulate, dissolved, and volatile matter. The methods are not intended for the determination of materials normally classified as "oily matter," such as vegetable oils, animal oils, and petroleum oils that are volatile at the drying temperature of the method or extractable with organic solvents. For the determination of oily matter in industrial waste water refer to the Method of Test for Oily Matter in Industrial Water Waste (ASTM Designation: D 1340).[2]

[1] Under the standardization procedure of the Society, these methods are under the jurisdiction of the ASTM Committee D-19 on Industrial Water. A list of members may be found in the ASTM Year Book.

Summary of Method

2. Particulate and dissolved matter are separated by filtration. Extractable material is removed from the particulate matter by solvent extraction. Particulate matter is determined by weighing the residue obtained on the filter after drying at 180 C. Dissolved matter is determined in the filtrate which is washed with solvent to remove the solvent-extractable materials, and is obtained by weighing the residue after evaporation and drying at 180 C. Volatile matter under each of the above classifications is determined by loss on heating the residues at 600 ± 25 C.

Definitions

3. (a) The terms "particulate matter," "dissolved matter," and "volatile matter," in these methods are defined in accordance with the Definitions of Terms Relating to Industrial Water

[2] Appears in this publication.

384

and Industrial Waste Water (ASTM Designation: D 1129),[2] as follows:

Particulate Matter.—That matter, exclusive of gases, existing in the non-liquid state which is dispersed in water to give a heterogeneous mixture.

Dissolved Matter.—That matter, exclusive of gases, which is dispersed in water to give a single phase of homogeneous liquid.

Volatile Matter.—That matter that is changed under conditions of the test from a solid or a liquid state to the gaseous state.

(*b*) For definitions of other terms used in these methods refer to Definitions D 1129.

Interferences

4. (*a*) Some dried residues readily absorb moisture. Rapid weighing is essential to this method. Some residues contain materials such as ammonium carbonate that decompose below 180 C; others contain liquids, such as glycerol and sulfuric acid, that will remain as a liquid residue at 180 C with or without solution of salts that might also be present.

(*b*) Rapid weighing of ignited residues also is important for the reason indicated in Paragraph (*a*). There is more likelihood of interferences since carbonates, organic matter, nitrite and nitrate nitrogen, water of hydration, chlorides, and sulfates may not be removed completely but only in part at 600 C. No single temperature is known that will eliminate all these interferences. However, at any temperature reproducible results should be obtained and, therefore, generally serve the intended purpose.

Apparatus

5. (*a*) *Sample Reservoir.*—A chemically-resistant container of 1 to 4 liters capacity.

(*b*) *Filter Crucible.*—An evenly distributed filter mat approximately 2 mm thick, composed of finely divided asbestos fiber, produced by pouring a slurry of acid-washed asbestos through a Gooch crucible under reduced pressure and washing with reagent water until the filtrate is clear.

(*c*) *Evaporating Dish.*—A straight-walled platinum dish, 80 to 100 mm in diameter, and approximately 200-ml capacity. A porcelain dish may be substituted for the platinum dish if the residue is not to be analyzed.

(*d*) *Heater.*—A controlled electric hot plate, infrared lamp, or steam bath for maintaining the temperature of the evaporating sample near the boiling point.

(*e*) *Separatory Funnels*, 250 and 500-ml capacity.

(*f*) *Centrifuge*, complete with conical tubes.

Reagents and Materials

6. *Solvent.*—Benzene, carbon tetrachloride, or chloroform, any of which shall be purchased or distilled so that the residue after evaporation shall be not more than 0.5 mg per 100 ml of solvent.

Sampling

7. (*a*) Collect the sample in accordance with the applicable method of the American Society for Testing and Materials, as follows:

D 510—Sampling Industrial Water[2]
D 1496—Sampling Homogeneous Industrial Waste Water.[2]

Procedure

8. (*a*) *Particulate Matter.*—Select a sample from the uniformly dispersed mixture of sufficient quantity to yield the maximum practical amount of particu-

late matter. Weigh the sample, and filter it through a filter crucible that has been ignited at 600 ± 25 C, cooled in a desiccator, and weighed. Withdraw a portion of the filtrate for use in rinsing the receptacle to transfer all sediment to the crucible. Use the withdrawn portion of the filtrate for this rinsing rather than water, to maintain equilibrium between the nondissolved matter and the sample. Remove solvent-extractable material by washing the residue with solvent in the filter crucible that was dried at 103 C, but not ignited. Wash the residue with solvent until 10 ml of the washings leave not more than 0.5 mg of residue on evaporation at 180 C. Discard the washings. Air-dry the sediment in the crucible for 5 min; then place the crucible in an oven at 180 C for 1 hr, cool in a desiccator, and weigh the filter crucible plus residue. Repeat the oven-drying operation until constant weight is obtained. "Constant weight" shall be considered as attained when the change in weight of the vessel plus the residue shall not be more than 0.5 mg between two successive operations involving heating, cooling in a desiccator, and weighing. Record the weight of the residue as "weight of particulate matter."

(b) If the sample does not filter readily, pretreat it prior to filtering, as follows: Transfer the sample to centrifuge tubes and centrifuge for a period of 5 to 10 min to compact the particulate matter. Remove the tubes from the centrifuge and return the supernatant liquid to a beaker. Rinse any retained material from the container into the centrifuge tubes with this supernatant liquid. Centrifuge sufficiently to compact any particulate matter. Pour the supernatant liquid through the filter crucible; then transfer quantitatively the centrifuged particulate matter to the crucible. Use a withdrawn portion of the

filtrate to rinse the solids in the centrifuge tubes into the crucible. Complete the determination as described in Paragraph (a).

(c) Dissolved Matter.—If the presence of solvent-extractable material is suspected, transfer a weighed volume of the filtrate from Paragraph (a) to a separatory funnel and extract with solvent. Wash with solvent until 10 ml of the washings leave not more than 0.5 mg of residue on evaporation at 180 C. Discard the washings. Transfer the solvent-extracted filtrate to an evaporating dish that previously has been ignited to 600 ± 25 C, cooled in a desiccator, and weighed. Fill to within approximately ¼ in. of the top of the evaporating dish. Heat the dish on a hot plate or under infrared lamps to evaporate the sample, but do not allow the sample in the dish to boil. Periodically add filtrate to the dish until the entire filtrate has been transferred. Rinse the filtrate container several times with water, adding the rinsings to the contents of the evaporating dish. Then evaporate the remainder of the material in the dish to near dryness. Dry the dish and its contents for one hour in an oven at 180 C. Cool in a desiccator and weigh the residue. Repeat until a constant weight is obtained. "Constant weight" shall be considered as attained when the change in weight of the vessel plus the residue shall be not more than 0.5 mg between two successive operations involving heating, cooling in a desiccator, and weighing. Record the weight of residue as "weight of dissolved matter." Ignite the dish and contents for 1 hr at 600 ± 25 C, cool in the desiccator, and reweigh. Record the loss in weight as "weight of volatile dissolved matter."

Calculations

9. Calculate the concentration of the

specific class of nonaqueous matter, in parts per million, as follows. Use the appropriate data for the class of matter being determined, and designate the results accordingly:

Particulate or dissolved matter, ppm

$$= \frac{A}{W} \times 1000$$

Volatile matter, ppm $= \frac{B}{W} \times 1000$

where:

A = grams of solid or dissolved matter,
B = grams of volatile matter,
W = kilograms of sample used.

Precision

10. Precision cannot be stated for this method. Precision is limited primarily by the nature of the residue and, to a lesser degree, the ability to obtain a representative portion of the sample, balance reproducibility, and drying temperature.

Standard Methods of Test for
ELECTRICAL CONDUCTIVITY OF INDUSTRIAL WATER AND INDUSTRIAL WASTE WATER[1]

ASTM Designation: D 1125 – 64
ADOPTED, 1964

This Standard of the American Society for Testing and Materials is issued under the fixed designation D 1125; the final number indicates the year of original adoption as standard or, in the case of revision, the year of last revision.

Scope and Application

1. These methods cover the measurement of the electrical conductivity of industrial water and industrial waste water. These methods are applicable for such purposes as the detection of ionized impurities dissolved in condensed steam,[2,3] the approximate determination of dissolved electrolytes in natural and treated waters, such as boiler feedwater, boiler water, evaporator salines, and cooling water. The following methods are included:

	Sections
Referee Method	9 to 15
Non-Referee Method	16 to 22

Definitions

2. (a) The term "electrical conductivity" in this method shall be defined in accordance with the Definitions of Terms Relating to Industrial Water and Industrial Waste Water (ASTM Designation: D 1129),[4] as follows:

Electrical Conductivity.—The reciprocal of the resistance in ohms measured between opposite faces of a centimeter cube of an aqueous solution at a specified temperature.

NOTE 1.—The electrical conductivity shall be expressed in micromhos per centimeter at t C. The actual resistance, R, of the cell is measured in ohms. The conductance, $\frac{1}{R}$, is directly proportional to the cross-sectional area, A, inversely proportional to the length of the path, L, and directly proportional to the constant, K. The latter is the conductivity measured between opposite faces of a centimeter cube. Mathematically,

$$\frac{1}{R} = \frac{KA}{L}, \text{ or } K = \frac{L}{AR} = \frac{cm}{sq\ cm \times ohms} = $$
$$\text{mhos per cm.}$$

[1] Under the standardization procedure of the Society, these methods are under the jurisdiction of the ASTM Committee D-19 on Industrial Water. A list of members may be found in the ASTM Year Book.

[2] See the Methods of Test for Deposit-Forming Impurities in Steam (ASTM Designation: D 2186), which appear in this publication.

[3] Where the principal interest in the use of conductivity methods is to determine steam purity, reference may be made to the "Methods for Determination of Quality and Purity of Steam," *ASME Power Test Code*, Supplement on Instruments and Apparatus, Part 19.11. These methods may be used also for checking the correctness of water analyses. See J. R. Rossum, "Conductance Method for Checking Accuracy of Water Analyses," *Analytical Chemistry*, Vol. 21, p. 631 (1949).

[4] Appears in this publication.

The numerical value of this expression multiplied by 1,000,000 is the electrical conductivity in micromhos per centimeter.

(b) For definitions of other terms used in these methods, refer to Definitions D 1129.

Apparatus

3. (a) *Measuring Circuit.*—Instruments may be battery, or a-c or d-c line, operated. In any case, the conductivity cell shall be energized with alternating current at an approximately constant frequency within the range 25 to 3000 cycles per sec. The instrument may be a manually operated Wheatstone Bridge, a deflection meter, or a self-balancing recorder or indicator. Calibration may be in conductance or resistance units. If manually operated, the null balance detector may be a galvanometer, headphone, or electron ray tube of sensitivity commensurate with the required precision of measurement.

(b) *Conductivity Cells:*

(1) Flow or in-line conductivity cells shall be used for measuring conductivity of 10 micromhos per cm or less. Cell constants from 0.01 to 0.1 are appropriate. The conductivity cell shall be mounted so that continuous flow of the sample through or past it is possible. The flow chamber and cell mounting shall retain calibration under conditions of pressure, flow and temperature change, and be resistant to corrosion. The chamber shall be equipped with means for accurate measurement of the temperature at the time of the conductivity measurement.

(2) Flow, in-line, dip-type, or pipet-type cells may be used for water having a conductivity greater than 10 micromhos per cm. Cell constants from 0.01 to 10 or greater may be used depending upon the conductivity of the water measured. A cell constant of approximately 0.01 to 0.1 is suitable for waters of lower conductivity (100 micromhos per cm and less). A cell constant of approximately 1.0 is suitable for waters of moderate conductivity (somewhat over 100 micromhos per cm.) A cell constant of 10 or higher is suitable for highly conductive waters. In each case, that cell shall be chosen which will preferably give a cell resistance in the range 500 to 10,000 ohms.

(3) Platinized electrodes (see Section 7) shall be used for determinations of conductivity by the referee method. Unplatinized electrodes may be used for field and routine laboratory testing of water having a conductivity below 0.1 micromho.

(c) *Thermometer.*—An ASTM Precision Thermometer having a range of −2 to 32 C and conforming to the requirements for thermometer 63C as prescribed in ASTM Specifications E 1.[5] The thermometer for the non-referee methods should be accurate to 0.5 C.

Purity of Reagents

4. (a) Reagent grade chemicals shall be used in all tests. Unless otherwise indicated, it is intended that all reagents shall conform to the specifications of the Committee on Analytical Reagents of the American Chemical Society, where such specifications are available.[6] Other grades may be used, provided it is first ascertained that the reagent is of sufficiently high purity to permit its use without lessening the accuracy of the determination.

(b) Unless otherwise indicated, references to water shall be understood to mean reagent water conforming to the Specifications for Reagent Water (ASTM

[5] 1967 Book of ASTM Standards, Part 30.
[6] "Reagent Chemicals, American Chemical Society Specifications," Am. Chem. Soc., Washington, D. C. For suggestions on the testing of reagents not listed by the American Chemical Society, see "Reagent Chemicals and Standards," by Joseph Rosin, D. Van Nostrand Co., Inc., New York, N. Y., and the "United States Pharmacopeia."

Designation: D 1193).[4] In making up the potassium chloride solutions for the referee method, use water stabilized to the laboratory atmosphere by aspirating air through the water from a fritted-glass or stainless steel gas dispersion tube. The equilibrium point is reached when the conductivity remains constant.

Reagents

5. (*a*) *Alcohol.*—95 per cent ethyl alcohol, isopropyl alcohol, or methyl alcohol.

tion A.—Dissolve 7.4365 g of KCl (weighed in air) in water and dilute to 1 liter at 20 ± 2 C.

(*i*) *Potassium Chloride Reference Solution B.*—Dissolve 0.7440 g of KCl (weighed in air) in water and dilute to 1 liter at 20 ± 2 C.

(*j*) *Potassium Chloride Reference Solution C.*—Dilute 100 ml of reference solution B to 1 liter with water at 20 ± 2 C shortly before using. Store the solution in a glass-stoppered bottle of chemical-resistant glass.

TABLE I.—ELECTRICAL CONDUCTIVITY VALUES ASSIGNED TO THE POTASSIUM CHLORIDE IN THE REFERENCE SOLUTIONS.

Reference Solution	Approximate Normality of Solution	Method of Preparation	Temperature, deg Cent	Electrical Conductivity, micromhos per cm[a]
A...............	0.1	7.4365 g KCl weighed in air per 1000 ml of solution at 20 C	0 18 25	7 138 11 167 12 856
B	0.01	0.7440 g KCl weighed in air per 1000 ml of solution at 20 C	0 18 25	773.6 1 220.5 1 408.8
C...............	0.001	Dilute 100 ml of solution B to 1000 ml at 20 C	25	146.93

* Excluding the conductivity of the water used to prepare the solutions.

(*b*) *Aqua Regia.*—Mix 3 volumes of concentrated hydrochloric acid (HCl, sp gr 1.19) with 1 volume of concentrated nitric acid (HNO_3, sp gr 1.42).

(*c*) *Ethyl Ether.*

(*d*) *Hydrochloric Acid (sp gr 1.19).*—Concentrated hydrochloric acid (HCl).

(*e*) *Hydrochloric Acid (1:1).*—Mix 1 volume of concentrated HCl (sp gr 1.19) with 1 volume of water.

(*f*) *Platinizing Solution.*—Dissolve 1.5 g of chloroplatinic acid ($H_2PtCl_6 \cdot 6H_2O$) in 50 ml of water containing 0.0125 g of lead acetate ($Pb(C_2H_3O_2)_2$).

(*g*) *Potassium Chloride* (KCl), dried at 105 C for 2 hr.

(*h*) *Potassium Chloride Reference Solu-*

Note 2.—The electrical conductivity of each of the reference solutions is given in Table I. The values for electrical conductivities for the solutions are those of G. Jones and B. C. Bradshaw;[7] the data of T. Shedlovsky[8] are used for solution C. Solutions A and B were prepared by Jones and Bradshaw by dissolving 7.4191 and 0.7453 g respectively of KCl (in vacuum) per 1000 g of solution (in vacuum). The method of preparation given in Table I includes the corrections to weights of KCl (in air against brass weights) per liter of solution at 20 C and assumes the density of KCl = 1.98, density of brass = 8.4, and the density of air = 0.00118. The densities of 0.10 N and 0.010 N KCl at 20 C, 1.00280 and 0.99871 g per ml, respectively, were inter-

[7] *Journal,* Am. Chem. Soc., Vol. 55, p. 1780 (1933).

[8] *Journal,* Am. Chem. Soc., Vol. 54, p. 1411 (1932).

polated from the data in the International Critical Tables.[9] Solution C may be prepared with sufficient accuracy by a tenfold dilution of solution B.

Sampling

6. (*a*) Samples shall be collected in accordance with the applicable method of the American Society for Testing and Materials as follows:

D 510—Sampling Industrial Water,[4]
D 860—Sampling Water from Boilers,[4]
D 1066—Sampling Steam,[4]
D 1496—Sampling Homogeneous Industrial Waste Water.[4]

(*b*) Avoid exposure of the sample to atmospheres containing ammonia or acidic gases. Protect the sample to avoid gain or loss of dissolved gases, particularly if there is some delay before the conductivity measurements are made. Use a flow-type cell for sampling and measuring condensed steam or water having a conductivity of less than 10 micromhos per cm.

Preparation of Electrodes

7. (*a*) A "broad" null position in the case of a manually operated instrument and sluggishness in rebalancing or stepwise action of an automatic recorder or an indicator may be an indication of deteriorated electrode surfaces. If such conditions are noted or if the cell constant as checked does not fall within reasonable limits of its nominal value, it is necessary to clean and replatinize the electrodes. In general, no mechanical cleaning should be attempted. Platinized electrodes are unnecessary for field and routine laboratory testing of water having a conductivity below 0.1 micromho.

(*b*) A suitable cleaning solution consists of an agitated mixture of 1 part by volume of isopropyl alcohol, 1 part of ethyl ether, and 1 part of HCl (1:1).

[9] International Critical Tables, Vol. 3, p. 87 (1928).

After cleaning, thoroughly flush the cell with water. If the old platinum black coating is to be removed, judicious application of aqua regia to the electrodes, or electrolysis in HCl (sp gr 1.19) is frequently successful. Alternatively, the cell manufacturer's instructions should be followed for cleaning the electrodes.

(*c*) Platinize the electrodes of the cells with H_2PtCl_6 solution. A suitable plating apparatus consists of a 6-volt d-c supply, a variable resistor, a milliammeter, and an electrode. The deposit should present a black, velvety appearance and should adhere well to the electrode surface. The procedure for platinizing is not critical. Good platinized coatings are obtained using from 1.5 to 3 coulombs per sq cm of electrode area. For example, for an electrode having a total area (both sides) of 10 sq cm, the plating time at a current of 20 ma would be from $12\frac{1}{2}$ to 25 min. The current density may be from 1 to 4 ma per sq cm of electrode area. The electrodes shall be plated one at a time with the aid of an extra electrode. During the plating the solution shall be agitated gently. When not in use, the cells shall be filled with water to prevent the drying out of the electrodes while in storage.

Calibration

8. (*a*) *Measuring Instrument.*—A calibrating resistor is usually furnished with conductivity recorders and indicators by the manufacturer, together with information as to the correct scale reading the instrument shall assume when this resistor is connected to the recorder or indicator in place of the conductivity cell. Follow the manufacturer's instructions and periodically check the instrument. When lead wires between the instrument and the cell are long, check the installation at least once by connecting the calibrating resistor at

the far end of the lead wire and noting the difference, if any, in reading with the long lead wire in the circuit. Check portable- or manually-operated instruments in a similar manner with one or several calibrating resistors. Note errors of significant magnitude and correct subsequent conductivity readings.

(b) *Conductivity Cells.*—For field and routine laboratory testing, check conductivity cells for cell constant by comparing instrument readings taken with the cell in question against readings on the same sample or series of samples taken with a conductivity cell of known or certified cell constant. Exercise care to insure that both working and reference cells are at the same temperature or, alternatively, at different but known temperatures so that a correction as later described can be applied. Resistance-reading instruments will indicate in direct proportion to the cell constant, while conductance-reading instruments will indicate in inverse proportion to cell constant. Conductivity cells provided with platinized electrodes may be calibrated with reference solutions in accordance with Section 11.

REFEREE METHOD

Application

9. This method is applicable to the measurement of the electrical conductivity of industrial water and industrial waste water when a somewhat greater degree of precision and accuracy is required than can be obtained by use of of field and routine laboratory methods.

Summary of Method

10. The conductivity is measured at 25 C, avoiding the use of a temperature correction and thus eliminating a major source of error in the measurement.

Determination of Cell Constant

11. (a) For the purposes of this method, the cell constant of the con-

ductivity cell used shall be known within ± 1 per cent. The manufacturer's certification of the cell constant within this accuracy shall be considered satisfactory. If the conductivity cell has been in service subsequent to this certification, it shall be rechecked by the manufacturer, or in the laboratory.

(b) Rinse the conductivity cell several times with water, then at least twice with the reference solution that has a conductivity nearest to that of the sample under test (Table I). Control the solution temperature to 25 ± 0.1 C. Measure the resistance of the cell. Repeat the measurement on additional portions of the reference solution until the value obtained remains constant to within the limit of the precision specified in Section 15.

(c) For instruments reading measured resistance in ohms, calculate the cell constant, J, as follows:

$$J = \frac{R}{1{,}000{,}000} \times (K_1 + K_2)$$

where:

R = measured resistance of the cell in ohms,

K_1 = conductivity, in micromhos per centimeter, of the KCl in the reference solution at the temperature of measurement (Table I), and

K_2 = conductivity, in micromhos per centimeter, at the same temperature of measurement of the water used to prepare the reference solution.

(d) For instruments reading measured conductance, in mhos, calculate the cell constant, J, as follows:

$$J = \frac{K_1 + K_2}{1{,}000{,}000 \times K_x}$$

where:

K_1 = conductivity, in micromhos per centimeter, of the KCl in the reference solution at the temperature of measurement (Table I),

K_2 = conductivity, in micromhos per centimeter, at the same temperature of measurement, of the water used to prepare the reference solution, and

K_x = measured conductance, in mhos (1/ohms).

Procedure

12. (a) *Conductivity Below 10 Micromhos per cm.*—Use a flow-type conductivity cell. Adjust the sample stream, known to be free of corrosion products and extraneous contamination, to a proper flow rate and bring the temperature to 25 C ± 0.1 C. Allow sufficient time to reach equalization of temperatures. Read the conductance.

(b) *Conductivity Above 10 Micromhos per cm.*—Either a flow-type, dip-type, or pipet-type cell may be used. If a flow-type cell is used, proceed as described in Paragraph (a). If another type is used, rinse the cell thoroughly several times with water and then two or more times with the sample. Adjust the temperature to 25 C ± 0.1 C. Read the resistance or conductance. Allow sufficient time for equalization of temperatures.

Calculation

13. (a) For instruments reading measured resistance, in ohms, calculate the conductivity of the sample as follows:

$$K = \frac{J}{R} \times 1,000,000$$

where:

K = conductivity of the sample, in micromhos per centimeter, at 25 C,

J = cell constant of conductivity cell, in reciprocal centimeters, and

R = measured resistance of the cell,

in ohms, when filled with the sample.

(b) For instruments reading measured conductance, in mhos, calculate the conductivity of the sample as follows:

$$K = JK_x \times 1,000,000$$

where:

K = conductivity of the sample, in micromhos per cm, at 25 C,

J = constant of conductivity cell, in reciprocal centimeters, and

K_x = measured conductance, in mhos (1/ohms).

Report

14. Report the conductivity at 25 C in terms of micromhos per centimeter to the nearest 1 per cent of the determined conductivity.

Precision

15. Results obtained should not differ by more than 1 per cent of the conductivity.

NON-REFEREE METHOD

Application

16. This method is applicable to field and routine measurements of the electrical conductivity of industrial water and industrial waste water.

Summary of Method

17. This method utilizes a flow-type conductivity cell to sample a continuous stream of the water under test, or, in the case of samples having conductivities greater than 10 micromhos per cm, any other convenient type of conductivity cell for taking a static sample. Temperature correction methods are also provided.

Procedure

18. (a) *Conductivity Below 10 Micromhos per cm.*—Use a flow-type conductivity cell. Adjust the sample stream,

known to be free of corrosion products and extraneous contamination, to a proper flow rate and bring the temperature to a steady value as near 25 C as possible. Read the temperature to the nearest 0.5 C. If the measuring instrument is provided with a manual temperature compensator, adjust this to the sample temperature value. If an automatic temperature compensator is provided, no adjustment is necessary but sufficient time must be allowed to permit equalization of temperatures. Read the conductivity. If the instrument has no means of temperature compensation, determine a temperature correction in accordance with the instructions in Section 19 to convert readings to 25 C.

(b) *Conductivity Above 10 Micromhos per cm.*—Either a flow-type, dip-type, or pipet-type cell may be used. If a flow-type cell is used, proceed as described in Paragraph (a). If another type is used, rinse the conductivity cell thoroughly several times with water and then two or more times with the sample. Determine the resistance or the conductance, and the temperature (to the nearest 0.5 C), on successive portions of the sample until a constant value is obtained. If the measuring instrument is provided with a manual temperature compensator, adjust this to the sample temperature value before reading the instrument. If an automatic temperature compensator is provided, no adjustment is necessary, but sufficient time must be allowed to permit equalization of temperature. If the instrument has no means of temperature compensation, determine a temperature correction in accordance with the instructions in Section 19 to convert readings to 25 C.

Temperature Coefficient of Conductivity

19. (a) Water solutions of electrolytes have temperature coefficients of conduc-

tivity as high as 3 per cent per deg Cent. The coefficient varies somewhat depending upon the composition of the electrolyte. To avoid making a correction, it is necessary to hold the temperature of the sample to 25 ± 0.5 C. If this cannot be done, the temperature coefficient must be determined and a correction applied. This requires a series of conductivity and temperature measurements on the sample over the required temperature range.

(b) In static systems, exercise care to avoid change of composition caused by loss of volatile constituents or by pick-up of contaminants from the air or the containing vessel during the series of measurements.

(c) In flowing systems, split the sample into two or more streams, running each through a suitable heat exchanger and flow-type conductivity cell. Provide means for variable heating or cooling so that the desired range of temperatures will be covered. Regulate the rate of flow through each cell so that each cell is measuring the same time fraction of the sample to eliminate the effect of a variable sample.

(d) From the data obtained, plot conductivity against temperature. From this curve a table of temperature correction factors may be prepared, or the ratio of conductivity at temperature, T, to conductivity at 25 C may be plotted against temperature, T, and this ratio or correction factor, Q, taken from the smoothed curve.

(e) When using an instrument provided with a manual or automatic temperature compensator, follow the manufacturer's instructions to calibrate the compensator or check its accuracy and applicability to the sample being tested.

Calculations

20. (a) For instruments reading meas-

ured resistance in ohms, calculate the conductivity of the sample as follows:

$$K = \frac{J}{R \times Q} \times 1{,}000{,}000$$

where:

K = conductivity of the sample, in micromhos per centimeter, at 25 C,

R = measured resistance of the cell, in ohms, when filled with the sample,

J = cell constant of conductivity cell, in reciprocal centimeters, and

Q = temperature correction factor.

(b) For instruments reading measured conductance, in mhos, calculate the conductivity of the sample as follows:

$$K = \frac{JK_x}{Q} \times 1{,}000{,}000$$

where:

K = conductivity of the sample, in micromhos per centimeter, at 25 C,

J = cell constant of conductivity cell, in reciprocal centimeters,

Q = temperature correction factor, and

K_x = measured conductance, in mhos (1/ohms).

(c) Automatic recorders and indicators provided with temperature compensators, when used with conductivity cells of the required cell constant, usually read directly in terms of micromhos per centimeter referred to 25 C. No calculations are necessary if the compensator is corrected for the solution in the cell.

Report

21. Report the value of the conductivity at 25 C in terms of micromhos per centimeter to the nearest 3 per cent of the determined conductivity.

Precision

22. Results obtained should not differ by more than 3 per cent of the conductivity.

Standard Methods of Test for

HARDNESS IN INDUSTRIAL WATER[1]

ASTM Designation: D 1126 – 65

ADOPTED, 1957; LAST REVISED, 1965

This Standard of the American Society for Testing and Materials is issued under the fixed designation D 1126; the final number indicates the year of original adoption as standard or, in the case of revision, the year of last revision.

Scope

1. (a) These methods[2] cover the determination of hardness in industrial water. The following two methods are included:

	Sections
Referee Method (Gravimetric)	5 to 10
Non-Referee Method (Volumetric Titration)	11 to 17

(b) The referee method is the most dependable for industrial water of unknown composition. The non-referee method is simpler but less accurate in the presence of interferences. When interferences do not exceed the specified limits in concentration, the non-referee method is as accurate as the referee method.

Definitions

2. (a) The term "hardness" in these methods is defined in accordance with the Definitions of Terms Relating to Industrial Water and Industrial Waste Water (ASTM Designation: D 1129),[3] as follows:

Hardness.—A characteristic of water generally accepted to represent the total concentration of calcium and magnesium ions.

NOTE 1.—Hardness is also caused by other polyvalent cations which seldom are present in more than trace amounts. Strontium will be determined with calcium in both the referee and non-referee methods. The interfering effects of other cations such as aluminum, barium, iron, manganese, and zinc may be eliminated by addition of appropriate inhibitors.

(b) For definitions of other terms used in these methods, refer to Definitions D 1129.[3]

Purity of Reagents

3. (a) Reagent grade chemicals shall be used in all tests. Unless otherwise

---

[1] Under the standardization procedure of the Society, these methods are under the jurisdiction of the ASTM Committee D-19 on Industrial Water. A list of members may be found in the ASTM Year Book.

[2] These methods conform essentially to the recommendations made by the Joint Committee on Uniformity of Methods of Water Examination in March, 1959.

---

[3] Appears in this publication.

indicated, it is intended that all reagents shall conform to the specifications of the Committee on Analytical Reagents of the American Chemical Society, where such specifications are available.[4] Other grades may be used, provided it is first ascertained that the reagent is of sufficiently high purity to permit its use without lessening the accuracy of the determination.

(b) Unless otherwise indicated, references to water shall be understood to mean reagent water conforming to the Specifications for Reagent Water (ASTM Designation: D 1193).[3]

Sampling

4. Collect the sample in accordance with the applicable method of the American Society for Testing and Materials, as follows:

D 510—Sampling Industrial Water,[3]
D 860—Sampling Water from Boilers,[3]
D 1066—Sampling Steam.[3]

REFEREE METHOD

(Gravimetric Determination of Calcium and Magnesium Ions)

Application

5. This method can be applied to the determination of calcium and magnesium ion concentration in any industrial water. The total hardness may be calculated from the results of these determinations.

Principle of Method

6. The calcium ion concentration is gravimetrically determined by the precipitation of calcium oxalate, which is

then ignited to calcium oxide. The magnesium ion concentration is gravimetrically determined by the precipitation of magnesium ammonium orthophosphate, which is then ignited to magnesium pyrophosphate. The total hardness is derived from the sum of the calcium ion content and the magnesium ion content of the sample.

Reagents

7. See the Method of Test for Calcium Ion and Magnesium Ion in Industrial Water (ASTM Designation: D 511).[3]

Procedure

8. Proceed in accordance with the procedure given in Method D 511.

Calculation

9. Calculate the total hardness in the sample from the calcium and magnesium content as follows:

$$\text{Total hardness, epm (Note 2)} = \frac{A}{20.04} + \frac{B}{12.16}$$

where:

A = calcium ion, in parts per million, present in the sample, and

B = magnesium ion, in parts per million, present in the sample.

Note 2.—To convert hardness in equivalents per million to equivalent $CaCO_3$ in parts per million, multiply by 50.

Precision

10. Calcium and magnesium hardness in concentrations below 0.5 epm can be determined with a precision of 0.01 epm, and in concentrations above 0.5 epm with a precision of 0.02 epm.

---

[4] "Reagent Chemicals, American Chemical Society Specifications," Am. Chem. Soc., Washington, D. C. For suggestions on the testing of reagents not listed by the American Chemical Society, see "Reagent Chemicals and Standards," by Joseph Rosin, D. Van Nostrand Co., Inc., New York, N. Y., and the "United States Pharmacopeia."

[5] By publication of this method, the American Society for Testing and Materials does not undertake to insure anyone utilizing the method against liability for infringement of Letters Patent nor assume any such liability, nor should this publication be construed as a recommendation of any patented or proprietary re agents or procedure that may be involved.

Non-Referee Method[5]

(Volumetric Titration)

Application

11. This method is applicable to raw water, treated water, and boiler water. It is not suitable for highly colored waters, which obscure the color change of the indicator. It is applicable to concentrations covering the range of 0 to 24 epm, and is capable of differentiating between calcium and magnesium hardness.

Principle of Method

12. Calcium and magnesium ions in water are sequestered by the addition of sodium ethylenediamine tetraacetate. The end point of the reaction is detected by means of Chrome Black T, color index 14645, which has a red color in the presence of calcium and magnesium and a blue color when they are sequestered.

Interferences

13. The substances shown in Table I do not interfere with this determination if they are present in concentrations not in excess of those indicated.

Reagents

14. (a) *Ammonium Hydroxide Solution* (*1:4*).—Mix 1 volume of NH_4OH (sp gr 0.90) with 4 volumes of water.

(b) *Buffer Solution*.—Prepare the buffer solution in three steps as follows:

(1) Dissolve 40 g of sodium tetraborate ($Na_2B_4O_7 \cdot 10H_2O$) in 800 ml of water.

(2) Dissolve 10 g of sodium hydroxide (NaOH), 10 g of sodium sulfide (Na_2S), and 10 g of potassium sodium tartrate ($KNaC_4H_4O_6 \cdot 4H_2O$) in 100 ml of water.

(3) When cool, mix the two solutions and add 1 g of magnesium disodium ethylenediamine tetraacetate, having a Mg to EDTA mole ratio of 1:1.[6] Complex any excess magnesium with standard sodium ethylenediamine tetraacetate solution (1 ml = 1.0 mg $CaCO_3$), if

TABLE I.—FREEDOM OF REACTION FROM INTERFERENCES.

Substance	Maximum Concentration Without Interference in the Total Hardness Test, ppm	Maximum Concentration Without Interference in the Calcium Hardness Test, ppm
Aluminum, Al^{+++}	20	5
Ammonium, NH_4^+	a	2 000
Bicarbonate, HCO_3^-	...	500
Bromine, Br	...	2
Cadmium, Cd^{++}	20	...
Carbonate, CO_3^{--}	1 000	50
Chloride, Cl^-	10 000	...
Chlorine, Cl	...	2
Chromate, CrO_4^{--}	500	500
Cobalt, Co^{++}	0.3	...
Copper, Cu^{++}	20	2
Iron, ferric, Fe^{+++}	10[b]	20
Iron, ferrous, Fe^{++}	10[b]	20
Lead, Pb^{++}	20	5
Manganese, Mn^{++}	1[c]	10[c]
Nickel, Ni^{++}	0.5[d]	...
Nitrate, NO_3^-	500	500
Nitrite, NO_2^-	500	500
Phosphate, PO_4^{---}	100	...
Silicate, SiO_3^{--}	200	100
Strontium, Sr^{++}	e	e
Sulfate, SO_4^{--}	10 000	10 000
Sulfite, SO_3^{--}	500	500
Tannin, Quebracho	200	50
Tin, stannic, Sn^{++++}	10	5
Tin, stannous, Sn^{++}	10	5
Zinc, Zn^{++}	20	5

[a] No data are available.

[b] Iron will not interfere in concentrations up to 200 ppm. However, the red color of the end point may return in about 30 sec.

[c] Manganese will not interfere in concentrations up to 10 ppm if a few crystals of $K_4Fe(CN)_6 \cdot 3H_2O$ are added to the buffer immediately before use.

[d] Accurate results can be obtained in the presence of 1 ppm nickel, but the end point is slow under these conditions.

[e] If strontium is present, it will be titrated with calcium and magnesium.

[6] Magnesium disodium ethylenediamine tetraacetate, supplied by the Fisher Scientific Co., Pittsburgh, Pa., Catalogue No. M-294, and Ganes' Chemical Works, Inc., New York 17, N. Y., have been found satisfactory for this purpose.

necessary. Make up to 1 liter with water. Keep the solution bottle stoppered when not in use. The reagent will be effective for at least one month.

(c) *Calcium Indicator*.[7]—Mix 0.20 g of ammonium purpurate and 100 g of NaCl by grinding them together to 40 to 50 mesh size.

(d) *Hardness Indicator*.—Add 1 ml of Na_2CO_3 solution (30 g per liter) to 30 ml of water. Add 1.0 g of Chrome Black T, color index 14645 and mix. Adjust the pH of the solution to 10.5 by addition of Na_2CO_3 solution (30 g per liter). Dilute the solution to 100 ml with isopropanol (99 per cent); ethanol (95 per cent) or methanol are also satisfactory. Store the solution in a tightly stoppered, dark-colored bottle to reduce deterioration due to air and light (Note 3). This solution has a storage life of about one month.

NOTE 3.—The indicator can be prepared, stored, and used in powder form rather than liquid form. The powder has a storage life of at least one year. It is prepared by grinding 0.2 g of Chrome Black T with 80 g of powdered sodium chloride (NaCl). A dark-colored bottle should be used for storage. Suitable powdered hardness indicator is available from several commercial sources.

(e) *Hydrochloric Acid* (1:4).—Mix 1 volume of concentrated hydrochloric acid (HCl, sp gr 1.19) with 4 volumes of water.

(f) *Sodium Carbonate Solution* (30 g per liter).—Dissolve 30 g of sodium carbonate (Na_2CO_3) in water and dilute to 1 liter.

(g) *Sodium Ethylenediamine Tetraacetate, Standard Solution* (1 ml = 1.0 mg $CaCO_3$).—Dissolve 4.0 g of disodium ethylenediamine tetraacetate dihydrate in approximately 800 ml of water. Adjust the pH of the solution to 10.5 with

NaOH solution (50 g per liter). Adjust the strength of this solution against calcium chloride ($CaCl_2$) solution (1 ml = 0.2 mg $CaCO_3$) (Note 4) so that 1 ml of the standard solution will be equivalent to 1.0 mg of $CaCO_3$. Store the standard solution, preferably in polyethylene, plastic, or hard rubber bottles, and restandardize monthly. If soft glass bottles are used, restandardize at least once a week.

NOTE 4.—The $CaCl_2$ solution may be prepared as follows: Dissolve 0.20 g of $CaCO_3$ in HCl (1:4), adding the HCl very slowly and keeping the dish containing the solution shielded with a watch glass to prevent loss by spattering. When all of the $CaCO_3$ has been dissolved, evaporate the solution to dryness, add 5 ml of water, and evaporate to dryness again. Repeat the addition of water and evaporation to dryness several times to ensure complete expulsion of free acid. Dissolve the final residue in water, and dilute to 1 liter in a volumetric flask.

(h) *Sodium Hydroxide Solution* (50 g per liter).—Dissolve 50 g of sodium hydroxide (NaOH) in water and dilute to 1 liter.

Procedure

15. (a) *Total Hardness*.—Measure 50 ml of the sample into a white porcelain casserole or evaporating dish. Adjust the pH of the sample, if necessary, to 7 to 10 by adding NH_4OH solution or HCl solution. Add 0.5 ml of buffer solution and stir. Add 2 or 3 drops of hardness indicator and stir (Note 5). Add standard sodium ethylenediamine tetraacetate solution slowly from a buret with continuous stirring until the color changes from red to blue. The titration should be completed within 5 min after the buffer addition. If the titration requires more than 5 ml of the titrating solution, dilute the sample and repeat the test.

NOTE 5.—If powdered indicator is used, add a sufficient quantity of it to produce the required depth of color (approximately 0.2 g).

---

[7] Murexide, Catalogue No. 6373, Eastman Kodak Co., Rochester, N. Y., is satisfactory for this purpose

(b) *Low Total Hardness.*—Determine low total hardness values (0 to 0.1 epm) by using the procedure given in Paragraph (a), but use a 100-ml sample and titrate by means of a microburet. When employing a 100-ml sample, add twice as much of the reagents as indicated in Paragraph (a).

(c) *Calcium Hardness.*—Measure 50 ml of the sample into a white porcelain casserole or evaporating dish. Add 2 ml of NaOH solution and stir. Add approximately 0.2 g of calcium indicator and stir. Add standard sodium ethylenediamine tetraacetate solution slowly from a buret with continuous stirring, until the color changes from salmon pink to orchid purple. The titration should be completed within 5 min after the buffer addition. If the titration requires more than 5 ml of the titrating solution, dilute the sample to avoid precipitation of some of the calcium, and repeat the test.

Calculation

16. (a) Calculate the hardness of the sample as follows:

$$\text{Hardness, epm} = \frac{20C}{S}$$

where:

C = milliliters of standard sodium ethylenediamine tetraacetate solution added in titrating hardness, and

S = milliliters of sample taken.

(b) Calculate the calcium hardness of the sample as follows:

$$\text{Calcium hardness, epm} = \frac{20D}{S}$$

where:

D = milliliters of standard sodium ethylenediamine tetraacetate solution added in titrating calcium hardness, and

S = milliliters of sample taken for the test.

(c) Calculate the magnesium hardness of the sample as follows:

$$\text{Magnesium hardness, epm} = E - F$$

where:

E = total hardness, epm, and

F = calcium hardness, epm.

Precision[8]

17. (a) The precision of the method for the determination of calcium may be expressed as follows:

$$S_T = 0.0048$$

where:

S_T = over-all precision expressed in epm of calcium hardness determined.

(b) The precision of the method for the determination of total hardness may be expressed as follows:

$$S_T = 0.0056$$

where:

S_T = over-all precision expressed in emp of total hardness determined.

_____

[8] Supporting data and literature references pertinent to this method are given in Appendix I to the Report of Committee D-19, *Proceedings*, Am. Soc. Testing Mats., Vol. 53 (1953).

Standard Method for

IDENTIFICATION OF TYPES OF MICROORGANISMS AND MICROSCOPIC MATTER IN INDUSTRIAL WATER AND INDUSTRIAL WASTE WATER[1]

ASTM Designation: D 1128 – 60

ADOPTED, 1960

This Standard of the American Society for Testing and Materials is issued under the fixed designation D 1128; the final number indicates the year of original adoption as standard or, in the case of revision, the year of last revision.

Scope and Application

1. This method covers the identification by microscopic examination of bacterial cells, mold filaments, algae, protozoa and other small animals, and such particles of inert material as may be found in industrial water and industrial waste water.

Summary of Method

2. The particulate matter in the water is examined under the microscope. By referring to Table I, the observed particles are identified as to general type. The specific identification of bacteria, molds, etc., must be left to trained microbiologists.[2]

Definitions

3. For definitions of terms used in this method, refer to the Definitions of Terms Relating to Industrial Water and Industrial Waste Water (ASTM Designation: D 1129).[3]

Apparatus and Materials

4. (a) *Centrifuge,* having a variable speed motor, but capable of attaining 2400 rpm.

(b) *Centrifuge Tubes,* with conical bottom 50-ml.

(c) *Microscope, Compound,* with at least 10X ocular and 10X, 43X, and 90X objectives, substage condenser, and preferably mechanical stage.

(d) *Light Source.*—A 75 to 100-w, nitrogen-filled, tungsten filament bulb with a "daylite" filter.

(e) *Immersion Oil.*—A good immersion oil—cedar, Shillaber, or equivalent.

(f) *Pipets.*—Satisfactory pipets can be made by taking a length of 8 mm OD

[1] Under the standardization procedure of the Society, this method is under the jurisdiction of the ASTM Committee D-19 on Industrial Water. A list of members may be found in the ASTM Year Book.
[2] Reference may be made to the "Standard Methods for Examination of Water and Wastewater," Am. Public Health Assn., Inc., New York, N. Y., current edition.
[3] Appears in this publication.

soft glass tubing 400 mm long, pulling out at the middle in a bunsen flame until the pulled out portion is 2 to 3 mm in diameter, and then cooling and cutting through the pulled-out portion. A 5-ml rubber bulb, medicine dropper type, may be used for the upper end.

(g) *Slides and Cover Glasses.*—Standard 3 by 1-in. noncorrosive slides. Cover glasses, round or square type $\frac{3}{4}$ in. in diameter, clean and grease free.

Note.—Clean cover glasses and slides as follows: (1) Place the cover glasses and slides in glacial acetic acid for 15 min; then wash in distilled water. Place in alcohol (95 per cent) for 5 min and dry with a clean towel. Pass through a bunsen flame before using.

(h) *Field Sampling Case* comprising: Facilities for keeping samples cold but not frozen, and out of sunlight; six to twelve wide mouthed bottles, 400 to 1000-ml capacity; with glass or polyethylene covers; marking pencil; thermometer; pH kit; dipper on a handle 5 to 6 ft long; 18-in. square of soft cloth, or soft laboratory towels.

Purity of Reagents

5. (a) Reagent grade chemicals shall be used in all tests. Unless otherwise indicated, it is intended that all reagents shall conform to the specifications of the Committee on Analytical Reagents of the American Chemical Society, where such specifications are available.[4] Other grades may be used, provided it is first ascertained that the reagent is of sufficiently high purity to permit its use without lessening the accuracy of the determinations.

(b) Unless otherwise indicated, refer-

---

[4] "Reagent Chemicals, American Chemical Society Specifications," Am. Chem. Soc., Washington, D. C. For suggestions on the testing of reagents not listed by the American Chemical Society, see "Reagent Chemicals and Standards," by Joseph Rosin, D. Van Nostrand Co., Inc., New York, N. Y., and the "United States Pharmacopeia."

ences to water shall be understood to mean reagent water conforming to the Specifications for Reagent Water (ASTM Designation: D 1193).[3] In addition, reagent water used for this method shall be sterile.

Reagents and Materials

6. (a) *Ammonium Oxalate – Crystal Violet Solution.*—Prepare Hucker's modification of the Gram stain as follows:

(1) Prepare Solution A:

Crystal violet (90 per cent dye content). 2.0 g
Ethyl alcohol (95 per cent)........... 20   ml

(2) Prepare Solution B:

Ammonium oxalate................. 0.8 g
Water........................... 80   ml

(3) Mix Solutions A and B:

(b) *Counterstain for Gram Stain.*—Prepare as follows:

Safranin 0 (2.5 per cent solution in alcohol 95 per cent)................... 10   m
Water............................ 100   m

(c) *Dorner's Nigrosin Solution.*—Prepare as follows:

(1) Prepare an aqueous Nigrosin solution as follows:

Nigrosin (water-soluble, certified by the Commission on Standardization of Biological Stains, Geneva, N. Y)...... 10 g
Water............................ 100   m

(2) Immerse in boiling water bath for 30 min; then add as a preservative:

Formalin......................... 0.5 ml

(3) Filter through double filter paper and store in sterile serological test tubes, about 5 ml to the tube.

(d) *Ethyl Alcohol (95 per cent).*

(e) *Loeffler's Methylene Blue.*—Prepare as follows:

(1) Prepare Solution A:

Methylene blue (90 per cent dye content)........................... 0.3 g
Ethyl alcohol (95 per cent)........... 30   ml

(2) Prepare Solution B:

Potassium hydroxide (KOH) solution
(0.1 g KOH per liter)............. 100 ml

(3) Mix Solutions A and B:

(f) *Lugol's Iodine Solution.*—Prepare Gram's modification of Lugol's solution as follows:

Iodine........................... 1.0 g
Potassium iodide (KI)............. 2.0 g
Water........................... 300 ml

Mix the iodine and KI with 5 ml of water in a small beaker. Stir thoroughly and then dilute with 300 ml of water.

Sampling

7. (a) Collect the sample in accordance with the applicable method of the American Society for Testing and Materials as follows:

D 510—Sampling Industrial Water,[3]
D 1496—Sampling Homogeneous Industrial Waste Water.[3]

(b) The sample shall be representative of conditions at the point taken. The sampling point should be chosen so that general, not highly localized, conditions are sampled. Never completely fill sample bottles and never permit to stand in direct sunlight.

Procedure

8. (a) In examining water samples microscopically, first describe the physical appearance of the sample. Indicate the color of the sample, its turbidity, and the relative amount, color, and consistency of any sediment or flocculent material contained in the sample.

(b) When samples contain a visible sediment, obtain the specimen for microscopic examination by use of a pipet. Place a small drop of the sediment so obtained upon a glass slide.

(c) If the sample contains no visible sediment, centrifuge 100 ml (two tubes) for 5 min at 2400 rpm. Then pipet or siphon off all but 3 to 6 drops from the tube. Mix the remaining catch by spurting in and out of the small pipet; then place a drop of the mixed catch on a slide, add a cover glass, and examine.

(d) Bring the specimen into focus with the low-power objective of the microscope, examine briefly, and then observe more closely with the "high-dry" objective. In examining wet mounts prepared as described in Paragraph (c), it will be found that contrast between such hyaline (colorless) structures as bacterial cells and the water in which they are suspended is poor in the presence of excessive illumination. This can be remedied by partly closing the iris diaphragm of the substage condenser, lowering the condenser, or readjusting the angle of the substage mirror, or by a combination of these operations.

(e) Structures may be found with the "high-dry" objective that warrant greater magnification, and for this purpose the oil-immersion lens shall be used. Swinging the "high-dry" lens out of the way, place a drop of immersion oil on the cover glass over the area illuminated by the light entering from the substage condenser. Swing the oil-immersion objective into place. Watching the lowest point of this objective *from the side, carefully* lower it with the coarse adjustment until it is immersed in the oil and nearly touching the cover glass. Then, looking through the eyepiece, bring the specimen into focus by raising or lowering the objective with the fine adjustment. The amount of light entering upon the specimen may need adjusting at this point. If the cover glass tends to "float" about on the drop of sample, put two spots of vaseline on the slide at opposite edges of the drop between slide and cover glass; these will anchor the cover glass in place.

(*f*) Bacterial cells may be more definitely differentiated from crystalline or amorphous particles which are likely to be included in water samples by employing one of the various staining techniques, as follows:

(*1*) *Negative   Stainings.*—This method does not stain the bacteria but instead stains the background black. The bacterial cells then appear as light areas in a darkened field. However, only the outlines of the organisms are made apparent by this method. A method for negative staining is as follows: Place a small drop of the sediment on a glass slide, mix with an equal volume of Dorner's Nigrosin solution (Section 6(*c*)), and streak out with the narrow edge of another slide. The streak or film resulting should be thin, since thick smears are likely to crack and peel upon drying. Dry the slide in air and examine under the oil-immersion lens without a cover glass.

(*2*) *Staining with Aniline Dyes.*— Aniline dyes are employed whenever it is desirable to obtain, in addition to the outline of the bacterial cells, some indication as to their internal structure. Before employing the aniline dyes, place a small drop of the specimen on a glass slide and spread out in a thin film. Allow the film to air-dry and fix it by passing it through a Bunsen flame several times. Care shall be taken not to overheat the slide, as this tends to cause distortion.

A simple method for staining with an aniline dye employs Loeffler's methylene blue solution (Section 6(*e*)). Flood the dye over the smear and allow to remain in contact with it for about 1 min. Wash off the dye with a gentle stream of cool water, and blot the slide dry between two pieces of blotting paper. Examine the slide under the oil-immersion lens. The bacterial cells will be stained blue; spores, if present will not take the stain; and granular structures will be a darker color than the cell.

Gram's differential stain offers a more detailed method, not only for definition of the cell structure, but also for classification of the organisms. The method is as follows: Apply the ammonium oxalate – crystal violet solution (Section 6(*a*)) for 60 sec, wash gently with water, and apply the iodine solution (Section 6(*j*)) for 60 sec and wash off with water. Apply ethyl alcohol (95 per cent) and renew until all but the thickest portion of the smear ceases to give off the purple dye (usually about 20 to 30 sec). Then blot the smear dry and examine under the oil-immersion lens. In this technique, the application of the alcohol is the important step and the one whereby the differentiation as to Gram-positive or Gram-negative is made. Those bacteria which will retain the violet-iodine combination are referred to as Gram-positive and exhibit a dark purple color when examined microscopically. Those which are decolorized by the alcohol and subsequently take up the counterstain are referred to as Gram-negative. Safranin used as a counterstain gives these a light red color. The Gram's stain is meant to be used for bacteria that are 24 hr old or less. As the bacteria becomes older, Gram-positive organisms frequently lose this characteristic and appear Gram-negative. The presence of Gram variable organisms may mean that the bacteria are of different ages or that different types are present.

(*g*) In examining stained smears, use the same general technique in focusing with the oil-immersion lens. However, in this case, maximum illumination is desired. Open the iris diaphragm completely, focus the substage condenser,

TABLE I.—PARTICULATE CONTENT OF WATER.[a]

I. LIVING ORGANISMS.—Show movement, reproduce, take up a variety of stains.
  A. *Algae* are green, blue green, brown, yellow, red, etc. Planktonic (free floating or swimming) or attached. Single celled, or a variety of colonial types.
    (1) *Blue Green Algae.*—Color not definitive since they may be otherwise. Never have definite chloroplasts.
    (2) *Green Algae.*—Always have definite apple green chloroplasts. May be motile, or not.
    (3) *Other Algae.*—Commonest other algae are: green euglenas (all with a red eyespot); cryptomonads which are usually olive green and vigorous swimmers by means of two flagella; diatoms, which are usually brown and frequently glide over the substrate (always have a silicious shell); yellow brown flagellates, usually maladorous if abundant; and dinoflagellates, usually also brown, but with one *encircling* and one swimming flagellum.
  B. *Bacteria.*—Maximum diameter less than 5 microns, except for sulfur bacteria, which are usually less than 2 microns. Cells rigid, except for *Spirochaetales*. Mostly spheres, rods, or spirals, but filamentous aggregates are common. One suborder contains stalked forms and one order contains branching cells in colonial aggregates. May be colored green or other shades.
  C. *Molds.*—Includes unicellular yeasts, which show definite budding; and tubular, branching, filamentous molds. A few yeasts are colored, but other molds are colorless. Mold filaments are of uniform diameter—opposite walls parallel in optical section; are segmented, and the ends are rounded.
  D. *Protozoa.*—They show a definite, often complex, organization, and are generally colorless and usually ingest solid food which may be bacteria, algae, or other protozoa. Movement is quick and fast for ciliates (many short locomotor hairs) and flagellates (long and few locomotor hairs or flagelle) and slow for amoeboid protozoa. It is difficult for an inexperienced observer to separate the ciliate protozoa from the remaining groups of microscopic animals. If a definite identification is required, it is suggested a biologist be consulted.
  E. *Rotifers.*—The term "wheel animalicules" is often applied to these. They generally show one or two small disks at the anterior end with what appear to be two small, turning wheels.
  F. *Worms.*—There are several kinds of these—all elongate and either flattened or round. Nematodes whip about vigorously in water—one kind is called "vinegar eel." They are round in cross section and their body contour is smooth. Bristle worms have clumps of stiff hairs at regular intervals along the body. Flatworms are ciliated, and have two black eyespots at their anterior end.
  G. *Other Small Animals.*—These might include certain eggs, water fleas, water mites, water bears, small snails, and small insect larvae. Space does not permit a description of them, but since they may sometimes occur in great abundance, it is suggested again that a biologist be consulted as to their significance, if numerous.

II. INERT MATTER:
  A. *Amorphous Matter*, including fecal pellets. Irregular to rounded shapes, not translucent black, gray, or brownish color.
  B. *Fibers.*—A variety of fibers, all elongate. May be vegetable (cellulose) or animal chitinous tracheal tubes of insects (characteristically spirally ringed), but they are inert and will not stain readily. Some vegetable hairs are triradiate, but are hollow, not solid as are sponge spicules.
  C. *Oil Droplets.*—Easily recognized by their refractive properties—a very black border, interior transparent.
  D. *Pollen.*—Usually rounded, each type of typical structure and shape. Yellow in color.
  E *Sand.*—Larger, angular, and translucent. Does not exhibit Brownian movement.
  F. *Silt.*—This may be granular matter of no special type of shape. If very small, the particles will exhibit the dancing Brownian movement, within a circumscribed area, but not move rapidly through a considerable distance as bacteria and protozoa do.
  G. *Sponge Spicules.*—Pointed. May be triradiate. Translucent.

[a]For illustrations of various organisms, see the "Standard Methods for Examination of Water and Wastewater," Twelfth Edition, pp. 691–731, Am. Public Health Assn., Inc. New York, N. Y. (1965).

and adjust the mirror so as to reflect light from the brightest part of the light source.

(*h*) For identification of crystalline material in water, follow the procedures given in the Method for Examination of Water-Formed Deposits by Chemical Microscopy (ASTM Designation: D 1245).[3]

Identification or Differentiation

9. Particulate matter likely to be found in water samples may be classified in accordance with the key in Table I.

Evaluation and Report

10. The report should indicate in a proportional way the categories of material in the sample examined and the degree to which the sample is concentrated, for example: "One hundred milliliters centrifuged, catch contained in 1 ml," and "Sample contained only mixture of bacteria," or "Sample contained only a few pollen grains." If the sample contains several categories of particulate matter, their relative order of abundance should be given.

Standard Definitions of
TERMS RELATING TO INDUSTRIAL WATER AND INDUSTRIAL WASTE WATER[1]

ASTM Designation: D 1129 – 66
ADOPTED, 1950; LAST REVISED, 1966

This Standard of the American Society for Testing and Materials is issued under the fixed designation D 1129; the number immediately following the designation indicates the year of original adoption or, in the case of revision, the year of last revision. A number in parentheses indicates the year of last reapproval.

Absolute Turbidity.—See Turbidity.

Absorbance.—The logarithm to the base 10 of the reciprocal of the relative transmittance, T.

$$A = \log_{10}\left(\frac{1}{T}\right) = -\log_{10} T$$

Absorbance thus expresses the excess absorption over that of a specified reference or standard. It is implied that compensation has been effected for reflectance losses, solvent absorption losses, and refractive effects, if present, and that attenuation by scattering is small compared with attenuation by absorption.

Accuracy.—A measure of the degree of conformity of a value generated by a specific procedure for the true value. The concept of accuracy comprises both precision and bias.

Acidity.—See Acidity-Alkalinity.

Acidity—Alkalinity:

Acidity.—The quantitative capacity of aqueous media to react with hydroxyl ions. (D 1884)[2]

Alkalinity.—The quantitative capacity of aqueous media to react with hydrogen ions. (D 1884)

Basicity.—See Alkalinity.

Free Mineral Acidity.—See Ion Exchange (Solid Phase).

Theoretical Free Mineral Acidity.—See Ion Exchange (Solid Phase).

Acute Toxicity.—See Bioassay.

Alkalinity.—See Acidity-Alkalinity.

Alkyl Benzene Sulfonate (ABS).—The generic name applied to the neutralized product resulting from the sulfonation of an alkylated benzene.

Anion-Exchange Material.—See Ion Exchange (Solid Phase)

Atom Fraction of an Isotope.—See Radioactivity.

Atom Per Cent of an Isotope.—See Radioactivity.

Backwash.—See Ion Exchange (Solid Phase).

Basicity.—See Acidity-Alkalinity.

Beta Energy, Maximum.—See Radioactivity.

Bias.—A persistent positive or negative deviation of the method average value from the true value.

Bioassay.—The determination of the effects of a substance on a test organism using standardized procedures.

Acute Toxicity.—Any direct lethal action of pollution to fresh-water fishes that is demonstrable within 96 hr or less. (D 1345)

---

[1] Under the standardization procedure of the Society, these definitions are under the jurisdiction of the ASTM Committee D-19 on Industrial Water. A list of members may be found in the ASTM Year Book.

[2] These designations refer to the ASTM Method to which the definition applies. Consult the Contents in Numeric Sequence for the latest edition of the method.

NOTE.—The lethal action includes both internal and external effects, but excludes indirect action such as depletion of dissolved oxygen through chemical or biochemical oxidation of the test material.

Critical Concentration Range.—The interval between the highest concentration at which all test animals survive for 48 hr and the lowest concentration at which all test animals die within 24 hr. (D 1345)

Diatoms.—Microscopic unicellular or colonial algae constituting the class *Bacillarieae* and having silicified cell walls. They are of great importance in self-purification of natural waters and as feed for many other forms of aquatic life.

Inhibitory Toxicity.—Any direct inhibitory action of pollutants on the rate of reproduction of diatoms which is demonstrable within seven days or less of testing.

Median Inhibitory Limit (IL_m).—The concentration of test material which decreases the amount of growth to fifty per cent of that in the controls, within a test period of seven days. It is the recommended measure or index of relative toxicity. Specifically, it is a concentration value derived by graphical interpolation and is based on the amount of growth made in seven days in the test flasks as compared with that made in a control.

Median Tolerance Limit (TL_m).—The concentration of pollutants at which 50 per cent of the test animals are able to survive for a specified period of exposure. (D 1345)

NOTE.—The exposure period may be 24, 48, or 96 hr. The 24-hr TL_m and the 48-hr TL_m generally should be determined whenever the toxicity is sufficiently pronounced to permit their determination.

Biochemical Oxygen Demand.—See Chemical Oxygen Demand.

Biological Deposits.—See Water-Formed Deposits.

Biological Tests.—Examination for the purpose of determining the presence, identity, numbers, or effects of the presence of any organism in industrial water. (D 510)

Boiler Water.—See Industrial Water.

Carrier.—See Radioactivity.

Cation-Exchange Material.—See Ion-Exchange (Solid Phase).

Chemical Oxygen Demand (COD).—Th amount of oxygen, expressed in parts pe million, consumed under specified condi tions in the oxidation of the organic an oxidizable inorganic matter contained i an industrial waste water, corrected fo the influence of chlorides. (D 1252)

Biochemical Oxygen Demand (BOD).- The quantity of oxygen required for th biological and chemical oxidation c water-borne substances under condition of test.

Chlorine Residual.—The amount of avail able chlorine present in industrial wate at any specified period, subsequent to th addition of chlorine. (D 1253)

Chlorine Requirement.—The amount o chlorine, expressed in parts per million required to achieve under specified con ditions the objectives of chlorination (D 1291)

Combined Available Chlorine Residual.- Residual consisting of chlorine combined with ammonia nitrogen or nitrogenou compounds. (D 1253)

Free Available Chloride Residual.—Re sidual consisting of hypochlorite ion (OCl), hypochlorous acid (HOCl), or combination thereof. (D 1253, D 1427)

Total Chlorine Residual.—Total amoun of chlorine residual present, without re gard to type. (D 1253, D 1427)

Chlorine Requirement.—See Chlorine Re sidual.

Circuit Reluctance.—The reluctance of th magnetic circuit is the sum of the reluc tances of each portion of the circuit (D 1341)

Combined Available Chlorine Residual.—Se Chlorine Residual.

Combined-Compound Formula.—See Multi ple Salts.

Combined-Oxide Formula.—See Multipl Salts.

Control Analysis.—The determination o specific ions or properties used as criteri of proper boiler operation. (D 860)

Corrosion Products.—See Water-Formed De posits.

Counter Background.—See Radioactivity.

Counter Beta-Particle Efficiency.—See Radio activity.

Counter Efficiency.—see Radioactivity.

Counter Gamma Efficiency.—See Radioactivity.

Critical Concentration Range.—See Bioassay.

Curie.—See Radioactivity.

Decontamination.—See Radioactivity.

Decontamination Factor.—See Radioactivity.

Diatoms.—See Bioassay.

Dissolved Matter.—See Matter.

Electrical Conductivity.—The reciprocal of the resistance in ohms measured between opposite faces of a centimeter cube of an aqueous solution at a specified temperature. (D 1125)

> Note.—The electrical conductivity shall be expressed in micromhos per centimeter at t C. The actual resistance, R, of the cell is measured in ohms. The conductance, $\frac{1}{R}$, is directly proportional to the cross-sectional area, A, inversely proportional to the length of the path, L, and directly proportional to the constant, K. The latter is the conductivity measured between opposite faces of a centimeter cube. Mathematically, $\frac{1}{R} = \frac{KA}{L}$, or $K = \frac{L}{AR} = \frac{cm}{sq\ cm \times ohms} = $ mhos per cm. The numerical value of this expression multiplied by 1,000,000 is the electrical conductivity in micromhos per centimeter.

Embrittlement Cracking.—A form of metal failure that occurs in steam boilers at riveted joints and at tube ends, the cracking being predominantly intercrystalline. (D 807)

> Note.—This form of cracking, which has been known as "caustic embrittlement," is believed to result from the action of certain constituents of concentrated boiler water upon steel under stress.

Equivalent per Million (epm).—See Reporting Results.

Fixed Matter.—See Matter.

Free Available Chlorine Residual.—See Chlorine Residual.

Free Mineral Acidity.—See Ion Exchange (Solid Phase).

Half-Life.—See Radioactivity.

Hardness.—A characteristic of water generally accepted to represent the total concentration of calcium and magnesium ions. (D 1126)

> Note.—Originally hardness was understood to be the capacity of a water for precipitating soap. Soap is precipitated chiefly by calcium and magnesium ions commonly present in industrial water but may also be precipitated by ions of other polyvalent metals, such as iron, manganese, and aluminum, and by hydrogen ions.
>
> For industrial water, hardness was originally measured by the amount of soap required to produce a stable lather. Measurement is usually made on a water sample, the alkalinity of which has been adjusted to eliminate the effect of hydrogen ions.
>
> Hardness is expressed fundamentally in terms of the chemical equivalents of metal ions capable of precipitating soap. It has commonly been expressed in terms of the equivalent amount of calcium carbonate.

Hydrogen Cycle.—See Ion Exchange (Solid Phase).

Industrial Waste Water.—See Industrial Water.

Industrial Water.—Water (including its impurities) used directly or indirectly in industrial processes. (D 510, D 1192)

Boiler Water.—A term construed to mean a representative sample of the circulating boiler water, after the generated steam has been separated, and before the incoming feed water or added chemical becomes mixed with it so that its composition is affected. (D 860)

Industrial Waste Water.—Water discharged from an industrial process as a result of formation or utilization in that process. (D 1496)

> Note.—Industrial waste water may have been utilized directly or indirectly, such as cooling water. Industrial waste water may be discharged into other processes, recovery systems, natural streams, or other receiving bodies.

Water-Borne Industrial Waste.—A water-borne substance (solids, liquids, or gases) resulting from an industrial operation or process and discharged into the water therefrom. (D 1496)

Inhibitory Toxicity.—See Bioassay.

Ion Exchange (Solid Phase).—A reversible process by which ions are interchanged between a solid and a liquid with no substantial structural changes of the solid. (D 1782)

Anion-Exchange Material.—An ion-exchange material capable of the reversible exchange of negatively charged ions.

Backwash.—That part of the operating cycle of an ion-exchange process wherein a reverse upward flow of water expands the bed, effecting such physical changes as loosening the bed to counteract compacting, stirring up and washing off light insoluble contaminants to clean the bed, or separating a mixed bed into its components to prepare it for regeneration. (D 1782)

Cation-Exchange Material.—An ion-exchange material capable of the reversible exchange of positively charged ions.

Free Mineral Acidity.—The quantitative capacity of aqueous media to react with hydroxyl ions to pH 4.3. (D 1782)

Hydrogen Cycle.—The operation of a cation-exchange cycle wherein the removal of specified cations from the influent water is accomplished by exchange with an equivalent amount of hydrogen ion from the exchange material. (D 1782)

Ion-Exchange Capacity (Volume Basis).—The number of milliequivalents of exchangeable ions per milliliter of backwashed and settled bed of ion-exchange material in its standard form.

Ion-Exchange Capacity (Weight Basis).—The number of milliequivalents of exchangeable ions per dry gram of ion-exchange material in its standard form.

Ion-Exchange Material.—An insoluble solid that has the ability to exchange reversibly certain ions in its structure, or attached to its surface as functional groups, with ions in a surrounding medium. (D 1782)

Ion-Exchange Resin.—A synthetic organic ion-exchange material.

Mixed Bed.—A physical mixture of anion-exchange material and cation exchange material.

Operating Cycle.—An ion-exchange process consisting of a backwash, regeneration, rinse, and service run. (D 1782)

Regeneration.—That part of the operating cycle of an ion-exchange process in which a specific chemical solution is passed through the ion-exchange bed to prepare it for a service run. (D 1782)

Regeneration Level.—The total weight of regenerant used per unit quantity of ion-exchange material in a single regeneration. (D 1782)

NOTE.—Regeneration level is usually expressed as pounds of regenerant per cubic foot of fully hydrated ion-exchange material, in a specific ionic form, measured after backwash and draining.

Rinse.—That part of the operating cycle of an ion-exchange process in which a specified water is passed through the bed of ion-exchange material to remove the residual regenerant solution. (D 1782)

Service Run.—That part of the operating cycle of an ion-exchange process in which an industrial or test water is passed through a bed of the ion-exchange material in order to remove specific ions from the water or to exchange them for an equivalent amount of a specific ion from the bed material. (D 1782)

Sodium Cycle.—The operation of a cation-exchange cycle wherein the removal of specified cations from the influent water is accomplished by exchange with an equivalent amount of sodium ion from the exchange material. (D 1782)

Theoretical Free Mineral Acidity.—The free mineral acidity that would result from the conversion of the anions of strong acids in solution to their respective free acids. (D 1782)

Ion-Exchange Capacity (Volume Basis).—See Ion Exchange (Solid Phase).

Ion-Exchange Capacity (Weight Basis).—See Ion Exchange (Solid Phase).

Ion Exchange Material.—See Ion Exchange (Solid Phase).

Ion Exchange Resin.—See Ion Exchange (Solid Phase).

Jackson Candle Turbidity.—See Turbidity.

Matter:

Dissolved Matter.—That matter, exclusive of gases, which is dispersed in water to give a single phase of homogeneous liquid. (D 1069)

Fixed Matter.—Residues remaining after ignition of particulate or dissolved matter or both (D 1888).

Oily Matter.—Hydrocarbons, hydrocarbon derivatives, and all liquid or unctuous substances that have boiling points of 90 C or above and are extractable from water at pH 5.0 or lower, using benzene as a solvent. (D 1340)

NOTE.—Chloroform or carbon tetrachloride may be substituted for benzene to avoid fire hazard or emulsion difficulties. The oily matter extracted by these solvents is, for practical purposes, the same material as that extracted by benzene.

Particulate Matter.—That matter, exclusive of gases, existing in the nonliquid state which is dispersed in water to give a heterogeneous mixture. (D 1069)

Total Matter.—The sum of the particulate matter and dissolved matter (D 1888).

Volatile Matter.—That matter that is changed under conditions of the test from a solid or a liquid state to the gaseous state. (D 1069, D 1888)

Median Inhibitory Limit.—See Bioassay.

Median Tolerance Limit.—See Bioassay.

Micromho.—See Electrical Conductivity.

Minimum Determinability.—The lowest value that can be determined within the stated precision of a method. Minimum determinability is expressed quantitatively in the same dimension that is used for reporting results of a test.

NOTE.—Minimum determinability corresponds to the lower limit of the range of quantitative applicability of a method. It does approach, but cannot equal or be less than, precision of a method. (See Sensitivity.)

Mixed Bed.—See Ion Exchange (Solid Phase).

Monitoring.—The continual sampling and automatic recording or signalling, or both, of water characteristics.

Multiple Salts.—Those salts whose composition may be written as a combination of two or more simple salts. Examples: burkeite, $Na_2CO_3 \cdot 2Na_2SO_4$, and atacamite, $CuCl_2 \cdot 3Cu(OH)_2$. (D 933)

Combined-Compound Formula.—A formula written in terms of the simple chemical formulae of the salts comprising the composition of the multiple salt. (See examples under Multiple Salts.) (D 933)

Combined-Oxide Formula.—A formula

which represents the constituents as "oxides" with the metallic oxides preceding the acid anhydrides each arranged in the order of increasing valence. Water of composition appears last. Examples: cancrinite, $3Na_2O \cdot 2CaO \cdot 3Al_2O_3 \cdot 2CO_2 \cdot 6SiO_2$, and analcite, $Na_2O \cdot Al_2O_3 \cdot 4SiO_2 \cdot 2H_2O$. (D 933)

Trivial Name.—A name that is not produced by any systematic procedure of naming. Trivial names may be derived from geographic locations, names of people, or from descriptive words. Examples: "aragonite" after Aragon, Spain; "wollastonite" in honor of the English chemist, W. H. Wollaston; and "magnetite" alluding to its highly magnetic property. (D 933)

Nephelometric Turbidity.—See Turbidity.

Normal Abundance of an Isotope.—See Radioactivity.

Nuclide.—See Radioactivity.

Odor:

Odor Intensity Index.—The number of times the concentration of the original sample is halved by addition of odor-free water to obtain the least definitely perceptible odor. (D 1292)

Threshold Odor Number.—The greatest dilution of the sample with odor-free water to yield the least definitely perceptible odor. (D 1292)

Odor Intensity Index.—See Odor.

Oily Matter.—See Matter.

Operating Cycle.—See Ion Exchange (Solid Phase).

Oxidation-Reduction Potential.—The electromotive force developed by a platinum electrode immersed in the water, referred to the standard hydrogen electrode (D 1498).

Particulate Matter.—See Matter.

Parts per Billion.—See Reporting Results.

Parts per Million.—See Reporting Results.

pH.—The pH of an aqueous solution or extract is defined in terms of E the electromotive force between a glass and reference electrode when immersed in the solution or extract, and E_s, the electromotive force obtained when the electrodes are immersed in a reference buffer solution (the assigned pH of which is designated pH_s), by the following equation:

$$pH = pH_s + \frac{(E - E_s)F}{2.3026RT}$$

where:

F = the Faraday,

R = the gas constant, and

T = the absolute temperature, (centigrade temperature + 273.16).

E and E_s are expressed in volts. (D 1293)

Phenolic Compounds.—Hydroxy derivatives of benzene and its condensed nuclei. (D 1783)

Precision.—The degree of agreement of repeated measurements of the same property, expressed in terms of dispersion of test results about the arithmetical mean result obtained by repetitive testing of a homogeneous sample under specified conditions. The precision of a method is expressed quantitatively as the standard deviation computed from the results of a series of controlled determinations.

Radioactive Daughter.—See Radioactivity.

Radioactivity.—Spontaneous nuclear disintegration with emission of corpuscular or electromagnetic radiation, or both.

Atom Fraction of an Isotope.—The number of atoms of the isotope divided by the total number of atoms of that element in the sample: This ratio is analogous to mol fraction. For example, using the isotopes of oxygen, the atom fraction of O^{18} is

$$\frac{O^{18}}{O^{16} + O^{17} + O^{18}}$$

Atom Per Cent of an Isotope.—The atom fraction of an isotope expressed in per cent.

Beta Energy, Maximum.—The maximum energy of the beta-particle energy spectrum produced during beta decay of a given radioactive species. (D 1890)

NOTE.—Since a given beta-particle emitter may decay to several different quantum states of the product nucleus, more than one maximum energy may be listed for a given radioactive species.

Carrier.—A weighable amount of a nonradioactive material which when associated with a radioactive substance will exchange with the radioactive substance and carry it through a chemical or physical process.

Counter Background.—In the measurement of radioactivity, the counting rate resulting from factors other than the radioactivity of the sample and reagents used. (D 1690, D 1890)

NOTE.—Counter background varies with the location, shielding of the detector, and the electronics; it includes cosmic rays, contaminating radioactivity, and electrical noise.

Counter Beta-Particle Efficiency.—In the measurement of radioactivity, that fraction of beta particle emitted by a source which is detected by the counter. (D 1890)

Counter Efficiency.—In the measurement of radioactivity, that fraction of the disintegrations occurring in a source which is detected by the counter. (D 1690, D 1890)

Counter Gamma Efficiency.—In the measurement of radioactivity, that fraction of gamma photons emitted by a source which is detected by the counter. (D 1690)

Curie.—A unit of radioactivity equivalent to 3.700×10^{10} atomic disintegrations per second or 2.220×10^{12} atomic disintegrations per minute. A microcurie is one-millionth of a curie (10^{-6} curie); a picocurie, one-millionth of a microcurie (10^{-12} curie). (D 1690, D 1890)

Decontamination.—In a radiochemical analysis, the elimination of material other than the radioelement being determined.

Decontamination Factor.—The ratio of the amount of foreign material present before a chemical or physical separation to that present afterward; for example, if 1 per cent remains, the decontamination factor is 100.

Half-Life.—The period of time in which one half of the radioactive atoms of a given radionuclide decay; an unvarying characteristic of a radionuclide.

Normal Abundance of an Isotope.—The abundance in atom per cent of the isotopes of an element as it is found in nature.

Nuclide.—An atomic species characterized by the constitution of its nucleus, specifically by the number of protons and neutrons.

Radioactive Daughter.—The direct radioactive decay product of a radionuclide.

Radioactively Homogeneous Water.—Water in which the radioactive material is uniformly dispersed throughout the volume of water sample and remains so until the measurement is completed, or until the sample is evaporated or precipitating reagents are added to the sample. (D 1690 and D 1890)

Radioisotopes.—Radionuclides having the same atomic number.

Radionuclide.—A radioactive nuclide.

Random Counting Error.—The error in a count rate determination due to the statistical nature of radioactive decay. The random counting error may be calculated as follows:

$$s = \sqrt{\frac{C_s}{t_s} + \frac{C_b}{t_b}}$$

where:

s = standard deviation in cpm,
C_s = total count rate in cpm,
C_b = background count rate in cpm,
t_s = time of count in minutes, and
t_b = time of background count in minutes.

Reagent Background.—In the measurement of radioactivity of water samples, the counting rate observed when a sample is replaced by mock sample salts or by reagent chemicals used for chemical separations. (D 1890)

NOTE.—Reagent background varies with the reagent chemicals and analytical methods used and may vary with reagents from different manufacturers and from different processing lots.

Resolution, Gamma.—The ratio (expressed as per cent) of the width in energy units of the observed photopeak of a gamma emitter at half the maximum count rate to the average energy of the photopeak.

Radioactively Homogeneous Water.—See Radioactivity.

Radioisotopes.—See Radioactivity.

Radionuclide.—See Radioactivity.

Random Counting Error.—See Radioactivity.

Reagent Background.—See Radioactivity.

Regeneration.—See Ion Exchange (Solid Phase).

Regeneration Level.—See Ion Exchange (Solid Phase).

Reporting Results:

Equivalent per Million (epm).—A unit chemical equivalent weight of solute per million unit weights of solution. Concentration in equivalents per million is calculated by dividing concentration in parts per million by the chemical combining weight of the substance or ion. (D 596)

NOTE.—This unit also has been called "milliequivalents per liter" and "milligram equivalents per kilogram." The latter term is precise, but the former will be in error if the specific gravity of the solution is not exactly 1.0.

Part per Billion (ppb).—A measure of proportion by weight, equivalent to a unit weight of solute per billion (10^9) unit weights of solution. (D 596)

NOTE.—A part per billion is generally considered equivalent to one millionth of a gram per liter, but this is not precise. A part per billion is equivalent to a milligram of solute per one thousand kilograms of solution.

Part per Million (ppm).—A measure of proportion by weight and equivalent to a unit weight of solute per million unit weights of solution. (D 596)

NOTE.—A part per million is generally considered equivalent to a milligram per liter, but this is not precise. A part per million is equivalent to a milligram of solute per kilogram of solution.

Residual Chlorine.—See Chlorine Residual.

Resolution, Gamma.—See Radioactivity.

Rinse.—See Ion Exchange (Solid Phase).

Sampling.—Obtaining of a portion representative of the material concerned.

Scale.—See Water-Formed Deposits.

Sensitivity.—The least amount or concentration that can be detected, not determined, by a method.

NOTE.—A numerical value of sensitivity must be less than either precision or minimum determinability of a given method and in some cases may be only a small fraction of the latter. (See Minimum Determinability.)

Service Run.—See Ion Exchange (Solid Phase).

Sludge.—See Water-Formed Deposits.

Sodium Cycle.—See Ion Exchange (Solid Phase).

Specific Gravity.—The ratio of the weight in air of a given volume of the sample to the weight in air of an equal volume of reagent water, both being determined at the standard reference temperature of 15.6 C (60 F). It is expressed as follows: Specific gravity, 15.6/15.6 C (60/60 F). (D 1429)

Sterile.—Free from any viable organism, either active or dormant. (D 510)

Surface Tension.—A property arising from molecular forces of the surface film of all liquids which tend to alter the contained volume of liquid into a form of minimum superficial area. (D 1590)

Note.—Surface tension is numerically equal to the force acting normal to an imaginary line of unit length in a surface. It is also numerically equal to the work required to enlarge the surface by unit area. The usual unit of measurement is dynes per centimeter.

Theoretical Free Mineral Acidity.—See Ion Exchange (Solid Phase).

Threshold Odor Number.—See Odor.

Total Chlorine Residual.—See Chlorine Residual.

Total Matter.—See Matter.

Transmittance.—The ratio of radiant power transmitted by the sample to the radiant power incident on the sample.

Note.—In practice, the sample is often a liquid or a gas contained in an absorption cell. In this case, the transmittance is the ratio of the radiant power transmitted by the sample in its cell to the radiant power transmitted by some clearly specified reference material in its cell, when both are measured under the same instrument conditions such as spectral position and slit width. In the case of solids not contained in a cell, the radiant power transmitted by the sample is also measured in the presence of that transmitted by a clearly specified reference material. This ratio is called relative transmittance, T.

Trivial Name.—See Multiple Salts.

Turbidity.—Reduction of transparency of a sample due to the presence of particulate matter. (1889)

Absolute Turbidity.—The fractional decrease of incident monochromatic light through the sample, integrating both scattered and transmitted light. (D 1889)

Note.—For a small amount of scattering experienced in essentially colorless solutions, absolute turbidity of a 1-cm layer corresponds to the extinction coefficient in the equation expressing Lambert's law.

Jackson Candle Turbidity.—An empirical measure of turbidity in special apparatus, based on the measurement of the depth of a column of water sample that is just sufficient to extinguish the image of a burning standard candle observed vertically through the sample. (D 1889)

Nephelometric Turbidity.—An empirical measure of turbidity based on a measurement of the light scattering characteristics (Tyndall effect) of the particulate matter in the sample. (D 1889)

Volatile Matter.—See Matter.

Water.—See Industrial Water.

Water-Borne Industrial Waste.—See Industrial Water.

Water-Formed Deposits.—Any accumulation of insoluble material derived from water or formed by the reaction of water upon surfaces in contact with water. (D 887, D 933)

Note.—Deposits formed from or by water in all its phases may be further classified as scale, sludge, corrosion products, or biological deposits. The over-all composition of a deposit or some part of a deposit may be determined by chemical or spectrographic analysis; the constituents actually present as chemical substances may be identified by microscope or X-ray diffraction studies. Organisms may be identified by microscopic or biological methods.

Biological Deposits.—Water-formed deposits of organisms or the products of their life processes. (D 887, D 933)

Note.—The biological deposits may be composed of microscopic organisms, as in slimes, or of macroscopic types such as barnacles or mussels. Slimes are usually composed of deposits of a gelatinous or filamentous nature.

Corrosion Products.—A result of chemical or electrochmical reaction between a metal and its environment (D 887).

Note.—A corrosion product resulting from the action of water, such as rust, usually consists of insoluble material deposited on or near the corroded area; corrosion products may, however, be deposited a considerable distance from the point at which the metal is undergoing attack.

Scale.—A deposit formed from solution directly in place upon a confining surface. (D 887, D 933)

Note.—Scale is a deposit that usually will retain its physical shape when mechanical means are used to remove it from the surface on which it is deposited. Scale, which may or may not adhere to the underlying surface, is usually crystalline and dense, frequently laminated, and occasionally columnar in structure.

Mill scale, formed on iron or steel heated in an atmosphere containing oxygen, consists chiefly of magnetic iron oxide, Fe_3O_4.

Sludge.—A water-formed sedimentary deposit. (D 887, D 933)

Note.—The water-formed sedimentary deposit may include all suspended solids carried by the water. Sludge usually does not cohere sufficiently to retain its physical shape when mechanical means are used to remove it from the surface on which it deposits, but it may be baked in place and be hard and adherent.

Standard Specifications for
SUBSTITUTE OCEAN WATER[1]

ASTM Designation: D 1141 – 52 (1965)

ADOPTED, 1952; REAPPROVED, 1965

This Standard of the American Society for Testing and Materials is issued under the fixed designation D 1141; the number immediately following the designation indicates the year of original adoption or, in the case of revision, the year of last revision. A number in parentheses indicates the year of last reapproval.

Scope

1. (a) These specifications cover the preparation of solutions containing inorganic salts in proportions and concentrations representative of ocean water.[2]

NOTE 1—Since the concentration of ocean water varies with sampling location, the gross concentration employed herein is an average of many reliable individual analyses. Trace elements, occurring naturally in concentrations below 0.005 ppm, are not included.

(b) These specifications provide three stock solutions, each relatively concentrated but stable in storage. For preparation of substitute ocean water, aliquots of the first two stock solutions, with added salt, are combined in larger volume. An added refinement in adjustment of heavy-metal concentration is provided by the addition of a small aliquot of the third stock solution to the previous solution.

Application

2. This substitute ocean water may be used for laboratory testing where a reproducible solution simulating sea water is required. Examples are for tests on oil contamination, detergency evaluation, and corrosion testing.

NOTE 2—The lack of organic matter, suspended matter, and marine life in this solution does not permit unqualified acceptance of test results as representing performance in actual ocean water. Where corrosion is involved, the results obtained from laboratory tests may not approximate those secured under natural testing conditions which differ greatly from those of the laboratory, and especially where effects of velocity, salt atmospheres, or organic constituents

---

[1] Under the standardization procedure of the Society, these specifications are under the jurisdiction of the ASTM Committee D-19 on Industrial Water. A list of members may be found in the ASTM Year Book.

[2] These specifications are based upon the following studies:

May and Black, "Synthetic Ocean Water," *Naval Research Laboratory Report P-2909*, August, 1946.

T. P. May and A. L. Alexander, "Spray Testing with Natural and Synthetic Sea Water, Part I—Corrosion Characteristics in the Testing of Metals," *Proceedings*, Am. Soc. Testing Mats., Vol. 50 (1950).

A. L. Alexander and T. P. May, "Spray Testing with Natural and Synthetic Sea Water, Part II—A Study of Organic Coatings," *Proceedings*, Am. Soc. Testing Mats., Vol. 50 (1950).

are involved. Also the rapid depletion of reacting elements present in low concentrations suggests caution in direct application of results.

Reagents

3. (a) *Purity of Reagents*—Reagent grade chemicals shall be used in all solutions. Unless otherwise indicated, it is intended that all reagents shall conform to the specifications of the Committee on Analytical Reagents of the American Chemical Society where such specifications are available.[3] Other grades may be used, provided it is first ascertained that the reagent is of sufficiently high purity to permit its use without lessening the accuracy of the determination.

(b) *Purity of Water*—Unless otherwise indicated, references to water shall be understood to mean reagent water conforming to ASTM Specifications D 1193, for Reagent Water.[4]

(c) *Stock Solution No. 1*—Dissolve the indicated amounts of the following salts in water and dilute to a total volume of 7.0 liters. Store in well-stoppered glass containers.

$MgCl_2 \cdot 6H_2O$	3889.0 g
$CaCl_2$ (anhydrous)	405.6 g
$SrCl_2 \cdot 6H_2O$	14.8 g

(d) *Stock Solution No. 2*—Dissolve the indicated amounts of the following salts in water and dilute to a total volume of 7.0 liters. Store in well-stoppered glass containers.

KCl	486.2 g
$NaHCO_3$	140.7 g
KBr	70.4 g
H_3BO_3	19.0 g
NaF	2.1 g

(e) *Stock Solution No. 3*—Dissolve the indicated amounts of the following salts in water and dilute to a total volume of 10.0 liters. Store in well-stoppered amber glass containers.

$Ba(NO_3)_2$	0.994 g
$Mn(NO_3)_2 \cdot 6H_2O$	0.546 g
$Cu(NO_3)_2 \cdot 3H_2O$	0.396 g
$Zn(NO_3)_2 \cdot 6H_2O$	0.151 g
$Pb(NO_3)_2$	0.066 g
$AgNO_3$	0.0049 g

NOTE 3—To make the addition of $AgNO_3$ in the above solution, dissolve 0.049 g of $AgNO_3$ in water and dilute to 1 liter. Add 100 ml of this solution to Stock Solution No. 3 before diluting to 10.0 liters.

Preparation of Substitute Ocean Water

4. Dissolve 245.34 g of sodium chloride (NaCl) and 40.94 g of anhydrous sodium sulfate (Na_2SO_4) in 8 to 9 liters of water. Add slowly with vigorous stirring, 200 ml of Stock Solution No. 1 and then 100 ml of Stock Solution No. 2. Dilute to 10.0 liters. Adjust the pH to 8.2 with 0.1 N sodium hydroxide (NaOH) solution. Only a few milliliters of NaOH solution should be required.

NOTE 4—The solution should be prepared and the pH adjusted immediately prior to use.

Preparation of Substitute Ocean Water with Heavy Metals

5. Add 10 ml of Stock Solution No. 3 slowly, and with vigorous stirring, to 10.0 liters of the substitute ocean water prepared as described in Section 4.

---

[3] "Reagent Chemicals, American Chemical Society Specifications," Am. Chemical Soc., Washington, D. C. For suggestions on the testing of reagents not listed by the American Chemical Society, see "Reagent Chemicals and Standards," by Joseph Rosin, D. Van Nostrand Co., Inc., New York, N. Y., and the "United States Pharmacopeia."

[4] Appears in this publication.

(See Appendix on p. 418.)

APPENDIX

The substitute ocean water prepared in accordance with Section 4 will have the composition shown above the broken line in Table I. The substitute ocean water with heavy metals, prepared in accordance with Section 5, will have the complete composition shown in Table I.

TABLE 1—CHEMICAL COMPOSITION OF OF SUBSTITUTE OCEAN WATER.[a,b]

Compound	Concentration, g per liter
NaCl	24.53
MgCl₂	5.20
Na₂SO₄	4.09
CaCl₂	1.16
KCl	0.695
NaHCO₃	0.201
KBr	0.101
H₃BO₃	0.027
SrCl₂	0.025
NaF	0.003
Ba(NO₃)₂	0.0000994
Mn(NO₃)₂	0.0000340
Cu(NO₃)₂	0.0000308
Zn(NO₃)₂	0.0000096
Pb(NO₃)₂	0.0000066
AgNO₃	0.00000049

[a] Chlorinity of this substitute ocean water is 19.38. Chlorinity, as used in these specifications, is an oceanographic term and is a measure of total halides in sea water which are precipitated by silver nitrate. It is numerically defined as the weight of silver required to completely precipitate the halogens in 0.3285 kg of ocean water.

[b] The pH (after adjustment with 0.1 N NaOH) is 8.2.

Standard Method of Test for

CHLOROFORM-EXTRACTABLE MATTER IN INDUSTRIAL WATER AND INDUSTRIAL WASTE WATER[1]

ASTM Designation: D 1178 – 60

ADOPTED, 1960

This Standard of the American Society for Testing and Materials is issued under the fixed designation D 1178; the final number indicates the year of original adoption as standard or, in the case of revision, the year of last revision.

Scope and Application

1. (*a*) This method covers the separation of chloroform-extractable matter[2,3] from industrial water and industrial waste water, and the gravimetric determination of that portion of the extract which is not lost upon evaporation of the chloroform. This residue may contain one or more members of several classes of compounds, among which are heavy oils and fats, trace amounts of phenols, rubber and certain resins, asphaltenes and carbenes, and decomposition products of tannin.

(*b*) This method is applicable to the determination of heavy oils in industrial water and industrial waste water. It is not intended to determine materials that volatilize under the conditions of test nor to determine specific oils, greases, and organic compounds. When such information is desired, the residue obtained by this method may be subjected to further extraction with specific solvents agreed upon by the interested parties.

NOTE 1.—The Joint Committee on Uniformity of Methods of Water Examination has concluded that uniformity of methods for the determination of grease and oily matter is not practical on the basis of present technical knowledge.

Commonly used solvents are hexane, petroleum ether, benzene, chloroform, or carbon

---

[1] Under the standardization procedure of the Society, this method is under the jurisdiction of the ASTM Committee D-19 on Industrial Water. A list of members may be found in the ASTM Year Book.

[2] For further information on this method, see the following references:

C. A. Noll and W. J. Tomlinson, "Fixing and Determining Oil in Feed Water and Boiler Water," *Industrial and Engineering Chemistry*, Analytical Edition, Vol. 15, p. 629 (1943).

H. D. Kirschman and R. Pomeroy, "Determination of Oil in Oilfield Waste Waters," *Analytical Chemistry*, Vol. 21, p. 793 (1949).

[3] The American Society for Testing and Materials agrees with the conclusion reached in November, 1959, by the Joint Committee on Uniformity of Methods of Water Examination, which states that uniformity of methods for the determination of grease and oily matter is not practical on the basis of present technical knowledge.

tetrachloride. These solvents exert selective extraction of specific greases and oily constituents. In addition, nonoily materials, such as phenolic type material and colloidal sulfur, are selectively extracted to varying degrees by these solvents. The selectivity of extraction is affected by the sample-to-solvent ratio.

Oily matter and grease may be of mineral, animal, or vegetable origin. The solvent action exerted on material of such different chemical structure will vary to a marked degree. Thus, application of a test method for oily matter or grease to such materials will necessarily produce a variety of results depending on the solvent used. In one case, a solvent may be an excellent extractant of mineral oil and a poor extractant of vegetable oil. In another case, a second solvent may be a poor extractant for mineral oil but excellent for extracting vegetable oil.

The definition of grease and oily matter by necessity is based on the procedure used because of the above considerations. The source of the grease or oily matter, the solvent used, the sample-to-solvent ratio, the pH of the sample, and the inclusion of nonoily matter will dictate the material determined and influence the interpretation of the results obtained.

Principle of Method

2. The sample of water is acidified to a pH of 3 to 4, after which the sample and chloroform are mechanically mixed. The extractable matter is the residue left after evaporation of the separated chloroform at room temperature, or on a water bath, depending on the temperature of the sample source.

Definitions

3. For definitions of terms used in this method, refer to the Definitions of Terms Relating to Industrial Water and Industrial Waste Water (ASTM Designation: D 1129).[3a]

Apparatus

4. *Stirring Apparatus.*—The stirring apparatus shall be equipped with a noncorrodible impeller of the type having a hollow cross-tube with a hole at the

bottom center, or an impeller of equivalent efficiency. It shall be capable of operating at 1250 to 1750 rpm in water and shall be of suitable size to enter a 1-liter, wide-mouth Erlenmeyer flask.

Purity of Reagents

5. (a) Reagent grade chemicals shall be used in all tests. Unless otherwise indicated, it is intended that all reagents shall conform to the specifications of the Committee on Analytical Reagents of the American Chemical Society, where such specifications are available.[4] Other grades may be used, provided it is first ascertained that the reagent is of sufficiently high purity to permit its use without lessening the accuracy of the determination.

(b) Unless otherwise indicated, references to water shall be understood to mean water conforming to the requirements for reagent water in the Specifications for Reagent Water (ASTM Designation: D 1193).[3]

Reagents

6. (a) *Chloroform.*

(b) *Hydrochloric Acid (1:9).*—Mix 1 volume of concentrated hydrochloric acid (HCl, sp gr 1.19) with 9 volumes of water.

Sampling

7. Collect the sample in a weighed, glass-stoppered, 1000-ml, wide-mouth Erlenmeyer flask of chemically resistant glass (Notes 2 and 3). If the sample is to be obtained through a sample line, flush the line thoroughly. Fill the flask immediately to approximately three fourths its height, thus collecting about

---

[3a] Appears in this publication.

[4] "Reagent Chemicals, American Chemical Society Specifications." Am. Chem. Soc., Washington, D. C. For suggestions on the testing of reagents not listed by the American Chemical Society, see "Reagent Chemicals and Standards," by Joseph Rosin, D. Van Nostrand Co., Inc., New York, N. Y., and the "United States Pharmacopeia."

900 ml of sample. Otherwise, collect the sample in accordance with the applicable method of the American Society for Testing and Materials, as follows:

D 510—Sampling Industrial Water,[3a]
D 860—Sampling Water from Boilers.[3a]

NOTE 2.—The sample may be collected in cork-stoppered flasks, provided the stoppers are wrapped in metal foil.

NOTE 3.—Flasks of 2000-ml capacity may be used when the extractable matter content is less than 5 ppm.

Procedure

8. (*a*) Weigh the flask and its contents to the nearest 1 g and obtain the weight of sample by difference.

(*b*) Withdraw a few drops of the sample and test its pH value with indicator paper or other suitable means. If this value is above 4, adjust the pH to a value between 3 and 4 by addition of HCl (1:9).

(*c*) Add 100 ml of chloroform to the flask and stir mechanically for 15 min at a rate of 1250 to 1750 rpm. Remove the stirrer and allow time for phases to separate; then transfer all the chloroform layer to a 500-ml separatory funnel by means of a glass siphon. No lubricant should be used on the stopcock of the funnel. Add 50 ml of chloroform to the flask and repeat the stirring for 15 min; then transfer the second portion of chloroform to the same separatory funnel.

(*d*) Draw off the chloroform layer from the separatory funnel through a dry, fat- and oil-free filter paper into a 250-ml beaker. If there is suspended matter at the interface, leave about 2 ml of the chloroform layer in the funnel. Add a 20-ml portion of fresh chloroform directly to the funnel, shake, and then withdraw the chloroform, using it as a wash for the filter.

(*e*) Evaporate the chloroform to about 20 ml on a boiling water bath; then transfer it quantitatively to a weighed platinum or silica evaporating dish. Again reduce the volume to 20 ml on a boiling water bath; then continue the evaporation at room temperature, covering the dish with a ribbed watch glass to protect the contents from contamination with dust. Weigh the dish periodically until constant weight is obtained (Note 4).

NOTE 4.—The evaporation may be completed on the boiling water bath if the sample was obtained from a source whose temperature was at or above 100 C.

Calculation

9. Calculate the concentration of chloroform-extractable matter in the acidified water sample in parts per million as follows:

Chloroform-extractable matter, ppm

$$= \frac{(W_1 - W_2)}{S} \times 1{,}000{,}000$$

where:
W_1 = weight, in grams, of dish plus residue,
W_2 = weight, in grams, of dish only, and
S = grams of sample used.

Precision and Accuracy[5]

10. Under the accepted definitions of precision and accuracy, values cannot be given because of the material being isolated (Note 5).

NOTE 5.—The effectiveness of chloroform as a solvent for organic materials has been demonstrated by Kirschman and Pomeroy.[6]

[5] Supporting data for this method appear in the Report of Committee D-19, *Proceedings*, Am. Soc. Testing Mats. Vol. 51, p. 421 (1951).
[6] H. D. Kirschman and R. Pomeroy, "Determination of Oil in Oilfield Waste Waters," *Analytical Chemistry*, Vol. 21, p. 793 (1949).

Standard Methods of Test for
FLUORIDE ION IN INDUSTRIAL WATER AND INDUSTRIAL WASTE WATER[1]

ASTM Designation: D 1179 - 61

ADOPTED, 1957; REVISED, 1958, 1961

This Standard of the American Society for Testing and Materials is issued under the fixed designation D 1179; the number immediately following the designation indicates the year of original adoption or, in the case of revision, the year of last revision. A number in parentheses indicates the year of last reapproval.

Scope

1. (a) These methods cover the determination of fluoride ion in industrial water and industrial waste water. Three methods are given as follows:

	Sections
Referee Method	5 to 10
Non-Referee Method A (Zirconium-Alizarin)	11 to 18
Non-Referee Method B (Zirconium-Eriochrome Cyanine)	19 to 27

[1] Under the standardization procedure of the Society, these methods are under the jurisdiction of the ASTM Committee D-19 on Industrial Water. A list of members may be found in the ASTM Year Book.

These methods have been adapted from analytical methods developed by the Branch of Quality of Water, U. S. Geological Survey, as published in "Methods for Collection and Analysis of Water Samples," U. S. Geological Survey Water-Supply Paper 1454, pp. 163–171 (1960). For a more thorough discussion, see W. L. Lamar and P. G. Drake, "Factors Affecting the Determination of Fluoride in Water with Zirconium-Alizarin," *Journal*, Am. Water Works Assn., Vol. 47, June, 1955, pp. 563–572, and L. L. Thatcher, "Modified Zirconium-Eriochrome Cyanine R Determination of Fluoride," *Analytical Chemistry*. Vol. 29, November, 1957, pp. 1709–1712.

(b) The Referee Method covers the accurate measurement of fluoride ion in water through isolation of the fluoride by distillation. The Non-Referee Methods provide more convenient and faster means of determining fluoride ion when interfering substances are not present or when they are within tolerable limits.

Definitions

2. For definitions of terms used in these methods, refer to the Definitions of Terms Relating to Industrial Water and Industrial Waste Water (ASTM Designation: D 1129).[2]

Purity of Reagents

3. (a) Reagent grade chemicals shall be used in all tests. Unless otherwise indicated, it is intended that all reagents shall conform to the specifications of the Committee on Analytical Reagents of the American Chemical Society,

[2] Appears in this publication.

where such specifications are available.[3] Other grades may be used, provided it is first ascertained that the reagent is of sufficiently high purity to permit its use without lessening the accuracy of the determination.

(b) Unless otherwise indicated, references to water shall be understood to mean reagent water conforming to the Specifications for Reagent Water (ASTM Designation: D 1193).[2] In addition, the water shall be made fluoride-free by distillation after alkalizing to phenolphthalein with sodium hydroxide.

Sampling

4. Collect the sample in accordance with the applicable method of the American Society for Testing and Materials, as follows:

D 510—Sampling Industrial Water,[2]
D 860—Sampling Water from Boilers,[2]
D 1066—Sampling Steam,[2]
D 1496—Sampling Homogeneous Industrial Waste Water.[2]

REFEREE METHOD[4]

Application

5. This method is applicable to the accurate determination of fluoride ion in all industrial water and industrial waste water.

Summary of Method

6. The fluoride is distilled from the sample as hydrofluorosilicic acid and is then determined colorimetrically as the zirconium-alizarin complex (Non-Referee Method A) or as the zirconium-Erio-

---

[3] "Reagent Chemicals, American Chemical Society Specifications," Am. Chem. Soc., Washington, D. C. For suggestions on the testing of reagents not listed by the American Chemical Society, see "Reagent Chemicals and Standards," by Joseph Rosin, D. Van Nostrand Co., Inc., New York, N. Y., and the "United States Pharmacopeia."
[4] Supporting data giving results of cooperative tests have been filed at ASTM Headquarters.

chrome Cyanine complex (Non-Referee Method B).

Interferences

7. Anions and cations generally found in industrial water offer no interference, because the fluoride ion is isolated by distillation.

Apparatus

8. *Distillation Assembly.*—A steam generator, a fluoride isolation still, and a distillate receiver, assembled as shown in Fig. 1. Rubber connections shall be used on the steam generator, and ground-glass joints shall be used on the fluoride isolation still.

Reagents

9. (a) *Phenolphthalein Indicator Solution (5 g per liter).*—Dissolve 0.5 g of phenolphthalein in 50 ml of ethyl alcohol (95 per cent) (Note 1). Dilute to 100 ml with water.

Note 1.—Specially denatured ethyl alcohol conforming to Formula No. 3A or 30 of the U. S. Bureau of Internal Revenue may be substituted for ethyl alcohol (95 per cent).

(b) *Silver Sulfate* (Ag_2SO_4), powder.
(c) *Sodium Hydroxide* (NaOH), pellets.
(d) *Sulfuric Acid (sp gr 1.84).*—Concentrated sulfuric acid (H_2SO_4).

Procedure

10. (a) Dissolve in 50 ml of H_2SO_4, by stirring, sufficient Ag_2SO_4 to precipitate the chloride present in the sample. A slight excess of Ag_2SO_4 will do no harm.

(b) Transfer 200 ml of the sample (Note 2) to the fluoride distillation flask, make alkaline to phenolphthalein with a pellet of NaOH, add some glass beads, and evaporate to a volume of about 50 ml, preferably using an electrical heating mantle. Care must be exercised to prevent bumping and consequent loss of sample.

34-1

NOTE 2.—If 200 ml of the sample contain more than 4000 mg of chloride, take a smaller aliquot so that the chloride in the sample aliquot will not exceed 4000 mg chloride.

(c) Allow the concentrated sample to cool and make slightly acid by dropwise addition of H_2SO_4. Connect the distilla-

distillation flask, regulating the addition of the solution by means of the stopcock on the separatory funnel. Tilt or shake flask M to thoroughly mix the H_2SO_4 - Ag_2SO_4 solution with the sample.

(d) Wash the acid from the tip of the funnel into the flask with water and

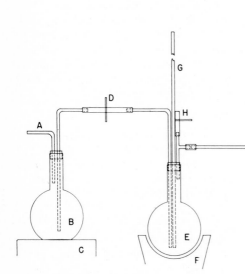
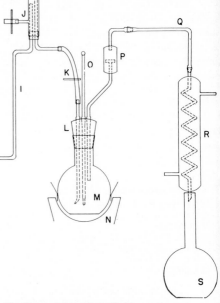

A—Pressure control tube.
B—Hot-water reservoir, 1000-ml.
C—Hot plate.
D—Hot-water supply tube clamp.
E—Steam generator flask, 1000-ml.
F—Heating mantle.
G—Pressure relief tube.
H—Steam regulation tube—Hoffman clamp.
I—Glass steam line (asbestos covered).
J—Steam trap (asbestos covered)—clamp on relief water drain.

K—Steam inlet tube—Hoffman clamp.
L—Fluoride distillation flask adapter.
M—Fluoride distillation flask, 300-ml.
N—Heating mantle with asbestos shield.
O—Thermometer, 250 C.
P—Trap.
Q—Condenser adapter.
R—Condenser.
S—Distillate receiving flask, 200-ml.

FIG. 1.—Distillation Assembly for Fluoride Isolation.

tion assembly except for the steam inlet tube, K (Fig. 1). In place of the steam inlet tube insert a long-stem cylindrical separatory funnel. Start a flow of cooling water through the condenser. Close the stopcock on the separatory funnel, and introduce into the funnel 50 ml of the H_2SO_4 - Ag_2SO_4 solution. Slowly add the H_2SO_4 - Ag_2SO_4 solution to the fluoride

remove the separatory funnel. In its place insert the steam inlet tube and connect it to the steam trap, J (Fig. 1). Make the water in the steam generator slightly alkaline to phenolphthalein with NaOH and start the flow of steam through the sample by opening the clamp on the steam inlet, K, and closing the clamp on the steam regulation tube

H. Adjust the clamp on the steam regula
tion tube so that a hydrostatic head of
20 to 40 cm is maintained in the steam
generator pressure relief tube, *G* (Note 3).

NOTE 3.—The hot water reservoir, *B*, is used
to supply boiling water to the steam generator.
The pressure control tube, *A*, serves as a steam
release. When boiling water is needed in the
steam generator, *E*, clamp *D* is released and air
pressure is applied to tube *A*.

(*e*) Apply heat to the distillation flask
by means of the heating mantle, *N*.
Prevent undue heating of the flask walls
by means of a shield of asbestos at the
top of the mantle. Do not apply heat
above the surface of the liquid in the
flask. Maintain the temperature of the
sample at 135 to 145 C during the distillation by the adjustment of steam flow
and the application of heat to the fluoride
distillation flask. Collect 200 ml of
distillate in a 200-ml volumetric flask.

(*f*) Complete the determination of
the fluoride concentration by either the
zirconium-alizarin method, in accordance with Sections 14 to 18, or the
zirconium-Eriochrome Cyanine method,
in accordance with Sections 22 to 27.

NON-REFEREE METHOD A

(Zirconium-Alizarin Method)

Application

11. This visual method is applicable
to the determination of fluoride in
industrial water and industrial waste
water when interfering substances are
absent or within tolerable limits. Corrections for interfering substances may be
applied to a limited extent. This method
is more subject to interference than
Method B, but it does not require as
exacting a technique and may be less
time-consuming, depending on the circumstances.

Summary of Method

12. The determination of fluoride in
water with the zirconium-alizarin reagent

is based on the property of the fluoride
ion to form the zirconium fluoride complex. This results in a proportionate
subtraction of zirconium from the zirconium-alizarin reagent. When fluoride
is present, the reaction results in variations of color intensity and in a color
range from pink to yellow-green, with
intermediate color combinations depending on the concentration of fluoride
ion present.

Interferences

13. (*a*) The zirconium-alizarin fluoride
reaction is subject to interferences.
Certain ions affect the reaction in such a
manner that the fluoride concentration
appears to be higher than its true value,
while other ions have the opposite
effect. Limited corrections may be applied for interfering substances. However, when the effect of any substance
present is not known, or when the
composition of the water is not known,
prior isolation of the fluoride by the
Referee Method is required. Specific
interferences are discussed briefly in
Paragraphs (*b*) to (*i*) and in the literature.[5]

(*b*) The following ions are tolerable
in the concentrations shown and cause
little interference in much higher concentrations: calcium, magnesium, and
potassium, 200 ppm; nitrate, 300 ppm,
and sodium, 1000 ppm.

(*c*) Aluminum ion causes a negative
error, due to formation of aluminum
fluoride complex. The error depends
on the concentrations of both fluoride
and aluminum. Figure 2 shows a correction curve for aluminum that is
valid for reaction periods of 1 hr and 7
to 18 hr.

---

[5] Supporting data pertinent to this method are
given in Appendix I to the Report of Committee
D-19, *Proceedings*, Am. Soc. Testing Mats.,
Vol. 55, p. 548 (1955).

(*d*) The presence of hexavalent chromium causes a positive error in the fluoride determination. This effect varies inversely with the concentration of fluoride and directly with the concentration of chromium and reaction time. The maximum fluoride error caused by hexavalent chromium is as follows:

lation as described in the referee method.

(*e*) Ferrous and ferric iron up to 1.5 mg in the sample aliquot do not cause significant interference. However, 2.5 mg of iron interferes seriously by obscuring the reaction color. Manganese does not produce any significant interferences in quantities as high as 2.5 mg.

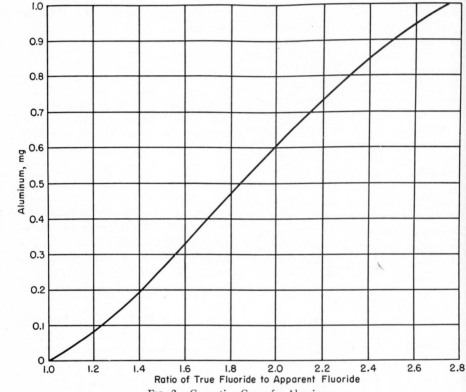

FIG. 2.—Correction Curve for Aluminum.

For 1-hr readings, the fluoride error will not exceed +0.005 mg F when the hexavalent chromium in the sample aliquot does not exceed 0.05 mg. For 7 to 18-hr readings, the fluoride error will also not exceed +0.005 mg F when the hexavalent chromium does not exceed 0.01 mg. When the chromium in the sample aliquot exceeds 0.01 mg, the fluoride readings should be taken at 1 hr; and when it exceeds 0.05 mg, the fluoride should be isolated by distil-

(*f*) The interference of nitrate is negligible. The presence of sulfate increases the fluoride indication while chloride and basicity (alkalinity) decrease the fluoride indication. These interferences are substantially additive up to 100 mg of sulfate, 200 mg of chloride, and basicity equivalent to 50 mg of alkalinity as $CaCO_3$ in the sample aliquot. The effect of the basicity is the same regardless of whether due to bicarbonate, carbonate, or hydroxide.

Figure 3 shows correction curves for sulfate, chloride, and basicity that are valid for reaction periods of 1 hr and 7 to 18 hr.

(g) Phosphates as PO_4 or as $(NaPO_3)_6$ are similar in their effects and decrease or increase the fluoride indication depending upon the quantities of phosphate

the error is not more than 0.004 mg fluoride.

(2) For 1-hr readings when the phosphate does not exceed 0.20 mg, the error is not more than 0.007 mg fluoride.

(3) For 7 to 18-hr readings when the phosphate does not exceed 0.20

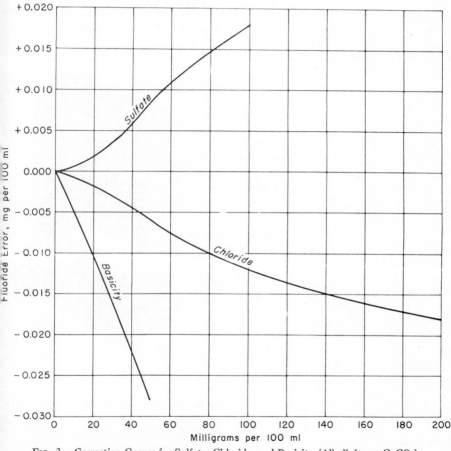

FIG. 3.—Correction Curves for Sulfate, Chloride, and Basicity (Alkalinity as $CaCO_3$).

and fluoride present. These effects vary with reaction time. When the quantity of the fluoride in the sample aliquot is not more than 0.10 mg, the maximum of the variable interferences of phosphates as PO_4 is as follows:

(1) For 1-hr readings when the phosphate does not exceed 0.10 mg,

mg, the error is not more than 0.004 mg fluoride (Note 4).

If the quantity of phosphate in the sample aliquot exceeds the above limits, fluoride should be isolated by distillation (Referee Method).

Note 4.—For the above ranges of fluoride and phosphate, the errors are mostly negative.

However, for several combinations of the higher concentrations of fluoride and the lower concentrations of phosphate, the error is positive with the maximum positive error occurring for the combination of 0.10 mg of fluoride and 0.01 mg of phosphate.

(*h*) Acidity increases the fluoride indication below pH 4.5, but at pH 3.5 the effect is only +0.002 mg of fluoride (Note 5).

Note 5.—Although the hydrogen ion effect may be counteracted by applying corrections or by carefully adjusting the pH of the sample to 4.5 to 6.0 with NaOH, samples low in pH are apt to contain other constituents that make distillation advisable.

(*i*) The reaction color may be obscured by turbidity and interfering color. Visually, most analysts can tolerate color or turbidity, or both, up to 20 units together. When there is noticeable turbidity it is recommended that it be removed by filtration through a membrane-type filter. The limit of color that can be tolerated visually may be extended by making the comparison (Section 16(*d*)) as follows: Place the tube containing the sample plus reagent above a similar tube containing the same volume of water. Place the tube containing the appropriate standard above a tube containing a duplicate volume of the sample without the reagent, acidify with 5 ml of H_2SO_4 (1:16), and add 5 ml of water so that each tube will contain equal volumes. View through the entire length of the liquid columns, preferably by using a simply constructed two-hole Nessler tube support.

Apparatus

14. (*a*) *Nessler Color Comparison Tubes.*—Matched tubes of 100-ml capacity.

(*b*) *Nessler Tube Support.*—This is optional. A suggested type is shown in Fig. 4.

Reagents

15. (*a*) *Sodium Arsenite Solution* (*2 g per liter*).—Dissolve 2 g of sodium

arsenite ($NaAsO_2$) in water and dilute to 1 liter.

(*b*) *Sodium Fluoride, Standard Solution* (*1 ml = 0.01 mg F*).—Dissolve 0.2210 g of sodium fluoride (NaF) in water and dilute to 1 liter. Dilute 100 ml of this stock solution to 1 liter with water. Store in chemical-resistant glass or polyethylene.

(*c*) *Sodium Hydroxide Solution* (*20 g per liter*).—Dissolve 20 g of sodium

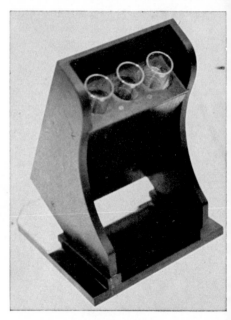

Fig. 4.—Nessler Tube Support.

hydroxide (NaOH) in water and dilute to 1 liter.

(*d*) *Sulfuric Acid* (*1:16*).—Dilute 29.1 ml of concentrated sulfuric acid (H_2SO_4, sp gr 1.84) to 500 ml by carefully adding the H_2SO_4 to the water.

Note 6.—In the preparation of the H_2SO_4 (1:16), it is essential that the exact volumes prescribed in Section 15(*d*) be used, since the concentration of this reagent is more critical than is usually the case where a dilution ratio is used to express the concentration although not so critical as to require standardization of the reagent.

(e) Zirconium-Alizarin Reagent. — Dissolve 1.84 g of zirconylnitrate $(ZrO(NO_3)_2 \cdot 2H_2O)$ or 2.22 g of zirconyl chloride $(ZrOCl_2 \cdot 8H_2O)$ in 250 ml of water (Note 7). A turbid solution may result if impure chemicals are used, but it should not be filtered. When pure chemicals are used, a clear solution will be obtained. Dissolve 0.37 g of alizarin monosodium sulfonate in 250 ml of water. Add 25 ml of the zirconyl solution to 50 to 100 ml of water. Add slowly with constant stirring 25 ml of the alizarin solution. Dilute to 500 ml with water. Mix well, and add 500 ml of H_2SO_4 (1:16) (Note 8).

Note 7.—If a turbid zirconyl solution results, it should not be filtered because this turbidity may be due to some insolubility of the zirconyl salt rather than to impurities. However, if the turbidity persists after mixing the zirconyl solution with the alizarin and H_2SO_4, the reagent should be discarded.

Note 8.—The acid indicator should be clear, and is ready for use after about 1 hr. This reagent is quite stable, particularly when stored in the dark. Refrigeration is not necessary. In event a precipitate forms or a poor color range develops, a new reagent should be prepared.

Procedure

16. *(a)* Transfer 100 ml, or less, of sample containing not more than 0.14 mg of fluoride to a Nessler tube. If the volume of the sample taken is less than 100 ml, dilute it to 100 ml with water (Note 9).

Note 9.—While concentrations of the fluoride ion as high as 0.14 mg can be compared, the accuracy is improved if the amount of fluoride in the aliquot taken is limited to not more than 0.10 mg.

(b) If chlorine is present, remove it by adding a slight excess of $NaAsO_2$ solution. Use 0.1 ml for each 0.1 mg of chlorine in the sample aliquot plus 0.1 ml excess.

(c) Prepare a series of standards from NaF solution (1 ml = 0.01 mg F) covering the anticipated range of the samples in increments of 0.01 mg F.

Dilute each standard to 100 ml with water and transfer to Nessler tubes (standards may also be prepared directly in Nessler tubes). Add exactly 10 ml of the zirconium-alizarin reagent to each sample and standard and mix well.

(d) Compare the samples with the standards, with the Nessler tubes preferably in a support, using diffused light or a fluorescent daylight lamp, by viewing through the length of the tube. The readings may be made at the end of a 60-min reaction time when the reagent is added to all tubes within 2 min, provided both the samples and the standards are maintained at the same temperature. If the results are not needed promptly, the most satisfactory procedure is to make comparisons after a reaction time of 7 to 18 hr, when the color range is better and when the temperature and time used in adding the reagent are not critical (Note 10).

Note 10.—When the reaction time is not less than 7 hr, differences up to 1 hr in the ages of the samples and standards are permissible. Inspection of the samples will indicate any concentration of fluoride requiring a smaller aliquot, which may be taken and prepared within the 1-hr limit and included in the series of comparisons.

Calculation

17. Calculate the concentration of fluoride ion, in parts per million, as follows:

$$\text{Fluoride, ppm} = (F \pm A)R \times \frac{1000}{VG}$$

where:

A = fluoride error, in milligrams in the 100-ml test volume, due to the total effect of interference by chloride or sulfate ions, or basicity (alkalinity as $CaCO_3$), or any combination of these as found from Fig. 3,

F = milligrams of fluoride in the 100 ml of reference standard matched by the sample,

R = ratio correction for interference by the milligrams of aluminum ion in the 100-ml test volume as found from Fig. 2,

V = milliliters of sample used in the 100-ml test volume compared with the reference standard, and

G = specific gravity of sample (considered as 1 for waters containing less than 5000 ppm of dissolved solids).

Precision and Accuracy

18. (a) The precision of this method, in parts per million, varies with the volume, V, in milliliters of the sample as follows:

$$\text{Precision, ppm} = \frac{1}{V}$$

(b) The accuracy of this method varies with both the volume, V, in milliliters of the sample and with the type and extent of interfering substances present. Within the tolerable limits specified, the accuracy, in parts per million will range from $\pm 2/V$ to $\pm 10/V$, depending upon the type and extent of interfering substances present.

Non-Referee Method B

(Zirconium-Eriochrome

Cyanine Method)

Application

19. This method is applicable to the determination of fluoride in industrial water when interfering substances are absent or within tolerable limits.

Summary of Method

20. In acid solution, zirconium reacts with Eriochrome Cyanine R to form a red complex ion. The fluoride ion forms a more stable complex with zirconium (ZrF_6^{--}) and withdraws proportional zirconium from the organic complex to produce a bleaching effect.

Interferences

21. (a) The following ions are tolerable in the concentrations shown: Aluminum, iron, manganese, zinc, cyanide, and boron as tetraborate, 10 ppm; hexavalent chromium, nickel, copper, lead, and cadmium, 5 ppm; metaphosphate (PO_3), 1.0 ppm, and orthophosphate (PO_4), 10 ppm; free chlorine, 7 ppm; silica and magnesium, 100 ppm; calcium, 500 ppm; sodium, 6000 ppm; bicarbonate, 2000 ppm; chloride, 10,000 ppm; and nitrate, 2000 ppm.[6]

(b) Aluminum complexes the fluoride ion resulting in low values. This complex, up to at least 10 ppm aluminum, is destroyed in time (Note 11) by the action of the reagent.

Note 11.—At least 6-hr standing is recommended for samples containing appreciable aluminum.

(c) Thiosemicarbazide is used to inhibit the effect of free chlorine, chromate, and other strong oxidizing agents. With this reagent, accurate fluoride results can be obtained on samples containing as much as 7 ppm free chlorine and 5 ppm hexavalent chromium.

(d) Bicarbonate over 2000 ppm has an effect on the results, and excessive concentrations should be neutralized by adding 0.1 ml of hydrochloric acid (1:5) for each 10 mg of bicarbonate in the test sample.

(e) Sulfate interferes by forming a complex with zirconium resulting in an increase in apparent fluoride concentration. This interference is eliminated by precipitating the sulfate as barium sulfate. However, the sulfate in the test sample must not exceed approximately 10 mg.

---

[6] Supporting data pertinent to this method are given in the Appendix to the Report of Committee D-19. *Proceedings*, Am. Soc. Testing Mats., Vol. 58 (1958).

Apparatus

22. *Spectrophotometer* suitable for use at 540 mμ and equipped with 40 to 50-mm rectangular cells.

Reagents

23. (*a*) *Barium Chloride,* (BaCl$_2$·2H$_2$O).

(*b*) *Color Correction Solution.*—Dissolve 4 g of barium chloride (BaCl$_2$·2H$_2$O) in 500 ml of water, add 75 ml HCl (sp gr 1.19), and dilute to 1 liter with water.

(*c*) *Eriochrome Cyanine R Solution* (*9.0 g per liter*).—Dissolve 1.80 g of Eriochrome Cyanine R in water and dilute to 200 ml.[7]

(*d*) *Fluoride Indicator.*—Add 20.0 ml of the Eriochrome Cyanine R solution to approximately 500 ml of water and stir. While stirring, add 10.0 ml of ZrO(NO$_3$)$_2$·2H$_2$O (2.0 g per liter). Add 75 ml of HCl (sp gr 1.19) and 4 g of BaCl$_2$·2H$_2$O. Dissolve and dilute to 1 liter with water. The reagent mixture is stable for four months.

(*e*) *Hydrochloric Acid (sp gr 1.19).*—Concentrated hydrochloric acid (HCl).

(*f*) *Sodium Fluoride, Standard Solution (1 ml = 0.01 mg F).*—See Section 15(*b*).

(*g*) *Thiosemicarbazide*, powder.

(*h*) *Zirconyl Nitrate Solution (2.0 g per liter).*—Dissolve 0.40 g of zirconyl nitrate (ZrO(NO$_3$)$_2$·2H$_2$O) in 100 ml of HCl (sp gr 1.19). Dilute to 200 ml with water

Calibration

24. (*a*) Prepare a series of fluoride standards containing from 0.00 to 0.03 mg fluoride by diluting measured vol-

[7] In selecting the optimum wavelength, the color density of the solution must be considered as well as the sensitivity. Samples of indicator from different sources may vary considerably in color. The National Aniline product labeled "Alizarol Cyanone RC" has been found satisfactory for this purpose.

umes of the fluoride solution (1 ml = 0.010 mg F), so that a 10.00-ml aliquot of each dilution will contain the desired quantity of fluoride.

(*b*) Pipet 10.0-ml portions of the fluoride standards into graduates or Nessler tubes, and proceed as directed in Section 25. Plot absorbance against fluoride concentration (Note 12).

Note 12.—A separate calibration curve must be made for each photometer and a recalibration must be made if any alterations of the instrument are made or if new reagents are prepared. Check the curve with each series of tests by running two or more solutions of known fluoride concentration.

Procedure

25. (*a*) Transfer 10.0 ml or less, of sample containing less than 0.03 mg of fluoride into a graduate or Nessler tube. If the volume of sample taken is less than 10.0 ml, dilute it to 10.0 ml with water.

(*b*) Add a few milligrams of solid thiosemicarbazide from the tip of a microspatula. Stir and let stand 5 to 10 min.

(*c*) Add 25.0 ml of the fluoride indicator solution. If the sample contains sulfate, a precipitate will develop. Place the samples near the photometer and allow to stand overnight. The standing time is necessary to eliminate the aluminum interference and to permit the settling of barium sulfate.

(*d*) For each significantly colored sample, make up a color correction sample by adding 25.0 ml of color correction solution to the same volume of sample used in the analysis. The color correction samples, blank, and necessary standards are prepared at the same time as the samples and allowed to stand overnight.

(*e*) Decant the clear supernatant solution (Note 13) into the cells, taking care not to disturb the barium sulfate (BaSO$_4$) precipitate. Determine the absorbance at 540 mμ in a spectrophotometer, using 40 to 50-mm rectangular cells. The absorbance of each sample is measured against a blank of 10.0 ml of water plus 25.0 ml of fluoride indicator solution. Set the blank to read at a selected point in the upper range of the absorbance scale. This selected point should be sufficient to cover the fluoride range and permit maximum use of the spectrophotomer.

NOTE 13.—At the time of reading, all solutions should be at the same temperature and within 3 C of the temperature at which the calibration curve was prepared. Temperature variations may occur if the reference solution is allowed to remain in the spectrophotometer during prolonged testing.

(f) To correct for color in the sample, measure the absorbance of the color correction sample against water and subtract this value from the measured absorbance of the test sample.

(g) Determine the concentration of the fluoride ion in milligrams from the standard fluoride curve.

Calculation

26. Calculate the concentration of fluoride ion in parts per million as follows:

$$\text{Fluoride, ppm} = \frac{F}{VG} \times 1000$$

where:

V = milliliters of sample used,
F = milligrams of fluoride in test sample volume, and
G = specific gravity of sample (considered 1 for waters containing less than 5000 ppm of disssolved solids).

Precision and Accuracy[6]

27. (a) The precision of this method, in parts per million, varies with the volume, V, in milliliters of the sample as follows:

$$\text{Precision, ppm} = \frac{0.1}{V}$$

(b) The accuracy of this method varies with both the volume, V, of the sample in milliliters and with the type and extent of interfering substances present. Within the tolerable limits specified, the accuracy, in parts per million, will range from $\pm0.2/V$ to $\pm1/V$ depending upon the type and extent of interfering substance present.

APPROVED AS
USA STANDARD Z111.2-1964 (2nd ed.)
BY USA STANDARDS INSTITUTE
UDC 663.61:621.1.013.3:545.05

Standard Specifications for

EQUIPMENT FOR SAMPLING INDUSTRIAL WATER AND STEAM[1]

ASTM Designation: D 1192 – 64

ADOPTED, 1964

This Standard of the American Society for Testing and Materials is issued under the fixed designation D 1192; the final number indicates the year of original adoption as standard or, in the case of revision, the year of last revision.

Scope

1. These specifications cover the basic requirements for equipment to be used for the collection of samples of industrial water and steam and for their handling from the time they are taken to the time of analysis.

Application

2. (*a*) These specifications cover only that equipment which is commonly used for the sampling of water and steam. They do not cover specialized equipment required for, and unique to, a specific test or method of analysis. The specifications cover items such as valves, fittings, piping, cooling coils and condensers, degassers, sample containers, and packaging materials, but specifically exclude such items as sampling tubes or nozzles that are used for obtaining or collecting steam or water samples, and apparatus used in subsequent methods of test and analysis.

(*b*) For information on specialized sampling equipment, reference shall be made to the applicable method of the American Society for Testing and Materials, as follows:

	ASTM Designation[a]
Plant or confined waters	D 510
Boiler water	D 860
Steam	D 1066
Dissolved oxygen in industrial water	D 888

[a] These designations refer to the following methods of the American Society for Testing and Materials:
D 510—Sampling Industrial Water,[2]
D 860—Sampling Water from Boilers,[2]
D 1066—Sampling Steam,[2] and
D 888—Tests for Dissolved Oxygen in Industrial Water.[2]

Definitions

3. (*a*) The term "industrial water" in these specifications is defined in ac-

[1] Under the standardization procedure of the Society, these specifications are under the jurisdiction of the ASTM Committee D-19 on Industrial Water. A list of members may be found in the ASTM Year Book.

[2] Appears in this publication.

cordance with ASTM Definitions D 1129, Terms Relating to Industrial Water and Industrial Waste Water,[2] as follows:

Industrial Water—Water (including its impurities) used directly or indirectly in industrial processes.

(*b*) For definitions of other terms used in these specifications, refer to Definitions D 1129.

Sampling Lines

4. (*a*) Sampling lines shall be as short as possible and of the smallest practicable bore to facilitate flushing and to

Pipe (seamless ferritic alloy-steel for high-temperature service).......   A 335
Tubing (seamless carbon-steel for high-temperature service).......   A 179
Tubing (seamless alloy-steel for high-temperature service).......   A 269

---

[a] These designations refer to the following specifications of the American Society for Testing and Materials:

A 106—Seamless Carbon-Steel Pipe for High-Temperature Service,[3]

A 335—Seamless Ferritic Alloy Steel Pipe for High-Temperature Service,[3]

A 179—Seamless Cold-Drawn Low-Carbon Steel Heat-Exchanger and Condenser Tubes,[3] and

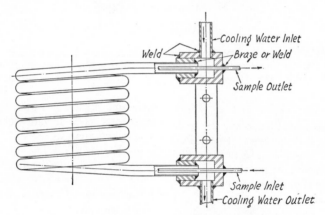

FIG. 1—Double-Tube Helical Coil Heat Exchanger.

reduce time lag. The lines shall have sufficient strength to prevent structural failure. Pressure piping shall be designed in accordance with the latest issue of the American Standard Code for Pressure Piping (ASA No. B31.1). Where small diameter capillary tubing is used, it shall be protected by placing it inside larger diameter pipe of adequate structural strength. The material from which the sampling lines are made shall conform to the requirements of the applicable specifications of the American Society for Testing and Materials, as follows:

ASTM Designation[a]

Pipe (seamless carbon-steel for high-temperature service).......   A 106

A 269—Seamless and Welded Austenitic Stainless Steel Tubing for General Service.[3]

(*b*) Carbon steel pipe or tubing is satisfactory for sampling lines for boiler water and industrial waters. For sampling high-purity waters such as condensed steam from boilers and evaporators or corrosive waters, the sampling lines shall be made of stainless steel that is at least as resistant to steam as 18 per cent chromium - 8 per cent nickel steel. All sample lines should be pitched downward at least 10 deg to prevent settling or separation of solids contained

---

[3] 1967 Book of ASTM Standards, Part 1.

by the water sample. Traps and pockets in which condensate or sludge might settle shall be avoided, since they may be partially emptied with changes in flow conditions and may result in sample contamination. Expansion loops or other means shall be provided to prevent undue buckling and bending when large temperature changes occur. Such buckling and bending may damage the lines and allied equipment.

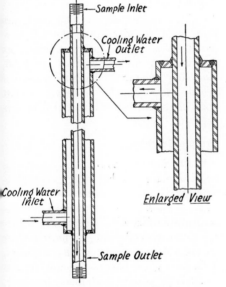

FIG. 2—Vertical-Tube Heat Exchanger.

Valves and Fittings

5. (a) Valves and fittings shall be made from materials similar to those used in the sampling lines. The materials shall conform to the requirements of the applicable specifications of the American Society for Testing and Materials, as follows:

ASTM Designation[a]

Steel (suitable for fusion welding up to 850 F)	A 216
Steel (carbon forged)	A 105
Steel (alloy steel castings for use up to 1100 F)	A 217

Steel (ferritic and austenitic steel castings for use up to 1100 F) .... A 351
Steel (wrought carbon steel and ferritic alloy steel welding fittings).. A 234

[a] These designations refer to the following specifications of the American Society for Testing and Materials:

A 216—Carbon-Steel Castings Suitable for Fusion Welding for High-Temperature Service,[3]

A 105—Forged or Rolled Steel Pipe Flanges, Forged Fittings, and Valves and Parts for High-Temperature Service,[3]

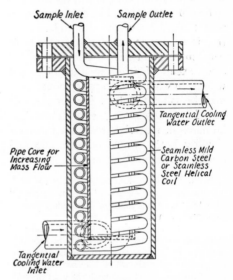

FIG. 3—Submerged Helical Coil Heat Exchanger.

A 217—Alloy Steel Castings for Pressure Containing Parts Suitable for High-Temperature Service,[3]

A 351—Ferritic and Austenitic Steel Castings for High-Temperature Service,[3] and

A 234—Welding Fittings, Factory-Made Wrought Carbon Steel and Ferritic Alloy Steel.[3]

(b) At least one shut-off valve shall be placed immediately after the point from which the sample of steam or water is withdrawn, so that the sampling line may be isolated when desired. Valves shall be placed both at the sample inlet and at the sample outlet of the sample cooler and condenser. Means should be provided for locking or wiring the inlet valve in the wide-open position when in use. This practice will ensure condensation at the highest pressure and will minimize the possibility of sample condensation or dilution in the event a leak develops in the cooling coil.

Sample Cooler or Condenser

6. (*a*) If steam is to be sampled, the cooler and condenser must be designed so that sufficient sample can be obtained to be representative. The cooler and condenser shall be made of stainless steel that is at least as resistant to steam as 18 per cent chromium - 8 per cent nickel steel except for boiler and high pH waters, in which case copper, monel, etc., may be substituted on the sample side coil. In all cases, the coil or tubes shall be made of materials resistant to corrosion by both sample on one side and cooling water on the other.

NOTE 1—The scaling tendencies of the cooling waters available should be given careful consideration when selecting a sample cooler or condenser. A water that contains considerable slime or algae may also cause rapid fouling of the cooler so that its efficiency may be seriously impaired. If it is necessary to use such a water, the sample cooler should be one that can readily and effectively be cleaned with the least possible delay. A concentric, helical coil type cooler (Fig. 1) is susceptible to plugging and fouling. In the case of the other two types of coolers (Figs. 2 and 3), the scale may be dislodged while the coil is in service by a scale-cracking or thermal-shocking procedure such as is used in an evaporator. The scale in the latter two types will fall to the bottom and can be removed periodically by mechanical or chemical cleaning. However, where good cooling water is available, or where suitable treated cooling water is used, any of the three types shown is acceptable.

(*b*) The tube through which the sample will flow shall be continuous and shall extend completely through the cooling jacket, so there will be no possibility of sample contamination or dilution from the cooling water. The tube shall be of sufficient strength to withstand the full pressure of the fluid being sampled. The diameter of the tube shall be small so that storage within the coil is low and the time lag of sample through the condenser will be a minimum. The cooler shall be so constructed as to provide at least the calculated cooling surface requirement. (See the Appendix for details of calculation.)

Degassers

7. Degassers shall be made of corrosion-resistant materials similar to those described in Section 6. The degassers shall be designed to take the full flow required for representative sampling as described in ASTM Method D 1066, Sampling Steam.[2] The piping ahead of the degasser shall be arranged so that none of the sample is diverted from the degasser.

Sample Containers

8. (*a*) Sample containers shall be made of materials that will not contaminate the sample and, before use, shall be cleaned thoroughly to remove all extraneous surface dirt. Chemically resistant glass, polyethylene, or hard rubber are suitable materials for the containers. Soda-lime glass bottles are not recommended as sample containers; however, if properly coated with paraffin, such bottles are suitable for the collection and storage of water for most analyses.

NOTE 2—New, chemically resistant glass containers shall be aged by allowing them to stand full of distilled water for several days. Aging may be hastened by a preliminary treatment with dilute sodium hydroxide solution. Only polyethylene or hard rubber containers shall be used for samples in which small amounts of hardness, silica, sodium, or potassium are to be determined.

(*b*) The closures for the sample containers shall be glass stoppers, new cork stoppers that have been thoroughly washed, or plastic caps with suitable liners.

Sample Labels

9. Space shall be provided for the following information on an etched area of the bottle, a gummed label, or a cardboard or linen tag securely affixed to the container:

Sample number,

Date and time of sampling,

Source of sample,

Point of sampling (designated in sufficient detail to enable anyone to collect a second sample from the identical spot from which the first sample was taken),

Temperature and rate of flow of the fluid in the equipment from which the sample was taken,

Temperature of sample,

Results of field tests made on the sample, and

Signature of sampler.

Sample Shipping Containers

10. (a) The stoppers closing the sample containers shall be fixed in place by wire, tape, or cord to prevent leakage in transit. The sample containers shall be of such size that when filled with the desired amount of sample, space roughly equivalent to 1 per cent of the volumetric capacity of the containers will be available for expansion of the liquid.

(b) The sample shipping container shall be a case (wood preferred) having a separate compartment for each sample container. The compartment around each sample container shall be lined with corrugated paper, felt, or similar material; or the sample containers shall be held in place with spring clips, sawdust, excelsior, or similar material.

Shipping Labels

11. The addresses of consignee and consignor shall be plainly printed upon two sides of the outer container, or attached firmly thereon by cards or labels. Warning and descriptive labels shall be attached to the outer container, such as "Fragile," "Liquid," "Glass," "Handle with Care," "This Side Up," etc., when applicable. In cold weather, the label "Keep from Freezing" shall be attached to the outer container.

APPENDIX

CALCULATION OF COOLING SURFACE REQUIREMENTS

A1. (a) The surface requirements of equipment used for condensing and cooling steam, originally saturated, can be determined with sufficient accuracy from Eq 1, if the sampling rate (Note 3), cooling water temperature, and initial sample conditions are known.

$$A = 1130 \frac{f}{U \Delta t_m} \dots \dots \dots (1)$$

where:

A = surface requirement, in square feet,

f = sample rate, in pounds per hour,

Δt_m = mean temperature difference, in degrees Fahrenheit, and

U = over-all heat transfer coefficient, in British thermal units per degree Fahrenheit per hour. (For the coolers shown in Figs.

1 and 3, $U = 200$. For the cooler shown in Fig. 2, $U = 150$.)

NOTE 3—In the case of steam, the sampling rate corresponds to that given under Section 9(e) of Method D 1066.

(b) The surface requirements will be increased 7 per cent above those found by Eq 1 for each 100 F of superheat, when superheated steam is to be sampled.

A2. The mean temperature difference is found from a knowledge of the sample and cooling water temperatures entering and leaving the sample cooler. It represents the average of the terminal differences at both ends of the sample cooler, as shown in Eq 2.

$$t_m = \frac{(T_1 - T_2) + (t_1 - t_2)}{2} \quad \ldots\ldots(2)$$

where:

t_m = mean temperature difference, in degrees Fahrenheit,

T_1 = sample temperature, entering cooler, in degrees Fahrenheit,

T_2 = sample temperature, leaving cooler, in degrees Fahrenheit,

t_1 = coolant temperature, entering cooler, in degrees Fahrenheit, and

t_2 = coolant temperature, leaving cooler, in degrees Fahrenheit.

TABLE 1—AVAILABLE COOLING SURFACE PER 20-FT LENGTH OF TUBING AND PIPE FOR USE IN SAMPLE COOLERS.

Diameter		External Surface per 20-ft Length, sq ft	
Tubing, OD, in.	Pipe, Nominal Size, in.	Tubing	Pipe
1/4	1/4	1.41	2.83
3/8	3/8	2.11	3.54
1/2	1/2	2.81	4.40
3/4	3/4	. . .	5.50
7/8	7/8	4.92	. . .
1	1	5.81	6.88

A3. The cooling coil may be constructed from a continuous length of tubing having the required surface, or may be constructed by placing two or more cooling coils in series. The number of sample coolers required can be determined from Table 1 and Eqs 1 and 2.

Example—Assume that it is desired to select a sample cooler to be used on a boiler operating at 1200 psi absolute pressure. For the particular nozzle design selected, the sampling rate for representative sampling is 120 lb per hr. The available cooling water temperature is 70 F, and it is desirable to maintain an outlet temperature of 140 F. The required sample temperature is 90 F. It is desired to use a sample cooler of the type shown in Fig. 3, using 1/2-in. pipe. The mean temperature difference is then:

$$t_m = \frac{(567.2 - 90) + (70 - 140)}{2} = 203.6 \text{ F}$$

For a sampling rate of 120 lb per hr and a mean temperature difference of 203.6 F, Eq 1 gives a surface requirement:

$$A = 1130 \frac{120}{200 \times 203.6} = 3.33 \text{ sq ft}$$

For a surface requirement of 3.33 sq ft, and using 1/2-in. pipe, Table 1 indicates that one cooler would be adequate since it will contain 4.40 sq ft of surface.

In the case of boiler water, where it is not necessary to fulfill requirements for representative sampling, and where the minimum sampling rate has been given as 500 ml per min (66.3 lb per hr), the surface requirements for cooling this quantity of water at a pressure ranging from 200 to 2600 psi to 70 F, for example, will be 0.9 sq ft for the coolers shown in Figs. 1 and 3, while the cooler shown in Fig. 2 will require 1.2 sq ft of surface. Table 1 indicates that one cooler of any of these types would be adequate to cool the minimum quantity; and where the larger diameter tubing or pipe could be used, one cooler would be adequate to cool several times the minimum quantity of water.

Standard Specifications for

REAGENT WATER[1]

ASTM Designation: D 1193 – 66

ADOPTED, 1956; LAST REVISED, 1966

This Standard of the American Society for Testing and Materials is issued under the fixed designation D 1193; the number immediately following the designation indicates the year of original adoption or, in the case of revision, the year of last revision. A number in parentheses indicates the year of last reapproval.

1. Scope

1.1 These specifications cover requirements for water suitable for use in methods of chemical analysis and physical testing. Two grades of reagent water are specified:

Referee Reagent Water, and

Non-Referee Reagent Water.

1.2 Referee reagent water may be prepared by the distillation of a water having an electrical conductivity, maximum, of 20 micromhos/cm at 25 C (77 F) followed by polishing with a mixed bed of ion-exchange materials.

1.3 Non-referee grade reagent water may be prepared by single distillation.

1.4 Referee reagent water shall be used in referee analysis. Non-referee reagent water is suitable for use in general laboratory testing.

2. Significance

2.1 The method of preparing referee reagent water adds organic contaminants to the water by contact with the ion-exchange materials.

2.1.1 The dissolved or particulate organic contamination would normally range from 1 to 5 ppb.

2.2 The quality of the effluent water depends upon the type, age, and method of regeneration of the ion-exchange materials. Likewise, the flow rate through the ion-exchange resin bed will change the conductivity of the effluent water. The instructions of the manufacturer of the resins or the resin cartridge bed should be followed.

2.3 Reagent water should be protected from atmospheric contamination and from solution of container and tubing materials.

2.3.1 Extreme care must be exercised in handling samples when making analyses. Sample containers and tubing should be made of TFE-fluorocarbon, block tin, quartz, 18-8 stainless steel, polyethylene, or other material proven to be sufficiently resistant to chemical attack.

3. Definitions

3.1 The terms "particulate matter," "dissolved matter," "total matter," and others related to water constituents determined in these methods, are defined in

[1] Under the standardization procedure of the Society, these specifications are under the jurisdiction of the ASTM Committee D-19 on Industrial Water. A list of members may be found in the ASTM Year Book.

accordance with ASTM Definitions D 1129, Terms Relating to Industrial Water and Industrial Waste Water,[2] as follows:

3.1.1 *Particulate Matter*—That matter, exclusive of gases, existing in the nonliquid state which is dispersed in water to give a heterogeneous mixture.

3.1.2 *Dissolved Matter*—That matter, exclusive of gases, which is dispersed in water to give a single phase of homogeneous liquid.

3.1.3 *Total Matter*—The sum of the particulate and dissolved matter.

3.2 For definitions of other terms used in these specifications, refer to Definitions D 1129.

4. Reagents

4.1 *Potassium Permanganate Solution (0.316 g/liter)*—Dissolve 0.316 g of potassium permanganate ($KMnO_4$) (ACS reagent grade) in water and dilute to 1 liter with water in a volumetric flask.

4.2 *Sulfuric Acid (sp gr 1.84)*—Concentrated sulfuric acid (H_2SO_4), ACS reagent grade.

4.3 *Water*—Unless otherwise indicated, references to water shall be understood to mean referee reagent water as specified in these specifications.

5. Requirements

5.1 Reagent water shall conform to the following requirements:

---
[2] Appears in this publication.

	Referee	Non Refere
Total matter, max, ppm	0.1	2.0
Electrical conductivity, max, micromhos per cm at 25 C (77 F)	0.1	5.0
Consumption of potassium permanganate	pass test	pass test

5.2 Additional requirements concer ing specific contaminants or method preparation may be included in the specifications by mutual agreement b tween the parties concerned.

6. Methods of Test

6.1 *Total Matter*—Determine tot matter in accordance with Method A ASTM Methods D 1888, Test for Pa ticulate and Dissolved Matter in I dustrial Water.[2]

6.2 *Electrical Conductivity*—Determi: the electrical conductivity in accordan with ASTM Methods D 1125, Test f Electrical Conductivity of Industri Water and Industrial Waste Water.[2]

6.3 *Consumption of Potassium P, manganate*—Determine consumption potassium permanganate by adding 0. ml of $KMnO_4$ solution (0.316 g/liter) t mixture of 500 ml of the reagent wat and 1 ml of H_2SO_4 in a stoppered bott of chemically-resistant glass. Consid the reagent water as having passed t: test if the permanganate color does n disappear completely after standing f 1 hr at room temperature.

Standard Method for
EXAMINATION OF WATER-FORMED DEPOSITS BY CHEMICAL MICROSCOPY[1]

ASTM Designation: D 1245 – 55 (1965)
ADOPTED, 1955; REAPPROVED, 1965

This Standard of the American Society for Testing and Materials is issued under the fixed designation D 1245; the number immediately following the designation indicates the year of original adoption or, in the case of revision, the year of last revision. A number in parentheses indicates the year of last reapproval.

Note.—Editorial changes were made in Sections 7 and 10 in June, 1959.

Scope and Application

1. (*a*) This method describes a procedure for the examination of water-formed deposits by means of chemical microscopy. The procedures of chemical microscopy are applicable to all water-formed deposits. They are much less time consuming than chemical macroanalysis, and, when they can be supplemented by optical data, sufficient information may be obtained to make complete chemical analysis unnecessary. The sample required is small. The method can be applied in cases where there is not sufficient sample available for a macroanalysis.

(*b*) The petrographic procedure which is a part of this method is limited to deposits that are composed of individual particles or crystals having a diameter of at least 10 μ, unless the particles have a characteristic form, cleavage, or highly specific identifying optical properties.

Principle of Method

2. The method is essentially chemical microscopic, supplemented by optical data obtained by the petrographic method. The identification of compounds is made by observing, under the microscope, characteristic reactions and precipitates resulting from the action of specific reagents on the solid sample or solutions thereof, and by measuring the optical properties.

Definitions

3. (*a*) For definitions of terms in this method relating specifically to industrial water and water-formed deposits, refer to the Standard Definitions of Terms Relating to Industrial Water and Industrial Waste Water (ASTM Designation: D 1129).[2]

(*b*) Certain terms in this method that relate specifically to chemical microscopy are defined as follows:

[1] Under the standardization procedure of the Society, this method is under the jurisdiction of the ASTM Committee D-19 on Industrial Water. A list of members may be found in the ASTM Year Book.

[2] Appears in this publication.

Petrographic.—Pertaining to the description of rocks or rocklike substances. Such description is usually in terms of morphology and optical properties.

Index of Refraction.—The numerical expression of the ratio of the velocity of light in a vacuum to the velocity of light in a substance.

Isotropic.—Having the same optical properties in all directions.

Anisotropic.—Having optical properties which vary with changing direction.

Extinction Angle.—The angle between the extinction position and some plane, edge, or line in a crystal.

Extinction Position.—The position in which an anisotropic crystal, between crossed nicol prisms, exhibits complete darkness.

Dispersion.—The variation of index of refraction with wave length.

Solid Solution.—A homogeneous mixture of two or more components, in the solid state, retaining substantially the structure of one of the components.

Interferences

4. Deposits containing solid solutions present a complication in that the optical data vary throughout such a system, and, unless the presence of this complication is known, the analysis may be in error. Extremely fine material, especially if dark colored, may cloud over and obscure details of otherwise recognizable particles.

Apparatus

5. (a) *Reagent Bottles for Immersion Liquids.*—Glass dropping bottles of 30-ml capacity. These bottles shall be equipped with ground-glass stoppers with dropping rods integral with the stoppers. Dropping bottles with rubber bulbs are unsatisfactory because of the effect of some of the immersion liquids on the rubber. It is essential that the bottles be marked with the refractive index of the contained liquid.

(b) *Box or Block* suitable for containing and storing the immersion liquid bottles.

(c) *Mortar and Pestle,* of tool steel mullite, or aluminum oxide.

(d) *Micro Spatula.*

(e) *Sample Vials,* 45 by 15 mm.

(f) *Porcelain Crucibles.*—No. 0 is a useful size.

(g) *Micro Gas Burner or Micro Electric Heater.*

(h) *Glass Rods,* 150 by 5 mm for transferring drops, and 75 by 1 mm for stirring and leading reagent drops on the slides.

(i) *Microscope Slides,* of selected grade, 1 by 3 or 1 by 2 in. Etched ends are preferred.

(j) *Cover Glasses,* No. 1 or No. 2 thickness, round or square cover glasses. The round, No. 2 thickness cover glasses are preferred.

(k) *Petrographic Microscope.*—A microscope equipped with a circular rotating stage, graduated in degrees. The optical system shall include two polarizing prisms, one mounted below the condenser and the other just above the objective; 4×, 10×, and 45× objectives; and 5× and 10× eyepieces fitted with crosshairs. The optic axis of the microscope shall be adjustable so that it can be brought into coincidence with the center of rotation of the revolving stage. A Bertrand-Amici lens equipped with an iris diaphragm, or a sliding stop ocular, shall be used for viewing interference figures. A quartz wedge, gypsum plate, and standard mica plate are necessary external accessories.

(l) *Light Source.*—Microscope lamp with concentrated filament bulb and a focusing lens.

(m) *Small Alloy Magnet.*

Note 1.—The sizes of apparatus specified in Paragraphs (c) to (m) have been found most convenient. Other sizes may be used.

27–31

Purity of Reagents

6. (a) Reagent grade chemicals shall be used in all tests. Unless otherwise indicated, it is intended that all reagents shall conform to the specifications of the Committee on Analytical Reagents of the American Chemical Society, where such specifications are available.[3] Other grades may be used, provided it is first ascertained that the reagent is of sufficiently high purity to permit its use without lessening the accuracy of the determination.

(b) Unless otherwise indicated, references to water shall be understood to mean non-referee reagent water conforming to the Specifications for Reagent Water (ASTM Designation: D 1193).[2]

Reagents

7. (a) Nitric Acid (sp gr 1.42).—Concentrated nitric acid (HNO₃).

(b) Nitric Acid (1:19).—Mix 1 volume of HNO₃ (sp gr 1.42) with 19 volumes of water.

(c) Hydrochloric Acid (sp gr 1.19).—Concentrated hydrochloric acid (HCl).

(d) Hydrochloric Acid (1:4).—Mix 1 volume of HCl (sp gr 1:19) with 4 volumes of water.

(e) Chloroform or Carbon Tetrachloride.

(f) Phenolphthalein Indicator Solution.

(g) Silver Nitrate Solution.—Dissolve 1 g of AgNO₃ in 20 ml of water and add five drops of HNO₃ (sp gr 1.42).

(h) Sulfuric Acid (sp gr 1.84).—Concentrated sulfuric acid (H₂SO₄).

(i) Sulfuric Acid (1:19).—Mix 1 volume of H₂SO₄ (sp gr 1.84) with 19 volumes of water.

(j) Ammonium Molybdate Solution.—Dissolve 1 g of ammonium molybdate ((NH₄)₆Mo₇O₂₄·4H₂O) in 10 ml of water and add 5 drops of NHO₃ (sp gr 1.42).

(k) Ammonium Hydroxide (sp gr 0.90).—Concentrated ammonium hydroxide (NH₄OH).

(l) Diammonium Phosphate Solution.—Dissolve 1 g of (NH₄)₂HPO₄ in 10 ml of water.

(m) Cesium Sulfate.—Cs₂SO₄ crystals, 10- to 20-mesh.

(n) Potassium Mercuric Thiocyanate Solution.—Prepare freshly precipitated Hg(CNS)₂ by adding a concentrated solution of Hg(NO₃)₂ to a concentrated solution of KCNS. Filter and air-dry the precipitate. To one part Hg(CNS)₂ add three parts KCNS, dissolve in a minimum quantity of water, and evaporate in a desiccator. Collect the first crop of tabular crystals of K₂Hg(CNS)₄, wash with alcohol, and dry. Dissolve 10 g of the crystals in water and dilute to 100 ml.

(o) Zinc Uranyl Acetate Solution.—Dissolve 1 g of UO₂(C₂H₃O₂)₂·2H₂O and 0.1 ml of glacial acetic acid in 5 ml of water. Dissolve 3 g of Zn(C₂H₃O₂)₂·2H₂O and 0.1 ml of glacial acetic acid in 5 ml of water. Warm if necessary to complete solution. Mix the two solutions and store in a chemically resistant glass bottle. If precipitation occurs, filter the solution before use.

(p) Chloroplatinic Acid Solution.—Dissolve 1 g of H₂PtCl₆·6H₂O in 5 ml of water and add 0.5 ml of HCl (sp gr 1.19).

(q) Sodium Bismuthate.—Powdered NaBiO₃.

(r) Potassium Iodide Solution.—Prepare a KI solution on the slide at the time of test by dissolving a small crystal (10- to 20-mesh) of KI in a drop of water.

(s) Dimethylglyoxime Solution.—Prepare a solution on the slide by dissolving

[3] "Reagent Chemicals, American Chemical Society Specifications," Am. Chem. Soc., Washington, D.C. For suggestions on the testing of reagents not listed by the American Chemical Society, see "Reagent Chemicals and Standards," by Joseph Rosin, D. Van Nostrand Co., Inc., New York, N. Y., and the "United States Pharmacopeia."

a small amount of powdered dimethyl-glyoxime in a drop of water.

(*t*) *Refractive Index Standards.*—A set of liquids having refractive indices ranging from 1.40 to 1.74 in steps of 0.01. In the range from 1.45 to 1.65, it is desirable to have liquids available in steps of 0.005. Directions for the preparation of suitable liquids are given in U. S. Geological Survey Bulletin No. 848 (1)[4] or "Elements of Optical Mineralogy" (2). The index of refraction of these liquids must be checked prior to their use, as they may change from loss of more volatile constituents.

Sampling

8. Collect the sample in accordance with the Standard Method of Field Sampling of Water-Formed Deposits (ASTM Designation: D 887).[2]

Laboratory Preparation of Samples

9. (*a*) Dry a small, representative portion of the deposit at 105 C for 1 hr. Retain a portion of the dried deposit in its unground form. Crush a second portion of the dried deposit in the mortar. Avoid grinding, since this produces an excessive amount of very fine material which is of little or no value when the optical method is applied.

(*b*) Place a portion of the crushed sample (approximately 0.1 g or less) in a porcelain crucible, add 4 drops of HNO_3 (sp gr 1.42), and evaporate to dryness over the microburner. Add 1 ml of water, warm, and stir with a glass rod. Allow the insoluble material to settle. Withdraw portions of the supernatant liquid, henceforth referred to as the test solution, on the end of a glass rod and transfer to a slide for carrying out certain of the tests described in Section 10. Make other tests on portions of the original or crushed sample.

---

[4] The boldface numbers in parentheses refer to the references listed at the end of this method.

Chemical Microscopic Procedures

10. (*a*) The microscopic tests in this section are intended to reveal the major components of a deposit. Elements present in low percentages usually must be concentrated by macro separation methods before these tests are applied. For a more detailed discussion of these tests refer to Chamot and Mason (3).

(*b*) *Evolution of Gas with Dilute Acid.*— Place a small piece of the unground deposit on a slide and observe under the 4× objective. Allow a drop of HCl (1:4) to flow onto the sample, or guide it to the particle by means of a glass rod. Evolution of gas bubbles usually indicates carbonates, sulfites, sulfides, or metals. Effervescence due to carbonates is usually violent, and of short duration. The gas evolution due to sulfites and sulfides is usually less vigorous, and that due to hydrogen evolution from a metal is usually of considerable duration. The slide used for this test should be preserved and examined after an hour. If sodium salts are present, evaporation of some of the solution will have deposited cubic crystals of NaCl. If appreciable amounts of calcium and sulfate ions were present characteristic clumps of $CaSO_4 \cdot 2H_2O$ needles will be formed.

(*c*) *Magnetic Material.*—Place some of the crushed sample on a slide and bring the magnet under the slide. As the magnet moves under the slide, any magnetic material in the sample will respond to the magnetic field.

NOTE 2.—A coating of magnetite on nonmagnetic particles may give an erroneous indication of the total amount of magnetic material actually present.

(*d*) *Water-Soluble Components.*—Add a drop of water to a portion of crushed sample on a microscope slide and warm over the microburner. Set aside to evaporate. If water-soluble components are present they will crystallize at the edge of the drop.

(e) *Material Soluble in Organic Solvents.*—Add a drop of organic solvent (chloroform or carbon tetrachloride) to a portion of the crushed sample. Allow to evaporate and examine the slide for a residue of soluble matter.

(f) *Alkaline Material.*—Spread some of the crushed sample on a slide and cover with a drop of water. Allow a drop of phenolphthalein solution to flow into the drop. The presence of alkaline material will be indicated by the pink solution surrounding the alkaline components of the deposit.

(g) *Combustible Matter.*—Gently heat a portion of the deposit on a spatula and note the odor. Heat more strongly and note the type of combustion which takes place. Rapid, spontaneous ignition may indicate nitrates. A glowing indicates carbon or organic matter. Substances like cotton, wool, rubber, sulfur, or sulfites can be identified by their odor. A steady luminous flame may indicate oil or asphalt.

(h) *Metallic Elements.*—To a portion of the crushed sample on a slide, add a drop of $AgNO_3$ solution and examine under low power. The presence of metallic iron, copper, or other metals will be confirmed by the formation of feathery crystals of metallic silver.

(i) *Silicates.*—To a portion of the crushed sample on a slide, add HCl (sp gr 1.19) and warm. The presence of silicates which are attacked by acid will be indicated by the formation of a gelatinous scum on the surface of the test drop.

NOTE 3.—The presence of large amounts of organic matter may obscure this test. Gentle ignition may permit removal of organic matter.

(j) *Calcium.*—Add a drop of H_2SO_4 (1:19) to the preceding test drop. The presence of calcium will be confirmed by the formation of masses of radiating needles of $CaSO_4 \cdot 2H_2O$.

(k) *Orthophosphate.*—To a drop of test solution, add a drop of $(NH_4)_6Mo_7O_{24}$ so-

lution acidified with HNO_3. Orthophosphates yield a lemon-yellow precipitate of $(NH_4)_3PO_4 \cdot 12MoO_3 \cdot xH_2O$ in the form of minute granules which develop into highly refractive discs, spheres, octahedra, and sometimes cubes.

(l) *Magnesium.*—Place a drop of test solution on a slide, add a drop of NH_4OH (sp gr 0.90), and evaporate to dryness. Add a drop of NH_4OH to the residue and warm gently. Without disturbing the residue, draw the clear liquid to a clean area and evaporate to dryness. Then add a drop of water, allow to stand a few moments, and add a small drop of $(NH_4)_2HPO_4$ and a drop of NH_4OH (sp gr 0.90). The presence of magnesium will be confirmed by the formation of large feathery stars and crosses which, on standing, develop into plates or rectangular prisms. If the amount of magnesium is low, a period of 1 min or more may be required for the development of the crystals.

(m) *Aluminum.*—Place a small portion of the crushed sample on the end of a slide and add a small drop of H_2SO_4 (sp gr 1.84). Evaporate to dryness over the microburner, cool, and add a drop of water and warm gently. Lead the solution to a clean portion of the slide; then add a crystal of Cs_2SO_4. If aluminum is present, crystals of cesium "alum" will separate in large, well-formed, colorless octahedra.

(n) *Ferric Iron, Zinc, Copper, and Cobalt.*—Place a drop of the test solution on a slide. Place a drop of $K_2Hg(CNS)_4$ solution beside the test drop and, by means of a glass rod, draw the drop of reagent into the test drop in such a manner as to form a narrow channel of liquid between the two drops. If the test solution does not turn blood red, ferric iron is absent. Examine the preparation under the 10X objective. The presence of zinc will be confirmed by the formation of white feathery crosses which appear black by transmitted light. The presence of copper will cause formation of greenish-yellow, mossy dendrites, or boat-shaped crystals, or both. Cobalt will give rise to deep blue orthorhombic prisms. If the test drop turns red, indicating the presence of ferric ion, take a test drop and evaporate to dryness with 1 drop of NH₄OH (sp gr 0.90). Then cover the residue with a drop of NH₄OH (sp gr 0.90) and warm gently. Without disturbing the residue, draw the drop to a clean area and evaporate to dryness. Then cover the residue with a drop of water, allow to stand for a few moments, and, with a glass rod, lead the solution to a clean area of the slide. Add a drop of K₂Hg(SCN)₄ solution and examine under the 10× objective for zinc, copper, and cobalt as described above.

(o) *Sodium.*—Evaporate a drop of test solution to dryness. Place a drop of water on the residue and then lead it to a clean area of the slide. Add a drop of zinc uranyl acetate solution. The presence of sodium is indicated by the formation of monoclinic crystals. These crystals are usually colorless but, if large, may be faintly yellow.

(p) *Potassium.*—Evaporate a drop of test solution to dryness and treat with a drop of water, after which transfer it to a clean area of the slide. Add a drop of H₂PtCl₆ solution and observe under the 10× objective. Deep yellow octahedra are formed if potassium is present. The crystals may have a hexagonal aspect under certain conditions. If ammonium compounds are present, ignite a portion of the sample to drive off NH₃ compounds before testing for potassium.

(q) *Manganese.*—Add 2 drops of HCl (sp gr 1.19) to a small portion of the crushed sample on a slide and evaporate to dryness. Add 2 drops of HNO₃ (1:19), warm, and allow to cool. Add a small amount of powdered NaBiO₃ and stir with a glass rod. The development

of a magenta color indicates the presence of manganese.

(r) *Lead.*—To a drop of test solution, add a crystal of KI. The presence of lead will be indicated by the formation of bright yellow, thin scales and hexagonal plates that may appear greenish, brownish, or even gray by transmitted light.

(s) *Nickel.*—To a large drop of test solution add NH₄OH (sp gr 0.90) and warm gently. Draw the solution from the insoluble material by means of a glass rod to a clean slide and evaporate to dryness. Treat the residue with additional NH₄OH and add to the original drop. Allow a drop of dimethylglyoxime solution to flow into the drop. A rose-pink or magenta-colored precipitate will be formed if nickel is present. Under high power the precipitate will be shown to consist of fine needles.

Petrographic Procedure

Note 4.—Detailed procedures for petrographic examination are described in the literature (1, 2, 3, 4, 5).

11. (a) *Determination of Crystalline Habit.*—Place a drop of immersion liquid (index of refraction, $N = 1.57$) on a slide and mark the index of refraction of the liquid on the frosted end of the slide. Sprinkle some of the crushed sample over this liquid and cover with a cover glass. Examine under 450×. Observe and record any unique crystal habit or cleavage. Insert the upper nicol prism and rotate the stage. Record whether isotropic or anisotropic crystals, or both, are present. Isotropic crystals, and anisotropic crystals oriented with an optic axis parallel to that of the microscope, will remain dark in all positions of rotation. Anisotropic crystals will be alternately bright and dark on rotation of the stage and will exhibit either two or three indices of refraction.

(b) *Determination of Extinction Angle.*—If any of the crystals is elongated, determine the extinction angle. The extinction angle is observed between the extinction position and some recognizable crystallographic direction such as a cleavage plane. Measure the angle by means of the graduated scale on the rotating stage. Position the crystal carefully so that the intersection of the crosshairs intersects the cleavage plane.

(c) *Determination of Index of Refraction.*—Use the Becke line test to determine whether the particle under examination has an index above or below that of the liquid in which the crystal is immersed. The slide prepared in accordance with Paragraph (a) may be used for the preliminary examination. The Becke line is a bright line seen at the contact zone between a crystal and a liquid having a different refractive index. Make the determination as follows.

(1) Choose a crystal near the center of the field and focus the microscope. Partially close the diaphragm of the substage condenser in order to obtain central illumination. Raise the tube of the microscope by means of the fine adjustment and observe a narrow white line which will appear just inside or outside the boundary of the fragment with the surrounding liquid. If, on raising the tube, the line moves into the crystal, the index of refraction of the crystal is greater than that of the liquid. If the index of refraction of the crystal is less than that of the liquid, the line will move into the liquid. If the indices of the crystal and the liquid are identical, the boundary of the crystal will become very difficult to see. Due to the dispersion of the liquid, that is, the variation of index of refraction of the liquid with wave length, the boundary will not disappear. Complete disappearance can occur only if monochromatic light is used.

NOTE 5.—The determination of refractive indices of any component in a mixture is complicated by the necessity of recognizing the component in the series of liquid mounts. In other words, the material must be sufficiently characteristic in appearance to be recognized from mount to mount without reasonable doubt.

(2) Choose a recognizable component of the deposit for determination of index of refraction. Choose an appropriate liquid and prepare a second slide with the higher or lower liquid, whichever is indicated by the preliminary test. By this procedure a liquid will be found that most nearly matches the index of the crystal. If the crystal, on rotation of the stage, alternately darkens and becomes bright, the crystal is anisotropic and may exhibit two or three indices of refraction. Choose a particle that shows a high order interference color. Turn the stage to extinction, remove the upper nicol prism, and apply the Becke line test. Rotate the stage 90 deg and repeat the test. Prepare additional slides with different liquids until the highest and lowest indices of the component are determined. The highest and lowest indices of the crystal will not be exhibited unless the crystal is exactly oriented relative to the plane of the lower nicol prism. The crystals which exhibit the highest order of interference color between crossed nicol prisms are most nearly oriented in the proper position to exhibit the highest and lowest indices of refraction. An anisotropic crystal which remains dark, or nearly so, on rotation of the stage will exhibit the beta index of refraction.

(d) *Sign of Elongation.*—If the crystals are elongated, record the sign of elongation. The sign of elongation is positive in those crystals in which the higher index is exhibited parallel to the axis of elongation and negative in those in which the lower index is exhibited in this position.

Interpretation of Data

12. Identification of crystals is made by comparing the determined optical data with that which is published in the literature or with data determined from pedigreed samples. The refractive indices are the most important of the optical constants, and often identification can be made by this determination alone. Confirmatory information, however from other optical constants and from chemical microscopic tests make the identification more positive.

NOTE 6.—Extensive tables of optical data are contained in reference sources such as Winchell (4) and Larsen and Berman (1). Some data are included in the chemical handbooks. More recently published data may be found in *Chemical Abstracts* under the headings: Refractive Index Optical Properties, Minerals, Microscopy, and Petrography.

REFERENCES

(1) L. S. Larsen and H. Berman, "The Microscope Determination of the Nonopaque Minerals," Bulletin 848, U. S. Geological Survey (1934).

(2) A. N. Winchell, "Elements of Optical Mineralogy," John Wiley & Sons, Inc., New York, N. Y., Part I, p. 80 (1937).

(3) Chamot and Mason, "Handbook of Chemical Microscopy," John Wiley & Sons, Inc. New York, N. Y., Volume II.

(4) A. N. Winchell, "The Microscopic Character of Artificial Inorganic Substances or Artificial Minerals," John Wiley & Sons, Inc. New York, N. Y.

(5) A. N. Winchell, "Elements of Optical Mineralogy," John Wiley & Sons, Inc., New York, N. Y., Part II.

Standard Method of Test for
IODIDE AND BROMIDE IONS IN INDUSTRIAL WATER[1]

ASTM Designation: D 1246 – 55 (1965)
ADOPTED, 1955; REAPPROVED, 1965

This Standard of the American Society for Testing and Materials is issued under the fixed designation D 1246; the number immediately following the designation indicates the year of original adoption or, in the case of revision, the year of last revision. A number in parentheses indicates the year of last reapproval.

NOTE.—Editorial changes were made in Section 6 in June, 1960.

Scope and Application

1. This method covers the titrimetric determination of iodide or bromide ions, or both, in industrial water. It may be applied to the determination of iodide and bromide ions in the presence of chloride ions, in industrial waters, including industrial waste water, brine, and sea water.

Summary of Method

2. (a) The iodide, in a buffered solution, is oxidized by bromine to iodate, the excess bromine subsequently being decomposed. Iodine equivalent to the iodate is then liberated from added potassium iodide and titrated.

(b) Iodide and bromide, occurring together are oxidized to iodate and bromate, respectively by hypochlorite, the excess hypochlorite subsequently being decomposed. Iodine equivalent to the combined iodate and bromate is then liberated from added potassium iodide and titrated. Bromide is calculated from the difference in titrations.

Definitions

3. For definitions of terms used in this method, refer to the Definitions of Terms Relating to Industrial Water and Industrial Waste Water (ASTM Designation: D 1129).[2]

Interferences

4. Iron, manganese, and organic matter interfere with the basic reactions of this method, but are removed by preliminary treatment with calcium oxide when necessary.

Purity of Reagents

5. (a) Reagent grade chemicals shall be used in all tests. Unless otherwise indicated, it is intended that all reagents shall conform to the specifications of the Committee on Analytical Reagents of the American Chemical Society, where such specifications are available.[3] Other

---

[1] Under the standardization procedure of the Society, this method is under the jurisdiction of the ASTM Committee D-19 on Industrial Water. A list of members may be found in the ASTM Year Book.

[2] Appears in this publication.
[3] "Reagent Chemicals, American Chemical Society Specifications," Am. Chem. Soc., Washington, D. C. For suggestions on the testing of reagents not listed by the American Chemical Society, see "Reagent Chemicals and Standards," by Joseph Rosin, D. Van Nostrand Co., Inc., New York, N. Y., and the "United States Pharmocopeia."

grades may be used, provided it is first ascertained that the reagent is of sufficiently high purity to permit its use without lessening the accuracy of the determination.

Note 1.—The purity of the reagents should be checked by determining a blank, following the procedure given in Section 8.

(*b*) Unless otherwise indicated, reference to water shall be understood to mean reagent water conforming to the Specifications for Reagent Water (ASTM Designation: D 1193).[2]

Reagents

6. (*a*) *Acetic Acid* (*1:8*).—Mix 1 volume of glacial acetic acid with 8 volumes of water.

(*b*) *Bromine Water* (*saturated*).—Add to 250 ml of water, slightly more liquid bromine than will dissolve on shaking. Store in a glass-stoppered, actinic glass bottle.

(*c*) *Calcium Carbonate* ($CaCO_3$), powdered.

(*d*) *Calcium Oxide*.—Anhydrous, powdered CaO.

(*e*) *Hydrochloric Acid* (*1:4*).—Mix 1 volume of HCl (sp gr 1.19) with 4 volumes of water.

(*f*) *Methyl Red Indicator* (*0.1 g per liter*).—Dissolve 0.01 g of water-soluble methyl red in water and dilute to 100 ml.

(*g*) *Potassium Fluoride* ($KF \cdot 2H_2O$), crystals.

(*h*) *Potassium Hypochlorite Solution* (*44 g KClO per liter*).—Dissolve 61.7 g of potassium hydroxide (KOH) in 1 liter of water. Then, pass approximately 35 g of bromine-free chlorine into the KOH solution while continually cooling and stirring. Store in actinic glassware.

(*i*) *Potassium Iodide* (KI), crystals.

Note 2.—The potassium iodide must be free from iodates. This may be ascertained by dissolving 0.1 to 0.2 g of KI in about 5 ml of water, acidifying with 1 or 2 drops of H_2SO_4 (sp gr 1.84), and adding 2 to 3 ml of starch indicator. Immediate appearance of a blue color indicates

the presence of iodate; slow color formation is due to atmospheric oxidation.

(*j*) *Sodium Acetate Solution* (*275 g per liter*).—Dissolve 275 g of sodium acetate trihydrate ($NaC_2H_3O_2 \cdot 3H_2O$) in water, dilute to 1 liter, and filter.

(*k*) *Sodium Chloride* (NaCl), crystals, which, in addition to conforming to ACS specifications, shall also be free from iodide, iodate, bromide, and bromate.

(*l*) *Sodium Formate Solution* (*500 g per liter*).—Dissolve 50 g of sodium formate ($NaCHO_2$) in hot water and dilute to 100 ml.

(*m*) *Sodium Molybdate Solution* (*10 g per liter*).—Dissolve 1 g of sodium molybdate ($Na_2MoO_4 \cdot 2H_2O$) in water, and dilute to 100 ml.

(*n*) *Sodium Thiosulfate Stock Solution*.—Clean a 1-liter glass-stoppered bottle with dichromate - sulfuric acid cleaning solution and rinse thoroughly with hot water. Dissolve 25 g of sodium thiosulfate ($Na_2S_2O_3 \cdot 5H_2O$) in water that has been previously boiled and cooled. Dilute this solution to 1 liter with previously boiled and cooled water. Stopper the bottle and mix by continuous shaking, with periodic inversion. Preserve the solution by adding 1 g of sodium carbonate (Na_2CO_3).

(*o*) *Sodium Thiosulfate, Standard Solution* (*0.01 N*).—Transfer 100 ml of the $Na_2S_2O_3$ stock solution (Paragraph (*n*)) to a 1000-ml volumetric flask, add 900 ml of water, and mix thoroughly. Dissolve 0.3567 g of recrystallized potassium iodate (KIO_3, previously dried 2 hr at 180 C) in water and dilute to 1000 ml. Pipet 25 ml of the KIO_3 solution into a 250-ml iodine flask; then add successively 75 ml of water, 0.5 g of KI crystals, and (after solution is complete) 10 ml of H_2SO_4 (1:4). Allow the stoppered flask to stand 5 min in the dark; then titrate with the $Na_2S_2O_3$ solution being standardized, using 2 to 3 ml of starch indicator as the end point is approached. Calculate the normality of the standard sodium thiosulfate solution as follows:

$$N = \frac{0.25}{S}$$

where:

N = normality of the $Na_2S_2O_3$ solution, and

S = milliliters of standard $Na_2S_2O_3$ solution required for titration of the solution.

(*p*) *Starch Indicator.*—Make a paste of 1 g of arrowroot starch or soluble iodometric starch with cold water. Pour the paste into 100 ml of boiling water and boil for several minutes. Store in a glass-stoppered bottle in a cool place. Starch solution, prepared in this manner, will remain chemically stable for 2 or 3 days.

(*q*) *Sulfuric Acid (1:4).*—Add 1 volume of concentrated sulfuric acid (H_2SO_4, sp gr 1.84) to 4 volumes of water, and mix.

Sampling

7. Collect the sample in accordance with the Methods of Sampling Industrial Water (ASTM Designation: D 510).[2]

Procedure

8. (*a*) If the sample contains soluble iron, manganese, or organic matter, shake approximately 400 ml of the sample with a slight excess of CaO. Filter the suspension through a dry filter paper, discarding the first 75 ml of filtrate.

NOTE 3.—Paragraphs (*b*) and (*c*) refer to the procedure for the determination of iodide, alone; and Paragraphs (*d*) and (*e*) refer to the procedure for the determination of iodide and bromide, together. If only iodide ion concentration is desired, Paragraphs (*d*) and (*e*) and subsequent references to the second iodine flask may be disregarded.

(*b*) Measure 100 ml of sample (or filtrate obtained in Paragraph (*a*)), or a fraction thereof to contain not more than 5 mg of iodide, into a 250-ml iodine flask, diluting with water to approximately

100 ml if the sample taken was smaller in volume. Add a drop of methyl red indicator solution and barely acidify with H_2SO_4 (1:4). Add 15 ml of sodium acetate solution and 5 ml of acetic acid (1:8). Add sufficient bromine water to produce a light yellow color, mix, and allow to stand 5 min.

(*c*) Reduce the excess bromine by adding sodium formate solution until the yellow tinge in the sample disappears; then add an excess of 1 ml of the sodium formate solution. Wash down the sides of the flask with a small amount of water and blow out bromine vapors by the use of a syringe and a glass tube inserted through the mouth of the flask. Add 0.5 g of $KF \cdot 2H_2O$ if any iron precipitates at this point.

(*d*) Measure 100 ml of sample (or filtrate obtained in Paragraph (*a*)), or a fraction thereof to contain not more than 5 mg of bromide, into a second 250-ml iodine flask, diluting with water to approximately 100 ml if the sample taken was smaller in volume. Add sufficient NaCl to produce a 3-g chloride content in the sample. Add a drop of methyl red indicator solution and neutralize the solution with HCl (1:4), add 10 ml of KClO solution, followed by 1 ml of HCl (1:4) and sufficient $CaCO_3$ to produce an excess of approximately 0.1 g. Heat the solution to boiling and maintain this temperature for about 8 min.

NOTE 4.—For waters high in bromide concentration, use a quantity of sample to contain not more than 25 mg of bromide. It is recommended in this case to use 0.05 N $Na_2S_2O_3$ solution in Paragraph (*f*). Standard $Na_2S_2O_3$ solution of this strength may be prepared by substituting 500 ml of stock solution and 500 ml of water for the quantities given in Section 6(*o*).

(*e*) Reduce the excess KClO by adding 2 ml of sodium formate solution, taking precautions to wash down the sides of the flask with a small amount of hot water. Keep the solution hot for an additional 8 min. Cool, add several drops of Na_2MoO_4 solution, and, if any iron precipitates at this point, add 0.5 g of $KF \cdot 2H_2O$.

(f) Dissolve about 1 g of KI in the solutions prepared in Paragraphs (c) and (e); then add 10 ml of H_2SO_4 (1:4) to each flask. Let the two flasks stand 5 min in the dark; then titrate the liberated iodine with 0.01 N $Na_2S_2O_3$ solution to a starch end point, adding 2 to 3 ml of starch indicator as the end point is approached. Disregard the return of blue color after the end point has been reached.

Calculation

9. Calculate the concentration of iodide ions and bromide ions in parts per million as follows:

$$\text{Iodide, ppm} = \frac{21{,}150 \times AN_1}{SD}$$

$$\text{Bromide, ppm} = 13{,}320 \times \left(\frac{BN_2}{TD} - \frac{AN_1}{SD} \right)$$

where:

A = milliliters of $Na_2S_2O_3$ solution required for titration of the solution from Section 8(b),

B = milliliters of $Na_2S_2O_3$ solution re-

quired for titration of the solution from Section 8(d),

D = specific gravity of sample (considered as 1.000 for water containing less than 5000 ppm of dissolved solids),

N_1 = normality of $Na_2S_2O_3$ solution used for titrating iodide only,

N_2 = normality of $Na_2S_2O_3$ solution used for titrating iodide and bromide together,

S = milliliters of sample used for the iodide determination, and

T = milliliters of sample used for the iodide-plus-bromide determination.

Precision and Accuracy

10. The precision and accuracy of this method, in parts per million, which vary with the volume, V, of the sample in milliliters, can be calculated as follows:

	Iodide	Bromide
Precision, ppm	$\dfrac{10}{V}$	$\dfrac{30}{V}$
Accuracy, ppm	$\pm \dfrac{10}{V}$	$\pm \dfrac{80}{V}$

Standard Method of Test for

CHEMICAL OXYGEN DEMAND (DICHROMATE OXYGEN DEMAND) OF INDUSTRIAL WASTE WATER[1]

ASTM Designation: D 1252 – 60

ADOPTED, 1960

This Standard of the American Society for Testing and Materials is issued under the fixed designation D 1252; the final number indicates the year of original adoption as standard or, in the case of revision, the year of last revision.

Scope and Application

1. (*a*) This method describes a procedure for determining the quantity of oxygen which an industrial waste water will consume from a dichromate solution under specified conditions.

(*b*) This method for chemical oxygen demand is recommended as a supplement to the biochemical oxygen demand (BOD) test, but not as a substitute for it (Note 1).

NOTE 1.—In spite of weaknesses inherent in a biological assay, the biochemical oxygen demand (BOD) is the only test which indicates directly the quantity of oxygen that will be utilized by natural agencies in stabilizing organic matter. However, the test for chemical oxygen demand (COD) may be used in evaluating the treatment and control of industrial waste water, and may be correlated with the BOD. Since these tests, COD and BOD, are not uniformly effective in oxidizing organic chemical compounds, there is no inherent constant relationship between the results of these tests for all industrial waste waters. If the basic composition of an industrial waste water continues to be relatively uniform, a fairly constant correlation may be expected between these parameters. For a BOD method of test, refer to ASTM Method D 2329, Test for Biochemical Oxygen Demand of Industrial Water and Industrial Waste Water.[2]

(*c*) This method can be applied to individual concentrated industrial wastes and to the combined effluents from a chemical plant. Ferrous iron, nitrites, sulfites, sulfides, halides, etc., are oxidized as well as organic constituents. Chlorides are quantitatively oxidized by this method, with 1 ppm of chloride as Cl⁻ exerting the equivalent of 0.226 ppm chemical oxygen demand. Therefore, small amounts of organic matter cannot be reliably determined in the presence of a high chloride content, such as would be found in sea water. Furthermore, low

[1] Under the standardization procedure of the Society, this method is under the jurisdiction of the ASTM Committee D-19 on Industrial Water. A list of members may be found in the ASTM Year Book.

This method has been adapted from an analytical method developed (investigations conducted) at the Environmental Health Center of the U. S. Public Health Service, Cincinnati, Ohio.

[2] Appears in this publication.

results may be obtained under certain conditions, since not all organic compounds are completely oxidized (see Section 10).

Principle of Method

2. Organic (see Section 10) and oxidizable inorganic material present in an industrial waste water is oxidized by a standard potassium dichromate solution in 50 per cent by volume of sulfuric acid. The excess dichromate is then titrated with a standard ferrous ammonium sulfate solution, using ortho-phenanthroline ferrous complex as an internal indicator.

Definitions

3. (a) The term "chemical oxygen demand (COD)" in this method is defined in accordance with the Definitions of Terms Relating to Industrial Water and Industrial Waste Water (ASTM Designation: D 1129),[2] as follows:

Chemical Oxygen Demand (COD).— The amount of oxygen, expressed in parts per million, consumed under specified conditions in the oxidation of the organic and oxidizable inorganic matter contained in an industrial waste water, corrected for the influence of chlorides.

(b) For definitions of other terms used in this method, refer to Definitions D 1129.

Apparatus

4. *Reflux Apparatus.*—The apparatus, shall consist of a 300-ml round-bottom boiling flask or Erlenmeyer flask made of heat-resistant glass, connected to a Friedrichs condenser by means of a ground-glass joint. An equivalent reflux apparatus may be substituted, provided a ground-glass connection is used between the flask and the condenser, and provided the flask is made of heat-resistant glass.

Purity of Reagents

5. (a) Reagent grade chemicals shall be used in all tests. Unless otherwise indicated, it is intended that all reagents shall conform to the specifications of the Committee on Analytical Reagents of the American Chemical Society, where such specifications are available.[3] Other grades of reagents may be used, provided it is first ascertained that the reagent is of sufficiently high purity to permit its use without lessening the accuracy of the determination.

(b) Unless otherwise indicated, references to water shall be understood to mean reagent water conforming to the Specifications for Reagent Water (ASTM Designation: D 1193).[2] In addition, reagent water used for this method shall be free of material that is oxidizable by dichromate under the specified conditions of test.

Reagents

6. (a) *Ferrous Ammonium Sulfate, Standard Solution (0.25 N).*—Dissolve 98.0 g of $FeSO_4 \cdot (NH_4)_2SO_4 \cdot 6H_2O$ in water. Add 20 ml of H_2SO_4, cool, and dilute to 1 liter. Standardize this solution daily if chemical oxygen demand determinations are made on a daily basis; otherwise, standardize before using. For standardization, dilute 25.0 ml of 0.25 N $K_2Cr_2O_7$ solution to about 250 ml. Add 20 ml of H_2SO_4, and allow the solution to cool. Titrate the cooled solution with the ferrous ammonium sulfate solution being standardized, using the phenanthroline ferrous sulfate indicator, as directed in Section 8 (c).

[3] "Reagent Chemicals, American Chemical Society Specifications," Am. Chem. Soc., Washington, D. C. For suggestions on the testing of reagents not listed by the American Chemical Society, see "Reagent Chemicals and Standards," by Joseph Rosin, D. Van Nostrand Co., Inc., New York, N.Y., and the "United States Pharmacopeia."

(b) *Phenanthroline Ferrous Sulfate Indicator Solution.*—Dissolve 1.48 g of 1, 10-(ortho)-phenanthroline monohydrate, together with 0.70 g of $FeSO_4 \cdot 7H_2O$, in 100 ml of water. This indicator may be purchased already prepared.[4]

(c) *Potassium Dichromate, Standard Solution (0.25 N).*—Dissolve 12.2588 g of $K_2Cr_2O_7$, previously dried at 103 C for 2 hr, in water and dilute to 1 liter in a volumetric flask.

(d) *Silver Sulfate.*—Powdered Ag_2SO_4.

(e) *Sulfuric Acid (sp gr 1.84).*—Concentrated sulfuric acid (H_2SO_4).

Sampling

7. Collect the sample in accordance with the Methods of Sampling Industrial Water (ASTM Designation: D 510).[3]

Procedure

8. (a) To 25.0 ml of 0.2500 N $K_2Cr_2O_7$ solution and the necessary dilution water (Note 2) add cautiously 75 ml of H_2SO_4. Cool to room temperature or lower. To the cooled mixture add the sample with thorough mixing (**Caution, Note 3**). Add pumice granules or glass beads to prevent bumping, attach the flask to the condenser, and reflux the mixture for 2 hr (Note 4).

Note 2.—If the sample size is less than 50 ml, it is advantageous to add the necessary amount of dilution water to the $K_2Cr_2O_7$ solution before the addition of the H_2SO_4 rather than diluting the sample to 50 ml. The sample is added to the cooled mixture to minimize the loss of volatile compounds that may be present.

Note 3: Caution.—Care must be taken to assure that the contents of the flask are well mixed. If not, superheating may result, and the mixture may be blown out of the side-arm of the flask.

Note 4.—For some waste waters the 2-hr reflux period is not necessary. The reflux period necessary to give the maximum oxidation for an individual waste water may be determined, and a shorter period of refluxing may be permissible.

[4] The indicator solution manufactured by the G. Frederick Smith Chemical Co., Columbus, Ohio, and available from laboratory chemical suppliers, is satisfactory for this purpose.

(b) Allow the flask to cool, and wash down the condenser with about 25 ml of water. Transfer the mixture to a 500-ml Erlenmeyer flask, washing out the reflux flask three or four times with water. Carefully dilute the acid solution to about 350 ml with water, and again allow the solution to cool. Titrate the excess dichromate with 0.25 N ferrous ammonium sulfate solution to a phenanthroline ferrous sulfate end point. Add two or three drops of the indicator near the end of the titration. The color change will be sharp, changing from a blue-green to a reddish blue.

(c) *Blank.*—Simultaneously run a blank determination, following the details given in Paragraphs (a) and (b), but using reagent water in place of the sample.

(d) If it is anticipated that organic compounds, such as straight chain acids and alcohols, are present in the waste water and will resist oxidation by dichromate, add 1 g of Ag_2SO_4 directly to the mixture before refluxing, or add the Ag_2SO_4 dissolved in the H_2SO_4 at the rate of 1 g for every 75 ml of acid. The use of this catalyst is precluded in those cases where compounds are present that will react with silver. If such compounds are present (especially high chloride concentration), modify the procedure as described in Paragraph (g).

(e) For waste water of low (5 to 50 ppm) chemical oxygen demand, a more dilute solution of $K_2Cr_2O_7$ may be used. A 0.025 N solution is recommended. However, if a 0.025 N solution is used, the sample size should be selected so that the dichromate reduction is not less than 25 per cent nor more than 50 per cent.

(f) Determine the chloride content of the sample by the Methods of Test for Chloride Ion in Industrial Water and Industrial Waste Water (ASTM Designation: D 512).[2]

(g) When high chloride concentrations are present, reflux the mixture for 1 hr in the absence of the Ag_2SO_4 catalyst. This will volatilize the chloride as free chlorine. Stop the refluxing, allow to cool, and then add 1 g of Ag_2SO_4 (Note 5). Continue refluxing for 1 hr, then proceed as described in Paragraph (b).

Note 5.—A special flask carrying a side arm to facilitate the introduction of the Ag_2SO_4 is preferable. The catalyst may also be made in pellet form, each pellet containing about 1 g of Ag_2SO_4. This makes introduction of the catalyst into the reflux mixture easier.

Calculation

9. Calculate the chemical oxygen demand (COD) in the sample, in parts per million, as follows:

Chemical oxygen demand (COD), ppm

$$= \frac{(A - B)N \times 8000}{S} - (0.226C)$$

where:

A = milliliters of $FeSO_4(NH_4)_2SO_4$ solution required for titration of the blank,

B = milliliters of $FeSO_4(NH_4)_2SO_4$ solution required for titration of the sample,

C = chloride ion content of the sample, in parts per million,

N = normality of the $FeSO_4(NH_4)_2SO_4$ solution, and

S = milliliters of sample taken for the test.

Precision and Accuracy[5]

10. (a) The precision of this method is shown in the following table by typical examples of the coefficient of variation, expressed in per cent, obtained during a statistical evaluation of the procedure:

Compound or Waste	Coefficient of Variation, per cent	
	Without Ag_2SO_4	With Ag_2SO_4
Glycocoll................	0.8	0.7
Distillery waste.........	1.8	0.6
2-amino-8-naphthol-6-sulfonic acid..........	0.5	0.8
Sodium lauryl sulfate....	1.0	1.3
Oil refinery waste caustic.	0.7	1.3

(b) The accuracy of this method depends upon the type of organic compound being oxidized. In many cases accuracy is improved by the use of Ag_2SO_4 as a catalyst. Typical results of the accuracy obtained are given in the following table:

Compound	Results Obtained, per cent of theoretical	
	Without Ag_2SO_4	With Ag_2SO_4
Acetic acid.............	2.4	95.1
Alpha-amino-n-caproic acid	97.7	98.5
n-Butyric acid..........	71.8	96.1
o-Cresol................	83.2	95.8
Furoic acid.............	83.6	97.6
Pyridine	1.3	0.8

[5] Supporting data and literature references pertinent to this method are given in Appendix I to the Report of Committee D-19, see *Proceedings*, Am. Soc. Testing Mats., Vol. 53, pp. 470-474 (1953).

Standard Methods of Test for
RESIDUAL CHLORINE IN INDUSTRIAL WATER[1]

ASTM Designation: D 1253 – 57 (1965)

ADOPTED, 1957; REAPPROVED, 1965

This Standard of the American Society for Testing and Materials is issued under the fixed designation D 1253; the number immediately following the designation indicates the year of original adoption or, in the case of revision, the year of last revision. A number in parentheses indicates the year of last reapproval.

Note.—Editorial changes were made in Section 9 in September, 1958, and in Footnote 8 in June, 1959.

Scope

1. (a) These methods cover procedures for the determination of residual chlorine in industrial water. Provision is made for the determination of total chlorine, free available chlorine, and combined available chlorine in the presence of the amount of color, turbidity, iron, manganese, chromium, nitrites, and organic matter normally present. Three methods are given, as follows:

	Sections
Referee Method (Amperometric Titration Method)	5 to 15
Non-Referee Method A (Colorimetric Method)	16 to 24
Non-Referee Method B (Dilution – Colorimetric Method)	25 to 31

(b) The referee method is amperometric, and is not subject to commonly encountered interferences. This method is applicable to all types of industrial water having a residual chlorine content of not more than 5 ppm. Non-referee method A is colorimetric, and is subject to interferences by certain ions and by elevated temperatures. This method is not applicable to highly colored or turbid water.

Non-referee method B is a dilution-colorimetric method subject to interferences similar to non-referee method A, but is applicable to water containing high amounts of residual chlorine.

(c) Methods for the determination of residual chlorine in water containing appreciable amounts of industrial waste are given in the Methods of Test for Residual Chlorine in Industrial Waste Water (ASTM Designation: D 1427).[2]

Definitions

2. (a) The terms "residual chlorine (chlorine residual)," "total chlorine residual," "free available chlorine residual," and "combined available chlorine residual" in these methods are defined in accordance with the Standard Definitions of Terms Relating to Industrial Water and Industrial Waste Water (ASTM Designation: D 1129),[2] as follows:

Residual Chlorine (Chlorine Residual).—The amount of available chlorine present in industrial water at any specified period, subsequent to the addition of chlorine.

Total Chlorine Residual.—Total

---

[1] Under the standardization procedure of the Society, these methods are under the jurisdiction of the ASTM Committee D-19 on Industrial Water. A list of members may be found in the ASTM Year Book.

[2] Appears in this publication.

457

amount of chlorine residual present, without regard to type.

Free Available Chlorine Residual.— Residual consisting of hypochlorite ions (OCl), hypochlorous acid (HOCl), or a combination thereof.

Combined Available Chlorine Residual. —Residual consisting of chlorine combined with ammonia nitrogen or nitrogenous compounds.

NOTE 1.—Chlorine present as chloride is not included in these definitions, nor determined by these methods.

(b) For definitions of other terms used in these methods, refer to Definitions D 1129.

Purity of Reagents

3. (a) Reagent grade chemicals shall be used in all tests. Unless otherwise indicated, it is intended that all reagents shall conform to the specifications of the Committee on Analytical Reagents of the American Chemical Society, where such specifications are available.[3] Other grades may be used, provided it is first ascertained that the reagent is of sufficiently high purity to permit its use without lessening the accuracy of the determination.

(b) Unless otherwise indicated, references to water shall be understood to mean reagent water conforming to the Specifications for Reagent Water (ASTM Designation: D 1193).[2] In addition, the water shall be free of chlorine demand. Prepare the water by adding approximately 20 ppm available chlorine and adjusting the pH to be between 7.0 and 9.0. Protect the prepared water from sunlight for 1 week; then expose it to sunlight until no residual chlorine remains. If desirable, the final dechlorina-

[3] "Reagent Chemicals, American Chemical Society Specifications," Am. Chem. Soc., Washington, D. C. For suggestions on the testing of reagents not listed by the American Chemical Society, see "Reagent Chemicals and Standards," by Joseph Rosin. D. Van Nostrand Co., Inc., New York, N. Y., and the "United States Pharmacopeia."

tion may be effected with sodium arsenite solution prepared as directed in Section 9 (c).

Sampling

4. Collect the sample in accordance with the Methods of Sampling Industrial Water (ASTM Designation: D 510).[2] Take care that the sample is representative, and keep it away from direct sunlight prior to analysis.

NOTE 2.—All tests should be made as soon as possible after collection of the sample (not more than 5 min) because the residual chlorine may diminish with time, due to the chlorine demand of the sample. Where time of contact is important, the elapsed time between the addition of chlorine and the determination of chlorine should be taken into account.

REFEREE METHOD

(Amperometric Titration Method)

Application

5. This method is applicable to all types of industrial water, regardless of temperature, color, and turbidity. It may be used to determine the amount of total chlorine, free available chlorine, or combined available chlorine present in industrial water up to a concentration of 5 ppm.

Principle of Method

6. This is an amperometric titration method utilizing phenylarseneoxide as the titrating agent. When the cell of the titrator is immersed in a sample containing chlorine, current is generated; but as phenylarseneoxide is added, the chlorine is neutralized and the generation of current ceases. When chlorine is present as a chloramine, potassium iodide is added, releasing iodine which is titrated in a similar manner. The iodine content is calculated in terms of free chlorine.

Interferences

7. Values of pH above 8.0 interfere by slowing down the rate of reaction. This interference is eliminated by buffering all samples to pH 7.0 or less. Erratic behavior of the apparatus in the presence of cupric ions has been reported. Cuprous

and silver ions tend to poison the electrode.

Apparatus

8. *Amperometric Titration Apparatus.*
—See Fig. 1.[4, 5]

$Na_2HPO_4 \cdot 12H_2O$ in water and dilute to 1 liter.

(c) *Iodine Solution (12.7 g per liter).*[6]
—Dissolve 25 g of KI in 50 ml of water. Add 12.7 g of iodine crystals and stir until solution is complete. Dilute to 1

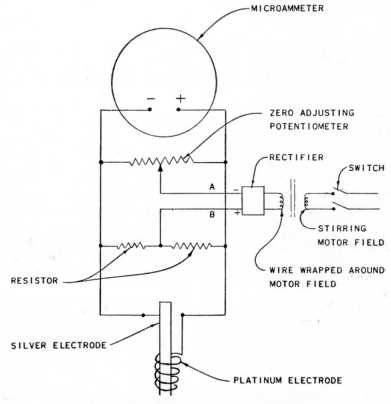

FIG. 1.—Wiring Diagram of Amperometric Titrator.

Reagents

9. *(a) Buffer Solution A (pH 4.0).*—Dissolve 243 g of sodium acetate trihydrate and 480 g of glacial acetic acid in water and dilute to 1 liter.

(b) Buffer Solution B (pH 7.0).—Dissolve 25.4 g of KH_2PO_4 and 86 g of

liter with water and store the solution in a dark bottle.

(d) Iodine Solution (0.0282 N).[7]—Transfer to a 1-liter volumetric flask 25 g of KI dissolved in a small amount of water, and the calculated amount of approximately 0.1 N iodine solution that has been standardized against sodium arsenite. Dilute to 1 liter and store in a cool, dark place. Standardize daily as follows: Place 5 to 10 ml of 0.1 N arsenite

---

[4] Further details of assembly may be found in *Water and Sewage Works*, May, 1949, p. 171; *Journal American Water Works Association*, Vol. 34, pp. 1227–1240 (1942); and *Analytical Chemistry*, Vol. 19, pp. 200–204 (1947).
[5] The commercial apparatus and phenylarsenoxide available from Wallace & Tiernan, Inc., Newark, N. J., have been found satisfactory for this purpose.

---

[6] Reagent used for standardizing purposes only.

solution in a flask and titrate with this solution, using starch solution as an indicator. Discard and prepare fresh solution if standardization shows a change in normality.

(e) *Phenylarseneoxide, Standard Solution (0.00564 N).*—Dissolve 0.8 g phenylarseneoxide[5] in 150 ml of NaOH solution (12 g per liter). To 110 ml of this solution add 800 ml of water, and bring to a pH of 9.0 by adding HCl (1:1). (This should require about 2 ml of HCl (1:1).) Continue acidification with HCl (1:1) until a pH of 6 to 7 is reached, as indicated by a glass-electrode system; then dilute to a total volume of 1 liter. Standardize to 0.00564 N against 0.0282 N iodine solution, using the titrator as the end-point indicator. Add 1 ml of chloroform for preservation.

(f) *Potassium Iodide Solution (50 g per liter).*—Dissolve 50 g of KI in water and dilute to 1 liter.

(g) *Sodium Arsenite, Standard Solution (0.10 N).*[6]—Dissolve 4.946 g of dried arsenous oxide, As_2O_3, in 40 ml of NaOH solution (250 g NaOH per liter). Heat the solution to about 35 C and stir until the solution is clear and the surface free from floating material. Dilute to approximately 250 ml with water, saturate with CO_2, then dilute to 1 liter. Store the solution in a dark bottle.

Alternatively, standard sodium arsenite solution may be prepared as follows: Dissolve 4.946 g of dried As_2O_3 in 40 ml of NaOH solution (50 g NaOH per liter), acidify very slightly with H_2SO_4 or HCl, and dilute to 1 liter with water.

Calibration[7]

10. When equipment has been out of service for a day or more, check the

[7] Calibrate commercial apparatus in accordance with the detailed instructions supplied by the manufacturer. Glassware should be conditioned with water containing at least 10 ppm of residual chlorine for at least 2 hr before use and then rinsed with water having zero chlorine demand.

electrode for sensitivity by noting the rapidity of the pointer deflections, before beginning formal titrations. If the pointer responds slowly after addition of KI, add a small amount of iodine. If it responds slowly to free chlorine, sensitize it by adding more chlorine.

Determination of Total Chlorine Residual

11. Add 1 ml of KI solution to 200 ml of sample (Note 3); then follow immediately with 1 ml of buffer solution A. Immerse the electrode in the sample, start the stirring motor, and add phenylarseneoxide solution dropwise from a buret. The galvanometer pointer will move counterclockwise after the addition of each drop if chlorine is present. Wait a few seconds between successive additions of phenylarseneoxide to allow time for completion of the reaction. When the pointer no longer moves on addition of 1 drop of solution, record the total volume of phenylarseneoxide solution added.

Note 3.—For residual chlorine concentration of 2.0 ppm or less, use 200 ml of sample. For greater concentrations use 100 ml of sample. It is preferable that the size of the sample be such that not more than 2 ml of 0.00564 N phenylarseneoxide solution will be required to complete the titration.

Determination of Free Available Chlorine Residual

12. Add 1 ml of buffer solution B to 200 ml of sample (Note 3), then proceed as described in Section 11, starting with the second sentence (Note 4).

Note 4.—The presence of free available chlorine is characterized by a rapid deflection of the galvanometer pointer. Slight counterclockwise movements of the pointer after addition of individual drops of phenylarseneoxide denote a drift effect rather than the presence of free available chlorine. Check by repeating the titration on a fresh sample.

Determination of Combined Available Chlorine Residual

13. After determining the free available chlorine residual, add 1 ml of KI so-

lution and 1 ml of buffer solution A, and repeat the phenylarseneoxide titration as described in Section 11, starting with the second sentence.

Calculation

14. Calculate the various types of chlorine residual, in parts per million, as follows:

$$\text{Chlorine residual, ppm} = \frac{200A}{S}$$

where:

A = milliliters of phenylarseneoxide solution (0.00564 N) required for the titration in Section 11, 12, or 13, depending on the specific type of chlorine residual determined, and

S = milliliters of sample used.

Precision

15. The precision of this method is 0.02 ppm for residual chlorine values not greater than 5.0 ppm.

Non-Referee Method A
(Colorimetric Method)

Application

16. This method is applicable to the determination of total chlorine residual, free available chlorine residual, and combined available chlorine residual in industrial waters, except those high in color and turbidity. It is applicable to rapid control determinations of chlorine residuals not in excess of 10 ppm. Sensitivity is greatest for chlorine residuals of less than 1.0 ppm.

Principle of Method

17. Residual chlorine (total, free, or combined) reacts under acid conditions (optimum pH 1.2), with ortho-tolidine to form the yellow holoquinone of ortho-tolidine dihydrochloride. The color developed is approximately proportional to the amount of chlorine residual present, and is quantitatively evaluated by comparison with standard colors. Sodium arsenite fixes the color developed in the free available chlorine test, giving ample

time to make color comparisons, and neutralizes all chlorine residual present in the compensation cell.

Note 5.—Careful attention to such details as temperature, time of contact after addition of ortho-tolidine, time of addition of sodium arsenite, and intensity and quality of light source results in greater sensitivity of the test.

Interferences

18. Temperatures greater than 15 C prevent determination of free available chlorine residual, but do not interfere with the determination of total chlorine residual or combined available chlorine residual. High color and turbidity of the sample will interfere.

Apparatus

19. (a) Color Comparator of the slide or disc type.

(b) Light Source suitable for use with the type of comparator employed (Note 6).

Note 6.—A fluorescent "daylight" lamp assembly is a suitable light source for color comparators, and can be used without a color filter. Some comparators are equipped with a light source other than fluorescent. The standards in such sets cannot be used with other light sources because of the special compensations employed for the particular light source provided. When a filament "daylight" lamp assembly is used, it is essential that it include a color filter and diffuser glass. The diffuser glass must be placed in contact with the color filter, and on the sample side. The light source should be a 150-w Mazda "C" lamp with clear envelope. The color filter should be equivalent of a Corning Glass "daylight" No. 5900, having a thickness equivalent to 163 micro-reciprocal degrees (mr°). The diffuser glass should be thin flashed opal without color tint.

(c) Chlorine Standards.—Glass or sealed permanent liquid standards.[8]

(d) Viewing Cells suitable for use with the type of comparator employed (Note 7).

Note 7.—Viewing cells are available in a variety of shapes and volumes depending upon

---

[8] N. S. Chamberlin and J. R. Glass, "Colorimetric Determination of Chlorine Residuals up to 10 ppm with Ortho-tolidine," *Journal American Water Works Association*, Vol. 35, Aug., 1943, p. 1065, and Sept., 1943, p. 1205. It is recommended that commercially available standards be used rather than laboratory-prepared standards, due to the difficulty of achieving stability and accuracy.

the comparator for which they are designed. The small sizes of 10- and 15-ml capacity are recommended in the test for free available chlorine. These sizes can be manipulated quickly. This allows the reading to be made within 5 sec, as stipulated. When larger cells are used, the manipulations are slowed to the point where the reading cannot be made within the stipulated 5-sec interval.

Reagents

20. (a) *Sodium Arsenite Solution (5 g Na_2HAsO_3 per liter).*—Dissolve 5 g of Na_2HAsO_3 in 1 liter of water. Mix, and store in a glass-stoppered bottle.

(b) *Ortho-tolidine Solution (1.0 g ortho-tolidine per liter).*—Dissolve 1.34 g of ortho-tolidine dihydrochloride in 500 ml of water. Add this solution, with constant stirring, to 500 ml of a mixture of 350 ml of water and 150 ml of HCl (sp gr 1.19). Store for not more than six months in a brown, glass-stoppered bottle and in a cool place not below −20 C.

Determination of Total Chlorine Residual

21. (a) Select two viewing cells equal in size, shape, viewing depth, color, and volume.

(b) Fill one of the two cells to the mark with sample. Add 1 ml of Na_2HAsO_3 solution per 100 ml of sample; mix, and add 5 ml of ortho-tolidine solution per 100 ml of sample (Notes 8 and 9). Place this cell with its contents in the comparator behind the chlorine standard to compensate for color and turbidity.

NOTE 8.—This order of addition ensures full production of color, and at the same time accomplishes the desired amount of mixing.

NOTE 9.—Always keep the ratio of arsenite or ortho-tolidine at the same value when using other than 100-ml cells.

(c) Add 5 ml of ortho-tolidine solution per 100 ml of sample to the second cell. Fill the second cell to the mark with sample, and place it in the reading position of the comparator. Match the maximum color produced, which normally

takes place within 5 min, with the color of the standard.

Determination of Free Available Chlorine Residual

22. (a) Cool the sample to 15 C or less and proceed as directed in Section 21 (b), using 10- or 15-ml viewing cells.

(b) Add 5 ml of ortho-tolidine solution per 100 ml of sample to the second cell (Note 9). Fill to the mark with sample and, within 5 sec, add 1 ml of Na_2HAsO_3 solution per 100 ml of sample and mix. Place the cell in position, and compare the color produced with the standard color.

Calculation

23. (a) *Total Chlorine Residual.*—The value of the chlorine standard most closely matching the color of the sample solution in Section 21 (c) is the amount of total chlorine present. Interpolation between values is permissible.

(b) *Free Available Chlorine Residual.*—The value of the chlorine standard most closely matching the color of the sample solution in Section 22 (b) is the amount of free available chlorine present. Interpolation between values is permissible.

(c) *Combined Available Chlorine Residuals.*—The difference between the amounts of total chlorine residual and free available chlorine residual is the amount of combined available chlorine residual present.

Precision

24. The precision of this method is a function of the quality of the standards. The precision is normally 0.05 ppm for residuals of less than 0.5 ppm, and 0.10 ppm for residuals between 0.5 and 1.0 ppm.

NON-REFEREE METHOD B
(Dilution - Colorimetric Method)

Application

25. This method is applicable to the determination of total chlorine residuals

16–1

only, where the concentration exceeds 1 ppm. It is particularly adaptable to the determination of high residuals (10 to 300 ppm) used in the disinfection of water mains, tanks, etc., where an approximation is adequate. The method has the advantage of ease of manipulation.

Principle of Method

26. A known volume of the sample under test is diluted with a known volume of water containing a known volume of dilute ortho-tolidine. The solution is compared with chlorine color standards, and the total chlorine residual corresponding to the matching standard is corrected for dilution.

Apparatus

27. See Section 19.

Reagents

28. *Ortho-tolidine Solution.*—See Section 20 (*b*).

Procedure

29. (*a*) Fill one of two viewing cells with water, and place it in the comparator behind the chlorine standard.

(*b*) Pour 5 ml of ortho-tolidine solution into a 100-ml cylinder, add the desired amount of diluent water, and mix. Add sufficient sample to make 100 ml of solution (Note 10).

NOTE 10.—Addition of dilute ortho-tolidine to the sample will lead to erroneous results. Care in manipulation is of prime importance. Choose a ratio of diluent water to sample, always using 5 ml of ortho-tolidine solution, to provide a match in color with chlorine standards equivalent to less than 0.5 ppm residual chlorine.

(*c*) Pour the diluted sample solution into the second viewing cell, and compare the color against chlorine standards.

Calculation

30. Calculate the total chlorine residual as follows:

$$\text{Total chlorine residual, ppm} = \frac{100C}{S}$$

where:

C = the value of the chlorine standard most closely matching the color of the diluted sample solution in Section 29 (*c*), and

S = milliliters of sample contained in 100 ml of the diluted sample solution.

Precision

31. The precision of this method is 15 per cent of the total chlorine residual determined.

Tentative Methods of Test for

NITRITE ION IN INDUSTRIAL WATER[1]

ASTM Designation: D 1254 – 63 T

ISSUED, 1963

These Tentative Methods have been approved by the sponsoring committee and accepted by the Society in accordance with established procedures, for use pending adoption as standard. Suggestions for revisions should be addressed to the Society at 1916 Race St., Philadelphia 3, Pa.

Scope

1. These methods[2] cover the determination of nitrite ion in industrial water. Two methods are given as follows:

	Sections
Referee Method (Colorimetric Method)	5 to 13
Non-Referee Method (Volumetric Method)	14 to 20

Definitions

2. For definitions of terms used in this method, refer to the Definitions of Terms Relating to Industrial Water and Industrial Waste Water (ASTM Designation: D 1129).[3]

Purity of Reagents

3. (a) Reagent grade chemicals shall be used in all tests. Unless otherwise indicated, it is intended that all reagents shall conform to the specifications of the Committee on Analytical Reagents of the American Chemical Society, where such specifications are available.[4] Other grades may be used, provided it is first ascertained that the reagent is of sufficiently high purity to permit its use without lessening the accuracy of the determination.

---

[1] Under the standardization procedure of the Society, these methods are under the jurisdiction of the ASTM Committee D-19 on Industrial Water. A list of members may be found in the ASTM Year Book.

[2] Supporting data relating to this method may be found in B. F. Rider and M. G. Mellon, "Colorimetric Determination of Nitrites," *Industrial and Engineering Chemistry*, Analytical Edition, Vol. 18, p. 96 (1946) and in Appendix I to the 1957 Report of Committee D-19, *Proceedings*, Am. Soc. Testing Mats., Vol. 57 (1957).

[3] Appears in this publication.

[4] "Reagent Chemicals, American Chemical Society Specifications," Am. Chemical Soc., Washington, D. C. For suggestions on the testing of reagents not listed by the American Chemical Society, see "Reagent Chemicals and Standards," by Joseph Rosin, D. Van Nostrand Co., Inc., New York, N. Y., and the "United States Pharmacopeia."

(b) Unless otherwise indicated, references to water shall mean reagent water conforming to the Specifications for Reagent Water (ASTM Designation: D 1193).[3] In addition, reagent water used for these methods shall be free of nitrite ion and sterile. Nitrite-free water can be obtained by distillation of water or by ion exchange methods, with care to prevent absorption of nitrous fumes in the prepared water. Sterile nitrite-free water can be prepared by heating distilled water in an autoclave for 15 min at 15 psi pressure.

Sampling

4. Collect the samples in accordance with the applicable methods of the American Society for Testing and Materials, as follows, using sterile bottles. Nitrite ion should be determined as soon as possible after sampling, even when sterile bottles are used.

D 510—Sampling Industrial Water,[3]
D 860—Sampling Water From Boilers,[3]
D 1066—Sampling Steam.[3]

Referee Method

(Colorimetric Method)

Application

5. This method is applicable to industrial waters that are not highly polluted and contain not more than approximately 0.5 ppm nitrite. The method can be extended by careful dilution with water (Section 3(b)).

Summary of Method

6. The diazonium compound formed by diazotation of sulfanilic acid by nitrite ion in the water sample under strongly acid conditions is coupled at pH 2.0 to 2.5 with alpha-naphthylamine hydrochloride to produce a reddish purple color (azo dye). Photometric measurement at approximately 520 mμ, or visual comparison is made between color developed with the sample and color developed with known standards.

Interferences

7. (a) The following do not interfere when present in concentrations up to 1000 times that of the nitrite: barium, beryllium, calcium, lead (II), lithium, magnesium, manganese (II), nickel (II), potassium, sodium, strontium, thorium, uranyl, zinc, arsenate, benzoate, borate, bromide, chloride, citrate, fluoride, formate, iodate, lactate, molybdate, nitrate, oxalate, phosphate, pyrophosphate, salicylate, selenate, sulfate, tartrate, tetraborate, and thiocyanate.

(b) The interfering ions fall into various classes, as follows: amines, oxidizing agents, and reducing agents destroy nitrites. Some ions complex the nitrite and retard its activity. Some ions precipitate under reaction conditions; others upset the acidity conditions; and still others interfere because of their own color.

(1) Amines such as ammonia, urea, and aliphatic primary amines (HNH_2, NH_2CONH_2, and RNH_2) react with nitrites to liberate gaseous nitrogen. Small concentrations of ammonium ion do not interfere, but high concentrations should be avoided.

(2) Nitrites are destroyed by reducing ions such as iodide, iron (II), chlorostannite, sulfide, thiosulfate, and sulfite, which must be absent from the sample. Strong oxidizing ions such as permanganate, chlorate, trisulfatocerate, perchlorate, periodate, peroxydisulfate, and tungstate should be absent. Other oxidizing ions such as dichromate, iodate, and selenate do not destroy nitrite in extreme dilutions in the normal time allowed, but they may on longer standing.

(3) Mercury (I) and silver precipitate as their chlorides, and bismuth and antimony (III) presumably as their

oxychlorides in the presence of the hydrochloric acid used. Lead (II) also precipitates as its chloride in concentrated solution but redissolves at room temperature upon dilution to 400 ppm and causes no interference. Chloroplatinate, iron (III), gold (III), and

(6) Purple ions, such as cobalt (II), which absorb green light, should be limited in concentration; whereas green ions, such as nickel (II) have little effect. Pale yellow ions, such as uranyl, show little interference; whereas more intensely yellow dichromate should

TABLE I.—EFFECTS OF INTERFERENCES.

Ion	Added as	Present, ppm	Error, per cent	Amount Permissible, ppm
Au^{+++}	AuCl$_3$	5	ppt	0
Sb^{+++}	SbCl$_3$	400	ppt	0
Bi^{+++}	Bi(NO$_3$)$_3$	400	ppt	0
Ce^{++++}	(NH$_4$)$_2$Ce(NO$_3$)$_6$	20	new hue	0
Cr^{+++}	Cr$_2$(SO$_4$)$_3$	80	3	40
Co^{++}	Co(NO$_3$)$_2$	400	8	100
Cu^{++}	CuSO$_4$	20	7	0
Fe^{++}	FeSO$_4$	40	4	0
Fe^{+++}	FeCl$_3$	10	ppt	0
Hg^{++}	Hg(NO$_3$)$_2$	400	50	0
Hg$_2$$^{++}$	Hg$_2$(NO$_3$)$_2$	400	ppt	0
Ag$^+$	AgNO$_3$	400	ppt	0
C$_2$H$_3$O$_2$$^-$	NaC$_2$H$_3$O$_2$	400	3	200
CO$_3$$^-$	Na$_2$CO$_3$	200	2	200
ClO$_3$$^-$	KClO$_3$	40	4	0
PtCl$_6$$^-$	H$_2$PtCl$_6$	80	2	80
SnCl$_6$$^-$	H$_2$SnCl$_6$	80	3	40
SnCl$_4$$^{--}$	H$_2$SnCl$_4$	40	90	0
CN$^-$	KCN	200	4	100
Cr$_2$O$_7$$^-$	K$_2$Cr$_2$O$_7$	80	2	80
I$^-$	KI	10	3	0
ClO$_4$$^-$	KClO$_4$	400	15	0
IO$_4$$^-$	KIO$_4$	20	3	0
MnO$_4$$^-$	KMnO$_4$	1	14	0
S$_2$O$_8$$^-$	(NH$_4$)$_2$S$_2$O$_8$	400	37	0
SiO$_3$$^-$	Na$_2$SiO$_3$	400	5	200
SO$_3$$^-$	Na$_2$SO$_3$	40	88	0
S$^-$	Na$_2$S	10	80	0
S$_2$O$_3$$^-$	Na$_2$SO$_3$	40	23	0
WO$_4$$^{--}$	Na$_2$WO$_4$	40	3	10
VO$_3$$^-$	KVO$_3$	20	ppt	0

metavanadate ions form precipitates with 1-aminonaphthalene.

(4) Alkali salts of ions such as carbonate, acetate, cyanide, and silicate reduce the acidity of the system and should be present only in limited quantities.

(5) Mercury (II) causes high results, whereas copper (II) catalyzes the decomposition of the diazonium salt, causing low results. Both should be absent.

be limited to 80 ppm. Chromium (III) should be limited to 40 ppm. All these colored ions change the hue of the system and must be absent for visual comparison.

(c) Effects of interferences are shown in Table I.

Apparatus

8. (a) *Photometer.*—Spectrophotometer or filter photometer suited for use in the range of 515 to 530 mμ. Filter pho-

tometers and photometric practice prescribed in this method shall conform to the Recommended Practice for Photometric Methods for Chemical Analysis of Metals (ASTM Designation: E 60).[5, 6]

(b) *Nessler Tubes.*—Matched Nessler tubes (American Public Health Association Standard) about 300 mm long, 17-mm inside diameter, and marked for 50 ml at 225 ± 1.5 mm from inside the bottom.

Reagents

9. (a) *Acetic Acid (1:3).*—Mix 1 volume of glacial acetic acid (CH₃COOH) with 3 volumes of water.

(b) *Alpha-Naphthylamine Hydrochloride Solution (6 g per liter).*—Dissolve 0.60 g of 1-aminonaphthalene hydrochloride and 1 ml of concentrated hydrochloric acid (HCl, sp gr 1.19) in water and dilute to 100 ml.

(c) *Aluminum Hydroxide Gel.*—Dissolve approximately 125 g of potassium aluminum sulfate (KAl(SO₄)₂·12H₂O) in 1 liter of water (Note). Precipitate the aluminum by slowly adding ammonium hydroxide (NH₄OH, sp gr 0.90) in 5 to 10-ml increments. Wash the precipitate in a large jar by decantation with water until free of chlorides and ammonia. The resultant product is a paste or gel. Test the decanted wash water for freedom from chlorides and ammonia by addition of a few drops of silver nitrate (AgNO₃) solution (100 g per liter) and phenolphthalein indicator solution.

Note.—Alternatively, aluminum hydroxide (Al(OH)₃) for use in this method may be prepared by electrolyzing ammonia-free water, using aluminum electrodes. Wash the precipitate as described in Paragraph (c).

(d) *Sodium Acetate Solution (275 g per liter).*—Dissolve 27.5 g of sodium

acetate trihydrate (NaC₂H₃O₂·3H₂O) in water, dilute to 100 ml, and filter.

(e) *Sodium Nitrite, Stock Solution (1 ml = 0.2000 mg NO₂⁻).*—Dissolve 0.3000 g of sodium nitrite (NaNO₂) in water and dilute to 1 liter with water. Sodium nitrite is easily reduced; especially in the presence of moisture, and fresh bottles of this reagent only are to be used. Store in a sterilized bottle and add 1 ml of chloroform. Prepare sterile bottles for storing nitrite solutions by heating for 1 hr at 170 C in an air oven. For greatest accuracy analyze in accordance with the non-referee method.

(f) *Sodium Nitrite, Standard Solution (1 ml = 0.0010 mg NO₂⁻).*—Dilute 100 ml of sodium nitrite stock solution (Paragraph (e)) to 1 liter with water. In turn, dilute 50 ml of this latter dilution to 1 liter with water. Store in a sterilized bottle and add 1 ml of chloroform. Make fresh daily.

(g) *Sulfanilic Acid Solution (6 g per liter).*—Dissolve 0.60 g of 4-aminobenzene sulfonic acid in 70 ml of hot water, cool the solution, add 20 ml of concentrated hydrochloric acid (HCl, sp gr 1.19), dilute to 100 ml with water, and mix thoroughly.

Calibration

10. (a) Dilute 0.0, 1.0, 2.0, 3.0, 4.0, 5.0, 10.0, 15.0, 20.0, and 25.0 ml of NaNO₂ solution (1 ml = 0.0010 mg NO₂⁻) to 50 ml with water. These dilutions correspond to nitrite contents of 0.00, 0.02, 0.04, 0.06, 0.08, 0.10, 0.20, 0.30, 0.40, and 0.50 ppm, respectively.

(b) Add 1.0 ml of sulfanilic acid solution to each of the solutions prepared as described in Paragraph (a) and allow to stand between 3 and 10 min. Add 1.0 ml of alphanaphthylamine hydrochloride solution to each, mix thoroughly, and allow to stand between 10 and 30 min in diffuse light after buffering the

---

[5] The spectrophotometers shall conform to ASTM Recommended Practice E 275, Describing and Measuring Performance of Spectrophotometers, *1967 Book of ASTM Standards,* Part 30.
[6] 1967 Book of ASTM Standards, Part 32.

system to a pH of 2.0 to 2.5 with NaC$_2$H$_3$O$_2$ solution. This generally requires about 1 ml of NaC$_2$H$_3$O$_2$ solution.

(c) Measure the transmittance or absorbance at approximately 520 mμ, and plot the values obtained for the known standards against the parts per million of nitrite ion. Prepare an independent calibration curve for each photometer, and check it from time to time. Do not use curves prepared for a specific photometer with a different instrument.

Procedure

11. (a) If the sample to be analyzed has a pH greater than 10, adjust it to a pH of approximately 7 by adding CH$_3$COOH (1:3).

(b) If the sample to be analyzed has significant color (more than 30 APHA),[7] add 3 ml of Al(OH)$_3$ gel to 500 ml of sample. Shake thoroughly, and then allow the precipitate to settle. Decant or filter the solution to obtain a clear, colorless sample.

(c) Place 50 ml of clear sample in a flask or beaker, add 1.0 ml of sulfanilic acid solution, and allow to stand between 3 and 10 min. Add 1.0 ml of alpha-naphthylamine hydrochloride solution, mix thoroughly, and allow to stand between 10 and 30 min after buffering the system to a pH of 2.0 to 2.5 with NaC$_2$H$_3$O$_2$ solution. Measure the transmittance or absorbance at approximately 520 mμ by means of a photometer; or, in the absence of a photometer, make a visual comparison in Nessler tubes between the sample and the standards, prepared immediately before use in accordance with Section 10(a) and (b).

(d) If the color intensity obtained is greater than that of the known stand-

ards, or is outside the range of the photometer, repeat the determination using a sample diluted with a measured amount of water.

(e) Record the nitrite concentration equivalent to the transmittance, absorbance, or known standard selected, as the case may be, as the "observed NO$_2^-$ equivalent."

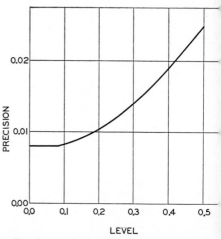

FIG. 1.—Precision Versus Level, Both as ppm Nitrite Ion.

Calculation

12. Calculate the concentration of nitrite ion in the sample, in parts per million, as follows:

$$\text{Nitrite ion, ppm} = A \times \left(1 + \frac{D}{S}\right)$$

where:

A = observed NO$_2^-$ equivalent,
D = milliliters of diluent water added to the sample, and
S = milliliters of sample used.

Precision

13. The precision of the method varies with the length of light path in the cell used. In the absence of interferences, reliable results are obtained

[7] See "Standard Methods for the Examination of Water, Sewage, and Industrial Wastes," Tenth Edition, Am. Public Health Assn., Inc., New York, N. Y., pp. 87–89 (1955)

when a 20-mm cell is employed, if the concentration of nitrite ion is between 0.02 and 0.50 ppm, expressed as NO_2^-. The precision is as shown in Fig. 1.

Non-Referee Method

(Volumetric Method)

Application

14. (a) This method covers the titrimetric determination of nitrite in industrial water and is applicable to waters containing nitrite in concentrations from about 3 to 600 ppm of nitrite ion. Higher concentrations may be determined by either using a smaller aliquot, or by employing more concentrated potassium permanganate and sodium oxalate solutions.

(b) The method is applicable where a complete freedom from interferences is not required and is particularly applicable in those systems containing high nitrite content, added as a corrosion inhibitor.

Summary of Method

15. A measured volume of sample is added below the surface of a known volume of acidified potassium permanganate. Under these conditions nitrite ions react only with permanganate ions. The solution is heated to complete the reaction. Excess permanganate is determined by adding a measured amount of sodium oxalate (excess), followed by back titration with standard permanganate solution.

Interferences

16. Reducing agents interfere with this method since it is essentially a means of measuring the reducing tendency. This does not detract from the utility of the method in many cases such as when nitrite is added to industrial water as a corrosion inhibitor and is present in relatively large quantities since then a small error is of little

consequence. However, in those instances where relatively large quantities of other reducing agents are present the method is of lesser application.

Reagents

17. (a) *Potassium Permanganate, Standard Solution (0.04 N).*—Dissolve 2.50 g of potassium permanganate ($KMnO_4$) in 2 liters of boiling water in a Florence flask. Cover with a beaker and simmer for $\frac{1}{2}$ hr. Cool to room temperature. Filter twice by gravity through a fritted-glass filter and store in a dark-colored, glass-stoppered bottle. Pipet triplicate 50-ml aliquots of the $Na_2C_2O_4$ solution (0.04 N) into a 500-

TABLE II.—SAMPLE VOLUMES FOR NITRITE SOLUTIONS.

Nitrite Nitrogen, ppm	Sample Volume, ml
300 to 600	50
150 to 300	100
Less than 150	200

ml Erlenmeyer flask and add 100 ml of water. Heat to 90 C and add 10 ml of sulfuric acid (H_2SO_4, 1:1). Titrate rapidly with potassium permanganate solution to a slight pink end point, persistent for 1 min. Calculate the normality of the $KMnO_4$ solution. If necessary, adjust the normality to slightly less than the normality of the $Na_2C_2O_4$ solution and restandardize.

(b) *Sodium Oxalate, Standard Solution (0.04 N).*—Dry National Bureau of Standards oxidimetric grade sodium oxalate ($Na_2C_2O_4$) or equivalent, at 105 C for 1 hr and cool in a desiccator. Weigh 5.360 g, dissolve in water, and dilute to 2.0 liters. Store in a chemical-resistant borosilicate glass container. Sodium oxalate solutions are subject to deterioration by microorganisms and should be prepared at time of use.

(c) Sulfuric Acid (1:1).—Carefully mix 1 volume of concentrated sulfuric acid (H_2SO_4, sp gr 1.84) with 1 volume of water.

Procedure

18. *(a)* Nitrite solutions, especially in the presence of microbiological contamination, are unstable. Analyze with minimum delay as follows: Add 50.0 ml of the $KMnO_4$ solution and 10 ml of H_2SO_4 (1:1) for each 50-ml sample up to a maximum of 30 ml of acid, to a 500-ml Erlenmeyer flask. Pipet a volume of sample containing 0.6 to 30.0 mg of nitrite ion, to the flask by immersing the tip of the pipet below the surface of the $KMnO_4$ solution; the pipet should yield the required volume in one filling. A suitable sample volume is shown in Table II. Immediately warm the mixture in the Erlenmeyer flask to 90 C and add 50 ml of NaC_2O_4 solution. Titrate with $KMnO_4$ solution, using a microburet if the titration is less than 10 ml, to a faint pink end point, persistent for 1 min.

(b) Determine the blank at the time of analysis by repeating the procedure described in Paragraph *(a)* in duplicate, using water equal in volume to the sample. (See Section 3*(b)*.)

Calculation

19. Calculate the parts per million of nitrite ion (NO_2^-) as follows:

$$NO_2^-, ppm = \frac{(V_x - V_a) \times N \times 23,004}{V_s}$$

where:

V_x = milliliters of $KMnO_4$ required for titration of the sample,

V_a = milliliters of $KMnO_4$ required for titration of the blank,

N = normality of the $KMnO_4$, and

V_s = milliliters of sample used.

Precision

20. In the absence of interferences and on the basis of two operators in one laboratory, precision may be stated as follows:

$$S_C = 0.00318X + 0.539$$

where:

S_C = precision expressed as parts per million of nitrite ion (NO_2^-), and

X = nitrite content expressed as parts per million of nitrite ion (NO_2^-).

Tentative Method of Test for

SULFIDES IN INDUSTRIAL WATER AND INDUSTRIAL WASTE WATER[1]

ASTM Designation: D 1255 – 65 T

ISSUED, 1965

This Tentative Method has been approved by the sponsoring committee and accepted by the Society in accordance with established procedures, for use pending adoption as standard. Suggestions for revisions should be addressed to the Society at 1916 Race St., Philadelphia, Pa. 19103.

1. Scope

1.1 This method covers a non-referee colorimetric procedure for the determination of total sulfides, dissolved sulfides, and hydrogen sulfide in industrial water and industrial waste water.

1.2 The method may be applied to the analysis of industrial waste water containing sulfide ion concentration from 0.1 to 20 ppm. Greater concentrations of sulfide ion may result in color inhibition. However, this method may be applied to the analysis of water containing more than 20 ppm of sulfide ion by diluting the sample and correcting the final results to compensate for such dilution.

1.3 The method is divided according to specific application as follows:

	Section
Determination of Total Sulfides	8
Determination of Dissolved Sulfides	9
Determination of Hydrogen Sulfide	10

2. Principle of Method

2.1 This method is based upon the action of p-amino dimethylaniline oxalate and ferric chloride on aqueous solutions of the sulfide ion to form methylene blue.

3. Definitions

3.1 For definitions of terms used in this method, refer to ASTM Definitions D 1129, Terms Relating to Industrial Water and Industrial Waste Water.[2]

4. Interferences[3]

4.1 Sulfite or thiosulfate ions in excess of 10 ppm reduce color development. Increasing the addition of ferric chloride ($FeCl_3$) solution to six drops and the contact time before the addition of di-ammonium phosphate ((NH_4)$_2$HPO$_4$) to 5 min will permit use of the method in the presence of sulfite or thiosulfate in concentrations up to 50 ppm.

---

[1] Under the standardization procedure of the Society, this method is under the jurisdiction of the ASTM Committee D-19 on Industrial Water. A list of members may be found in the ASTM Year Book.

[2] Appears in this publication.
[3] R. Pomeroy, *Petroleum Engineer*, September, 1944, p. 156.

4.2 Reduced sulfur compounds, such as polysulfides and hyposulfites, which decompose in acid to form sulfides, will be determined as sulfide.

4.3 Dye intermediates, iron cyanides, and iodides in concentrations greater than 10 ppm will interfere. Metallic cyanides can cause a blue color interference.

4.4 Cyanide ions in concentrations greater than 500 ppm will retard the formation of color.

4.5 Concentrations of carbonates greater than 2000 ppm will interfere due to sweeping out of the hydrogen sulfide by the carbon dioxide liberated by the acid addition.

5. Apparatus

5.1 *Color Comparison Tubes*—Matched test tubes or Nessler tubes of about 15-ml capacity, with 7.5-ml graduation marks.

5.2 *Dropping Pipets*, calibrated and graduated to deliver 0.5 and 1.6 ml of water.

5.3 *Dropping Pipets*, calibrated to deliver between 19.5 and 20.5 drops/ml of methylene blue solution.

5.4 *Dropping Pipets*, calibrated to deliver between 18 and 22 drops/ml of ferric chloride solution.

5.5 *Glass-Stoppered Bottle* (300 ml)—A biochemical oxygen demand (BOD) bottle or equivalent.

6. Reagents

6.1 *Purity of Reagents*—Reagent grade chemicals shall be used in all tests. Unless otherwise indicated, it is intended that all reagents shall conform to the specifications of the Committee on Analytical Reagents of the American Chemical Society, where such specifica-

tions are available.[4] Other grades may b used, provided it is first ascertained tha the reagent is of sufficiently high purit; to permit its use without lessening th accuracy of the determination.

6.2 *Purity of Water*—Unless otherwis indicated, references to water shall be un derstood to mean reagent water conform ing to ASTM Specifications D 1193, fo Reagent Water.[2]

6.3 *Aluminum Chloride Solution (69 g/liter)*—Because of the hygroscopi and caking tendency of this chemical, i will be convenient to purchase 100-g o ¼-lb bottles of the aluminum chlorid hexahydrate ($AlCl_3 \cdot 6H_2O$). Dissolve th contents of a previously unopened 100-, bottle of this salt in 144 ml of water, o the contents of a ¼-lb bottle in 164 ml o water.

6.4 *Amine-Sulfuric Acid, Stock Solu tion*—This solution may be prepared a follows: dissolve 26.6 g of *p*-amino-di methylaniline oxalate[5] in a cold mixtur of 50 ml of concentrated sulfuric aci (H_2SO_4, sp gr 1.84) and 20 ml of water cool, then dilute to 100 ml with water Store in a dark glass bottle.

6.5 *Amine-Sulfuric Acid Reagent*— Dilute 25 ml of stock solution with 97 ml of H_2SO_4 (1:1). Store in a dark glas bottle.

6.6 *Diammonium Phosphate Solutio* *(400 g/liter)*—Dissolve 40 g of diam monium phosphate (($NH_4)_2HPO_4$) i water and dilute to 100 ml.

---

[4] "Reagent Chemicals, American Chemic; Society Specifications," Am. Chemical Soc Washington, D. C. For suggestions on th testing of reagents not listed by the America Chemical Society, see "Reagent Chemicals an Standards," by Joseph Rosin, D. Van Nostran Co., Inc., New York, N. Y., and the "Unite States Pharmacopeia."

[5] *p*-Amino dimethylaniline oxalate obtair able as *N,N*-Dimethyl-*p*-phenylenediamin oxalate, Eastman Catalog No. 5672, has bee found satisfactory for this purpose. The excer tional stability of the oxalate salt of the diamir compound was noted by I. Nusbaum, *Sewa*; *and Industrial Wastes*, Vol. 25, p. 512 (1953 who suggested its use in the sulfide method.

6.7 *Ferric Chloride Solution (1000 g/ liter)*—Dissolve 100 g of ferric chloride ($FeCl_3 \cdot 6H_2O$) in water and dilute to 100 ml.

6.8 *Iodine Solution (0.025 N)*—Dissolve 15 g of iodate-free potassium iodide (KI) in 25 ml of water and add 3.2 g (theoretical = 3.173 g) of iodine. After the iodine has dissolved, dilute to 1 liter. Since iodine solutions are photochemically decomposed by light, this solution should be stored in a dark colored or covered bottle and must be protected from direct sunlight as much as possible.

6.8.1 Standardize the iodine solution as follows: titrate 25.0 ml of the iodine solution with 0.025 N $Na_2S_2O_3$ to a light yellow color. Add 5 drops of starch indicator. Continue the titration to the disappearance of the blue color.

6.8.2 Calculate the normality of the iodine solution as follows:

$$N = \frac{N' \times V'}{25.0}$$

where:

N = normality of the iodine solution,

N' = normality of the $Na_2S_2O_3$ solution, and

V' = milliliters of $Na_2S_2O_3$ solution required for the titration of the solution.

6.9 *Methylene Blue Solution A (1 drop = 1.0 ppm Sulfide Ion)*—Dissolve 1 g of methylene blue[6] dye in water and dilute to 1 liter.

6.9.1 Standardize the methylene blue solution as follows: Determine the number of drops of methylene blue solution A that will produce a color equivalent to that obtained with the sulfide solution

(6.13) in accordance with 8.2. A diluted sulfide solution can be used if a less intense color is preferred. After making this analysis, adjust the methylene blue solution either by diluting with water or adding more dye so that 1 drop is equivalent to 1.0 mg/liter of sulfide ion.

6.10 *Methylene Blue Solution B (1 drop = 0.1 ppm Sulfide Ion)*—Dilute 100 ml of solution A to 1 liter with water.

6.11 *Sodium Carbonate Solution (50 g/liter)*—Dissolve 5.0 g of anhydrous sodium carbonate (Na_2CO_3) in water and dilute to 100 ml.

6.12 *Sodium Hydroxide Solution (200 g/liter)*—Dissolve 20 g of sodium hydroxide (NaOH) pellets in water and dilute to 100 ml.

6.13 *Sodium Sulfide, Standard Solutions*—Prepare as follows:

6.13.1 *Stock Solution (2000 ppm S^{--})*—Dissolve 8.20 g of sodium sulfide trihydrate ($Na_2S \cdot 3H_2O$)[7] in boiled, cooled water. The sodium sulfide should be weighed out from a well-stoppered weighing bottle. Dilute to 1 liter in a volumetric flask. If the weight of $Na_2S \cdot 3H_2O$ used is other than the recommended amount, calculate the sulfide concentration as follows:

$$A = 242.8 \times B$$

where:

A = concentration of sulfide, ppm, and

B = grams of $Na_2S \cdot 3H_2O$ in 1 liter.

The stock solution should be prepared fresh each day.

6.13.2 *Standard Solution (20 ppm S^{--})*—Take 10.0 ml of the stock solution or an appropriate aliquot which contains 20.0 mg of sulfide and dilute to 1 liter with boiled, cooled water. This solution should be prepared as needed, since it is unstable.

---

[6] Use the USP grade of the dye, or one certified by the Biological Stain Commission. The percentage of actual dye content should be reported on the label and should be 84 per cent or more. This solution will be only approximately the correct strength and must be standardized against sulfide solution of known strength and adjusted so that 1 drop of solution is equivalent to 1.0 ppm sulfide.

[7] Sodium sulfide, technical flakes, 60 per cent, $Na_2S \cdot 3 H_2O$, Mallinckrodt No. 8032, has been found satisfactory for this purpose.

6.13.2.1 To standardize, pipet 100 ml into an Erlenmeyer flask and immediately add 10.0 ml of 0.025 N iodine solution. Titrate the residual iodine with 0.025 N $Na_2S_2O_3$ solution, using starch indicator at the end point. A blank should be run on the reagents. Calculate the sulfide concentration of the Na_2S solution as follows:

$$A = ((10.0 - C) - D) \times 4$$

where:
A = sulfide concentration of the Na_2S solution, ppm,
C = milliliters of 0.025 N $Na_2S_2O_3$ solution required for titration of the solution, and
D = milliliters of 0.025 N iodine solution used for the reagent blank.

6.14 *Sodium   Thiosulfate   Solution* (*0.025 N*)[8]— Dissolve 6.205 g of sodium thiosulfate ($Na_2S_2O_3 \cdot 5H_2O$) in freshly boiled and cooled water and dilute to 1 liter. Stabilize the solution by dissolving 0.4 g of Na_2CO_3. Standardize against potassium dichromate ($K_2Cr_2O_7$) as follows: Dissolve 2 g of iodate-free potassium iodide (KI) (Note 1) and 2 g of sodium bicarbonate ($NaHCO_3$) in 300 ml of water in a 500-ml Erlenmeyer flask and add concentrated hydrochloric acid (HCl, sp gr 1.19) slowly, while swirling the flask, until evolution of CO_2 ceases. Add a 10-ml excess of HCl, mix, and then dissolve 0.0245 g of dried $K_2Cr_2O_7$ (Note 2). Wash down the inside of the flask with a small amount of water without agitating the flask, and allow to stand for 10 min. Titrate with the $Na_2S_2O_3$ solution, using starch solution as the indicator, until the color just changes from blue to the green color of the chromic salt.

6.14.1 Calculate the normality of the $Na_2S_2O_3$ solution as follows:

[8] Reagent used for standardization purposes only.

$$N = \frac{A}{12.25B} \times 1000$$

where:
N = normality of the $Na_2S_2O_3$ solution,
A = grams of $K_2Cr_2O_7$ used, and
B = milliliters of $Na_2S_2O_3$ solution required for titration of the solution.

Note 1—Suitable iodate-free KI will not yield a blue color when 1 g is dissolved in freshly boiled reagent grade water (deaerated) treated with 5 drops (0.25 ml) of sulfuric acid (H_2SO_4, 1:39) and 1 ml of freshly prepared starch solution.

Note 2—To ensure properly dried $K_2Cr_2O_7$, the salt should be heated in a platinum crucible to a point just above its fusion point (396 C, 745 F), taking care to exclude all dust and organic matter. The fused salt, after cooling, should be crushed to a powder in an agate mortar and kept in a glass-stoppered bottle. Potassium dichromate that has been merely dried at 100 to 105 C (212 to 221 F) is not satisfactory to use for this reagent.

6.15 *Starch Indicator*—Make a paste of 1 g of arrowroot starch or soluble iodimetric starch with cold water. Pour the paste into 100 ml of boiling water and boil for several minutes. Store in a glass-stoppered bottle in a cool place. Starch solution, prepared in this manner, will remain chemically stable for two or three days.

6.16 *Sulfuric Acid* (*1 : 1*)—Carefully pour 1 volume of concentrated sulfuric acid (H_2SO_4, sp gr 1.84) into 1 volume of water, with constant stirring. Several liters should be made at a time.

6.17 *Zinc Acetate Solution* (*240 g/ liter*)—Dissolve 24.0 g of zinc acetate ($ZnC_2H_3O_2 \cdot 2H_2O$) in water and dilute to 100 ml.

7. Sampling

7.1 Collect the sample in accordance with ASTM Methods D 510, Sampling Industrial Water,[2] keeping the sample out of contact with air insofar as possible. When sampling shallow flows in drains where the usual methods and apparatus cannot be employed, take the sample with a minimum of splashing and aeration. Make the determination within 1 min of the time of sampling.

7.2 Samples to be tested for total sulfides only may be preserved by adding 2 ml of zinc acetate solution to each liter of sample. Analyze samples so preserved within 6 hr of the time of sampling.

8. Determination of Total Sulfides

8.1 Add three or four drops of zinc acetate solution to 100 ml of sample and follow with a few drops of Na_2CO_3 solution. Allow the precipitated ZnS to settle; then decant the clear liquid. Add sufficient water to the precipitated slurry

contact time. One to five minutes after the color first appears (see 4.1), add 1.6 ml of $(NH_4)_2HPO_4$ solution to each tube.

8.4 Add methylene blue solution A or B, depending on the sulfide concentration and the desired accuracy of the test, dropwise, to the contents of the second tube until the color imparted by the methylene blue matches that developed in the first tube.

8.5 Record the total number of drops of each methylene blue solution added to the contents of the second tube.

9. Determination of Dissolved Sulfides

9.1 Fill a 300-ml glass-stoppered bottle with sample and eliminate air bubbles.

TABLE 1—CONVERSION FACTORS FOR HYDROGEN SULFIDE CONCENTRATION.

pH	Factor	pH	Factor	pH	Factor
5.0	0.98	6.8	0.44	7.7	0.091
5.4	0.95	6.9	0.39	7.8	0.073
5.8	0.89	7.0	0.33	7.9	0.059
6.0	0.83	7.1	0.29	8.0	0.048
6.2	0.76	7.2	0.24	8.2	0.031
6.4	0.67	7.3	0.23	8.4	0.020
6.5	0.61	7.4	0.17	8.8	0.0079
6.6	0.56	7.5	0.14	9.2	0.0032
6.7	0.50	7.6	0.11	9.6	0.0013

to restore the volume of sample to 100 ml, and mix thoroughly. Where interferences are known to be absent, this paragraph may be omitted.

8.2 Fill two color comparison tubes to the 7.5-ml marks with sample. Add to one tube 0.5 ml of amine sulfuric acid reagent and 3 drops of $FeCl_3$ solution; stopper and mix the contents immediately by inverting the tube slowly, only once. Add to the other tube 0.5 ml of H_2SO_4 (1:1) and three drops of $FeCl_3$ solution; stopper and mix the contents immediately by inverting the tube slowly only once.

8.3 The presence of sulfide ion will be indicated by the immediate appearance of blue color in the first tube. Complete color development requires about 1 min

Add 0.5 ml of $AlCl_3$ solution and 0.5 ml of NaOH solution. Stopper the bottle and flocculate the precipitate by rotating the bottle back and forth about a transverse axis. Allow the floc to settle.

9.2 Proceed with the clear supernatant liquid as directed in 8.2 to 8.5.

10. Determination of Hydrogen Sulfide[9]

10.1 Determine the dissolved sulfides as described in 9. Determination of Dissolved Sulfides. Determine the pH in accordance with ASTM Method D 1293, Test for pH of Industrial Water and Industrial Waste Water.[2] Calculate the

[9] R. Pomeroy, "Hydrogen Sulfide in Sewage," *Sewage Works Journal*, Vol. 13 (1941), p. 498.

concentration of H_2S in the sample in accordance with 11.2.

11. Calculation

11.1 Calculate the concentration of total sulfides and dissolved sulfides, in parts per million in the sample as received, as follows:

$$\text{Total sulfides, ppm} = E + 0.1F$$
$$\text{Dissolved sulfides, ppm} = H + 0.1G$$

where:

E = drops of methylene blue solution A added to the second tube in the determination of total sulfides,

F = drops of methylene blue solution B added to the second tube in the determination of total sulfides,

H = drops of methylene blue solution A added to the second tube in the determination of dissolved sulfides, and

G = drops of methylene blue solution B added to the second tube in the determination of dissolved sulfides.

11.2 Calculate the concentration of H_2S, in parts per million in the sample as received, as follows:

$$\text{Hydrogen sulfide, ppm} = J \times K$$

where:

J = concentration, ppm, of dissolved sulfides, and

K = conversion factor at the determined pH, as shown in Table 1.

12. Precision[9,10]

12.1 The precision of this method depends on the accuracy with which the colors are matched, and is better for clear samples than for turbid samples. Color intensity is reproducible as far as can be determined visually. The precision of this method may be expressed as follows:

$$S_0 = 0.04X + 0.10$$

where:

S_0 = single operator precision, and

X = concentration of sulfide, ppm.

[10] R. Pomeroy, "Sulfide Determination," *Sewage Works Journal*, Vol. 8 (1936), p. 572.

Standard Scheme for

ANALYSIS OF INDUSTRIAL WATER AND INDUSTRIAL WASTE WATER[1]

ASTM Designation: D 1256 – 61

ADOPTED, 1961

This Standard of the American Society for Testing and Materials is issued under the fixed designation D 1256; the final number indicates the year of original adoption as standard or, in the case of revision, the year of last revision.

Scope and Application

1. (*a*) This is a systematic scheme for the examination of industrial water and industrial waste water. The order of application of methods for chemical and physical measurements permits the determination of existing constituents and properties in logical sequence.

(*b*) This scheme is intended to aid the water analyst in choosing an analytical course that he can follow to determine one or all of the constituents or properties of industrial water. The outline indicates by general groupings of water constituents and properties the general procedures that must be followed in obtaining the sample, depending upon the information desired. By further subgrouping it also indicates what general precautions must be observed in preserving the character of the sample with respect to the desired analysis.

(*c*) There are four schematic outlines. The first (Fig. 1) shows the general schematic relationship of the principal groups of samples. The remaining three (Tables I to III) list the constituents and properties that can be determined on each group of samples.

(*d*) The constituents or properties in each group appear in alphabetical order, where possible. Where a simple, acceptable test for a given constituent or property is desirable in providing information useful in subsequent analyses to be performed on a sample, it is indicated by an asterisk. For example, a colorimetric silica determination would indicate the volume of sample that would contain silicon compounds equivalent to at least 10 mg of SiO_2, as specified in the referee method for SiO_2 in the Methods of Test for Silica in Industrial Water and Industrial Waste Water (ASTM Designation: D 859).[2] Completion of such a simple preliminary test would save considerable time.

(*e*) Each constituent or property of a

[1] Under the standardization procedure of the Society, this scheme for analysis is under the jurisdiction of the ASTM Committee D-19 on Industrial Water. A list of members may be found in the ASTM Year Book.

[2] Appears in this publication.

sample group that is listed without indentation from the margin (see Tables I to III) indicates that a separate portion is required for the analysis for that particular constituent. Where an analytical scheme is possible or desirable, and one or more constituents may be determined on a single sample by a scheme of successive analyses of filtrates or aliquots, the constituents determined in the scheme are indented in reference to the appropriate preceding constituent.

Apparatus, Reagents, and Materials

2. Descriptions of apparatus, reagents, and materials appear in the specific ASTM methods and specifications referred to later in this scheme for analysis.

Sampling

3. Sampling procedures shall follow applicable methods of the American Society for Testing and Materials.

[3] *Special Technical Publication No. 148-I,* January, 1960; also Second Printing, February, 1961; Third Printing, February, 1963; Fourth Printing, February, 1965; Fifth Printing, April, 1966; and Sixth Printing, April, 1967.

Procedure

4. (a) Use the methods of test of the American Society for Testing Materials as indicated by the ASTM designations shown in the schematic outlines (Tables I to III). Year numbers have been omitted from these ASTM designations. The responsibility for use of the latest revision of a given ASTM method rests with the analyst. In this connection, the attention of the analyst is directed to the fact that such methods may be revised annually.

(b) Where an ASTM designation is not shown in these schematic outlines, the analyst should refer to the ASTM Manual on Industrial Water and Industrial Waste Water.[3]

Report

5. Methods for reporting analytical results should follow those described in the Method of Reporting Results of Analysis of Industrial Water and Industrial Waste Water (ASTM Designation: D 596)[2] when applicable.

(See Tables I to III, pp. 480 to 482.)

SAMPLE SOURCE

Sampling procedures shall be in accordance with the applicable ASTM methods.

SAMPLES FOR PROPERTIES AND CONSTITUENTS AFFECTED BY AIR CONTACT

In order to obtain the true concentration of properties and constituents affected by air contact during sampling, or during the interval between sampling and analysis, it is necessary to employ special methods or equipment, or both, for sampling, and, preferably, to carry out the determinations immediately. If determinations are not made immediately in the field, it must be realized that laboratory results reported for these constituents are based on the sample in an as-received condition, and are not necessarily representative of the water sampled, since the laboratory usually has no control over, or knowledge of, the sampling methods used. (Note 1.)

SAMPLES FOR PROPERTIES AND CONSTITUENTS UNAFFECTED BY AIR CONTACT

Samples for which these properties and constituents are to be determined may or may not be filtered in the laboratory prior to analysis, depending upon the nature and the amount of undissolved material, the method of analysis used, and the specific information required. If the analysis is to be representative of the sample as collected at the source, the amount and composition of the undissolved material present should be determined. Spectrographic and X-ray diffraction examination of the undissolved material is of value in connection with these procedures. (Note 1.)

FLOW SAMPLES

(See Table I) Flow samples shall be used in determining these properties and constituents at the sample source. This information may be continuously and automatically determined, indicated, and recorded.

SEPARATE SAMPLES

(See Table II) Samples for which these properties and constituents are to be determined require that the sample containers be sealed against air contact during the interval between sampling and analysis; or the samples must be chemically fixed immediately after sampling.

SEPARATE PORTIONS OF A SINGLE SAMPLE

(See Table III) Separate portions of a single sample may be used for determining these properties and constituents individually or, in some cases, in a sequence of analyses. The customary precautions against contamination by air-borne solids, or too long storage in unsuitable containers (Note 1) must be observed in the case of samples to be analyzed for these constituents.

SEPARATE SAMPLES

Samples for the determination of chloroform extractable matter and floating liquids must be collected separately in glass-stoppered flasks of chemically resistant glass. Samples may also be collected in cork-stoppered flasks, provided the stoppers are wrapped in metal foil.

Note 1.—If the property or constituent to be determined may be affected by reaction of the sample with the sample container, a separate sample should be collected in a special container that will not itself contaminate the sample. Containers of polyethylene or similar material are generally satisfactory for this purpose.

Fig. 1.—Outline of Principal Sample Groups.

42–37

TABLE I.—PROPERTIES AND CONSTITUENTS AFFECTED BY AIR CONTACT.

Flow samples shall be used in determining these properties and constituents at the sample source This information may be continuously and automatically determined, indicated, and recorded.

Electrical Conductivity: D 1125
Hydrogen: Thermal Conductivity Method (Note 2)
Oxygen: Thermal Conductivity Method (Note 2)
pH (Hydrogen Ion): E 70, D 1293

NOTE 2.—Where an ASTM method is not indicated, refer to the ASTM Manual on Indus trial Water.[4]

TABLE II.—PROPERTIES AND CONSTITUENTS AFFECTED BY AIR CONTACT.

Samples for which these properties and constituents are to be determined require that the sampl containers be sealed against air contact during the interval between sampling and analysis; or th samples must be chemically fixed immediately after sampling.

Acidity and Basicity: D 1884
Ammonia and Ammonium Ion: D 1426
    AMMONIA: calculated
    AMMONIUM ION: calculated
Bicarbonate Ion: (see Carbon Dioxide)
Bisulfite Ion: (see Sulfur Dioxide)
Calcium and Magnesium Hardness: D 1126 (Note 3)
    CALCIUM HARDNESS: D 1126 (Note 3)
    MAGNESIUM: (Note 3)
Carbon Dioxide, Carbonate, Bicarbonate: D 513
    CARBON DIOXIDE: calculated (Note 4)
    CARBONATE ION: calculated (Note 4)
    BICARBONATE ION: calculated (Note 4)
Chlorine Residual: D 1253, D 1427
Chlorine Requirement: D 1291
Hardness: (see Calcium and Magnesium Hardness) (Note 3)
Hydrazine: D 1385
Hydroxide Ion: D 514
Iron, Ferric: D 1068
Iron, Ferrous: D 1068
Nitrite Ion: D 1254
Oxygen, Dissolved: D 888
pH: E 70 (Note 3), D 1293
Phenolic-Type Compounds: (Note 2)
Sulfides and Hydrogen Sulfide: D 1255 (also see Notes 2 and 4)
    HYDROGEN SULFIDE
    SULFIDES
Sulfur Dioxide, Sulfite, and Bisulfites: (Note 2)
    BISULFIDE ION: calculated (Note 4)
    SULFITE ION: calculated (Note 4), D 1339
    SULFUR DIOXIDE: calculated (Note 4)

NOTE 3.—These properties and constituents are usually determined on separate portions of single sample that has not been sealed against air contact, because, in most instances, it either not possible or not practical to obtain separate, sealed or chemically fixed samples fo these determinations. When determinations of these properties and constituents are requeste on samples that have not been protected against air contact or that have not been chemicall fixed, note should be made qualifying the analytical results in this regard.

NOTE 4.—In order to calculate these constituents correctly, the pH value of the sample mus be noted simultaneously with the taking of the sample. The truest pH value would be from flowing source.

TABLE III.—PROPERTIES AND CONSTITUENTS NOT AFFECTED BY AIR CONTACT
(Note 5).

Separate portions of a single sample may be used for determining these properties and constituents individually, or in some cases, in a sequence of analyses. The customary precautions against contamination by air-borne solids, or too long storage in unsuitable containers (Note 1), must be observed in the case of samples to be analyzed for these constituents.

*Aluminum: D 857
Barium: (Note 2)
Bromide Ion: (see Iodide Ion)
Calcium: D 511 or D 1126 (see also Silica and Solids)
*Calcium and Magnesium Hardness: D 1126 (Note 5)
    CALCIUM HARDNESS
    MAGNESIUM HARDNESS
Chemical Oxygen Demand (Dichromate): D 1252
*Chlorides: D 512
Chloroform-Extractable Matter: D 1178 (see Fig. 1—Samples for Constituents Unaffected by Air Contact)
Copper: (Note 2)
Cyanide: (Note 2)
Fluoride Ion: D 1179
Hardness: (see Calcium and Magnesium Hardness)
Hydroxide Ion: D 514
Iodide and Bromide Ion: D 1246
    IODIDE ION
    BROMIDE ION
*Iron, Total: D 1068, D 1497
Lead: (Note 2)
*Magnesium: (see Calcium and Magnesium Hardness)
*Manganese: D 858 (Note 5)
Nitrate: D 992 (Note 5)
Odor: D 1292
Organic Material: (see Solids) (Notes 2 and 5)
*Phosphate, Ortho-: D 515
    PHOSPHATE, ORTHO-, TRIBASIC: calculated (Note 4)
    PHOSPHATE, ORTHO-, DIBASIC: calculated (Note 4)
    PHOSPHATE, ORTHO-, Monobasic: calculated (Note 4)
Potassium: D 1127, D 1428
*Silica: D 859 (see also Solids)
    CALCIUM: D 511
    MAGNESIUM: D 511
    SULFATE: D 516
Sodium: D 1127, D 1428
*Solids: D 1888 (see Notes 5 and 6) [also estimated from Electrical Conductivity (D 1125)
    ORGANIC: D 1888
      Silica: D 859
      Calcium: D 511
      Magnesium: D 511
      Sulfate: D 516
    SILICA: D 859
      Calcium: D 511
      Magnesium: D 511
      Sulfate: D 516
Sulfate: D 516 (see also Solids and Note 5)
Tannin and Lignin: (Note 2)

(See Notes 5 and 6 on p. 482.)

NOTE 5.—These constituents generally are not rapidly affected by air contact; however, many in this category are affected to some degree over a period of time not only by air (oxidation), but also by storage, container material, light, temperature changes, etc. For example, high-carbonate water containing an appreciable amount of calcium and magnesium may suffer a loss of CO_2, thus effecting a change in the dissolved solids. For this reason, certain constituents such as calcium and magnesium are included in both Tables I and III.

NOTE 6.—The analytical scheme outlined in Table III is intended primarily to apply to total solids. To be a true analysis of the sample as received it may be necessary to separate the solids into floating solids, suspended solids, settled solids, and dissolved solids. Analyses of any or all of these various types of solids can then be made using a scheme similar to the suggestions made in the ASTM Manual on Industrial Water,[3] covering analysis of water-formed deposits or, if the quantities involved in any of these solids categories are insufficient for chemical analysis, X-ray diffraction and spectrographic examination may be of value.

Standard Method of Test for

CHLORINE REQUIREMENT OF INDUSTRIAL WATER AND INDUSTRIAL WASTE WATER[1]

ASTM Designation: D 1291 – 57 (1965)

ADOPTED, 1957; REAPPROVED, 1965

This Standard of the American Society for Testing and Materials is issued under the fixed designation D 1291; the number immediately following the designation indicates the year of original adoption or, in the case of revision, the year of last revision. A number in parentheses indicates the year of last reapproval.

Scope and Application

1. (*a*) This method describes a procedure for determining the quantity of chlorine required to obtain a specific objective in the treatment by chlorination of industrial water, including industrial waste water.

(*b*) This method can be applied to all types of industrial water, including solutions of individual concentrated industrial wastes, and to the combined waste water effluents from an industrial plant.

(*c*) This method is recommended as a means of establishing, prior to possible plant application, the quantity of chlorine required to achieve any of the following objectives:

(*1*) Elimination of pathogens in the water,

(*2*) Destruction or modification of decomposable organic substances so as to reduce the biochemical oxygen demand of the water,

(*3*) Elimination or reduction of taste and odors in the water,

(*4*) Separation of grease in waste water by eliminating the protective colloidal effect of proteins present, and

(*5*) Destruction or modification of substances in the waste water that react directly with oxygen, such as ammonia, cyanates, cyanides, ferrous iron, nitrites, phenol, phosphorus, sulfides, sulfites, thiocyanates, and other oxidizable constituents.

Principle of Method

2. A cholorinating solution, such as chlorine water or hypochlorite solution, of known strength is applied in increasing increments of chlorine concentration to a series of portions of the individual sample of water to be tested. The conditions of pH and chlorine contact time are those specified for the particular objective of chlorination. The maximum chlorine applied is more than sufficient to attain the specific objective, as determined by the specific test for the objective.

NOTE 1.—It is frequently advantageous, since it may be a means of controlling subsequent chlorination, to apply one of the Standard

[1] Under the standardization procedure of the Society, this method is under the jurisdiction of the ASTM Committee D-19 on Industrial Water. A list of members may be found in the ASTM Year Book.

483

Methods of Test for Residual Chlorine in Industrial Water (ASTM Designation: D 1253)[2] in parallel with the specific test for the objective. The chlorine requirement is determined by interpolation of the test data.

Definitions

3. (a) The term "chlorine requirement" in this method is defined in accordance with the Definitions of Terms Relating to Industrial Water and Industrial Waste Water (ASTM Designation: D 1129),[2] as follows:

Chlorine Requirement.—The amount of chlorine, expressed in parts per million, required to achieve under specified conditions the objectives of chlorination.

(b) For definitions of other terms used in this method, refer to Definitions D 1129.

Precautions

4. (a) The area used for the test must not be in direct sunlight.

(b) The temperature of the water just prior to, or immediately after, chlorination must not exceed 50 C.

Apparatus

5. *pH Apparatus.*—Use the apparatus specified in the Tentative Method for Determination of pH of Aqueous Solutions with the Glass Electrode (ASTM Designation: E 70)[2] or, if the sample is industrial waste water, use the apparatus specified in the Method of Test for pH of Industrial Water and Industrial Waste Water (ASTM Designation: D 1293).[2]

Purity of Reagents

6. (a) Reagent grade chemicals shall be used in all tests. Unless otherwise indicated, it is intended that all reagents shall conform to the specifications of the Committee on Analytical Reagents of the American Chemical Society, where

such specifications are available.[3] Other grades may be used, provided it is first ascertained that the reagent is of sufficiently high purity to permit its use without lessening the accuracy of the determination.

(b) Unless otherwise indicated, references to water shall be understood to mean reagent water conforming to the Specifications for Reagent Water (ASTM Designation: D 1193).[2]

Reagents

7. (a) *Standard Potassium Dichromate Solution (0.10 N).*[4]—Dissolve 4.904 g of $K_2Cr_2O_7$, previously dried at 103 C for 2 hr, in water and dilute to 1 liter in a volumetric flask.

(b) *Potassium Iodide Solution (50 g KI per liter).*[4]—Dissolve 50 g of KI in 1 liter of freshly boiled and cooled water.

(c) *Sulfuric Acid (sp gr 1.84).*[4]

(d) *Starch Solution.*[4]—Make a paste of 1 g of arrowroot starch or soluble iodometric starch with cold water. Pour the paste into 100 ml of boiling water and boil for several minutes. Store in a glass-stoppered bottle in a cold place. Starch solution, prepared in this manner, will remain chemically stable for 2 to 3 days.

(e) *Standard Sodium Thiosulfate Solution (0.10 N).*[4]—Clean a 1 liter glass-stoppered bottle with dichromate - sulfuric acid cleaning solution and rinse thoroughly with hot water. Dissolve 25 g of $Na_2S_2O_3 \cdot 5H_2O$ in water that has been previously boiled and cooled. Dilute this solution to 1 liter with water, previously boiled and cooled. Stopper the bottle, and mix the solution by continuous shaking, with periodic inversion.

---

[3] "Reagent Chemicals, American Chemical Society Specifications," Am. Chem. Soc., Washington, D.C. For suggestions on the testing of reagents not listed by the American Chemical Society, see "Reagent Chemicals and Standards," by Joseph Rosin, D. Van Nostrand Co., Inc., New York. N.Y. and the "United States Pharmacopeia."

[4] Reagent used for standardization only.

---

[2] Appears in this publication.

Preserve the solution by adding 1 g of Na_2CO_3. Standardize by adding, while stirring constantly, 1 ml of H_2SO_4, 10 ml of 0.10 N $K_2Cr_2O_7$ solution, and 10 ml of KI solution to 80 ml of water. Allow to stand for about 5 min; then titrate with the $Na_2S_2O_3$ solution being standardized, using starch solution as an indicator.

(f) *Acetic Acid Solution* (1:1).[4]—Mix equal volumes of glacial acetic acid and water.

(g) *Standard Chlorine Water* (1 ml = 0.5 to 3 mg available chlorine).—(See precautions in Section 4.) Pass gaseous chlorine through water until the solution contains 0.5 to 3.0 mg available chlorine per milliliter, depending upon the maximum expected chlorine requirement of the sample. Store the chlorinating solution in a glass-stoppered, brown bottle, and replace with freshly prepared reagent when the strength of solution is depleted 20 per cent. Restandardize the solution just prior to use by adding, while mixing thoroughly, 10 ml of the chlorine water to be standardized to a glass-stoppered flask or bottle containing 10 ml of acetic acid (1:1) and 10 ml. KI solution. Titrate with 0.10–$Na_2S_2O_3$ solution, using starch solution as an indicator. Calculate the strength of the standard chlorine water, in milligrams of available chlorine per milliliter of solution, as follows:

$$\text{Available chlorine, mg per ml} = \frac{A \times 3.546}{B}$$

where:
A = milliliters of 0.10 N $Na_2S_2O_3$ solution used in the titration, and
B = milliliters of chlorinating solution titrated.

(h) *Standard Sodium Hypochlorite Solution* (1 ml = 0.5 to 100 mg available chlorine). (See precautions in Section 4.) Use a commercial sodium hypochlorite or bleach solution containing 1 to 10 g of available chlorine per 100 ml of solu-

tion,[5] diluted with water, when necessary, to give a solution containing 0.5 to 100 mg available chlorine per mililiter, depending upon the maximum expected chlorine requirement of the sample. These solutions, undiluted or diluted, shall be standardized just prior to use. Standardize and store the solutions in accordance with Paragraph (g), except that for a solution containing 3.0 to 20 mg available chlorine a 5-ml sample shall be used, and for a solution containing 20 to 100 mg available chlorine a 1-ml sample shall be used. Confirm the 1-ml sample titrations by repeating the standardization.

(i) *Standard Calcium Hypochlorite Solution* (1 ml = 0.5 to 100 mg available chlorine).—(See precautions in Section 4.) Use a commercial high-test calcium hypochlorite powder (70 per cent available chlorine, by weight). Dissolve 145 g of the hypochlorite in 1 liter of water. Allow to clarify by settling; then decant the supernatant solution containing approximately 100 mg available chlorine per milliliter. Use undiluted, or dilute with water to give a solution containing 0.5 to 100 mg of available chlorine per milliliter, depending upon the maximum expected chlorine requirement of the sample. These solutions, undiluted or diluted, must be standardized just prior to use. Standardize and store the solutions in accordance with Paragraph (h).

(j) *Hydrochloric Acid* (1:1).—Mix equal volumes of HCl (sp gr 1.19) and water.

(k) *Sodium Hydroxide Solution* (11.25 g NaOH per liter).—Dissolve 11.25 g NaOH in water and dilute to 1 liter.

(l) *Calcium Hydroxide Solution* (10.7 g $Ca(OH)_2$ per liter).—Weigh out 10.7 g of 100 per cent hydrated lime and suspend in water. Dilute the suspension to

---

[5] The concentration of the commercial solution is ordinarily expressed in terms of "trade %," which is numerically equivalent to grams of available chlorine per 100 ml of solution.

1 liter. Shake well each time before using.

(*m*) *Reagents* prescribed in the Standard Methods of Test for Residual Chlorine in Industrial Water (ASTM Designation: D 1253).[2]

(*n*) *Sodium Sulfite Solution* (*100 g Na₂SO₃ per liter*).—Dissolve 10 g anhydrous Na_2SO_3 in water and dilute to 100 ml. Heat the solution to boiling if a bacteriological test is to be run on the dechlorinated sample. Prepare fresh solution daily.

(*o*) *Reagents* required to test for the specific quality, the destroying, modifying, or enhancing of which is the objective of chlorination.

Sampling

8. Collect the sample in accordance with the Tentative Methods of Sampling Industrial Water (ASTM Designation: D 510).[2]

Procedure

Establishing Conditions of Test

9. (*a*) Ascertain the optimum pH range and the optimum time of chlorine contact required to achieve the objective of chlorination from past experience, from a survey of the literature, by experimentation, or from plant conditions.

(*b*) Estimate the total chlorine requirement necessary to achieve the objective of chlorination. On the basis of this estimate determine the experimental additions of chlorinating solution such that there shall be not less than five equal increments of the total estimated requirements. The largest increment of chlorination should be more than sufficient to obtain the objective of chlorination. The lowest increment should be 20 per cent of the maximum.

(*c*) Choose the chlorinating solution. When the anticipated chlorine requirement is less than 600 ppm, use the chlori-

nating solution to be used in ultimate plant treatment. When the anticipated chlorine requirement is 600 ppm or more, use the appropriate hypochlorite solution.

(*d*) In each of a series of clean 1-liter glass containers, place a 500-ml portion of the sample. (Observe the precautions in Section 4.)

Trial Chlorination

(*e*) To the first of the series of 500-ml portions of the sample, add the amount of chlorinating solution anticipated to be sufficient to achieve the objective of chlorination (Notes 2 and 3). Stir gently and constantly during the addition.

NOTE 2.—It is the purpose of the trial chlorination to supply experimental information on the required chlorine dosage and the necessary pH adjustments to simplify and expedite the test.

NOTE 3.—The volume of chlorinated sample shall not be more than 600 ml unless the chlorine requirement is in excess of 20,000 ppm. This requires that the chlorinating solution shall contain the desired amount of chlorine to be added in 100 ml or less. In no case shall the chlorinating solution contain more than 100 mg of available chlorine per milliliter.

(*f*) Immediately determine the pH of the chlorinated sample in accordance with the Tentative Method for Determination of pH of Aqueous Solutions with the Glass Electrode (ASTM Designation: E 70),[2] or, if the sample is industrial waste water, in accordance with the Standard Method of Test for pH of Industrial Water and Industrial Waste Water (ASTM Designation: D 1293).[2]

(*g*) If the pH is within the optimum range, proceed as described in Paragraph (*h*). If the pH is higher than the optimum range, adjust the pH as described in Paragraph (*j*). If the pH is lower than the optimum, discard the sample, adjust the pH of the second of the series of sample portions as described in Paragraphs (*k*) and (*l*), and repeat Paragraphs (*e*) and (*f*).

(*h*) After pH adjustment, allow the chlorinated sample to stand the predetermined time selected for chlorination. On completion of the predetermined time of contact, withdraw a portion of the chlorinated sample and immediately determine the residual chlorine in accordance with the appropriate method given in the Standard Methods of Test for Residual Chlorine in Industrial Water (ASTM Designation: D 1253);[2,6,7] or determine the specific quality, the destroying, modifying, or enhancing of which is the objective of chlorination; or determine both the residual chlorine and the appropriate specific quality, if required.

Note 4.—In case the trial chlorination reveals that the requirements were underestimated, it should be planned to use additional equal increments of chlorinating solution so as to add somewhat more than 100 per cent of the actual chlorine requirement. If the trial chlorination reveals that the requirements have been appreciably overestimated, it should be planned to use a sufficient number of smaller equal increments of chlorination, so that the smallest increment is approximately 20 per cent of the chlorine requirement.

pH Adjustment

(*i*) If the pH of the chlorinated sample is within the optimum range, pH adjustment is unnecessary.

(*j*) If the pH of the chlorinated sample is higher than the optimum range, proceed as follows (Note 5): Add, slowly and dropwise, HCl (1:1) to the chlorinated sample until the pH of the sample has reached the upper limit of the optimum range.

Note 5.—pH adjustment is required when the pH of the chlorinated sample is higher than the optimum pH range for accomplishing the objective of chlorination, because no reaction will ensue when the pH is greater than 10. A rapid

[6] H. C. Marks, R. R. Joiner, F. B. Strandskov, "Amperometric Titration of Residual Chlorine in Sewage," *Water and Sewage Works*, Vol. 95, p. 175 (1948).
[7] R. V. Day, D. H. Horchler, H. C. Marks, "Residual Chlorine Methods & Disinfection of Sewage," *Industrial and Engineering Chemistry*, Vol. 45, p. 1001 (1953).

reaction (which itself lowers the pH) may ensue when the pH is less than 10. Therefore, the HCl solution must be added with caution.

(*k*) If the pH of the chlorinated sample is lower than the optimum range, discard the sample and proceed with another of the series of sample portions, as follows: Add sufficient NaOH solution or $Ca(OH)_2$ solution (Note 6) to bring the pH of the unchlorinated sample portion to the mid-point of the optimum pH range.

Note 6.—NaOH solution is recommended, but $Ca(OH)_2$ solution may be used if the presence of the calcium ion is required.

(*l*) If the chlorinating solution to be used is chlorine water, add an additional 0.1 ml of the NaOH solution or $Ca(OH)_2$ solution for each milligram of available chlorine to be applied to the sample. If the chlorinating solution to be used is hypochlorite solution, there need be no additional NaOH or $Ca(OH)_2$ solution added.

Chlorination

(*m*) On the basis of information obtained by the trial chlorination, it is possible to anticipate the requirements for pH adjustment and to select the desired incremental additions of chlorinating solution. Starting with the smallest increment of chlorine addition, individually and in turn, add each successively larger increment to separate 500-ml portions of the sample (Note 7).

Note 7.—One increment of chlorine addition should be applied to each of the sample portions, with not less than five such sample portions being used for the test. The minimum total addition should be 20 per cent of the maximum. The maximum addition should be sufficient to adequately achieve the objective of chlorination.

(*n*) After the addition of each separate increment of chlorination, determine the pH by the appropriate method (see Paragraph (*f*)).

(*o*) If the pH is within the optimum

range, proceed with the chlorination of the next sample portion using the next higher increment of chlorination. If the pH is higher than the optimum range, acidify as described in Paragraph (j). If the pH drops below the optimum range, discard the sample and proceed as described in Paragraph (k) and (l).

(p) Allow each portion of chlorinated sample to stand for a time predetermined in accordance with Paragraph (a). Withdraw a portion of the sample and determine the residual chlorine by the appropriate method given in Methods D 1253.[2] Immediately (Note 8) after a portion of the sample is withdrawn for the residual chlorine determination, add 0.5 ml of Na_2SO_3 solution to the remainder of the sample portion.

NOTE 8.—The immediate addition of the dechlorinating agent is important, not only because of the interference of oxidizing agents in the tests pertaining to the objectives of chlorination, but because it definitely fixes the chlorine contact time.

(q) Determine the specific quality, the destroying, modifying, or enhancing of which is the objective of chlorination (Note 9).

NOTE 9.—Use ASTM Methods for all determinations, where such methods are available.

Calculation

10. (a) Calculate the chlorine dosage, in parts per million, for each increment of chlorination as follows:

$$\text{Chlorine dosage, ppm} = 2\,AB$$

where:

A = milliliters of chlorinating solution added to 500 ml of sample, and

B = milligrams of available chlorine per milliliter of the chlorinating solution.

(b) Plot the results of the chlorine residual tests, or the tests for the specific quality which constitutes the objective of chlorination, against the corresponding chlorine dosage in parts per million for each increment of chlorination. By interpolation of the curve plotted, determine the chlorine requirement in parts per million of chlorine.

Standard Method of Test for

ODOR IN INDUSTRIAL WATER AND INDUSTRIAL WASTE WATER[1]

ASTM Designation: D 1292 – 65

ADOPTED, 1963; REVISED, 1965

This Standard of the American Society for Testing and Materials is issued under the fixed designation D 1292; the final number indicates the year of original adoption as standard or, in the case of revision, the year of last revision.

Scope

1. (*a*) This method[2] covers the determination of the odor (that is, the property that affects the sense of smell) of industrial water and industrial waste water. A suggested system for classifying odors is given as Appendix I. The method is applicable to the determination of odor intensity in terms of odor intensity index or threshold odor number.

(*b*) Industrial effluents may carry myriad of compounds, difficult to measure individually, which contribute to odor problems. Combinations of compounds can cause an odor intensity or develop a characteristic that cannot be anticipated from odors of the individual substances.

(*c*) Because of the variation in human sensitivity, high precision in determining odor intensity is not possible. There will not always be agreement on odor characteristics by various testers. Odor analysis provides the tool to measure variation in odor intensity at a given sampling point. The degree of variation may indicate the magnitude or importance of an odor problem. Determining the cause of the variation or the source of the objectionable characteristic may define the odor problem better than analysis for individual compounds.

Summary of Method

2. A sample of water is diluted with odor-free water until a dilution is obtained that has the least definitely perceptible odor. The test is made by two or more testers. One makes dilutions and the others determine odor intensity. Samples are tested in generally increasing concentration of odorant, although not in consecutive sequence of dilutions, until the odor is perceived. The persons making the test select the odorous sample from among three flasks, two of which contain odor-free water. Odor is measured without regard to the presence

[1] Under the standardization procedure of the Society, this method is under the jurisdiction of the ASTM Committee D-19 on Industrial Water. A list of members may be found in the ASTM Year Book.

[2] This method is based on a procedure proposed by the Dow Chemical Co. in a private communication.

of suspended matter or immiscible substances in the sample. Cognizance is taken of the fact that there is no absolute odor value and that the test is to be used for comparison only. The test is carried out at 40 C.

Definitions

3. (a) The terms "odor intensity index" and "threshold odor number" in this method are defined in accordance with the Definitions of Terms Relating to Industrial Water and Industrial Waste Water (ASTM Designation: D 1129),[3] as follows:

Odor Intensity Index.—The number of times the concentration of the original sample is halved by addition of odor-free water to obtain the least definitely perceptible odor.

Threshold Odor Number.—The greatest dilution of the sample with odor-free water to yield the least definitely perceptible odor.

(b) For definitions of other terms used in this method, refer to Definitions D 1129.

Precautions

4. (a) The area used for the test shall be free of interfering odors.[4] An ideal laboratory has a separate room equipped with activated-carbon filtered inlet air of controlled, constant temperature and humidity. A relative humidity of 50 per cent is recommended wherever control is feasible. Cleanliness is an absolute necessity. All equipment used in the test shall be clean and free of odor and shall be restricted to use for odor determination. An odorless detergent[5] shall be used to cleanse the

hands and faces of the persons participating in the test from tobacco, shaving preparation, cosmetic, and other odors. Testers shall not smoke, chew tobacco or gum, or eat food of pronounced taste or odor for at least 30 min prior to the determination.

(b) The physical condition of the participants is important. The odor tester shall be free from any conditions affecting the olfactory system. Prolonged use of the sense of smell causes olfactory fatigue. Repeated smelling of the same odor has the same effect. Therefore, for prolonged testing, frequent rest periods, preferably in fresh, odor-free air, are necessary for recuperation. Under ordinary circumstances no operator shall carry out odor tests for longer than 15 min without rest in order to avoid olfactory fatigue. This is an average time. Stronger odorants may dull olfactory response within a few minutes while waters of good quality may be tested over longer time intervals. If personnel is limited, the testers may check their observations after allowing sufficient time to relax the olfactory system.

(c) Not all persons are capable of carrying out this test. The testers should be thoroughly screened to obtain the best possible precision, especially for research purposes. However, if due care is exercised, most persons qualify for routine work. At least two testers are necessary, but more are preferred: one to make the preliminary screening and prepare the dilutions and the other or others to make the actual odor determination. The testers making the determination shall not know the dilutions; in no case shall they make the dilutions. Dilutions shall be tested by presenting samples ranging from lower to higher concentrations but they must not be presented in sequence. Insertion of a set of blanks or lower concentrations

---

[3] Appears in this publication.
[4] Robert A. Baker, "Critical Evaluation of Olfactory Measurement," *Journal,* Water Pollution Control Federation, Vol. 34, No. 6, pp. 582–591, June, 1962.
[5] Surety Hand Soap, Surety Manufacturing Co., Inc., 2541 Archer Ave., Chicago, Ill., or equivalent products.

into the series is recommended. This lessens the chance of memorizing odors or guessing.

(d) Color is often imparted by various contaminants in waste water. This color is often evident below perceptible odor levels. A colored lighting system may be used to eliminate color bias in selection of the odor-containing flask by the testers. Photographic safelights with interchangeable filters are useful for this purpose.

(e) Turbidity in some waste waters may be evident below perceptible odor levels. The colored lighting system described in Paragraph (d), may not eliminate this bias. In such instances external masking of the flasks may be necessary. Painting the flasks to make them opaque is a means of masking turbidity.

(f) For maximum control the odor laboratory should be divided into two areas separating the sample preparation and the odor detection activities.[5] This allows isolation of the dilution operator from the odor tester and permits greater control of background odor in the odor measuring area.

Apparatus

5. (a) *Constant-Temperature Bath*, capable of maintaining a temperature of 40 ± 1 C.

(b) *Sample Bottles, Glass-Stoppered.*— Biochemical oxygen demand (BOD) bottles are satisfactory for this purpose.

(c) *Flasks*, 500-ml, wide-mouth Erlenmeyer, glass-stoppered or covered by watch glasses.

Reagents

6. (a) *Activated Carbon.*—Water purification grade. Carbon should be renewed after treating approximately 20 liters of water, or more often as necessary.

(b) *Water, Odor-Free.*—Prepare odor-free water by passing reagent water conforming to the Specifications for Reagent Water (ASTM Designation: D 1193),[3] or tap water through a glass column 3 ft long and 2 in. in diameter, packed with granular activated carbon, at a flow rate of less than 11 liters per hr. Use glass connections and tubing in making the system. The column ends may be packed with glass wool to support the carbon. Test the column effluent at 40 C. This is necessary since the quantities and nature of impurities in the water will affect useful carbon life. It has been found that columns used infrequently may develop a biological growth which imparts odor. To check the condition of the column after an idle period (such as a weekend) a simple test is recommended. Fill a short glass tube with fresh carbon and filter water through it. The reagent water so prepared should be checked against the column effluent to be sure a subtle odor is not present. Odor-free water should not be stored but should be prepared on the day the test is made. In order to save time during analyses, maintain the supply of odor-free water at 40 ± 1 C.

Sampling

7. (a) Collect the sample in accordance with the applicable method of the American Society for Testing and Materials as follows:

D   510—Sampling Industrial Water,[3]
D   860—Sampling Water from Boilers,[3]
D 1066—Sampling Steam,[3]
D 1496—Sampling Homogeneous Industrial Waste Water.[3]

(b) Determine odor on separate, freshly-obtained samples. Sampling is very important. Glass-stoppered bottles shall be used and shall be completely filled. Although larger volumes may be necessary in some cases, the standard BOD bottles are ideal for this use. If the sample is at a temperature greater than 40 C, cool it before testing for odor.

(c) Storage of water may lead to errors through modification of odor intensity and character. Biological, chemical, and physical reactions are factors in this degradation. If the analysis cannot be made promptly, refrigerate the sample during storage. Although this will not guarantee that odor changes will not take place, it minimizes the effect in most cases. Store the sample in a glass-stoppered bottle to minimize contamination with refrigerator odors. Precooling the sample in an ice bath and in an odor-free atmosphere before refrigeration is advised.

(d) Record the sample temperature at the time of collection. This frequently is useful when relating laboratory results to field conditions.

Preliminary Test

8. (a) Preparation of a test series can be greatly simplified if an approximation of odor intensity is first made as follows: Thoroughly scrub all glassware with a brush and odorless detergent.[6] Rinse with tap water and clean with chromic acid solution. Rinse with reagent water, rinse with odor-free water, and store filled with odor-free water. Check all flasks to make sure no residual odor exists by testing with 200 ml of odor-free water at 40 C.

(b) To determine the estimated order of magnitude of the odor intensity, the dilution tester shall pipet 25 ml of sample into a clean, glass-stoppered (or watch-glass covered) 500-ml conical flask. Dilute this to a total volume of 200 ml by adding 175 ml of odor-free water at 40 C. For this preliminary test the dilution water may be added from a graduated cylinder. Do not allow the

[6] Alconox, obtainable from Alconox Inc., New York 3, N. Y., has been found satisfactory for this purpose.

pipet or the sample solution to touch the neck of the flask. Stopper and warm the flask to 40 C in a water bath. Avoid prolonged or direct heating.

(c) Mix by vigorously swirling three or four times, remove the stopper, and place the nose at the top of the flask. Test for odor, using normal inhalation. Compare with a flask containing odor-free water. Note whether odor is detected. If odor is not detected, prepare lower dilutions successively in clean flasks until the odor is just perceptible. It usually is convenient to make a series of dilutions at the beginning. Odor testing however must be from the highest dilution toward lower dilutions.

(d) If the odor is detected in the initial dilution, dilute at least 12.5 ml of original sample to a measured volume and record this primary dilution. Make subsequent lower dilutions and record the aliquot at which odor is just perceptible. Calculate the estimated order of magnitude of the odor intensity in accordance with Section 10.

Procedure

9. (a) The choice of dilutions for odor measurement depends on the order of magnitude of odor intensity determined in accordance with Section 8. The tester who determined the odor intensity in the preliminary test shall now assume the role of making the dilutions for the other tester or testers, but shall do no testing himself. Primary dilutions shall contain at least 12.5 ml of sample. If greater dilutions are necessary, add odor-free water to the primary dilution. Such subsequent dilutions shall be used in the evaluation.

(b) The dilution tester shall code three clean, odor-free flasks for the test, adding approximately half the estimated quantity of sample (preliminary test) to one of the flasks. Dilute the contents of each flask to a total volume of 200 ml with odor-free water. Stopper each flask and adjust the temperature to 40 C in a water bath. Vigorously swirl the stoppered flasks and present them to the odor tester. In presenting the flasks to the tester the position of the odor-containing

fails to detect an odor, the dilution tester then shall decrease the dilution (increase the concentration) until a dilution is found at which the odor is perceptible, using the same procedure. The dilution tester shall record the

TABLE I.—DILUTION OF SAMPLE AND REPORTING OF RESULTS.

	Volume Transferred to Odor Flask, ml[a]	Threshold Odor Number (Dilution Factor)	Odor Intensity Index (OII)
Original sample...	200	1	0
	100	2	1
	50	4	2
	25	8	3
	12.5	16	4
Dilution A (25 ml of original sample diluted to 200 ml)............	50	32	5
	25	64	6
	12.5	128	7
Dilution B (25 ml of dilution A diluted to 200 ml)................	50	256	8
	25	512	9
	12.5	1024	10
Dilution C (25 ml of dilution B diluted to 200 ml)...............	50	2050	11
	25	4100	12
	12.5	8200	13
Dilution D (25 ml of dilution C diluted to 200 ml)...............	50	16 400	14
	25	32 800	15
	12.5	65 500	16
Dilution E (25 ml of dilution D diluted to 200 ml)...............	50	131 000	17
	25	262 000	18
	12.5	524 000	19
	6.25	1 050 000	20

[a] Volume in odor flask made up to 200 ml with odor-free water.

flask in the array shall be randomized. The odor tester shall swirl a flask vigorously exercising care to avoid spilling the contents. The flasks shall be held by the flat bottom with a finger on the cover or stopper during swirling. This minimizes imparting an odor near the opening of the flask prior to testing. Swirling distributes the odorous substance uniformly in the vapor space. The tester shall remove the stopper or watch glass cover, place his nose at the top of the flask and test for odor using normal inhalation. If the odor tester

results. The samples shall be given to the tester in generally increasing concentration but not in a sequence of higher concentrations. Sets of blanks, all flasks containing odor-free water, and some lower concentrations shall be inserted during the testing to eliminate guessing or anticipation of the threshold level.

(c) If there is odor perception, the dilution tester shall empty all the flasks and prepare two blanks of odor-free water and one 200-ml dilution containing half as much sample as in Paragraph (b). Repeat this procedure until the odor tester fails to detect an odor. At this point the dilution tester shall make up the least perceptible dilution and the odor tester shall repeat the test. If the odor tester fails to confirm his first result, then the dilution tester shall double the sample concentration until perception is again obtained.

Calculation

10. (a) Calculate the odor intensity as odor intensity index as follows:

$$\text{Odor intensity index} = 3.3 \log \left(\frac{200}{A}\right) + 3D$$

where:

A = milliliters of sample or milliliters of aliquot of the primary dilution used, and

D = number of 25:175 primary dilutions required to reach the determinable magnitude of odor intensity.

(b) The odor intensity may be calculated as threshold odor number if desired by the procedure described in Appendix II.

Report

11. (a) Record the highest dilution at which the odor is just perceptible and calculate the odor intensity index (Table I shows the relationship between odor intensity index and sample dilu-tion.) Report the average and the range of the odor intensity index obtained by two or more odor testers.

(b) Report the elapsed time between sampling and analysis if this exceeds 30 min.

Precision and Accuracy[7]

12. (a) There is no absolute threshold odor number. The threshold odor number reflects the opinion of the tester at the time of testing.

(b) Duplicate values for odor intensity index obtained by a tester with an odorant at a given time have been shown to agree within approximately one index number.[5] The value may vary for an individual with time of day or from day to day.

(c) Person-person and person-chemical interactions exist. The results will be modified by the choice of panelists, panel size, and chemical stimuli, all other factors being equal. The following data demonstrate the order of variability:

Chemical	Variance	Degrees of Freedom	Standard Deviation	95 Per Cent Confidence Limits
n-butanol...	1.028	18	1.01	0.76, 1.49
m-cresol....	0.125	4	0.35	0.21, 1.01

[7] Supporting data for this method have been filed at ASTM Headquarters.

APPENDIX I

SUGGESTED ODOR CLASSIFICATION

A1. (a) The types of odors present in waste water will vary widely. Describe the odor type when desired. Table II will be helpful as a guide in classifying the odor as to type. Often the initial sample odor differs from odors determined at various dilutions. If this odor fractionation occurs, report the first odor characteristic as well as intermediate and final odor character. Record corresponding dilutions. Judge the degrees of sweetness, pungency, smokiness, and rottenness of the odor at the desired dilution. If the characteristic being judged is high in intensity, rate that characteristic as "100"; if medium, rate it as "50"; and if low, rate it as "0". Intermediate ratings may be used, but this practice is not recommended.

(b) The odor class can be established by comparison with the perception levels of odor characteristics shown in Table II. Thus, if an odor is rated a "100" in sweetness, "50" in pungency, "0" in smokiness, and "50" in rottenness, the odor should be described as "estery" or "alcoholic." Reference to the chemical types that produce these odors will guide the operator in determining whether the odor should be reported as "estery" or "alcoholic."

TABLE II.—ODORS CLASSIFIED BY CHEMICAL TYPES.

Sweetness	Pungency	Smokiness	Rottenness	Odor Class	Chemical Types	Examples
100	50	0 to 50	50	Estery	esters, ethers, lower ketones	lacquer, solvents, most fruits, many flowers.
100	50 to 100	0 to 100	50	Alcoholic	phenols and cresols, alcohols, hydrocarbons	creosote, tars, smokes, alcohol, liquor, rose and spicy flowers, spices and herbs.
50	50	0 to 50	50	Carbonyl	aldehydes, higher ketones	rancid fats, butter, stone fruits and nuts, violets, grasses and vegetables.
50	100	0 to 50	50	Acidic	acid anhydrides, organic acids, sulfur dioxide	vinegar, perspiration, rancid oils, resins, body odor, garbage.
100	50 to 100	50 to 100	0 to 100	Halide	quinones, oxides and ozone, halides, nitrogen compounds	insecticides, weed killers, musty and moldy odors, husks, medicinal odors, earth, peat.
50	50	100	100	Sulfury	selenium compounds, arsenicals, mercaptans, sulfides	skunks, bears, foxes, rotting fish and meat, cabbage, onion, sewage.
100	50	50	100	Unsaturated	acetylene derivatives, butadiene, isoprene	paint thinners, varnish, kerosine, turpentine, essential oils, cucumber.
100	50	0 to 50	100	Basic	vinyl monomers, amines, alkaloids, ammonia	fecal odors, manure, fish and shellfish, stale flowers such as lilac, lily, jasmine, and honeysuckle.

Column header: Odor Characteristics[a]

[a] The degree of odor characteristic perceived is designated as follows:
100 indicates a high level of perception,
50 indicates a medium level of perception, and
0 indicates a low level of perception.

APPENDIX II

THRESHOLD ODOR NUMBER

B1. (a) Odor intensity is frequently reported as threshold odor number which may be calculated as follows:

$$\text{Threshold odor number} = \frac{200}{A} \times 8^{D}$$

(*b*) The relationship to odor dilution is presented in Table I. When reporting threshold odor values, give the median and range of values obtained by two or more testers. Threshold odor numbers cannot be averaged.

(*c*) The average person finds it difficult to grasp the significance of the high numerical values obtained when using threshold odor number to report strong odor. Consequently, the odor intensity index is recommended because it represents the number of times the sample had to be diluted in half to reach the threshold level.

Appendix III

Suggested Odor Intensity Report Form

Sample No.: 17462   *Sample Source:* Plant ABC Effluent   *Date:* July 7   *Time:* 10:00 am
Test Conditions: Temp. 70 F; Rel. Humidity 55 per cent

Dilutions	Volume	OII	Tester		
			RAB	FLJ	MML
Original sample...............	200	0			
	100	1			
	50	2			
	25	3			
	12.5	4			
Dilution A: 25 ml of original sample / 200 ml	50	5			
	25	6			
	12.5	7	++++ (7)		++++ (7)
Dilution B: 25 ml of dilution A / 200 ml	50	8	— — — — Bᵃ	++++ (8)	BB + — — —
	25	9	— — — — B	— — — — B	— — — —
	12.5	10	—	— — — —	— —
Dilution C: 25 ml of dilution B / 200 ml	50	11			
	25	12			
	12.5	13			

ᵃ Set of odor-free blanks.

The above report sheet illustrates the sequence of sample dilution presentation and method of recording results for the determination of threshold odor by three testers. The first tester was given dilutions of the sample corresponding to odor intensity index values of 10, 9, 8, and 7 in that order. The tester failed to identify the first three dilutions but did identify the last dilution. The results were recorded vertically upward in the first column as —, —, —, and +. Then dilution 9, a set of blanks, and dilutions 8 and 7 were presented in that order. Only dilution 7 was identified. The results were recorded as —, B, —, and + in the second vertical column moving upward. The tests were continued until four positive identifications were made at dilution 7. The final results of (7), (8), and (7) respectively were recorded in the columns for each of the three testers. This report form is presented only as a guide and may be modified.

APPENDIX IV

ODOR THRESHOLD CONCENTRATIONS FOR VARIOUS CHEMICALS[8]

Chemical	No. of Panelists	No. of Observations	Threshold Odor Level,[a] ppm	
			Average	Range
cetic acid	9	9	24.3	5.07 to 81.2
cetone	12	17	40.9	1.29 to 330
cetophenone	17	154	0.17	0.0039 to 2.02
crylonitrile	16	104	18.6	0.0031 to 50.4
llyl chloride[b]	10	10	14 700	3660 to 29 300
-Amyl acetate	18	139	0.08	0.0017 to 0.86
niline	8	8	70.1	2.0 to 128
enzene[c]	13	18	31.3	0.84 to 53.6
-Butanol	32	167	2.5	0.012 to 25.3
-Chlorophenol	16	24	1.24	0.02 to 20.4
-Cresol	13	21	0.65	0.016 to 4.1
-Cresol	29	147	0.68	0.016 to 4.0
ichloroisopropylether	8	8	0.32	0.017 to 1.1
-4 Dichlorophenol	10	94	0.21	0.02 to 1.35
imethylamine	12	29	23.2	0.01 to 42.5
thylacrylate	9	9	0.0067	0.0018 to 0.0141
ormaldehyde	10	11	49.9	0.8 to 102
-Mercaptoethanol	9	9	0.64	0.07 to 1.1
esitylene[c]	13	19	0.027	0.00024 to 0.062
lethylamine	10	10	3.33	0.65 to 5.23
ethyl ethyl pyridine	16	20	0.05	0.0017 to 0.225
lethyl vinyl pyridine	8	8	0.04	0.015 to 0.12
-Naphthol[c]	14	20	1.29	0.01 to 11.4
ctyl alcohol[c]	10	10	0.13	0.0087 to 0.56
henol	12	20	5.9	0.016 to 16.7
yridine	13	130	0.82	0.007 to 7.7
uinoline	11	17	0.71	0.016 to 4.3
tyrene[c]	16	23	0.73	0.02 to 2.6
hiophenol[b]	10	10	13.5	2.05 to 32.8
rimethylamine	10	10	1.7	0.04 to 5.17
ylene[c]	16	21	2.21	0.26 to 4.13
-Butyl mercaptan	8	94	0.006	0.001 to 0.06

[a] Threshold values based upon pure substances.

[b] Threshold of a saturated aqueous solution. Solubility data not available.

[c] Dilutions started with saturated aqueous solution at room temperature; solubility data obained from literature for correction back to pure substances.

The threshold odor levels for 32 organic hemicals are presented. For some chemicals ese results were calculated from solubility ata. Where solubility data were not available, e results are based on a saturated aqueous lution as the starting sample. For all other chemicals the threshold is based on the pure substance.

A cautionary note regarding field use of threshold data obtained with pure substances may be appropriate. These substances, in mixtures, may produce odors greater than or less than expected on the basis of direct addition, and the effect noted in mixtures, whether synergism or antagonism, may be quite marked, depending on the chemicals involved.

[8] Reprinted with permission from *Journal of merican Water Works Association*, Vol. 55, uly, 1963, pp. 913–916.

Standard Method of Test for
pH OF INDUSTRIAL WATER AND INDUSTRIAL WASTE WATER[1]

ASTM Designation: D 1293 – 65
ADOPTED, 1965

This Standard of the American Society for Testing and Materials is issued under the fixed designation D 1293; the final number indicates the year of original adoption as standard or, in the case of revision, the year of last revision.

Scope

1. (a) This method covers the electrometric measurement of the pH of industrial water and industrial waste water by means of the glass electrode.[2] The procedure for measuring batch samples is given in Section 8(a) and (b), and for measuring flowing samples, in Section 8(c), (d), and (e).

Definitions

2. (a) The term "pH" in this method is defined in accordance with the Definitions of Terms Relating to Industrial Water and Industrial Waste Water

(ASTM Designation: D 1129),[3] as follows:

pH.—The pH of an aqueous solution or extract is defined in terms of E, the electromotive force between a glass and reference electrode when immersed in the solution or extract, in volts, and E_s, the electromotive force obtained when the electrodes are immersed in a reference buffer solution (the assigned pH of which is designated pH_s), in volts, as follows:

$$pH = pH_s + \frac{(E - E_s)F}{2.3026\,RT}$$

where:

F = Faraday,
R = gas constant, and
T = the absolute temperature, $t\,C +$ 273.16.

Values of the factor $F/(2.3026\,RT)$ a different temperatures are given i Table I. (See Appendix, Section A1 fo comment on the meaning of the term pH.)

[1] Under the standardization procedure of the Society, this method is under the jurisdiction of the ASTM Committee D-19 on Industrial Water. A list of members may be found in the ASTM Year Book.

[2] This method has been adapted in part from the Method for Determination of pH of Aqueous Solutions with the Glass Electrode (ASTM Designation: E 70), which appears in this publication.

[3] Appears in this publication.

52–39

(*b*) For definitions of other terms used in this method, refer to Definitions D 1129.

Interferences

3. (*a*) The glass electrode reliably measures pH in nearly all aqueous solu-

TABLE I. VALUES OF F/(2.3026 RT)[a]

Temperature, deg Cent	$F/(2.3026\ RT)$, volts⁻¹
0.........	18.452
5.........	18.120
10.........	17.800
15.........	17.491
20.........	17.193
25.........	16.904
30.........	16.626
35.........	16.356
40.........	16.095
45.........	15.842
50.........	15.597
55.........	15.359
60.........	15.129
65.........	14.905
70.........	14.688
75.........	14.477
80.........	14.272
85.........	14.073
90.........	13.879
95.........	13.690

[a] The data of the table were calculated using a precise value of the logarithmic conversion factor (2.302585) and values of the fundamental constants from F. D. Rossini, F. T. Gucker, Jr., H. L. Johnston, L. Pauling, and G. W. Vinal, "Status of the Values of the Fundamental Constants for Physical Chemistry as of July 1, 1951," *Journal*, Am. Chemical Soc., Vol. 74, p. 2699 (1952) as follows:

F = 96,493.1 ± 1.0 coulombs per equivalent
R = 8.31439 ± 0.00034 joules per deg mole
$T_{0 deg C}$ = 273.160 ± 0.010 K

tions and in general is not subject to solution interference from color, turbidity, colloidal matter, oxidants, or reductants. Below pH 1.0 the electrode is subject to a so-called acid error, and in alkaline solutions above pH 10.0 it may be subject to a sodium ion error. In addition, a few substances appear to poison the glass electrode. A discussion of this subject is given in the Appendix, Section A3.

Apparatus

4. (*a*) *pH Meter.*—A pH meter with associated glass and reference electrodes. There shall be two permissible types of meter, designated types I and II. The choice of meter will depend upon the desired precision of the measurement. Where best results are desired or in case of dispute, meters of type I shall be used. The two types are differentiated on the basis of their electrical characteristics. These requirements are listed in Table II.

(*b*) *Reference Electrode.*—A calomel, silver-silver chloride, or other reference electrode of constant potential shall be used. If a saturated calomel electrode is used, some potassium chloride crystals shall be contained in the saturated potassium chloride solution. The design of the electrode shall permit for each measurement a fresh liquid junction to be formed between the solution of potassium chloride and the buffer standard or test solution and shall allow traces of solution to be removed by washing. To ensure the desired slow outward flow of reference electrode solution, keep the solution pressure inside the liquid junction somewhat in excess of that outside the junction. In nonpressurized applications this requirement can be met by maintaining the inside solution level higher than the outside solution level. The reference electrode and junction shall perform satisfactorily as required in the standardizing procedure described in Section 7. A discussion of reference electrodes is given in the Appendix, Section A2.

(*c*) *Glass Electrode.*—The pH response of the glass electrode shall conform to the requirements set forth in Section 7. If the glass electrode is used outside the electrode compartment of the meter, the lead wire shall be shielded. Measurements at pH greater than 10.0 shall be made with a high-alkalinity type of electrode to reduce the possibility of sodium ion errors.

(d) *Electrode Treatment.*—New glass electrodes and those that have been stored dry shall be conditioned and

Unless otherwise indicated, it is intended that all reagents shall conform to the specifications of the Committee on Analytical Reagents of the American Chemical Society, where such specifications are available.[4] Other grades may be used, provided it is first ascertained that the reagent is of sufficiently high

TABLE II.—ELECTRICAL CHARACTERISTICS OF METERS.

	Type I Meter	Type II Meter
Vacuum-tube operation	yes	yes
Type of measuring circuit	potentiometric	calibrated direct deflection meter
Method for detection of balance	null indicator (ammeter, galvanometer, or electron-ray tube)	direct deflection
Maximum grid current drawn from glass electrode during measurement	2×10^{-12} amp	5×10^{-11}
Standard cell for calibration of working battery	yes	no
Scale:		
Units shown	millivolts, pH or both	millivolts, pH, or both
Minimum range, pH	0 to 13	0 to 13[a]
Minimum range, mv	0 to ±1100	0 to ±400
Maximum value of smallest ruled interval	0.1 pH, 10 mv	0.1 pH, 10 mv
Asymmetry potential compensator	yes	yes
Temperature compensator (automatic or manual)	yes	optional[b]
Minimum range, deg Cent	10 to 40	10 to 40
Maximum value of smallest graduation, deg Cent	2	2
Power supply, batteries or 110-v ac	either	either

[a] A double scale may be provided.
[b] If a temperature compensator is not provided, the instrument shall be furnished with suitable charts giving corrections for each degree from 10 to 40 C for various pH readings.

maintained as recommended by the manufacturer. If the assembly is in intermittent use, keep the immersible ends of the electrodes in water between measurements. For prolonged storage, glass electrodes may be allowed to become dry, but the junction and filling openings of reference electrodes should be capped to reduce evaporation.

Reagents

5. (a) Reagent grade chemicals shall be used in all tests, except as specifically noted for preparation of reference buffer solutions described in Paragraph (c).

purity to permit its use without lessening the accuracy of the determination.

(b) Unless otherwise indicated, references to water shall be understood to mean reagent water conforming to Specifications for Reagent Water (ASTM Designation: D 1193).[3] The water used for the preparation of the reference

---

[4] "Reagent Chemicals, American Chemical Society Specifications," Am. Chemical Soc., Washington, D. C. For suggestions on the testing of reagents not listed by the American Chemical Society, see "Reagent Chemicals and Standards," by Joseph Rosin, D. Van Nostrand Co., Inc., New York, N. Y. and the "United States Pharmacopeia."

buffer solutions of Paragraphs (c), (d), (e), (f), (g), and (h) shall be of referee grade. In addition, the water used for the reference buffer solutions of Paragraphs (c), (d) and (e) shall be boiled for 15 min or purged with air free of carbon dioxide and shall be protected with a soda-lime tube or equivalent while cooling and storing. Precautions shall be taken to prevent contamination

Standards. Table IV identifies the buffer salts by their NBS numbers. Subject the buffer salts to a drying procedure prior to use only as recommended in Table IV. Keep the five reference buffer solutions with pH less than 9.5 in bottles of chemically resistant glass or polyethylene. Keep the calcium hydroxide solution in a polyethylene bottle. Keep the reference buffer solutions well

TABLE III.—pH OF REFERENCE BUFFER SOLUTIONS.[a]

Temperature, deg C	Tetroxalate Solution	Tartrate Solution	Phthalate Solution	Phosphate Solution	Borax Solution	Calcium Hydroxide Solution
0...................	1.67	....	4.00	6.98	9.46	13.42
5...................	1.67	....	4.00	6.95	9.40	13.21
10...................	1.67	....	4.00	6.92	9.33	13.00
15...................	1.67	....	4.00	6.90	9.28	12.81
20...................	1.68	....	4.00	6.88	9.23	12.63
25...................	1.68	3.56	4.01	6.87	9.18	12.45
30...................	1.68	3.55	4.02	6.85	9.14	12.29
35...................	1.69	3.55	4.02	6.84	9.10	12.13
40...................	1.69	3.55	4.04	6.84	9.07	11.98
45...................	1.70	3.55	4.05	6.83	9.04	11.84
50...................	1.71	3.55	4.06	6.83	9.01	11.71
55...................	1.72	3.55	4.08	6.83	8.99	11.57
60...................	1.72	3.56	4.09	6.84	8.96	11.45
70...................	1.74	3.58	4.13	6.85	8.92	....
80...................	1.77	3.61	4.16	6.86	8.89	....
90...................	1.79	3.65	4.21	6.88	8.85	....
95...................	1.81	3.67	4.23	6.89	8.83	....

[a] For a discussion of the manner in which these pH values were assigned, see R. G. Bates, "Revised Standard Values for pH Measurements from 0 to 95 C," *Journal of Research*, Nat. Bureau Standards, Vol. 66A, p. 179 (1962).

of the water with traces of the material used for protection against carbon dioxide. The pH of the carbon dioxide-free water shall be between 6.5 and 7.5 at 25 C.

(c) *Reference Buffer Solutions.*—The pH_s values of six recommended reference buffer solutions at several temperatures are listed in Table III.[5] Prepare five of these solutions from highly purified buffer salts sold specifically for this purpose by the National Bureau of

[5] Solutions used for standardization purposes only.

stoppered and replace them at an age of three months, or sooner if a visible change should occur in the solution.

(d) *Borax Reference Buffer Solution* (pH_s = 9.18 at 25 C).—Dissolve 3.80 g of sodium tetraborate decahydrate ($Na_2B_4O_7 \cdot 10H_2O$) in water and dilute to 1 liter.

(e) *Calcium Hydroxide Reference Buffer Solution* (pH_s = 12.45 at 25 C).—Prepare pure calcium hydroxide ($Ca(OH)_2$) from well-washed calcium carbonate ($CaCO_3$) of low-alkali grade by slowly heating the carbonate in a platinum dish at 1000 C and igniting for at least 45 min at that temperature. After cooling, add the calcined product slowly to water with stirring, heat the resultant suspension to boiling, cool, and filter through a funnel having a fritted-glass disk of medium porosity. Collect the solid from the filter, dry it in an oven at 110 C, and crush it to a uniform finely granular state. Vigorously shake a considerable excess of the finely granular product with water at 25 C in a stoppered polyethylene bottle. Allow the gross excess of solid to settle and filter the solution with suction through a fritted-glass funnel of medium porosity.

vigorously an excess of potassium hydrogen tartrate ($KHC_4H_4O_6$) with 100 to 300 ml of water at 25 C in a glass-stoppered bottle. Filter, if necessary, to remove suspended salt. Add a crystal of thymol (about 0.1 g) as a preservative.

(*i*) *Tetroxalate Reference Buffer Solution*, (pH_s = *1.68 at 25 C*).—Dissolve 12.61 g of potassium tetroxalate dihydrate ($KHC_2O_4 \cdot H_2C_2O_4 \cdot 2H_2O$) in water and dilute to 1 liter.

(*j*) *Other Buffer Solutions.*—A buffer solution of composition identical to one of the reference buffer solutions of Paragraphs (*c*) through (*i*) but of buffer material or solution source other than

TABLE IV.—NATIONAL BUREAU OF STANDARDS (NBS) MATERIALS FOR REFERENCE BUFFER SOLUTIONS.

NBS Standard Sample Designation[a]	Buffer Salt	Drying Procedure
187..................	Borax (sodium tetraborate deca-hydrate)	Drying not necessary (this salt should not be oven-dried)
186—II..............	Disodium hydrogen phosphate	2 hr in oven at 130 C
186—I...............	Potassium dihydrogen phosphate	2 hr in oven at 130 C
185..................	Potassium hydrogen phthalate	Drying not necessary
188..................	Potassium hydrogen tartrate	Drying not necessary
189..................	Potassium tetroxalate dihydrate	Should not be dried

[a] The buffer salts listed can be purchased from the U. S. Department of Commerce, National Bureau of Standards, Washington 25, D. C.

The filtrate is the reference buffer solution. Contamination of the solution with atmospheric carbon dioxide renders it turbid and is a cause for replacement.

(*f*) *Phosphate Reference Buffer Solution* (pH_s = *6.86 at 25 C*).—Dissolve 3.39 g of potassium dihydrogen phosphate (KH_2PO_4) and 3.53 g of anhydrous disodium hydrogen phosphate (Na_2HPO_4) in water and dilute to 1 liter.

(*g*) *Phthalate Reference Buffer Solution* (pH_s = *4.01 at 25 C*).—Dissolve 10.12 g of potassium hydrogen phthalate ($KHC_8H_4O_4$) in water and dilute to 1 liter.

(*h*) *Tartrate Reference Buffer Solution* (pH_s = *3.56 at 25 C*).—Shake

that specified may be used as a working standard in the method providing in each case such a solution is first checked against the corresponding reference buffer solution, using the procedures of the method, and is found to differ by not more than 0.02 pH.

Sampling

6. Collect the sample in accordance with the applicable method of the American Society for Testing and Materials, as follows:

D   510—Sampling Industrial Water,[3]
D   860—Sampling Water from Boilers,[3]
D 1066—Sampling Steam,[3] and
D 1496—Sampling Homogeneous Industrial Waste Water.[3]

Standardization of Assembly

7. (*a*) Turn on the instrument, allow it to warm up thoroughly, and bring it to electrical balance in accordance with the manufacturer's instructions. Wash the glass and reference electrodes and the sample cup with three changes of water or by means of a flowing stream from a wash bottle. Form a fresh liquid junction if a sleeve-type junction is used. Note the temperature of the test (unknown) solution and adjust the temperature dial of the meter to correspond.

(*b*) If the anticipated pH of the test solution is less than 10.0, select the two reference buffer solutions the pH$_s$ values of which are close to the anticipated pH and bracket this pH if possible (see Appendix, Section A3(*a*)). Warm or cool these reference solutions as necessary to match within 2 C the temperature of the unknown. Fill the sample cup with the first reference buffer solution and immerse the electrodes. In type I meters set the dial of the meter to equal the pH$_s$ value of the reference buffer solution at the temperature of the test, as read from Table III or interpolated from the data therein. Engage the operating button and rotate the standardization knob or asymmetry potential knob until the meter is brought to balance. In type II meters engage the operating button, turn the range switch if present to the proper position, and rotate the asymmetry potential knob until the reading of the dial corresponds to the known pH$_s$ of the reference buffer solution. Empty the sample cup and refill it with successive portions of the reference buffer solution and repeat the above procedure until two successive instrument readings are obtained, without changing the setting of the asymmetry potential knob, which readings differ from the pH$_s$ value of the buffer solution by not more than 0.02 pH. If the temperature of the electrodes differs appreciably from that of the solution, use several portions of solution and immerse the electrodes deeply to assure that both the electrodes and the solution are at the desired temperature. In doing this the level of the potassium chloride solution in the reference electrode must always be kept higher than that of the measured solution. To reduce the effects of thermal and electrical hysteresis, the temperature of electrodes, reference buffer solutions, and wash water should be kept as close to that of the unknown as possible.

(*c*) Wash the electrodes and sample cup three times with water. Place the second reference buffer solution in the sample cup, and measure the pH, either by simply reading the dial in the type II meter or by adjusting the balance point in the type I meter. Do not change the setting of the asymmetry knob in either case. Use additional portions of the second reference buffer solution, as before, until two successive readings differ by not more than 0.02 pH. The assembly shall be judged to be operating satisfactorily if the pH reading obtained for the second reference buffer solution agrees with its assigned pH$_s$ value within 0.03 unit for type I meters and 0.05 unit for type II meters.

(*d*) If the anticipated pH of the test solution is greater than 10.0, use the high-alkalinity type of electrode and observe the manufacturer's instructions. Use the borax reference buffer solution for initial standardization of the assembly. If the temperature of measurement is below 60 C use the calcium hydroxide reference buffer solution as the second standard. Since the pH$_s$ of this second solution changes significantly with temperature, note the temperature of the solution to the nearest degree Centigrade and use this reading to obtain the applicable pH_s by interpolation of the data of Table III. Judge the assembly to be operating satisfactorily if the reading obtained for the second reference solution does not differ from the assigned pH_s of this solution by more than 0.1. If the temperature of measurement is above 60 C and the pH greater than 10.0, standardize the instrument with borax solution alone, but beforehand check on the correct functioning of the high-alkalinity electrode by use of the two reference solutions at some temperature below 60 C (See Appendix, Section A4.(a) and (b)).

(e) If only an occasional pH determination is made, standardize the assembly each time it is used. In a long series of measurements, supplement initial and final standardizations by interim checks at regular intervals. Inasmuch as commercially available pH assemblies exhibit different degrees of measurement stability, carry out these checks at intervals of 30 min, unless it is ascertained that less frequent checking is satisfactory to ensure the performance described in Paragraphs (b) and (c). If the assembly is automatic and in continuous use under flowing conditions, standardize daily, using two reference buffer solutions to check the proper functioning of the electrodes, unless here again it is ascertained that less frequent checking is satisfactory to assure the performance described in Paragraphs (b) and (c).

Procedure

8. (a) *pH Determination of Batch Samples.*—After the assembly has been standardized with two reference buffer solutions as described in Section 7, wash the electrodes with three changes of water or by means of a flowing stream from a wash bottle. Place the sample in a clean glass beaker provided with a thermometer. If the measurement is made outside the electrode compartment of the pH meter, equip the beaker with a small laboratory-type mechanical stirrer having a glass agitator or with a magnetic stirring unit having an inert plastic impeller (see Appendix, Section A4(e)). Operate the stirrer during the period of pH measurement at a rate to prevent splashing and to avoid errors through sample loss or gain of acid or basic gases by interchange with the atmosphere, but when necessary, briskly enough to intermix the phases of a nonhomogeneous test solution. Insert the electrodes and determine a preliminary pH value. This value may drift somewhat and should be considered an estimated value. Measure successive portions of the sample until readings on two successive portions differ by no more than 0.03 unit, and show drifts of less than 0.02 unit in 1 min. In the case of well-buffered samples, two or three portions will usually be sufficient. Record the pH and temperature of the sample.

(b) Measure the pH of reagent water and slightly buffered solutions that are in equilibrium with air as described in Paragraph (a), except that the pH of successive portions of sample are measured, with agitation, until the observed results for two successive portions differ by no more than 0.1 unit. Six or more portions may be necessary. If the water sample or slightly buffered test solution is not in equilibrium with carbon dioxide of the atmosphere, make the measurements with externally mounted electrodes in a wide-mouth flask that has been flushed with carbon dioxide-free air. Protect the contents of the flask from exposure to air during the measurement. Because of experimental difficulties and possible uncertainties in making batch measurements on unbuffered or slightly buffered samples, a flow-type measurement as described in Paragraphs (c), (d), and (e) is preferred for such sample materials. The Appendix, Paragraph A4(c), describes precautions that should be taken if the electrical conductivity[6] of the sample is less than about 5 micromhos per cm.

(c) *pH Determination of Flowing Samples.*—Flow cells with accompanying electrode units are an important feature of industrial pH control. In conjunction with electronic recorders and recorder-controllers, they provide the continuous measurements necessary for fully automatic regulation of pH. The flow cell is particularly advantageous for the determination of the pH of water or of sparingly buffered solutions, but must be judiciously used where the test solution is of low conductivity. Simple dip measurements without agitation are subject to appreciable errors from inadequate washing of the electrodes, solubility of the glass, and absorption of carbon dioxide during the measurement. A rapid flow of solution past the electrode maintains a clean glass interface, retards the tendency for fine solids to collect at the surface, minimizes errors resulting from solubility of the glass, and protects the sample from atmospheric contaminants.

(d) The flow cell unit may be of metal, glass, rubber, or plastic (see Appendix, Section A4(d)). If of metal it should not have welded joints, and pipe connections if employed should all be of the same metal as the flow cell. The volume of the flow cell should be small to afford proper exchange of solution in contact with the electrodes. Provide means for monitoring the temperature of the solutions. Use equipment and leads that are free from tendency to pick up interfering electrical

charges. Observe special instructions as may be furnished by the manufacturer.

(e) In measuring the pH of flowing samples of water and slightly buffered solutions, maintain a flow rate sufficient to change the solution in the cell five times per minute. Do not read until the sample flow has been continued for at least 15 min subsequent to the standardization treatment of the electrodes in the reference buffer solution, or until a drift of less than 0.1 pH unit in 2 min is observed. If the pH of the flowing solution is changing, the glass electrode measurement may lag behind the true pH. Record the pH and temperature of the sample solution. If the electrical conductivity[6] of the sample is less than about 5 micromhos per cm, measurement errors can arise from streaming potentials, especially if the sample flow rate is excessive. Precautions in dealing with this problem are given in the Appendix, Section A4(d).

Calculation

9. (a) If the meter is calibrated in pH units the pH of the sample is obtained directly by reading the meter scale. If the meter reading is in voltage units, the pH of the sample is calculated by using the equation given in Section 2(b). The pH_s value for the calculation shall be selected to represent the reference buffer solution that is the closer in pH to that of the sample being determined.

Report

10. (a) Report the temperature of measurement to the nearest degree Centigrade. In all measurements except as noted below, report the pH of the test solution to the nearest 0.01 pH unit. Report the pH of the test solution to the nearest 0.1 pH unit when measurements are made under any one or more of the following circumstances: when measurements are made on reagent water or unbuffered solutions, when the pH is less

---

[6] See the Method of Test for Electrical Conductivity of Industrial Water and Industrial Waste Water (ASTM Designation: D 1125), which appears in this publication.

than 1.0 or greater than 12.0, where it may be necessary at high pH to standardize with the borax reference buffer solution only, and when measurements are made continuously and automatically on flowing samples.

Precision

11. (a) Because of the wide variability in measurement conditions and because of the changeable character of the pH of certain solutions, the precision of this method is 0.1 pH unit.

APPENDIX

MISCELLANEOUS NOTES ON GLASS ELECTRODE MEASUREMENTS AND EQUIPMENT

Meaning of the Term pH

A1. The term pH historically has referred to the hydrogen ion property of a solution and has been expressed as the logarithm to the base 10 of the reciprocal (negative logarithm) of the activity of hydrogen ions at a given temperature, as follows:

$$pH = \log 1/(H^+) = -\log (H^+)$$

where (H^+) = activity of hydrogen ions. Although this expression is helpful in giving meaning to the term pH and can be used as an approximate definition, it can not be rigorously upheld when applied to practical pH measurements. Accordingly it is desirable to establish a definition that can be upheld in terms of operations and calculations. The definition given in Section 2(a) is of this type and has gained wide acceptance.

Reference Electrodes

A2. (a) In making pH measurements with the glass electrode, the reference electrode used to complete the cell assembly functions simply as a source of reproducible potential. The absolute value of the reference electrode potential is of no consequence because of the way the measurements are made. The saturated calomel electrode has proven itself over the years to be a very satisfactory reference electrode system for measurements at constant or approximately constant temperature. This type of reference electrode is thus recommended for measurements at normal room temperatures, although other types of reference electrodes such as the silver-silver chloride electrode will also serve satisfactorily under these conditions.

(b) If a saturated electrode is used under significantly changeable temperature conditions, care must be taken to see that sufficient solid potassium chloride is present at all temperatures of use to ensure solution saturation throughout, both in the free solution in the electrode tube and in the solution permeating the electrode

element. Also before making measurements five or ten minutes or longer must be allowed for the electrode to accommodate itself to the new temperature condition. If the temperature falls appreciably, precipitation of potassium chloride may cause plugging of the liquid junction and hence may introduce a high resistance and a false potential at the junction. Any such accumulation of potassium chloride should be removed immediately.

(c) Reference electrodes of the unsaturated type have been used successfully in continuous, automatic pH recording applications where the temperature is likely to fluctuate. The solution concentration is established at a value equal to the potassium chloride concentration at saturation at the lowest temperature of use (for example, approximately 3.3 N for 0 C). Such a reference electrode system has the advantage of being free from the annoying effects caused by variable solubility, but entails some trouble to prepare the solution of required concentration and to keep it at the prescribed concentration value under plant conditions. It is advisable to follow the instrument manufacturer's recommendations in the matter of choosing and maintaining reference electrodes, as well as in other details of the equipment. Do not attempt to change an electrode from the saturated type to the unsaturated type (or vice versa) by merely changing the type of potassium chloride solution used.

Faulty Glass Electrode Response and Restorative Techniques

A3. (a) Detecting Faulty Electrodes.—The pH measuring assembly is standardized with two reference buffer solutions as described in Section 8 to check the linearity of response of the electrode combination at different pH values and to detect a faulty glass or reference electrode or an incorrect temperature compensation. The presence of a faulty electrode is indicated by failure to obtain a reasonably correct value for the pH of the second reference buffer solution after the meter has been standardized with the first. A cracked glass electrode will often yield pH readings that are essentially the same for both standards and should be discarded. It should be noted that although a normal glass electrode responds remarkably well to pH changes it is not necessarily a perfect pH measuring device and may slightly miss the requirements of Section 7 (c) if, for example, the pH span is made as great as 5 pH units (phthalate to borax).

(b) *Imperfect pH Response.*—In addition to the interferences mentioned in Paragraph A.4(a), the pH-responsive property of the glass electrode may be impaired by a few specific substances such as certain oily materials, some precipitates, and possibly certain dissolved constituents. A faulty condition will be recognized from the check with the two reference buffer solutions. If this should occur the electrode can likely be restored to normal by an appropriate cleaning procedure.

(c) *Glass Electrode Cleaning Techniques.*— Where emulsions of free oil and water are to be measured for pH, it is absolutely necessary that the electrodes be cleaned thoroughly after each measurement. This may be done by washing with soap or detergent and water, followed by several rinses with water, after which the lower third of the electrodes should be immersed in hydrochloric acid (HCl, 1:9) for 10 min to remove any film that may have formed. The electrode should be thoroughly rinsed by washing it in several changes of water before returning it to service.

(d) Where the sample contains sticky soaps, suspended particles, or precipitates, thorough cleaning after each measurement may be necessary. This may be done by using a solvent such as alcohol or benzol to clean the electrodes. If this fails, a chemical treatment designed to dissolve the particular deposited coating may prove successful. After final rinsing of the electrode in the solvent used, the lower third of the electrodes should be immersed in HCl (1:9) for 10 min to remove any film that may have formed. The electrode should be washed thoroughly in several changes of water, before subjecting it to the buffer checking procedure.

(e) If an electrode has failed to respond to the treatments suggested in Paragraphs (c) and (d), more drastic measures may be tried. A poisoned electrode can often be rejuvenated by treating it in chromic acid cleaning solution for a period of several minutes or longer if necessary. This treatment is particularly effective in cleaning foreign substances from the surface of the glass, but has the disadvantage of exerting a dehydrating effect on the glass. Consequently an electrode so treated, after thorough rinsing, should be allowed to stand in water overnight before using it to make measurements. Certain types of electrodes may not need so prolonged a period of water reconditioning and may be ready for making measurements after only 10 or 20 min of soaking. If the electrode fails to respond to the chromic acid cleaning solution treatment it may be subjected to a mild etching treatment in ammonium bifluoride solution. The electrode should be immersed for about 1 min in a 20 per cent solution of ammonium bifluoride (NH_4HF_2) in water, contained in a polyethylene cup. Since this treatment actually removes a portion of the bulb glass, it should be used only as a last resort and then only infrequently. Following the fluoride etch treatment an electrode should be thoroughly rinsed and conditioned as recommended for a new electrode.

Special Measurement Techniques

A4. (a) *Measurements on Alkaline Solutions.* —Although the high-alkalinity electrode exhibits a much lower sodium ion error than an ordinary glass electrode, the high-alkalinity electrode can nevertheless introduce an appreciable error when the sodium ion content and the pH or temperature of the solution are unusually high. If sodium ion error data are available from the electrode manufacturer, appropriate corrections may be applied to the measurement.

(b) With alkaline solutions, both in the standardization procedure and in the measurement of actual samples, there is a tendency for carbon dioxide of the air to react with the solution and hence to change its pH. For this reason all measurements with alkaline solutions should be made as promptly as possible and with the solution exposed to the air no longer than is absolutely necessary.

(c) *Batch Measurements on Test Solutions of Low Conductivity.*—In making measurements on samples having an electrical conductivity[6] lower than about 5 micromhos per cm the net electrical resistance of the sample interposed between the glass and reference electrodes may become high enough in value to introduce measuring difficulties. The junction of the reference electrode should be placed as close as possible to the pH-responsive bulb of the glass electrode. If this does not correct the difficulties, the sample should be protected from electrostatic charges by surrounding the nonconducting sample vessel with a grounded metallic shield.

(d) *Flow Measurements on Test Solutions of Low Conductivity.*—In making measurements on flowing samples having an electrical conductivity[6] lower than about 5 micromhos per cm, precautions must be taken to avoid difficulties from streaming potentials and interferences as noted in Paragraph (c). If available, special information from the instrument manufacturer regarding such measurements should be observed. It is desirable that the flow chamber be made of a conductive material such as stainless steel and that it be grounded. If for some reason a nonconductive flow cell is used, it is especially helpful to mount the electrode tips close together and with the line through the tips at right angles to the sample flow path. Because streaming potential increases with flow velocity, it is advisable to adjust the sample flow rate at a value not exceeding that needed to keep the flow cell properly flushed. This can be done by conveying the sample water to the flow cell through a short line leading from a constant-head overflow chamber. The line to the cell should be provided with suitable flow-controlling means.

(e) *Magnetic Stirring.*—Do not use magnetic stirring in those few instances where it may have an effect on pH measurement.

Tentative Methods of Test for
SULFITE ION IN INDUSTRIAL WATER[1]

ASTM Designation: D 1339 – 62 T
ISSUED, 1954; REVISED, 1962

These Tentative Methods have been approved by the sponsoring committee and accepted by the Society in accordance with established procedures for use pending adoption as standard. Suggestions for Revisions should be addressed to the Society at 1916 Race St., Philadelphia 3, Pa.

Scope

1. (*a*) These methods cover the volumetric determination of sulfite in industrial water. Three methods are given as follows:

	Range	Section
Referee Method A.	to 6 ppm Na_2SO_3	5 to 12
Referee Method B.	6 ppm Na_2SO_3 or higher	13 to 20
Non-Referee Method C......	3 ppm Na_2SO_3 or higher	21 to 27

(*b*) Method B may be used as a non-referee method for samples containing less than 6 ppm Na_2SO_3; the end point may then be determined with starch indicator.

Definitions

2. For definitions of terms used in these methods refer to the Definitions of Terms Relating to Industrial Water and Industrial Waste Water (ASTM Designation: D 1129).[2]

Purity of Reagents

3. (*a*) Reagent grade chemicals shall be used in all tests. Unless otherwise indicated, it is intended that all reagents shall conform to the specifications of the Committee on Analytical Reagents of the American Chemical Society, where such specifications are available.[3] Other grades may be used, provided it is first ascertained that the reagent is of sufficiently high purity to permit its use without lessening the accuracy of the determination.

(*b*) Unless otherwise indicated, references to water shall be understood to mean reagent water conforming to the Specifications for Reagent Water (ASTM

---

[2] Appears in this publication.
[3] "Reagent Chemicals, American Chemical Society Specifications," Am. Chemical Soc., Washington, D. C. For suggestions on the testing of reagents not listed by the American Chemical Society, see "Reagent Chemicals and Standards," by Joseph Rosin, D. Van Nostrand Co., Inc., New York, N. Y. and the "United States Pharmacopeia."

---

[1] Under the standardization procedure of the Society, these methods are under the jurisdiction of the ASTM Committee D-19 on Industrial Water. A list of members may be found in the ASTM Year Book.

Designation: D 1193).[2] In addition, reagent water used for these methods shall be sulfite-free.

Sampling

4. Special sampling instructions are included in Methods A and B. For Method C, collect a cooled (15 to 20 C), fresh, air-free sample in accordance with he applicable method of the American tociety for Testing and Materials, as follows:

D 510—Sampling Industrial Water,[2]
D 860—Sampling Water from Boilers.[2]

sulfides and certain heavy-metal ions react like sulfite with the iodine chloride and cause high results. Nitrite, if present, will oxidize sulfite when the sample is acidified.

Apparatus

8. (a) *Sample Tubes.*—Glass sample tubes as shown in Fig. 1, having a nominal capacity of 500 ml. The capacity of each tube shall be determined to the nearest milliliter.

(b) *Burets.*—Four 10-ml burets, having a stopcock bore not greater than 2 mm

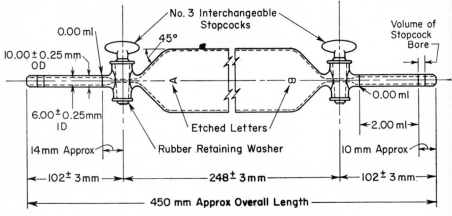

FIG. 1.—500–ml Sample Tube for Sulfite Determination.[4]

REFEREE METHOD A

Application

5. This method is applicable to the determination of sulfite ion in industrial water, especially boiler water and boiler feedwater, in which the range of sulfite ion concentration is 0.1 to 6 ppm.

Summary of Method

6. The sample is taken in a tube of special design to exclude air until the sulfite has been reacted with iodine chloride. The excess iodine chloride is determined by titration with thiosulfate. The range of the method is limited by reagent concentrations.

Interferences

7. Other reducing agents such as

and a maximum tip diameter not exceeding 3 mm.

(c) *Stirrer.*—A variable-speed motor-driven stirrer with a glass propeller.

(d) *Electrometric Dead Stop Indicating Apparatus,*[5] equipped with platinum

---

[4] McLean-type sampling tube, as modified by the Engineering Experiment Station, U. S. Navy, and by the Heat Exchange Institute. This figure is the same as Fig. 1 of the Methods of Test for Dissolved Oxygen in Industrial Water (ASTM Designation: D 888), which appears in this publication.

[5] R. C. Ulmer, J. M. Reynar, and J. M. Decker, "Applicability of the Schwartz-Gurney Method for Determining Dissolved Oxygen in Boiler Feedwater and Modification of the Method to Make It Especially Applicable in the Presence of Such Impurities as are Encountered in Power Plants," *Proceedings*, Am. Soc. Testing Mats., vol. 43, pp. 1261–1263 (1943).

electrodes, such that the assembly is sensitive to the addition of 0.05 ml of 0.005 N sodium thiosulfate (Na_2SO_3) to 500 ml of water.

Reagents

9. (*a*) *Hydrochloric Acid* (*1:1*).—Mix 1 volume of concentrated hydrochloric acid (HCl, sp gr 1.19) with 1 volume of water.

(*b*) *Potassium Dichromate.*—Heat potassium dichromate ($K_2Cr_2O_7$) in a platinum crucible to a temperature just above its fusion point (396 C), taking care to exclude all dust and organic matter. After cooling, crush the fused salt to a powder in an agate mortar and preserve in a glass-stoppered bottle.

(*c*) *Potassium Iodate, Standard Solution* (*0.025 N*).—Dissolve "x" g of potassium iodate (KIO_3), dried at 120 C, and 0.5 g of sodium bicarbonate ($NaHCO_3$) in water and dilute to 1 liter. ("x" = 8.92 times the normality of the standard sodium thiosulfate solution (Paragraph(*f*)).

(*d*) *Potassium Iodide.*—Potassium iodide (KI) such that no blue color will be obtained when 1 g is dissolved in freshly boiled water treated with 5 drops of 1 N sulfuric acid (H_2SO_4) and 1 ml of freshly prepared starch solution.

(*e*) *Potassium Iodide Solution* (*50 g per liter*).—Dissolve 50 g of iodate-free KI and 0.5 g of sodium bicarbonate ($NaHCO_3$) in freshly boiled and cooled water and dilute to 1 liter.

(*f*) *Sodium Thiosulfate, Standard Solution* (*0.10 N*).—Using a 1000-ml volumetric flask, dissolve 24.82 g of sodium thiosulfate ($Na_2S_2O_3 \cdot 5H_2O$) in approximately 800 ml of water that has just been boiled and cooled, and invert the flask at regular short intervals until the solid is dissolved. Stabilize the solution by dissolving in it in the same manner 1 g of sodium carbonate (Na_2CO_3), and make

up to 1 liter with the boiled water. Standardize against $K_2Cr_2O_7$ as follows:

Dissolve 2 g of iodate-free KI and 2 g of $NaHCO_3$ in 300 ml of water in a 500-ml Erlenmeyer flask and add hydrochloric acid (HCl, sp gr 1.19) slowly, while swirling the flask, until carbon dioxide (CO_2) gas evolution ceases. Add 10 ml excess of HCl, mix, and then dissolve 0.098 g of dried $K_2Cr_2O_7$. Wash down the inside of the flask with a small amount of water without agitating the flask, and allow to stand for 10 min. Titrate with the $Na_2S_2O_3$ solution, using starch solution as the indicator, until the color just changes from blue to the green color of the chromic salt.

Calculate the normality of the $Na_2S_2O_3$ solution as follows:

$$N = \frac{A}{49.04B} \times 1000$$

where:

N = normality of the $Na_2S_2O_3$ solution,

A = grams of potassium dichromate used, and

B = milliliters of $Na_2S_2O_3$ solution required for the titration.

(*g*) *Sodium Thiosulfate, Standard Solution* (*0.005 N*).—Transfer 25 ml of the 0.10 N $Na_2S_2O_3$ solution to a 500-ml volumetric flask. Dilute to the mark with water and mix completely. This solution should be prepared not more than 12 to 15 hr before using.

(*h*) *Starch Indicator.*—Make a paste of 1 g of arrowroot starch or soluble iodometric starch with cold water. Pour the paste into 100 ml of boiling water and boil for several minutes. Store in a glass-stoppered bottle in a cool place. Starch solution prepared in this manner will remain chemically stable for 2 or 3 days.

Procedure

10. (*a*) *Sampling.*—Arrange the sample tube in a support so that it is vertical, with its upper outlet free of hose connec-

tions and at a level higher than the valve for adjustment of sample flow. Connect the lower end to the sampling line by means of rubber tubing. The sampling line shall contain a suitable cooling coil if the water being sampled is above room temperature, in which case the sample shall be cooled to ambient-air temperature. If a cooling coil is used, the valve for cooling-water adjustment shall be at the inlet to the cooling coil, and the overflow shall be to a point of lower elevation. The valve for adjusting the flow of sample shall be at the outlet from the cooling coil. Adjust the sample to a rate that will fill the tube in 40 to 60 sec, and continue this flow long enough to provide at least ten changes of water in the sampling tube. If the sampling line is used intermittently, allow a suitably longer time for the first sample to ensure adequate flushing of the sampling line and cooling coil. Close the upper stopcock of the tube, and immediately close the lower stopcock and remove the tubing connection.

If the line being sampled is under such high pressure that the sampling tubes or connecting tubing may burst with the water hammer when the stopcocks are closed, throttle the sample flow with the control valve just before the sample is removed, but do not shut off the sample flow completely.

(b) *Fixing.*—Fill the three burets with HCl (1:1), KI solution, and 0.025 N KIO$_3$ solution, respectively. Flick the water from the upper nipple of the sample tube and fill the nipple to the upper calibration mark with HCl. If a bubble is entrapped in the nipple within or below the reagent, remove it by probing with a clean platinum wire until the bubble rises to the surface. Open the lower stopcock and admit the reagent by control with the upper stopcock until the meniscus in the nipple coincides with the lower calibration mark. If the

sample contains more than 800 ppm of NaOH, add 2 ml more of acid for each 1000 ppm of alkalinity or fraction thereof in excess of 800 ppm. Close both stopcocks and rinse both nipples with a fine stream of water. Mix the contents by shaking or rotation, and flick out the excess water from each nipple. Invert the tube and fill what is now the upper nipple with KI solution to the 2-ml calibration mark. Introduce the solution into the sample, repeating the stopcock control, the rinsing of both nipples, the shaking and rotating, and the flicking of water from the nipples. Again invert the tube and now introduce 2.0 ml of 0.025 N KIO$_3$ solution into the sample following the directions given above for adding the reagents and rinsing the nipples. Once more, shake and rotate the tube to mix the sample thoroughly.

(c) *Titration of Sample.*—Invert the sample tube and drain the sample into a clean 800-ml griffin low-form beaker by opening both stopcocks. Do not rinse or blow into the sampling tube, but shake the last drops from the nipple into the beaker. Add several drops of starch indicator to indicate the approach of the end point. Insert the electrodes of the electrometric dead-stop indicating apparatus into the sample, start the stirrer at low speed, and titrate the excess iodine chloride with 0.005 N Na$_2$S$_2$O$_3$ solution.

(d) *Determination of Blank.*—Make a blank titration of 500 ml of water containing no sulfite, to which have been added the three reagents that were added to the sample in Paragraph (b) (Note).

Note.—Alternately, if such tubes are available, one sample of 500 ml and one sample of 250 ml are collected simultaneously, fixed as described in Paragraph (b), and titrated as described in paragraph (c). The difference in the net amounts of 0.025 N KIO$_3$ solution used up by the sulfite content of the two samples will be the sulfite-ion equivalent of a 250-ml sample.

Calculation

11. (*a*) Calculate the concentration of sulfite, as parts per million of sodium sulfite (Na_2SO_3), as follows:

$$\text{Sulfite as } Na_2SO_3, \text{ ppm}, = \frac{63000N\ (10-A)}{S}$$

where:

N = normality of the $Na_2S_2O_3$ solution,

A = blank-corrected volume in milliliters of $Na_2S_2O_3$ solution required for titration of the excess of iodine, and

S = sampling-tube volume in milliliters minus 6.

(*b*) To convert parts per million of sodium sulfite to parts per million of sulfite ion, multiply by 0.635.

Precision[6]

12. The precision of the method is 0.2 ppm Na_2SO_3.

Referee Method B

Application

13. This method is applicable to the determination of sulfite ion in industrial water, especially boiler water and boiler feedwater, in which the sulfite concentration is higher than 6 ppm.

Summary of Method

14. Provision is made for the excluding of air from the sample while it is being taken. Potassium iodate is then added to form iodine chloride with potassium iodide and hydrochloric acid to oxidize the sulfite ion. The excess iodine chloride is titrated with sodium thiosulfate, using an electrometric indicator to show the end point.

Interferences

15. High results may be caused by the presence of other reducing materials such

---

[6] Supporting data have been filed at ASTM Headquarters.

as sulfide and ferrous iron. Low results may be caused by catalysts such as cobalt and copper that promote rapid oxidation of sulfite when the sample is exposed to air. Nitrite, if present, will oxidize sulfite when the sample is acidified.

Apparatus

16. (*a*) *Erlenmeyer Flask*, wide-mouth, 500-ml, fitted with inlet, outlet, and

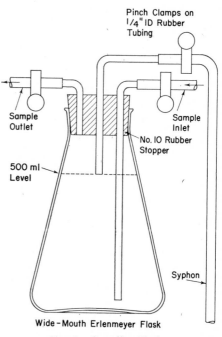

Fig. 2.—Sampling Flask.

syphon-leveling connections, as shown in Fig. 2.

(*b*) *Magnetic Stirring Apparatus*, with swinging support if electrometric end point-indicating apparatus is used.

(*c*) *Endpoint-Indicating Apparatus.*— See Section 8(*d*). This apparatus is not necessary for non-referee testing (See Section 1(*b*)).

Reagents

17. (*a*) *Hydrochloric Acid* (*1:1*).— Mix 1 volume of concentrated hydro-

chloric acid (HCl, sp gr 1.19) with 1 volume of water.

(*b*) *Potassium Iodate, Standard Solution (0.05 N).*—Dissolve "x" g of potassium iodate (KIO₃), dried at 120 C. and 0.5 gr of sodium bicarbonate (NaHCO₃) in water and dilute to 500.0 ml ("x" = 8.92 times the normality of the standard sodium thiosulfate solution).

(*c*) *Potassium Iodide (50 gr per liter).*— See Section 9(*e*).

(*d*) *Sodium Thiosulfate, Standard Solution (0.10 N).*—See Section 9(*f*).

(*e*) *Sodium Thiosulfate, Standard Solution (0.01 N).*—Transfer 50 ml of the 0.10 N Na₂S₂O₃ solution to a 500-ml volumetric flask. Dilute to the mark with water and mix completely. This solution should be prepared not more than 12 to 15 hr before using.

(*f*) *Starch Indicator.*—See Section 9(*h*).

Procedure

18. (*a*) Connect the sampling flask to the sampling cooler with rubber tubing so that the sample, at or slightly below room temperature, enters the bottom of the flask and overflows from the top. Overflow an estimated volume of five times the flask volume, allowing the syphon to fill during this step. Then close off the inlet connection and open the syphon to adjust the sample volume to 500 ml.

(*b*) *Fixing.*—Remove the stopper from the flask, set the flask on the magnetic stirrer platform, and operate the stirrer at low speed while 5 ml of HCl, 5 ml of KI, and 5.0 ml of KIO₃ are added immediately and in that order. If the sample contains more than 30 ppm of sulfite, use correspondingly larger amounts of reagents.

(*c*) *Titration.*—Add several drops of starch indicator to indicate the approach of the end point. Insert the electrodes

of the end point indicator into the sample and titrate the excess iodin chloride with 0 01 N Na₂S₂O₃ solution

(*d*) *Determination of Blank.*—Make a blank titration of 500 ml of water con taining no sulfite to which have been added in the same way and in the same volume the reagents used to fix the sample (Paragraph (*b*)).

Calculation

19. Calculate the concentration o sulfite as parts per million of sodium sulfite, as follows:

Sulfite as Na₂SO₃, ppm = 126 N (25 − A

where:

N = normality of the Na₂S₂O₃ solution and

A = blank-corrected volume in milli liters of the Na₂S₂O₃ solution re quired for titration of the excess o iodine chloride.

Precision[7]

20. Studies on the precision of thi method have not been completed.

NON-REFEREE METHOD C

Application

21. This method is particularly applic able for control tests where good pre cision is not required and the sulfite con tent is 3 ppm or higher.

Summary of Method

22. Iodine, liberated by potassium iodate solution, reacts with the sulfite in the water sample. An end point is reached when excess iodine is present, a shown by the blue color produced with starch indicator.

Interferences

23. Catalysts such as copper cause rapid oxidation of sulfite when the

[7] Supporting data will be submitted to ASTM Headquarters when compiled.

sample is exposed to air, and the rate of this reaction increases with temperature. Other reducing agents such as sulfides and ferrous iron will cause high results since they react like sulfite. Nitrite, if present, will oxidize sulfite when the sample is acidified.

Reagents

24. (a) *Hydrochloric acid (1:1).*—Mix 1 volume of concentrated hydrochloric acid (HCl, sp gr 1.19) with 1 volume of water.

(b) *Potassium Iodate, Standard Solution (1 ml = 1 mg Na₂SO₃).*—Dissolve 0.566 g of potassium iodate (KIO₃), dried at 120 C, and 0.5 g of sodium bicarbonate (NaHCO₃) in water, and dilute to 1 liter in a volumetric flask.

(c) *Potassium Iodide Solution (50 g per liter).*—See Section 9(e).

(d) *Starch Indicator.*—See Section 9(h).

Procedure

25. Pour 5 ml of HCl (1:1), into a 250-ml wide-mouth Erlenmeyer flask.

Rapidly pipet 100 ml of fresh sample into the acid, keeping the pipet tip below the surface. Add 1 ml of starch solution and 5 ml of KI solution. Immediately add KIO₃ solution dropwise from a buret while shaking the flask, until the first persistent blue color appears in the sample. Record the volume of KIO₃ solution used as S. Repeat the test, using 100 ml of water instead of sample, and record the volume of KIO₃ solution as B.

Calculation

26. Calculate the concentration of sulfite, as SO_3^{--} and as Na_2SO_3, in parts per million, as follows:

Sulfite as SO_3^{--}, ppm $= 6.35 (S - B)$
Sulfite as Na_2SO_3, ppm $= 10 (S - B)$

where:

S = milliliters of KIO₃ solution required for titration of the sample, and

B = milliliters of KIO₃ solution required for titration of the water blank.

Precision

27. Single operator precision of this method is 1 ppm Na₂ SO₃.

Standard Method of Test for
OILY MATTER IN INDUSTRIAL WASTE WATER[1]

ASTM Designation: D 1340 – 60

ADOPTED, 1956; REVISED, 1960

This Standard of the American Society for Testing and Materials is issued under the fixed designation D 1340; the final number indicates the year of original adoption as standard or, in the case of revision, the year of last revision.

Scope and Application

1. This method[2] covers the determination of oily matter[3] content of industrial waste water.

NOTE 1.—The Joint Committee on Uniformity of Methods of Water Examination has concluded that uniformity of methods for the determination of grease and oily matter is not practicable on the basis of present technical knowledge.

Commonly used solvents are hexane, petroleum ether, benzene, chloroform, or carbon tetrachloride. These solvents exert selective extraction of specific greases and oily constituents. In addition, nonoily materials, such as phenolic type material and colloidal sulfur, are selectively extracted to varying degrees by these solvents. The selectivity of extraction is affected by the sample-to-solvent ratio.

Oily matter and grease may be of mineral, animal, or vegetable origin. The solvent action exerted on material of such different chemical structure will vary to a marked degree. Thus application of a test method for oily matter on grease to such materials will necessarily produce a variety of results depending on the solvent used. In one case, a solvent may be an excellent extractant of mineral oil and a poor extractant of vegetable oil. In another case, a second solvent may be a poor extractant for mineral oil but excellent for extracting vegetable oil.

The definition of grease and oily matter by necessity is based on the procedure used because of the above considerations. The source of the grease or oily matter, the solvent used, the sample-to-solvent ratio, the pH of the sample, and the inclusion of nonoily matter will dictate the material determined and influence the interpretation of the results obtained.

Principle of Method

2. The sample is refluxed through a trap, and the volatile oily matter is collected and measured volumetrically in the reflux trap. The remaining sample is extracted with two successive portions of solvent, using mechanical agitation

[1] Under the standardization procedure of the Society, this method is under the jurisdiction of the ASTM Committee D-19 on Industrial Water. A list of members may be found in the ASTM Year Book.

[2] This method is based on methods developed by the Standard Inspection Laboratories of the Esso Standard Oil Co. and the Sun Oil Co. (see A. F. S. Musante, *Analytical Chemistry*, Vol. 23, pp. 1374–1379 (1951)), and is similar to part of API Method 731–53, "Determination of Volatile and Non-Volatile Oily Material," *Manual on Disposal of Refinery Wastes*, Vol. 4, American Petroleum Institute (1953).

[3] The American Society for Testing and Materials agrees with the conclusion reached in November, 1959, by the Joint Committee on Uniformity of Methods of Water Examination, which states that uniformity of methods for the determination of grease and oily matter is not practicable on the basis of present technical knowledge.

The solvent layer is separated from the water following each extraction, and the extracts are combined and reduced by distillation to remove the solvent. The residue is cooled and weighed, and the calculated results are reported as parts per million by weight.

Definitions

3. (a) The term "oily matter" in this method is defined in accordance

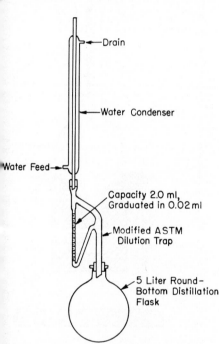

Fig. 1.—Preliminary Distillation Assembly.

with the Standard Definitions of Terms Relating to Industrial Water and Industrial Waste Water (ASTM Designation: D 1129),[4] as follows:

Oily Matter.—Hydrocarbons, hydrocarbon derivatives, and all liquid or unctuous substances that have boiling points of 90 C or above and are extractable from water at pH 5.0, or lower, using benzene as a solvent (Note 2).

---

[4] Appears in this publication.

Note 2.—Chloroform or carbon tetrachloride may be substituted for benzene to avoid fire hazard or emulsion difficulties. The oily matter extracted by these solvents is, for practical purposes, the same material as that extracted by benzene.

(b) For definitions of other terms used in this method, refer to Definitions D 1129.

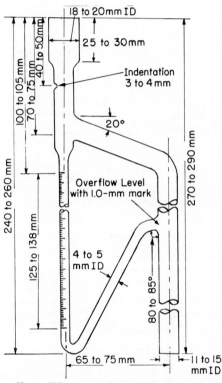

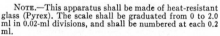

Note.—This apparatus shall be made of heat-resistant glass (Pyrex). The scale shall be graduated from 0 to 2.0 ml in 0.02-ml divisions, and shall be numbered at each 0.2 ml.

Fig. 2.—Modified ASTM-Type Receiver for Oil in Effluent Waters.

Apparatus

4. (a) *Preliminary Distillation Assembly* (see Fig. 1).—The assembly shall consist of a graduated trap[5] connected

---

[5] The receiving trap No. G-20166 and the extraction flask and funnel assembly No. G-20165, available from the Emil Greiner Co., 20-26 N. Moore St., New York 13, N. Y., are satisfactory for this purpose.

to a 5-liter round-bottom flask and to a water-cooled condenser. A detailed drawing of the trap is shown in Fig. 2.

(b) *Extraction Stirrer.*—Any motor having a speed of 2000 to 4000 rpm, and

round-bottom distillation flask by means of a ball-and-socket joint, for use when carbon tetrachloride or chloroform is

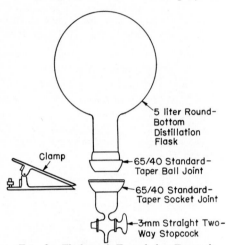

FIG. 3.—Flask and Funnel for Extraction With Carbon Tetrachloride or Chloroform.

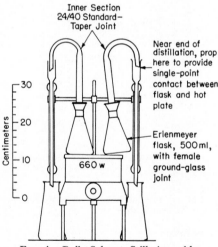

FIG. 4.—Bulk Solvent Still Assembly.

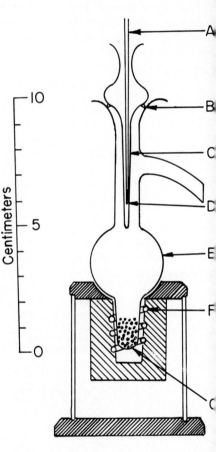

A—Thermocouple, 30 B & S gage wires.
B—Tips on thermowell to provide spacing, which prevent accumulation of condensed solvent.
C—Thin-wall glass capillary thermowell.
D—Thermocouple junction midway between flask and side-arm.
E—Miniature distilling flask, 10-ml capacity, 1 ml in sump.
F—Heating unit, 20-w, 25-v, consisting of 5 ft, 30 B & S gage Chromel wire coiled on ⅛-in. arbor and partially embedded in refractory support. Applied voltage adjusted to maintain temperature in heater between 290 and 300 C.
G—Glass particles, 1-mm size, fused in sump.

FIG. 5.—Miniature Still Assembly.

provided with an impeller small enough to enter the sample flask, may be used.

(c) *Extraction Flask and Funnel Assembly* (see Fig. 3).[5]—A funnel equipped with a stopcock and fitted to a 5-liter,

used as the solvent. The assembly permits inversion of the flask for withdrawing the solvent layer, and eliminates the necessity for transfer of the sample

(d) *Bulk Solvent Still Assembly* (see Fig. 4).—The assembly shall consist of a 500-ml Erlenmeyer flask provided with a 150-mm long, 22-mm diameter unpacked column, a 250-mm West-type condenser, and a 660-w, 6-in. diameter hot plate. Any equivalent assembly will be satisfactory.[6]

(e) *Miniature Still* (see Fig. 5).[6]—A suitable still may be made by enlarging a 28-mm diameter bulb in an 11-mm OD tube. The still should have about 10-ml capacity to the top of the bulb, about 1 ml of which will be in the sump. Particles of broken glass (less than 1 mm in size) shall be fused to the inside wall of the sump wall to promote bubble formation for smooth distillation. A generous flare shall be made at the top for laying the still on its side during weighing without danger of spilling the residual oil.

(f) *Thermowell* (see Fig. 5).[6]—The thermowell shall be constructed from 10-mm tubing by pulling out a thin-wall tube. The cross-sectional dimensions of the tube are not critical, but the mass of the portion of the well extending below the side-arm of the still should be kept low to allow the thermocouple to respond quickly to the rapid temperature changes which occur when the cut point of the distillation is approached. The inside diameter should be just large enough to permit the free movement of a thermocouple constructed of No. 30 B & S gage, enamel-covered wires. Three small tips should be provided on the well to prevent continuous circumferential contact with the flared top edge of the still, thus minimizing the

accumulation of condensed solvent at this point.

(g) *Miniature Still Heater* (see Fig. 5).[6]—A suitable heating element may be made from 5 ft of No. 30 B & S gage, Nichrome V or Chromel A wire, coiled on a ⅛-in. diameter arbor, and partially imbedded in an alundum cement block. Part of the coil shall be exposed to contact the miniature still sump wall. The above heater element is designed to operate at approximately 25 v and, preferably, should be controlled by means of a variable transformer.

(h) *Indicating Pyrometer.*—A calibrated, direct-reading pyrometer covering at least the range of 10 to 300 C.

Purity of Reagents

5. (a) Reagent grade chemicals shall be used in all tests. Unless otherwise indicated, it is intended that all reagents shall conform to the specifications of the Committee on Analytical Reagents of the American Chemical Society, where such specifications are available.[7] Other grades may be used, provided it is first ascertained that the reagent is of sufficiently high purity to permit its use without lessening the accuracy of the determination.

(b) Unless otherwise indicated, references to water shall be understood to mean reagent water conforming to the Specifications for Reagent Water (ASTM Designation: D 1193).[4]

Reagents and Materials

6. (a) *Hydrochloric Acid (sp gr 1.19).*

---

[6] The condenser equivalent to the unpacked column and West-type condenser and the miniature still assembly, including heater, flask, flask stand, thermocouple, and thermowell, available from the Emil Greiner Co., 20-26 N. Moore St., New York 13, N. Y., have been found satisfactory for this purpose. The heaters are also available in single or triple units, the latter with built-in voltmeter.

[7] "Reagent Chemicals, American Chemical Society Specifications," Am. Chem. Soc., Washington, D. C. For suggestions on the testing of reagents not listed by the American Chemical Society, see "Reagent Chemicals and Standards," by Joseph Rosin, D. Van Nostrand Co., Inc., New York, N. Y., and the "United States Pharmacopeia."

(b) *Dispersing Agent*.[8]—Dissolve 10 g of dioctyl sodium sulfosuccinate in 90 ml of water.

(c) *Solvent*.—Benzene, carbon tetra-chloride, or chloroform, any of which shall be distilled so that the residue after evaporation shall be not more than 0.5 mg per 100 ml of solvent.

Sampling

7. Collect a spot or composite sample at a point selected so as to obtain a representative sample of the waste water. Where possible, it is preferable to collect the sample in the 5-liter flask that is to be used in the preliminary distillation. Some means of protection, such as a box or bucket, should be provided for the flask in transporting the sample.

Procedure

Preliminary Distillation for Volatile Oily Matter

8. (a) Attach the trap and condenser to the 5-liter round-bottom flask containing 3000 to 3500 ml of sample, and turn on the condensing water. For the best results, the temperature of the water as it leaves the condenser should be at 5 C. Heat the flask until the sample boils freely. Continue the boiling until the volume of the condensed oily matter in the trap is constant for at least 15 min. Cool the flask to room temperature and remove the trap (Note 3). Stopper both ends of the trap, and immerse it in a water bath maintained at 15 C. When the contents of the trap have reached bath temperature, note and record the volume of oily matter to the nearest 0.02 ml.

Note 3.—Occasionally there may be a small portion of the oily matter that adheres to the lower part of the condenser tube. In this case,

[8] A 10 per cent aqueous solution of Aerosol OT as supplied by the Fisher Scientific Co., Pittsburgh, Pa., is satisfactory for this purpose.

partially dismantle the apparatus, hold the trap directly under the condenser tip, and touch the interior of the condenser tube with a copper wire previously dipped in a dispersing agent.

Extraction

(b) Acidify the sample in the flask with a measured volume of HCl (sp gr 1.19) to a pH of 5.0 or lower, and then add 150 ml of solvent. Insert the stirrer and adjust it so that the impeller dips into the aqueous layer to about 50 mm from the interface of the aqueous and solvent layers. Tilt the flask to about 30 deg off vertical to avoid vortex formation, and stir the contents for 15 sec.

(c) After stirring is completed, transfer the entire contents of the flask to a 4-liter separatory funnel, allow the funnel to stand quietly for about 1 min. and then draw the aqueous layer back into the round-bottom flask (Notes 4 and 5). Complete separation at this point is not essential. Repeat the extraction operation, using a second 150-ml portion of solvent, and again transfer the entire contents of the flask to the same separatory funnel. Allow the funnel to stand quietly for about 15 min, then carefully draw the aqueous layer into a graduated cylinder, measure its volume, and discard (Note 4). Transfer the extract to a clean 500-ml Erlenmeyer flask. Carefully rinse the round-bottom flask with a new 50-ml portion of solvent; then rinse the separatory funnel using the same 50 ml of solvent, and combine the rinsings with the extract in the 500-ml flask.

Note 4.—If carbon tetrachloride or chloroform is used, first withdraw the solvent through the stopcock into the 500-ml Erlenmeyer flask. Stopcock grease causes contamination of the extract. If a well-ground stopcock is used, water is a satisfactory lubricant. To prevent loss of sample at the glass interfaces, apply stopcock grease at the ends of the stopcock plug.

Note 5.—To handle extracts containing troublesome emulsions which hold large amounts of water, heat and filter through a small portion of glass wool, rinsing the latter throughly with solvent. The resulting filtrate usually consists of two layers, by which the water may be readily separated from the solvent. Measure the volume of separated water; then discard.

(*d*) If the solvent layer from the second extraction of a sample shows appreciable color or other evidence of relatively high oil content, repeat the extraction with a third portion of fresh solvent and combine the extracts.

Bulk Solvent Removal

(*e*) Set the Erlenmeyer flask on the hot plate, attach the column and condenser, and distill off the solvent at the rate of 20 to 22 ml per min to a volume of about 5 ml (Note 6). Near the end of the reduction step, tilt the distillation flask as shown in Fig. 4, so as to permit a better estimation of the volume of the residue and also to prevent overheating with resultant cracking of the residual oil and consequent loss of light end products (Note 7).

NOTE 6.—When rapid determinations are required, distill the first extract during the 15-min settling period required for the complete separation of the second extract. Then add the second extract, rinse with solvent, and reduce the volume as directed.

NOTE 7.—When the extract contains an unusually large quantity of oil, concentrate the extract by rapid distillation to a volume of about 10 to 15 ml. Transfer to a glass-stoppered 25-ml graduated cylinder, carefully rinsing the flask with solvent. After the transfer and rinsing is completed, bring the volume up to 25 ml with solvent, and mix. Use an aliquot portion in the miniature still for determination of oily matter. A final residue of between 0.1 and 1.0 ml is preferred.

Residual Solvent Removal

(*f*) Transfer the residue from the bulk solvent distillation operation, or an aliquot portion of a reduced extract containing an unusually large quantity of oily matter, to the dried and weighed miniature still by means of a small funnel, filling the bulb not more than half full. Place the still in the hot heater and start the distillation. In operation, adjust the voltage to a value sufficient to maintain the element at a temperature between 290 and 300 C, as measured by placing the bare thermocouple into the sump of an empty still in the heater, with the couple bent to make contact with one glass wall near the heating coils. Because this adjustment is critical (a 1-v variation will produce a marked change in the temperature), use a voltmeter while setting the voltage and to check the constancy of the line voltage. The heat output (about 20w) is sufficient to provide reasonably rapid distillation of solvent without bumping. Because the power consumption of the unit is low, and its life practically unlimited owing to the relatively low operating temperature, the heater may be operated continuously.

(*g*) The liquid in the still should start to boil briskly within 1 min after insertion of the still in the heater. The rate of distillation should be rapid enough to raise the top level of the ascending vapors, as indicated by wetting of the walls, above the top of the side-arm. As the distillation progresses and space becomes available, add any remaining residue and rinse the residue container with several milliliters of solvent, adding the rinsings to the still. Take care to complete the transfer operation well before all of the solvent has been distilled from the residue. As soon as the transfer operation has been completed, replace the small funnel with the thermowell, and adjust the thermocouple to a position about midway between the still bulb and the side-arm as shown in Fig. 5.

(*h*) As the distillation approaches the point of complete solvent removal, the temperature variations will follow either of two patterns, depending on the boiling range of the extracted oily matter.

A drop in the vapor temperature below the boiling point of the solvent generally indicates the absence of oily matter boiling below 200 C, while a gradual increase indicates the presence of components boiling between the boiling point of the solvent and 200 C. Consider the solvent to be completely removed 1 min after the temperature has dropped below 75 C, or when the temperature has reached 90 C (Note 8), whichever occurs first. Take the flask from the heater, remove the thermowell, and blow gently (without approaching closer than about 75 mm) into the top of the warm still to remove any solvent that may have condensed in the neck or side arm. Cool, wipe, and weigh the still containing the residual oily matter.

NOTE 8.—If carbon tetrachloride or chloroform is used, it will be necessary to establish different cut points.

Blank Determination

(i) Make a blank determination for each new stock of solvent. Agitate two 150-ml portions with 3000 ml of water, and reduce as directed in the procedure above. Cool the miniature still and weigh within 5 min, propping the still in a vertical position during the cooling and while on the analytical balance pan to avoid loss of the highly volatile pure solvent. This precaution and haste is not necessary during the determination of oily matter when the solvent remaining is in solution in the residual oil. Obtain the average weight of residue from five such determinations. The blank correction is an adjustment for the weight of solvent retained in the flask after the final distillation, plus compensation for any high-boiling residue in the solvent used.

Calculation

9. (a) Calculate the oily matter in the sample, in terms of parts per million, as follows:

$$\text{Volatile oily matter, ppm} = \frac{Ld}{W} \times 10^6$$

$$\text{Extracted oily matter, ppm} = \frac{H - B}{W} \times 10^6$$

Total oily matter, ppm

= volatile oily matter + extracted oily matter

where:

L = milliliters of volatile oily matter,
d = density, in grams per milliliter, of volatile oil (unless known, assume 0.8),
H = grams of extracted oil,
B = grams of residue from blank determination, and
W = grams of sample (the volume of water from the separatory funnel, corrected for amount of acid added, + the volume of water from the solvent-water emulsion, assuming each milliliter weighs 1 g).

Precision and Accuracy[9]

10. (a) Duplicate results by the same operator on samples taken simultaneously should not differ by more than 5 per cent of the mean.

(b) The error by this method is less than 10 per cent with respect to oily contaminants boiling above 90 C, when the cut point between volatile and nonvolatile oily matter lies in the 230 to 260 C boiling range. By omitting the initial reflux distillation step and starting with the extraction, the same accuracy is attained on oily matter boiling above 150 C.

[9] Supporting data pertinent to this method are given in the Appendix to the Report of Committee D-19, *Proceedings*, Am. Soc. Testing Mats., Vol. 54, p. 527 (1954).

APPROVED AS
USA STANDARD Z111.10-1964
BY USA STANDARDS INSTITUTE
UDC 621.181.021 :620.193

Standard Method for
DETERMINATION OF THICKNESS OF INTERNAL DEPOSITS ON TUBULAR HEAT EXCHANGE SURFACES[1,2]

ASTM Designation: D 1341 – 57 (1965)

ADOPTED, 1957; REAPPROVED, 1965

This Standard of the American Society for Testing and Materials is issued under the fixed designation D 1341; the number immediately following the designation indicates the year of original adoption or, in the case of revision, the year of last revision. A number in parentheses indicates the year of last reapproval.

Scope and Application

1. This method covers a procedure for the determination of deposit thickness on the inside surface of tubes, conduits, and tubular ducts constructed of magnetic material. It is intended primarily for the nondestructive examination of boiler tubes.

Principle of Method

2. (a) The method is based on the measurement of changes in the reluctance of a magnetic circuit which consists of the armature and pole pieces of the electromagnet employed, the deposit (if any) between the pole pieces and the tube surface, and the section of tube wall between the two pole pieces. The reluctance of the magnetic circuit is increased by an increase in the thickness of a deposit of nonmagnetic or semi-magnetic material between one or both pole pieces and the tube surface.

(b) The thickness of the deposit is correlated by calibration to the change in reluctance of the magnetic circuit.

Definitions

3. (a) *Circuit Reluctance.*—The reluctance of the magnetic circuit is the sum of the reluctance of each portion of the circuit.

(b) For definitions of terms used in this method relating specifically to magnetic testing, refer to the Definitions of Terms, Symbols, and Conversion Factors Relating to Magnetic Testing (ASTM Designation: A 340).[3]

Interferences and Limitations

4. (a) Deposits not capable of supporting the sensing element without a change in thickness of the deposit cause inaccurate results.

---

[1] Under the standardization procedure of the Society, this method is under the jurisdiction of the ASTM Committee D-19 on Industrial Water. A list of members may be found in the ASTM Year Book.

[2] By publication of this method, the American Society for Testing and Materials does not undertake to insure anyone utilizing the method against liability for infringement of Letters Patent nor assume any such liability, and such publication should not be construed as a recommendation of any patented or proprietary apparatus or procedure that may be involved.

[3] 1966 Book of ASTM Standards, Part 8.

523

(b) Tubes containing two or more bends in different planes prevent the use of the flat spring steel tape (see Section 5(b)).

(c) Bends cause false results whenever the radius of curvature is less than that for which the sensing element is designed.

(d) A constant a-c voltage source of 5 per cent regulation is a prerequisite to obtaining results of the indicated accuracy.

(e) The actual points of contact of the pole pieces and the deposit limit the extent of results obtained. Continuous measurements made during the traverse of a tube give a record of the deposit thickness only along the line of contact between the pole pieces and the deposit surface.

(f) A pitted tube surface causes erratic and inaccurate results.

NOTE 1.—The erratic results obtained when the pole pieces move over a pit in the tube surface can be used by an experienced operator as an aid in the identification and location of pits.

Apparatus

5. (a) Sensing Element Assembly.—A sensing element comprising an electromagnet enclosed in a non-magnetic casing, two hemispherically shaped pole pieces of the electromagnet to operate in sliding contact with the surface being explored, and a suitable mechanism to guide the sensing element and to exert sufficient pressure to keep the pole pieces in contact with the surface of the deposit or with the tube surface if no deposit is present.

(b) Tape.—A flat graduated spring steel tape with a coupling for attaching the sensing element to one end of the tape. The coupling shall be capable of being rotated coaxially with the tape to any position and locked, so that any desired segment of the tube surface may be explored.

(c) Gage.[4]—An electrical apparatus for measuring changes in the impedance of the sensing element caused by changes in the reluctance of the magnetic circuit. Such apparatus shall be calibrated to read deposit thickness in thousandths of an inch.

(d) Connector.—A flexible, suitably insulated two-wire conductor for connecting the sensing element to the electrical apparatus.[5]

Calibration

6. (a) Adjust the apparatus for zero by means of brass shims or glazed papers. Select a piece of tubing of the size and weight of those to be surveyed and long enough to accommodate the entire detector head with its carriages. Clean the tubing free of mill scale and thick rust by pickling or wire brushing. Cut brass shim stock or glazed paper, of 0.002-, 0.004-, and 0.006-in. thickness, to a size to fit under both contacts of the detector head. Adjust the instrument to the calibrating plate in accordance with instructions. Insert the detector head into the zeroing tube. Make the zero adjustment so that the meter reads slightly up scale from zero.

NOTE 2.—The instrument will not give a reading below the mechanical zero adjustment. Correct readings of shim thickness will not be obtained if the zero adjusting potentiometer is set on the wrong side of the true zero point.

(b) Slip the brass shims or glazed paper singly or in combinations under the contacts of the probe head, depending on the thickness of scale expected. Compare the instrument reading against the known thickness of the shims or paper. If the reading is heavy, remove the shims or paper and adjust the instrument setting toward zero. If the reading is

---

[4] The Turner Thickness Gage, Manufactured by Haskins-Turner Co., Jackson, Mich., has been found to be satisfactory for this purpose.
[5] Armored cable is recommended for this purpose.

light, adjust the setting away from zero. Repeat these adjustments until the shim thickness indicated is as nearly correct as possible.

(c) Make adjustments in the electrical apparatus to compensate for the effect of the internal diameter of the tube on the reluctance of the magnetic circuit.

(d) Check the calibration of the apparatus before making a series of tests, and recheck as often as necessary to insure reproducible results.

Procedure

7. Attach the sensing element to the spring steel tape and lock in the proper position to explore the desired segment of the tube. Push or pull the element with its attached conductor slowly through the tube, and continuously observe the readings. Stop the element at desired intervals, and record the readings of the gage.

Note 3.—In some instances it may be desirable first to run a suitable lead wire through the tube to be examined, attaching the lead wire to the end of the sensing element opposite the end to which the flat steel tape is attached. The passage of the sensing element through the tube can then be aided by maintaining tension on the lead wire.

Calculation

8. The readings of the electrical apparatus show the deposit thickness directly in thousandths of an inch.

Precision and Accuracy

9. An experienced operator can obtain results with a precision of 0.002 in. and an accuracy of 0.004 in. for continuous firm deposits of uniform thickness.

Standard Method of Test for

EVALUATING ACUTE TOXICITY OF INDUSTRIAL WASTE WATER TO FRESH-WATER FISHES[1]

ASTM Designation: D 1345 – 59 (1965)

ADOPTED, 1959; REAPPROVED, 1965

This Standard of the American Society for Testing and Materials is issued under the fixed designation D 1345; the number immediately following the designation indicates the year of original adoption or, in the case of revision, the year of last revision. A number in parentheses indicates the year of last reapproval.

Scope and Application

1. (a) This bio-assay procedure[2] is intended as a non-referee batch method (Note 1) for evaluating acute toxicity of wastes and of other water pollutants to fresh-water fishes. The test provides information on the relative acute toxicity (Note 2) of the substance tested under prescribed experimental conditions.

[1] Under the standardization procedure of the Society, this method is under the jurisdiction of the ASTM Committee D-19 on Industrial Water. A list of members may be found in the ASTM Year Book.

[2] This method is based in large part on the recommendations of the Committee on Research of the Federation of Sewage and Industrial Wastes Associations, and it is essentially the same as the first one of the so-called "Auxiliary Methods" described in the report of that committee: Doudoroff, *et al.*, "Bio-Assay Methods For The Evaluation of Acute Toxicity of Industrial Wastes To Fish," *Sewage and Industrial Wastes*, Vol. 23, No. 11, pp. 1380–1397 (1951). Many of the recommendations of that committee, in turn, derive directly from an earlier, more detailed and comprehensive publication by Hart, Doudoroff, and Greenbank, "The Evaluation of the Toxicity of Industrial Wastes, Chemicals and Other Substances to Fresh-Water Fishes," The Atlantic-Richfield Co., Philadelphia, Pa., 317 p. (1945). (Out of print.)

NOTE 1.—Tests may be performed using a standard reference water and reference chemicals (Section 6, Paragraphs (b) and (c)). The reference water is recommended for obtaining basic comparative research data. Test chemicals are recommended for standardizing the lot of fish under test.

NOTE 2.—Chronic or cumulative toxicity can interfere seriously with the growth and reproduction of organisms and may eventually cause death. This method detects only acute toxicity.

(b) The test is applicable to industrial waste water and to the determination of the toxicity of pure chemical compounds in water solution. Wastes having volatile or readily oxidizable constitutents (Note 3) and excessive biochemical or other oxygen demand (Note 4) may also be tested by this method.

NOTE 3.—The concentration of highly volatile and unstable toxicants may decline throughout the test. In the case of highly volatile toxicants, it may be possible to obtain more reliable data by substituting initial oxygenation of the diluent in place of the standard controlled artificial oxygenation procedure. In the case of readily oxidizable constituents, it may be advisable to use test solution renewal techniques.

NOTE 4.—A distinction is made between

526

death due to deficiency of dissolved oxygen in polluted water and death due to toxicity. In order to detect and evaluate the direct lethality of test material, it is necessary to maintain adequate dissolved oxygen concentrations during toxicity tests.

(c) The results of the test data are reported in terms of median tolerance limits (Section 2(b)). The critical concentration range may be reported, also, as supplementary information (Section 2(c)).

(d) The test data is applicable for use as a guide in estimating "safe concentrations" of the discharge of industrial wastes (see Appendix III).

Definitions

2. (a) The terms "acute toxicity," "median tolerance limit (TL_m)," and "critical concentration range" in this method are defined in accordance with the Definitions of Terms Relating to Industrial Water and Industrial Waste Water (ASTM Designation: D 1129),[3] as follows:

Acute Toxicity.—Any direct lethal action of pollution to fresh-water fishes that is demonstrable within 96 hr or less (Note 5).

NOTE 5.—The lethal action includes both internal and external effects, but excludes indirect action such as depletion of dissolved oxygen through chemical or biochemical oxidation of the test material.

Median Tolerance Limit (TL_m).—The concentration of pollutants at which 50 per cent of the test animals are able to survive for a specified period of exposure (Note 6).

NOTE 6.—The exposure period may be 24, 48, or 96 hr. The 24-hr TL_m and the 48-hr TL_m generally should be determined whenever the toxicity is sufficiently pronounced to permit their determination.

Critical Concentration Range.—The interval between the highest concentration at which all test animals survive for 48 hr and the lowest concentration at which all test animals die within 24 hr.

(b) For definitions of other terms used in this method, refer to Definitions D 1129.

Interferences

3. (a) If the toxic constituent of a waste is volatile, there is a tendency for the toxicity of the test solution to decrease throughout the duration of the test.

(b) Volatile toxic substances may be developed in the test solution as a result of chemical action. For example, when a nonvolatile, strongly acidic substance is dissolved in the dilution water, it reacts with the carbonates naturally present in the water and releases carbon dioxide which may be injurious either directly, by its toxic action, or by holding in solution other toxic components such as heavy metals. Therefore, acid solutions or solutions containing salts which hydrolyze to form acid solutions must be regarded as volatile substances.

(c) Strongly alkaline solutions may exhibit changes similar to those usually attributed to volatility of toxic compounds by undergoing gradual neutralization by absorption of carbon dioxide from the fish or from the air used for aeration.

(d) Substances which are ordinarily considered to be nonvolatile may form toxic volatile products by hydrolysis. For example, the toxic salt sodium cyanide, when in dilute solution, is hydrolyzed in part to hydrocyanic acid. Materials reacting in this manner may have to be considered as volatile, even though the volatility is the property of the secondary product.

---

[3] Appears in this publication.

(e) Certain chemicals such as phenol may undergo oxidation to a less toxic oxidation product. If the rate of oxidation proceeds so slowly that the change in toxicity over a 24-hr period cannot be detected readily by biological tests, the substance may be regarded as stable insofar as the test is concerned. On the other hand, if the oxidation proceeds rapidly, it usually will be complete before any toxicity test can be performed (Note 7).

NOTE 7.—It will be evident that if a toxic material undergoes very rapid oxidation to a nontoxic form, there need be no concern over the inability of the test procedure to measure the toxicity of the material before oxidation, since the toxicity of such a material will not present a disposal problem.

(f) Some highly toxic metals form insoluble or only very slightly soluble carbonates or hydroxides, and these may form insoluble precipitates when their soluble salts are added to the dilution water in preparing test dilutions. The actual concentration of toxic metals in the test dilutions will, therefore, depend upon the concentration and kind of ions in the dilution water. Under these conditions, the value obtained for the median tolerance limit for such a toxic metal may vary with the dilution water used by different investigators. For this reason, the composition of the dilution water is reported with the median tolerance limits, and the formation of any precipitate or turbidity in the test dilutions is recorded.

Apparatus

4. (a) Aquaria.—Several aquaria for maintaining and acclimatizing fish to be used as test animals. These aquaria shall be equipped with facilities for maintaining a uniform temperature (±1 C) so that the test animals may be acclimated to the test temperature (Section 10(a)).

(b) Uniform-Temperature Test Facilities, for maintaining a uniform temperature throughout the test period so that deviations shall not exceed 1 C above or below the average test temperature selected and reported. These facilities may consist of a constant-temperature room in which to perform the experiments, or of a large constant-temperature bath, having transparent walls, in which to immerse the test containers.

(c) Test Containers, consisting of 5-gal glass bottles with wide mouths, capable of accommodating 3-hole No. 12 rubber stoppers through which two glass tubes of 7 mm OD extend almost to the bottom of the container. The third hole in the rubber stopper is required as a vent. Through these tubes, compressed air or oxygen, or both, can be introduced at a constant rate regulated by means of suitable pressure-control devices. The test container shall always be filled to a fixed level at the base of the neck, so that the surface of the test liquid in contact with the overlying atmosphere has a diameter less than one half the diameter of the bottle.

(d) Source of Compressed Air, Carbon Dioxide, and Oxygen.—Equipped with suitable pressure-control valves to maintain constant rates of delivery.

Purity of Reagents

5. (a) Reagent grade chemicals shall be used in all tests. Unless otherwise indicated, it is intended that all reagents shall conform to the specifications of the Committee on Analytical Reagents of the American Chemical Society, where such specifications are available.[4] Other grades may be used, provided it is first

---

[4] "Reagent Chemicals, American Chemical Society Specifications," Am. Chem. Soc. Washington, D. C. For suggestions on the testing of reagents not listed by the American Chemical Society, see "Reagent Chemicals and Standards," by Joseph Rosin, D. Van Nostrand Co., Inc., New York, N. Y., and the "United States Pharmacopeia."

ascertained that the reagent is of sufficiently high purity to permit its use without lessening the accuracy of the determination.

(b) Unless otherwise indicated, references to water shall be understood to mean reagent water conforming to the Specifications for Reagent Water (ASTM Designation: D 1193).[3]

Reagents and Materials

6. (a) *Dilution Water.*—The purpose of the bio-assay will determine the type of dilution water to be used in the preparation of test solutions of the test substance. In evaluating the toxicity of a waste for obtaining safe disposal rates, the most desirable dilution water is that water into which the waste is to be discharged. Unless there are specific reasons to the contrary, it is advisable to obtain the dilution water from the receiving body of water at a point where there is no industrial pollution from any source. If unpolluted dilution water cannot be obtained from the body of water under consideration, water of similar quality, with respect to its dissolved mineral content, shall be obtained or prepared from some other source. Such water can be prepared by adding appropriate chemicals to available natural water of suitable quality, which may first be diluted, if necessary, with reagent water. As a general rule, the calcium, magnesium, sulfate, and total dissolved solids content of this substituted water, and especially its total alkalinity, should not differ from those of the water receiving the waste tested by more than 25 per cent.

If the purpose of the test is to obtain comparative data (on pure chemical compounds) among different laboratories, then the standard reference water as prescribed in Paragraph (b) shall be used as a dilution water.

(b) *Standard Reference Water:*[5]

(1) *Stock Solution 1.*—Dissolve 71.0 g $MgSO_4 \cdot 7H_2O$, 6.5 g K_2SO_4, and 0.2 g $MnSO_4 \cdot 4H_2O$ in water, and dilute to 1 liter.

(2) *Stock Solution 2.*—Dissolve 18.6 g $CaCl_2 \cdot 2H_2O$ in water, and dilute to 1 liter.

(3) *Stock Solution 3.*—Dissolve 25.0 g $NaHCO_3$, 3.0 g NH_4NO_3, and 1.1 g $K_2HPO_4 \cdot 3H_2O$ in water, and dilute to 1 liter.

(4) *Stock Solution 4.*—Dissolve 32.2 g CaO in water, and dilute to 1 liter. Bubble CO_2 gas through this mixture to make a $CaCO_3$ slurry.

(5) *Stock Solution 5.*—Dissolve 62.6 g $Na_2SiO_3 \cdot 9H_2O$ in water, and dilute to 1 liter.

(6) *Stock Solution 6.*—Dissolve 1.2 g $FeCl_3 \cdot 6H_2O$ in water, and dilute to 1 liter.

For each liter of standard reference water to be prepared, add 1 ml each of solutions 1, 2, and 3. Disperse pure CO_2 gas into this solution by means of a gas diffuser for 15 min. The pH of the solution at this point should be about 4.3. Add 1 ml of solution 4 to each liter of standard reference water, and introduce CO_2 gas until the solution becomes clear. The pH at this point should be about 5.1. Then diffuse compressed air through the solution for 25 min, to raise the pH to about 7.9. Add 1 ml each of solutions 5 and 6 to each liter of water, and aerate for 60 min. The final pH of 7.9 remains constant within 0.1 pH units.

(c) *Reference Test Chemical.*—Each investigator may select at his own discretion any pure chemical compound to be used as a reference test chemical. Toxicity tests on this chemical may be run as often as required to provide the

---

[5] This reference water is U. S. mean dilution water as described by R. F. Weston in "Conductivity as an Aid in Water Analysis," presented at the 110th meeting of the American Chemical Society September, 1946.

investigator with information relative to the reproducibility of the test data with that chemical. It is desirable to repeat toxicity tests using the reference chemical with each new batch of fish after they have been properly acclimated. The reference chemical will thus serve as an indicator of the consistency of toxicity results obtainable from different batches of fish. If the test results on a new batch of fish do not fall within the control limits established by previous tests, it is possible that other data obtained using this batch of fish, also will compare unfavorably. It is recommended that the standard reference water (Paragraph (b)) be employed as the dilution water for use with the reference chemical.

Sampling

7. (a) Collect the sample in accordance with the Tentative Methods of Sampling Industrial Water (ASTM Designation: D 510).[3]

(b) Prepare all dilutions required for a single toxicity evaluation from the same sample of waste, portions of which shall be stored until needed at a temperature of 0 to 4 C in completely filled, tightly stoppered bottles. Keep the duration of such storage to a minimum, and report storage time along with the source and nature of the sample.

(c) Uniformly disperse, by agitation, any undissolved material present in a sample of waste water before withdrawing a measured portion for mixing with dilution water. However, avoid violent agitation and unnecessary exposure of the sample to the atmosphere.

Calibration and Standardization

8. Before filling the test containers, it is necessary to determine a suitable aeration rate so that the loss of any dissolved volatile substance from the liquid in the test container will not be excessive. This involves determining the

total number of bubbles of air or oxygen, or both, to be released per minute in a given test container which is filled with the test solution to a given (fixed) level. After the apparatus has been thus calibrated, the same constant "bubbling rate" must be maintained throughout each test, although the ratio of the number of air bubbles to the number of oxygen bubbles released per minute may be varied as necessary (Note 8). The dissolved oxygen content of test solutions shall not fall below 4 ppm when warm-water fishes are used as test animals, or below 5 ppm when cold-water fishes are used; and it shall not exceed the saturation value at the experimental temperature (Section 10 (a)). Calibrate as follows:

Fill the test container to the fixed level with clean soft water having an alkalinity to methyl orange indicator not in excess of 40 ppm as $CaCO_3$. Dissolve CO_2 gas in the water to obtain a concentration between 50 and 100 ppm of free CO_2. Then establish an aeration rate (in terms of the number of bubbles of air or oxygen released per minute, counted with the aid of a stop watch) by experiment, such that the amount of CO_2 lost from this solution in 24 hr under these experimental conditions will not exceed 67 per cent of the initial free CO_2 (Note 9).

Note 8.—In many cases, the use of air alone will be sufficient to maintain an adequate dissolved oxygen content. If the wastes being tested exert a high oxygen demand, then air and oxygen, or oxygen alone, may be required.

Note 9.—In order to maintain the liquid surface at a uniform level in the test container during a bio-assay, it is necessary to compensate for any volume of test solution removed for analysis by adding an equivalent volume of test solution to the 5-gal bottle.

Test Animals

9. (a) In determining the kinds of fish to be used as test animals, the species

selected should not be resistant to adverse water quality conditions, but should withstand captivity well. They should be species which are common in unpolluted portions of the body of water receiving the waste to be tested, or at least species which are known to inhabit similar waters in the same major watershed. If available, species which are deemed important locally should be given preference.

(*b*) Although any fish species which suits the purpose of the investigation may be used, species belonging to any of the following widely distributed and important families are particularly recommended, and should be selected unless there is good reason for making a different choice:

Centrarchidae (sunfishes, basses, crappies),
Salmonidae (trouts, charrs, salmons),
Cyprinidae (true minnows, exclusive of carp and goldfish), and
Catostomidae (suckers).

(*c*) The fish used for each individual toxicity evaluation shall all be of the same species. They should be identified at least as to genus, and preferably as to species. The correct scientific name[6] shall be stated when the test results are reported.

(*d*) The fish shall be obtained from any single common source (stream, lake, hatchery, etc.), but preferably from the body of water receiving the pollutant tested. The fish should all be collected and brought to the laboratory at about the same time. Stocks of fish for test purposes may be kept initially in any suitable containers (for example, small ponds, live-boxes, screened pens, concrete

or wooden tanks, glass aquaria, etc.) and in any water of suitable quality and temperature in which they can be kept in good condition until they are needed.

(*e*) Test animals should be acclimatized for 10 days or longer to conditions similar to those under which the tests are to be performed, with regard especially to the temperature and the chemical properties (or source) of the water.

(*f*) The fish should be fed at regular intervals at least three times a week, and preferably daily, during the acclimatization period, but should not be fed for a period of about 2 days before they are used in a test. The fish should not be fed during the test.

(*g*) The length of the largest fish used in an individual bio-assay should be not more than 1.5 times the length of the smallest specimen used. Small specimens, averaging between 2 and 3 in. in length, are the most convenient and desirable test animals.

(*h*) The percentage of specimens dying or becoming seriously diseased in the acclimatizing aquarium during a period of four days immediately preceding a test shall be less than 10 per cent. Otherwise, the test animal lot shall be deemed unfit for use until the incidence of disease and the mortality rate decline sufficiently. Specimens used for test purposes shall show no evident symptoms of disease or abnormalities of appearance or behavior at the time of their transfer to test containers.

(*i*) Test animals shall be transferred from the acclimatizing aquarium to the test containers within 30 min after the preparation of the waste dilutions. This time interval should be uniform and should be recorded. Test animals should be transferred only with small-meshed dip-nets of soft material. They should not be allowed to rest on any dry surface, nor be held out of water any longer than necessary.

[6] The following reference is a helpful guide to the nomenclature of fishes: "A List of Common and Scientific Names of the Better Known Fishes of the United States and Canada," *Special Publication No. 1*, American Fisheries Society, 45 p. (1948).

(*j*) Any specimen that has been accidentally dropped during transfer or otherwise mishandled during transfer shall be rejected and not used for test purposes until its health and freedom from injury have been established. All test animals should be selected, and graded according to size in advance, so as to avoid any unnecessary handling just before the test.

(*k*) The weight of all fish in a test container shall not exceed 2 g per liter of liquid medium tested, and preferably the weight should be about 1 g per liter of liquid tested.

Procedure

10. (*a*) Using a diffuser and compressed air or oxygen as required, aerate the dilution water at or near the test temperature (Notes 10, 11, and 12), which shall be between 20 and 25 C for warm-water fishes such as *Centrarchidae* and most *Cyprinidae*, and between 12 and 18 C for cold-water fishes such as *Salmonidae*.

Note 10.—It is assumed that the dissolved oxygen in the test material is insufficient to provide 5 ppm of oxygen in the test dilution. This will occur frequently with industrial wastes, and aeration of the dilution water is undertaken to insure an adequate initial dissolved oxygen concentration in the test dilutions. To attain this end, oxygenation of the dilution water with oxygen may be required for those cases in which the sample exerts an oxygen demand. It is not permissible, however, to allow the dissolved oxygen content of test dilutions to exceed the saturation value at the test temperature. When difficulty is encountered in obtaining adequate and persistent dissolved oxygen concentrations, it is advisable to determine the oxygen demand of the sample. It will then be possible to calculate the quantity of oxygen that must be dissolved in the dilution water to provide an initial concentration of 5 ppm in the test dilution. With many industrial wastes having excessive oxygen demands, it may not be possible to obtain sufficient dissolved oxygen by this method. In such cases, the waste shall be aerated with air or oxygen prior to running the toxicity test. It shall be clearly stated in the report that the median

tolerance limit (TL_m) applies to aerated samples. Rapid aeration or oxygenation with diffusion equipment should be avoided if the waste or test solution contains volatile components.

Note 11.—It may be necessary or desirable to test undiluted wastes. To do this, run a dissolved oxygen determination directly on the waste. If a sufficient dissolved oxygen content is available, proceed in accordance with Paragraph (*c*). If the waste is deficient in dissolved oxygen, aerate with air or oxygen to obtain an adequate dissolved oxygen content, and then proceed as directed in Paragraph (*c*). In this latter case report the aeration of the waste together with the toxicity results.

Note 12.—In general, no difficulty will be encountered in obtaining adequate dissolved oxygen concentrations when testing pure chemicals.

(*b*) Prepare trial dilutions of the highest and lowest concentrations of waste to be tested in conveniently small volumes. From each, siphon off sufficient material for dissolved oxygen determinations, and discard the remaining portions of each dilution (Note 13).

Note 13.—It is desirable to obtain this information before preparing dilutions in the 5-gal test containers.

(*c*) If adequate dissolved oxygen concentrations are indicated in the trial dilutions, or in the waste material if undiluted waste is to be tested (Note 11), prepare the appropriate dilutions in the test containers so as to provide an adequate range of concentrations for testing (Appendix I). Prepare each dilution in sufficient quantity to fill each test container to the fixed level established in the calibration procedure (Section 8). Retain a portion of each dilution in separate containers for use in maintaining the liquid surface in the test containers at a uniform level, after samples have been withdrawn for determination of dissolved oxygen or other tests. Place the filled test containers in a constant-temperature bath.

(*d*) Determine the dissolved oxygen

content of the dilutions in the test containers, using a minimum volume of test solution. If an adequate dissolved oxygen content is obtained, replace the volume of test solution which was withdrawn from each test container for the dissolved oxygen tests as prescribed in Paragraph (c). Discard any dilution in which a deficiency of oxygen is found (Note 14), and prepare another.

Note 14.—The minimum permissible concentration of dissolved oxygen is 4 ppm when warm-water fishes are used, and 5 ppm when cold-water fishes are used.

(e) When adequate and persistent dissolved oxygen contents are obtained, transfer the test animals to the test dilutions. At least ten test animals shall be used for testing each experimental concentration of the substance under investigation. Fewer than ten may be used, however, in preliminary tests performed in order to determine what critical concentrations should be tested with the larger number of fish. No more than 30 min shall elapse between preparing the dilutions and adding the test animals.

(f) Stopper the test containers with the rubber stoppers containing glass tubes (Section 4 (c)) and start aerating (Note 15) at the rate established in the calibration procedure (Section 8).

Note 15.—The purpose of the aeration is to insure the maintenance of an adequate dissolved oxygen concentration in the test solutions and to compensate for the oxygen utilized by the test animals. It is essential, however, to maintain throughout the toxicity test the same constant "bubbling rate" established in the calibration procedure (Section 8), in order to minimize loss of volatile material from the test solution. This requires frequent checking throughout the test. Whether air, air and oxygen, or oxygen alone is used will depend on the nature of the material being tested. This can be decided by running dissolved oxygen determinations.

(g) As often as necessary during the test, siphon off samples of the test material for dissolved oxygen determinations or other tests. On the basis of the dissolved oxygen results, vary as required the ratio of the number of air bubbles to the number of oxygen bubbles released per minute, but maintain the same constant "bubbling rate" (Notes 15 and 16).

Note 16.—In the case of highly volatile test material, it may be advisable to eliminate aeration and to introduce the required amount of oxygen with the dilution water. This can be done by dispersing compressed oxygen gas through the water in a tall cylinder. It is not advisable to use initial oxygen concentrations higher than approximately twice saturation for the test conditions.

(h) If, at the end of 24 hr, some of the test animals have died while the dissolved oxygen content of the liquid tested remains adequate, measurable toxicity is indicated. As long as some of the test animals live, continue the test for 48 hr.

Note 17.—In the case of highly unstable test material, it may be necessary to renew the test material once every 24 hr or at convenient shorter intervals. This can be accomplished by periodically transferring the test animals quickly by means of a dip-net to a test container with fresh test material. Renewal of the test material at intervals of 24 hr is often both convenient and sufficient, but shorter intervals such as 12 hr or 8 hr sometimes are necessary or advisable. The need for test material renewal can be determined by checking the toxicity of solutions under test for 8 to 24 hr against the toxicity of fresh test solutions.

(i) Record the number of fish that have died at the end of 24 and 48 hr, respectively (Note 18).

Note 18.—Test animals are recorded as "dead" at the time of observation only if respiratory and other movements, either spontaneous or in response to mild mechanical stimulation (such as prodding of the animal or pressing its tail with a glass rod), cannot be readily detected during an observation period of about 5 min. Dead fish should be removed as soon as they are observed.

(*j*) Set up additional tests, if necessary, using different concentrations in order to delimit the critical concentration range (Appendix I).

(*k*) When the critical concentration range has been approximately determined, evaluate the toxicity of the pollutant by carefully testing several concentrations near and within the apparent limits of this range, using the suggested test concentrations given in Appendix I.

(*l*) Carry the final tests through a period of at least 48 hr. If, at the end of this period, more than half of the test animals survive at the highest concentration that can be properly tested, continue the test for a total of 96 hr.

Only when it has been shown that more than 50 per cent of the test animals survive for 96 hr at this maximal test concentration, may the substance under investigation be reported as not having acute toxicity that is demonstrable and measurable by the method described.

Calculation and Report

11. (*a*) The calculation of median tolerance limits by interpolation is explained in Appendix II.

(*b*) Reporting, interpretation, and use of bio-assay results are discussed in Appendix III.

Precision and Accuracy

12. Due to the large number of variables encountered in such tests, no limits for precision and accuracy are given.

APPENDIX I

SUGGESTED EXPERIMENTAL CONCENTRATIONS

A1. (a) In order to determine the median tolerance limit, TL_m, any appropriate concentrations of the waste assayed may be tested. It is more convenient, however, to select the concentration values from the logarithmic series shown in Table I.

TABLE I.—A GUIDE TO THE SELECTION OF EXPERIMENTAL CONCENTRATIONS, BASED ON PROGRESSIVE BISECTION OF INTERVALS ON A LOGARITHMIC SCALE.

		Concentrations		
(1)	(2)	(3)	(4)	(5)
10.0	...	...	...	...
...	...	...	...	8.7
...	...	...	7.5	...
...	...	...	...	6.5
...	...	5.6	...	...
...	...	...	...	4.9
...	...	...	4.2	...
...	...	...	...	3.7
...	3.2	...	...	...
...	...	...	...	2.8
...	...	...	2.4	...
...	...	...	...	2.1
...	...	1.8	...	...
...	...	...	...	1.55
...	...	...	1.35	...
...	...	...	...	1.15
1.0	...	...	...	...

(b) The values in Table I can represent concentrations expressed either as per cent by volume or as parts per million by weight. The values shown may be multiplied or divided, as necessary, by any multiple of ten. For example, the two values in column 1 may be 10.0 and 1.0, as shown, or they may be 100 and 10, or 1.0 and 0.1, etc. The figures are arranged in five vertical columns in the order (from left to right) in which the corresponding concentrations can be tested, for the purpose of gradually delimiting the critical concentration range and locating a median tolerance limit. Each value is approximately midway between the next higher and lower values shown in the preceding columns, when these are plotted on a logarithmic scale.

(c) A series of concentrations, such as 0.1, 1.0, 10 and 100 per cent (column 1) may be tested first. Then appropriate concentrations from column 2, column 3, etc., may be tested. A value may be selected from each column which bisects (on a logarithmic scale) the concentration interval, or range, within which a median tolerance limit that is to be evaluated has been shown to be located by preceding tests. For example, if the 24-hr TL_m and the 48 hr TL_m of a waste are to be determined, and if it has been found already that all the test animals survive for 48 hr in a 1 per cent waste dilution, whereas all die within 24 hr in a 10 per cent dilution, the concentration to be tested next (from column 2) is 3.2 per cent. If all the test animals survive for 48 hr at this concentration, the concentration to be tested next (from column 3) is 5.6 per cent.

(d) Time can be saved by performing concurrent tests of several appropriate concentrations shown in two or more successive columns. Thus, for the hypothetical waste discussed above, 1.8, 3.2 and 5.6 per cent dilutions may be tested simultaneously.

(e) When the critical concentration range has been adequately delimited by the procedures described in Paragraphs (c) and (d), only those concentrations in the right hand columns of Table I that are apparently within this range need be tested. It is not always necessary to test concentrations shown in column 5. However, increased accuracy often can be achieved by testing appropriate concentrations in this column, especially when the critical concentration range has been found to be relatively narrow. For example, if no test animals live for 24 hr in a 5.6 per cent waste dilution, whereas all survive for 48 hr in a 3.2 per cent dilution, all intermediate concentrations in columns 4 and 5 (namely, 4.2, 3.7, and 4.9 per cent) can well be included in the series of test concentrations.

(f) Other similar series of test concentrations, such as those in Table II, may be tested concurrently. For example, concentrations shown in column 1 may be tested first. If additional tests are deemed advisable for reducing the intervals between test concentrations within the critical range so determined, only the ap-

TABLE II.—A GUIDE TO THE SELEC-
TION OF EXPERIMENTAL CONCENTRA-
TIONS BASED ON DECILOG INTERVALS.

Concentrations		Log Concentrations
(1)	(2)	
10.00	....	1.00
....	7.94 (or 7.9)	0.90
6.31 (or 6.3)	....	0.80
....	5.01 (or 5.0)	0.70
3.98 (or 4.0)	....	0.60
....	3.16 (or 3.15)	0.50
2.51 (or 2.5)	....	0.40
....	1.99 (or 2.0)	0.30
1.58 (or 1.6)	....	0.20
....	1.26 (or 1.25)	0.10
1.00	....	0.00

propriate critical concentrations from column 2 then may be tested.

(g) The magnitude of suitable intervals between the concentrations tested for establishing a median tolerance limit by interpolation cannot be definitely prescribed. It depends on the re-quired degree of accuracy and on the nature of the experimental data. When two test concentrations, of which one is above and one is below the median tolerance limit, have proved unquestionably lethal to some (for example, 20 per cent or more), but not all, of the test animals, determination of survival percentages at intermediate concentrations generally is not essential. Otherwise, the accuracy and reliability of the estimate of TL_m can often be markedly improved by reducing the intervals between the test concentrations. However, the testing of more concentrations may not be justifiable when the increased accuracy thus achieved can have no practical import. The intervals between the concentrations included in Table II (columns 1 and 2), and even those included in the first four columns only of Table I, are believed to be sufficiently small under most circumstances. It will be noted that the difference between any one of these concentrations and the next higher concentration of the series is not much more than one fourth, nor much less than one fifth of the higher value. Intervals that are narrower or wider are not recommended unless they are clearly advantageous and adequate.

APPENDIX II

EXAMPLE OF THE DERIVATION OF MEDIAN TOLERANCE LIMITS BY STRAIGHT-LINE GRAPHICAL INTERPOLATION

A2. Hypothetical experimental data are presented in Table III, which show the numbers of test animals used for testing different dilutions of a liquid industrial waste or effluent, and the numbers surviving after exposure periods of 24 and 48 hr. These experimental

TABLE III.—EXPERIMENTAL DATA.

Concentration, percentage waste by volume	Number of Test Animals	Number of Test Animals Surviving After	
		24 hr	48 hr
100............	10	0	0
75............	10	3	0
56............	10	8	1
42............	10	10	6
32............	10	10	9

results are plotted in Fig. 1, which illustrates the estimation of median tolerance limits by the straight-line graphical interpolation method. The 24-hr and 48-hr median tolerance limits are shown to be about 67 and 44 per cent by volume of waste, respectively.

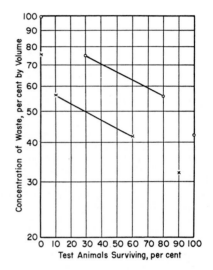

FIG. 1.—Estimation of Median Tolerance Limits by Straight-Line Graphical Interpolation.

APPENDIX III

REPORTING, INTERPRETATION, AND USE OF BIO-ASSAY RESULTS

A3. (a) The kind of fish used as test animals, their source and average size, the source of the dilution water and its mineral content (at least, total alkalinity, hardness, pH, etc.), and the experimental temperature always should be stated in the report. Other pertinent data, such as the volume of test liquid, the number and weight of fish in each test container, and a summary of the results of chemical determinations made in the course of the experiment, such as dissolved oxygen and pH values, also should be reported.

(b) A complete report should include, in addition to the median tolerance limits determined, a concise table of the experimental data on which these values are based; that is, the numbers of fish used and the observed percentages of survival at the different test concentrations near and within the critical range.

(c) The median tolerance limits are only useful indices of the relative toxicity of the substance tested under certain experimental conditions. They obviously do not represent concentrations which may be deemed safe, or harmless, in fish habitats subject to pollution. Therefore, when estimating safe disposal rates or dilution ratios for industrial wastes on the basis of the toxicity evaluations, liberal safety factors are required. The following tentative formula for the estimation of presumably safe concentrations has been suggested:[2]

$$C = \frac{48\text{-hr } TL_m \times 0.3}{S^2}$$

where:

C = the presumably harmless concentration, expressed in the same units as the 48-hr TL_m,

$$S = \frac{24\text{-hr } TL_m}{48\text{-hr } TL_m}, \text{ and}$$

The factor 0.3 and the exponent 2 = tentative safety factors.

The above formula has not been generally accepted and its use may be quite misleading in many cases.

(d) There are numerous factors that influence the results of the bio-assay which should be considered in the application of the test data to field conditions. For example, the test conditions limit the volume of test solution per fish. Since in some cases it is possible for the fish to oxidize or otherwise alter the composition of the test material, there are cases in which 24-hr and 48-hr TL_m results cannot be obtained as such because of the effect of the fish on the toxic material. Materials such as phenol are oxidized by the fish. In this case, if the fish are not killed in the first hour or so, they will generally survive indefinitely. The test results in such a case probably indicate a lower degree of toxicity than would occur in nature. In some cases, the toxic material is volatile. Such materials would be lost rapidly from solution in turbulent streams and slowly in sluggish streams. The test data indicate the anticipated toxicity in a sluggish stream and therefore indicate a higher toxicity than would be expected in nature from a turbulent stream. The composition of the dilution water in the test solution may affect the results appreciably. Experience has indicated that such characteristics as hardness, alkalinity, pH, and organic content of the water may affect the toxicity of a given material. It is for this reason that a standard reference water is recommended when comparative tests are required, and in determining the toxicity of pure chemical compounds. Furthermore, the use of a test reference chemical in addition to a standard reference water provides a convenient method for comparing different batches of fish under the same conditions.

(e) Test data apply only to the species of test animals. More sensitive forms may be present in the stream. In testing programs, it is advantageous to use fish that have about the same sensitivity as the "game" fish indigenous to the stream under consideration.

(f) This test procedure measures short-time effects only. Effects of prolonged exposure are not measured, nor is the effect of the test substance on the food supply of the fish.

(g) Toxicity results indicate the toxicity for only that size and species of fish used in the test. Sometimes the fry are more sensitive to toxic materials than the adult fish; on other occasions, the reverse is true.

(h) This test procedure is not adaptable to control testing for continuous discharges, because of the time delay in obtaining results.

APPENDIX IV

BIBLIOGRAPHY

(1) P. Duodoroff, "Biological Observations and Toxicity Bio-Assays in the Control of Industrial Wastes," *Proceedings*, Sixth Industrial Wastes Conference, Purdue University Engineering Bulletin, Extension Series No. 76, pp. 88–104 (1951).

(2) P. Duodoroff, "Some Recent Developments in the Study of Toxic Industrial Wastes," *Proceedings*, Fourth Annual Pacific Northwest Industrial Waste Conference, State College of Washington, Pullman, Wash., pp. 21–25 (1952).

(3) P. Duodoroff and M. Katz, "Critical Review of Literature on the Toxicity of Industrial Wastes and Their Components to Fish. I. Alkalies, Acids, and Inorganic Gases," *Sewage and Industrial Wastes*, Vol. 22, No. 11, p. 1432 (1950).

(4) P. Duodoroff and M. Katz, "Critical Review of Literature on the Toxicity of Industrial Wastes and Their Components to Fish. II. The Metals as Salts," *Sewage and Industrial Wastes*, Vol. 25, No. 7, pp. 802–839 (1953).

(5) M. M. Ellis, B. A. Westfall and M. D. Ellis, "Determination of Water Quality," *Research Report 9*, U. S. Fish and Wildlife Service, p. 122 (1946).

(6) L. Freeman, "A Standardized Method for Determining Toxicity of Pure Compounds to Fish," *Sewage and Industrial Wastes*, Vol. 25, No. 7, pp. 845–848 (1953).

(7) W. B. Hart, P. Duodoroff and J. Greenbank, "The Evaluation of the Toxicity of Industrial Wastes, Chemicals and Other Substances to Fresh-Water Fishes," The Atlantic Refining Co., Philadelphia, Pa., 317 p. (1945). (Out of print.)

(8) W. B. Hart, R. F. Weston and J. G. DeMann, "An Apparatus for Oxygenating Test Solutions in Which Fish are Used as Test Animals for Evaluating Toxicity," *Transactions American Fisheries Society (1945)*, Vol. 75, p. 228 (1948).

(9) D. W. M. Herbert, "Measurement of Toxicity of Substances to Fish," The Institute of Sewage Purification, p. 8 (1952)

(10) H. Turnbull, J. G. DeMann and R. F. Weston, "The Toxicity of Various Refinery Materials to Fresh Water Fish," *Industrial and Engineering Chemistry*, Vol. 46, No. 2, pp. 324–333 (1954).

(11) W. M. VanHorn, "The Biological Indices of Stream Quality," *Proceedings*, Fifth Industrial Waste Conference (1949), *Purdue University Engineering Bulletin*, Extension Series No. 72, p. 215 (1950).

Standard Method of Test for
HYDRAZINE IN INDUSTRIAL WATER[1]

ASTM Designation: D 1385 – 64

ADOPTED, 1964

This Standard of the American Society for Testing and Materials is issued under the fixed designation D 1385; the final number indicates the year of original adoption as standard or, in the case of revision, the year of last revision.

Scope and Application

1. This method[2] covers the colorimetric determination of hydrazine in industrial water.

Summary of Method

2. Para-dimethylaminobenzaldehyde produces a specific, yellow reaction product with hydrazine. The intensity of the yellow color is proportional to the amount of hydrazine in the water, and follows Beer's law.

Definitions

3. For definitions of terms used in this method, refer to the Definitions of Terms Relating to Industrial Water and Industrial Waste Water (ASTM Designation: D 1129).[3]

Interferences

4. (a) The substances normally present in industrial water do not interfere with the test; however, the hydrazine content may be diminished by oxidizing agents collected with the sample or absorbed by it prior to testing.

(b) Colors in the prescribed wavelengths also interfere, as do other dark colors or turbidities that cannot be overcome by the prescribed treatment.

Apparatus

5. *Colorimeter or Photometer.*—A Duboscq-type colorimeter, or a filter photometer or spectrophotometer suitable for measurements at 458 mμ. Table I shows the ranges to which various photometers are applicable. The quantities are based on a band width of 10 mμ and are increased by approximately 10

[1] Under the standardization procedure of the Society, this method is under the jurisdiction of the ASTM Committee D-19 on Industrial Water. A list of members may be found in the ASTM Year Book.

[2] For further information on this method, the following references may be of interest:

G. W. Watt and J. D. Chrisp, "Spectrophotometric Method for the Determination of Hydrazine," *Analytical Chemistry*, Vol. 24, No. 12, pp. 2006–2008 (1952).

Paul R. Wood, "Determination of Maleic Hydrazide Residues in Plant and Animal Tissue," *Analytical Chemistry*, Vol. 25, No. 12, pp 1879-1883 (1953).

[3] Appears in this publication.

per cent for a band width of 40 mμ. Certain photoelectric filter photometers are capable of measurements at 425 mμ, but not at 458 mμ. Measurements may be made at 425 mμ, with a reduction in sensitivity of approximately 50 per cent of that possible at 458 mμ.

Purity of Reagents

6. (a) Reagent grade chemicals shall be used in all tests. Unless otherwise indicated, it is intended that all reagents shall conform to the specifications of the Committee on Analytical Reagents of the American Chemical Society, where such specifications are available.[4] Other grades may be used, provided it is first ascertained that the reagent is of sufficiently high purity to permit its use without lessening the accuracy of the determination.

TABLE I.—APPLICATION RANGES OF PHOTOMETERS.

Scale Length, mm/per cent transmission	Solution Thickness, mm	Range, micrograms of N_2H_4 in 60 ml of final solution
1	10	0.20 to 25.0
	50	0.05 to 5.0
2.5	10	0.08 to 25.0
	50	0.02 to 5.0
5.0	10	0.05 to 25.0
	50	0.01 to 5.0

(b) Unless otherwise indicated, references to water shall be understood to mean reagent water conforming to the Specifications for Reagent Water (ASTM Designation: D 1193).[3] In addition, water shall be freshly boiled and free of dissolved oxygen.

(c) The purity of hydrazine dihydro-chloride may be established by iodimetric methods, making certain that all water used is oxygen-free and that all flasks and pipets used are purged with nitrogen. The water for this reagent is best prepared by boiling and then cooling under a nitrogen blanket.

(d) Para-dimethylaminobenzaldehyde reagents obtained from different manufacturers produce different intensities of color in solution. It is necessary that each new supply of reagent be tested on standard solutions before using with previously determined calibration curves.

Reagents

7. (a) *Hydrazine, Standard Solution* (*1 ml = 0.1 mg N_2H_4*). —Dissolve 0.328 g of hydrazine dihydrochloride ($N_2H_4 \cdot$ 2 HCl)[5] in 100 ml of water and 10.00 ml of HCl (sp gr 1.19). Dilute with water to 1 liter in a volumetric flask, and mix.

(b) *Hydrochloric Acid* (*sp gr 1.19*).— Concentrated hydrochloric acid (HCl).

(c) *Hydrochloric Acid* (*1:9*).—Mix 1 volume of HCl (sp gr 1.19) with 9 volumes of water.

(d) *Hydrochloric Acid* (*1:99*). —Mix 1 volume of HCl (sp gr 1.19) with 99 volumes of water.

(e) *Para-Dimethylaminobenzaldehyde Solution.*—Dissolve 4.0 g of *p*-dimethyl-aminobenzaldehyde[6] in 200 ml of methyl alcohol (CH_3OH) and 20 ml of HCl (sp gr 1.19). Store in a dark bottle out of direct sunlight.

Sampling

8. (a) Collect the sample in accordance with the applicable method of the American Society for Testing and Materials, as follows:

D 510—Sampling Industrial Water,[3]
D 860—Sampling Water from Boilers,[3]
D 1066—Sampling Steam.[3]

---

[4] "Reagent Chemicals, American Chemical Society Specifications," Am. Chem. Soc., Washington, D. C. For suggestions on the testing of reagents not listed by the American Chemical Society, see "Reagent Chemicals and Standards," by Joseph Rosin, D. Van Nostrand Co., Inc., New York, N. Y., and the "United States Pharmacopeia."

[5] Eastman reagent chemical No. 1117 has been found satisfactory for this purpose.
[6] Eastman reagent chemical No. 95 has been found satisfactory for this purpose.

(*b*) Analyze the sample as soon after collection as practicable, since hydrazine undergoes auto-oxidation as well as oxidation by oxidizing agents. Such agents may be in the sample or may enter the sample from the atmosphere. If it is suspected that oxidation of the hydrazine in the sample is occurring in the interval between collection and analysis, or if the sample is not to be analyzed immediately, collect under acid. Place 5.0 ml of HCl (1:9) in a 50-ml volumetric flask, and collect sufficient sample in the flask to bring the total volume to 50 ml.

Calibration

9. (*a*) Prepare a series of hydrazine standards by diluting measured volumes of the hydrazine solution (1 ml = 0.1 mg N_2H_4) with HCl (1:99), so that a 50.0-ml aliquot of each dilution will contain the desired quantity of hydrazine.

(*b*) Pipet 50.0-ml portions of the hydrazine standards into 100-ml beakers, flasks, or cylinders, and proceed as directed in Section 10, except do not add more acid. Plot transmittance against micrograms of hydrazine (Note).

NOTE—A separate calibration curve must be made for each photometer and a recalibration must be made if it is necessary to change the cell, lamp, or filter, or if any other alterations of instrument or reagents are made. Check the curve with each series of tests by running two or more solutions of known hydrazine concentrations.

Procedure

10. (*a*) To a 100-ml beaker, flask, or cylinder, add from a buret exactly 5.0 ml of HCl (1:9), unless the sample was collected under acid, in which case, proceed directly as described in Paragraph (*b*), except to use HCl (1:99) instead of water for diluting to 50.0 ml.

(*b*) By means of a graduated pipet, transfer to the 100-ml beaker, flask or cylinder a portion of the sample that will contain approximately 0.20 to 5.0

μg of N_2H_4. Add water from a graduated buret or pipet to make a final volume of exactly 50.0 ml, and mix. Add 10.0 ml of *p*-dimethylaminobenzaldehyde solution with a pipet, and mix. Let the mixture stand at least 10 min and not more than 100 min. Measure and compare the color by means of any of the apparatus listed in Section 5. Make photometric measurements at approximately 458 mμ.

(*c*) In photometric procedures, with water showing no appreciable color, prepare a blank containing no added hydrazine in order to correct for the color of the unreacted *p*-dimethylaminobenzaldehyde and any optical effects involved in adjusting the photometer for 100 per cent transmission.

(*d*) In the case of highly-colored water, prepare a blank by using the sample, after having first oxidized the hydrazine in the sample by suitable means. Determine the completeness of the oxidation of the hydrazine by making a plot of the percentage transmittance (compared to water to which the reagents have been added) *versus* wavelength for the spectral region 400 to 500 mμ, and noting whether the characteristic dip of para-dimethylaminobenzalazine occurs at 458 mμ.

Calculation

11. Calculate the hydrazine concentration, in parts per million, as follows:

$$\text{Hydrazine, ppm} = \frac{W}{S}$$

where:

W = micrograms of hydrazine found in accordance with Section 10, and
S = milliliters of sample.

Precision and Accuracy

12. (*a*) The precision can be estimated as follows:

$$\text{Precision, ppm} = \frac{3}{SLT}$$

where:

S = milliliters of sample,
L = millimeters of photometer scale length for each 1 per cent transmission, and
T = millimeters of light path length through solution.

(b) The agreement among five different laboratories expressed as the standard deviation of the mean of the results of each laboratory about the mean of the results of all laboratories participating was calculated and found to correspond to approximately four times the precision.

(c) The accuracy of the method has not been established.

Standard Methods of Test for

AMMONIA IN INDUSTRIAL WATER AND INDUSTRIAL WASTE WATER[1]

ASTM Designation: D 1426 – 58 (1965)

ADOPTED, 1958; REAPPROVED, 1965

This Standard of the American Society for Testing and Materials is issued under the fixed designation D 1426; the number immediately following the designation indicates the year of original adoption or, in the case of revision, the year of last revision. A number in parentheses indicates the year of last reapproval.

Scope and Application

1. (a) These methods[2] cover the determination of ammonia and ammonium ions present in industrial water and industrial waste water. Two methods are given, as follows:

	Section
Referee Method (Distillation Method)	6 to 12
Non-Referee Method (Direct Nesslerization Method)	13 to 21

(b) The Referee Method is applicable to all types of industrial water, including industrial waste water, for the determination of ammonia concentrations usually encountered in such waters. The Non-Referee Method may be used for the rapid routine determination of

ammonia in such waters. In both methods, all determinations should be carried out at room temperature (25 to 30 C).

Definitions

2. For definitions of terms used in these methods, refer to the Definitions of Terms Relating to Industrial Water and Industrial Waste Water (ASTM Designation: D 1129).[3]

Interferences

3. Certain interferences are common to both the Referee and Non-Referee Methods. Glycine, urea, glutamic acid, and acetamide, for example, hydrolyze very slowly in solution on standing; but, of these, only urea will hydrolyze on distillation at a pH of 7.4. Glycine is the only one of these compounds that will react with Nessler's reagent to give the characteristic yellow color in the time required in the test. Some amines, how-

---

[1] Under the standardization procedure of the Society, these methods are under the jurisdiction of the ASTM Committee D-19 on Industrial Water. A list of members may be found in the ASTM Year Book.

[2] Supporting data relating to the referee method may be found in Appendix I to the 1956 Report of Committee D-19, *Proceedings*, Am. Soc. Testing Mats., Vol. 56 (1956).

[3] Appears in this publication.

ever, react to produce turbidity. Hydrazine interferes at all levels of concentration. The extent of interference depends on the amount of hydrazine present.

Purity of Reagents

4. (a) Reagent grade chemicals shall be used in all tests. Unless otherwise indicated, it is intended that all reagents shall conform to the specifications of the Committee on Analytical Reagents of the American Chemical Society, where such specifications are available.[4] Other grades of reagents may be used, provided it is first ascertained that the reagent is of sufficiently high purity to permit its use without lessening the accuracy of the determination.

(b) Unless otherwise indicated, references to water shall be understood to mean reagent water conforming to the Specifications for Reagent Water (ASTM Designation: D 1193).[3] In addition, this water shall be free of ammonia nitrogen. Such water is best prepared by the passage of distilled water through an ion-exchange column containing a strongly acidic cation-exchange resin mixed with a strongly basic anion-exchange resin. These resins should also be selected so that organic compounds which might subsequently interfere with the ammonia determination will be removed (Note 1).[5]

Note 1.—The regeneration of the ion-exchange column should be carried out according to the instructions of the manufacturer.

Sampling

5. Collect the samples in accordance with the applicable methods of the American Society for Testing and Materials, as follows:

D 510—Sampling Industrial Water,[3]
D 860—Sampling Water from Boilers,[3]
D 1066—Sampling Steam.[3]

REFEREE METHOD

(Distillation Method)

Application

6. This method is applicable to all types of industrial water and industrial waste water where the greatest degree of precision and accuracy is required.

Summary of Method

7. The sample is buffered at a pH of 7.4 to inhibit hydrolysis of organic nitrogen compounds, and distilled into a solution of boric acid where the ammonia nitrogen is determined colorimetrically by Nesslerization or acidimetrically with standard sulfuric acid, using methyl red as an indicator. In the analysis of steam condensates, the distillation may be carried out at a pH of 11.0 or higher to expedite ammonia recovery.

Apparatus

8. (a) Distillation Apparatus.—An all-glass still consisting of a 1- or 2-liter flask, preferably double-necked to facilitate sample addition. The center neck is connected in series with a spray trap (Kjeldahl), a water-cooled condenser, and a long narrow delivery tube which extends nearly to the bottom of a suitable receiver marked at 300 or 350 ml. The outer neck carries a glass-stoppered funnel to facilitate sample addition. The outlet of this funnel shall extend below the liquid level in the flask.

(b) Nessler Tubes.—Matched Nessler tubes (APHA Standard) about 300 mm long, 17 mm inside diameter, and

[4] "Reagent Chemicals, American Chemical Society Specifications," Am. Chem. Soc., Washington, D. C. For suggestions on the testing of reagents not listed by the American Chemical Society, see "Reagent Chemicals and Standards," by Joseph Rosin, D. Van Nostrand Co., Inc., New York, N. Y., and the "United States Pharmacopeia."

[5] Resins similar to XE-75 or M.B.-1 have been found satisfactory for this purpose.

marked for 50 ml at 225 ± 1.5 mm from inside the bottom.

(c) *Photometer.*—Filter photometer or spectrophotometer suitable for absorbance measurements at 460 mμ.

(d) *Stoppers.*—Rubber stoppers, size No. 2, to fit Nessler tubes. These stoppers shall be boiled in 1.0 per cent H_2SO_4 (1:99), rinsed, boiled in NaOH solution (1 g NaOH per liter), rinsed, allowed to stand in dilute Nessler reagent for 30 min, and then rinsed again.

Reagents

9. (a) *Ammonium Chloride, Standard Solution (1 ml = 0.01 mg N).*—Dissolve 3.819 g of NH_4Cl in water and dilute to 1 liter in a volumetric flask. Dilute 10 ml of this stock solution to 1 liter in a volumetric flask.

(b) *Boric Acid Solution.*—Dissolve 20 g of H_3BO_3 in water and dilute to 1 liter.

(c) *Methyl Red Indicator (1 g per liter).*—Dissolve 0.1 g of water-soluble methyl red in water and dilute to 100 ml.

(d) *Nessler Reagent.*—Dissolve 100 g of anhydrous HgI_2 and 70 g of anhydrous KI in a small volume of water, and add this mixture slowly, with stirring, to a cooled solution of 160 g of NaOH in 500 ml of water. Dilute the mixture to 1 liter. If this reagent is stored in a chemically resistant bottle out of direct sunlight, it will remain stable up to a period of 1 yr (Note 2).

NOTE 2.—This reagent should give the characteristic color with ammonia within 10 min after addition, and should not produce a precipitate with small amounts of ammonia (0.04 mg in a 50-ml volume).

(e) *Phosphate Buffer Solution.*—Dissolve 14.3 g of KH_2PO_4 and 68.8 g of K_2HPO_4 in water and dilute to 1 liter.

(f) *Sulfuric Acid, Standard (0.02 N).*—Prepare a solution of H_2SO_4 (sp gr 1.84) such that 1 ml = 0.28 mg of ammonia nitrogen, and standardize (Note 3).

NOTE 3.—Other normalities of standard acid may be used. If the analyst so desires, a standard solution of $KH(IO_3)_2$ may be substituted for the standard H_2SO_4. In this case, the biiodate is a primary standard.

Procedure

10. (a) *Distillation.*—Add 500 ml of water and 10 ml of phosphate buffer to the still. Distill until two 50-ml portions of the distillate are shown to be ammonia-free when tested with Nessler reagent. Cool, and add sample and water to attain a final volume of about 550 ml. Distill 300 ml at a rate of between 6 and 10 ml per min into 50 ml of H_3BO_3 solution. Remove the receiver and mix. Collect an additional 50 ml to check for complete ammonia removal.

(b) Normally, the still and buffer are ready for immediate re-use if the pH is found to be correct on checking, and nitrogen compounds are absent. The need for 25 ml of buffer is indicated if the pH is not 7.4 at the end of the distillation period. If more than 1 mg of ammonia is present, an additional 50 ml of H_3BO_3 solution should be added to the receiver at the start to prevent loss of ammonia. In determining ammonia nitrogen in steam condensates, the sample may be added without cooling the still.

(c) *Volumetric Determination.*—To the distillate, add three drops of methyl red indicator and titrate the ammonia nitrogen obtained with standard H_2SO_4, matching the end point against a blank containing the same volume of water and H_3BO_3 solution.

(d) *Colorimetric Determination.* — Prepare a series of 14 Nessler tubes containing the following volumes of standard NH_4Cl solution diluted to 50 ml with water: 0.0, 0.2, 0.4, 0.6, 0.8, 1.0,

1.2, 1.4, 1.7, 2.0, 2.5, 3.0, 3.5, and 4.0 ml. Select a distillate volume containing no more than 0.04 mg of ammonia nitrogen and dilute to 50 ml. Mix, add 1 ml of Nessler reagent, and remix. Compare the color developed after 10 min with standards. If the ammonia nitrogen concentration is below 0.008 mg (in the 50-ml tube), compare after 30 min. If a photometer is used, make the readings after 20 to 30 min at 460 mμ. A compensatory blank should be used and the concentration determined from a previously prepared calibration curve (Note 4).

Note 4.—Some types of samples may give more consistent photometer readings if a protective colloid, such as gelatin or gum arabic, is added.

Calculation

11. (a) Calculate the ammonia concentration, in parts per million nitrogen, in the original sample as follows:

$$\text{Ammonia, as nitrogen, ppm} = \frac{A \times N_1 \times 14{,}000}{S}$$

$$\text{Ammonia, as nitrogen, ppm} = \frac{B \times C \times 10}{D \times S}$$

where:

A = milliliters of standard H_2SO_4 used in titrating,
N_1 = normality of the standard H_2SO_4,
S = milliliters of original sample used for distillation,
B = milliliters of NH_4Cl solution (1 ml = 0.01 mg N_2) used in the colorimetric determination,
C = milliliters of total distillate (plus H_3BO_3), and
D = milliliters of distillate used in the 50-ml Nessler tube.

(b) Calculate the ammonia concentration, in parts per million of free ammonia, in the original sample as follows:

$$\text{Ammonia, ppm} = E \times 1.2158$$

where:

E = parts per million of ammonia nitrogen.

Precision and Accuracy

12. The precision and accuracy will vary depending on the type of water being examined.

Non-Referee Method

(Direct Nesslerization Method)

Application

13. This method is suitable for the rapid, routine determination of ammonia nitrogen in industrial water and industrial waste water.

Summary of Method

14. Turbid samples may be clarified with $ZnSO_4$ and $NaOH$ solution; the precipitated $Zn(OH)_2$ is filtered off, discarding the first 25 ml of filtrate, and the ammonia is determined on an aliquot of the remaining clear filtrate by direct Nesslerization.

Interferences

15. See Section 3.

Apparatus

16. See Section 8 (b), (c), and (d).

Reagents

17. (a) Ammonium Chloride, Standard Solution.—See Section 9 (a).

(b) Cobaltous Chloride Solution (12 g per liter).—Dissolve 12 g of $CoCl_2 \cdot 6H_2O$ in 200 ml of water, add 100 ml of HCl (sp gr 1.19), and dilute to 1 liter.

(c) Nessler Reagent.—See Section 9 (d).

(*d*) *Potassium Chloroplatinate Solution (2 g per liter).*—Dissolve 2 g of K₂PtCl₆ in 350 ml of water, add 100 ml of HCl (sp gr 1.19), and dilute to 1 liter.

(*e*) *Sodium Hydroxide Solution (250 g per liter).*—Dissolve 250 g of NaOH in water, and dilute to 1 liter.

(*f*) *Sodium-Potassium Tartrate Solution (500 g per liter).*—Dissolve 500 g of sodium-potassium tartrate tetra-

TABLE I.—PERMANENT STANDARDS.

NH₃ as N₂, mg	Platinum Solution, ml	Cobalt Solution, ml
0.000	1.2	0.0
0.002	2.8	0.0
0.004	4.7	0.1
0.007	5.9	0.2
0.010	7.7	0.5
0.014	9.9	1.1
0.017	11.4	1.7
0.020	12.7	2.2
0.025	15.0	3.3
0.030	17.3	4.5
0.035	19.0	5.7
0.040	19.7	7.1
0.045	19.9	8.7
0.050	20.0	10.4
0.060	20.0	15.0
0.070	20.0	22.0

hydrate in 1 liter of water. Boil until ammonia-free, and dilute to 1 liter.

(*g*) *Zinc Sulfate Solution (100 g per liter).*—Dissolve 100 g of ZnSO₄·7H₂O in water and dilute to 1 liter.

Permanent Standards

18. Measure the volumes of platinum and cobalt solutions indicated in Table I into 50-ml Nessler tubes and dilute to the mark with water. These standards should be compared with temporary standards (Section 10 (*d*)) and the tints modified to match the time and reagents used. They will keep for 6 to 8 months if stored in a dark place and kept stoppered (Note 5).

Note 5.—These standards shall not be used in the referee method, but may be used for rapid routine determinations.

Procedure

19. If the samples contain turbidity, add one ml of ZnSO₄ solution to 100 ml of sample and mix. Add NaOH solution with gentle mixing until the pH is about 10.5. Allow to settle, and filter through filter paper, discarding the first 25 ml of filtrate. Dilute an aliquot portion to 50 ml in a Nessler tube. Add 2 drops of sodium-potassium tartrate solution to prevent cloudy tubes, and mix. Add 1 ml of Nessler solution, and compare with either temporary or permanent standards in accordance with Section 10 (*d*), substituting "sample" fo "distillate" (Note 4).

Calculations

20. (*a*) Calculate the ammonia concentration, in parts per million of nitrogen, in the original sample as follows:

$$\text{Ammonia, as nitrogen, ppm} = \frac{A \times 10}{S}$$

where:

A = milliliters of NH₄Cl solution (1 ml = 0.01 mg N₂) used, and

S = milliliters of sample.

(*b*) Permanent standards are made to read directly in milligrams of ammonia nitrogen. When these standards are used, calculate the ammonia concentration, in parts per million of nitrogen, in the original sample as follows:

$$\text{Ammonia, as nitrogen, ppm} = \frac{B \times 1000}{S}$$

where:

B = milligrams of nitrogen, and

S = milliliters of sample.

34-4

(c) Calculate the ammonia concentration, in parts per million of free ammonia, in the original sample as follows

Ammonia, ppm $= E \times 1.2158$

where:

E = parts per million of ammonia nitrogen.

Precision and Accuracy

21. The minimum readable concentration of ammonia nitrogen with Nessler's reagent is about 0.003 mg in a 50-ml Nessler tube. Results are normally reproducible within about 5 per cent of the amount determined.

Standard Methods of Test for
RESIDUAL CHLORINE IN INDUSTRIAL WASTE WATER[1]

ASTM Designation: D 1427 – 58 (1965)
ADOPTED, 1958; REAPPROVED, 1965

This Standard of the American Society for Testing and Materials is issued under the fixed designation D 1427; the number immediately following the designation indicates the year of original adoption or, in the case of revision, the year of last revision. A number in parentheses indicates the year of last reapproval.

NOTE.—An editorial change was made in Footnote 9 in June, 1959.

Scope and Application

1. (a) These methods cover non-referee procedures for the determination of residual chlorine in industrial waste water. A referee method and two non-referee methods for the determination of residual chlorine in industrial water other than that containing waste are given in the Methods of Test for Residual Chlorine in Industrial Water (ASTM Designation: D 1253).[2] Provision is made in these methods for the determination of total chlorine and free available chlorine. Provision is also made for the determination of the total chlorine in the presence of most of the interfering constituents found in industrial waste water, either through choice of the method employed or by a modification of the same. Two methods are given, as follows:

	Section
Non-Referee Method A (Starch-Iodide Titration Method)	6 to 11
Non-Referee Method B (Amperometric Titration Method)	12 to 20

(b) Both methods are applicable to the determination of total chlorine in industrial waste water. Only non-referee method B is applicable to the determination of free available chlorine in industrial waste water

(c) The type of residual chlorine to be determined depends on the objective of chlorination. When a free chlorine residual is not required, a determination of the total chlorine normally suffices regardless of the composition of the chlorine residual.

(d) Modifications of these methods are provided to eliminate one or more interferences present either initially in the industrial waste water or present subsequent to chlorination. The methods are most dependable when used with industrial waste water of known composition.

[1] Under the standardization procedure of the Society, these methods are under the jurisdiction of the ASTM Committee D-19 on Industrial Water. A list of members may be found in the ASTM Year Book.

[2] Appears in this publication.

Definitions

2. (*a*) The terms "residual chlorine (chlorine residual)," "total chlorine residual," and "free available chlorine residual," in these methods are defined in accordance with the Definitions of Terms Relating to Industrial Water and Industrial Waste Water (ASTM Designation: D 1129),[2] as follows:

Residual Chlorine (Chlorine Residual). —The amount of available chlorine present in industrial water at any specified period, subsequent to the addition of chlorine.

Total Chlorine Residual. — Total amount of chlorine residual present, without regard to type.

Free Available Chlorine Residual.— Residual consisting of hypochlorite ions (OCl), hypochlorous acid (HOCl), or a combination thereof.

(*b*) For definitions of other terms used in these methods, refer to Definitions D 1129.

Purity of Reagents

3. (*a*) Reagent grade chemicals shall be used in all tests. Unless otherwise indicated, it is intended that all reagents shall conform to the specifications of the Committee on Analytical Reagents of the American Chemical Society, where such specifications are available.[3] Other grades may be used, provided it is first ascertained that the reagent is of sufficiently high purity to permit its use without lessening the accuracy of the determination.

(*b*) Unless otherwise indicated, reference to water shall be understood to mean reagent water conforming to the Specifications for Reagent Water (ASTM Designation: D 1193).[2] In addition, the water shall be free from chlorine demand. Prepare the water by adding approximately 20 ppm available chlorine and adjusting the pH to be between 7.0 and 9.0. Protect the prepared water from sunlight for 1 week, then expose it to sunlight until no residual chlorine remains. If desirable, the final dechlorination may be effected with sodium arsenite solution prepared as directed in Section 4 (*g*).

Reagents

4. (*a*) *Buffer Solution A (pH 4.0).*— Dissolve 243 g of sodium acetate trihydrate and 480 g of glacial acetic acid in water and dilute to 1 liter.

(*b*) *Buffer Solution B (pH 7.0).*—Dissolve 25.4 g of KH_2PO_4 and 86 g of $Na_2HPO_4 \cdot 12H_2O$ in water and dilute to 1 liter.

(*c*) *Iodine Solution (12.7 g per liter).*[4]— Dissolve 25 g of KI in 50 ml of water. Add 12.7 g of iodine crystals and stir until solution is complete. Dilute to 1 liter with water and store the solution in a dark bottle.

(*d*) *Iodine, Standard Solution (0.0282 N).*—Transfer to a 1-liter volumetric flask 25 g of KI, dissolved in a small amount of water, and the calculated amount of approximately 0.1 N iodine solution that has been standardized against sodium arsenite. Dilute to 1 liter and store in a cool, dark place. Standardize daily as follows: Place 5 to 10 ml of 0.1 N arsenite solution in a flask and titrate with this solution, using starch solution as an indicator. Discard and prepare fresh solution if standardization shows a change in normality.

(*e*) *Phenylarseneoxide, Standard Solution (0.00564 N).*—Dissolve 0.8 g of

---

[3] "Reagent Chemicals, American Chemical Society Specifications," Am. Chem. Soc., Washington, D. C. For suggestions on the testing of reagents not listed by the American Chemical Society, see "Reagent Chemicals and Standards," by Joseph Rosin, D. Van Nostrand Co., Inc., New York, N. Y., and the "United States Pharmacopeia."

[4] Reagent used for standardization purposes only.

phenylarseneoxide in 150 ml of NaOH (12 g per liter). To 110 ml of this solution add 800 ml of water, and bring to a pH of 9.0 by adding HCl (1:1). (This should require about 2 ml of HCl (1:1).) Continue acidification with HCl (1:1) until a pH of 6 to 7 is reached, as indicated by a glass-electrode system; then dilute to a total volume of 1 liter. Add 1 ml of chloroform for preservation. Standardize to 0.00564 N against 0.0282 N iodine solution, using the titrator as the end-point indicator.

(*f*) *Potassium Iodide Solution (50 g per liter).*—Dissolve 50 g of KI in water and dilute to 1 liter.

(*g*) *Sodium Arsenite, Standard Solution (0.10 N).*[5]—Dissolve 4.946 g of dried As_2O_3 in 40 ml of NaOH solution (250 g NaOH per liter). Heat the solution to about 35 C and stir until the solution is clear and the surface free from floating material. Dilute to approximately 250 ml with water, saturate with CO_2, and then dilute to 1 liter. Store the solution in a dark bottle. Alternatively, standard sodium arsenite solution may be prepared as follows: Dissolve 4.946 g of dried As_2O_3 in 40 ml of NaOH solution (50 g per liter), acidify very slightly with H_2SO_4 or HCl, and dilute to 1 liter with water.

(*h*) *Starch Indicator.*—Make a paste of 1 g of arrowroot starch or soluble iodometric starch with cold water. Pour the paste into 100 ml of boiling water and boil for several minutes. Store in a glass-stoppered bottle in a cold place. Starch solution, prepared in this manner, will remain chemically stable for two to three days.

Sampling

5. Collect the sample in accordance with the Methods of Sampling Indus-trial Water (ASTM Designation D 510).[2] Take care that the sample is representative, and keep it away from direct sunlight prior to analysis (Note 1).

Note 1.—All determinations should be made immediately after collection of the sample, as the residual chlorine may diminish with time due to the continuing chlorine demand of the sample. When time of chlorine contact is of the utmost importance, the elapsed time between the addition of the chlorine and the determination of any residual chlorine should be taken into account.

Non-Referee Method A

(Starch-Iodide Titration Method)

Application

6. (*a*) This method is applicable to the determination of only total chlorine residual in all types of industrial waste water, except those having a color and turbidity high enough after dilution to the limit of the required precision to interfere with the visual colorimetric end point of the titration.

(*b*) The rate of chlorine addition may require a qualitative knowledge of total chlorine residual immediately after addition of chlorine. Such qualitative information normally suffices for control of chlorine addition to achieve, under specified conditions of total chlorine residual, the objectives of chlorination.

Summary of Method

7. (*a*) This is an iodometric titration for only total chlorine residual, utilizing iodine as the titrating agent in a back-titration as in Paragraph (*b*), or one utilizing phenylarseneoxide as the titrating agent in a direct titration as in Paragraph (*c*).

(*b*) When a sample is treated with a measured excess of standard phenylarseneoxide solution followed by the addition of iodide, the iodine liberated at the proper pH is stoichiometrically proportional to the total chlorine present. The liberated iodine reacts with the phenylarseneoxide before any is lost to other extraneous reactions. The excess phenylarseneoxide is titrated with standard iodine solution in the presence of starch until the phenylarseneoxide is completely oxidized. The end point of the titration is the next addition of standard iodine solution that causes a faint blue color to persist in the sample.

(c) When a sample is treated with iodide, the iodine liberated at the proper pH is stoichiometrically proportional to the total chlorine present. The iodine so liberated is titrated with standard phenylarseneoxide solution in the presence of starch until the iodine is completely reduced. The endpoint of the titration is the next addition of the phenylarseneoxide solution that causes the blue color to disappear in the sample.

Interferences

8. (a) *Organic Matter* that is unaffected by combined available chlorine (chloramines) acts as a mild reducing agent to react with liberated iodine. Where such organic matter is known to be present, proceed in accordance with Section 9 (a). Organic matter that is rapidly and continually being consumed by free available chlorine cannot be determined quantitatively.

(b) *Manganic Manganese*, in concentrations as low as 1.0 ppm, liberates iodine from iodide at a pH of 4.0.

(c) *Ferric Iron, Ferricyanide, and Nitrites*, in concentrations up to 1000 ppm, do not interfere at a pH of 4.0.

(d) *Chromates* reduce phenylarseneoxide to an appreciable extent before excess phenylarseneoxide can be titrated with standard iodine. In the presence of chromates, proceed in accordance with Section 9 (b).

(e) *Excessive Color and Turbidity* that is not reduced sufficiently by dilution of the sample, interfere with this method. If these are present, use Non-Referee Method B (Amperometric Titration Method).

Procedure

9. (a) *Back-Titration.*—To a measured 10-ml portion of 0.00564 N phenylarseneoxide solution in a 500-ml casserole or Erlenmeyer flask, add 1 ml of KI solution and 200 ml of the sample (Notes 2 and 3), while stirring. Follow immediately with sufficient buffer solution A to insure a pH of 4.0. Add 1 ml of starch solution and then, with stirring, add 0.0282 N iodine solution dropwise from a buret. Wait a few seconds between successive additions, and continue the titration until the next addition permits a faint blue color to persist. Record the total volume of iodine solution added.

NOTE 2.—If the color and turbidity of the sample interfere with detection of the end point, dilute the phenylarseneoxide and KI mixture with water. Add an appropriately reduced volume of sample to bring the total volume of the mixture to be titrated to 200 to 225 ml. Proceed with the titration as described.

NOTE 3.—For residual chlorine concentrations of 10 ppm or less, use a 200-ml sample, color and turbidity permitting (see Section 8 (e)). For residual chlorine concentrations between 10 and 25 ppm, increase the phenylarseneoxide solution to a maximum of 25 ml. The formation of a blue color on addition of starch indicates that insufficient phenylarseneoxide is present. In this case, repeat the procedure, using a greater amount of phenylarseneoxide solution. If the amount of phenylarseneoxide solution required exceeds 25 ml, repeat the procedure using an appropriately reduced volume of sample in accordance with Note 2.

(b) *Direct Titration.*—To a 200-ml sample (Notes 2 and 3) in a 500-ml casserole or Erlenmeyer flask add 1 ml of KI solution, while stirring. Follow immediately with buffer solution A, sufficient to insure a pH of 4.0. Add 0.00564 N phenylarseneoxide solution, while stirring, dropwise from a buret until the color is reduced to a pale but discernible yellow color. Add 1 ml of starch solution and continue the drop-wise addition of the phenylarseneoxide solution, while stirring, until the next addition discharges the blue color. Record the total volume of phenylarseneoxide solution added.

Calculation

10. (a) For the back-titration, calculate the total chlorine residual, in parts per million, as follows:

$$\text{Chlorine residual, ppm} = \frac{A - 5I}{S} \times 200$$

where:
A = milliliters of 0.00564 N phenyl-arseneoxide solution added as described in Section 9 (a),
I = milliliters of 0.0282 N iodine solution required for the titration described in Section 9 (a), and
S = milliliters of sample used.

(b) For the direct titration, calculate the total chlorine residual, in parts per million, as follows.

$$\text{Chlorine residual, ppm} = \frac{200A}{S}$$

where:
A = milliliters of 0.00564 N phenyl-arseneoxide solution required for the titration described in Section 9 (b), and
S = milliliters of sample used.

Precision and Accuracy

11. (a) The precision of the back-titration method may be expressed as:

$$\text{Precision} = \frac{20}{S}$$

(b) The precision of the direct titration method may be expressed as:

$$\text{Precision} = \frac{4}{S}$$

(c) No statement of accuracy can be valid due to the multiple effects of interferences; to the continuous chlorine requirement for all reducing constituents present; and to the continuous varia-tion of concentratior of these constit-uents, each with its specific (but different) chlorine requirement for each sample.

Non-Referee Method B

(Amperometric Titration Method)

Application

12. (a) The method is applicable to all types of industrial waste water, re-gardless of temperature, color, and turbidity, providing the method is modified in accordance with the pres-ence of certain constituents in the industrial waste water. It may be used to determine the amount of total chlorine and free available chlorine present in any concentration in indus-trial waste water.

(b) The rate of chlorine addition may require a qualitative knowledge of total chlorine residual or free available chlorine residual immediately after addi-tion of chlorine. Such qualitative in-formation normally suffices for control of chlorine addition to achieve, undei specified conditions of total chlorine residual or free available chlorine resid-ual, the objectives of chlorination.

Summary of Method

13. (a) This is an amperometric titration for total chlorine residual utilizing iodine as the titrating agent in a back-titration as in Paragraph (b), or for total chlorine residual utilizing phenylarseneoxide as the titrating agent

in a direct titration as in Paragraph (c) and for free available chlorine as in Paragraph (d).

(b) When a sample is treated with a measured excess of standard phenylarseneoxide solution followed by the addition of iodide, the iodine liberated at the proper pH is stoichiometrically proportional to the total chlorine present. The iodine liberated reacts with the phenylarseneoxide before any is lost to other extraneous reactions. When the cell is immersed in a sample so treated, no current is generated due to halogens nor is any further current generated, as the excess phenylarseneoxide is titrated with standard iodine solution until the phenylarseneoxide is completely oxidized. The end point of the titration is the next addition of standard iodine solution that causes further current to be generated and a microammeter response or pointer deflection.

(c) When the cell is immersed in a sample containing iodide at the proper pH, the iodine liberated is stoichiometrically proportional to the total chlorine present and the current generated is proportional to the iodine and the total chlorine. As standard phenylarseneoxide solution is added, the current generated becomes less, the end point of the titration being the next addition of standard phenylarseneoxide solution that causes no further reduction in current or in microammeter response or pointer deflection.

(d) When the cell is immersed in a sample at the proper pH and which contains free available chlorine, the current generated becomes less as standard phenylarseneoxide solution is added, until the free available chlorine is completely reduced. The end point of the titration is the next addition of standard phenylarseneoxide solution that causes no further reduction in

current or in microammeter response or pointer deflection.

Interferences[5, 6, 7]

14. (a) The interferences for this method are identical to those described in Section 8 (a) to (d).

(b) Nitrogen trichloride is often present as the end product of the chlorination of industrial waste water, and titrates partly as free available chlorine and partly as combined available chlorine. This error can only be avoided in the determination of the total chlorine residual.

(c) Exposure of high concentrations of free available chlorine causes a film-type polarization which reverses very slowly. This may be avoided by use of the back-titration or, if the direct titration must be used, by diluting the sample with water until the solution titrated contains no more than 10 ppm free available chlorine.

(d) Dichloramine is the principal end product of the chlorination of industrial waste water containing ammonia or nitrogenous organic compounds. It is often extremely high after dilution, and produces four to five times as much current as monochloramine. The current produced by even less than 5 ppm dichloramine may be so great as to cause the microammeter pointer to be off the right side of the scale even at the end point in the free available chlorine titration. This may be overcome by inserting an opposing voltage on the microammeter by disconnecting the leads, A and B of Fig. 1, on the

---

[5] H. C. Marks, R. R. Joiner, and F. B. Strandskov, "Amperometric Titration of Residual Chlorine in Sewage," *Water and Sewage Works*, Vol. 95, p. 175, May, 1948.

[6] R. V. Day, D. H. Horchler, and H. C. Marks, "Residual Chlorine Methods and Disinfection of Sewage," *Industrial and Engineering Chemistry*, Vol. 45, p. 1001 (1953).

[7] H. C. Marks and N. S. Chamberlin, "Determination of Residual Chlorine in Metal Finishing Wastes," *Analytical Chemistry*, Vol. 24, p. 1885 (1953).

rectifier and connecting them to another source, such as a 1.5-v dry cell.

(e) Silver in the soluble silver cyanide complex ion in concentrations as low as

Apparatus

15. *Amperometric Titration Apparatus.*[8]—See Fig. 1 for the wiring diagram of this apparatus (Note 4).

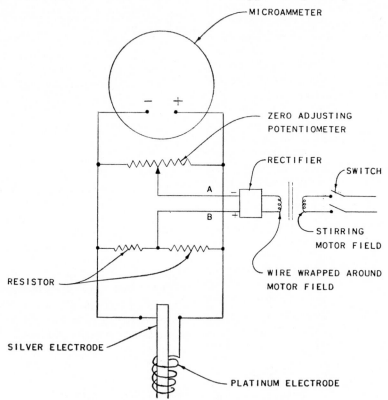

FIG. 1.—Wiring Diagram of Amperometric Titrator.

1.0 ppm silver, poisons the cell at pH 4.0 but not at 7.0; and the silver ion, in absence of the cyanide complex, gives extensive response in the current at pH 4.0 and gradually poisons the amperometric titrator cell at all pH levels. This may be avoided by using Non-Referee Method A for total chlorine.

(f) Cuprous copper in the soluble copper cyanide ion in concentrations at least as low as 5 ppm copper, poisons the cell at pH 4.0 and 7.0. (Cadmium, nickelous nickel, and zinc ions are without effect on the cell.) This is avoided by using Non-Referee Method A for total chlorine.

NOTE 4.—This apparatus is identical with the apparatus used in the Methods of Test for Residual Chlorine in Industrial Water (ASTM Designation: D 1253).[2]

Calibration[9]

16. When the titrator has been out of service for a day or more, check the

---

[8] The apparatus available from Wallace & Tiernan, Inc., Newark, N. J., has been found satisfactory for this purpose.
[9] Calibrate commercial apparatus in accordance with the detailed instructions supplied by the manufacturer. Glassware should be conditioned with water containing at least 10 ppm of residual chlorine for at least 2 hr before use and then rinsed with water having zero chlorine demand.

electrode for sensitivity by noting the rapidity of the pointer deflection before beginning formal titrations. If the pointer responds slowly after the addition of KI solution, add a small amount of iodine. If it responds slowly to free available chlorine, sensitize it by adding more chlorine.

Procedure for Total Chlorine Residual

17. (a) *Back-Titration.*—To a measured 10-ml portion of 0.00564 N phenylarseneoxide solution in the titrator jar add 1 ml of KI solution and 200 ml of the sample (Note 5). Immediately immerse the cell in the sample and start the stirring motor. Follow immediately with sufficient buffer solution A to insure a pH of 4.0. With the potentiometer, adjust the microammeter pointer to the left side of the scale so that the pointer can deflect clockwise. Add 0.0282 N iodine solution dropwise from the buret, wait a few seconds between successive additions, and continue until the next addition permits the pointer to abruptly deflect clockwise and, in so doing, persist in the clockwise position. Record the total volume of iodine solution added.

Note 5.—For residual chlorine concentrations of 10 ppm or less, use a 200-ml sample. For residual chlorine concentrations between 10 and 25 ppm, increase the phenylarseneoxide solution to a maximum of 25 ml. The abrupt deflection of the pointer clockwise on the first addition of iodine solution indicates that insufficient phenylarseneoxide is present. In this case, repeat the procedure, using a greater amount of phenylarseneoxide solution. If the amount of phenylarseneoxide solution required exceeds 25 ml, repeat the procedure by diluting the phenylarseneoxide and KI mixture with water. Add an appropriately reduced volume of the sample to bring the total volume of the mixture to be titrated to 200 to 225 ml. Proceed with the titration as described.

(b) *Direct Titration.*—With the cell immersed in a 200-ml sample (Note 4), start the stirring motor and add 1 ml of KI solution. Follow immediately with buffer solution A, sufficient to insure a pH of 4.0. With the potentiometer, adjust the microammeter pointer to the right side of the scale so that the pointer can deflect counterclockwise. Add 0.00564 N phenylarseneoxide solution dropwise from the buret, waiting a few seconds between successive additions. When the microammeter pointer reaches the bottom of the scale, readjust as above with the potentiometer. Continue until the next addition of phenylarseneoxide solution produces no further counterclockwise movement of the pointer. Record the total volume of phenylarseneoxide solution added.

Procedure for Free Available Chlorine

18. With the cell immersed in a 200-ml sample (Note 4), start the stirring motor. Follow immediately with buffer solution B or, if necessary, buffer solution A, sufficient to insure a pH of 7.0. Then proceed as described in Section 17 (b), starting with the addition of standard phenylarseneoxide solution from the buret.

Calculation

19. (a) For the back-titration, calculate the total chlorine residual, in parts per million, as follows:

$$\text{Chlorine residual, ppm} = \frac{A - 5I}{S} \times 200$$

where:
A = milliliters of 0.00564 N phenylarseneoxide solution added as described in Section 17 (a),
I = milliliters of 0.0282 N iodine solution required for the titration described in Section 17 (a),
S = milliliters of sample used.

(b) For the direct titration, calculate the total chlorine residual, in parts per million, as follows:

$$\text{Chlorine residual, ppm} = \frac{200A}{S}$$

where:

A = milliliters of 0.00564 N phenyl-arseneoxide solution required for the titration described in Section 17 (b), and

S = milliliters of sample used.

(c) Calculate the free available chlorine, in parts per million, as follows:

$$\text{Free available chlorine, ppm} = \frac{200A}{S}$$

where:

A = milliliters of 0.00564 N phenyl-arseneoxide solution required for the titration described in Section 18, and

S = milliliters of sample used.

Precision and Accuracy

20. (a) The precision of the back-titration method may be expressed as:

$$\text{Precision} = \frac{20}{S}$$

(b) The precision of the direct titration methods (Sections 17 (b) and 18) may be expressed as:

$$\text{Precision} = \frac{4}{S}$$

(c) No statement of accuracy can be valid due to the multiple effects of interferences; to the continuous chlorine requirement for all reducing constituents present; and to the continuous variation of concentration of these constituents, each with its specific (but different) chlorine requirement for each sample.

Standard Methods of Test for
SODIUM AND POTASSIUM IN INDUSTRIAL WATER AND WATER-FORMED DEPOSITS BY FLAME PHOTOMETRY[1]

ASTM Designation: D 1428 – 64
ADOPTED, 1964.[2]

This Standard of the American Society for Testing and Materials is issued under the fixed designation D 1428; the final number indicates the year of original adoption as standard or, in the case of revision, the year of last revision.

Scope

1. These methods cover the determination of sodium and potassium in industrial water and water-formed deposits using direct measuring-type flame photometers.

	Sections
Method A. Analysis of Industrial Water	8 to 13
Method B. Analysis of Trace Amounts of Sodium in Low-Solids Industrial Water	14 to 22
Method C. Analysis of Water-Formed Deposits	23 to 28

[1] Under the standardization procedure of the Society, these methods are under the jurisdiction of the ASTM Committee D-19 on Industrial Water. A list of members may be found in the ASTM Year Book.

[2] Revised and adopted as standard August 31, 1964, by action of the Society at the Annual Meeting and confirming letter ballot.

Prior to their present adoption as standard, these methods were published as tentative from 1956 to 1961, being revised in 1956 and 1961. They were adopted in 1961 and published as standard until 1962. They were revised and reverted to tentative in 1962 and published as such until 1964. The Method of Test for Sodium in High-Purity Industrial Water by Flame Photometry (ASTM Designation: D 1887) was incorporated in the 1962 revision.

Summary of Methods

2. When a solution containing salts of sodium or potassium is atomized into a gas flame, light that is characteristic of these elements is emitted, the intensity being a function of concentration. Salts of many other elements cause similar emission. The flame photometer consists of apparatus for giving a reproducible amount of emitted light for a given concentration of element in the test solution, and for determining the intensity of such emission as a function of concentration of the element without excessive interference from other emitted light (Note 1).

NOTE 1.—Specifically, for a given element light of wavelengths other than that characteristic of the element to be determined must be eliminated before accurate intensity measurements can be made. This is accomplished by selective filtration of the emitted light, by use of interference filters, or by a suitable slit arrangement in light-dispersing devices, such as prism or grating monochromators.

Definitions

3. For definitions of terms used in this method, refer to the Definitions of

Terms Relating to Industrial Water and Industrial Waste Water (ASTM Designation: D 1129).[3]

Interferences

4. (a) Radiation interference caused by elements other than that being determined is the greatest contributor to error in flame photometry. Some effects are positive and others negative. Of the elements encountered in these analyses, the greatest effect is that of one alkali metal on another. The foreign-element effects cannot be entirely compensated for without employing calibration standards closely duplicating the composition of the sample. However, the effects may be minimized by operating at the lowest practical sodium or potassium concentration range or by removal of the interfering elements. For example, aluminum has a depressing effect on alkali-metal emission, which may be of serious consequence. The amount of aluminum normally present in any type of industrial water has been found to have a negligible effect on alkali-metal determination. However, aluminum in water-formed deposits should be removed from the solution prior to flame photometry if its concentration has been found, by preliminary tests, to exceed that of the alkali metal being determined.

(b) Self-absorption causes the curve of intensity versus concentration to decrease in slope at higher concentrations, tending to reduce accuracy. Bracketing the unknown by known standard solutions and interpolating linearly between the two minimize this interference so as to render it practically negligible.

(c) Suspended matter which may interfere mechanically by clogging the burner shall be removed by filtration prior to analysis. Organic coloring matter

does not cause interference and need not be removed.

Apparatus and Materials

5. (a) Flame Photometer.—The instrument shall consist of an atomizer and burner; suitable pressure-regulating devices and gages for fuel and air or oxygen; an optical system, consisting of suitable light-dispersing or filtering devices capable of preventing excessive interference from light of wavelengths other than that being measured; and a photosensitive indicating device.

(b) Supply of Fuel and Air or Oxygen.— The supplies of fuel and air or oxygen shall be maintained at pressures somewhat higher than the controlled operating pressure of the instrument.

Purity of Reagents

6. (a) Reagent grade chemicals shall be used in all tests. Unless otherwise indicated, it is intended that all reagents shall conform to the specifications of the Committee on Analytical Reagents of the American Chemical Society, where such specifications are available.[4] Other grades may be used, provided it is first ascertained that the reagent is of sufficiently high purity to permit its use without lessening the accuracy of the determination.

(b) Unless otherwise indicated, references to water shall be understood to mean reagent water conforming to the requirements for the referee grade in the Specifications for Reagent Water (ASTM Designation: D 1193).[3] In addition, the sodium or potassium content shall not exceed 0.01 ppm, or 1 per cent

---

[3] Appears in this publication.

[4] "Reagent Chemicals, American Chemical Society Specifications," Am. Chemical Soc., Washington, D. C. For suggestions on the testing of reagents not listed by the American Chemical Society, see "Reagent Chemicals and Standards," by Joseph Rosin, D. Van Nostrand Co., Inc., New York, N. Y. and the "United States Pharmacopeia."

of the maximum concentration in the range to be covered, whichever is greater (Note 2).

Note 2.—The effluent from a mixed-bed deionizing unit having a specific conductance of 0.09 micromho may be assumed to contain not more than 0.01 ppm of sodium ion or potassium ion. If such water then be stored in a closed alkali-metal-free container, such as one made of polyethylene or stainless steel, subsequent increase in conductivity, usually due to absorption of gases, will not invalidate its use for this purpose. Instructions for the preparation of mixed-bed deionizers are available from manufacturers of ion-exchange resins.

Sampling

7. Collect the sample in accordance with the applicable method of the American Society for Testing and Materials, as follows:

D 510—Sampling Industrial Water,[3]
D 860—Sampling Water from Boilers,[3]
D 887—Field Sampling of Water-Formed Deposits,[3]
D 1066—Sampling Steam.[3]

Method A. Analysis of Industrial Water

Application

8. Sodium and potassium present in any type of industrial water may be determined by this method. The method is especially recommended for concentrations of sodium and potassium between 1 and 100 ppm. For samples containing less than 1 ppm sodium, Method B is recommended.

Reagents

9. Prepare the following stock solutions from reagents that have been dried to constant weight at 105 C. Store these stock solutions in polyethylene or equally alkali-metal-free containers.

(a) Potassium Chloride Solution (1.9068 g per liter).—Dissolve 1.9068 g of potassium chloride (KCl) in water and dilute to 1 liter with water. This solution contains 1000 ppm of potassium ion.

(b) Sodium Chloride Solution (2.5418 g per liter).—Dissolve 2.5418 g of sodium chloride (NaCl) in water and dilute to 1 liter with water. This solution contains 1000 ppm of sodium ion.

Calibration and Standardization[5]

10. Calibrate and standardize as follows:

(a) By diluting the stock solutions described in Section 9, prepare eleven solutions of sodium and potassium for each operating range, that is, 0 to 1, 0 to 10, and 0 to 100 ppm, so that within each range there are equally spaced standards in tenths of the maximum.

(b) Turn the instrument on.

(c) Select the proper photocell, either red-sensitive or blue-sensitive (Note 3), open the slit width to about one fourth of the maximum opening, set the instrument to the maximum sensitivity range, and balance the meter to obtain electrical equilibrium.

Note 3.—A photomultiplier tube or blue-sensitive phototube having a range of 320 to 620 mμ, is required for the sodium determination; and a red-sensitive phototube having a range of 620 to 1200 mμ, is required for the potassium determination.

(d) Feed fuel and air or oxygen to the burner and ignite the emitted mixture. Adjust fuel and air or oxygen pressures (Note 4), set the scale-reading dial at about 95 per cent of full scale, introduce a solution containing the maximum amount of sodium or potassium in the range to be covered, and allow the emitted light to strike the selected photocell.

[5] The exact method of operation varies with different instruments; hence, no attempt is made here to describe in detail the steps for putting the instrument into operation.

Note 4.—Use the fuel and air or oxygen pressures, and procedures for warm-up time, prescribed by the instrument manufacturer.

(e) Select the proper filter, if a filter-type instrument is used. For instruments employing spectral dispersing devices, turn the wavelength dial back and forth slowly and carefully in the vicinity of the desired wavelength, 589 mμ for sodium and 768 mμ for potassium. The galvanometer can be made to pass through a maximum deflection. This wavelength setting produces maximum sensitivity, and should not be disturbed during the test for the element to be determined.

(f) Continue to atomize the maximum standard of the range to be covered, and set the scale-reading dial at exactly full scale (100 or 1000) (Note 5). Adjust the gain so as to balance the galvanometer needle.

Note 5.—For instruments equipped with a variable slit, carry out the procedure described in Paragraph (e) with the slit width between fully closed and one fourth open for a preliminary test. In determining the proper slit width for optimum instrument performance, consideration must be given to the fact that the intensity of the emission line is approximately proportional to the slit width, whereas continuous background intensity increases as the square of the slit width. A decrease in slit width results in decreased illumination of the phototube for a given concentration and is compensated for by increasing the gain of the instrument. The most favorable operating conditions are obtained with the smallest slit width that does not result in instability of the galvanometer needle when it is set to give full-scale reading with the maximum standard in the range to be covered.

When altering the slit width, determine background by atomizing a zero standard, and check for sensitivity setting and instrument stability with the maximum standard in the range to be covered.

Lower ranges require wider slit widths. Determine and record the optimum slit width for each range and element to be covered. Use these values in all subsequent tests.

(g) Determine the emission intensity of all standards. With instruments em-ploying spectral dispersing devices, repeat the procedure described in Paragraph (e) for the wavelength setting when changing from one element to another. With instruments equipped with a movable slit, be certain to change the slit width to the value determined, as suggested in Note 5, when changing to a different range or element.

(h) Plot emission intensity (scale reading) versus concentration on linear graph paper. For the lower ranges, the curve thus prepared approximates a straight line but may not intersect zero because of background intensity. At higher ranges the curves show a decrease in slope with increasing concentration. Record on graphs all data in regard to slit widths used in different ranges and elements, fuel pressure, and air or oxygen pressure.

Procedure

11. (a) No preliminary treatment of the sample is needed, except filtration through an 11-cm ashless filter paper of medium retentiveness, if the sample contains suspended material.

(b) Turn the instrument on and feed fuel and air or oxygen to the burner. Ignite the emitted mixture. For instruments with an adjustable slit, set the width to the value determined as suggested in Note 5 for the particular range and element to be determined.

(c) Place the scale-reading dial at 100 (or 1000). Atomize the sample and allow its emitted light to strike the photocell. Select the wavelength established in accordance with Section 10(e) and adjust the gain to balance the galvanometer. Determine the emission intensity of the sample (Note 6).

Note 6.—If the concentration of the element in the sample is found to be greater than the maximum standard employed in Section 10(d), dilute the original sample with water to bring the concentration within the range.

If the concentration of the element in the sample is less than one tenth of the value of the maximum standard, use the next lower range. If change of range is necessary, repeat the procedure from the beginning of this section.

(*d*) Refer to the curve prepared in accordance with Section 10(*h*) and select the standards that immediately bracket the emission intensity of the sample. Determine the emission intensities of the bracketing standards, and a check emission intensity value for the sample. Record these values. Repeat the determination of emission intensity of the bracketing standards and the sample and record as above.

Calculations

12. (*a*) Calculate the concentration of sodium or potassium ions, in parts per million, from the first set of data as follows:

$$X = \left[\frac{(A - B)(c - b)}{(a - b)} + B \right] \times D$$

where:

X = sodium ion or potassium ion in the sample, in parts per million,

A = parts per million of ion corresponding to X for the upper bracketing sample,

B = parts per million of ion corresponding to X for the lower bracketing sample,

a = emission intensity of the upper bracketing standard,

b = emission intensity of the lower bracketing standard,

c = emission intensity of the sample and

D = number of dilutions.

(*b*) Repeat the calculation for the second set of data and average the two values of X to obtain the result to be reported.

Precision

13. The over-all precision of the method is as follows:

for sodium:

$$S_T = 0.011X + 0.64$$

for potassium:

$$S_T = 0.009 + 0.45$$

where:

S_T = over-all precision in parts per million, and

X = concentration of sodium or potassium determined in sample.

METHOD B. ANALYSIS OF TRACE AMOUNTS OF SODIUM IN LOW-SOLIDS INDUSTRIAL WATER

Application

14. This method is applicable to the determination of trace amounts of sodium ion in such industrial waters having low solids content as condensate and deionized water. It is specifically applicable to concentrations of sodium from 0.25 to 1000 ppb. Many authorities claim that it is possible to detect much less than 0.25 ppb. While this is true, it can be done only with certain types of equipment and with very close control of the many variables in flame photometry.[6]

---

[6] For further information on this method the following references may be of interest:

C. A. Bishoff, J. K. Brown, and H. L. Kahler, "Conductivity versus Sodium by Flame Spectrophotometer in Steam Purity Tests," ASME Paper 56-A-196, Am. Soc. Mechanical Engineers.

E. E. Coulter and T. M. Campbell, "Steam Purity Determination by Tracer Techniques," Symposium on Steam Quality, *ASTM STP No. 192*, Am. Soc. Testing Mats., pp. 13–26 (1956).

E. A. Pirsh and F. G. Raynor, "Instrumentation for the Determination of Steam Purity," Engineers' Society of Western Pennsylvania, Seventeenth Annual Water Conference Proceedings, pp. 79–88 (1956).

J. K. Rice, "Steam Quality Measurements by Flame Photometer," Engineers' Society of Western Pennsylvania, Seventeenth Annual Water Conference Proceedings, pp. 89–101 (1956).

Interferences

15. In the analysis of low solids industrial water, radiation interferences caused by elements other than sodium are negligible. The principal errors encountered are variations in flame background and contamination of the flame by air-borne dusts. Because of the abundance of sodium in all atmospheric dust, it is necessary to filter air entering the burner housing. There should be no smoking in the vicinity of the photometer since cigarette smoke is heavily contaminated with sodium and potassium. Equipment and procedures for minimizing these effects are described in Sections 16(*b*) and 18(*b*).

Apparatus and Materials

16. (*a*) *Flame Photometer.*—The instrument shall consist of an atomizer and burner suitable for hydrogen as fuel, pressure-regulating devices[7] capable of maintaining constant oxygen and hydrogen pressure for duration of the test, an optical system capable of isolating the desired radiation, a photomultiplier tube as a light-measuring and amplifying device, and a method for indicating the intensity of the measured emitted light.

(*b*) *Air Filter*[8] *and Blower.*[9]—For analysis of low-solids water it is necessary to introduce filtered air into and around the burner housing. This is accomplished by means of a blower and a filter capable of removing 99.97 per cent of all particles larger than 0.3 μ. The filter and blower are mounted as a single unit and placed under the burner housing. To accomplish this, it is necessary to cut a hole in the table top beneath the burner housing. The hole

---

[7] Valves available from Stratos, a division of Fairchild Engine and Airplane Corp., have been found satisfactory for this purpose.
[8] A space air filter from the Mine Safety Co., Pittsburgh, Pa., has been found satisfactory for this purpose.
[9] Any 50 to 100-cu ft per min blower may be used.

should have the same dimensions as the burner housing. This arrangement is most satisfactory for permanent installations. As an alternative, the discharge from the blower-filter could be connected to a hose about 2 in. in diameter and introduced through the side opposite the door of the burner housing.

(*c*) *Oxygen and Hydrogen.*—A supply of oxygen and hydrogen maintained at a pressure somewhat greater than the controlled operating pressures of the instrument.

(*d*) *Polyethylene or Tetrafluoroethylene (Teflon) Sample Cups.*—The glass sample holders supplied with most flame photometers are not suitable when analyzing low-solids water. Contamination of the sample by contact with the fingers in handling these small cups is a distinct possibility. Errors due to creeping and the wettability of the glass must also be considered. Therefore, it is strongly recommended that sample cups be made from polyethylene or tetrafluoroethylene (Teflon) rods. Handles made from either plastic or metal should be attached to these cups to facilitate handling and prevent pickup of sodium from perspiration on the fingers.

(*e*) *Polyethylene or Tetrafluoroethylene (Teflon) Bottles*, 8-oz, with caps of the same material.

(*f*) *Polyethylene, Tetrafluoroethylene (Teflon), or Stainless Steel Container.*

(*g*) *Vinyl (Tygon) Tubing.*

(*h*) *Rubber Gloves or "Fingers."*

Reagents

17. (*a*) *Sodium Chloride (0.2542 g per liter).*—Dry sodium chloride (NaCl) at constant weight at 105 C. Dissolve 0.2542 g of NaCl in water and dilute to 1 liter with water. Dilute 10 ml of this solution to 1 liter and store in polyethylene or equally alkali-metal-free con-

tainers. The latter solution contains 1000 ppb sodium. This solution can be further diluted to provide a known standard of any sodium concentration less than 1000 ppb Na^+.

(b) *Water.*—The sodium content shall not exceed 1.0 ppb (Note 7).

Note 7.—Single distilled water passed through a mixed bed deionizing unit composed of strong cation and anion resins can produce an effluent containing less than 1.0 ppb sodium. If such water then be stored in a closed alkali metal-free container, such as one made of polyethylene, tetrafluoroethylene (Teflon), or stainless steel, subsequent increase in conductivity, usually due to absorption of gases, will not invalidate its use for this purpose. Instructions for the preparation of mixed bed deionizers are available from ion-exchange manufacturers.

Sampling

18. (a) Collect the sample in accordance with the applicable method of the American Society for Testing and Materials as follows, with modifications as given in Paragraph (b):

D 510—Sampling Industrial Water,[3]
D 860—Sampling Water from Boilers,[3]
D 1066—Sampling Steam.[3]

(b) A special sampling technique is required for low solids water as follows: Thoroughly flush the sample line; attach vinyl tubing, sufficiently long to reach the bottom of the sample container, and adjust the flow rate to approximately 1 pt per min. When cooling is necessary, regulate the cooling water to reduce the temperature to less than 100 F. Start sample collection by placing the loose end of the tubing in a container of sufficient size to completely immerse the sample bottle. When the container is overflowing, withdraw the sampling tube from the container and rinse the outside surfaces of the bottle with the flowing sample. Insert the end of the tube into the sample bottle and then immerse the bottle in the container.

Allow the sample bottle and container to overflow for a period of not less than 30 min. During this period, allow the bottle caps to soak in the container with the concave side down. At the end of the overflow period, carefully remove the sampling tube from the bottle and lower the end to the bottom of the container. During this operation, care must be exercised to avoid touching any part of the wetted tube surfaces or the water itself with the hands; where necessary, employ tongs which shall be allowed to stand in the container while the sample is being collected. Using the same tongs, hold the bottle under the surface of the water and, using rubber "fingers" which have been thoroughly rinsed, cap the bottle. It may then be removed from the container.

Calibration and Standardization[10]

19. (a) Calibrate and standardize the instrument as follows:

(1) Prepare at least three standards to cover the expected range of the sample by diluting the 1000-ppb solution described in Section 17(a). The concentration of the standards of course will vary according to the range for which the instrument is to be calibrated. In general, the standards should be selected to give a zero, middle, and maximum point for the calibration curve. However, once the calibration curve has been ascertained, daily calibrations can be made by using only the maximum standard for a given range.

(2) Turn on the instrument.

(3) Set the instrument to the maximum sensitivity range and place the photomultiplier tube in operating position. Balance the meter to obtain electrical equilibrium.

[10] The exact method of operation varies with different instruments; hence, no attempt is made here to describe in detail the steps for putting the instrument into operation.

(4) Feed fuel and oxygen to the burner and ignite the emitted mixture. Adjust fuel and oxygen pressure (Note 8), set the scale-reading dial at about 95 per cent of a full scale, introduce the maximum sodium standard in the range to be covered, and allow the emitted light to strike the photomultiplier tube. Adjust the slit width until the galvanometer needle reads zero for null balancing-type instruments or 50 per cent transmittance for direct-reading instruments.

NOTE 8.—Use the fuel and oxygen pressures and procedures for warm-up time prescribed by the instrument manufacturer.

(5) Rotate the wavelength dial back and forth slowly and carefully in the vicinity of 589 mμ. In this manner, the galvanometer can be made to pass through a maximum deflection to the left. The point where the needle shows maximum deflection to the left is the proper wavelength setting. Every time the wavelength dial is moved, the wavelength setting must be checked.

(6) Continue to atomize the maximum standard of the range to be covered and set the scale-reading dial at exactly full scale (100 per cent transmittance). Adjust the slit width so as to balance the galvanometer for null balancing instruments or until the instrument reads 100 per cent transmittance for direct-reading instruments.

(7) Determine the emission intensity of the standards. Record the readings.

(8) Determine the scale reading of the sodium-free reagent water by aspirating reagent water into the flame until successive scale readings differ by not more than 0.10 per cent of full scale. Record the reading. Continue to aspirate the reagent water and make scale readings at +5 mμ and −5 mμ from the wavelength reading found in Step (5).

Record and average the readings. This average offset scale reading corresponds to zero concentration of sodium.

(9) Plot on linear or log-log paper the net emission intensity in scale units for the standards. Net emission intensity is the difference between total emission intensity found in Step (7) and the average offset scale reading obtained in Step (8). A straight line should result. Now calculate the sodium in the reagent water by referring to the calibration curve. If the sodium content exceeds 0.5 per cent of the maximum standard, prepare new standards allowing for the sodium in the reagent water. Repeat Steps (6) to (9). In this manner, the sodium content of the reagent water can always be checked and compensated for in preparing the standards. It is recognized that this method is not theoretically correct, but the percentage of error is very low. Record on graph paper all data in regard to slit width, degree of amplification, range of test in parts per billion, fuel pressure, and oxygen pressure.

(b) Store the standards in containers that will not cause their contamination with sodium and exercise care that the containers will not be open for any appreciable length of time. The portions of standards withdrawn from bottles and not used must be discarded and never returned to the bottles.

Procedure

20. Determine the sodium in the sample as follows:

(1) Proceed in accordance with Section 19(a)(1) to (6).

(2) Rinse the atomizer by aspirating sodium-free reagent water.

(3) Atomize the sample and determine the scale reading of the emission intensity. Repeat with fresh portions of

the sample until successive scale readings are within ± 1.0 per cent of the average scale reading.

Calculations

21. Calculate the concentration of sodium ion, in parts per billion, in accordance with the calibration curve of the emission intensity versus sodium concentration as described in Section 19(a)(9).

Precision[11]

22. The precision of this method is 0.9 ppb $+$ 0.6 per cent of the concentration determined in the range 0.25 to 1000 ppb.

METHOD C. ANALYSIS OF WATER-FORMED DEPOSITS

Application

23. Sodium and potassium present in any type of water-formed deposit may be determined by this method. Deposits must be dissolved, for which a procedure is included in the method. Because of the normally high concentration of other cations relative to the sodium and potassium concentrations, this method may not be satisfactory for the analysis of deposits in which the concentration of sodium or potassium is less than 0.1 per cent. For a discussion of interferences, refer to Section 4.

Reagents

24. (a) Prepare stock solutions of sodium and potassium as described in Section 9.

(b) *Hydrochloric Acid (sp gr 1.19).*—Concentrated hydrochloric acid (HCl).

(c) *Hydrochloric Acid (1:19).*—Add 5 ml of concentrated HCl (sp gr 1.19) to 95 ml of water.

(d) *Hydrofluoric Acid (48 per cent).*

(e) *Sulfuric Acid (1:4).*—Carefully mix 1 volume of concentrated sulfuric acid (H$_2$SO$_4$, sp gr 1.84) with 4 volumes of water.

Calibration and Standardization

25. Calibrate and standardize as follows:

(a) Prepare eleven solutions of sodium and potassium for ranges of 0 to 10 and 0 to 100 ppm, as described in Section 10(a), each standard containing 5 ml of HCl (sp gr 1.19) per 100 ml of solution.

(b) Complete the standardization and calibration as described in Sections 10(a) through (h), using the standard solutions prepared in accordance with Paragraph (a).

Procedure

26. (a) Grind about 20 g of the deposit so that it will pass through a No. 100 (149-μ) sieve. Mix the sieved material well. Weigh 1.000 g of the sample into a platinum crucible and ignite for 30 min at a maximum temperature of 700 C to remove organic matter.

(b) Transfer the ignited sample to a 250-ml heat-resistant glass beaker or platinum dish, moisten with water, and add 25 to 50 ml of HCl (sp gr 1.19). Cover the beaker with a ribbed watch glass, heat the solution to boiling, and evaporate to dryness on a steam bath. Moisten the residue with 75 ml of water and add exactly 25 ml of HCl (sp gr 1.19). Repeat the digestion and evaporation to dryness until a clear solution is obtained. Heat the solution to about 50 C and then filter through an 11-cm ashless filter paper of medium retentiveness. Wash the residue with water (Note 9), and save the filtrate and washings.

---

[11] Supporting data giving results of cooperative tests have been filed at ASTM Headquarters.

NOTE 9.—If the amount of residue is negligible, omit the step described in the following Paragraph (c).

(c) Remove the filter paper from the funnel, transfer to a platinum crucible, and ignite at 700 C for 30 min. Cool and add a few milliliters of H_2SO_4 (1:4) and 5 to 10 ml of HF (48 per cent). Evaporate the solution to fumes on a hot plate. Cool, and repeat the HF treatment. Again evaporate until fuming ceases, then ignite for 15 min at 700 C. Cool, dissolve the residue in not more than 2 ml of HCl (sp gr 1.19) with water as needed, and digest for 15 min on a steam bath. Filter, if necessary, wash with hot water, and add the filtrate to that obtained in Paragraph (b).

(d) Dilute the filtrate to 500 ml in a volumetric flask. This solution contains the silica-free inorganic portion of the deposit in a concentration equivalent to 2000 ppm of the original sample, and approximately 5 ml of HCl (sp gr 1.19) per 100-ml sample.

(e) Follow the procedure described in Section 11(a) (Note 10), using the standards prepared in accordance with Section 25(a).

NOTE 10.—If the concentration of the element in the sample is found to be greater than the maximum standard employed, dilute the sample with HCl (1:19) to bring the concentration within range.

Calculations

27. (a) Calculate the concentration of sodium or potassium ions, in parts per million, as described in Section 12 (Note 11).

NOTE 11.—Since the solution for analysis contained the ignited, silica-free portion of 1.000 g of the original sample in 500 ml, the concentration of the solution in terms of the original sample is 2000 ppm.

(b) Calculate the equivalent sodium or potassium oxide as follows:

$$Na_2O, \text{ per cent} = \frac{X}{2000} \times 1.348 \times 100$$

$$K_2O, \text{ per cent} = \frac{X}{2000} \times 1.205 \times 100$$

where:

X = concentration of sodium or potassium ions, in parts per million.

Precision[12]

28. The precision of this method is 5.0 per cent for sodium and 9.0 per cent for potassium.

[12] Supporting data for this method will be found in the paper by R. K. Scott, V. M. Marcy, and J. J. Hronas, "The Flame Photometer in the Analysis of Water and Water-Formed Deposits," Symposium on Flame Photometry, *ASTM STP No. 116*, Am. Soc. Testing Mats., p. 105 (1951).

Standard Methods of Test for

SPECIFIC GRAVITY OF INDUSTRIAL WATER AND INDUSTRIAL WASTE WATER[1]

ASTM Designation: D 1429 – 60

ADOPTED, 1960

This Standard of the American Society for Testing and Materials is issued under the fixed designation D 1429; the final number indicates the year of original adoption as standard or, in the case of revision, the year of last revision.

Scope and Application

1. These methods describe a referee and a non-referee procedure for determining the specific gravity of industrial water and industrial waste water free of separable oil. The referee method is applicable to clear samples or those containing only a moderate amount of suspended solids. The non-referee method is applicable to samples of mud or sludge. The methods are designated as follows:

	Sections
Referee Method (Pycnometer Method)	6 to 9
Non-Referee Method (Erlenmeyer Flask Method)	10 to 13

Definitions

2. (a) The term "specific gravity" in these methods is defined in accordance with the Definitions of Terms Relating to Industrial Water and Industrial Waste Water (ASTM Designation: D 1129).[2]

Specific Gravity.—The ratio of the weight in air of a given volume of the sample to the weight in air of an equal volume of reagent water, both being determined at the standard reference temperature of 15.6 C (60 F). It is expressed as follows:

Specific gravity, 15.6/15.6 C (60/60 F)....

(b) For definitions of other terms used in this method, refer to Definitions D 1129.

Apparatus

3. (a) *Bath.*—Constant-temperature bath designed to maintain a temperature of 15.6 ± 1 C (60 ± 1.8 F). If any other temperature must be used due to local

[1] Under the standardization procedure of the Society, these methods are under the jurisdiction of the ASTM Committee D-19 on Industrial Water. A list of members may be found in the ASTM Year Book.

[2] Appears in this publication.

conditions, appropriate corrections shall be made.

(b) *Pycnometer.*—Cylindrical or conical glass vessel carefully ground to receive an accurately fitting glass stopper provided with a hole approximately 1.0 to 2.0 mm in diameter, centrally located in reference to the vertical axis. The top surface of the stopper shall be smooth and substantially plane, and the lower surface shall be concave in order to allow all air to escape through the bore. The height of the concave

Reagents

4. *Reagent Water,* conforming to the Specifications for Reagent Water (ASTM Designation: D 1193).[2]

Sampling

5. (a) Collect the sample in accordance with the applicable method of the American Society for Testing and Materials, as follows:

D 510—Sampling Industrial Water,[2]
D 860—Sampling Water from Boilers,[2]
D 1066—Sampling Steam.[2]

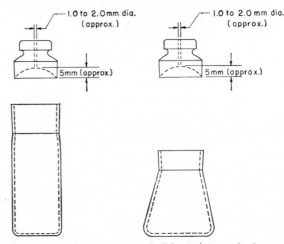

NOTE.—The ground-glass joint shall be 24/12 standard taper.
FIG. 1.—Suitable Pycnometers.

section shall be approximately 5 mm at the center. The stoppered pycnometer shall have a capacity of about 24 to 30 ml, and shall weigh not more than 40 g. Suitable pycnometers are shown in Fig. 1.

(c) *Thermometer.*—An ASTM Gravity Thermometer having a range of −20 to +102 C or −5 to +215 F, as specified, and conforming to the requirements for thermometer 12C or 12F, respectively, as prescribed in ASTM Specifications E 1.[3]

---

[3] 1967 Book of ASTM Standards, Part 30.

(b) In view of the lack of a standard method for sampling mud or sludge, no instructions are given for sampling this type of material.

REFEREE METHOD

(Pycnometer Method)

Summary of Method

6. The sample is introduced into a pycnometer, stabilized at the desired temperature, and weighed. The specific gravity is calculated from this weight and the previously determined weight of

reagent water that is required to fill the pycnometer at the same temperature.

Procedure

7. (a) Weigh a clean, dry, calibrated pycnometer, complete with stopper, on an analytical balance, and record this weight to the nearest 0.1 mg, as P.

(b) Remove the stopper and fill the pycnometer with recently boiled reagent water that has been cooled to room temperature, to within several millimeters of the top. Remove air bubbles. Immerse the unstoppered pycnometer up to the neck in a constant-temperature bath maintained at 15.6 ± 1 C (60 ± 1.8 F). Allow the pycnometer to remain in the bath for a period of time sufficient to establish temperature equilibrium. Twenty minutes is usually sufficient.

(c) After temperature equilibrium has been established, and before removing from the bath, firmly insert the stopper and remove the excess water from the top of the stopper, taking care to leave the capillary filled. Remove the stoppered pycnometer from the bath and wipe it dry. Immediately weigh the pycnometer, and record this weight to the nearest 0.1 mg, as W.

(d) Empty the reagent water from the pycnometer and dry, or rinse with the sample to be tested.

(e) Using the sample to be tested, repeat the procedure given in Paragraphs (b) and (c), recording the weight of the pycnometer containing the sample under test as S.

Calculations

8. Calculate the specific gravity of the sample as follows:

$$\text{Specific gravity} = \frac{S - P}{W - P}$$

where:

P = weight of the empty pycnometer,

S = weight of the pycnometer and contained sample, and

W = weight of the pycnometer and contained reagent water.

Precision and Accuracy

9. (a) *Precision.*—Results should not differ from the arithmetical mean by more than the following amounts:

Different operators and apparatus........ 0.002

(b) *Accuracy.*—The limit of accuracy of the test is ±0.0005 specific gravity.

NON-REFEREE METHOD

(Erlenmeyer Flask Method)

Summary of Method

10. (a) The sample of mud or sludge is thoroughly stirred and poured into a wide-mouth Erlenmeyer flask until it is somewhat more than level full, the excess being struck off with a spatula blade. The specific gravity is calculated from this weight and the previously determined weight of water required to fill the flask completely.

(b) If the sample is of a plastic solid consistency, the flask is partly filled with the sample and weighed. Water is then added to fill the flask completely, and the total weight is taken. The specific gravity is calculated from the weight of the volume of water displaced by the sample.

Procedure

11. (a) Clean, dry, and weigh the Erlenmeyer flask to the nearest 0.1 g, and record this weight as F.

(b) Fill the flask with reagent water or tap water. Both flask and water shall be at temperature equilibrium. Weigh the filled flask and record this weight as W. Empty and dry the flask.

(c) If the sample flows readily, fill the flask completely with the sample, leveling the upper surface with a flat-bladed

34-82

spatula held at an angle of 45 deg with the rim of the flask. Weigh, and record this weight as S.

(d) Mix the sample thoroughly by stirring, but do not shake. If the sample does not flow readily, add sufficient sample to approximately half fill the flask, without exerting pressure, and weigh. Record the weight of the flask and sample as R. Fill the flask containing the sample completely with reagent water or tap water, whichever was used in accordance with Paragraph (b), taking care to remove all entrained air bubbles, and weigh again. Record this weight as T.

Calculations

12. (a) In the case of free-flowing samples, calculate the specific gravity of the sample as follows:

$$\text{Specific gravity} = \frac{S - F}{W - F}$$

where:

F = weight of the empty flask,

S = weight of the flask completely filled with sample, and

W = weight of the flask and contained water.

(b) In the case of samples which do not flow readily, calculate the specific gravity of the sample as follows:

$$\text{Specific gravity} = \frac{R - F}{(W - F) - (T - R)}$$

where:

F = weight of the empty flask,

R = weight of the flask partly filled with sample,

T = weight of the flask partly filled with sample, plus water added to fill remaining volume, and

W = weight of the flask and contained water.

Precision and Accuracy

13. Results with a precision of 0.005 can be obtained. No statement of accuracy is possible.

APPROVED AS
USA STANDARD Z111.3-1964
BY USA STANDARDS INSTITUTE
UDC 663.61:543.3

Standard Methods of

SAMPLING HOMOGENEOUS INDUSTRIAL WASTE WATER[1]

ASTM Designation: D 1496 – 64

ADOPTED, 1964

This Standard of the American Society for Testing and Materials is issued under the fixed designation D 1496; the final number indicates the year of original adoption as standard or, in the case of revision, the year of last revision.

Scope and Application

1. (*a*) These methods cover the sampling at atmospheric or higher pressures of homogeneous industrial waste water for physical and chemical tests.

(*b*) These methods are applicable to sampling homogeneous industrial waste water from sources such as pipe lines and conduits, processing tanks and vats, spray ponds, towers, and filters, at atmospheric or higher pressures for chemical or physical tests. Certain test methods require special handling of samples. For additional information refer to sampling methods governing such test methods.

(*c*) Normal variations in processes and in equipment from plant to plant preclude the possibility of specifying standard methods of sampling that are applicable in all cases. Definite principles have, however, been established as a basis for the formulation of procedures for sampling that are applicable in general and probably applicable in most specific cases. Where modifications of these procedures are necessary, they may be made by the exercise of trained judgment in each individual case.

(*d*) Changes that may be necessary in these procedures under specific circumstances may be made in any particular case by mutual agreement of the parties concerned.

Summary of Methods

2. The following general rules are applicable to all sampling methods:

(*a*) The samples must represent the conditions existing at the point taken.

(*b*) The samples must be of sufficient volume and must be taken frequently enough to permit an accuracy of testing requisite for the desired objective, as conditioned by the methods of analysis to be employed.

(*c*) The samples must be collected, packed, shipped, and manipulated prior to analysis in a manner that safeguards against change in the particular constituents or properties to be examined.

---

[1] Under the standardization procedure of the Society, these methods are under the jurisdiction of the ASTM Committee D-19 on Industrial Water. A list of members may be found in the ASTM Year Book.

14-61

TABLE I.—VOLUME OF SAMPLE REQUIRED FOR DETERMINATION OF THE
VARIOUS CONSTITUENTS OF INDUSTRIAL WASTE WATER.

	Volume of Sample,[a] ml		Volume of Sample,[a] ml
PHYSICAL TESTS		*Miscellaneous:*	
*Color and Odor	100 to 500	pH, colorimetric	10 to 20
*Corrosivity	flowing sample	Polyphosphates	100 to 200
*Electrical conductivity	100	Silica	50 to 1000
*pH, electrometric	100	Solids, dissolved	100 to 20 000
*Specific gravity	100	Solids, suspended	50 to 1000
*Temperature	flowing sample	Tannin and lignin	100 to 200
*Toxicity	1000 to 20 000		
*Turbidity	100 to 1000	*Cations:*	
		Aluminum, Al^{+++}	100 to 1000
CHEMICAL TESTS		†Ammonium, NH_4^+	25 to 500
Dissolved Gases:		Antimony, Sb^{+++} to	
†Ammonia, NH_3	100	Sb^{+++++}	100 to 1000
†Carbon Dioxide, free		Arsenic, As^{+++} to As^{+++++}	100 to 1000
CO_2	100	Barium, Ba^{++}	100 to 1000
†Chlorine, free Cl_2	100	Cadmium, Cd^{++}	100 to 1000
†Hydrogen, H_2	1000	Calcium, Ca^{++}	100 to 1000
†Hydrogen sulfide, H_2S	500	Chromium, Cr^{+++} to	
†Oxygen, O_2	250 to 1000	Cr^{++++++}	100 to 1000
†Sulfur Dioxide, free SO_2	100	Copper, Cu^{++}	100 to 4000
		†Iron, Fe^{++} and Fe^{+++}	100 to 1000
		Lead, Pb^{++}	100 to 4000
Miscellaneous:		Magnesium, Mg^{++}	100 to 1000
Acidity and alkalinity	100	Manganese, Mn^{++} to	
†Bacteria, iron	100	$Mn^{+++++++}$	100 to 1000
†Bacteria, sulfate-reduc-		Mercury, Hg^+ and Hg^{++}	100 to 1000
ing	100	Potassium, K^+	100 to 1000
†Biochemical oxygen de-		Nickel, Ni^{++}	100 to 1000
mand	100 to 500	Silver, Ag^+	100 to 1000
Carbon dioxide, total CO_2		Sodium, Na^+	100 to 1000
(including CO_3^{--}, HCO_3^-,		Strontium, Sr^{++}	100 to 1000
and free)	100 to 200	Tin, Sn^{++} and Sn^{++++}	100 to 1000
†Chemical oxygen demand		Zinc, Zn^{++}	100 to 1000
(dichromate)	50 to 100		
†Chlorine requirement	2000 to 4000	*Anions:*	
†Chlorine, total residual		Bicarbonate, HCO_3^-	100 to 200
Cl_2, (including OCl^-,		Bromide, Br^-	25 to 100
$HOCl$, NH_2Cl, $NHCl_2$,		Carbonate, CO_3^{--}	100 to 200
and free)	100 to 200	Chloride, Cl^-	25 to 100
Chloroform-extractable		Cyanide, Cn^-	25 to 100
matter	1000	Fluoride, Fl^-	25 to 100
Detergents	100 to 200	Hydroxide, OH^-	50 to 100
Hardness	50 to 100	Iodide, I^-	25 to 100
†Hydrazine	50 to 100	Nitrate, NO_3^-	10 to 100
†Microorganisms	100 to 200	Nitrite, NO_2^-	50 to 100
Volatile and filming		Phosphate, ortho, PO_4^{---},	
amines	500 to 1000	HPO_4^{--}, $H_2PO_4^-$	50 to 100
Oily matter	3000 to 5000	Sulfate, SO_4^{--}, HSO_4^-	100 to 1000
Organic nitrogen	500 to 1000	†Sulfide, S^{--}, HS^-	100 to 500
†Phenolic compounds	800 to 4000	†Sulfite, SO_3^{--}, HSO_3^-	50 to 500

[a] Volumes specified in this table should be considered as a guide for the approximate quantity of sample necessary for the particular analysis. The exact quantity used should be consistent with the volume prescribed in the standard method of analysis, whenever the volume is specified.

* Aliquot may be used for other determinations.

† Samples for unstable constituents must be obtained in separate containers, preserved as prescribed, completely filled and sealed against all exposure.

14-59

Definitions

3. (a) The terms "industrial waste water" and "water-borne industrial waste" in these methods are defined in accordance with the Definitions of Terms Relating to Industrial Water and Industrial Waste Water (ASTM Designation: D 1129)[2], as follows:

Industrial Waste Water.—Water discharged from an industrial process as a result of formation or utilization in that process (Note 1).

Note 1.—Industrial waste water may have been utilized directly or indirectly as cooling water. Industrial waste water may be discharged into other processes, recovery systems, natural streams, or other receiving bodies.

Water-Borne Industrial Waste.—A water-borne substance (solids, liquids, or gases) resulting from an industrial operation or process, and discharged into the water therefrom.

(b) For definitions of other terms used in these methods, refer to Definitions D 1129.

Apparatus

4. (a) For apparatus required for sampling, such as valves, sample lines, sample coolers, sample containers and shipping containers, refer to the Specifications for Equipment for Sampling Industrial Water and Steam (ASTM Designation: D 1192).[2]

(b) Refer to the apparatus description in the applicable test method if ·pecial apparatus is required for any specific test.

(c) When contact with the air causes a change in the concentration or characteristics of a constituent to be determined, such as dissolved oxygen, carbon dioxide, or other constituent listed as "unstable" in Table I, use the applicable apparatus specified in Paragraph (a) (Note 2).

---

[2] Appears in this publication.

Note 2.—The apparatus described in the Methods of Test for Dissolved Oxygen in Industrial Water (ASTM Designation: D 888)[2] is frequently convenient for this purpose.

Composite Samples

5. (a) Composite samples may be made by mutual agreement of the interested parties by combining individual samples taken at frequent intervals or by means of an automatic sampler. In either case, indicate whether the volume of sample is proportional to the rate of flow. At the end of a definite period, mix the composite sample thoroughly so that determinations on a portion of the composite sample will represent the average for the stable constituents.

(b) Variations of unstable constituents, for which individual samples are specified in Table I, may be determined by analysis on the individual samples.

(c) In sampling process-effluent waters, collect composite samples covering periods of 12 hr or less, in at least one 24-hr period. Collect increments for composite samples at regular intervals from 15 min to 1 hr, and in proportion to the rate of flow of the effluent water. This may be conveniently done by taking a simple multiple in milliliters of the flow in gallons per minute or other unit of flow. Choose a suitable factor to give the proper volume (about 4 liters) for the composite sample.

Temperature Adjustment of Samples

6. Where samples of industrial waste water are taken at other than ambient temperature, use coils as described in ASTM Specifications D 1192 to adjust the sample approximately to the ambient temperature (Note 3).

Note 3.—Some test methods require adjustment of sample to other than ambient temperatures. Carry out such temperature adjustment as required.

Volume of Sample

7. (a) Obtain at least 2 liters of water in the sample for analysis (Note 4).

Note 4.—A sample containing 4 liters of water is preferable; and, in some cases, a sample containing as much as 20 liters may be necessary. The number of tests to be made and the amount required for each test by the procedure employed determine the size of the sample above the minimum specified. It is always desirable to have excess sample for checking analyses or for further analysis at a later date.

(*b*) The estimates in Table I cover the volumes of sample required for the usual determinations that are made on industrial waste water as well as for several tests that are made for special purposes.

Point of Sampling

8. (*a*) Choose the point of sampling with extreme care so that a representative sample of the industrial waste water to be tested is obtained.

(*b*) Because of a wide variety of conditions found in industrial plants, it is not possible to prescribe the exact point of sampling. Choose the location of the sampling point with respect to the information desired and in conformity to local conditions.

(*c*) It is desirable to take a series of samples from any source of industrial waste water to determine whether differences in composition are likely to exist, before final selection of the sampling point.

(*d*) Choose sampling points in pipelines, conduits, tanks, vats, filters, zeolite and chemical water softeners, deionizing processes, surface condensers, evaporators, or condensate return lines with respect to the characteristics of the individual piece of equipment containing the material to be tested, the character and changes occurring between the inlet and outlet water, and rate of passage through the equipment. Again take care a representative sample is insured by allowing mixing to take place. Avoid taking the sample along the wall of the pipe or conduit but take it within the stream.

(*e*) Insert nozzles to sampling cocks into the pipe line or piece of equipment to such a depth as to prevent pipe surface sampling. Choose a point along the length of the pipe where there will be a minimum disturbance of flow due to fittings.

(*f*) In the absence of any other sampling connections, take samples from water-level or gage-glass drain lines or petcocks. Such samples are not representative of the average composition of the water in the vessel and are not to be used in cases of dispute.

Preparation of Sample Bottles

9. Prepare and clean sample containers according to the procedures referred to in Section 4. Rinse the sample containers with reagent water conforming to the Specifications for Reagent Water (ASTM Designation: D 1193)[2] and dry by draining.

Taking the Sample

10. (*a*) Regulate the rate of flow in the sample line to not more than 500 ml per min, after first flushing the sample line at a rate sufficiently high to remove all sediment and gas pockets. In special cases where dissolved gases are released from solution by the drop in pressure, note this on the label.

(*b*) When sampling water from cocks or valves, insert the sample line, or a thoroughly washed glass tube or sulfur-free rubber tube extension of the sample line, into the sampling bottle so that it touches the bottom. Allow a volume of water equal to at least ten times the volume of the sample container to flow into and overflow from the container before the sample is taken.

(*c*) Where contact with air would cause a change in the concentration or characteristics of a constituent to be determined, secure the sample without contact with air and completely fill the container (Notes 5 and 6).

Note 5.—When the apparatus referred to in Note 1 is applicable, take the sample out of contact with air by one of the procedures described therein.

Note 6.—The following constituents require the above precautions:

Oxygen	Hardness
Total carbon dioxide	Hydrogen
Total ammonia	Sulfur dioxide
Hydrogen sulfide	Ammonium
Free chlorine	Iron
pH	Acidity and basicity (alkalinity)

(d) For sampling of unconfined industrial waste water at any specific depth in ponds, lagoons, reservoirs, etc. where contact with air or agitation of the water would cause a change in concentration or characteristics of a constituent to be determined, use a sampling apparatus so constructed that the solution at the depth to be sampled flows through a tube to the bottom of the container, and that a volume of sample equal to four to ten times the volume of the receiving container passes through it. When no determinations of dissolved gases are made, any less complicated apparatus may be used that will permit the collection of a sample at a desired depth, or of an integrated sample containing waste water from all points in a vertical section.

(e) When samples are to be shipped, do not fill the bottle entirely, in order to allow some room for expansion when subjected to a change in temperature (Note 7).

Note 7.—An air space of 10 to 25 ml usually suffices for this purpose, although this does not protect against bursting of the container due to freezing.

Preservation of Samples

11. Add chemical preservatives to samples only as specified in specific test methods.

Time Interval Between Collection and Analysis of Samples

12. (a) In general, allow as short a time as possible to elapse between the collection of a sample and its analysis. Under some conditions, analysis in the field is necessary to secure reliable results. The actual time that may be allowed to intervene between the collection and analysis of a sample varies with the type of examination to be conducted, the character of the sample, and the time interval allowable for applying corrective treatment.

(b) On the statement of an analysis, specify the length of time elapsed between collection and analysis of the sample.

(c) Make the determination of dissolved gases, such as oxygen, hydrogen sulfide, and carbon dioxide, at the source; except that in some cases such constituents may be fixed and determined later as specified in the specific test methods.

Labeling and Transportation of Samples

13. Refer to Sections 10 (e) and 12 (a) and to the Specifications for Equipment for Sampling Industrial Water and Steam (ASTM Designation: D 1192).[2]

Standard Method of Test for

OXIDATION-REDUCTION POTENTIAL OF INDUSTRIAL WATER[1]

ASTM Designation: D 1498 – 59 (1965)

ADOPTED, 1959; REAPPROVED, 1965

This Standard of the American Society for Testing and Materials is issued under the fixed designation D 1498; the number immediately following the designation indicates the year of original adoption or, in the case of revision, the year of last revision. A number in parentheses indicates the year of last reapproval.

Scope and Application

1. This method describes the apparatus and procedure for the electrometric measurement of oxidation-reduction potentials of industrial water. It does not deal with the manner in which the solutions are prepared, the theoretical interpretation of the oxidation-reduction potential, or the establishment of a standard oxidation-reduction potential for any given system. It is applicable to all types of industrial water at temperatures below 38 C. It is particularly valuable where oxidation or reduction are pertinent properties, as in chlorinated waters.

Summary of Method

2. The oxidation-reduction potential of the water is measured, using a calomel electrode-noble metal electrode and an appropriate meter. The measured value is corrected to express the oxidation-reduction potential referred to the normal hydrogen electrode.

Definitions

3. (a) The term "oxidation-reduction potential" in this method is defined in accordance with the Definitions of Terms Relating to Industrial Water and Industrial Waste Water (ASTM Designation: D 1129),[2] as follows:

Oxidation-Reduction Potential.—The electromotive force developed by a platinum electrode immersed in the water, referred to the standard hydrogen electrode.

(b) For definition of other terms used in this method, refer to Definitions D 1129.

---

[1] Under the standardization procedure of the Society, this method is under the jurisdiction of the ASTM Committee D-19 on Industrial Water. A list of members may be found in the ASTM Year Book.

[2] Appears in this publication.

Limitations

4. Reproducible oxidation-reduction potentials cannot be obtained for chemical systems that are not reversible. The measurement of end point potential in oxidation-reduction titrations is sometimes of this type.

Apparatus

5. (a) *Meter.*—Three types of meters may be used. The electrical characteristics of the meters and operating characteristics of the three assemblies are given in Table I. The choice will depend

calomel electrode with an excess of solid potassium chloride and an excess of calomel surrounding the pure mercury component. The junction between the saturated potassium chloride solution of the reference electrode and the test solution shall permit easy washing to remove traces of solution from the previous determination and shall be of such construction that a fresh junction can be formed for each test. The electrical resistance of the junction, measured with alternating current and with saturated potassium chloride solution inside and

TABLE I.—ELECTRICAL CHARACTERISTICS OF METERS AND OPERATING PERFORMANCE OF ASSEMBLIES.

	Type A Meter	Type B Meter	Type C Meter
Vacuum tube operation................	yes	yes	no
Type of measuring circuit..............	potentiometric	direct reading	potentiometric
Method for detection of balance point....	null indicator (galvanometer or electron-ray tube)	direct	galvanometer[a]
Maximum current flowing in input circuit..	10^{-10} amp	10^{-10} amp	
Standard cell for calibration............	yes	optional	yes
Scale units.........................	millivolts	millivolts	millivolts
Minimum range......................	0 to ± 1100	0 to $\pm 1100^b$	1 to ± 1100
Maximum value of smallest ruled interval.	10 mv	10 mv	10 mv
Power supply batteries or 115, ac........	either	either	batteries

[a] Minimum sensitivity equivalent to 0.0005 μa at one meter.
[b] A double scale may be provided.

on the accuracy desired in the determination. For routine determination, types A, B, or C may be used. For reference work, or in the case of dispute, types A or C should be used. These type designations are based on the electrical characteristics of the meters and the operating performance of the assembly. Although pH meters are included, electrical shielding is not necessary to the extent that it is in the Method of Test for pH of Industrial Water and Industrial Waste Water (ASTM Designation: D 1293)[2] or in the Method for Determination of pH of Aqueous Solutions with the Glass Electrode (ASTM Designation: E 70).[2]

(b) *Reference Electrode.* — Saturated

outside the junction, should not exceed 5000 ohms. The design of the electrode shall permit the calomel electrode to assume the same temperature as the test solution and the oxidation-reduction electrode.

(c) *Oxidation-Reduction Electrodes.*— Three inert metal oxidation-reduction electrodes, preferably of smooth pure platinum, but gold or other noble metal may be used in those cases where such metal is not attacked by the test solution. The construction of the electrode shall be such that only the noble metal comes in contact with the test solution. The supporting member must be inert to the corrosive action of the cleaning solutions described later. The area of the noble metal in contact with the test solution should be approximately 1 sq cm.

Purity of Reagents and Materials

6. (a) Reagent grade chemicals shall be used in all tests. Unless otherwise indicated, it is intended that all reagents shall conform to the specifications of the Committee on Analytical Reagents of the American Chemical Society, where such specifications are available.[3] Other grades may be used, provided it is first ascertained that the reagent is of sufficiently high purity to permit its use without lessening the accuracy of the determination.

(b) *Water.*—Unless otherwise indicated, references to water shall be understood to mean reagent water conforming to Specifications for Reagent Water (ASTM Designation: D 1193).[2]

Reagents and Materials

7. (a) *Aqua Regia.*—Mix three volumes of concentrated hydrochloric acid (HCl, sp gr 1.19) with one volume of concentrated nitric acid (HNO$_3$, sp gr 1.42).

(b) *Chromic Acid Cleaning Solution.*—Dissolve about 5 g of potassium dichromate (K$_2$Cr$_2$O$_7$) in 500 ml of concentrated sulfuric acid (H$_2$SO$_4$, sp gr 1.84).

(c) *Detergent.*—Use any commercially available "low-suds" liquid or solid detergent.

(d) *Iodine Solution.*—Dissolve 1.0 g of crushed iodine crystals in a small amount of water containing 2.0 g of potassium iodide (KI). Dilute this solution to 300 ml with water.

(e) *Nitric Acid Solution (1:1).*—Mix

---

[3] "Reagent Chemicals, American Chemical Society Specifications," Am. Chem. Soc., Washington, D. C. For suggestions on the testing of reagents not listed by the American Chemical Society, see "Reagent Chemicals and Standards," by Joseph Rosin, D. Van Nostrand Co., Inc., New York, N. Y., and "The United States Pharmacopeia."

equal volumes of concentrated nitric acid (HNO$_3$, sp gr 1.42) and water.

(f) *Potassium Chloride, Saturated Solution.*—Dissolve 35 g of potassium chloride (KCl) in 100 ml of warm water. Allow the solution to cool to room temperature. Decant the clear solution as required.

(g) *Potassium Iodide Solution (50 g per liter).*—Dissolve 5.0 g of potassium iodide (KI) in 100 ml of water. Acidify to litmus by adding sulfuric acid (sp gr 1.84).

(h) *Tincture of Iodine.*—Add 7 g of crushed iodine crystals and 5 g of potassium iodide (KI) to 5 ml of water. Make up the mixture to 100 ml with denatured ethyl alcohol.

Sampling

8. Collect the sample in accordance with the applicable methods of the American Society for Testing and Materials, as follows:

D 510—Sampling Industrial Water,[2]
D 860—Sampling Water from Boilers,[2]
D 1066—Sampling Steam.[2]

Calibration and Standardization

9. (a) *Standardization of the Meter.*—When pH meters of type A or type B are used, check the scale to be sure that it represents true voltage. For the type B meter in which the pH scale and the voltage scale may be inseparable, the temperature compensating adjustment must be set at the appropriate value to make the voltage scale correct. The zero control (sometimes called the asymmetry or the standardizing potential control) of the pH meter must be adjusted until the voltage reading on the meter is zero. Follow the instrument manufacturer's instructions in ascertaining whether or not the temperature compensator affects the voltage reading. If it does, make the appropriate setting. If voltages greater than 1100 mv are

involved, it may be desirable to use a standard cell of known voltage between the meter and the measuring electrode. The voltage reading is the algebraic sum of the standard cell value and the voltage reading of the meter.

(b) Before using electronic type meters (A and B), turn them on, allow them to warm up thoroughly, and bring them in to electrical balance by carefully following the manufacturer's instructions.

(c) The potentiometer of the type C meter does not require the above precautions, but it must have the slide-wire current standardized as explained in the manufacturer's instructions.

Procedure

10. (a) When new metal electrodes are used, remove traces of foreign matter (welding residue, etc.). Immerse the new oxidation-reduction electrode in aqua regia, warm to 70 C, and allow to stand for a period of about 1 min. This solution dissolves the noble metal as well as any foreign matter so that the electrode shall not be allowed to stand in it longer than the time specified. The above treatment in aqua regia may also be used cautiously to recondition an electrode that has become unreliable in its operation.

(b) Just before measurement, clean the electrode in HNO_3 (1:1). Warm the solution and electrode gradually to boiling. Maintain it just below the boiling point for about 5 min, and then allow the solution and electrode to cool. Wash the electrode in water several times and place it in the test solution. It is desirable to clean the electrode daily. An alternative cleaning procedure is to immerse the electrode at room temperature in chromic acid cleaning mixture and then rinse it thoroughly with water. Preliminary cleaning with a detergent sometimes is desirable to remove oily residues. In these cleaning operations particular care must be exercised to protect the glass - metal seals from

sudden changes of temperature, which might crack them.

(c) For a type C meter, connect the cell in series with a 1-megohm resistor. This resistor prevents the flow of excessive current during measurement. Errors due to polarization of the oxidation-reduction electrode thereby become insignificant even with a potentiometer galvanometer system. This resistor should not be used with the type A or type B pH meters.

NOTE 1.—To insure proper polarity in connecting the electrodes to the meter, the following polarity check is suggested. Place the saturated calomel reference electrode and the metal electrode in the KI solution acidified with H_2SO_4. Add a few drops of iodine solution or tincture of iodine. The voltage of the electrode system can be read only when the metal electrode is connected to the positive terminal of the instrument. This fixes the polarity of the instrument terminals.

NOTE 2.—If a precision of greater than 5 mv is desired, control the temperature of the assembly to within ±1 C. Higher precision will require closer control of temperature. Electrodes, test solutions, and wash water must be allowed to stand for a sufficient time to obtain thermal equilibrium at the temperature of measurement, in order to reduce to a negligible value the effects of the thermal or electrical hysteresis of the reference electrode.

(d) After the meter has been standardized as specified in Section 9, immerse the electrode pair in the test solution and allow the cell to reach thermal equilibrium. Read the voltage (Note 3). Repeat this reading at least two more times, using different oxidation-reduction electrodes each time connected in turn to the measuring assembly. These readings should agree within ±5 mv. If they do not, substitute an additional electrode or electrodes until readings are obtained that do agree. Take the average voltage given by three electrode systems.

NOTE 3.—In some systems that are poorly poised, the voltage will continue to change for some time after immersion.

(*e*) In transferring the electrodes from one test solution to another, exercise care in cleaning them thoroughly with water. Shake excess water gently from the electrodes before immersing them in the next solution. Keep the metal electrode and the lower part of the calomel electrode immersed in water during intervals between tests.

Calculation

11. Calculate the oxidation-reduction potential of the sample, in millivolts, referred to the hydrogen scale as follows:

Oxidation-reduction potential, $mv = E - C$

where:

E = electromotive force, in millivolts, of the cell, and

C = potential, in millivolts, of the saturated calomel electrode referred to the hydrogen scale (Note 4).

Note. 4—The potential of the saturated calomel electrode at 25 C is 244.0 mv. As the temperature increases, the potential increases at the rate of 0.25 mv for each degree Centigrade increase. Thus, at 35 C the potential would be 246.5 mv. The sign of the electromotive force of the cell is negative if the calomel electrode is negative with respect to the metal electrode and positive if the calomel electrode is positive with respect to the metal electrode. (The above directions conform with the American Convention regarding the sign of the electrode potential introduced by G. N. Lewis and adopted by the International Critical Tables.)

Report

12. Report the oxidation-reduction potential value to the nearest millivolt. Where considered to be appropriate, the temperature at which the measurement was made, the noble metal electrode used, the value of C, and the known limits of error may also be reported.

Precision and Accuracy

13. With type A and type C meters, the precision is ±5 mv. With type B meters the precision is ±10 mv.

Standard Methods of Test for

DISSOLVED AND GASEOUS HYDROGEN IN INDUSTRIAL WATER[1]

ASTM Designation: D 1588 – 60

ADOPTED, 1960

This Standard of the American Society for Testing and Materials is issued under the fixed designation D 1588; the final number indicates the year of original adoption as standard or, in the case of revision, the year of last revision.

Scope

1. (*a*) These methods cover procedures for collection and measurement of dissolved and gaseous hydrogen in industrial water. Two methods are given, as follows:

	Sections
Referee Method (Thermal Conductivity Method)	4 to 9
Non-Referee Method (Volumetric Method)	10 to 16

(*c*) The referee method entails the separation of hydrogen and its measurement by thermal conductivity. The non-referee method entails the separation of hydrogen and its measurement volumetrically.

Definitions

2. For definitions of terms used in these methods, refer to the Definitions of Terms Relating to Industrial Water and Industrial Waste Water (ASTM Designation: D 1129).[2]

Purity of Reagents

3. (*a*) Reagent grade chemicals shall be used in all tests. Unless otherwise indicated, it is intended that all reagents shall conform to the specifications of the Committee on Analytical Reagents or the American Chemical Society, where such specifications are available.[3] Other grades may be used, provided it is first ascertained that the reagent is of sufficiently high purity to permit its use without lessening the accuracy of the determination.

(*b*) Unless otherwise indicated, references to water shall be understood to mean reagent water conforming to Speci-

---

[1] Under the standardization procedure of the Society, these methods are under the jurisdiction of the ASTM Committee D-19 on Industrial Water. A list of members may be found in the ASTM Year Book.

[2] Appears in this publication.
[3] "Reagent Chemicals, American Chemical Society Specifications," Am. Chem. Soc., Washington, D. C. For suggestions on the testing of reagents not listed by the American Chemical Society, see "Reagent Chemicals and Standards," by Joseph Rosin, D. Van Nostrand Co., Inc., New York, N. Y., and "The United States Pharmacopeia."

fications for Reagent Water (ASTM Designation: D 1193).[2]

Sampling

4. Collect the sample in accordance with the applicable method of the

for the accurate measurement of low concentrations of hydrogen in steam condensates but may be extended to other industrial waters of similar character.

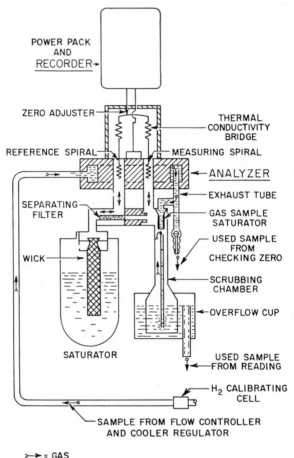

POWER PACK
AND
RECORDER→

ZERO ADJUSTER

THERMAL
CONDUCTIVITY
BRIDGE

REFERENCE SPIRAL

MEASURING SPIRAL

ANALYZER

EXHAUST TUBE

SEPARATING
FILTER

GAS SAMPLE
SATURATOR

USED SAMPLE
FROM
CHECKING ZERO

WICK

SCRUBBING
CHAMBER

OVERFLOW CUP

SATURATOR

USED SAMPLE
FROM READING

H_2 CALIBRATING
CELL

SAMPLE FROM FLOW CONTROLLER
AND COOLER REGULATOR

>—→ = GAS
○—→ = SAMPLE WATER

Fig. 1.—Dissolved Hydrogen Analyzer-Recorder (Flow Diagram).

American Society for Testing and Materials, as follows:

D 510 —Sampling Industrial Water,[2]
D 860 —Sampling Water from Boilers,[2]
D 1066—Sampling Steam.[2]

REFEREE METHOD

(Thermal Conductivity Method)

Application

5. This method is especially suitable

Summary of Method

6. Dissolved and gaseous hydrogen are scrubbed with air from a sample that has been cooled or warmed to a standard temperature. The thermal conductivity of the mixture of air and hydrogen, saturated with water, is compared with the thermal conductivity of air, saturated with water. The difference

in thermal conductivities causes imbalance of a Wheatstone bridge that is a part of the instrument that measures, indicates, and records the hydrogen concentration in the sample.

Apparatus[4]

7. The sample shall flow continuously to the instrument through stainless steel or copper tubing. Figure 1 shows the measuring cell and gas scrubbing apparatus. The assembled apparatus shall consist of the following basic parts:

(a) *Analyzer.*—A pair of thermal conductivity elements, each enclosed in a separate cell, both of which are in a metal block. The analyzer shall be maintained at constant temperature by the flow of sample through the block.

(b) *Cooler Regulator.*—A cooler regulator capable of controlling the sample temperature between 95 and 105 F. For high-temperature samples a two-step cooler is recommended. Precoolers of the concentric double coil or water chamber coil type, with parallel flow of cooling water, may be employed. The final cooler shall contain an automatic regulating element that will maintain the specified temperature.

(c) *Flow Controller.*—A flow controller that will maintain sample flow to the instrument at between 400 and 600 ml per min and one that will maintain sample flow to the analyzer cell at between 295 and 345 ml per min. Corrosion-resistant capillary tubing, orifices, valves, and a constant head device may be used for this purpose.

(d) *Hydrogen Calibrating Cell.*—A d-c electrolytic cell capable of generating hydrogen.

(e) *Recorder.*—A recorder that records the difference in thermal conductivity of the gases in the two cells in terms of

[4] This method, as written, is based on the Hydrogen Recorder made by the Cambridge Instrument Co., Inc.

hydrogen concentration. The instrument shall be calibrated in parts per billion and shall cover two ranges, 0 to 20 ppb and 0 to 40 ppb. A switch shall be provided to shift from one range to the other.

(f) *Saturator.*—A wick, one end of which is immersed in a container of water, serving as the air saturator.

(g) *Scrubbing Chamber.*—A scrubber suitable for removing hydrogen from the flowing sample by scrubbing it with air.

(h) *Accessory Parts.*—Power pack, thermometers, pressure and temperature regulators, and a frame for supporting the assembled parts.

Calibration

8. (a) To calibrate the instrument for hydrogen, select a time when the hydrogen in the sample is reading a constant amount on the recorder. Then determine the flow of sample in milliliters per minute through the analyzer and turn on the hydrogen generator in the sample line in the cell block. Adjust the flow of electric current to the generator to 2 ma, as indicated by the meter. Calculate the amount of hydrogen generated as follows:

$$\text{Hydrogen, ppb} = \frac{630E}{S}$$

where:

E = milliamperes of electric current, and
S = milliliters of sample flow per minute.

(b) Disconnect the hydrogen generator and note whether the recorded hydrogen in the sample returns to the former value. The increase in hydrogen shown when the generator was operating should be equal to the calculated amount.

Procedure

9. (a) Start the flow of cooling water through the coolers. If the sample is at

a temperature of less than the specified temperature, use warm water in the primary cooler to warm the sample.

(*b*) Start the flow of sample (Note 1) through the coolers and analyzer equipment. Regulate the flow of sample to 500 ± 100 ml per min. At this time, flow of sample to the analyzer cell block should be 320 ± 25 ml per min. Check this flow from time to time and adjust as required. Turn on the electric current to the power pack and recorder drive motor.

NOTE 1.—The hydrogen recorder is not designed to withstand pressure above approximately 100 psi. Therefore, when samples from high pressure sources are being analyzed, precautions should be taken to avoid subjecting the equipment to those pressures. If precautions are not taken, damage of equipment or injury of personnel, or both, may result.

(*c*) Check the Wheatstone bridge current by moving the plug to the "check" position. The recorder pointer should now move to the standard line marked on the scale. If necessary, adjust the coarse and fine wire resistors until the scale mark is reached by the pointer.

(*d*) Check and adjust the electrical zero of the Wheatstone bridge and recorder as follows: Turn the cock on the water leaving the analyzer cell block to "open" position, thus bypassing the scrubbing chamber. Continue to operate in this manner until the recorder prints a straight line on the chart. If the line does not correspond to the standard zero point selected, adjust to standard position by turning the resistor knob on the cell block.

(*e*) Return the instrument to reading position by closing the cock on the cell block. The instrument should now read parts per billion of hydrogen in the sample.

(*f*) Check and adjust the sample

water flow and the temperature of the sample daily, or as required. Hold the temperature at 100 ± 5 F. Clean the sample-scrubbing venturi with a pipe cleaner periodically. Keep the glass tube for saturating air to the cell block filled with water.

Precision and Accuracy

10. The accuracy of this test is ±5 per cent if the reading is between 10 per cent of scale and full scale. Below this range, the accuracy is ±0.2 ppb.

NON-REFEREE METHOD

(Volumetric Method)

Application

11. This method is intended for the approximate determination of hydrogen in steam condensates, but it may be extended to other industrial waters of similar character.

Summary of Method

12. The gases, including hydrogen, in the water sample are removed by boiling, and collected. The collected gases are analyzed for hydrogen and the concentration of hydrogen in the sample in terms of parts per billion, is calculated.

Apparatus

13. (*a*) *Condensing Equipment.*[5]—The condenser may be used as a heater for samples that have been condensed and are too low in temperature.

(*b*) *Flow Controller*, as described in Section 7 (*c*).

_____

[5] The equipment available from the Elliott Co., Jeanette, Pa. has been found satisfactory for this purpose

(c) *Gas Collecting Tubes*, having a capacity of 250 ml, for transferring gas from the gas separator to the volumetric gas analysis apparatus.

(d) *Leveling Bulb*, having a capacity of 250 ml.

(e) *Volumetric Gas Analysis Apparatus*, Orsat-type, including adsorption bulbs for oxygen and carbon dioxide and a copper oxide reaction tube and heater for hydrogen.

Reagents and Materials

14. (a) *Confining Solution.*—Dissolve 200 g of sodium sulfate (Na_2SO_4) in 800 ml of sulfuric acid (H_2SO_4, 1:19) (Note 2). Add 0.5 ml of methyl orange indicator.

NOTE 2.—Mercury may be used as an alternative confining liquid.

(b) *Potassium Hydroxide Solution (800 g per liter).*—Dissolve 800 g of potassium hydroxide (KOH) in water and dilute to 1 liter.

(c) *Potassium Hydroxide Solution (530 g per liter).*—Dissolve 530 g of KOH in water and dilute to 1 liter.

(d) *Potassium Pyrogallate Solution (170 g per liter).*—Dissolve 800 g of KOH in water. Dissolve 170 g of pyrogallol in water. Mix the two solutions and dilute the mixture to 1 liter with water. Protect the solution from contact with air as provided for by the volumetric gas analysis apparatus being used.

Procedure

15. (a) Maintain the flow rate of the sample to the condensing equipment at 400 to 2000 ml per min. Maintain the temperature of the sample so that the temperature of the sample entering the separating apparatus shall be from 170 F to 180 F.

(b) Adjust the operating pressure of

the gas separating apparatus to the optimum value.

(c) Purge the apparatus of air by venting gases to waste. The time required can be determined by testing the evolved gases.

(d) After purging is complete, set the water levels of the gas collecting assembly for zero reading and start gas collection. Note the time and rate of sample flow. When the separated gas accumulated in the collecting assembly amounts to 25 to 100 ml, transfer it to the gas analyzer and continue collecting samples for analysis. Note the time required for collecting each sample.

(e) After a sample has been transferred to the gas analyzer, proceed in the usual way to measure temperature and total volume of gas collected. Then pass the gas in turn to the carbon dioxide and oxygen adsorption bulbs and measure the new volume obtained. Slowly pass the gas through the copper oxide reaction tube which shall be heated to 300 ± 10 F. When there is no further reduction in volume, return the gas to the measuring tube and obtain the new volume.

(f) Record the volume of gas removed in the copper oxide tube, corrected for temperature and pressure, as the volume of hydrogen in the sample.

Calculation

16. (a) For these calculations, 1 gram molecular weight or 2.016 g of hydrogen at 60 F and 30 in. of mercury pressure is assumed to occupy a space of 23.645 liters,[6] or 1 liter of hydrogen weighs 85 mg.

(b) Convert the milliliters of hydrogen

---

[6] See the calculations by W. S. Blanchard, Nat. Bureau Standards, *Science Paper No. 529.*

found at 60 F and 30 in. of mercury[7] to milligrams of hydrogen and calculate the hydrogen content of the sample, in parts per billion, as follows:

[7] For correction factors for converting gas volumes at different temperatures to 60 F, see Table IV of the Method of Test for Calorific Value of Gaseous Fuels by the Water-Flow Calorimeter (ASTM Designation: D 900), 1967 Book of ASTM Standards, Part 19.

$$\text{Hydrogen, ppb} = \frac{A}{B} \times 1000$$

where:

A = milligrams of hydrogen in the sample, and

B = liters of sample.

Standard Methods of Test for

DISSOLVED OXYGEN IN INDUSTRIAL WASTE WATER[1]

ASTM Designation: D 1589 – 60

ADOPTED, 1960

This Standard of the American Society for Testing and Materials is issued under the fixed designation D 1589; the final number indicates the year of original adoption as standard or, in the case of revision, the year of last revision.

Scope and Application

1. (*a*) These methods describe procedures for the determination of dissolved oxygen in industrial waste water in the presence of certain interfering substances. Common interfering substances which may occur in such water are nitrites, ferrous iron, organic material, sulfites, or other oxidizing or reducing substances. Provisions incorporated in this method will, in most cases, lessen the interference of such substances in the determination of dissolved oxygen. Four methods are given, as follows:

	Sections
Alsterberg (Azide) Method	7 to 11
Rideal-Stewart Method	12 to 16
Pomeroy - Kirshman - Alsterberg Method	17 to 21
Polarographic Method	22 to 28

(*b*) Selection of the method to use for the dissolved oxygen determination will be determined by the nature of the sample and the type or types of interferences present.

(*1*) The Alsterberg (azide) method is the most effective method for removing interference caused by nitrites. Nitrites are the most common interferences found in surface waters. This method can also be used in the absence of other interfering substances.

(*2*) The Rideal-Stewart (permanganate) method is used only in the presence of ferrous iron and not in the presence of organic matter.

(*3*) The Pomeroy-Kirshman-Alsterberg method is used for waters supersaturated with oxygen or those having a high organic content.

(*4*) The polarographic method is suggested for certain industrial wastes, particularly where sulfites are present. This method is in an early stage of development and is provisionally recommended only for

[1] Under the standardization procedure of the Society, these methods are under the jurisdiction of the ASTM Committee D-19 on Industrial Water. A list of members may be found in the ASTM Year Book.

wastes after dilution with natural water by a factor of 4 to 100.

Definitions

2. For definitions of terms used in these methods, refer to the Definitions of Terms Relating to Industrial Water and Industrial Waste Water (ASTM Designation: D 1129).[2]

Apparatus

3. (a) *Sample Bottles*, 250- or 300-ml capacity, with tapered ground-glass stoppers. Special bottles with pointed stoppers and flared mouths are available from supply houses, but regular types (tall- or low-form) are satisfactory.

(b) *Pipets*, 10-ml capacity, graduated in 0.1-ml divisions for adding all reagents except sulfuric acid. These pipets should have elongated tips of approximately 2 in. for adding reagents well below the surface in the sample bottle. Only the sulfuric acid used in the final step is allowed to run down the neck of the bottle into the sample.

Purity of Reagents

4. (a) Reagent grade chemicals shall be used in all tests. Unless otherwise indicated, it is intended that all reagents shall conform to the specifications of the Committee on Analytical Reagents of the American Chemical Society, where such specifications are available.[3] Other grades may be used, provided it is first ascertained that the reagent is of sufficiently high purity to permit its use without lessening the accuracy of the determination.

---

[2] Appears in this publication.
[3] "Reagent Chemicals, American Chemical Society Specifications," Am. Chem. Soc., Washington, D. C. For suggestions on the testing of reagents not listed by the American Chemical Society, see "Reagent Chemicals and Standards," by Joseph Rosin, D. Van Nostrand Co., Inc., New York, N. Y.. and the "United States Pharmacopoeia."

(b) Unless otherwise indicated, reference to water shall be understood to mean reagent water conforming to the Specifications for Reagent Water (ASTM Designation: D 1193).[2]

Sampling

5. (a) Collect the samples in accordance with the applicable method of the American Society for Testing and Materials, as follows:

D 510—Sampling Industrial Water,[2]
D1496—Sampling Homogeneous Industrial Waste Water.[2]

(b) Collect the samples in narrow-mouth glass-stoppered bottles of 250- or 300-ml capacity, taking care to prevent entrainment or solution of atmospheric oxygen.

(c) With water under pressure, connect a tube of inert material to the inlet and extend the tube outlet to the bottom of the sample bottle. Allow ten times the volume of the bottle to flow through to thoroughly flush the bottle and obtain a representative sample. Replace stoppers carefully to prevent trapping air bubbles.

(d) Where samples are collected at varying depths from the surface, a special sample bottle holder or weighted sampler with a removable air-tight cover should be used. This unit may be designed to collect several 250- or 300-ml samples at the same time, with rubber inlet tubes extending to the bottom of each bottle and the water after passing through the sample bottle or bottles, displacing the air from the container. When bubbles stop rising from the sampler, the unit is filled. Water temperature is taken from the excess water in the sampler.

Preservation of Samples

6. Do not delay the determination of dissolved oxygen for samples having an

iodine demand exceeding 0.1 ppm or containing ferrous iron. Samples may be preserved 4 to 8 hr by adding 0.7 ml of concentrated sulfuric acid (H_2SO_4, sp gr 1.84) and 1.0 ml of sodium azide (NaN_3) solution (20 g per liter) to the bottle containing the sample in which dissolved oxygen is to be determined. Biological activity will be inhibited and the dissolved oxygen retained by storing at the temperature of collection or by water sealing (inverting bottle in water) and maintaining at a temperature of 10 to 20 C. Complete the determination as soon as possible, using the appropriate procedure for determining the concentration of dissolved oxygen.

Alsterberg (Azide) Procedure

Application

7. This method is intended for use where more than 0.1 ppm of nitrite nitrogen and less than 0.1 ppm of ferrous iron are present. Other reducing or oxidizing materials should be absent. The method is applicable in the presence of 100 to 200 ppm ferric iron if 1 ml of fluoride solution is added before final acidification and the titration is carried out immediately.

Reagents

8. (a) *Alkaline Iodide - Sodium Azide Solution.*—Dissolve 500 g of sodium hydroxide (NaOH) (or 700 g of potassium hydroxide (KOH)) and 135 g of sodium iodide (NaI) (or 150 g of potassium iodide (KI)) in water and dilute to 950 ml. To the cooled solution add 10 g of sodium azide (NaN_3) dissolved in 40 ml of water. Add the NaN_3 solution slowly, with constant stirring. Chemically equivalent potassium and sodium salts may be used interchangeably. The solution should not give a color with starch indicator solution when diluted and acidified. Store the solution in a dark, rubber-stoppered bottle. This solution may be used in all of these methods except the Rideal-Stewart method.

(b) *Manganous Sulfate Solution (364 g per liter).*—Dissolve 364 g of manganous sulfate ($MnSO_4 \cdot H_2O$) in water, filter, and dilute to 1 liter. No more than a trace of iodine should be liberated when the solution is added to an acidified potassium iodide (KI) solution.

(c) *Potassium Biiodate, Standard Solution (0.025 N).*—Dissolve 0.8125 g of potassium biiodate ($KH(IO_3)_2$) in water and dilute to 1 liter in a volumetric flask.

(d) *Potassium Fluoride Solution (400 g per liter).*—Dissolve 40 g of potassium fluoride ($KF \cdot 2H_2O$) in water and dilute to 100 ml.

(e) *Sodium Thiosulfate, Standard Solution (0.1 N).*—Dissolve 25 g of sodium thiosulfate ($Na_2S_2O_3 \cdot 5H_2O$) in water and dilute to 1 liter in a volumetric flask. Preserve the thiosulfate solution by adding 5 ml of chloroform or 1 g of NaOH per liter. Determine the exact normality by titration against a solution of equivalent strength of $KH(IO_3)_2$ or potassium dichromate ($K_2Cr_2O_7$).

(f) *Sodium Thiosulfate, Standard Solution (0.025 N).*—Dilute the appropriate volume (nominally 250 ml) of standardized 0.1 N $Na_2S_2O_3$ solution to 1 liter. One milliliter of 0.025 N thiosulfate solution is equivalent to 0.2 mg of oxygen.

(g) *Starch Indicator.*—Emulsify 5 to 6 g of potato or arrowroot starch in a mortar with a few milliliters of cold water. Pour the emulsion into 1 liter of boiling water, allow to boil for a few minutes, and settle overnight. Use the clear, supernatant solution. If the starch solution is to be used for a period of several days, a preservative of 1.3 g of salicylic acid or a few drops of toluene should be added.

(h) *Sulfuric Acid (sp gr 1.84).*—Concentrated sulfuric acid (H_2SO_4)

One milliliter is equivalent to about 3 ml of the alkaline iodide reagent.

Procedure

9. (*a*) Add 2.0 ml of $MnSO_4$ solution to the sample as collected in a sample bottle, followed by 2.0 ml of alkaline iodide - sodium azide solution well below the surface of the liquid (Note 1). Carefully replace the stopper to exclude air bubbles, and mix by inverting the bottle several times. Repeat the mixing a second time after the floc has settled, leaving a clear supernatant solution. Water high in chloride requires a 10-min contact period with the precipitate. When the floc has settled, leaving at least 100 ml of clear supernatant solution, remove the stopper and add 2.0 ml of H_2SO_4, allowing the acid to run down the neck of the bottle. If ferric iron (100 to 200 ppm) is present, add 1.0 ml of the KF solution before acidification. Restopper and mix by inversion until the iodine is uniformly distributed throughout the bottle. Titrate without delay 200 ml of original sample. A correction is necessary for the 4 ml of reagents added (2 ml of $MnSO_4$ solution and 2 ml of alkaline iodide - sodium azide solution). Where a 300-ml bottle is used the correct amount for titration is 203 ml.

NOTE 1.—Two milliliters of the alkaline iodide - sodium azide solution are used to insure better contact of the iodide - azide solution and sample with less agitation. With 250-ml bottles, 1 ml of the iodide - azide solution may be used if desired. In this procedure as in the succeeding ones all reagents except the H_2SO_4 are added well below the surface of the liquid.

(*b*) Rapidly titrate the 200 ml of sample with 0.025 *N* $Na_2S_2O_3$ solution to a pale, straw-yellow color. Add 1 to 2 ml of starch indicator. Continue the titration to the disappearance of the blue color (Note 2).

NOTE 2.—At the correct end point, one drop of 0.025 *N* $KH(IO_3)_2$ solution will cause the re-

turn of the blue color. If the end point is overrun, continue adding 0.025 *N* $KH(IO_3)_2$ solution until it reappears, noting the volume required. Subtract this value, minus the last drop of $KH(IO_3)_2$ (0.04 ml) from the volume of 0.025 *N* $Na_2S_2O_3$ solution used. Disregard the later reappearance of the blue color, which may be due to the catalytic effect of organic material or traces of uncomplexed metal salts.

Calculation

10. (*a*) Calculate the dissolved oxygen content of the sample as follows:

$$\text{Dissolved oxygen, ppm} = \frac{T \times 0.2}{200} \times 1000$$

where:

T = milliliters of 0.025 *N* $Na_2S_2O_3$ solution required for titration of the sample.

(*b*)

$$\text{Dissolved oxygen, ppm} = \frac{A}{0.698}$$

where:

A = milliliters of oxygen at 0 C and 760 mm.

NOTE 3.—If the percentage of saturation at 760 mm atmospheric pressure is desired, the dissolved oxygen found is compared with solubility data from standard solubility tables,[4] making corrections for barometric pressure and the aqueous vapor pressure, when necessary.

Precision and Accuracy

11. The precision and accuracy of this method cannot be stated since they will vary according to the interfering compounds present and their concentration.

RIDEAL-STEWART (PERMANGANATE) PROCEDURE

Application

12. This method is intended for use only on samples containing ferrous iron.

_____

[4] Tables of "Solubility of Oxygen in Water" will be found in standard handbooks, or in "Standard Methods for the Examination of Water and Wastewater of the APHA.

To overcome high ferric iron concentrations (up to hundreds of ppm) as may be encountered in some waste waters, add 1 ml of KF solution and titrate immediately upon acidification. The presence of 1 ppm of ferrous iron results in the apparent loss of 0.14 ppm dissolved oxygen.

Reagents

13. (a) *Alkaline Iodide Solution.*—Dissolve 500 g of sodium hydroxide (NaOH) (or 700 g of potassium hydroxide (KOH)) and 135 g of sodium iodide (NaI) (or 150 g of potassium iodide (KI)) in water and dilute to 1 liter. Chemically equivalent potassium and sodium salts may be used interchangeably. The solution should not give a color with starch indicator when diluted and acidified. Store the solution in a dark, rubber-stoppered bottle.

(b) *Manganous Sulfate Solution (364 g per liter).*—See Section 8 (b).

(c) *Potassium Fluoride Solution (400 g per liter).*—See Section 8(d).

(d) *Potassium Oxalate Solution (20 g per liter).*—Dissolve 2 g of potassium oxalate ($K_2C_2O_4 \cdot H_2O$) in 100 ml of water. One milliliter of this solution will reduce 1.1 ml of the $KMnO_4$ solution.

(e) *Potassium Permanganate Solution (6.3 g per liter).*—Dissolve 6.3 g of potassium permanganate ($KMnO_4$) in water and dilute to 1 liter. (With very high ferrous iron concentrations, solutions of $KMnO_4$ should be stronger so that 1 ml will satisfy the demand.)

(f) *Sodium Thiosulfate, Standard Solution (0.025 N).*—See Section 8 (f).

(g) *Sulfuric Acid (sp gr 1.84).*—Concentrated sulfuric acid (H_2SO_4).

Procedure

14. (a) Add to the sample 0.70 ml of H_2SO_4, followed by 1.0 ml of $KMnO_4$ solution. Where high iron is present, also add 1.0 ml of KF solution. Stopper and mix by inversion. The acid should be added with a 1-ml pipet graduated in 0.1-ml divisions. Add sufficient $KMnO_4$ solution to maintain a violet tinge for 5 min. If the color does not persist for 5 min, add more $KMnO_4$ solution, but avoid large excesses. In those cases where more than 5 ml of $KMnO_4$ solution is required, a stronger solution of this reagent may be used to avoid dilution of the sample.

(b) After 5 min, completely destroy the permanganate color by adding 0.5 to 1.0 ml of $K_2C_2O_4$ solution. Mix the sample well and allow it to stand in the dark. Low results are caused by excess oxalate, so that it is essential to add only sufficient oxalate to completely decolorize the permanganate without having an excess of more than 0.5 ml. Complete decolorization should be obtained in 2 to 10 min. If the sample cannot be decolorized without a large excess of oxalate, the dissolved oxygen results will be of doubtful value.

(c) After complete decolorization of the permanganate, add 2 ml of $MnSO_4$ solution and 3 ml of alkaline iodide solution. Stopper the bottle and mix its contents. After the precipitate has settled, leaving a clear supernatant liquid, remix for 20 sec and allow to settle until approximately 100 ml of clear supernatant solution is present. Acidify with 2.0 ml of H_2SO_4. Samples with a high iron content should be titrated at once with $Na_2S_2O_3$ solution as directed in Section 9(b) (Note 4).

NOTE 4.—A total of 6.7 ml of reagents having been added (0.7 ml of acid, 1 ml of $KMnO_4$ solution, 2 ml of $MnSO_4$ solution and 3 ml of alkaline iodide solution) the volume of sample for titration is 205 ml. A slight error occurs due to the dissolved oxygen of the $KMnO_4$ solution, but rather than complicate the correction further, this error is ignored.

Calculation

15. Calculate the dissolved oxygen content of the sample, in terms of parts per million, as described in Section 10 (a) and (b).

Precision and Accuracy

16. See Section 11.

POMEROY-KIRSHMAN-ALSTERBERG PROCEDURE

Application

17. (a) This method is intended for use with samples containing a high dissolved oxygen content (15 ppm or more) or those with high organic content as may be found in certain waste waters. Practically a saturated solution of alkaline iodide is used to provide sufficient iodide for samples supersaturated with oxygen. Sodium iodide is used because of the limited solubility of the potassium salt.

(b) The higher concentration of iodide lessens interferences by organic matter and reduces the loss of free iodine during the determination. A sharper end point in the titration is also obtained.

Reagents

18. (a) *Alkaline Iodide – Sodium Azide Solution.*—Dissolve 400 g of sodium hydroxide (NaOH) in 500 ml of freshly boiled and cooled water. Cool the water slightly and dissolve 900 g of sodium iodide (NaI). Dissolve 10 g of sodium azide (NaN_3) in 40 ml of water. Slowly add, with stirring, the azide solution to the alkaline iodide solution, bringing the total volume to at least 1 liter.

(b) *Sodium Thiosulfate, Standard Solution (0.10 N).* —See Section 8 (e).

(c) *Sodium Thiosulfate, Standard Solution (0.025 N).*—See Section 8 (f).

(d) *Starch Indicator.*—See Section 8 (g).

(e) *Sulfuric Acid (sp gr 1.84).*—See Section 8 (h).

Procedure

19. Add to the sample as collected 2.0 ml of $MnSO_4$ solution followed by 2.0 ml of alkaline iodide - sodium azide solution. Stopper and mix by inverting the bottle. After the precipitate has settled, add 2.0 ml of H_2SO_4 (sp gr 1.84). Mix and titrate, following directions as given in Section 9 (b).

Calculation

20. Calculate the dissolved oxygen content of the sample, in terms of parts per million as described in Section 10 (a) and (b).

Precision and Accuracy

21. See Section 11.

POLAROGRAPHIC PROCEDURE

Application

22. (a) Since this method is in the developmental stage, it can only be provisionally recommended for wastes after dilution with natural water by a factor of 4 to 100.

(b) Gaseous or volatile oxidants stronger than molecular oxygen will be discharged at the voltage used. The nitrogen stream used will remove these gases so that their diffusion currents will not appear in the blank reading. Free halogens are the most representative types of these interferences. Certain heavy metal ions and high concentrations of soaps or detergents may cause errors, unless the operating voltage is determined in their presence. The waste itself may be used to determine the necessary electrode potential in order to minimize or reduce such errors.

Apparatus

23. (a) *Polarograph.*

(b) *Electrodes.*

Reagents

24. (a) *Alkaline Iodide - Sodium Azide Solution.*—See Section 8 (a).

(b) *Manganous Sulfate Solution (364 g per liter).*—See Section 8 (b).

(c) *Methyl Red Indicator (1 g per liter).*—Dissolve 0.1 g of water-soluble methyl red in water and dilute to 100 ml with water.

(d) *Nitrogen.*—Water-pumped nitrogen.

(e) *Potassium Chloride Solution (0.75 g per liter).*—Dissolve 0.75 g of potassium chloride (KCl) in water and dilute to 1 liter.

(f) *Potassium Fluoride Solution (400 g KF per liter).*—See Section 8 (d).

(g) *Sodium Thiosulfate, Standard Solution (0.10 N).*—See Section 8 (e).

(h) *Sodium Thiosulfate, Standard Solution (0.025 N).*—See Section 8 (f).

(i) *Sulfuric Acid (sp gr 1.84).*—See Section 8 (h).

Calibration and Standardization

25. (a) Assemble, adjust, and test the instrument as specified in the manufacturer's instructions.

(b) Operating voltages from 0.3 to 1.0 v have been recommended by various investigators. More reliable results should be obtained by each laboratory determining the best operating voltage for its instrument, under the prevailing conditions with the particular type of waste being investigated.

(c) Aerate the KCl solution for a few minutes. Saturation is not necessary. Introduce sample into the instrument and add the stock solution of methyl red to bring the final concentration of methyl red to approximately 15 ppm. Vary the electrode voltage in steps of 0.02 v from 0 to 2 v. Read and record

the current of the galvanometer deflection at each voltage. As the mercury drop grows, the current increases and abruptly decreases when the drop falls. The reading taken occurs at the point of maximum deflection.

(d) Prepare a graph of the data obtained with the voltage as the abscissa and the indicated current as the ordinate. This graph will show two waves. In the procedure given in Section 26 use the voltage at the center of the curve plateau between the two waves.

(e) Aerate the sample to be tested and place it in the cell of the instrument. Vary the electrode voltage in steps of 0.02 volt from 0 to 3 v, or until the current becomes too great for measurement. Record the galvanometer reading at each increment of voltage. Deoxygenate the sample for 5 min with a rapid stream of nitrogen. Raise the gas tube above the level of the sample. Gently pass nitrogen over the sample surface while taking a second set of readings at the same voltages previously used.

(f) Prepare a graph of the data obtained with the voltage as the abscissa and the difference between the two indicated currents at each voltage as the ordinate. In the procedure given in Section 26, use the voltage at the midpoint of the best plateau in the curve obtained.

(g) Prepare a series of standard samples of aerated KCl solution by passing through the solutions air, oxygen, or nitrogen until the series covers the desired range of dissolved oxygen concentrations in steps of no more than 1 ppm as measured by the Alsterberg procedure given in Section 9. Also apply this procedure to an unaerated standard sample.

(h) Determine the galvanometer reading for each member of the series of standard samples by applying the procedure given in Section 26. Prepare a calibration curve, plotting the differences in the galvanometer readings for the unaerated solution and the aerated solutions against the concentrations obtained by the Alsterberg procedure in Paragraph (g).

Procedure

26. (a) Introduce the sample to be tested into the cell of the instrument. Add 0.15 ml of methyl red indicator solution for each 10 ml of sample taken. Apply the voltage determined in accordance with Section 25 (f) to the electrode. Record the galvanometer reading (Note 5). Record the temperature.

NOTE 5.—Care should be taken when the sample is introduced into the cell so that the minimum amount of aeration occurs. The operations described in Paragraph (a) must be performed rapidly to avoid changes in dissolved oxygen concentration due to exposure of the sample to the air. If the galvanometer reading is taken within 30 sec, the sample need not be protected from exposure to the air.

(b) Remove the dissolved oxygen from the sample by bubbling nitrogen rapidly through it for 5 min. Raise the gas tube above the sample surface. Record the galvanometer reading while the nitrogen flows gently above the sample.

(c) Correct the difference between the galvanometer readings recorded in accordance with Paragraphs (a) and (b), using the equation given in Section 27. Convert the difference in corrected galvanometer readings to dissolved oxygen concentration from the calibration curve prepared in Section 25 (h).

Temperature Correction

27. Calculate the difference in galvanometer readings at 20 C as follows:

$$G = [0.014 \times G_1 \times (20 - t)] + G_1$$

where:

G = difference in galvanometer readings at 20 C,

G_1 = difference in galvanometer readings at test temperature, and

t = test temperature.

From the corrected difference in galvanometer readings at 20 C, the ppm of dissolved oxygen can be determined from the calibration curve (Note 6).

NOTE 6.—The temperature coefficient of the diffusion current at 20 C will vary, depending upon the type of solution used. The value of 1.4 per cent per degree will apply to most industrial waste waters.

Precision and Accuracy

28. Data are unavailable on the precision and accuracy of this method when applied to industrial waste waters.

Standard Method of Test for
SURFACE TENSION OF INDUSTRIAL WATER AND INDUSTRIAL WASTE WATER[1]

ASTM Designation: D 1590 – 60
ADOPTED, 1960

This Standard of the American Society for Testing and Materials is issued under the fixed designation D 1590; the final number indicates the year of original adoption as standard or, in the case of revision, the year of last revision.

Scope and Application

1. (*a*) This method covers the procedure for quantitative measurement of the surface tension of industrial water and industrial waste water. The method is based on instrumental measurement by the ring method and offers the most precise and accurate determination.

(*b*) This test is not intended to show any direct relationship between surface tension and concentration of surface-active agents.

Summary of Method

2. (*a*) The method is based on measurement of the force required to detach a ring from the surface of the sample.

Definitions

3. (*a*) The term "surface tension" in this method is defined in accordance with the Definitions of Terms Relating to Industrial Water and Industrial Waste Water (ASTM Designation: D 1129),[2] as follows:

Surface Tension.—A property arising from molecular forces of the surface film of all liquids which tend to alter the contained volume of liquid into a form of minimum superficial area.

NOTE 1.—Surface tension is numerically equal to the force acting normal to an imaginary line of unit length in a surface. It is also numerically equal to the work required to enlarge the surface by unit area. The usual unit of measurement is dynes per centimeter.[3]

(*b*) For definitions of other terms used in this method, refer to Definitions D 1129.

Apparatus

4. (*a*) *Tensiometer.*[4] —A sensitive torsion balance provided with means for

---

[1] Under the standardization procedure of the Society, this method is under the jurisdiction of the ASTM Committee D-19 on Industrial Water. A list of members may be found in the ASTM Year Book.

[2] Appears in this publication.

[3] The surface tension of pure water is given in the International Critical Tables as 72.75 dynes per cm at 20 C.

[4] Either the du Nouy precision tensiometer equipped with a 4-cm circumference ring or the du Nouy interfacial tensiometer with a 6-cm ring may be used for this purpose.

applying a slowly increasing force to a platinum-iridium ring in contact with the surface of the sample. The apparatus shall be provided with a graduated scale to give readings in dynes of force when properly calibrated.

(b) *Ring*, accurately constructed of platinum-iridium wire. The ring shall be circular, in one plane, free of bends or irregularities. The circumference and ratio of diameter of the ring, R, to the diameter of the wire, r, shall be known to the third significant figure. The ring shall be suspended vertically from the instrument so that the plane of the ring is parallel to the surface of the sample being tested.

(c) *Measurement Vessel*, no smaller than 6 cm in diameter, and such that the ring will be in a flat area of the sample surface and well removed from the meniscus effect near the edge of the container. A crystallizing dish having approximate dimensions of 60 by 35 mm has been found satisfactory.

(d) *Centrifuge.*—Heavy-duty type equipped with suitable head to carry four 100-ml capacity tubes and having a minimum operating speed of 1500 rpm.

Sampling

5. (a) Collect the samples in accordance with the applicable methods of the American Society for Testing and Materials, as follows:

D   510—Sampling Industrial Water,[2]
D   860—Sampling Water from Boilers,[2]
D 1066—Sampling Steam,[2]
D 1496—Sampling Homogeneous Industrial Waste Water.[2]

(b) Use only glass-stoppered vessels as sample containers.

(c) Clean with chromic-sulfuric acid cleaning solution all glassware that will come in contact with the sample and rinse thoroughly with distilled water for each sample (Note 2).

NOTE 2.—The recommended cleaning procedure comprises a 1-hr soak in chromic-sulfuric acid, five rinses with distilled water after acid is removed by distilled water, and storage in distilled water overnight. Glassware for this test should be kept segregated and stored in distilled water. On removal from storage and just prior to use, ten rinses with distilled water are recommended.

(d) To avoid potential errors that may result from suspended solids or free oil in the samples as collected, centrifuge an appropriate volume for 30 min at 1500 rpm. Pipet the actual sample portion to the measurement vessel directly from the centrifuge tubes.

Calibration and Standardization

6. (a) Level the tensiometer and adjust the length of the torsion arm by means of weights and the adjustments provided in accordance with the manufacturer's directions. This calibration procedure adjusts the instrument so that each unit of the graduated scale represents a pull on the ring of 1 dyne per cm.

(b) From the calibration weight and instrument reading, calculate the grams of pull on the ring represented by each scale division. Use this value for calculating the conversion factor, F, which is employed to give corrected surface tension values.

Procedure

7. (a) After the tensiometer has been calibrated, check the level and insert the freshly-cleaned platinum ring (Note 3). Level the plane of the ring and set the measuring dial at zero. Adjust the ring to the zero position.

NOTE 3.—For each sample, the platinum ring must be freshly cleaned by immersion in methyl ethyl ketone, permitted to dry, then immersed in hydrochloric acid (1:6—1 volume of HCl (sp gr 1.19) mixed with 6 volumes of distilled water) and rinsed thoroughly in distilled water. The ring is again immersed in methyl ethyl ketone, permitted to dry and then heated to a white heat in the oxidizing portion of a gas

13-78

flame. Successive measurements on the same sample will require cleaning and flaming the ring for each determination.

(b) Place the sample to be tested in the thoroughly cleaned measurement vessel on the sample platform. Raise the sample platform by means of the adjusting screw until the ring is completely submerged, but not to exceed 3 mm.

(c) Permit the sample surface to age for 30 ± 5 sec.

(d) Lower the platform slowly by means of the adjusting screw, at the same time increasing the torque of the ring system by means of the dial adjustment. These two simultaneous adjustments must be carefully made so that the ring system remains constantly in the zero position. Record the dial reading when the ring breaks free of the water film. Complete the break within 60 ± 5 sec after starting measurement.

(e) Make at least two measurements each on separate sample portions, making additional measurements in accordance with the magnitude of the over-all variation of the first two.

(f) Measure and report temperatures of tested sample portions.

Calculation

8. (a) Calculate the corrected surface tension of the sample as follows:

Surface tension, dynes per cm = PF

where:
P = scale reading in dynes per cm when film breaks, and
F = correction factor.

(b) Values of F in terms of two compounded parameters, R^3/V and R/r have been compiled and tabulated by Harkins and Jordan [5] In order to look up F in the tables, the vlaues of these two parameters must be calculated. Values

for R, the mean radius of the ring in centimeters, and r, the radius of the wire in the ring in centimeters, are furnished by the manufacturer with each ring. The value of V may be calculated as follows:

$$V = \frac{M}{D - d}$$

where:
M = weight of liquid raised above free surface of the liquid (equivalent to dial reading multiplied by factor derived in Section 6 (b)),
D = density of liquid, and
d = density of air saturated with vapor of the liquid.

Report

9. (a) Report the results as surface tension, dynes per centimeter, at the sample temperature in degrees Centigrade.

(b) If it is desirable to convert the surface tension values to some standard temperature, a correction factor of 0.14 dynes per cm per deg Cent may be used. This correction is subtracted when the test temperature is lower than the reporting standard temperature and is added if the test temperature is higher.

Precision and Accuracy

10. (a) The precision of this method is 0.3 dyne per cm.

(b) No limit of accuracy can be stated because of the absence of experimental data.

---

[5] W. D. Harkins and H. F. Jordan, "A Method for Determination of Surface and Interfacial Tension from the Maximum Pull on a Ring," Journal Am. Chemical Soc., Vol. 52, p. 1751 (1930). These tables are also published in "Physical Methods of Organic Chemistry," Interscience Publishers, Inc., New York, N. Y., Vol. 1, pp. 182–184 (1945).

Standard Method of Test for
EFFECT OF WATER IN TUBULAR HEAT EXCHANGERS[1]

ASTM Designation: D 1591 – 64

ADOPTED, 1964

This Standard of the American Society for Testing and Materials is issued under the fixed designation D 1591; the final number indicates the year of original adoption as standard or, in the case of revision, the year of last revision.

Scope

1. This method covers the determination of the tendency of an industrial water to cause corrosion or to form deposits when flowing through a metallic tube in a heat exchanger.

Summary of Method

2. The determination of the corroding or depositing tendency of a water in tubular heat exchangers requires that the water chosen must be passed through a cylindrical test device at the actual or proposed use temperature and at the actual or proposed use flow rate. The test specimen for the test device should be identical in composition and diameter with that being used for or considered for the operating heat exchanger. Variations in material or size may be used for specific investigational purposes. This is a qualitative procedure, and does not take into consideration hot wall effects.

Definitions

3. For definitions of terms used in this method, refer to the Definitions of Terms Relating to Industrial Water and Industrial Waste Water (ASTM Designation: D 1129).[2]

Interferences

4. Interferences in this test method include any effects caused by the initial surface condition of the specimen, any electrolysis effects resulting from contact of dissimilar metals in the installation, any factors causing deviation from normal water flow pattern, and factors causing metal stress. The initial surface condition of the test specimen should be identical with that of the operating heat exchanger and any deviation from this condition should be regarded as an interference. Care must be exercised in the installation to avoid electrical contact of the test specimen with adjacent piping. Such contact introduces the interference of electrolytic corrosion due

[1] Under the standardization procedure of the Society, this method is under the jurisdiction of the ASTM Committee D-19 on Industrial Water. A list of members may be found in the ASTM Year Book.

[2] Appears in this publication.

to dissimilar metals. Any factor that tends to cause deviation from a normal flow pattern of the water passing through the test device interferes with the method. Internal burrs or flaring on the ends of the test specimen, sharp bends close to the test device, change in cross-sectional diameter of the flow adjacent to the test device, and change in the shape of the cross-section of the flow adjacent to the test device all tend to cause such deviation. Factors causing metal stress include cold working in cutting of the specimen, rolling operations, flaring of the tube end, welding and cold forming, and are interferences in so far as the specimen deviates from the actual tube.

Apparatus

5. (a) *Test Piece.*—A section of tubing of the same composition and diameter as the actual heat exchanger tubes. The minimum length of tubing should be twelve times the outside diameter of the tubing.

(b) *Connecting Tubing.*—Neoprene, tetrafluroethylene, polyethylene, or other flexible connecting tubing. Temperature and pressure conditions should guide the selection of the connectors. For smaller diameters, two pieces, each 3 in. long, are sufficient for each test device. For larger diameters, two 4-in. pieces are recommended. As an alternative, where pressure and temperature conditions make it necessary, use metallic couplings of the same composition as the test specimen.

(c) *Hose Clamps* of any suitable type.

(d) *Piping.*—Suitable piping to and from the test device.

(e) *Specimen Holders.*—Suitable insulated clamps or supports for the test specimen, if required.

(f) *Control Devices.*—Suitable apparatus for measuring flow rate, controlling flow rate, and measuring temperature.

Procedure

6. (a) Install the test device to receive water having the same composition and temperature characteristics as those in the actual or proposed heat exchanger (Note 1).

Note 1.—One method to comply with these specifications is to take a stream of water from the inlet to the actual heat exchanger to the test device, and a second stream from the outlet line leading away from the exchanger to a second test device. On the outlet end, care should be exercised to locate the test unit close to the point of discharge of the water from the heat exchanger. Care should be taken with regard to the installation of the discharge from the specimen to make sure the test unit runs full of water.

(b) Adjust the flow of water through the test device so that the flow rate approximates that of the actual exchanger.

(c) Check and record flow rate as often as required to assure uniformity of flow (at least once per day).

(d) Adopt a standard duration time for all tests on a given water (Note 2).

Note 2.—The chosen test period may be as short as four weeks or as long as several years. Specific choice should be based on anticipated severity of corroding or depositing tendency of the water, longer periods being required for less severe conditions.

(e) Remove the test piece and immediately sample the deposit or corrosion products for microbiological examination, if such is to be made. Sampling shall be done in accordance with the Method of Field Sampling of Water-Formed Deposits (ASTM Designation: D 887).[2]

(f) Sample the deposit for chemical and physical analysis in accordance with Method D 887.

(g) Cut the tube longitudinally, without using lubricant, and examine the interior surface in accordance with Section 11 of the Recommended Practice

for Conducting Plant Corrosion Tests
(ASTM Designation: A 224).[3]

Report

7. The report shall include the
following:

(*1*) Conditions of test.

(*2*) Pertinent analysis of water and
variations that may affect results.

(*3*) Diagram showing test apparatus
and position in the water circuit.

(*4*) Suitable pictures of test specimens
before service.

---

[3] 1967 Book of ASTM Standards, Part 3.

(*5*) Visual and pictorial description of
internal surface of specimen after test
before deposits have been removed.

(*6*) Description of method employed
in cleaning the surface.

(*7*) Notation of size, shape, and distribution of pits.

(*8*) A report on any over-all thinning
of the tube wall together with a statement from the manufacturer of the
tolerance in thickness (variation in
thickness) of the initial tube wall.

(*9*) Results of microbiological analysis
and chemical and physical analysis of
the deposit, where applicable.

Standard Methods of Test for

TOTAL CHROMIUM IN INDUSTRIAL WATER AND INDUSTRIAL WASTE WATER[1]

ASTM Designation: D 1687 – 61

ADOPTED, 1961

This Standard of the American Society for Testing and Materials is issued under the fixed designation D 1687; the final number indicates the year of original adoption as standard or, in the case of revision, the year of last revision.

Scope and Application

1. These methods cover the determination of total chromium in industrial water and in industrial waste water. Under certain conditions the methods can be adapted for the determination of hexavalent chromium. Two methods are included:

	Sections
Method A.[2] Permanganate Oxidation	7 to 13
Method B.[3] Hypobromite Oxidation	14 to 20

Summary of Methods

2. (a) The methods depend on the sensitive color reaction between hexavalent chromium and s-diphenylcarbazide in acid solution. The limit of detection of chromium by this reaction is about 0.01 ppm in the solution read on the colorimeter. By suitable dilution of sample, amounts up to 50 ppm may be readily measured.

(b) Selection of the proper procedure for preparation of the sample is a function of the composition of the sample. Both Methods A and B are best adapted to measure 5 to 50 μg of chromium (0.5 to 5.0 ppm) in a 10-ml sample. More concentrated solutions may be aliquotted before analysis.

In general, Method A is applicable where organic matter is low or easily oxidized. Method B is applicable in the presence of large amounts of refractory organic matter, as in tannery wastes.

Definitions

3. For definitions of terms used in these methods, refer to the Definitions of Terms Relating to Industrial Water

[1] Under the standardization procedure of the Society, these methods are under the jurisdiction of the ASTM Committee D-19 on Industrial Water. A list of members may be found in the ASTM Year Book.

[2] Method A is based on the procedure of B. E. Saltzman, "Microdetermination of Chromium with Diphenylcarbazide by Permanganate Oxidation," *Analytical Chemistry*, Vol. 24, pp. 1016–1020 (1952).

[3] Method B is based on the procedure of C. H. Grogan, H. J. Cahnmann, and E. Lethco, "Microdetermination of Chromium in Small Samples of Various Biological Media," *Analytical Chemistry*, Vol. 27, pp. 983–986 (1955).

and Industrial Waste Water (ASTM Designation: D 1129).[4]

Interferences

4. (a) To develop the color quantitatively, all the chromium must be converted to the hexavalent condition and any organic matter destroyed. The color reaction for chromium is quite specific. With Method A, iron in excess of 1000 ppm, vanadium in excess of 4 ppm, and molybdenum and mercury in amounts over 200 ppm may interfere. For Method B, iron in excess of 50 ppm and other precipitable hydroxides may interfere. Hence, these elements, if present in excess of the above quantities, must be removed or converted to a noninterfering complex.

(b) It has been found that samples high in chloride ion (over 250 ppm Cl) do not give complete recovery of chromium, possibly because of loss as chromyl chloride. In this case, it is desirable to remove the chloride by precipitation with silver nitrate, or to supplement the oxidation by the use of silver peroxide and filtering or centrifuging to remove the insoluble silver salts (Caution, Note 1).

NOTE 1: Caution.—Sodium azide should not be used in this case if Method A is employed. Excess permanganate may then be destroyed by the use of dilute hydrochloric acid[5] or nitrite and sulfamate.[6]

(c) Large amounts of phosphate and alkali earth metal may cause precipitation and loss of chromium during the alkaline oxidation of Method B. If this occurs, an acid oxidation, as in Method A, should be used.

(d) Since the reaction is characteristic of hexavalent chromium, this determination can sometimes be carried out directly by addition of acid and s-diphenylcarbazide to the sample. Caution must be exercised, since if the solution contains materials capable of reducing chromium to the trivalent condition on acidification (cyanides, thiosulfate, organic matter) an incorrect result will be obtained. Under such conditions the rigorous determination of hexavalent chromium becomes a very difficult problem. However, this reduction frequently occurs slowly and usable results can be obtained if the analysis is completed immediately after acidification.

Purity of Reagents

5. (a) Reagent grade chemicals shall be used in all tests. Unless otherwise indicated, it is intended that all reagents shall conform to the specifications of the Committee on Analytical Reagents of the American Chemical Society, where such specifications are available.[7] Other grades may be used, provided it is first ascertained that the reagent is of sufficiently high purity to permit its use without lessening the accuracy of the determination.

(b) Unless otherwise indicated, references to water shall be understood to mean reagent water conforming to Specifications for Reagent Water (ASTM Designation: D 1193).[4]

Sampling

6. Collect the sample in accordance with the applicable method of the Ameri-

[4] Appears in this publication.
[5] E. J. Serfass, R. F. Muraca, and D. G. Gardner, "Analytical Determination of Trace Constituents in Metal Finishing Effluents. VI. The Colorimetric Determination of Chromium in Effluents," *Plating*, Vol. 42, pp. 64–68 (1955).
[6] P. G. Butts, A. R. Gahler, and M. G. Mellon, "Colorimetric Determination of Metals in Sewage and Industrial Wastes," *Sewage and Industrial Wastes*, Vol. 22, p. 1552 (1950).

[7] "Reagent Chemicals, American Chemical Society Specifications,' Am. Chemical Soc., Washington, D. C. For suggestions on the testing of reagents not listed by the American Chemical Society, see "Reagent Chemicals and Standards", by Joseph Rosin, D. Van Nostrand Co., Inc., New York, N Y. and the "United States Pharmacopeia."

can Society for Testing and Materials, as follows:

D 510—Sampling Industrial Water,[4]
D 860—Sampling Water from Boilers,[4]
D 1496—Sampling Homogeneous Industrial Waste Water.[4]

METHOD A. PERMANGANATE OXIDATION

Summary of Method

7. The sample is oxidized by acid treatment, followed by potassium permanganate treatment. A color is developed in acid solution with s-diphenylcarbazide. This color is measured by means of a spectrophotometer or photoelectric colorimeter and the color related to the chromium content of the sample.

Apparatus

8. *Photometer.*—Spectrophotometer or filter photometer suitable for use at 540 mμ and equipped with a 10-mm cell.

Reagents

9. (*a*) *Ammonium Hydroxide (1:1).*— Mix equal volumes of concentrated ammonium hydroxide (NH_4OH, sp gr 0.90) and water.

(*b*) *Nitric Acid (sp gr 1.42).*—Concentrated nitric acid (HNO_3). Reagent grade nitric acid (HNO_3) frequently may contain sufficient chromium to interfere in this method. It may be purified by distillation in all-glass equipment. Such a distillation often may need to be repeated.

(*c*) *Potassium Dichromate, Standard Solution (1 ml = 5 µg Cr).*—Dissolve 1.41 g of potassium dichromate ($K_2Cr_2O_7$) in water and dilute to 1000 ml in a volumetric flask. Pipet 10 ml of this solution into a 1000-ml volumetric flask and dilute to the mark. One milliliter of this finally-diluted solution corresponds to 0.5 ppm chromium in a 10-ml sample carried through the entire procedure.

(*d*) *Potassium Permanganate Solution (3.16 g per liter).*—Dissolve 3.16 g of potassium permanganate ($KMnO_4$) in water and dilute to 1 liter.

(*e*) *s-Diphenylcarbazide Solution (5 g per liter).*—Add 4.0 g of phthalic anhydride to 80 ml of ethanol (95 per cent) and shake for a few minutes. Add 0.5 g of 1,5-diphenylcarbohydrazide (Note 2) and dilute to 100 ml with ethanol (95 per cent). Shake occasionally to dissolve the phthalic anhydride. This solution is usable for about six months if stored in a cool, dark place. New calibration curves should be prepared at least monthly.

NOTE 2.—The proper chemical name of the compound used for developing color in this method is 1,5-diphenylcarbohydrazide, and it is so listed by some suppliers. The name generally used in the literature is s-diphenylcarbazide, and this name has been used elsewhere in the text of these methods.

(*f*) *Sodium Azide Solution (50 g per liter).*—Dissolve 5 g of sodium azide (NaN_3) in water and dilute to 100 ml (**Caution,** Note 3).

NOTE 3: **Caution.**—Solid sodium azide is normally used in the method. This reagent may explode if heated or struck. Heavy metal azides are subject to detonation. The use of azide must be avoided if the sample contains appreciable amounts of ions that form insoluble azides, such as lead or silver (see Section 4(b)).

(*g*) *Sodium Dihydrogen Phosphate Solution (138 g per liter).*—Dissolve 138 g of sodium dihydrogen phosphate (NaH_2PO_4) in water and dilute to 1 liter.

(*h*) *Sulfuric Acid (sp gr 1.84).*—Concentrated sulfuric acid (H_2SO_4).

(*i*) *Sulfuric Acid (1:49).*—Mix 1 volume of H_2SO_4 (sp gr 1.84), cautiously and with stirring, with 49 volumes of water.

(*j*) *Wash Acid.*—Mix 50 ml of HNO_3 (sp gr 1.42) with 150 ml of concentrated hydrochloric acid (HCl, sp gr 1.19) and add 200 ml of water.

Calibration

10. (*a*) Prepare a series of chromium standards containing from 0.0 to 50 μg chromium by diluting measured volumes of $K_2Cr_2O_7$ solution (1 ml = 5 μg Cr), so that a 10-ml aliquot of each dilution will contain the desired quantity of chromium.

(*b*) Pipet 10-ml portions of the chromium standards into 125-ml Erlenmeyer flasks and proceed as directed in Section 11. Plot absorbance against chromium concentration (Note 4).

NOTE 4.—A separate calibration curve must be made for each photometer and a recalibration must be made if any alterations of the instrument are made or if new reagents are prepared.

Procedure[8]

11. (*a*) Pipet 10 ml of the sample into a 125-ml Erlenmeyer flask (Note 5). If a blank has not been run on reagents, use 10 ml of water and carry through the analysis.

NOTE 5.—All glassware should be rinsed in wash-acid and then with water before use.

(*b*) Add 5 ml of HNO_3 and evaporate just to dryness. Do not bake. Cool and add an additional 5 ml of HNO_3, followed by 2 ml of H_2SO_4 (sp gr 1.84). Evaporate to fumes, then heat gently for 1 min. If the residue is discolored by organic matter, cautiously add 2 ml of HNO_3, reduce to fumes, and repeat treatments as often as necessary (Note 6). It may be necessary to add more H_2SO_4 (sp gr 1.84) to prevent the mixture from becoming dry.

NOTE 6.—If organic matter is absent, omit the steps described in Paragraphs (*b*) and (*c*). Instead, add 1 ml of HNO_3 to the sample, boil, and proceed as described in Paragraph (*d*).

---

[8] The procedure as given handles interference from iron up to about 1000 ppm. For larger amounts or other uncommon interferences, consult the original reference by B. E. Saltzman (see Footnote 2).

If reducing impurities are absent, hexavalent chromium may be determined directly by omitting the steps described in Paragraphs (*b*) through (*g*). Add 13 ml of H_2SO_4 (1:49) and proceed as described in Paragraph (*h*).

(*c*) Cool the solution to room temperature. Add 17 ml of water and neutralize with NH_4OH (1:1). Add 13 ml of H_2SO_4 (1:49). Swirl and, if necessary, warm to achieve solution.

(*d*) Filter through a fine-texture, ashless filter paper[9] or centrifuge to obtain a clear solution. If a filter is used, wash it three times with 5-ml portions of water and combine the washings and filtrate. Collect the filtrate in a 250-ml beaker.

(*e*) Add 0.6 ml of $KMnO_4$ solution. Cover the beaker with a watch glass and heat on a steam bath for 20 min. If the pink color disappears, add an additional 0.6 ml of $KMnO_4$ solution to maintain a slight excess.

(*f*) After cooling the beaker, add sodium azide solution dropwise at the rate of a drop every 10 sec, swirling with each addition (**Caution,** Note 3). Use just enough azide (usually 3 to 5 drops) to destroy the permanganate color and any brownish tint. Cool at once to room temperature in a cold water bath.

(*g*) If any turbidity or precipitate is present at this point, filter through a fine-porosity porcelain crucible[10] or an asbestos mat, but do not use filter paper. Alternatively, clarify by centrifuging. If a filter is used, wash once with not more than 5 ml of water.

(*h*) Transfer the solution to a 50-ml volumetric flask and add 2 ml of the *s*-diphenylcarbazide solution. Mix and let stand 1 min.

(*i*) Add 5.0 ml of NaH_2PO_4 solution and let stand at least 5 min but not more than 30 min. Dilute to the mark.

---

[9] Whatman No. 42 paper has been found satisfactory for this purpose.

[10] A Selas crucible has been found satisfactory for this purpose.

(*j*) Measure the absorbance of the sample at 540 mμ in a spectrophotometer or filter photometer, using approximately a 10-mm cell, and setting the instrument for zero absorbance with water.

(*k*) Measure the absorbance at 540 mμ of the blank and subtract the absorbance of the blank from that of the sample. Convert the difference in absorbance to chromium content of the sample from the calibration curve prepared as directed in Section 10.

Calculation

12. Calculate the chromium concentration, in parts per million, as follows:

$$\text{Chromium, ppm} = \frac{W}{S \times G}$$

where:

W = micrograms of chromium found
S = milliliters of sample used, and
G = specific gravity of sample.

Precision and Accuracy[11]

13. Precision varies with the range of chromium content. The standard deviation increases from 0.04 ppm at 0.30 ppm chromium to 0.10 ppm at 6 ppm chromium. Accuracy is of the same order of magnitude.

METHOD B. HYPOBROMITE OXIDATION

Summary of Method

14. The sample is oxidized by acid treatment, followed by sodium hypobromite treatment. A color is developed in acid solution with *s*-diphenylcarbazide. This color is measured by means of a spectrophotometer or filter photometer and the color is related to the chromium content of the sample.

Apparatus

15. See Section 8.

---

[11] Supporting data giving results of cooperative tests have been filed at ASTM Headquarters.

Reagents

16. (*a*) *Hydrochloric Acid (sp gr 1.19).* —Concentrated hydrochloric acid (HCl). Reagent grade hydrochloric acid frequently may give an undesirably large blank. If this proves to be the case, satisfactory acid may be prepared by saturating reagent water, cooled in an ice bath, with gaseous hydrogen chloride that has been scrubbed with water and H_2SO_4 (sp gr 1.84) and passed through a solid carbon dioxide trap.

(*b*) *Hydrogen Peroxide (30 per cent).* — Concentrated hydrogen peroxide (H_2O_2).

(*c*) *Nitric Acid (sp gr 1.42).* —See Section 9 (*b*).

(*d*) *Phenol-Water Mixture (12 g phenol per liter).* —Dissolve 1.2 g of colorless phenol in 100 ml of water.

(*e*) *Potassium Dichromate, Standard Solution (1 ml = 5 μg Cr).* —See Section 9 (*c*).

(*f*) *s-Diphenylcarbazide Solution (5 g per liter).* —See Section 9 (*e*).

(*g*) *Sodium Hypobromite Solution.* — Add 6 ml of a saturated solution of bromine to 100 ml of sodium hydroxide solution (NaOH, 40 g per liter). Store the prepared solution in a dark bottle in a refrigerator.

(*h*) *Sulfuric Acid (1:9).* —Mix 1 volume of concentrated sulfuric acid (H_2SO_4, sp gr 1.84) cautiously and with stirring to 9 volumes of water. Without cooling, add potassium permanganate solution ($KMnO_4$, 10 g per liter) dropwise until a pale pink color persists for 1 min.

(*i*) *Wash Acid.* —See Section 9 (*j*).

Calibration

17. Proceed as directed in Section 10, except in Paragraph (*b*) proceed in accordance with Section 18 instead of with Section 11.

Procedure

18. (*a*) Pipet 10 ml of sample into a

25 by 150-mm, heat-resistant glass test tube (Notes 5 and 7). If a blank has not been run on reagents, use 10 ml of water and carry through the analysis. Add 0.5 ml of HNO₃ and 4 drops of H₂O₂. Mix by swirling and let stand 20 to 30 min.

NOTE 7.—If organic matter is absent, pipet 10 ml of sample into the test tube, add 2 ml of sodium hypobromite solution, mix, and heat in a boiling water bath for 10 to 20 min. Then proceed as described in Paragraph (d).

(b) Holding the tube in a suitable holder, heat it over a flame and boil gently. Hold the tube nearly horizontal to avoid losses. When water is removed, evaporate the acid slowly, allowing it to reflux (Note 8). The addition of HNO₃ and fuming may have to be repeated if large amounts of organic matter are present in order to obtain a white or yellowish ash. Do not allow the ash to bake. It is important to remove substantially all the HNO₃.

NOTE 8.—With samples containing much organic matter, remove the acid slowly to obtain maximum oxidation with each portion of acid. When the evaporation is properly performed, there will be a nearly dry residue at the bottom of the tube and several drops of acid on the tube wall which can be returned to the residue several times. Most of the oxidation takes place at this point in the procedure.

(c) Dissolve the ash by washing down the tube with 4 to 5 ml of water. Add 2 ml of sodium hypobromite solution, mix well, and heat in a boiling water bath for 10 to 20 min (Note 9).

NOTE 9.—Large amounts of phosphate and alkali earth metals may cause precipitation and loss of chromium at this point. If noticeable amounts of precipitate occur, an acid oxidation method such as Method A is preferred, although

the same ashing procedure as given here may be employed.

(d) From a microburet, add 1.16 ml of H₂SO₄ (1:9). The pH should be in the range 1.3 to 1.7 and a yellow-brown color due to free bromine should appear (Note 10).

NOTE 10.—If no brown color appears, either destruction of organic matter was incomplete, or the hypobromite solution needs renewing. In either case it is wise to reject the sample.

(e) Transfer the solution to a volumetric flask of the desired size (10 ml is adequate for 5 μg Cr). Rinse the tube into the flask with 2 to 3 ml of water and add 0.5 ml of phenol-water mixture to discharge the bromine color. Add 0.5 ml of s-diphenylcarbazide solution and dilute to the mark. Mix and let stand 1 min.

(f) Proceed in accordance with Section 11 (j) and (k).

Calculation

19. Calculate the chromium concentration, in parts per million, as follows:

$$\text{Chromium, ppm} = \frac{W}{S \times G}$$

where:

W = micrograms of chromium found
S = milliliters of sample used, and
G = specific gravity of sample.

Precision and Accuracy[11]

20. Precision varies with the range of chromium content. The standard deviation increases from 0.04 ppm at 0.30 ppm Cr to about 0.12 ppm at 6 ppm Cr. Accuracy is of the same order of magnitude.

Tentative Methods of Test for
COPPER IN INDUSTRIAL WATER AND INDUSTRIAL WASTE WATER[1]

ASTM Designation: D 1688 – 63 T

Issued, 1959; Last Revised, 1963

These Tentative Methods have been approved by the sponsoring committee and accepted by the Society in accordance with established procedures, for use pending adoption as standard. Suggestions for revisions should be addressed to the Society at 1916 Race St., Philadelphia 3, Pa.

Scope

1. (a) These methods cover the colorimetric determination of copper in industrial water and industrial waste water. The following three methods are included:

	Sections
Referee Method A (Neocuproine)..	6 to 15
Referee Method B (Neocuproine)..	16 to 25
Non-Referee Method C (Cuprethol)................	26 to 35

(b) Referee Method A covers the range of 0.05 ppm Cu or over. Referee Method B is an adaption of Method A for waters relatively free from interference to cover the range 0.002 to 0.100 ppm Cu. Non-Referee Method C is a rapid procedure for waters containing the same range of copper as Method A but having less interfering substances present.

Definitions

2. For definitions of terms used in these methods, refer to the Definitions of Terms Relating to Industrial Water and Industrial Waste Water (ASTM Designation: D 1129).[2]

Purity of Reagents

3. (a) Reagent grade chemicals shall be used in all tests. Unless otherwise indicated, it is intended that all reagents shall conform to specifications of the Committee on Analytical Reagents of the American Chemical Society, where such specifications are available.[3] Other grades may be used, provided it is first ascertained that the reagent is of sufficiently high purity to permit its use without lessening the accuracy of the determination.

(b) Unless otherwise indicated, refer-

[1] Under the standardization procedure of the Society, these methods are under the jurisdiction of the ASTM Committee D-19 on Industrial Water. A list of members may be found in the ASTM Year Book.

[2] Appears in this publication.

[3] "Reagent Chemicals, American Chemical Society Specifications," Am. Chemical Soc., Washington, D. C. For suggestions on the testing of reagents not listed by the American Chemical Society, see "Reagent Chemicals and Standards," by Joseph Rosin, D. Van Nostrand Co., Inc., New York, N. Y., and the "United States Pharmacopeia."

ences to water shall be understood to mean reagent water conforming to the Specifications for Reagent Water (ASTM Designation: D 1193).[4] In addition, the water used for these methods shall be copper-free.

Sampling

4. (a) Collect the sample in accordance with the applicable method of the American Society for Testing and Materials, as follows:

D   510—Sampling Industrial Water,[2]
D   860—Sampling Water from Boilers,[2]
D 1066—Sampling Steam,[2]
D 1496—Sampling Homogeneous Industrial Waste Water.[2]

(b) Since some of the copper in the sample may plate out on the surface of the container, collect the sample in a bottle to which concentrated hydrochloric acid (HCl, sp gr 1.19) has been added. The volume of acid should be sufficient to neutralize the sample to pH 4 plus exactly 2.0 ml for every liter of sample. When acidified samples are analyzed, a correction for the dilution should be made for the added acid. A polyethylene bottle must be used in collecting the sample when copper is to be determined in accordance with Method B.

Cleaning of Glassware

5. Contamination from unclean sample containers and glassware is a great source of error in the test, particularly with Method B. Soak all new glassware (for both sampling and testing) in hot nitric acid (HNO₃, 1:9) for several hours. To be certain that the new glassware is conditioned for Method B, rinse it with water and run a copper determination (blank) on copper-free water. Repeat the test until copper in the blank is reduced to a value representing less than

---

[4] Appears in this publication.

4 ppb Cu. After determinations in accordance with Method B, always rinse the glassware with the organic solvent, followed by water. Soak the glassware in HNO₃ (1:9) until used again for determination using Method B. Discard any glassware that appears etched or scratched.

REFEREE METHOD A

(Neocuproine)

Application

6. This method is applicable to the determination of copper in industrial water and industrial waste water containing 0.05 ppm Cu or more.

Summary of Method

7. (a) The method is based on the measurement of the intensity of the yellow color of the cuprous complex of 2,9-dimethyl-1,10-phenanthroline (neocuproine).[5] Full development of the color takes place over the pH range from 2.3 to 9.0.[6] However, a buffer solution is used to produce an aqueous phase with a pH of 4.0 to 6.0.

(b) The copper is reduced with hydroxylamine hydrochloride and the pH of the solution is adjusted with a sodium citrate solution. The cuprous ion is then reacted with 2,9-dimethyl-1,10-phenanthroline and the yellow complex extracted with chloroform.[6, 7, 8] Any of the usual photoelectric or visual

---

[5] Neocuproine, obtainable from the G. Frederick Smith Chemical Co., Columbus, Ohio, has been found satisfactory for this purpose.
[6] A. R. Gahler, "Colorimetric Determination of Copper with Neo-Cuproine," *Analytical Chemistry*, Vol. 26, No. 3, p. 577 (1954).
[7] A. R. Goulston and A. A. Deacutis, "Spectrophotometric Determination of Copper in Titanium," *Analytical Chemistry*, Vol. 29, pp 750–753, May, 1957.
[8] H. Diehl and G. F. Smith, "The Copper Reagents: Cuproine, Neocuproine, and Bathocuproine," The G. Frederick Smith Chemical Co., Columbus, Ohio, pp. 25–31 (1958).

methods may be used for measuring or comparing the color. The method follows Beer's Law up to a concentration of 5 ppm Cu. The maximum absorption occurs at 457 mμ.

Interferences

8. None of the ions commonly found in industrial water or industrial waste water interfere with the test.[9, 10] Possible interferences from sulfide, cyanide, organic matter, and chromium are eliminated in the test.

TABLE I.—APPLICATION RANGES OF APPARATUS FOR MEASUREMENT OF COLOR FOR METHOD A.

Apparatus for Color Measurement	Range Covered, ppm[a]
Nessler tube, 300-mm	0.05 to 2.0
Filter photometer (blue filter):[b]	
23-mm cell.	0.1 to 3.0
50-mm cell.	0.05 to 1.5
Spectrophotometer (457 mμ),	
10-mm cell.	0.2 to 5.0

[a] For the usual 50-ml sample.
[b] A Fisher No. 425 filter or a Klett-Summerson No. 44 filter, or equivalent, has been found suitable for this purpose.

Apparatus

9. (a) *Nessler Tubes or Photometer.*— A set of 50-ml Nessler tubes or a photometer may be used for evaluating the intensity of the color produced.

(b) The relation of the over-all sensitivity of the method to the thickness of the solution viewed and the apparatus used for measurement of the color is shown in Table I.

[9] G. F. Smith and W. H. McCurdy, "2,9-Dimethyl-1,10-phenanthroline, New Specific in Spectrophotometric Determination of Copper," *Analytical Chemistry,* Vol. 24, No. 2, p. 371 (1952).
[10] C. L. Luke and M. E. Campbell, "Determination of Impurities in Germanium and Silicon," *Analytical Chemistry,* Vol. 25, p. 1588 (1953).

Photometric Practice

10. Photometers and photometric practice described in this method shall conform to the Recommended Practice for Photometric Methods for Chemical Analysis of Metals (ASTM Designation: E 60).[11]

Reagents

11. (a) *Ammonium Hydroxide (sp gr 0.90).*—Concentrated ammonium hydroxide (NH_4OH).

(b) *Chloroform* ($CHCl_3$).

(c) *Copper, Standard Solution (1 ml = 0.02 mg Cu).*—Weigh 0.200 g of electrolytic copper. Place it in a 250-ml beaker under a hood, add 3 ml of water and 3 ml of HNO_3 (sp gr 1.42), and cover the beaker with a watch glass. After the metal has completely dissolved, add 1 ml of H_2SO_4 (sp gr 1.84) and heat on a hot plate just short of complete dryness. Do not bake the residue. Cool the residue, wash down the sides of the beaker and the bottom of the watch glass, and again evaporate the solution nearly to dryness to expel the HNO_3. Cool the residue, dissolve it in water, and dilute the solution to 1 liter. Make the standard as needed by diluting 100 ml of the prepared solution to 1 liter with water. One milliliter of the standard contains 0.02 mg Cu or when diluted to 50 ml with water it represents a 0.4 ppm Cu solution.

(d) *Hydrochloric Acid (sp gr 1.19).*— Concentrated hydrochloric acid (HCl).

(e) *Hydroxylamine Hydrochloride Solution (200 g per liter).*—Dissolve 40 g of hydroxylamine hydrochloride ($NH_2OH \cdot HCl$) in water and dilute to 200 ml.

(f) *Isopropyl Alcohol.*

(g) *Neocuproine Solution (1 g per liter).*—Dissolve 0.1 g of neocuproine (2,9-dimethyl-1,10-phenanthroline)[5] in 50 ml of isopropyl alcohol. Dilute the solution to 100 ml with water.

[11] 1967 Book of ASTM Standards, Part 32.

(h) *Nitric Acid* (*sp gr 1.42*).—Concentrated nitric acid (HNO_3).

(i) *Sodium Citrate Solution* (*250 g per liter*).—Dissolve 250 g of hydrated sodium citrate ($Na_3C_6H_5O_7 \cdot 2H_2O$) in water and dilute to 1 liter. Add 10 ml of $NH_2OH \cdot HCl$ solution and 10 ml of neocuproine solution. Extract copper impurities in the solution with 50 ml of $CHCl_3$, discarding the chloroform layer.

(j) *Sulfuric Acid* (*sp gr 1.84*).—Concentrated sulfuric acid (H_2SO_4).

Calibration and Standardization

12. (a) Prepare a series of standard copper solutions to cover the range specified in Table I. Prepare the standards by adding 0.1 ml of HCl (sp gr 1.19) to suitable volumes of standard copper solution in 125-ml Squibb separatory funnels and dilute each to 50 ml with water. Also include a zero standard (blank) in this series by diluting only 0.1 ml of HCl to 50 ml. Proceed as directed in Section 13(b), beginning with the addition of $NH_2OH \cdot HCl$ solution.

(b) If the copper content is to be determined by visual comparison in Nessler tubes, transfer each organic extract to the 50-ml tubes.

(c) If the copper content is to be determined by means of a photometer, measure the color of the organic extract obtained from each treated standard solution. For the initial photometer setting, use the organic extract from the blank determination as a reference solution. Prepare a calibration curve, plotting the results on semilog graph paper. Plot the percentage of transmittance along the vertical single cycle log axis and milligrams along the horizontal linear axis. If the scale of the photometer reads directly in absorbance, use ordinary graph paper for plotting absorbance versus milligrams of copper.

Procedure

13. (a) If the water contains interfering substances such as organic matter, sulfide, cyanide, or chromium (when the ratio of chromium to copper is greater than 5 to 1), the following preliminary sample treatment is required: Transfer 100 ml of the acidified shaken sample to a 250-ml beaker, add 1 ml of H_2SO_4 (sp gr 1.84), and 5 ml of HNO_3 (sp gr 1.42). Evaporate the sample to dense white sulfur trioxide fumes on a hot plate, taking the necessary precautions to minimize bumping. Repeat the treatment with an additional 5 ml of HNO_3 if the solution remains colored. If organic matter is difficult to destroy, repeat the treatment with 5 ml of HNO_3 and 5 ml of either hydrogen peroxide (H_2O_2) or perchloric acid ($HClO_4$) (Notes 1 and 2). Evaporate the solution to complete dryness. Rinse the sides of the beaker and watch glass with water and again evaporate the solution to dryness to completely expel the HNO_3. Add about 80 ml of water to the residue, bring solution to a boil, cool, and, if turbid, filter. Adjust the pH to 4 to 6 by dropwise addition of NH_4OH (sp gr 0.90) and use of suitable pH test paper (Note 3). Add 0.2 ml of HCl (sp gr 1.19) and dilute the solution to 100 ml in a volumetric flask with water.

NOTE 1: **Caution.**—Warm $HClO_4$ solutions react explosively with organic matter such as oil, paper, starch, wood, etc., the explosive force being directly proportional to the exposed surface area of the organic matter. The presence of HNO_3 prevents this spontaneous reaction and is positive insurance against exploding during evaporations of water samples with $HClO_4$, even if they contain organic matter. The preboil with HNO_3 will remove most organic matter; however, if the original samples contain large quantities of organic matter, such as oil films, chunks of wood, or coal dust, the organic matter should be removed by a suitable method before analysis.[12]

NOTE 2.—If the sample is high in chromium, volatilize the chromium as the chloride by add-

---

[12] Precautions for the use of $HClO_4$ are available in "Chemical Safety Data Sheet SD-11," published by the Manufacturing Chemists' Association of the United States.

ing 2 ml of HCl (sp gr 1.19) and again evaporating to dryness.

NOTE 3.—No internal indicators should be used to adjust the pH. A pH meter or an external indicator such as narrow range pH paper may be used, taking care not to contaminate the sample.

(b) Transfer a 50-ml aliquot of the above filtrate if preliminary sample treatment is required, or 50 ml of the original acidified sample if the water is free from the listed interference, to a 125-ml Squibb separatory funnel (Notes 4 and 5). Add 5 ml of $NH_2OH \cdot HCl$ solution, 10 ml of sodium citrate solution, and 10 ml of neocuproine solution to the sample in the funnel, shaking the funnel and its contents for 30 sec between each addition. Add 20 ml of $CHCl_3$ and shake the funnel vigorously for 30 sec. Allow the funnel to stand 5 min to permit aqueous and chloroform layers to separate. Drain the chloroform layer into a dry flask and repeat the extraction step with 20 ml of $CHCl_3$, combining the $CHCl_3$ extracts in the flask. Dilute combined extracts in a volumetric flask to 50 ml with isopropyl alcohol.

NOTE 4.—If the sample contains more than the maximum concentration of copper listed in Table I for the applicable apparatus, a smaller size sample diluted to 50 ml with water containing 0.2 ml HCl (sp gr 1.19) per 100 ml should be taken for analysis. Filter the acidified sample if turbid.

NOTE 5.—Separatory funnels with polytetrafluoroethylene (Teflon) stopcocks are preferred. Use silicone grease to lubricate glass stopcocks, but use only the minimum amount needed.

(c) If the determination is made by means of 50-ml Nessler tubes, transfer the $CHCl_3$ extract to the Nessler tube and compare the color with previously prepared standards.

(d) If a photometer is to be used, always carry out a blank determination by treating a solution prepared by adding 0.2 ml HCl (sp gr 1.19) to 100 ml of water as described in Paragraphs (a)

and (b) or a solution prepared by adding 0.1 ml HCl (sp gr 1.19) to 50 ml water as described in Paragraphs (a) and (b). Measure transmittance or absorbance of the test solution, using the organic extract obtained from the blank determination as reference solution for the initial photometer setting.

Calculation

14. Calculate the concentration of copper, in parts per million, as follows:

$$\text{Copper, ppm} = \frac{W \times 1000}{S}$$

where:

W = milligrams of copper found in accordance with Sections 12 and 13, and

S = milliliters of aliquot or sample used in accordance with Section 13(b).

Precision[13]

15. When the colored organic extract is measured in a photometer, the over-all precision of the method is as follows:

$$S_T = 0.008X + 0.01$$

where:

S_T = precision in parts per million, and

X = concentration of copper in sample in parts per million.

REFEREE METHOD B

(Neocuproine Method)

Application

16. This method is applicable to the determination of copper in industrial waters such as steam condensate and deionized water. It is specifically applicable to concentrations of copper from 2 to 1000 ppb.

---

[13] Supporting data giving results of cooperative tests have been filed at ASTM Headquarters.

Summary of Method

17. Refer to Section 7(a) and (b). In Method B a choice between chloroform and isoamyl alcohol is given as the organic solvent used for extraction. The maximum absorption occurs at 457 mμ when chloroform is the extractant and at 454 mμ when isoamyl alcohol is the extractant.

Interferences

18. None of the ions commonly found in low-solids industrial water interferes with the test.[9, 10]

Apparatus

19. (a) Nessler Tubes or Photometer.— A set of matched 50-ml Nessler tubes or a photometer may be used for evaluating the intensity of the color produced.

(b) The relation of the over-all sensitivity of the method to the thickness of the solution viewed and the apparatus used for measurement of the color is shown in Table II.

Photometric Practice

20. Photometers and photometric practice prescribed in this method shall conform to the Recommended Practice for Photometric Methods for Chemical Analysis of Metals (ASTM Designation: E 60).[11]

Reagents

21. (a) Chloroform Solvent.—Mix 9 volumes of chloroform (CHCl₃) with 1 volume of isopropyl alcohol.

(b) Copper, Standard Solution (1 ml = 4 μg Cu).—Dilute 200 ml of copper solution (1 ml = 0.02 mg Cu) described in Section 11(c) as needed to 1 liter with water. One milliliter of this standard solution contains 4 μg of copper or, when diluted to 200 ml with water, it contains 20 ppb of copper.

(c) Hydrochloric Acid (sp gr 1.19).— Concentrated hydrochloric acid (HCl).

(d) Hydroxylamine Hydrochloride Solution (200 g per liter).—Remove traces of copper from the solution prepared as described in Section 11(e) by treating in a separatory funnel with neocuproine solution and chloroform solvent as described in Section 23(a) and (b). Discard the organic extract.

(e) Isoamyl Alcohol, copper-free.

(f) Isopropyl Alcohol, copper-free.

(g) Neocuproine Solution (1 g per liter).—See Section 11(g) for preparation.

(h) Sodium Acetate Solution (275 g per liter).—Dissolve 55 g of sodium

TABLE II.—APPLICATION RANGES OF APPARATUS FOR MEASUREMENT OF COLOR FOR METHOD B.

Apparatus for Color Measurement	Range Covered, ppb[a]
Nessler tube, 300-mm.......	5 to 250
Filter photometer (blue filter):[b]	
23-mm cell...............	10 to 600
50-mm cell...............	5 to 250
Spectrophotometer (457 to 454 mμ):	
10-mm cell...............	20 to 1000
100-mm cell.............	2 to 100

[a] For the usual 200-ml sample.
[b] A Fisher No. 425 filter or a Klett-Summerson No. 44 filter, or equivalent, has been found suitable for this purpose.

acetate trihydrate (NaC₂H₃O₂·3H₂O) in water and dilute to 200 ml. Remove traces of copper from the solution by treating in a separatory funnel with NH₂OH·HCl, neocuproine, and chloroform solvent solutions as described in Section 23(a) and (b). Discard the organic extract.

Calibration and Standardization

22. (a) Prepare a series of standard copper solutions to cover the range specified in Table II for the measuring apparatus to be used. Prepare the standards in 250-ml Squibb separatory funnels by adding 0.4 ml of HCl to suitable volumes of the standard copper solution (1 ml =

4 µg Cu) and diluting each to 200 ml
with water. Also include a zero standard
(blank) in the series by diluting 0.4 ml
of acid to 200 ml.

(b) If the copper content is to be determined by visual comparisons in
Nessler tubes, proceed as directed in
Section 23(a) and (b) and then transfer
each organic extract to a Nessler tube
and dilute to the 50-ml graduation with
isopropyl alcohol.

(c) If the copper content is to be determined by means of a photometer,
proceed as directed in Section 23(a)
and (b) and measure the color of the
organic liquid obtained from each treated
standard solution. For the initial
photometer setting, use the organic
liquid from the blank determination as
a reference solution. Prepare a calibration curve, plotting the results on semilog graph paper. Plot the percentage of
transmittance along the vertical single
cycle log axis and the micrograms of
copper along the horizontal linear axis.
If the scale of the photometer reads
directly in absorbance, use ordinary
graph paper for plotting absorbance
versus micrograms of copper.

Procedure

23. (a) Transfer 200 ml of the acidified
sample having a temperature of 20 to
30 C to a 250-ml separatory funnel
(Notes 5 and 6). Add 1 ml of
NH$_2$OH·HCl solution and mix by
shaking. Next, add 10 ml of NaC$_2$H$_3$O$_2$
solution and again shake. Then add 2 to
4 ml of neocuproine solution (Note 7)
and shake the funnel and contents for
1 min.

NOTE 6.—If the sample contains more than
the maximum concentration of copper listed in
Table II for the applicable apparatus, a smaller
size sample diluted to 200 ml with water should
be taken for analysis. The dilution water should
be copper-free and contain 0.4 ml of HCl per
200 ml solution.

NOTE 7.—Normally, 2 ml of neocuproine
solution is sufficient in a test. However, 4 ml of

the reagent is suggested when the sample contains more than 100 µg of copper or when it is
high in heavy metal ions.

(b) To the solution in the funnel add
25 ml of chloroform solvent (Note 8)
and shake the funnel vigorously for at
least 1 min. Allow to stand 5 min to
permit the aqueous and chloroform
layers to separate. Completely drain off
the chloroform layer into a suitable,
dry 50-ml Erlenmeyer flask and add to it
10 ml of isopropyl alcohol to clear the
solution.

NOTE 8.—Isoamyl alcohol may be used in
place of chloroform solvent for extraction
purposes. Since the alcohol is lighter than water,
the aqueous layer is discarded and the alcohol
layer is collected in a suitable container. Add
10 ml of isopropyl alcohol to clear the solution.
Make spectrophotometric measurements at 454
mµ when isoamyl alcohol is used as the extractant.

(c) If the determination is to be made
by means of Nessler tubes, transfer the
organic extract to the Nessler tube.
Dilute to the 50-ml mark with isopropyl
alcohol, mix, and compare with the previously prepared standards.

(d) If a photometer is to be used,
measure the transmittance or absorbance
of the organic test solution, using a mixture of 25 ml of chloroform solvent and
10 ml of isopropyl alcohol (Notes 9 and
10) as the reference solution for the
initial photometer setting. Make spectrophotometric measurements at a wavelength of 457 mµ when chloroform is
used as the extractant.

NOTE 9.—If the organic test solution is not
sufficient to fill the optical cell, dilute the solution to 50 ml with isopropyl alcohol. The same
dilution must be used, however, in Section 22.
Precision is decreased when the volume of the
organic test solution is increased.

NOTE 10.—The blank determination made
for calibration purposes in Section 22 compensates for copper in both the reagents and the
200 ml of water. When the test sample contains
less than 10 ppb Cu, it is important in Paragraph
(d) to compensate only for the copper in the
reagents and not to include the few ppb Cu

found in many supposedly copper-free waters. The reagent blank is found by extracting the copper from two 200-ml aliquots of copper-free water. Use the normal volumes of reagent in one and twice the normal volumes of HCl, $NH_2OH \cdot HCl$ solution, $NaC_2H_3O_2$, and neocuproine solution in the other. All reagents, including HCl, should be from the same bottles as those employed during the test on unknown

TABLE III.—APPLICATION RANGES OF APPARATUS FOR MEASUREMENT OF COLOR FOR METHOD C.

Apparatus for Color Measurement	Range Covered, ppm[a]
Nessler tube, 300-mm	0.05 to 1.0
Filter photometer (blue filter):[b]	
20-mm cell	0.1 to 2.0
50-mm cell	0.05 to 1.0
Spectrophotometer (435 mμ),	
10-mm cell	0.2 to 4.0

[a] For the usual 100-ml sample.
[b] A Fisher No. 425 filter or a Klett-Summerson No. 44 filter, or the equivalent, has been found suitable for this purpose.

samples. Measure the color of the organic extract obtained from the blank treated with double the normal volumes of reagents, using the organic extract from the normal blank as reference solution for the initial photometer setting. Correct the value for copper in micrograms found in the unknown sample in Paragraph (d) by subtracting from it the value for the reagent blank.

Calculation

24. Calculate the concentration of copper, in parts per billion, as follows:

$$\text{Copper, ppb} = \frac{W \times 1000}{S}$$

where:

W = micrograms of copper determined in accordance with Sections 22 and 23, and

S = milliliters of sample used.

Precision[14]

25. When the colored test solution is measured in a spectrophotometer equipped with 100-mm cells, the over-all precision of the method is as follows:

$$S_T = 0.008X + 0.9$$

where:

S_T = precision in parts per billion, and
X = concentration of copper in sample in parts per billion.

NON-REFEREE METHOD C

(Cuprethol Method)

Application

26. This method is applicable to the determination of copper in industrial water containing 0.05 ppm Cu or more. Method A should be used if the water contains such interferences as cyanide, sulfide, nickel, bismuth, mercury, cobalt, and high concentrations of organic matter. Method C is preferred for relatively unpolluted waters since it does not involve an organic extraction step; hence, a determination can be made more rapidly with Method C.

Summary of Method

27. Cupric ions form a yellow-colored chelate with cuprethol, the trivial name for the reagent, bis-(2-hydroxyethyl)-dithiocarbamate. The colored compound formed at a pH between 5 and 6 is soluble[14, 15]. The maximum absorption occurs at 435 mμ and Beer's law is valid up to a copper concentration of 2 ppm. Any of the usual photoelectric or visual methods may be used for measuring or comparing the color.

Interferences

28. No interference is shown by 1000 ppm of sodium, potassium, ammonium, magnesium, chloride, nitrate, phosphate, and silicate. It is believed that excessive

---

[14] E. Geiger and H. G. Muller, "Substituted Dithiocarbonic Acid Reagent for Copper," *Helvetica Chimica Acta*, Vol. 26, p. 996 (1943).
[15] W. C. Woelfel, "Colorimetric Determination of Copper with Carbon Disulfide and Diethanolamine—An Improved Dithiocarbamate Reagent," *Analytical Chemistry*, Vol. 20, p. 772 (1948).

concentrations of interfering ions will rarely be encountered in unpolluted waters to render the method inapplicable. Bismuth, cobalt, mercurous, nickel, cyanide, and sulfide ions interfere most seriously. Use of pyrophosphate overcomes the possible interference from iron.

Apparatus

29. (a) *Nessler Tubes or Photometer.* A set of 50-ml matched Nessler tubes or a photometer may be used for evaluating the intensity of the color produced.

(b) The relation of the over-all sensitivity of the method to the thickness of solution viewed and the apparatus used for measurement of the color is shown in Table III.

Photometric Practice

30. Photometers and photometric practice prescribed in this method shall conform to the Recommended Practice for Photometric Methods for Chemical Analysis of Metals (ASTM Designation: E 60).[11]

Reagents

31. (a) *Acetate-Phthalate Buffer.*—Prepare an acetate solution by dissolving 100 g of sodium acetate trihydrate ($NaC_2H_3O_2 \cdot 3H_2O$) in water and diluting the solution to 500 ml with water. Make up a phthalate solution by dissolving 50 g of potassium acid phthalate (HOOC·C_6H_4COOK) in 230 ml of water heated to a temperature of about 80 C. While the phthalate solution is still warm, add sufficient phthalate solution to the acetate solution to produce a buffer having a pH of 5.4 as measured with a pH meter. Usually about 150 ml of the phthalate solution is required.

(b) *Copper, Standard Solution (1 ml = 0.02 mg Cu).*—Prepare a solution (1 ml = 0.02 mg Cu) as described in Section 11(c). One milliliter of that solution when diluted to 100 ml will represent a 0.2 ppm Cu solution.

(c) *Cuprethol Solution.*—Prepare two solutions, one with 4.0 g of diethanolamine dissolved in 200 ml of methyl alcohol and the other with 3.0 ml of carbon disulfide dissolved in 200 ml of methyl alcohol. As needed, make up the cuprethol solution by mixing equal volumes of the two alcoholic solutions. The two alcoholic solutions are quite stable but the mixture is stable for only about one week. The mixture slowly decomposes forming sulfur which causes a turbidity when used in the test.

(d) *Hydrochloric Acid (sp gr 1.19).*—Concentrated hydrochloric acid (HCl).

(e) *Sodium Hydroxide Solution (100 g per liter).*—Dissolve 10.0 g of sodium hydroxide (NaOH) in water and dilute to 100 ml with water.

(f) *Sodium Pyrophosphate Solution (30 g per liter).*—Dissolve 30 g of sodium pyrophosphate ($Na_4P_2O_7 \cdot 10H_2O$) in water and dilute to 1 liter.

Calibration and Standardization

32. (a) Prepare a series of standard copper solutions to cover the range specified in Table III. The standards are prepared by diluting suitable volume of standard copper solution to 100 ml with water. Also include a zero standard in this series. Proceed as directed in Section 33(a), beginning with the addition of $Na_4P_2O_7$ solution.

(b) If the copper content is to be determined by visual comparison in Nessler tubes, transfer a portion of each treated standard to a tube to fill to 50-ml mark.

(c) If the copper content is to be determined by means of a photometer, measure the color of each treated standard. Use water as a reference solution for the initial photometer setting. Prepare a calibration curve, plotting the results on semilog graph paper. Plot the percentage of transmittance along the vertical single cycle log axis and milligrams along the horizontal linear axis. If the scale of the photometer reads directly in absorbance, use ordinary graph paper for plotting absorbance versus milligrams of copper.

Procedure

33. (*a*) Transfer 100 ml of acidified clear sample (Note 11) to a beaker (see Section 4(*b*)) and heat on a hot plate until the volume is reduced to about 90 ml. Cool the sample to room temperature. Neutralize it with NaOH solution to a pH of 5 to 6, using narrow range pH paper. About 1 ml of NaOH solution is required. Dilute the solution to exactly 100 ml with water. Add 1 ml of $Na_4P_2O_7$ solution, 5 ml of acetate-phthalate buffer, and 1 ml of cuprethol solution to the neutralized sample, mixing the sample after each addition. Allow the solution to stand at least 10 min but no more than 30 min for color development.

NOTE 11.—If the sample contains more than the maximum concentration of copper listed in Table III for the applicable apparatus, a smaller size sample diluted to 100 ml with water should be taken for analysis. Filter the acidified, boiled sample if turbid.

(*b*) If the determination is to be made by means of 50-ml Nessler tubes, transfer a portion of the colored solution to fill a tube to 50-ml mark and compare its color with those of previously prepared standards.

(*c*) If a photometer is to be employed, measure the transmittance or absorbance of the yellow-colored test solution, using water as the reference solution for the initial photometer setting. If the acidified, boiled sample is colored or turbid after filtration, for compensation purposes use a prepared blank instead of water in the initial photometer setting. Prepare the blank by treating the acidified sample as described in Paragraph (*a*) but substituting 1 ml of methyl alcohol in place of cuprethol solution.

Calculation

34. Calculate the concentration of copper in parts per million as follows:

$$\text{Copper, ppm} = \frac{W \times 1000}{S}$$

where:

W = milligrams of copper found in accordance with Sections 32 and 33, and

S = milliliters of sample used in Section 33(*a*).

Precision[13]

35. The single operator and over-all precisions of the method can be expressed as follows:

$$S_0 = 0.005X + 0.006, \text{ and}$$
$$S_T = 0.044X + 0.008$$

where:

S_0 = single operator precision in ppm,
S_T = over-all precision in ppm, and
X = concentration of copper in sample in ppm.

Standard Method for

MEASUREMENT OF GAMMA RADIOACTIVITY OF INDUSTRIAL WATER AND INDUSTRIAL WASTE WATER[1]

ASTM Designation: D 1690 – 61

ADOPTED, 1961

This Standard of the American Society for Testing and Materials is issued under the fixed designation D 1690; the final number indicates the year of original adoption as standard or, in the case of revision, the year of last revision.

Scope and Application

1. (a) This method covers the measurement of gamma radioactivity of industrial water and industrial waste water. It is applicable to gamma emitters in the energy range above 0.1 Mev and in the concentration range of 10^{-2} to 10^{-5} microcuries per milliliter of radioactively homogeneous water.

(b) The method can be used for either absolute or relative determinations. In tracer work, the results may be expressed by comparison with an initial concentration which is taken as 100 per cent. For radioassay it may be expressed in terms of a known isotopic standard if the radionuclides concerned are known or it may be expressed arbitrarily in terms of some other standard such as cesium-137. General information on

radioactivity and measurement of radiation has been published.[2]

Summary of Method

2. Gamma radioactivity is measured by a scintillation counter. Gamma photons from a test sample enter a detector crystal, each transferring all or part of its energy to it. The crystal then emits light photons, the number of which is proportional to the energy the crystal received from the gamma photon. By the use of suitable light-collecting and electronic apparatus a pulse is obtained that is proportional to the amount of energy transferred to the crystal. The number of pulses in a given time is related to the disintegration rates of the radionuclides in the test sample and the relationship may be found by use of standardized preparations of radionuclides.

[1] Under the standardization procedure of the Society, this method is under the jurisdiction of the ASTM Committee D-19 on Industrial Water. A list of members may be found in the ASTM Year Book.

[2] G. Friedlander and J. W. Kennedy, "Nuclear and Radiochemistry," John Wiley & Sons, Inc., New York, N. Y. (1955).
W. J. Price, "Nuclear Radiation Detection," McGraw-Hill Book Co., Inc., New York, N. Y.

Definitions

3. (a) *Counter Efficiency.*—In the measurement of radioactivity, that fraction of the disintegrations occurring in a source which is detected by the counter.

(b) *Counter Gamma Efficiency.*—In the measurement of radioactivity, that fraction of gamma photons emitted by a source which is detected by the counter.

(c) *Curie.*—A unit of radioactivity equivalent to 3.700×10^{10} atomic disintegrations per second or 2.220×10^{12} atomic disintegrations per minute. A microcurie is one-millionth of a curie (10^{-6} curie); a picocurie, one-millionth of a microcurie (10^{-12} curie).

(d) *Counter Background.*—In the measurement of radioactivity, the counting rate resulting from factors other than the radioactivity of the sample and reagents used (Note 1).

Note 1.—Counter background varies with the location, shielding of the detector, and the electronics; it includes cosmic rays, contaminating radioactivity, and electrical noise.

(e) *Radioactively Homogeneous Water.*—Water in which the radioactive material is uniformly dispersed throughout the volume of water sample and remains so until the measurement is completed, or until the sample is evaporated or precipitating reagents are added to the sample.

(f) For definitions of other terms used in this method, refer to the Definitions of Terms Relating to Industrial Water and Industrial Waste Water (ASTM Designation: D 1129)[3] (Note 2).

Note 2.—For terms not defined in this method or in Definitions D 1129, reference may be made to other published glossaries, such as the USA Standard Glossary of Terms in Nuclear Science and Technology (USASI Designation: N1.1—1957).

---

[3] Appears in this publication.

Interferences

4. If the specimen contains a concentration of dissolved solids greater than 10,000 ppm, the observed counting rate may be low because of self-absorption. One may eliminate this error by preparing the standard in a solution of similar composition (Note 3).

Note 3.—The solution in which the standard is prepared must be like the specimen in that it contains concentrations of the same or neighboring elements that are within 10 per cent of those contained in the specimen.

Apparatus

5. (a) *Scintillation Counter*, consisting of the following components:

(1) *Crystal.*—A sodium iodide crystal "activated" with about 1 per cent thallium iodide, cylindrical, 2 in. in diameter by $1\frac{3}{4}$ in. in height, 2 in. in diameter by 2 in. in height, or 3 in. in diameter by 3 in. in height, and hermetically sealed in an opaque container with a transparent window. The crystal shall contain less than 5 ppm of potassium, shall be free of other radioactive materials, and shall be colorless and free of visible defects. In order to establish freedom from other radioactive materials, the manufacturer shall supply the gamma spectrum of the background of the crystal, between 0.08 and 3 Mev, showing absence of visible radionuclide peaks. The crystal shall be attached to and optically coupled to a multiplier phototube. The detector assembly shall be surrounded by an external-radiation shield made of massive metal, equivalent to at least 2 in. of lead. The shield shall have a door or port for inserting and removing specimens.

(2) *Power Supply*, high-voltage, of range sufficient to operate the multiplier phototube. The power supply

shall be regulated to 0.1 per cent, with a ripple of not more than 0.01 per cent.

(3) *Amplifier*, compatible with the multiplier phototube, having an external control labeled "pulse height" or "gain." This control permits discrimination against low-energy radiation and electronic "noise."

(4) *Scaler*, with a scaling ratio at least 512, and preferably 1000, and with a resolving time no greater than 5 μsec. The scaler shall have capacity for storing and visually displaying at least 9×10^5 counts.

(b) *Container for Test Specimen*, having an inside diameter at the base approximately equal to or less than the diameter of the crystal.

(c) *Absorber*, aluminum, $\frac{1}{4}$ in. in thickness and having a diameter equal to or greater than the crystal diameter; kept on top of the crystal at all times.

Purity of Reagents

6. (a) Reagent grade chemicals shall be used in all tests. Unless otherwise indicated, it is intended that all reagents shall conform to the specifications of the Committee on Analytical Reagents of the American Chemical Society, where such specifications are available.[4] Other grades may be used, provided it is first ascertained that the reagent is of sufficiently high purity to permit its use without lessening the accuracy of the determination.

(b) Unless otherwise indicated, reference to water shall be understood to mean reagent water conforming to the Specifications for Reagent Water (ASTM Designation: D 1193).[3]

---

[4] "Reagent Chemicals, American Chemical Society Specifications." Am. Chemical Soc., Washington, D. C. For suggestions on the testing of reagents not listed by the American Chemical Society, see "Reagent Chemicals and Standards" by Joseph Rosin, D. Van Nostrand Co., Inc., New York, N. Y., and the "United States Pharmacopeia."

Reagent

7. *Hydrochloric Acid (sp gr 1.19).*— Concentrated hydrochloric acid (HCl).

Sampling

8. (a) Collect the sample in accordance with the applicable method of the American Society for Testing and Materials, as follows:

D 510—Sampling Industrial Water,[3]
D 860—Sampling Water from Boilers,[3]
D 1496—Sampling Homogeneous Industrial Waste Water.[3]

(b) Preserve the sample in a radioactively homogeneous state (Note 4).

NOTE 4.—A sample may be made radioactively homogeneous by addition of a reagent in which the radioelements or compounds of the radioelements present in the sample would be soluble in large concentrations. Addition of acids, complexing agents, or like stable carriers may be used to obtain homogeneity. Consideration of the chemical nature of the radioelements and compounds present and the subsequent chemistry of the method will indicate the action to be taken.

Calibration and Standardization for General Measurements

9. (a) Put the instrument into operation according to the manufacturer's instructions. Place an appropriate volume of a solution of known concentration of cesium-137 (10^{-2} to 10^{-3} microcuries per ml) in a container, and place the container on the detector. In all measurements, volumes of samples and standard, as well as the container, must be identical.

(b) Set the gain control or pulse height selector to approximately the center of its range. Turn the "count" switch to "count" position. Raise the voltage until a counting rate of about 300 counts per minute is obtained. Advance the voltage in increments of convenient size (25 to 50 v). Determine the counting rate of the standard at four or more settings of gain control or pulse height selector at each voltage setting. Also measure the background counting rate at each of the settings, using a container of reagent water.

(c) Plot the ratio of net counting rate of standard to background counting rate against pulse height or gain, using the voltage that gives the highest values of the ratio. The ratio should rise initially as pulse height setting is increased (or as gain is lowered), then reach an approximately constant value. The setting of pulse height, or gain, that corresponds to a value near the shoulder of the curve, but definitely on the plateau, should be used. Test the validity of the setting by measuring the counting rate of a source (liquid or solid) of photons of approximately 0.1-Mev energy as a function of pulse height or gain.[5]

(d) A plot of the ratio of the net counting rate of the standard to the background counting rate should show a plateau, which should include the operating point selected by use of cesium-137. If this is not true, choose a new setting such that it is included in both plateaus. The instrument is now ready to use. The counting rate of the cesium standard and background must be checked at least daily, but the plateaus require redetermination only if standard and background rates change appreciably.

Calibration and Standardization for Tracer Experiments

10. Place an appropriate volume of a reference solution of the tracer (10^{-2} to 10^{-3} microcuries per ml) in a container, and place the container on the detector. Throughout an experiment, volumes must be kept constant. Determine proper setting of voltage and

pulse height or gain, as directed in Section 9.

Procedure

11. Place the test specimen in a container and place the container on the detector. Simultaneously start the operation of the scaler and timer. After a time interval sufficiently long to attain the desired precision, stop the scaler and timer. Record the reading of the register and any other indicator of accumulated counts (usually "interpolation lights"). If the background counting rate has not been determined the same day with sufficient precision, measure it. If room temperature has changed more than 2.5 C, count both background and standard.

Calculations

12. Results may be expressed in observed counts per minute (cpm) per milliliter. This method is useful for comparing activities of a group of samples, as in tracer experiments. Results may also be reported in terms of equivalent cesium-137 activity, employing the efficiency experimentally determined by use of a standard solution of cesium-137. If it is known that only one nuclide is present, its disintegration rate may be determined by use of an efficiency value determined by use of a standard of that nuclide obtained from the National Bureau of Standards or other supplier. The results may be calculated as follows:

$$\text{Gamma activity, cpm} = \frac{A}{t} - B$$

$$\text{Gamma activity, cpm per ml} = \frac{1}{V}\left(\frac{A}{t} - B\right)$$

where:

A = total counts accumulated,
B = background in counts per minute,
t = time of counting in minutes, and
V = milliliters of test specimen.

---

[5] Natural uranium, 0.093 Mev, and cadmium-109, 0.087 Mev, have been found satisfactory for this purpose.

Gamma activity equivalent to cesium-137, disintegrations per min (dpm) per ml $= \dfrac{G}{E_{Cs}}$

where:

$E_{Cs} =$ efficiency of counter for Cs^{137} (fraction), and

$G =$ gamma activity in counts per minute per milliliter.

Gamma activity as radionuclide X,

$$\text{dpm per ml} = \frac{G}{E_X}$$

where:

$E_X =$ efficiency of counter for radionuclide X (fraction), and

$G =$ gamma activity in counts per minute per milliliter.

Gamma activity, microcuries per ml

$$= \frac{\text{dpm per ml}}{2.22 \times 10^6}$$

Precision and Accuracy

13. Precision of counting-rate determinations may be calculated by published methods reported elsewhere.[6] Accuracy is calculated from the accuracy of the standard (data furnished by supplier), appropriately combined with precision of measurement.

———

[6] G. Friedlander and J. W. Kennedy, "Nuclear and Radiochemistry," John Wiley & Sons, Inc., New York, N. Y., pp. 252–269 (1955).

Tentative Method of Test for
ZINC IN INDUSTRIAL WATER AND INDUSTRIAL WASTE WATER[1]

ASTM Designation: D 1691 – 64 T
ISSUED, 1959; REVISED, 1964

This Tentative Method has been approved by the sponsoring committee and accepted by the Society in accordance with established procedures, for use pending adoption as standard. Suggestions for revisions should be addressed to the Society at 1916 Race St., Philadelphia 3, Pa.

Scope and Application

1. (*a*) This method covers the colorimetric determination of zinc in industrial water and industrial waste water. Interferences from many metals are eliminated or minimized in this method.

(*b*) A large portion of precipitated or suspended zinc is dissolved and measured in the test when a shaken sample is analyzed. Total zinc will be determined if insoluble zinc compounds are solubilized by acid treatment as given in Note 3. Dissolved zinc is determined on a filtered sample.

Summary of Method[2]

2. (*a*) Zinc forms a blue-colored complex with 2-carboxy-2′-hydroxy-5′-sulfoformazylbenzene (zincon) in a solution buffered to pH 9.0.

(*b*) The blue-colored zinc - zincon complex is masked at the low zinc concentration range of the test by the intense brick red color of the zincon indicator solution. The color obeys Beer's law up to a concentration of 5 ppm of zinc. As little as 0.02 ppm zinc can be detected when measurements are made with a spectrophotometer or a filter-type photometer equipped with a narrow band filter. However, many heavy metals react with zincon to cause serious interferences. The effect of these metallic ions is eliminated by the use of cyanide and chloral hydrate (**Caution,** Note 1). The cyanide reacts to form complexes with many metals including zinc. When chloral hydrate is added, only the zinc cyanide complex is destroyed and the zinc ion is released, enabling it to react with zincon.

NOTE 1: **Caution.**—Cyanide and chloral hydrate solutions are extremely poisonous if taken internally or if the fumes are inhaled. Safety pipets should always be used when measuring these solutions.

[1] Under the standardization procedure of the Society, this method is under the jurisdiction of the ASTM Committee D-19 on Industrial Water. A list of members may be found in the ASTM Year Book.

[2] For further information on this method the following references may be of interest:

J. A. Platte and V. M. Marcy, "Photometric Determination of Zinc with Zincon—Application to Water Containing Heavy Metals," *Analytical Chemistry*, Vol. 31, p. 1266 (1959).

R. M. Rush and J. H. Yoe, "Colorimetric Determination of Zinc and Copper with 2-carboxy-2′-hydroxy-5′-sulfoformazylbenzene," *Analytical Chemistry*, Vol. 26, p. 1345 (1954).

38–67

Definitions

3. For definitions of terms used in this method, refer to the Definitions of Terms Relating to Industrial Water and Industrial Waste Water (ASTM Designation: D 1129).[3]

Interferences[3]

4. (a) Metals that form stable cyanide complexes do not interfere with the test. As much as 30 ppm copper, 30 ppm cobalt, 20 ppm nickel, 10 ppm

TABLE I.—METHODS OF COLOR MEASUREMENT.

	Range Covered, ppm
Filter photometer (red filter, 620 mμ, with band pass of 20 mμ or less):	
10-mm cell................	0.1 to 5.0
23-mm cell................	0.05 to 2.5
Spectrophotometer (620 mμ):	
10-mm cell................	0.05 to 5.0
23-mm cell................	0.02 to 2.5

chromium, 9 ppm ferrous iron, 7 ppm ferric iron, 5 ppm aluminum, and 5 ppm manganese will not interfere. Anions normally present in industrial waters and industrial waste waters, such as phosphate, sulfate, and chloride, have no effect on the method. Up to 20 ppm polyphosphate and 50 ppm chromate may also be present.

(b) Compensation for turbidity, color, and interfering metals present in the sample not complexed with cyanide is possible by following the procedure described in Section 9(d).

Apparatus

5. *Photometer.*—A spectrophotometer or filter photometer suitable for measurements at 620 mμ (Note 2). Use of a spectrophotometer is recommended; however, any filter photometer equipped

with a narrow band pass filter of 20 mμ or less may be employed. Table I shows ranges for various photometers and cell depths.

NOTE 2—Filter photometers and photometric practices prescribed in this method shall conform to the Recommended Practice for Photometric Methods for Chemical Analysis of Metals (ASTM Designation: E 60)[4] and spectrophotometers shall conform to the Recommended Practice for Describing and Measuring Performance of Spectrophotometers (ASTM Designation: E 275).[5]

Reagents

6. (a) Reagent grade chemicals shall be used in all tests. Unless otherwise indicated, it is intended that all reagents shall conform to the specifications of the Committee on Analytical Reagents of the American Chemical Society, where such specifications are available.[6] Other grades may be used, provided it is first ascertained that the reagent is of sufficiently high purity to permit its use without lessening the accuracy of the determination. The purity of the reagents shall be checked by determining a blank, following the procedure given in Section 9(a), (b), and (c).

(b) Unless otherwise indicated, reference to water shall be understood to mean reagent water conforming to the Specifications for Reagent Water (ASTM Designation: D 1193).[3]

(c) *Buffer Solution (pH 9.0).*—Dilute 213 ml of sodium hydroxide solution (NaOH, 40 g per liter) to about 600 ml with water. Dissolve 37.3 g of potassium chloride (KCl) and 31.0 g of boric acid (H_3BO_3) in the solution and dilute to 1 liter. This reagent when diluted with 10

---

[3] Appears in this publication.

[4] *1967 Book of ASTM Standards*, Part 32.

[5] *1967 Book of ASTM Standards*, Part 30.

[6] "Reagent Chemicals, American Chemical Society Specifications," Am. Chem. Soc., Washington, D. C. For suggestions on the testing of reagents not listed by the American Chemical Society, see "Reagent Chemicals and Standards," by Joseph Rosin, D. Van Nostrand Co., Inc., New York, N. Y., and the "United States Pharmacopeia."

ml of water as described in Section 9 has a pH of 9.0.

(d) *Chloral Hydrate Solution (100 g per liter).*—Dissolve 10.0 g of chloral hydrate $(CCl_3CH(OH)_2)$ in 50 ml of water and dilute to 100 ml. Handle this poisonous reagent with care.

(e) *Hydrochloric Acid (sp gr 1.19).*—Concentrated hydrochloric acid (HCl).

(f) *Potassium Cyanide Solution (10 g per liter).*—Dissolve 1.00 g of potassium cyanide (KCN) in 50 ml of water and dilute to 100 ml. This solution is stable for 60 days if kept in a well-capped bottle. Use great care in handling this poisonous reagent.

(g) *Sodium Ascorbate.*[7]—Fine, granular sodium ascorbate. This reagent is needed only when the sample is estimated to contain more than 0.2 ppm manganese.

(h) *Sodium Hydroxide Solution (40 g per liter).*—Dissolve 40.0 g of sodium hydroxide (NaOH) in about 500 ml water and dilute to 1 liter.

(i) *Sodium Hydroxide Solution (240 g per liter).*—Dissolve 24.0 g of NaOH in 75 ml water and dilute to 100 ml.

(j) *Zinc, Standard Solution (1 ml = 0.1 mg Zn).*—Dissolve 0.2745 g of zinc sulfate $(ZnSO_4 \cdot H_2O)$ in 200 ml of water and dilute to 1 liter. This solution may be further diluted for convenience and accuracy in the preparation of the calibration standards; however, in such a case, the above indicated strength is altered and the change in concentration should be noted.

(k) *Zincon Solution (1.3 g per liter).*[8]—Dissolve 0.260 g of powdered 2-carboxy-2'-hydroxy-5'-sulformazylbenzene in approximately 100 ml of methyl alcohol by heating gently (below 50 C) and stirring

---

[7] Fine, granular sodium ascorbate, available from Hoffmann-La Roche Inc., Nutley, N. J. has been found satisfactory for this purpose.

[8] Zincon from La Motte Chemical Products Co., Chestertown, Md. has been found satisfactory for this purpose.

until the solid is completely in solution. Cool to room temperature and transfer to a 200-ml volumetric flask. Rinse the beaker several times with methyl alcohol, adding the rinses to the volumetric flask. Dilute to the mark with methyl alcohol, mix well, and store in a brown bottle. This solution is stable for a minimum period of three months. Stability is improved if the solution is refrigerated.

Sampling

7. Collect the sample in accordance with the applicable methods of the American Society for Testing and Materials as follows:

D 510—Sampling Industrial Waters,[3]
D 860—Sampling Water from Boilers,[3]
D 1066—Sampling Steam,[3]
D 1496—Sampling Homogeneous Industrial Waste Water.[3]

Calibration

8. (a) Prepare a series of standards to cover the expected range of zinc concentration by diluting the standard zinc solution. Make up each standard to a volume of 10 ml with water and proceed as described in Section 9(a), (b), and (c).

(b) Simultaneously, carry out a blank determination using 10 ml of water and all reagents, except for the standard zinc solution. Correct readings of the standards for this blank value. For photometer comparisons, prepare a calibration curve by plotting the absorbances of the standards against the zinc content of the standards.

Procedure

9. (a) Transfer a 10-ml aliquot sample (Note 3) containing 0.0002 to 0.05 mg zinc to a clean 100-ml flask.

NOTE 3.—Take a filtered sample if dissolved zinc is desired, otherwise a large portion of precipitated or suspended zinc compounds shall be dissolved and measured in the test. To determine the total zinc content the following preliminary sample treatment is suggested: add 1.0

ml HCl (sp gr 1.19) to 50 ml of shaken sample. Heat the solution to boiling and continue to boil for 5 min. Cool and then neutralize the solution to pH 7 by adding dropwise NaOH (240 g per liter) using pH paper. Dilute the solution to exactly 50 ml in a volumetric flask and proceed as described in Section 9(*a*), (*b*), and (*c*).

(*b*) Add the following reagents in order, mixing after addition of each: 0.5 g sodium ascorbate, 1 ml cyanide solution (**Caution,** Note 1), 5 ml buffer solution, 3 ml zincon solution, and 3 ml chloral hydrate solution (**Caution,** Note 1).

(*c*) Measure the color of the solution within 2 to 5 min by means of the photometer. In photometric work, with water showing no appreciable color, carry a blank containing no added zinc through the procedure in order to correct for the color of the unreacted zincon and any optical effects involved in adjusting the photometer for zero absorbance.

(*d*) In order to compensate for color, turbidity, or interfering metals not complexed with cyanide, use as reference solution the sample treated as described in Section 9(*a*), and (*b*), except that 3 ml water shall be added in place of 3 ml chloral hydrate.

Calculation

10. Calculate the concentration of zinc, in parts per million, as follows:

$$\text{Zinc, ppm} = \frac{W}{SG} \times 1000$$

where:
W = milligrams of zinc read from the calibration curve,
S = milliliters of sample used, and
G = specific gravity of the sample.

Precision and Accuracy[9]

11. The precision of this method is as follows:

$$S_T = 0.05 \text{ ppm zinc}$$
$$S_O = 0.03 \text{ ppm zinc}$$

where:
S_T = over-all precision, and
S_O = single operator precision.

---

[9] Supporting data giving results of cooperative tests have been filed at ASTM Headquarters.

APPROVED AS
USA STANDARD Z111.4-1964
BY USA STANDARDS INSTITUTE
UDC 663.61:620.1

Tentative Methods of Test for
OPERATING PERFORMANCE OF CATION-EXCHANGE MATERIALS[1]

ASTM Designation: D 1782 – 62 T
ISSUED, 1960; REVISED, 1962

These Tentative Methods have been approved by the sponsoring committee and accepted by the Society in accordance with established procedures, for use pending adoption as standard. Suggestions for revisions should be addressed to the Society at 1916 Race St., Philadelphia 3, Pa.

Scope

1. (a) These methods cover the determination of the operating capacity of cation-exchange materials when used for the removal of calcium, magnesium, and sodium ions from industrial water. It is intended for use in testing both new and used materials. The following two methods are included:

	Sections
Method A. Sodium Cycle	6 to 11
Method B. Hydrogen Cycle	12 to 17

(b) Method A covers the removal of calcium and magnesium ions only, while Method B covers the removal of calcium, magnesium, and sodium ions from industrial water.

Definitions

2. (a) Certain terms in these methods that relate specifically to ion exchange are defined as follows:

Free Mineral Acidity.—The quantitative capacity of aqueous media to react with hydroxyl ions to pH 4.3.

Hydrogen Cycle.—The operation of a cation-exchange cycle wherein the removal of specified cations from the influent water is accomplished by exchange with an equivalent amount of hydrogen ion from the exchange material.

Theoretical Free Mineral Acidity.—The free mineral acidity that would result from the conversion of the anions of strong acids in solution to their respective free acids.

(b) For definitions of other terms used in these methods, refer to the Definitions of Terms Relating to Industrial Water and Industrial Waste Water (ASTM Designation: D 1129).[2]

Apparatus

3. *Test Assembly* (Fig. 1) consisting of the following:

(a) *Column*, transparent, vertically-supported, 2.5 ± 0.25 cm (1.0 ± 0.1 in.) inside diameter and approximately 150 cm (60 in.) long. The bottom of the

[1] Under the standardization procedure of the Society, these methods are under the jurisdiction of the ASTM Committee D-19 on Industrial Water. A list of members may be found in the ASTM Year Book.

[2] Appears in this publication.

52-55

column shall be closed and provided with an outlet of approximately 6 mm inside diameter. Connections shall be provided at top and bottom for admission and removal of solutions as described in that the distance from the sample to the column outlet is at least 5 cm. A suggested supporting bed utilizes quartz, gravel, glass beads, or other material 0.15 to 0.35 cm in diameter, insoluble in

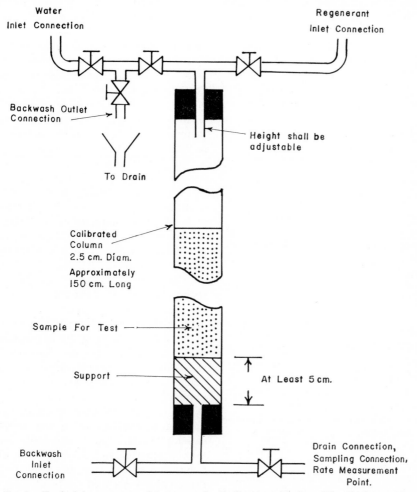

FIG. 1.—Typical Arrangement of Apparatus for Performance Testing of Ion-Exchange Materials

Section 9. Adequate means for measuring and regulating flow shall be provided.

Calibrate the column in such a manner that the volume readings required by the method can be made. Make all measurements at 25 ± 5 C.

(b) *Support* for the sample, so designed

the reagents used, and retained on a corrosion-resistant screen. However, other supports may be used at the discretion of the interested parties.

Purity of Reagents

4. (a) Reagent grade chemicals shall

be used in all tests. Unless otherwise indicated, it is intended that all reagents shall conform to the specifications of the Committee on Analytical Reagents of the American Chemical Society, where such specifications are available.[3] Other grades may be used, provided it is first ascertained that the reagent is of sufficiently high purity to permit its use without lessening the accuracy of the determination.

(b) Unless otherwise indicated, references to water shall be understood to mean reagent water conforming to the Specifications for Reagent Water (ASTM Designation: D 1193).[2]

Sampling

5. (a) This sampling procedure is for use in obtaining a representative sample either from a shipment of new ion-exchange material in the manufacturer's original packages or from a bed of used material.

(b) If the complete shipment is indicated by the manufacturer's marking to consist of only one batch or run of material, the number of packages selected for sampling shall be not less than 10 per cent of the packages in the batch and not less than 3 packages, except that when less than 3 packages are involved a sample shall be taken from each package. Choose at random the packages selected for sampling or, in case the manufacturer has marked the packages to indicate the order in which they were filled from his batch, make the selection with reference to this order of filling if desired by the purchaser. If the shipment consists of more than one batch or run of material, sample each batch separately and blend the samples of each batch to produce one composite sample for examination.

(c) Carefully open the packages selected making sure that no extraneous contamination is introduced. Insert a sampling device, such as a grain type sampler, that takes a core not less than $\frac{1}{2}$ in. in diameter into the package being sampled so that it will take a core of the material from substantially the entire length of the package. Combine material thus taken from individual packages and thoroughly mix and quarter until the sample is of the desired size. In the mixing and quartering process, take care to avoid loss of moisture from the sample and to avoid alteration of its physical characteristics. Obtain a minimum of 1 qt for testing. If this procedure does not obtain a large enough sample, take more than one core from each package at points well distributed within the package. Take the same number of cores from each package.

(d) Sample beds of used material by taking cores comprising the full depth of the bed at points well distributed over the bed area. Combine the cores and throughly mix and quarter until a minimum sample of 1 qt is obtained. Where beds are too deep or the internal mechanical construction is too complicated to permit use of this procedure, take a sufficient number of samples distributed over the area and throughout the depth of the bed so that a representative sample results.

(e) Transfer the laboratory sample to a 2-liter beaker and add enough water to bring the water level up to that of the ion-exchange material and soak for 1 hr (Note 1). Mix the sample thoroughly and transfer a representative portion of it to fill a 400-ml beaker. Use this portion of sample in the procedure.

---

[3] "Reagent Chemicals, American Chemical Society Specifications," Am. Chemical Soc., Washington, D. C. For suggestions on the testing of reagents not listed by the American Chemical Society, see "Reagent Chemicals and Standards," by Joseph Rosin, D. Van Nostrand Co., Inc., New York, N. Y., and the "United States Pharmacopeia."

NOTE 1.—Where new materials are shipped dry, follow the manufacturer's instructions for pre-conditioning.

METHOD A. SODIUM CYCLE

Scope

6. This method is designed to simulate operating conditions on a sodium cycle used for the removal of calcium and magnesium ions from industrial water.

Summary of Method

7. The method consists of repeated cycles of backwash, brine regeneration, rinse, and exhaustion of the sample in the form of a bed in a transparent column. The exhausting medium used is an ion-exchange test water.

Reagents and Materials

8. (a) *Brine Regenerants:*

(1) For synthetic organic ion-exchange materials:

Sodium Chloride (100 g per liter).—Dissolve 100.0 g of sodium chloride (NaCl) in 800 ml of water and dilute to 1 liter in a volumetric flask.

(2) For all other ion-exchange materials:

Sodium Chloride (50 g per liter).—Dissolve 50.0 g of NaCl in 800 ml of water and dilute to 1 liter in a volumetric flask.

(b) *Cation-Exchange Test Water A (10 epm).*—Dissolve enough calcium chloride ($CaCl_2 \cdot 2H_2O$) and magnesium sulfate ($MgSO_4 \cdot 7H_2O$) in water to make a solution containing, in each liter, 0.49 g $CaCl_2 \cdot 2H_2O$ and 0.415 g $MgSO_4 \cdot 7H_2O$. Adjust the pH to 7.5 by the addition of Na_2CO_3 (30 g per liter) and determine the hardness of the solution in accordance with the Methods of Test for Hardness in Industrial Water (ASTM Designation: D 1126).[3] The hardness of the test water shall be 10.0 ± 0.5 epm. Use the determined hardness in calculating operating capacity as indicated in Section 9(a). This test water shall be used for all tests.

(c) *Sodium Carbonate Solution (30 g per liter).*—Dissolve 30 g of sodium carbonate (Na_2CO_3) in water and dilute to 1 liter.

(d) *Hardness Test Reagents.*—For reagents used in determining hardness, refer to Methods D 1126.

Procedure

9. (a) Adjust the temperature of the water and all solutions to be used in the procedure to 25 ± 5 C and maintain this temperature throughout the test.

(b) Fill the column about half full of water and add sufficient sample to give a bed height of 75 ± 7.5 cm above the

TABLE I.—AMOUNT OF BRINE RE-GENERANT REQUIRED FOR USE IN METHOD A.

Type of Exchange Material	Brine Re-gen-erant, g per liter	Rate of Flow ml brine per min per ml of ex-changer	Contact Time, min	Regeneration Level	
				lb per cu ft	g per liter
Synthetic organic .	100	0.032	30	6.00	96.1
Greensand	50	0.027	15	1.25	20.0
Synthetic siliceous	50	0.080	20	5.00	80.1
Carbonaceous. . . .	50	0.067	15	3.15	50.5

top of the support. To avoid drying out the bed, maintain a layer of liquid at least 2 to 3 cm deep above the top of the bed at all times during the procedure.

(c) Backwash with water for 10 min, using a flow rate that will maintain a 50 per cent expansion of the bed. If the supernatant liquid is clear at this point, proceed at once to Paragraph (d). If the liquid is cloudy (indicating the presence of light, insoluble, extraneous matter), adjust the backwash outlet tube to a height above the bed equal to 75 per cent of the bed height. Continue back-washing at the same rate until the effluent is clear.

(d) Allow the bed to settle and drain at a rate of approximately 100 ml per min until the water level is 2 to 3 cm above the top of the bed. *Do not jar.* Record the volume, in milliliters, of ion-exchange material. Repeat the 10-min backwash until two successive readings of volume agree within 5 ml. The average of these two readings shall be the sample volume for new materials shipped in the sodium form.

(*e*) Exhaust the ion exchanger with cation-exchange test water A at a flow rate of 0.33 ml per min per ml of exchanger, as measured in Paragraph (*d*). Maintain a head of liquid not less than 5 cm above the top of the bed. Continue the run until the effluent shows 0.2 epm (or other agreed-upon hardness level) when tested in accordance with the Methods of Test for Hardness in Industrial Water (ASTM Designation: D 1126).[2] Record the volume of test water used.

(*f*) Repeat the 10-min backwash and drain as described in Paragraphs (*c*) and (*d*). When testing new material shipped in the sodium form, only one backwash is necessary at this point because a determination of volume has already been made. However, used materials must have a volume determination made here as described in Paragraph (*d*). Use this sample volume determined on the exhausted material in calculating the capacity of used ion exchange materials.

(*g*) Determine the amount of brine regenerant and rate required, from Table I. For use with Table I, the volume of sample for new material shall be that determined in accordance with Paragraph (*d*) and for used material shall be that determined in accordance with Paragraph (*f*).

(*h*) Pass the specified volume of brine regenerant through the bed at the specified rate until only a 2- to 3-cm layer of liquid remains above the bed. Rinse the bed with water, using the same rate, until one bed-volume of liquid has been displaced. Increase the rinse rate to approximately 100 ml per min. Test for hardness at 3-min intervals by adding 0.5 ml of buffer solution to 50 ml of the effluent followed by 3 drops of hardness indicator and 0.5 ml of sodium ethylenediamine tetraacetate solution (1 ml = 1.0 mg $CaCO_3$), with stirring. If a blue color develops, the effluent contains 0.2 epm or less hardness and the rinse is completed. If the color is red, the end point has not been reached. Continue the rinse until the effluent shows 0.2 epm or less hardness.

(*i*) Repeat the service run described in Paragraph (*e*).

(*j*) Repeat the cycle, beginning with a single backwash (Paragraph (*f*)), omitting the determination of bed volume. Continue with a regeneration and rinse (Paragraph (*h*)), and end with a service run (Paragraph (*e*)). Repeat the cycle until each of three successive runs agrees within ±5 per cent of their average capacity as calculated in accordance with Section 10.

Calculation and Report

10. (*a*) Calculate the operating capacity, in milliequivalents per milliliter, of the ion-exchange material as follows:

$$\text{Capacity, meq per ml} = \frac{A \times B}{S}$$

where:

A = hardness of test water in equivalents per million,

B = liters of test water used in service run, and

S = milliliters of sample in the bed. For new materials, this refers to the average volume of the material in the sodium form as determined in Section 9(*d*). For used materials, it is the average volume of the material in the exhausted form as determined in Section 9(*f*).

(*b*) Calculate the operating capacity,

in kilograins of calcium carbonate per cubic foot, as follows:

Capacity, kilograins of CaCO₃ per cu ft
$$= C \times 21.8$$

where:

C = capacity in milliequivalents per milliliter of ion-exchange material (Paragraph (a)).

(c) Report the capacity of the tested material as the average of three successive service runs that agree within ±5 per cent of their average capacity.

Precision[4]

11. The over-all precision of this method is 6 per cent of the reported capacity. The precision of successive runs within a test by a single operator is 2.4 per cent. Since this is an empirical performance test, no basis is available for estimation of accuracy.

METHOD B. HYDROGEN CYCLE

Scope

12. This method is designed to simulate operating conditions on a hydrogen cycle used for the removal of sodium, calcium, and magnesium ions from industrial water.

Summary of Method

13. The method consists of repeated cycles of backwash, acid regeneration, rinse, and exhaustion of the sample in the form of a bed in a transparent column. The exhausting medium used is an ion-exchange test water.

Reagents and Materials

14. (a) Acid Regenerants:
(1) Hydrochloric Acid (100 g per liter).—Carefully pour 227 ml of concentrated hydrochloric acid (HCl, sp gr 1.19)

---

[4] Supporting data giving results of cooperative tests have been filed at ASTM Headquarters.

into 500 ml of water, stirring constantly. Cool to 25 ± 5 C and dilute to 1 liter in a volumetric flask.

(2) Sulfuric Acid (20 g per liter).—Carefully pour 11.2 ml of concentrated sulfuric acid (H_2SO_4, sp gr 1.84) into 500 ml of water, stirring constantly. Cool to 25 ± 5 C and dilute to 1 liter in a volumetric flask.

(b) Alkalinity Test Reagents.—For reagents used in determining alkalinity, refer to the Methods of Test for Acidity and Alkalinity of Industrial Water (ASTM Designation: D 1884).[2]

(c) Cation-Exchange Test Water B (10 epm).—Dissolve enough sodium bicarbonate ($NaHCO_3$) in water to make a solution containing in each liter 0.21 g $NaHCO_3$. Determine the alkalinity of the solution in accordance with Methods D 1884, titrating to the methyl purple end point. The alkalinity of the solution shall be 2.50 ± 0.13 epm. Dissolve in this solution enough calcium chloride ($CaCl_2 \cdot 2H_2O$) and magnesium sulfate ($MgSO_4 \cdot 7H_2O$) to make a solution containing in each liter 0.368 g $CaCl_2 \cdot 2H_2O$ and 0.311 g $MgSO_4 \cdot 7H_2O$. Determine the total hardness of the solution in accordance with the Methods of Test for Hardness in Industrial Water (ASTM Designation: D 1126).[2] The total hardness of the solution shall be 7.50 ± 0.38 epm. Record the total hardness as epm of theoretical free mineral acidity for use in Section 15(c). Record the total strength of the solution as epm of alkalinity plus hardness for use in Section 16. This test water shall be used for all tests.

(d) Free Mineral Acidity Test Reagents.—For reagents used in determining the free mineral acidity, refer to Methods D 1884.

(e) Hardness Test Reagents.—For reagents used in determining hardness. refer to Methods D 1126.

Procedure

15. (*a*) Refer to Section 9(*a*), (*b*), and (*c*).

(*b*) Allow the bed to settle and drain at a rate of approximately 100 ml per min until the water level is 2 to 3 cm above the top of the bed. *Do not jar.* Record the volume, in milliliters, of ion-exchange material.

(*c*) Exhaust the ion exchanger with cation-exchange test water B at a flow rate of 0.33 ml per min per ml of exchanger as measured in Paragraph (*b*). Maintain a head of liquid not less than 5 cm above the top of the bed. Continue the run until the free mineral acidity of the effluent has decreased to 0.90 of the

regenerant through the bed at the specified rate until only a 2 to 3-cm layer of liquid remains above the bed. Rinse the bed with water, using the same rate, until one bed-volume of liquid has been displaced. Increase the rinse rate to approximately 100 ml per min, and rinse for 20 min. To 25 ml of the effluent add 0.2 ml of methyl purple indicator and 0.25 ml of 0.02 N NaOH (Note 3). If a green color develops, the effluent contains 10 ppm or less of free mineral acid calculated as $CaCO_3$ and the rinse is completed. If a purple or gray color develops, the rinse is not completed. Continue the rinse until a 25-ml portion of the effluent does show 10 ppm or less free mineral acidity.

TABLE II.—AMOUNT OF ACID REGENERANT REQUIRED FOR USE IN METHOD B

Type of Exchange Material	Acid Regenerant, g per liter	Rate of Flow ml acid per min per ml of exchanger	Contact Time, min	Regeneration Level	
				lb per cu ft	g per liter
Synthetic organic............{	100 (HCl)	0.037	30	7.00	112
	20 (H_2SO_4)	0.212	30	8.00	128
Carbonaceous.................	20 (H_2SO_4)	0.107	15	2.00	32.0

theoretical free mineral acidity of the test water. Determine the free mineral acidity of the effluent in accordance with Methods D 1884, titrating to the methyl purple end point. Record the volume of test water used.

(*d*) Repeat the 10-min backwash and drain as described in Section 9(*c*) and in Paragraph (*b*), until two successive readings of volume agree within 5 ml. The average of these two readings shall be the sample volume for all subsequent operations.

(*e*) Determine the amount of acid regenerant and the rate required from Table II, using the sample volume determined in accordance with Paragraph (*d*). The kind of acid used for synthetic organic materials shall be as agreed upon by the interested parties.

(*f*) Pass the specified volume of acid

Note 2.—For the methyl purple indicator and standard sodium hydroxide, refer to Methods D 1884.

(*g*) Repeat the service run described in Paragraph (*c*).

(*h*) Repeat the cycle, beginning with a single backwash (Paragraph (*d*)), omitting the determination of the bed volume. Continue with a regeneration and rinse (Paragraph (*f*)), and end with a service run (Paragraph (*c*)). Repeat the cycle until each of three successive runs agrees within ±5 per cent of their average capacity as calculated in accordance with Section 16.

Calculation and Report

16. (*a*) Calculate the operating capacity, in milliequivalents per milliliter, of the ion-exchange material as follows:

$$\text{Capacity, meq per ml} = \frac{A \times B}{S}$$

where:

A = total strength of test water in equivalents per million; it equals the sum of the alkalinity and the hardness,

B = liters of test water used in service run, and

S = milliliters of sample in the bed; this refers to the average volume of the material in the exhausted form as determined in Section 15(d).

(*b*) Calculate the operating capacity, in kilograins of calcium carbonate per cubic foot, as follows:

Capacity, kilograins of $CaCO_3$ per cu ft
$$= C \times 21.8$$

where:

C = capacity in milliequivalents per milliliter of ion-exchange material (Paragraph (*a*)).

(*c*) Report the capacity of the tested material as the average of three successive service runs that agree within ±5 per cent of their average capacity.

Precision[4]

17. The over-all precision of this method is 6 per cent of the reported capacity. The precision of successive runs within a test by a single operator is 2.8 per cent. Since this is an empirical performance test, no basis is available for estimation of accuracy.

Standard Methods of Test for

PHENOLIC COMPOUNDS IN INDUSTRIAL WATER AND INDUSTRIAL WASTE WATER[1]

ASTM Designation: D 1783 – 62

ADOPTED, 1962

This Standard of the American Society for Testing and Materials is issued under the fixed designation D 1783; the final number indicates the year of original adoption as standard or, in the case of revision, the year of last revision.

Scope and Application

1. (*a*) These methods cover preparation of the sample and determination of the concentration of phenolic compounds in industrial water and industrial waste water. Phenolic compounds with a substituent in the *para* position usually do not produce color with 4-aminoantipyrine. However, *para* substituents of the phenol such as a carboxyl, halogen, hydroxyl, methoxyl or sulfonic acid group, are expelled. Such phenolic compounds produce color with 4-aminoantipyrine.

(*b*) The methods are divided according to specific application as follows:

Sections

Method A. Chloroform Extraction
Method..................... 9 to 16

Method B. Direct Colorimetric
Method.................... 17 to 24

Definitions

2. (*a*) The term "phenolic compounds" in these methods is defined in accordance with the Definitions of Terms Relating to Industrial Water and Industrial Waste Water (ASTM Designation: D 1129),[2] as follows:

Phenolic Compounds.—Hydroxy derivatives of benzene and its condensed nuclei.

(*b*) For definitions of other terms used in these methods, refer to Definitions D 1129.

Interferences

3. (*a*) Common interferences that may occur in industrial waters and industrial waste waters are phenol-decomposing bacteria, reducing substances, and strongly alkaline conditions of the sample. Provisions incorporated in this

[1] Under the standardization procedure of the Society, these methods are under the jurisdiction of the ASTM Committee D-19 on Industrial Water. A list of members may be found in the ASTM Year Book.

[2] Appears in this publication.

method will minimize the effects of such interferences.

(b) Treatment procedures required prior to the analysis for removal of interfering compounds may result in the unavoidable elimination or loss of certain types of phenolic compounds. It is beyond the scope of these methods to describe procedures for overcoming all of the possible interferences that may be encountered in the methods, particularly with highly contaminated water and industrial waste water. The procedures used must be revised to meet the specific requirements.

(c) A few methods for eliminating certain interferences are suggested. (See Section 6 for descriptions of reagents required.)

(1) *Oxidizing Agents.*—If the sample smells of chlorine, or if iodine is liberated from potassium iodide on acidification of the sample, the oxidizing agents so indicated should be removed immediately after sampling. The presence of oxidizing agents in the sample may oxidize some or all of the phenols in a short time. Ferrous sulfate or sodium arsenite solution may be added to destroy all of the oxidizing substances. Excess ferrous sulfate or sodium arsenite do not interfere since they are removed in the distillation procedure.

(2) *Sulfur Compounds.*—Compounds that liberate hydrogen sulfide (H_2S) or sulfur dioxide (SO_2) on acidification may interfere with the phenol determination. Treatment of the acidified sample with copper sulfate usually eliminates such interference. Acidify the sample with H_2SO_4 or HCl until just acid to methyl orange. Then add a sufficient quantity of $CuSO_4$ solution to give a light blue color to the sample or until no more copper sulfide (CuS) precipitate is formed. Excessive amounts of H_2S or SO_2 may be removed from the acidified sample by a brief aeration treatment or stirring before the addition of the $CuSO_4$ solution, or both.

(3) *Oils and Tar.*—If the sample contains oil or tar, some phenolic compounds may be dissolved in these materials. An alkaline extraction, in the absence of $CuSO_4$ (Note 1), may be used to eliminate the tar or oil. Adjust the pH of the sample to 12 to 12.5 with NaOH pellets to avoid extraction of the phenols. Extract the mixture with carbon tetrachloride (CCl_4). Discard the oil- or tar-containing layer. Remove any CCl_4 remaining in the aqueous portion of the sample by gentle heating.

Note 1.—The presence of $CuSO_4$ would be detrimental since it would be converted to cupric hydroxide ($Cu(OH)_2$) by the NaOH. The $Cu(OH)_2$ acts as an oxidizing agent on phenols.

Apparatus

4. (a) *Büchner-Type Funnel with Coarse Fritted Disk.*[3]—At least three funnels are needed for determination of phenolic compounds by Method A. These funnels are not used in Method B.

(b) *Photometer.*[4]—A spectrophotometer or filter photometer, suitable for use at 460 mμ (Method A) or at 510 mμ (Method B), and accommodating a cell that gives a light path of 1.0 to 10 cm shall be used. The size of the cell used will depend on the absorbance of the colored solutions being measured and the characteristics of the photometer. In general, if the absorbances are greater than 1.0 with a larger cell, the next smaller size cell should be used.

(c) *Distillation Apparatus.*—A 1-liter, heat-resistant, distilling flask attached to

---

[3] A 15-ml coarse filter funnel, Corning No. 36060, has been found satisfactory for this purpose.

[4] A discussion of photometers and photometric practice is given in the Recommended Practice for Photometric Methods for Chemical Analysis of Metals (ASTM Designation: E 60), 1967 Book of ASTM Standards, Part 32.

a Graham condenser by means of a glass joint.

(d) *Filter Paper.*—Medium-texture, 11-cm filter paper may be used for filtration of the chloroform extracts in place of the Büchner-type funnels and anhydrous sodium sulfate.

(e) *pH Meter.*—This apparatus shall conform to the requirements given in the Method for Determination of pH of Aqueous Solutions with the Glass Electrode (ASTM Designation: E 70).[2]

Purity of Reagents

5. (a) Reagent grade chemicals shall be used in all tests. Unless otherwise indicated, it is intended that all reagents shall conform to the specifications of the Committee on Analytical Reagents of the American Chemical Society, where such specifications are available.[5] Other grades may be used, provided it is first ascertained that the reagent is of sufficiently high purity to permit its use without lessening the accuracy of the determination.

(b) Unless otherwise indicated, references to water shall be understood to mean water conforming to the Specifications for Reagent Water (ASTM Designation: D 1193).[2] Deionized water shall not be used. In addition, water used for these methods shall be free of phenolic compounds, residual chlorine, and substances that interfere with the test.

Reagents

6. (a) *4-Aminoantipyrine Solution (20 g per liter).*—Dissolve 2.0 g of 4-aminoantipyrine in water and dilute to 100 ml. Prepare this reagent fresh as used.

[5] "Reagent Chemicals, American Chemical Society Specifications," Am. Chemical Soc., Washington, D. C. For suggestions on the testing of reagents not listed by the American Chemical Society, see "Reagent Chemicals and Standards," by Joseph Rosin, D. Van Nostrand Co., Inc., New York, N. Y., and the "United States Pharmacopeia."

Note 2.—The melting point of a satisfactory grade of 4-aminoantipyrine ranges from 108.0 to 109.5 C. If the melting point is lower than 108 C, the compound should be recrystallized from benzene.

(b) *Ammonium Chloride Solution (20 g per liter).*—Dissolve 20 g of ammonium chloride (NH4Cl) in water and dilute to 1 liter.

(c) *Ammonium Hydroxide (sp gr 0.90).*—Concentrated ammonium hydroxide (NH4OH).

(d) *Chloroform* (CHCl3).

(e) *Copper Sulfate* (CuSO4·5H2O).

(f) *Copper Sulfate Solution (100 g per liter).*—Dissolve 100 g of CuSO4·5H2O in water and dilute to 1 liter.

(g) *Hydrochloric Acid (sp gr 1.19).*—Concentrated hydrochloric acid (HCl).

(h) *Phenol Standard Solutions.*—Prepare as follows:

(1) *Stock Solution (1.00 g per liter).*—Dissolve 1.00 g of phenol (C6H5OH) in freshly boiled and cooled water. Dilute to 1000 ml with freshly boiled and cooled water. Prepare a fresh stock solution within 30 days of use.

(2) *Intermediate Solution (1 ml = 0.01 mg Phenol).*—Dilute 10.0 ml of the stock solution to 1000 ml with freshly boiled and cooled water. Prepare this solution fresh on the day it is used.

(3) *Phenol Standard Solution (1 ml = 0.001 mg Phenol).*—Dilute 50 ml of the intermediate solution to 500 ml with freshly boiled and cooled water. Prepare this solution fresh within 2 hr of use.

(i) *Phosphoric Acid (85 per cent).*—Concentrated phosphoric acid (H3PO4).

(j) *Phosphoric Acid Solution (1:9).*—Mix 1 volume of H3PO4 (85 per cent) with 9 volumes of water.

(k) *Potassium Ferricyanide Solution (80 g per liter).*—Dissolve 8.0 g of potassium ferricyanide (K3Fe(CN)6) in water and dilute to 100 ml. Filter if necessary.

Prepare a fresh solution within 1 week of use.

(*l*) *Sodium Sulfate,* (Na$_2$SO$_4$), anhydrous and granular.

(*m*) *Sulfuric Acid (sp gr 1.84).*—Concentrated sulfuric acid (H$_2$SO$_4$).

Sampling

7. (*a*) Collect the sample in accordance with the applicable method of the American Society for Testing and Materials, as follows:

D 510—Sampling Industrial Water,[2]
D 1496—Sampling Homogeneous Industrial Waste Water.[2]

(*b*) When samples are composited, the samples or the composite sample shall be chilled immediately and kept at a temperature of not more than 10 C during the compositing period. The collection time for a single composite sample shall not exceed 4 hr. If longer sampling periods are necessary, a series of composite samples shall be collected. Such composite samples shall then be preserved in accordance with Section 8 until analyzed.

Preservation of Samples

8. (*a*) Phenolic compounds in water are subject to both chemical and biochemical oxidation. Unless the samples are analyzed within 4 hr after collection, they shall be preserved when collected. Acidify the samples to a pH of approximately 4.0 with H$_3$PO$_4$, HCl, or H$_2$SO$_4$.

NOTE 3: **Caution.**—Acidification of certain samples may produce vigorous evolution of carbon dioxide (CO$_2$), sulfur dioxide (SO$_2$), hydrogen sulfide (H$_2$S), or other gases. Therefore, the acidification should be done cautiously, and the sample should be stirred during the process. Obviously, the evolution of gases must be completed before the sample may be stoppered.

(*b*) Inhibit biochemical oxidation of phenolic compounds in the sample by adding 1.0 g of CuSO$_4$·5H$_2$O per liter of sample. To further minimize any changes in the phenolic content of the sample, it should be kept cold, preferably below 10 C. Analyze preserved samples within 24 hr after collection.

METHOD A. CHLOROFORM EXTRACTION METHOD

Application

9. This method is applicable to industrial water or industrial waste water that contains from 5 to 1000 ppb (1.0 ppm) of phenolic compounds.

Summary of Method

10. This is a photometric method, based on the reaction of steam-distillable phenolic compounds with 4-aminoantipyrine at a pH of 10.0 ± 0.2 in the presence of potassium ferricyanide. The antipyrine dye formed is extracted from the aqueous solution with chloroform and the absorbance is measured at 460 mμ. The concentration of phenolic compounds in the sample is expressed in terms of ppb of phenol (C$_6$H$_5$OH).

Calibration

11. (*a*) Prepare a series of 500-ml phenol standards in freshly boiled and cooled water, containing 0, 5, 10, 20, 30, 40, and 50 ml of standard phenol solution (1 ml = 0.001 mg phenol). All solutions used must be at room temperature. One milliliter of the standard phenol solution contains 1 μg of phenol.

(*b*) Develop color in the series of standards and prepare the chloroform extracts according to the procedure prescribed in Section 13.

(*c*) Measure the absorbance of each standard at 460 mμ against the reagent blank as zero absorbance. Plot the absorbances against the corresponding weights in micrograms of phenol (Note 4).

NOTE 4.—A separate calibration curve must be made for each spectrophotometer or photoelectric colorimeter. Each curve must be checked periodically to ensure reproducibility.

Distillation Procedure

12. (*a*) Measure 500 ml of the sample into a beaker. Adjust the pH of the sample to approximately 4.0 with H_3PO_4 solution (1:9). Use methyl orange indicator solution or a pH meter to aid in the pH adjustment. If the sample was not preserved with $CuSO_4$, add 5 ml of $CuSO_4$ solution (100 g per liter). Transfer the mixture to the distillation apparatus. Use a 500-ml graduated cylinder as a receiver.

(*b*) Distill 450 ml of the sample. Stop the distillation and, when boiling ceases, add 50 ml of water to the distillation flask. Continue the distillation until a total of 500 ml has been collected.

(*c*) If the distillate is turbid, a second distillation may prove helpful. Acidify the turbid distillate with H_3PO_4 solution (1:9), add 5 ml of $CuSO_4$ solution, and then repeat the previously described distillation. The second distillation usually eliminates the turbidity. However, if the second distillate is also turbid, the screening procedure must be modified. An extraction process before the distillation should then be attempted to avoid turbidity in the distillate.

Preliminary Determination of Phenolic Compounds

13. (*a*) Transfer to a beaker the 500 ml of distillate, or a suitable aliquot diluted to 500 ml, containing no more than 50 μg of phenolic compounds. The distillate and all solutions used must be at room temperature. Trial and error tests may be necessary to determine the volume of a suitable aliquot. Also, prepare a blank consisting of 500 ml of water.

(*b*) Add 25 ml of NH_4Cl solution to each aliquot. Adjust the pH to 9.8 to 10.2 with NH_4OH. Transfer each mixture to a 1-liter separatory funnel. Add 3.0 ml of 4-aminoantipyrine solution (20

g per liter) and mix immediately, then add 3.0 ml of $K_3Fe(CN)_6$ solution and again mix immediately. Allow color to develop for 3 min (Note 5).

Note 5.—The solutions should be clear and have a light yellow color. If not, an interfering substance is indicated. The determination should be repeated after more complete treatment to eliminate the interference.

(*c*) Add exactly 25 ml of chloroform to each separatory funnel if a 1.0 to 5.0-cm cell is to be used in the colorimeter. Add 50 ml if a 10-cm cell is to be used. Shake the separatory funnel 10 times. When the chloroform has settled, again shake the separatory funnel 10 times and allow the chloroform to settle.

(*d*) Filter each of the chloroform extracts through separate fritted-glass funnels containing 5 g of anhydrous, granular Na_2SO_4, or through filter paper, directly into clean absorption cells as needed for absorbance measurements. Do not add additional chloroform.

(*e*) Using the chloroform extract of the reagent blank adjust the colorimeter to zero absorbance at 460 mμ. Measure the absorbance of the sample extract at the same wavelength. By reference to the calibration curve (Section 11) and the absorbance obtained on the sample extract, estimate the phenolic content of the sample.

Final Determination of Phenolic Compounds

14. (*a*) If the entire volume of distillate of the sample was used in the preliminary determination, prepare a second 500-ml of sample distillate in the same manner as the first.

(*b*) Transfer the 500-ml distillate, or suitable aliquot diluted to 500 ml, containing no more than 50 μg of phenol, to a beaker. The distillate and all solutions used must be at room temperature. Using as a guide the phenolic content obtained on the sample in the preliminary determination, prepare 500 ml of a standard phenol solution with a phenolic content approximately equal to the phenolic content of that portion of the sample being prepared for final analysis. Also, prepare a blank consisting of 500 ml of water only.

(c) Proceed as prescribed in Section 13(b) to (e), measuring absorbance of the sample and of the standard against that of the reagent zero blank at 460 mμ.

Calculation

15. Calculate the phenolic content of the sample, in parts per billion, as follows:

$$\text{Phenolic compound, ppb} = \frac{PA_s}{A_p} \times \frac{1000}{S}$$

where:

P = micrograms of phenol (Note 6) in 500 ml of the standard solution,

A_s = absorbance of the extract of the sample,

A_p = absorbance of the extract of the standard, and

S = milliliters of the original sample present in 500 ml of the solution reacted with 4-aminoantipyrine.

Note 6.—Since the ratio of the various phenolic compounds present in a given sample is unpredictable, phenol (C_6H_5OH) is used as a standard. Any color produced by the reaction of other phenolic compounds is reported as phenol. This value will represent the minimum concentration of phenolic compounds present in the sample.

Precision and Accuracy[6]

16. (a) The precision of this method depends on the interferences present and the skill of the analyst. Precision also varies with the concentration of phenolic compounds.

Round robin tests by six laboratories on sterilized phenol (C_6H_5OH) solutions gave the following over-all standard deviations ($\pm 1\ \sigma$):

Phenol Concentration in Solution, ppb	Standard Deviation, ppb
9.61	± 0.99
48.3	± 3.1
93.5	± 4.2

Precision values by a single operator were ± 0.89, ± 1.9, and ± 3.6 ppb, respectively.

(b) This method can be regarded only as an approximation of phenolic compounds in industrial waters and industrial waste waters. The concentration of phenolic compounds obtained represents the minimum amount of phenolic compounds present in the sample and, therefore, an expression of the accuracy of this method cannot be made.

Method B. Direct Photometric Method

Application

17. This method is applicable to industrial water or industrial waste water that contains more than 0.1 ppm (100 ppb) of phenolic compounds.

Summary of Method

18. This is a photometric method, based on the reaction of steam-distillable phenolic compounds with 4-aminoantipyrine at a pH of 10.0 $\pm$ 0.2 in the presence of potassium ferricyanide. The antipyrine color formed in aqueous solution is measured at 510 mμ. The concentration of phenolic compounds in the sample is expressed in terms of ppm of phenol (C_6H_5OH).

Calibration

19. (a) Prepare a series of 100-ml phenol standards in water containing 0, 10, 20, 30, 40, and 50 ml of intermediate standard phenol solution (1 ml = 0.01 mg phenol). All solutions used must be at room temperature.

(b) Develop color in the series of standards according to the procedure prescribed in Section 21.

(c) Measure the absorbance of each standard at 510 mμ against the reagent blank as zero absorbance. Plot the absorbances against the corresponding weight in milligrams of phenol (Note 4).

Distillation Procedure

20. See Section 12.

Preliminary Determination of Phenolic Compounds

21. (*a*) Transfer to a beaker 100 ml of distillate, or a suitable aliquot diluted to 100 ml, containing no more than 0.50 mg of phenolic compounds. The distillate and all solutions used must be at room temperature. Trial and error tests may be necessary to determine the volume of a suitable aliquot. Also, prepare a blank consisting of 100 ml of water.

(*b*) Add 5 ml of NH_4Cl solution to each. Adjust the pH to 9.8 to 10.2 with NH_4OH. Add 2.0 ml of 4-aminoantipyrine solution, mix immediately, then add 2.0 ml of $K_3Fe(CN)_6$ solution and again mix immediately.

(*c*) After 15 min, transfer the solutions to absorption cells and measure the absorbance of the sample solution against the zero absorbance of the reagent blank at 510 mμ. By reference to the calibration curve (Section 19) and the absorbance obtained on the sample solution, estimate the phenolic content of the sample.

Final Determination of Phenolic Compounds

22. (*a*) Transfer to a beaker another 100-ml portion of distillate, or a suitable aliquot diluted to 100 ml containing no more than 0.50 mg of phenolic compounds. The distillate and all solutions used must be at room temperature. Using as a guide the phenolic content obtained on the sample in the preliminary determination, prepare 100 ml of a standard phenol solution with a phenolic content approximately equal to the phenolic content of that portion of sample being prepared for final analysis.

Also prepare a blank consisting of 100 ml of water only.

(*b*) Proceed as prescribed in Section 21(*b*) and (*c*), measuring the absorbances of the sample and of the standard against that of the reagent zero blank at 510 mμ.

Calculation

23. Calculate the phenolic content of the sample, in parts per million, as follows:

$$\text{Phenolic compounds, ppm} = \frac{PA_s}{A_p} \times \frac{1000}{S}$$

where:

P = milligrams of phenol (Note 6) in 100 ml of the standard solution,

A_s = absorbance of the sample solution,

A_p = absorbance of the standard, and

S = milliliters of original sample present in 100 ml of the solution reacted with 4-aminoantipyrine.

Precision and Accuracy[6]

24. (*a*) The precision of this method depends on the interferences present and the skill of the analyst. Precision also varies with the concentration of the phenolic compounds.

Round robin tests by six laboratories on sterilized phenol (C_6H_5OH) solutions gave the following over-all standard deviations ($\pm 1\ \sigma$):

Phenol Concentration in Solution, ppm	Standard Deviation, ppm
4.68	± 0.18
48.2	± 1.48
97.0	± 1.58

Precision values by a single operator were ± 0.066, ± 0.63, and ± 0.60 ppm, respectively.

(*b*) This method can be regarded only as an approximation of phenolic compounds in industrial water and industrial waste water. The concentration of phenolic compounds obtained represents the minimum amount of phenolic compounds present in the sample and, therefore, an expression of the accuracy of this method cannot be made.

Tentative Methods of Test for

ACIDITY AND ALKALINITY OF INDUSTRIAL WATER[1]

ASTM Designation: D 1884 – 66 T

Issued, 1961; Revised, 1966

These Tentative Methods have been approved by the sponsoring committee and accepted by the Society in accordance with established procedures,
for use pending adoption as standard. Suggestions for revisions should
be addressed to the Society at 1916 Race St., Philadelphia, Pa. 19103.

1. Scope

1.1 These methods cover the determination of acidity or alkalinity of industrial water. Four methods are given
as follows:

	Sections
Referee Method (Electrometric Titration)	5 to 13
Non-Referee Method A (Elec-trometric or Color-Change Titration)	14 to 22
Non-Referee Method B (Color-Comparison Titration)	23 to 30
Non-Referee Method C (Elec-trometric or Color-Change Titration after Boiling)	31 to 39

1.2 In all the methods, hydrogen or
hydroxide ions present in water by virtue
of the dissociation or hydrolysis of its
solutes, or both, are neutralized by titration with standard alkali (acidity) or
standard acid (alkalinity). Of the four
procedures, the Referee Method is the
most precise and accurate. With it, a
titration curve is developed which defines inflection points and indicates
buffering capacity; the acidity or alkalinity relative to a particular pH can be
determined from the curve. The non-
referee methods are used to determine
acidity or alkalinity relative to a predesignated end point based on the change
in color of an internal indicator or the
equivalent pH measured electrometrically. They are suitable for routine control purposes.

1.3 When titrating to selected datum
points, the choice of end points will be
determined primarily by the applicable
process controls for the water; the choice
must be such, however, that significant
errors in titration due to inflection points
on a typical titration curve are avoided.
In some instances the titration end point
may be at a pH beyond that at which
the constituents of the water cease to
react with the acid or alkali. Conversely,
the desired end point may be such that
only a part of the neutralizing capacity
is measured.

2. Definitions

2.1 The terms "acidity" and "alkalinity" in these methods are defined in
accordance with ASTM Definitions

---

[1] Under the standardization procedure of the
Society, these methods are under the jurisdiction
of the ASTM Committee D-19 on Industrial
Water. A list of members may be found in the
ASTM Year Book.

D 1129, Terms Relating to Industrial Water and Industrial Waste Water,[2] as follows:

2.1.1 *Acidity*—The quantitative capacity of aqueous media to react with hydroxyl ions.

2.1.2 *Alkalinity*—The quantitative capacity of aqueous media to react with hydrogen ions.

2.2 For definitions of other terms used in these methods, refer to Definitions D 1129.

3. Purity of Reagents

3.1 Reagent grade chemicals, or equivalent, as defined in ASTM Methods E 200, Preparation, Standardization, and Storage of Standard Solutions for Chemical Analysis[2] shall be used in all tests.

3.2 Unless otherwise indicated, references to water shall be understood to mean reagent water conforming to ASTM Specifications D 1193, for Reagent Water,[2] referee grade. In addition, reagent water for this test shall be free of carbon dioxide (CO_2) and shall have a pH between 6.2 and 7.2 at 25 C (77 F). A procedure for the preparation of carbon dioxide-free water is given in Methods E 200.

4. Sampling

4.1 Collect the sample in accordance with the applicable method of the American Society for Testing and Materials, as follows:

D 510—Sampling Industrial Water,[2]
D 860—Sampling Water from Boilers,[2]
D 1066—Sampling Steam,[2] and
D 1192—Spec. for Equipment for Sampling Industrial Water and Steam.[2]

REFEREE METHOD

(Electrometric Titration)

5. Application

5.1 This method is applicable to the determination of acidity or alkalinity of all industrial waters that are free of constituents that interfere with electrometric pH measurements. It is used for the development of a titration curve that will define inflection points and indicate buffering capacity, if any. The acidity or alkalinity relative to a particular pH is determined from the curve.

6. Summary of Method

6.1 To develop a titration curve that will properly identify the inflection points, standard acid or alkali is added to the sample in small increments and a pH reading is taken after each addition. The cumulative volume of solution added is plotted against the observed pH values. All pH measurements are made electrometrically.

7. Interferences

7.1 Oily matter, soaps, suspended solids, and waste materials, sometimes found in industrial waters, may interfere with the pH measurement. Similarly, the development of a precipitate during titration may make the glass electrode sluggish and cause high results.

8. Apparatus

8.1 *Electrometric pH Measurement Apparatus*, conforming to the requirements given in ASTM Method D 1293, Test for pH of Industrial Water and Industrial Waste Water.[2]

9. Reagents

9.1 *Hydrochloric Acid, Standard Solution (0.02 N)* (Note 1)—Prepare and standardize as directed in Methods E 200, except that the titration shall be made electrometrically. The inflection point corresponding to the complete titration of carbonic acid salts will be very close to pH 3.9.

NOTE 1—Sulfuric acid having a normality of 0.02 N may be used instead of hydrochloric acid. Prepare and standardize in like manner.

---

[2] Appears in this publication.

9.2 *Sodium Hydroxide, Standard Solution (0.02 N)*—Prepare and standardize as directed in Methods E 200, except that the titration shall be made electrometrically. The inflection point corresponding to the complete titration of the phthalic acid salt will be very close to pH 8.6.

10. Procedure

10.1 Mount the glass and reference electrodes in two of the holes of a clean, three-hole rubber stopper chosen to fit a 400-ml, tall-form Berzelius beaker without spout. Place the electrodes in the beaker and standardize the pH meter. Rinse the electrodes, first with reagent water, then with a portion of the sample. Following the final rinse, drain the beaker and electrodes completely.

10.2 Pipet 100 ml of the sample into the beaker through the third hole in the stopper. Hold the tip of the pipet near the bottom of the beaker while discharging the sample.

10.3 Measure the pH of the sample in accordance with Method D 1293.

10.4 Add either 0.02 N acid or alkali solution, as indicated, in increments of 0.5 ml or less (Note 2). After each addition, mix the solution thoroughly; determine the pH when the mixture has reached equilibrium as indicated by a constant reading (Note 3). Mechanical stirring, preferably of the magnetic type, is required for this operation; mixing by means of a gas stream is not permitted. Continue the titration until the necessary data for the titration curve have been obtained.

NOTE 2—If the sample requires appreciably more than 10 ml of standard solution for its titration, use a 0.1 N solution, prepared and standardized in the same manner (see Methods E 200).

NOTE 3—The equilibrium time will vary with different waters. In some instances, a waiting period of 30 sec may be required. When developing a titration curve, it is particularly important that equilibrium conditions be attained.

10.5 To develop a titration curve, plot the cumulative milliliters of standard solution added to the sample aliquot against the observed pH values. The acidity or alkalinity relative to a particular pH may be determined from the curve.

11. Calculation

11.1 Calculate the acidity or alkalinity, in equivalents per million as follows:

$$\text{Acidity (or alkalinity), epm} = AN \times 10$$

where:

A = milliliters of standard acid or alkali required for the titration, and

N = normality of the standard solution.

12. Report

12.1 Report the results of titrations to specific end points as follows: "The acidity (or alkalinity) to pH at —— C = —— epm."

12.2 Appropriate factors for converting equivalents per million (epm) to other units are given in ASTM Method D 596, Reporting Results of Analysis of Industrial Water and Industrial Waste Water.[2]

13. Precision

13.1 No statement concerning the precision of this method can be made because of the transient nature of the equilibria involved and the pronounced variation in the characteristics of different waters.

Non-Referee Method A

(Electrometric or Color-Change Titration)

14. Application

14.1 This method covers the rapid, routine control measurement of acidity or alkalinity to predesignated end points of industrial water containing no materials that interfere with the titration by reason of color, precipitation, etc.

15. Summary of Method

15.1 The sample is titrated with standard acid or alkali to a designated pH, the end point being determined electrometrically or by the color change of an internal indicator.

16. Interferences

16.1 Natural color or the formation of a precipitate while titrating the sample may mask the color change of an internal indicator. Suspended solids may interfere in electrometric titrations also by making the glass electrode sluggish. Waste materials present in some industrial waters may interfere chemically with color titrations by destroying the indicator. Variable results may be experienced with waters containing oxidizing or reducing substances, depending on the equilibrium conditions and the manner in which the sample is handled.

17. Apparatus

17.1 *Electrometric pH Measurement Apparatus*—See 8.1.

18. Reagents

18.1 *Bromcresol Green Indicator (1 g/ liter)*—Dissolve 0.1 g of bromcresol green in 2.9 ml of 0.02 N sodium hydroxide (NaOH) solution. Dilute to 100 ml with water.

18.2 *Hydrochloric Acid, Standard (0.02 N)* (Note 1)—See 9.1, except that the acid may be standardized by colorimetric titration as directed in Methods E 200 when an indicator is used for sample titration.

18.3 *Methyl Orange Indicator (0.5 g/ liter)*—Dissolve 0.05 g of methyl orange in water and dilute to 100 ml.

18.4 *Methyl Purple Indicator*—Proprietary compound.

18.5 *Methyl Red Indicator (1 g/liter)*—Dissolve 0.1 g of water-soluble methyl red in water and dilute to 100 ml.

18.6 *Phenolphthalein Indicator (5.0 g liter)*—Dissolve 0.5 g of phenolphthalein in 50 ml of ethyl alcohol (95 per cent (Note 4) and dilute to 100 ml with water

NOTE 4—Specially denatured ethyl alcohol conforming to Formula No. 3A or 30 of the U. S Bureau of Internal Revenue may be substitute for ethyl alcohol (95 per cent).

18.7 *Sodium Hydroxide, Standard Solution (0.02 N)*—See 9.2, except that the alkali may be standardized by colorimetric titration as directed in Method E 200 when an indicator is used for sample titration.

19. Procedure

19.1 Pipet 100 ml of the sample into a 300-ml, tall-form beaker or 250-ml narrow-mouth Erlenmeyer flask. Place the pipet tip at the bottom of the container while discharging the sample.

19.2 Titrate the aliquot electrometrically to the pH corresponding to the desired end point (Note 5). When using an indicator, add 0.2 ml (Note 6) and titrate with 0.02 N acid (for alkalinity or 0.02 N NaOH solution (for acidity until a persistent color change is noted (Note 7). Add the standard solution in small increments, swirling the flask vigorously after each addition. As the end point is approached, a momentary change in color will be noted in that portion of the sample with which the reagent first mixes. From that point on make dropwise additions.

NOTE 5—The choice of end point will have been made to provide optimum data for the intended use or disposition of the water. When an indicator is used, those listed in 18.1 and 18. through 18.6 are the ones used most frequently others may be employed if it is to the user's advantage.

NOTE 6—After some practice, slightly more or less indicator may be preferred. The analys must use the same quantity of phenolphthalein at all times, however, because at a given pH, the intensity of one-color indicators depends on the quantity.

NOTE 7—If the sample requires appreciably more than 10 ml of 0.02 N solution for its titration, use a smaller aliquot, or a 0.1 N solution prepared and standardized in the same manner (see Methods E 200).

20. Calculation

20.1 Calculate the acidity or alkalinity in equivalents per million as follows:

$$\text{Acidity (or alkalinity), epm} = \frac{AN}{B} \times 1000$$

where:

A = milliliters of standard acid or alkali required for the titration,

N = normality of the standard solution, and

B = milliliters of sample titrated.

21. Report

21.1 Report the results of titrations as follows: "The acidity (or alkalinity) to ——— = ——— epm," indicating the pH end point or the name of the indicator used, for example, "The acidity to methyl orange = ——— epm."

22. Precision

22.1 See 13.

NON-REFEREE METHOD B

(Color-Comparison Titration)

23. Application

23.1 This method is applicable to routine control use in determining the acidity or alkalinity of industrial waters containing no materials that buffer at the end point or interfere with the titration because of color, precipitation, etc.

24. Summary of Method

24.1 The sample is titrated with standard acid or alkali to a predesignated pH, the end point being determined by comparison of the color developed by an added indicator with the color of a standard buffer solution containing the same added indicator.

25. Interferences

25.1 Natural color or the formation of a precipitate during the titration of a sample may mask or otherwise interfere with color comparison. Waste materials present in some industrial waters may interfere chemically with the titration by destroying the indicator. Variable results may be experienced with waters containing oxidizing or reducing substances, depending on the equilibrium conditions and the manner in which the sample is handled.

26. Reagents

26.1 *Buffer Solutions*—Prepare buffer solutions corresponding to the pH values, that is, the indicator end points, to which the samples are titrated.

26.2 *Hydrochloric Acid, Standard (0.02 N)*—See 18.2.

26.3 *Indicator Solutions*—Bromcresol green, methyl orange, methyl purple, methyl red, and phenolphthalein (see 18.1, 18.3, 18.4, 18.5, and 18.6, respectively).

26.4 *Sodium Hydroxide, Standard Solution (0.02 N)*—See 18.7.

27. Procedure

27.1 Pipet 100 ml of the sample into a 250-ml, narrow-mouth Erlenmeyer flask. Place the pipet tip at the bottom of the flask while discharging the sample.

27.2 Transfer to a second flask, identical with that used for the sample, a volume of the appropriate buffer solution equal to that of the sample. To both the buffer and the sample, add 0.2 ml (Note 8) of the appropriate indicator (Note 5). Stopper the flask containing the buffer solution and mix well.

NOTE 8—After some practice, slightly more or less indicator may be preferred, but the volume used in the buffer must always be the same as that used in the sample.

27.3 If the sample is acid relative to the buffer solution, titrate with 0.02 N NaOH solution (Note 7) until the color exactly matches that of the buffer. Add the reagent in small increments and swirl the flask vigorously after each addition; as the end point is approached, reduce the size of the increments. Calculate and report the results as acidity.

27.4 If the sample is alkaline relative to the buffer solution, titrate with 0.02 N acid (Note 7) until the color exactly matches that of the buffer. Calculate and report as alkalinity.

27.5 *Indicator Correction*—Using in place of the sample an equal volume of freshly boiled, but cool reagent water, proceed as described in 27.1, 27.2 and 27.3 or 27.4. Double the volume of indicator in both the water previously titrated and the buffer solution, and determine the volume of either standard acid or NaOH solution required to again secure a color match. The additional volume of standard acid or NaOH solution is the indicator correction.

28. Calculation

28.1 Calculate the acidity or alkalinity, in equivalents per million as follows:

Acidity (or alkalinity), epm

$$= \frac{(A \pm C)N}{B} \times 1000$$

where:
A = milliliters of standard acid or alkali required for titration of the sample,
C = indicator correction, in milliliters (Note 9),
N = normality of the standard solution, and
B = milliliters of sample titrated.

NOTE 9—If the reagent used for titrating the sample is the same as that required for the indicator correction, subtract the correction from the titration; otherwise add it.

29. Report

29.1 See 21.

30. Precision

30.1 See 13.

NON-REFEREE METHOD C

(Electrometric or Color-Change Titration after Boiling)

31. Application

31.1 This method is applicable to routine control measurement of acidity or alkalinity of industrial waters containing concentrations of slowly hydrolyzable materials sufficient to significantly delay attainment of equilibrium conditions at a titration end point. Volatile components contributing to the acidity or alkalinity of the water may be lost during sample pretreatment.

32. Summary of Method

32.1 The sample aliquot is boiled to accelerate chemical reactions for attaining equilibrium conditions, cooled, and titrated with standard acid or alkali to a predesignated end point. Titration may be carried out electrometrically or by means of an internal indicator using the color-change procedure (Non-Referee Method A).

33. Interferences

33.1 See 16.1.

33.2 Constituents contributing to the acidity or alkalinity may be volatilized when the sample is boiled, thus introducing some error in the determination.

34. Apparatus

34.1 See 8.1.

35. Reagents

35.1 *Hydrochloric Acid, Standard (0.02 N)* (Note 1)—See 18.2.

35.2 *Indicator Solutions*—Bromcresol

green, methyl orange, methyl purple, methyl red, and phenolphthalein (see 18.1, 18.3, 18.4, 18.5, and 18.6, respectively).

35.3 *Sodium Hydroxide, Standard Solution (0.02 N)*—See 18.7.

36. Procedure

36.1 Pipet 100 ml of the sample into a 250-ml, narrow-mouth Erlenmeyer flask.

36.2 Heat the sample to boiling and continue to boil for two minutes. Cool to room temperature out of contact with the air.

36.3 Titrate the cooled aliquot electrometrically to the pH corresponding to the desired end point or to the color change of the appropriate indicator, following the procedure given in 19.2.

37. Calculation

37.1 See 20.1.

38. Report

38.1 Report the results of titrations as follows: "The acidity (or alkalinity) (boiled) to —— = —— epm," indicating the pH or indicator used for the end point, for example, "The acidity (boiled) to methyl orange = —— epm."

39. Precision

39.1 See 13. Precision.

Standard Methods of Test for
NICKEL IN INDUSTRIAL WATER[1]

ASTM Designation: D 1886 – 65

ADOPTED, 1965

This Standard of the American Society for Testing and Materials is issued under the fixed designation D 1886; the final number indicates the year of original adoption as standard or, in the case of revision, the year of last revision.

Scope

1. These methods[2] cover the photometric determination of nickel in industrial water. Two methods are included as follows:

	Concentration Range, ppm	Sections
Method A	0.001 to 0.05	5 to 12
Method B:		
Using 100-mm absorption cells	0.01 to 0.1	
Using 10-mm absorption cells	0.1 to 5.0	13 to 20

Definitions

2. For definitions of terms used in these methods, refer to the Definitions of Terms Relating to Industrial Water and Industrial Waste Water (ASTM Designation: D 1129).[3]

Purity of Reagents

3. (a) Reagent grade chemicals shall be used in all tests. Unless otherwise indicated, it is intended that all reagents shall conform to the specifications of the Committee on Analytical Reagents of the American Chemical Society, where such specifications are available.[4] Other grades may be used, provided it is first ascertained that the reagent is of sufficiently high purity to permit its use without lessening the accuracy of the determination.

(b) Unless otherwise indicated, references to water shall be understood to mean reagent water conforming to the Specifications for Reagent Water (ASTM

[1] Under the standardization procedure of the Society, these methods are under the jurisdiction of the ASTM Committee D-19 on Industrial Water. A list of members may be found in the ASTM Year Book.

[2] For further information on these methods, see the following reference:

J. M. Chilton, "Simultaneous Colorimetric Determination of Copper, Cobalt, and Nickel as Diethyldithiocarbamates," *Analytical Chemistry*, Vol. 25, pp. 1274–1275 (1953).

[3] Appears in this publication.

[4] "Reagent Chemicals, American Chemical Society Specifications," Am. Chemical Soc., Washington, D. C. For suggestions on the testing of reagents not listed by the American Chemical Society, see "Reagent Chemicals and Standards," by Joseph Rosin, D. Van Nostrand Co., Inc., New York, N. Y., and the "United States Pharmacopeia."

Designation: D 1193).[3] In addition, the water must be nickel and copper-free.

Sampling

4. (a) Collect the sample in accordance with the applicable method of the American Society for Testing and Materials, as follows:

D 510—Sampling Industrial Water,[3]
D 860—Sampling Boiler Water from Boilers,[3]
D 1066—Sampling Steam.[3]

(b) If the sample is to be stored for some time before analysis, stabilize it by adding sufficient nickel and copper-free sulfuric acid to produce a pH of 2.0 or less.

METHOD A

Summary of Method

5. This method is based on the formation of a yellow-green complex of nickel with sodium diethyldithiocarbamate, at a pH of 8.5 to 9.0, in the presence of citrate. The color complex is extracted with carbon tetrachloride and the color intensity measured by means of a spectrophotometer. Correction is made for copper up to 0.100 ppm. Calculations are based on absorbance measurements at wavelengths of 328 and 436 mμ.

Interferences

6. (a) Bismuth and cobalt interfere directly by forming colored complexes soluble in carbon tetrachloride and absorbing at wavelengths very similar to those for nickel. If the amounts of cobalt and bismuth ions are known, corrections may be calculated from absorbances, as is done for copper in this method. If the amounts of cobalt and bismuth are not known, the method is not applicable.

(b) Cyanide interferes in all concen-trations by forming complex ions and by preventing formation of the desired colored complexes.

(c) Metals such as iron, titanium, uranium, and aluminum interfere by forming precipitates but may be kept in solution by adding extra citrate. Up to ten times the specified citrate may be used with no adverse effects, provided the blank contains the same amount.

(d) Still other metals, including cadmium, mercury, tin, and zinc, form precipitates with the reagent, but small concentrations do not interfere if sufficient reagent is present. When excessive quantities of these ions are present, the carbon tetrachloride will pick up precipitates, but such precipitates can be removed by centrifugation.

Apparatus

7. Spectrophotometer, suitable for measuring transmittance or absorbance, or both, at 328 and 436 mμ, and equipped with 10-mm matched silica cells and a hydrogen lamp (Notes 1 and 2).

NOTE 1.—Spectrophotometers and spectrophotometric practice prescribed in these methods shall conform to the Recommended Practice for Describing and Measuring Performance of Spectrophotometers (ASTM Designation: E 275).[5]

NOTE 2.—The over-all sensitivity should be such that a solution containing 0.02 ppm nickel and 0.05 ppm copper gives about 50 per cent transmittance at 328 mμ and about 55 per cent transmittance at 436 mμ.

Reagents

8. (a) Ammonium Hydroxide (1:1).— Mix 1 volume of concentrated ammonium hydroxide (NH$_4$OH, sp gr 0.90) with 1 volume of water.

(b) Citric Acid Solution (350 g per liter).—Dissolve 35 g of citric acid monohydrate in water and dilute to 100 ml.

---

[5] 1967 Book of ASTM Standards, Part 30.

(c) *Cleaning Solution.*[6]—Prepare a saturated water solution of sodium dichromate ($Na_2Cr_2O_7 \cdot 2H_2O$). To 32 ml of this solution add 1 liter of concentrated sulfuric acid (H_2SO_4, sp gr 1.84) (**Caution,** Note 3).

NOTE 3: **Caution.**—Always add the acid to the solution carefully. Never add the solution to the acid, as spattering may result.

(d) *Copper, Standard Solution (1 ml = 1 mg Cu).*—Place 1.000 g of copper (not less than 99.90 per cent Cu) in a 250-ml beaker, add 10 ml of water and 10 ml of concentrated nitric acid (HNO_3, sp gr 1.42), cover with a watch glass, and allow to stand until dissolved. Add 1 ml of concentrated sulfuric acid (H_2SO_4, sp gr 1.84) and evaporate to just short of complete dryness. Cool, add 5 ml more of H_2SO_4, and evaporate to dense white fumes (boiling should be very slow to prevent losses). Cool and dilute to 1 liter.

(e) *Hydrochloric Acid (1:1).*—Mix 1 volume of concentrated hydrochloric acid (HCl, sp gr 1.19) with 1 volume of water.

(f) *Nickel, Standard Solution (1 ml = 1 mg Ni).*—Place 1.000 g of nickel (not less than 99.90 per cent Ni) in a 250-ml beaker, add 10 ml of water and 10 ml of concentrated nitric acid (HNO_3, sp gr 1.42), cover with a watch glass, and allow to stand until dissolved. Add 1 ml of concentrated sulfuric acid (H_2SO_4, sp gr 1.84) and evaporate to just short of complete dryness. Cool, add 5 ml more of H_2SO_4, and evaporate to dense white fumes (boiling should be very slow, to prevent losses). Cool and dilute to 1 liter.

(g) *Phenol Red Indicator (0.2 g per liter).*—Grind 0.05 g of phenol red in a mortar with 1.4 ml of 0.1 N sodium hydroxide (NaOH) solution. Dilute to 250 ml with water.

---

[6] This reagent is used for preparation of apparatus only.

(h) *Sodium Diethyldithiocarbamate Solution (0.4 g per liter).*—Dissolve 0.1 g of sodium diethyldithiocarbamate trihydrate in 250 ml of water and filter. Extract twice with 20-ml portions of carbon tetrachloride (CCl_4). Filter through wet, water-washed filter paper.

(i) *Tetrasodium Pyrophosphate Solution (40 g per liter).*—Dissolve 4 g of tetrasodium pyrophosphate ($Na_4P_2O_7 \cdot 10H_2O$) in water and dilute to 100 ml.

Calibration and Standardization

9. (a) Both copper and nickel form similar complexes with diethyldithiocarbamate, except that the maximum absorbance of the two complexes occurs at different wavelengths. The maximum absorbance of the nickel complex occurs at about 328 mμ, whereas the maximum absorbance of the copper complex occurs at about 436 mμ. While the two complexes exhibit maximum absorbance at their respective wavelengths, some absorption occurs at the other wavelength and thus each interferes with the other. Such interference may be eliminated by calculation as follows:

$$\text{Nickel, ppm} = K_{328} \times A_{328} - K_{436} \times A_{436}$$

where A_{328} and A_{436} are the measured maximum absorbances at about 328 mμ and 436 mμ respectively (Note 4), while K_{328} and K_{436} are constants for the respective wavelengths. The constants K_{328} and K_{436} may be evaluated by the solution of two simultaneous equations, each expressing known but different nickel and copper contents. The values of these constants are then used for calculating the nickel content of an unknown solution. (When desired, the copper content can be calculated similarly.)

NOTE 4.—If the spectrophotometer used scans and records continuously (such as with Beckman Model DK-2), the maximum absorbances are easily measured. However, if the spectrophotometer does not scan continuously, appreciable error may result if the rotating prism is not in correct adjustment. Correct maximum absorbances may be measured by taking *sufficient readings* at 328 ± about 6 mμ and at 436 ± about 6 mμ to establish the maximum absorbances (or minimum transmittances) with certainty.

(*b*) Evaluate the constants K_{328} and K_{436} as follows:

(*1*) Prepare standards No. 1 and No. 2 by the appropriate dilution of the standard nickel and copper solutions (Note 5):

Standard No. 1.... 0.02 ppm Ni; 0.025 ppm Cu
Standard No. 2.... 0.02 ppm Ni; 0.050 ppm Cu

Note 5.—Any similar set of standards may be used, but these are in the range of concentration to which this procedure is adapted. The mathematics is simplified if each contains the same amount of nickel.

(*2*) Pipet 100 ml of each standard as well as a 100-ml portion of water (nickel and copper-free) into 125-ml separatory funnels and proceed as described in Section 10(*a*) and (*b*) or (*a*) and (*c*) (Note 6).

Note 6: *Example.*—The measured maximum absorbances for Standards No. 1 and No. 2 were found to be:

Standard No. 1:
$A_{328} = 0.2741$
$A_{436} = 0.1518$
Standard No. 2:
$A_{328} = 0.2907$
$A_{436} = 0.2464$

Substituting in the equation given in Paragraph (*a*):
Standard No. 1:
$0.02 = K_{328} \times 0.2741 - K_{436} \times 0.1518$
Standard No. 2:
$0.02 = K_{328} \times 0.2907 - K_{436} \times 0.2464$
Therefore,
$0.0166\ K_{328} = 0.0946\ K_{436}$
$K_{328} = 0.08080$
$K_{436} = 0.01417$

(*3*) Prepare Standards No. 3 and No. 4:

Standard No. 3.... 0.030 ppm Ni; 0.025 ppm Cu
Standard No. 4.... 0.030 ppm Ni; 0.050 ppm Cu

Proceed as in Step (*2*). Average the values of K_{328} and K_{436} respectively.

(*c*) Errors in the values of K_{328} and K_{436} can be minimized by running the determination described in Paragraph (*b*) in duplicate and using the over-all averages.

Procedure

10. (*a*) Pipet 100 ml of the sample into a 125-ml separatory funnel. Pipet a 100-ml portion of water (nickel and copper-free) into a second separatory funnel. (Notes 7 and 8). To each add 2 drops of phenol red indicator, 4 ml of tetrasodium pyrophosphate solution, and 1 ml of citric acid solution, swirling between each addition. Add NH$_4$OH(1:1) dropwise until the solution is violet (12 to 15 drops). Add 5 ml of sodium diethyldithiocarbamate solution, swirl, and then add exactly 5 ml of carbon tetrachloride. Shake vigorously for 5 min and allow the layers to separate for 10 min, swirling occasionally. Transfer the carbon tetrachloride extract to clean, dry 10-ml glass-stoppered long-necked flasks. Allow each to stand for a minimum of 5 min, swirling occasionally, to complete removal of dispersed water droplets. Proceed as described in Paragraphs in (*b*) or (*c*).

Note 7.—Glassware of unknown cleanliness should be conditioned before use. This may be done as follows: Clean with cleaning solution and rinse well with water; boil with concentrated HCl; rinse several times with water. Store glassware in HCl (1:1) when not in use. To make certain that glassware is properly conditioned, run blank nickel-copper determinations on nickel and copper-free water until results are constant. Between determinations wash glassware several times in series with water and methanol. Dry 1 hr and swing to remove methanol vapor.

Note 8.—During operations described in Paragraphs (*a*), (*b*), and (*c*), avoid direct sunlight as the color complex is light-sensitive. Artificial lighting is satisfactory.

(b) When using a double-beam spectrophotometer,[7] clean the cells by washing several times with water, methanol, and carbon tetrachloride separately (Note 9). Fill the reference and sample cells with carbon tetrachloride. Set the spectrophotometer at about 550 mμ, check at zero transmittance, and adjust if necessary; then check at 100 per cent transmission and adjust if needed. Scan from 550 mμ to somewhat below 328 mμ. If the cells are clean and the instrument balanced, the recorded scan will be a line at 100 per cent transmission and fluctuating only a small fraction of 1 per cent. Drain both cells, dry, and free from vapor. Place carbon tetrachloride extract from the blank in the reference cell and from the sample in the sample cell (use the same cell always for reference). Scan between about 550 mμ and somewhat below 328 mμ (Note 10), after exactly 20 min from the time shaking is completed as described in Paragraph (a). Read the minimum transmittance at about 328 and 436 mμ. If there is no minimum, read the transmittance at exactly 328 and 436 mμ. Convert to absorbance.

NOTE 9.—At times it may be necessary to soak the cells 1 or 2 hr in a mild commercial detergent, washing them with water, methanol, and carbon tetrachloride separately.

NOTE 10.—The over-all sensitivity should be such that a solution containing 0.02 ppm Ni and 0.05 ppm Cu gives about 50 per cent transmittance at 328 mμ and about 55 per cent transmittance at 436 mμ.

(c) When using a single-beam spectrophotometer,[8] clean the cells by washing several times with water, methanol, and carbon tetrachloride separately (Note 9). Fill the reference and sample cells with carbon tetrachloride. Set the spectrophotometer at 436 mμ. Adjust the

[7] The Beckman Model DK-2 spectrophotometer has been found satisfactory for this purpose.

[8] The Beckman Model DU spectrophotometer has been found satisfactory for this purpose.

absorbance of the reference cell to zero; then determine the absorbance of sample cell (use the same cell always for reference). Repeat at 328 mμ. If absorbances of the sample cell at the two wavelengths are zero, the cells may be considered clean. Drain the cells, dry, and free from vapor. After exactly 20 min from the time shaking is completed as described in Paragraph (a), fill the reference cell with carbon tetrachloride extract from the blank and the sample cell with extract from the sample. Set the spectrophotometer at 436 mμ and adjust the reference cell to zero absorbance. Determine the absorbance of the sample cell (Note 10) and record it. Make sufficient determinations at 436 ± 6 mμ to establish the maximum with certainty. Repeat at 328 ± 6 mμ. If there are no maxima, read at exactly 328 and 436 mμ.

Calculation

11. Calculate the nickel content of the sample, using the equation given in Section 9(a).

Precision[9]

12. The over-all and within-a-laboratory precisions are as follows:

$$S_T = 0.08 \ X$$
$$S_{CI} = 0.04 \ X$$

where:
S_T = over-all precision,
S_{CI} = precision within one laboratory, and
X = concentration of nickel determined, in parts per million.

METHOD B

Summary of Method

13. This method is based on the formation of a wine-red color complex of

[9] Supporting data giving results of cooperative tests have been filed at ASTM Headquarters.

nickel with ammoniacal dimethylglyoxime in the presence of iodine. The color is measured directly with a filter photometer or a spectrophotometer.

Interferences

14. Iron interference is eliminated by the addition of ammonium citrate. Copper up to 3 ppm does not interfere with the test.

Apparatus

15. *Photometer.*—A filter photometer (Note 11) or a spectrophotometer (Note 1) suitable for measurement at a wavelength of 530 mμ.

NOTE 11.—Filter photometers and photometric practice described in this method shall conform to the Recommended Practice for Photometric Methods for Chemical Analysis of Metals (ASTM Designation: E 60).[10]

Reagents

16. (*a*) *Ammonium Citrate Solution (575 g per liter).*—Dissolve 500 g of citric acid monohydrate in 675 ml of concentrated ammonium hydroxide (NH$_4$OH, sp gr 0.90), cool, and dilute to 1000 ml with water. Filter.

(*b*) *Ammonium Hydroxide (1:1).*—Mix 1 volume of concentrated ammonium hydroxide (sp gr 0.90) with 1 volume water and filter.

(*c*) *Dimethylglyoxime, Ammoniacal Solution.*—Dissolve 1 g of dimethylglyoxime in 500 ml concentrated ammonium hydroxide (sp gr 0.90), add 500 ml water, and filter. Prepare fresh after two weeks.

(*d*) *Iodine Solution (12.7 g per liter).*—Dissolve 6.35 g of iodine in a solution of 75 g of potassium iodide (KI) in 60 ml of water and dilute to 500 ml with water. Store in a dark stoppered bottle.

(*e*) *Nickel, Standard Solution (1 ml = 0.02 mg Ni).*—Place 1.000 g of nickel (not less than 99.90 per cent Ni) in a

[10] 1967 Book of ASTM Standards, Part 32.

250-ml beaker, add 10 ml of water and 10 ml of concentrated nitric acid (HNO$_3$, sp gr 1.42), cover with a watch glass, and allow to stand until dissolved. Add 1 ml of concentrated sulfuric acid (H$_2$SO$_4$, sp gr 1.84) and evaporate to just short of complete dryness. Cool, add 5 ml more of H$_2$SO$_4$, and evaporate to dense white fumes (boiling should be very slow to prevent losses). Dilute to 500 ml in a volumetric flask. Dilute 50 ml to 1 liter in a volumetric flask and finally dilute 50 ml of this solution to 250 ml in a volumetric flask.

Calibration and Standardization

17. (*a*) Pipet the corresponding portions of the standard nickel solution into 100-ml volumetric flasks to cover the range from 0 to 10 ppm. At least five concentrations other than 0 should be selected. Suggested amounts are 0, 1, 2, 5, 10 and 25 ml. These correspond to 0, 0.4, 0.8, 2.0, 4.0, and 10.0 ppm, respectively. Add water to make a volume to 50 ml. Continue in accordance with Section 18.

(*b*) Plot the transmittances against parts per million of nickel on semilogarithmic paper, using the logarithmic scale for the transmittance readings.

Procedure

18. (*a*) Measure 50-ml portions of the sample into each of two 100-ml volumetric flasks.

(*b*) Add 10 ml of ammonium citrate solution and 5 ml of iodine solution to each flask.

(*c*) To one flask add 20 ml of ammoniacal dimethylglyoxime solution. Dilute to 100 ml with water and allow to stand 10 min.

(*d*) To the other flask add 20 ml of NH$_4$OH (1:1). Dilute to 100 ml with water and allow to stand 10 min. Use this solution as the reference solution.

(*e*) Balance the photometer at 100

per cent transmission with the reference solution and read the transmittance of the sample. With a filter photometer, the transmittance readings are made using a green filter which transmits radiant energy of 530-mμ wavelengths. With a spectrophotometer, the transmittances are read at 530 mμ.

Calculation

19. Calculation is not required, as the nickel concentration in parts per million can be read directly from the calibration curve.

Precision[9]

20. The over-all and within-a-laboratory precisions are as follows:

$$S_T \;\; = 0.06\ X$$

$$S_{CI} = 0.04\ X$$

where:

S_T = over-all precision,

S_{CI} = precision within one laboratory, and

X = concentration of nickel determined, in parts per million.

Tentative Methods of Test for

PARTICULATE AND DISSOLVED MATTER IN INDUSTRIAL WATER[1]

ASTM Designation: D 1888 – 66 T

ISSUED, 1961; LAST REVISED, 1966

These Tentative Methods have been approved by the sponsoring committee and accepted by the Society in accordance with established procedures, for use pending adoption as standard. Suggestions for revisions should be addressed to the Society at 1916 Race St., Philadelphia, Pa. 19103.

1. Scope

1.1 These methods cover the determination of particulate, dissolved, and total matter, sometimes referred to as the suspended, dissolved, and total solids, in industrial water. Two procedures, consistent with the total matter content, are provided as follows:

	Sections
Method A. Particulate and Dissolved Matter in Water with 25 ppm or Less of Total Matter (Automatic Evaporation)	6 to 12
Method B. Particulate and Dissolved Matter in Water with More Than 25 ppm of Total Matter	13 to 19

1.2 The methods actually cover the determination of (1) the constituents of an industrial water that can be removed by filtration, and (2) the residue on evaporation to dryness of either filtered or unfiltered samples; as a result, they do not always measure water components as defined. Separation of particulate matter by filtration requires precise definition of the filtering medium since some materials that are in no sense dissolved, for example, certain colloids, may not be removed by the filter used. Secondly, an evaporation residue will usually differ in composition from the particulate and dissolved matter present in the water.

1.3 When particulate matter is determined separately (the sample is filtered and the residue quantitatively assessed), provision is made for the use of either a membrane filter that will remove all particles over 0.45μ in size or an asbestos fiber medium in a Gooch crucible. However, unless otherwise specified when results are reported, use of the membrane filter shall be assumed. It is further provided that all buoyant floating particles or large particulate agglomerations that cannot be dispersed throughout the sample by vigorous shaking need not be considered as fundamental constituents of the water under examination and may be excluded, therefore, from the test portion.

1.4 The methods include steps for the

[1] Under the standardization procedure of the Society, these methods are under the jurisdiction of the ASTM Committee D-19 on Industrial Water. A list of members may be found in the ASTM Year Book.

determination of volatile matter in the dry residue from either filtration or evaporation. They do not, however, cover water constituents that are (1) volatile at the boiling temperature, or (2) normally classified as "oily matter", which is extractable with organic solvents or volatile at the drying temperature of filtration residues. For the determination of the latter, refer to ASTM Method D 1340, Test for Oily Matter in Industrial Waste Water.[2]

2. Definitions

2.1 The terms "particulate matter," "dissolved matter," "total matter," and others related to water constituents determined in these methods, are defined in accordance with ASTM Definitions D 1129, Terms Relating to Industrial Water and Industrial Waste Water,[2] as follows:

2.1.1 *Particulate Matter*—That matter, exclusive of gases, existing in the nonliquid state which is dispersed in water to give a heterogeneous mixture.

2.1.2 *Dissolved Matter*—That matter, exclusive of gases, which is dispersed in water to give a single phase of homogeneous liquid.

2.1.3 *Total Matter*—The sum of the particulate and dissolved matter.

2.1.4 *Volatile Matter*—That matter that is changed under conditions of the test from a solid or a liquid state to the gaseous state.

2.1.5 *Fixed Matter*—Residues remaining after ignition of particulate or dissolved matter, or both.

2.2 For definitions of other terms used in these methods, refer to Definitions D 1129.

3. Interferences

3.1 Some evaporation residues readily absorb moisture; rapid weighing is essential to this method. Some residues contain materials, such as ammonium carbonate, that decompose below 103 C (217 F); others contain liquids, such as glycerol and sulfuric acid, that will remain as a liquid residue at 103 C (217 F) with or without solution of salts that might also be present.

3.2 Rapid weighing of ignited residues, also, is important because of possible moisture absorption. Furthermore, there is likelihood of interference from carbonates, organic matter, nitrite and nitrate nitrogen, water of hydration, chlorides, and sulfates which may be decomposed either completely or in part when ignited at 600 C (1112 F). No single temperature is known that will eliminate all these interferences. Reasonably reproducible results should be obtained, however, at the prescribed 600 C (1112 F).

3.3 Because the water being sampled is of necessity in contact with the sample container and tubing, it is important, especially in the case of glass, that the possible precipitation of cations or the absorption of substances originally present in the water, on these surfaces, be recognized.

4. Purity of Reagents

4.1 Unless otherwise specified, reagent grade chemicals or equivalent, as defined in ASTM Methods E 200, Preparation, Standardization, and Storage of Standard Solutions for Chemical Analysis[2] shall be used in all tests.

4.2 Unless otherwise indicated, references to water shall be understood to mean reagent water conforming to ASTM Specifications D 1193, for Reagent Water.[2] Referee grade reagent water shall be used for Method A and the non-referee grade for Method B.

4.3 Except for concentrated hydrochloric acid (HCl, sp gr 1.19), reagents including reagent water should be membrane-filtered prior to use.

---

[2] Appears in this publication.

5. Sampling

5.1 Collect the sample in accordance with the applicable method of the American Society for Testing and Materials, as follows:

D 510—Sampling Industrial Water,[2]
D 860—Sampling Water from Boilers,[2]
D 1066—Sampling Steam,[2] and
D 1192—Equipment for Sampling Industrial Water, and Steam.[2]

5.2 Because of the low concentration of total matter in some waters and the possible effects of aeration on others, sampling shall be carried out in a manner which reduces atmospheric exposure to a minimum. The type and size of the container shall be consistent with the nature of the water being sampled (see 8.1 and 15.1).

5.3 Samples containing 25 ppm or less of total matter on which only the total matter content is to be determined shall be immediately acidified with 0.2 ml of concentrated hydrochloric acid (HCl, sp gr 1.19) per liter of water to prevent iron deposition on the walls of the container. If particulate matter is to be separately determined, the sample, regardless of total matter content, shall be filtered as soon as possible (see 10.3) and then acidified.

METHOD A. PARTICULATE AND DISSOLVED MATTER IN INDUSTRIAL WATER WITH 25 PPM OR LESS OF TOTAL MATTER (AUTOMATIC EVAPORATION)

6. Application

6.1 This method is intended primarily for steam condensate and distilled or demineralized water that contains 5 ppm or less of total matter. Because of the automatic evaporation feature, the method is desirable for use, however, on all waters containing up to 25 ppm of total matter, particularly if a large residue is desired for chemical analysis.

7. Summary of Method

7.1 Total matter is determined by evaporation, or the particulate and dissolved matter are separated by filtration and individually evaluated. The particulate matter is dried, freed of oily matter by extraction, dried again, and weighed. The solution of dissolved matter is evaporated to dryness using a dish provided with a constant-level control. Sufficient sample is evaporated to give the desired accuracy for the measurement and provide ample material for other analytical requirements. The residue is dried and weighed. Volatile matter in any of the three classifications is subsequently removed by ignition. The total, particulate, dissolved, volatile, or fixed matter are then calculated from the various weights obtained.

8. Apparatus

8.1 *Sample Reservoir*—A covered, 20-liter (5-gal) container of corrosion-resistant metal, suitable plastic, or chemical-resistant glass with necessary tubular connections. Most waters with very low total matter exhibit a pH in the range from 6 to 9. For samples of such waters, containers of TFE-fluorocarbon, block tin, polyethylene, or chemical-resistant glass shall be selected with that order of preference, depending upon the purity.

8.2 *Automatic Evaporation Assembly*—A dust shield, constant-level device, heater, and evaporation dish. Typical assemblies are described in 8.2.1 and 8.2.2.

8.2.1 *Evaporation Assembly A (Fig. 1)*:

8.2.1.1 *Dust Shield*—A heat-resistant cover glass enclosing the Monel-sheathed ring heater, platinum evaporating dish, antenna, and electrical terminal posts, with provision for introducing the water sample through the base. Minimum practicable enclosed space is necessary to prevent condensation on the cover.

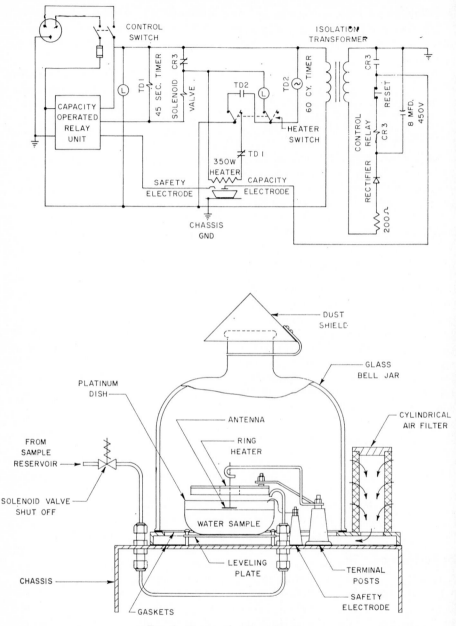

FIG. 1—Evaporation Assembly A.

The top of the dust shield is covered with a "dunce cap" to prevent foreign material from dropping into the dish while permitting free passage for the moisture-laden air. An open-bottom aluminum platform supporting two filter cylinders and having an opening under the glass cover is provided to supply filtered inlet air. Either a seal must be provided or filter material used between glass cover and the platform as well as between chassis and platform.

8.2.1.2 *Evaporator Assembly,* as shown

made conveniently of a flat coil of platinum wire (16 to 20-gage). The antenna is suspended from a stainless steel arm which makes contact with the electronic control circuit[3] through a terminal post.

FIG. 2—Evaporation Assembly B.

under the glass cover—The Monel-sheathed ring heater is suspended over the platinum evaporating dish by two stainless steel arms which are connected through the electronic control system to a power circuit containing a timer. The platinum dish is supported by an aluminum plate provided with leveling screws so that the distance from the dish to the heater can be adjusted. A stainless steel inlet tube is used for addition of sample at the pouring spout of the platinum vessel.

8.2.1.3 *Electronic Control Circuit*— Control of the water level in the platinum dish is effected by a capacitance-type electrode or antenna which can be

A change of the water level activates the shut-off valve[4]; if the water level in the

---

[3] The RCA Thermocap Relay Unit manufactured by the Niagara Electron Laboratories, Niagara Falls, N. Y., or equivalent, has been found satisfactory for this purpose.

[4] The electrically-operated valve (No. 5004141312) sold by Diamond Power Specialty Corp., Lancaster, Ohio, or an air-operated valve (No. 1000A 2-way Demi G 303 with No. 5049 stainless diaphragm) manufactured by the G. W. Dahl Co., Inc., Bristol, R. I., have been found satisfactory for this purpose. The Dahl valve must be coupled with a solenoid air valve such as the Skinner Electric Valve, 3-way, vented, No. V5D4200 manufactured by Skinner Electric Valve Div., The Skinner Chuck Co., 100 Edgewood Ave., New Britain, Conn., or its equivalent. It is imperative that new valves be tested to determine that contamination does not occur from mechanical wear on materials of construction.

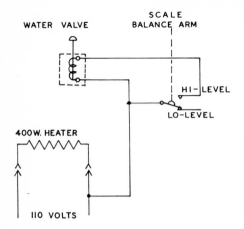

Fig. 3—Automatic Evaporation Circuit.

ture above the specified 103-C (217-F) level, should additional sample fail to reach the dish. Since the 45-sec timer automatically turns off the heater when sample flow is interrupted, an additional timer is incorporated which may be used upon completion of evaporation to keep the heater on for a specified time period to lower the water level in the dish and thus facilitate its removal from the test assembly. An overflow device is incorporated in the assembly, also. A platinum wire electrode is positioned so that its tip is suspended slightly above the normal water level in the platinum dish. This electrode serves as an addi-

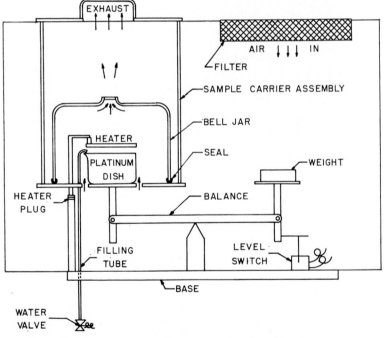

Fig. 4—Automatic Evaporation Assembly.

platinum dish does not return to the upper level control within 45 sec after reaching this lower level of capacitance control, the current to the ring heater is broken by means of a time interlock. The purpose of this interlock is to prevent the drying of the dish at a tempera-

tional upper-water level control should a failure occur in the capacitance system.

8.2.2 *Evaporation Assembly B (Figs. 2, 3 and 4)*[5]:

[5] An evaporator assembly of this type is available from Diamond Power Specialty Corp. Lancaster, Ohio. Parts for the assembly are also available from this manufacturer.

8.2.2.1 *Dust Shield*—The dust shield compartment consists of a heat-resistant glass bell jar equivalent to that used on assembly "A" and is contained in an enclosed dust-shielded compartment. Air is provided through an external filter source into this shielded sample compartment.

from the balance base and mounted in the dust shield compartment is a heater connection consisting of the necessary wiring connections and a Monel-sheathed ring heater similar to that used in evaporator assembly A. In addition, a solenoid water sample valve[4] is provided

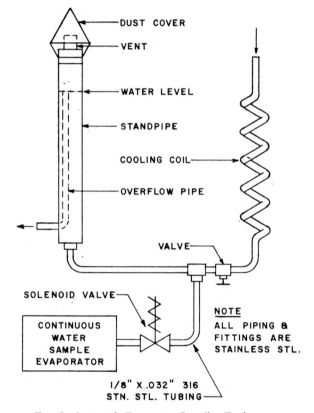

FIG. 5—Automatic Evaporator Sampling Equipment.

8.2.2.2 *Evaporator Assembly* — The evaporator assembly as shown schematically in Fig. 4 consists of a balance,[5,6] one arm of which extends into the dust shield compartment. The balance arm extending into the dust shield holds a platinum sample dish. Also extending into this compartment

with a $\frac{1}{8}$-in. (3.2-mm) outside diameter stainless steel tubing connection feeding into the shielded sample compartment and then to the platinum sample dish. Automatic sample addition is accomplished by a level switch on the counter balance arm and this actuates the water sample valve. Control is effected by counter balance arm. Action of the entire balance arm can be dampened by a dash pot. If desired, a timer mechanism

---

[6] The balance manufactured by the Fisher Scientific Co., Catalog No. 2-035, or its equivalent, has been found satisfactory for this purpose.

can be installed to record the volume of water evaporated. Calibration of this assembly is accomplished by using a calibrated sample reservoir and timing the addition and evaporation rate. This calibration will have to be carried out under atmospheric conditions similar to those pertaining at the actual sampling location.

8.2.2.3 *Wiring Diagram*—The wiring diagram for this assembly is also shown in Fig. 3.

8.3 *Sampling Device (See Fig. 5)*—A cooling coil with overflow pipe and solenoid valve suitable for sampling from a water source to a continuous sample evaporator. (The cooling coil is, of course, necessary only when sample is above room temperature.)

8.4 *Membrane Filter Assembly*—A borosilicate glass or stainless steel funnel with a flat, fritted base of the same material, and membrane filters (0.45-μ pore size) to fit.[7]

8.5 *Glass Petri Dish*—150-mm diameter.

8.6 *Filter Crucible*—A Gooch crucible containing an evenly distributed filter mat, approximately 5-mm thick and composed of finely divided asbestos fiber, produced by pouring a slurry of acid-washed asbestos into the crucible under slight suction.

8.7 *Evaporating Dish*—A straight-walled or round-bottom platinum dish of 80 to 100-mm diameter and approximately 200-ml capacity.

9. Reagents

9.1 *Chloroform or Benzene*, purified or USP grade.

9.2 *Ethyl Alcohol (95 per cent) (Note 1)*.

NOTE 1—Specially denatured ethyl alcohol conforming to Formula 3A or 30 of the U. S. Bureau of Internal Revenue may be substituted for ethyl alcohol (95 per cent).

[7] Suitable membrane filter holder and filters, HAWPO4700, are available from Millipore Co., Bedford, Mass.

9.3 *Hydrochloric Acid (sp gr 1.19)*—Concentrated hydrochloric acid (HCl).

10. Procedure

10.1 Select a volume of sample sufficient to yield an evaporation residue of approximately 25 mg if only the matter content is to be determined, or approximately 100 mg if the evaporation residue is to be analyzed.

10.2 If both particulate and dissolved matter are to be determined, proceed in accordance with 10.3; if only total matter is desired, follow the procedure starting with 10.4.

10.3 *Particulate Matter*—This water component is preferably separated by filtration using a membrane having a pore size of 0.45 μ (see 10.3.1); an alternative procedure using an asbestos fiber medium, generally considered to have a 5-μ pore size, is described in 10.3.2.

10.3.1 *Membrane Filtration*—Place $n + 1$ plain, white filter disks of the prescribed pore size in a 150-mm petri dish, where n equals the number of tests to be run. Place the dish and filters in a drying oven at 103 C for 15 min or in a vacuum desiccator for 30 min. If oven-dried, allow the filters to cool to room temperature while exposed to the air. Weigh each filter to the nearest 0.1 mg. With most balances it is desirable to have a polonium alpha emitter source to dispel effects of static electricity. Label filters with ball point pen and mark the extra filter C for "control." Proceed with the filtration in accordance with 10.3.1.1 through 10.3.1.5.

10.3.1.1 Place a weighed filter on the fritted base of the filter holder, and clamp the funnel portion of the apparatus in place on top of the filter. The filtration assembly shall be placed on a filter flask of appropriate size and with the aid of a vacuum from a vacuum-pressure pump or water aspirator, the sample shall be poured into the funnel and drawn through the filter into the filter flask. Where sample bottles are employed for collection of the sample, the entire contents of a sample bottle should be filtered. Wash the bottle with an appropriate quantity of filtered water (may be obtained from the filter flask) and pour this also into the filter funnel. Transfer sample and washings to sample reservoir. Dry the membrane by drawing air through the filter and wash with chloroform or benzene until 10 ml of the washings leave not more than 0.1 mg of residue on evaporation at 103 C. Air-dry the sediment for several minutes. Discard the washings. Release the vacuum and with flat-bladed forceps, remove the filter from the fritted base and place in the petri dish.

10.3.1.2 Wet the control filter (C) with the sample water from the filter flask, and place it also in the petri dish.

10.3.1.3 Place the petri dish in the drying oven at 103 C for 30 min; allow the filters to cool to room temperature and equilibrate to ambient humidity after removing from the oven, and reweigh.

10.3.1.4 Record the weight of particulate matter adjusted for the difference between final and initial weight of the test filter as "weight of particulate matter." A positive or negative adjustment shall be made in the event of any weight change occurring in the "control" filter.

10.3.1.5 Place the filter used in the particulate matter determination in a clean, ignited, small, porcelain crucible, which has been weighed, after ignition and cooling, to the nearest 0.1 mg. Add approximately 1 ml of ethyl alcohol and ignite with a match when the filter is fully wetted. After the alcohol has burned off, place the lid on the crucible and ignite it in the furnace at 600 ± 25 C for at least 30 min. Remove the crucible from the furnace and allow it to cool to room temperature in a desiccator. Remove the crucible cover and weigh the crucible to the nearest 0.1 mg (see 3.2). Record the loss in weight as "weight of volatile particulate matter" and the weight of the ignited residue as "weight of fixed particulate matter."

10.3.2 *Asbestos Fiber Filtration (Note 2)*—Filter the selected volume of sample through a filter crucible (see 8.6) that previously has been dried for 1 hr at 103 C, cooled in a desiccator, and weighed. After filtration, wash the filter crucible contents twice with water, transferring the filtrate and washings to the sample reservoir for subsequent determination of dissolved matter as described in 10.4. Dry the crucible contents by drawing air through the crucible for several minutes; then wash the crucible contents with chloroform or benzene until 10 ml of the washings leave not more than 0.1 mg of residue on evaporation at 103 C. Discard the washings. Air-dry the sediment for several minutes; then place the crucible in an oven at 103 C for 1 hr, cool in a desiccator, and weigh. Record the weight of the residue as "weight of particulate matter." Ignite the crucible contents for 30 min at 600 ± 25 C, cool in a desiccator, and reweigh (see 3.2). Record the loss in weight as "weight of volatile particulate matter" and the weight of the ignited residue as "weight of fixed particulate matter."

NOTE 2—Since asbestos fiber filters are generally considered to have a pore size of 5 μ, no process of coagulation shall be employed that will alter the content of either dissolved or particulate matter.

10.3.3 Immediately acidify the filtrate and washings with 0.2 ml of HCl (sp gr 1.19) per liter of water.

10.4 *Total Matter and Dissolved Matter*—Weigh a platinum dish that has been dried for 1 hr at 103 C and cooled in a desiccator. Using Evaporation Assembly A or B, start the evaporation of the selected volume of sample for total matter only or the filtrate and washings from the particulate matter removal (see 10.3), as follows:

10.4.1 *Evaporation Assembly A*—With the current off, insert the clean, weighed platinum dish (previously ignited at 600 ± 25 C) in the evaporator assembly and adjust the dish height by use of the leveling screws in the aluminum base. Antenna adjustments, if necessary, may also be made at this time, using the set screw provided at the end of the antenna arm. Turn on the circuit and heater switches and set the control knob on the relay to allow water to rise to the proper level with respect to the antenna and the desired water level in the dish. It is advisable to operate the relay with the water level as close to the antenna as possible. Observe the evaporator for a period of time to ascertain the satisfactory operation of the relay and assure the absence of boiling in the dish.

10.4.2 *Evaporation Assembly B*—Adjust the apparatus to the most rapid rate feasible without boiling. The adjustment is accomplished by the addition of 7 to 10-g weights to the tare weight of the evaporating dish on the counter weight arm of the balance. With the top of the shielded compartment removed, manually trip the level switch on the counter balance arm several times to actuate the water sample valve and flush out the sampling line. Then place a carefully cleaned and weighed platinum dish on the balance pan in the shielded compartment. Place a clean bell jar over the dish. Set the bell jar carefully on the seal mounted on the support plate in the dust shielded compartment (Fig. 4). Close the shield compartment leaving the vent open. Turn on the heater current and observe the operation long enough to assure satisfactory performance.

10.4.3 When evaporation is almost complete, remove the dish from the assembly, transfer to a 103-C oven, and heat to dryness. Continue heating for 1 hr, cool in a desiccator, and weigh (see 3.1). Record the weight of the residue as "weight of total matter" (or, if sample had been filtered, "dissolved matter"). Ignite the dish and contents for 1 hr at 600 ± 25 C, cool in a desiccator, and reweigh (see 3.2). Record the loss in weight as "weight of volatile matter" (or "volatile dissolved matter"), and the weight of the ignited residue as "weight of fixed matter" (or "fixed dissolved matter").

11. Calculation

11.1 Calculate the result of each specific determination in parts per million, as follows:

$$\text{Matter, ppm} = \frac{Wx}{V} \times 1000$$

where:

$Wx = W_1 =$ grams of total matter found,

$W_2 =$ grams of particulate matter found,

$W_3 =$ grams of dissolved matter found,

$W_4 =$ grams of volatile matter found,

$W_5 =$ grams of volatile particulate matter found,

$W_6 =$ grams of volatile dissolved matter found,

$W_7 =$ grams of fixed matter found,

$W_8 =$ grams of fixed particulate matter found, or

$W_9 =$ grams of fixed dissolved matter found, and

$V \quad =$ liters of sample used.

11.2 When particulate and dissolved matter have been separately determined, total matter, volatile matter, and fixed matter can be calculated by adding the two appropriate values.

11.3 If asbestos fiber filtration was used for the removal of particulate matter, it is mandatory that this be stated when reporting either particulate or dissolved matter. Otherwise, use of a membrane medium shall be assumed.

12. Precision

12.1 No statement can be made concerning the precision of this method. The precision is influenced by both the nature and the amount of entrained matter and by the effects of drying and ignition on its actual composition.

METHOD B. PARTICULATE AND DIS-
SOLVED MATTER IN INDUSTRIAL
WATER WITH MORE THAN 25
PPM OF TOTAL MATTER

13. Application

13.1 This method is primarily applicable to industrial water that will yield a residue on evaporation at 103 C of at least 25 mg/liter.

14. Summary of Method

14.1 Total matter is determined by evaporation of an appropriate aliquot, or the particulate and dissolved matter are separated by filtration and individually assessed. The particulate matter is dried and weighed. The dissolved matter is determined by weighing the residue obtained after evaporating the filtered sample. Volatile matter and fixed matter under any of the above classifications are determined by weighing the residues remaining after ignition at a temperature of 600 C.

15. Apparatus

15.1 *Sample Reservoir*—A chemical-resistant container of 1 to 4-liter capacity.

15.2 *Membrane Filter Assembly*—See 8.4.

15.3 *Glass Petri Dish*, 150-mm diameter.

15.4 *Filter Crucible*—See 8.6.

15.5 *Evaporating Dish*—A straight-wall or round-bottom platinum dish of 80 to 100-mm diameter and approximately 200-ml capacity. A porcelain dish may be substituted for the platinum dish if the residue is not to be analyzed.

15.6 *Heater*—A controlled electric hot plate, infrared lamp, or steam bath for maintaining the temperature of the evaporating sample near the boiling point.

16. Reagents

16.1 See 9.

17. Procedure

17.1 Weigh a quantity of sample sufficient to yield on evaporation approximately 25 mg of residue if only the amount is to be determined, or at least 100 mg if this residue is to be analyzed. The sample shall be well shaken before removing the aliquot and inclusion of floating material or agglomerates that cannot be dispersed shall be avoided. If only total matter is to be determined, without classification, proceed in accordance with 17.3. If both particulate and dissolved matter are to be determined, proceed in accordance with 17.2.

17.2 *Particulate Matter*—This determination shall preferably be made using a membrane filter following the procedure given in 10.3.1, except that a 0.2-mg residue from the solvent washings shall be permissible. The less desirable alternative use of an asbestos fiber medium is described in 10.3.2. In either case the filtrate shall be immediately acidified with 0.2 ml of HCl (sp gr 1.19)/liter of water unless the sample contains significant amounts of alkaline chemicals, for example, sodium hydroxide (NaOH), whose composition would be affected by the acid; acidification will prevent deposition of iron on the sample container.

17.3 *Total Matter and Dissolved Matter*—Transfer the sample aliquot provided for total matter determination (17.1) or the filtrate obtained from the particulate matter separation (17.2) to a sample reservoir having a valve-controlled outlet. Fill an evaporating dish that previously has been ignited at 600 ± 25 C for 1 hr, cooled in a desiccator, and weighed, to within approximately $\frac{1}{4}$ in. (6.3 mm) of the top with the sample from the reservoir. Heat the dish to evaporate the sample, but do not allow the sample to boil. Periodically add sample from the reservoir to the dish to prevent drying until the reservoir is empty. Rinse the reservoir several times with water, adding the rinsings to the contents of the evaporating dish. Then evaporate the remainder of the material in the dish to near dryness. Transfer to a 103-C oven and complete the evaporation. Dry the dish and its contents for 1 hr (see 3.1), cool in a desiccator, and weigh. Repeat the cycle of drying (1-hr periods), cooling, and weighing until loss in weight is no more than 4 per cent of the previous weight. Record the weight of residue as "weight of total matter" (or, if the sample had been filtered, "dissolved matter"). Ignite the dish contents for 30 min at 600 ± 25 C, cool in a desiccator, and reweigh (see 3.2). Record the loss in weight as "weight of volatile matter" (or "volatile dissolved matter") and the weight of the ignited residue as "weight of fixed matter" (or "fixed dissolved matter").

18. Calculation

18.1 See 11. Calculation.

19. Precision

19.1 See 12. Precision.

Standard Methods of Test for
TURBIDITY OF INDUSTRIAL WATER[1]

ASTM Designation: D 1889 – 66

ADOPTED, 1966

This Standard of the American Society for Testing and Materials is issued under the fixed designation D 1889; the number immediately following the designation indicates the year of original adoption or, in the case of revision, the year of last revision. A number in parentheses indicates the year of last reapproval.

Scope

1. These methods cover the determination of the turbidity of industrial water and industrial waste water. Measurements of both relative and absolute turbidity are employed. Three methods are included as follows:

	Sections
Jackson Candle Turbidity	5 to 9
Nephelometric Turbidity	10 to 16
Absolute Turbidity	17 to 22

Definitions

2. (*a*) The term "turbidity" in these methods is defined in accordance with the Definitions of Terms Relating to Industrial Water and Industrial Waste Water (ASTM Designation: D 1129),[2] as follows:

Turbidity.—Reduction of transparency of a sample due to the presence of particulate matter.

Jackson Candle Turbidity.—An empirical measure of turbidity in special apparatus, based on the measurement of the depth of a column of water sample that is just sufficient to extinguish the image of a burning standard candle observed vertically through the sample.

Nephelometric Turbidity.—An empirical measure of turbidity based on a measurement of the light-scattering characteristics (Tyndall effect) of the particulate matter in the sample (Note 1).

NOTE 1.—The measurement of nephelometric turbidity is accomplished by measuring the intensity of scattered light at 90 deg to the incident beam of light. Numerical values are obtained by comparison with the light-scattering characteristics of a known or an arbitrarily chosen material in an equivalent optical system. Comparison may also be made between transmitted light effect and scattered light effect.

Absolute Turbidity.—The fractional decrease of incident monochromatic light through the sample, inte-

---

[1] Under the standardization procedure of the Society, these methods are under the jurisdiction of the ASTM Committee D-19 on Industrial Water. A list of members may be found in the ASTM Year Book.
[2] Appears in this publication.

669

grating both scattered and transmitted light (Note 2).

Note 2.—For the small amount of scattering experienced in essentially colorless solutions, absolute turbidity of a 1-cm layer corresponds to the extinction coefficient in the equation expressing Lambert's Law.

(b) For definitions of other terms used in this method, refer to Definitions D 1129.

Purity of Reagent Water

3. Unless otherwise indicated, references to water shall be understood to mean reagent water conforming to the Specifications for Reagent Water (ASTM Designation: D 1193).[2]

Sampling

4. Collect the sample in accordance with the applicable method of the American Society for Testing and Materials, as follows:

D 510—Sampling Industrial Water,[2]
D 860—Sampling Water from Boilers,[2]
D 1066—Sampling Steam,[2]
D 1496—Sampling Homogeneous Industrial Waste Water.[2]

Jackson Candle Turbidity

Application

5. The Jackson candle turbidity method is suitable for measurement of light-scattering, by turbid waters, but it is not sufficiently sensitive for measurement of the turbidity of well water, filtered water, or clarified effluent samples. The range of applicability of the method is shown in Table I.

Summary of Method

6. This is an empirical measure of turbidity, based on the measurement of the depth of sample, in a special graduated vessel, that is just sufficient to extinguish the image of a burning standard candle observed vertically through the sample.

Apparatus

7. *Jackson Candle Turbidimeter.*[3]—This instrument consists of a graduated glass tube, a standard candle, a light shield surrounding the glass tube, and a support for the candle and tube. The glass tube and the candle shall be supported in a vertical position so that the center line

TABLE I.—GRADUATION OF JACKSON CANDLE TURBIDIMETER.

Depth of Liquid, cm	Turbidity	Depth of Liquid, cm	Turbidity
2.3	1000	11.4	190
2.6	900	12.0	180
2.9	800	12.7	170
3.2	700	13.5	160
3.5	650	14.4	150
3.8	600	15.4	140
4.1	550	16.6	130
4.5	500	18.0	120
4.9	450	19.6	110
5.5	400	21.5	100
5.6	390	22.6	95
5.8	380	23.8	90
5.9	370	25.1	85
6.1	360	26.5	80
6.3	350	28.1	75
6.4	340	29.8	70
6.6	330	31.8	65
6.8	320	34.1	60
7.0	310	36.7	55
7.3	300	39.8	50
7.5	290	43.5	45
7.8	280	48.1	40
8.1	270	54.0	35
8.4	260	61.8	30
8.7	250	72.9	25
9.1	240		
9.5	230		
9.9	220		
10.3	210		
10.8	200		

of the tube passes through the center line of the candle, the top of the support for the candle being 7.6 cm (3 in.) below the bottom of the tube. The glass tube shall be graduated either in turbidity or in

---

[3] This apparatus is available as a complete unit from laboratory supply houses.

centimeters. The relationship between Jackson candle turbidity and centimeters is shown in Table I. The glass tube shall have a flat, polished glass bottom. The candle shall be made of beeswax and spermaceti, gaged to burn within the limits of 114 to 126 grains per hr. The candle support shall have a spring or other device to keep the top of the candle pressed against the top of the support.

of samples, with both the standard candle and the alternative light source.

(*b*) Make the turbidity test by pouring the sample suspension into the glass tube until the image of the candle flame is no longer visible when viewed through the column of liquid. After the image has disappeared, the removal of 5 per cent of the suspension from the tube by suction, using a plastic tube and a rubber bulb,

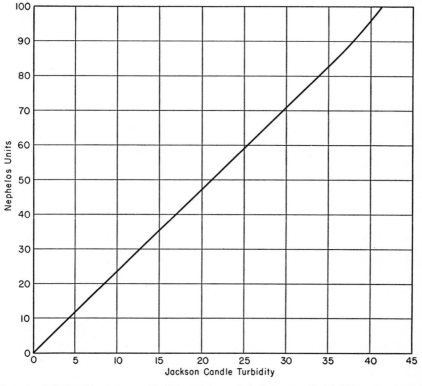

FIG. 1.—Relationship Between Nephelos Units and Jackson Candle Turbidity for 325-Mesh Diatomaceous Earth.

Procedure

8. (*a*) Make observations in a darkened room, with the glass tube enclosed in nonreflective material. It is allowable to substitute any other light source for the standard candle, but the instrument must then be calibrated, using a number

should again make the image of the flame visible. Take care to keep the glass tube clean, both inside and outside. Accumulations of dirt inside and soot and moisture outside will seriously interfere with the reliability of the results. In order to obtain reasonably consistent results, the candle flame must be kept to as nearly standard size and spacing as possible. This requires frequent trimming and adjusting. Do not keep the candle lighted for more than a few minutes at a time or flame size will increase.

(c) Figure 1 shows the approximate white-light relationship between the Jackson candle turbidity and nephelos standards, using 325-mesh diatomaceous earth,[4] suspended in water, settled for 24 hr, and the supernatant suspension pipetted out. This relationship will vary with different materials of suspension,

NEPHELOMETRIC TURBIDITY

Application

10. The nephelometric method covers the measurement of relative turbidity and is also applicable to the measurement of low turbidity.

Summary of Method

11. Nephelometric turbidity instruments measure scattered light at 90-deg or 90 and 270-deg angles to the incident beam. These instruments cannot be cali-

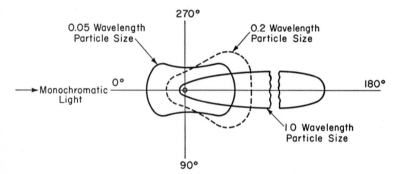

NOTE.—Typical polar diagrams of total scattered light for suspensions of approximately uniform size particles of various dimensions. The ratio of particle size dimension to incident wavelength results in a particular shape polar diagram for scattered light.

FIG. 2.—Rayleigh's Light-Scattering Observations for Uniform Small-Size Particles.

the size of the particles in suspension, and the wavelength of the light used for the nephelos determination.

Report

9. Report turbidity as the Jackson candle turbidity number between 25 and 1000 (Note 3).

NOTE 3.—The Jackson candle turbidity number is an arbitrary number and is not in terms of parts per million.

---

[4] Dicalite Speed Plus diatomaceous earth, 325-mesh, has been found satisfactory for this purpose.

brated accurately in terms of absolute turbidity, except in the case of fluids having uniform-size particles that are less than approximately one fifth of the wavelength of incident light (see Figs. 2 and 3). Nephelos standards have been prepared by thoroughly mixing suitable amounts of finely divided titanium dioxide (TiO_2) into partially polymerized polystyrene. Calibrated commercial standards in sealed tubes are available.

Apparatus

12. *Nephelometer or Calibrated Slit Turbidimeter.*

Calibration

13. Using nephelometric turbidity standards, obtain readings with at least instrument system physically and electrically in accordance with the manufacturer's instructions. Then replace the

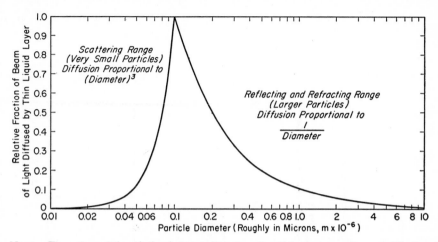

NOTE.—The nature of the relation between diameter of particles in suspension and diffusion of a beam of 0.47-μ blue light by a thin layer of suspension (constant percentage by weight of particle material).

FIG. 3.—Relation Between Particle Diameter and Light Diffusion.

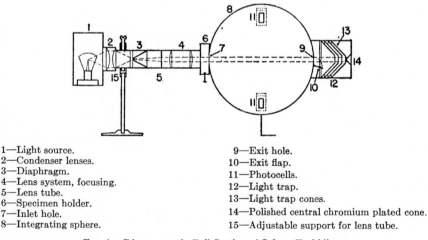

1—Light source.
2—Condenser lenses.
3—Diaphragm.
4—Lens system, focusing.
5—Lens tube.
6—Specimen holder.
7—Inlet hole.
8—Integrating sphere.

9—Exit hole.
10—Exit flap.
11—Photocells.
12—Light trap.
13—Light trap cones.
14—Polished central chromium plated cone.
15—Adjustable support for lens tube.

FIG. 4.—Diagrammatic Full Section of Sphere Turbidimeter.

three separate standards in order to calibrate the instrument.

Procedure

14. (*a*) *Instruments Using Nephelometric Standards.*—First balance the standards by the sample in an optically identical tube and record the reading. The straight line relationship for Tyndall effect for small amounts of scattered 90-deg or 90 and 270-deg light produces proportional readings for nephelometric

turbidity standards up to approximately 100 nephelos units. Therefore, the nephelometric turbidity of the sample can be calculated as the turbidity of the calibrated standard times the ratio of the readings.

(b) *Instruments Using Transmitted Light From Calibrated Slit As Reference.*— Follow the manufacturer's instructions in

estimate the mid-point of the interval of uniform-light intensity for the two fields by rotating the dial in one direction only towards higher values. This eliminates errors caused by lost motion in the mechanism.

Calculations

15. Calculate the nephelometric tur-

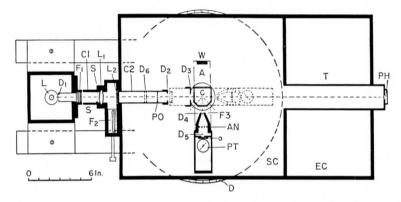

Optical System

A—Rotatable arm attached to disk.
AN—Analyzer.
C—Semioctagonal cell.
C_1—Shutter collimating tube.
C_2—Scattering beam collimating tube.
D—Graduated disk.
D_1—Lamp diaphragm.
D_2—Removable collimating tube diaphragm.
D_3—Cell table diaphragm.
D—Nosepiece diaphragm.
D—Cathode diaphragm.
D_6—Collimating tube diaphragm.
EC—Electrical compartment.
F_1—Monochromatic filter.
F_2—Neutral filters.

F_3—Location of filters used for correcting for fluorescence.
L—Mercury lamp.
L_1—Achromatic lens.
L_2—Planocylindrical lens.
O—Opal glass depolarizing diffusor. (Required for 931A photomultiplier tube but not for 1P21 tube.)
PH—Covered peephole.
PT—Photomultiplier tube.
PO—Demountable polarizer.
S—Photographic shutter.
SC—Scattering compartment.
T—Light-trap tube.
W—Working standard.

FIG. 5.—Schematic Diagram of Instrument for Measuring Absolute Turbidity, Dissymmetry and Depolarization of Liquids.

detail. This type of turbidimeter utilizes a fixed ratio of scattered light to transmitted light intensity. A calibrated slit adjusts the quantity of light for transmission from the single light source until the observer matches the final intensity of the light for the different paths. The instrument uses a special cell for the sample.

(c) For all calibrated slit instruments,

bidity, in nephelos units, as follows:

Nephelometric turbidity $= A \times B$

where:

$A =$ instrument reading of scattered light, and

$B =$ nephelos units per unit of instrument reading.

Report

16. Report results as nephelos units.

Absolute Turbidity

Application

17. The absolute turbidity method covers the measurement of both the scattered and the transmitted light. The method, using the integrating-sphere apparatus, is not subject to a particle size limitation.

Summary of Method

18. An integrating-sphere type of absolute turbidity instrument measures all of the scattered light. For most industrial water problems, the particle size is greater than one fifth of the wavelength of light, and thus back-scattering is much less than 90-deg or forward-scattering (see Figs. 2 and 3). The apparatus shown in Fig. 4 is arranged to give the summation of most of the scattered light for such suspensions and solutions. From this summation the approximate absolute turbidity can be calculated.

Apparatus

19. (a) Instruments for measuring absolute turbidity are commercially available or can be constructed for particular needs. The best instrument for the particular problem will depend on the average size of the light-scattering particles in the suspension (see Figs. 2 and 3). If the particle-size averages one twentieth the wavelength of light, an instrument as shown in Fig. 5 should be used to determine absolute turbidity.

(b) To determine approximate absolute turbidity where the particle size is sufficiently large to neglect the back-scattering, a simplified integrating

sphere instrument can be constructed.[5] This instrument, as shown in Fig. 4, has eliminated many interference problems by mounting the test cell at the outer surface of the sphere and integrating only the forward and side-scattered light. If the test cell is mounted internally in the sphere to integrate all of the scattered light, many corrections must be applied because the sample cell cannot be made infinitely small relative to the size of the sphere. The external sample cell results in more uniform reflected light within the sphere. Since the sensitive surface of the barrier-layer photocells are illuminated diffusely, difficulties caused by variations in sensitivity of different parts of their sensitive surface are thus reduced.

Procedure

20. After the instrument has been properly adjusted and calibrated for instrument error dark current, etc., obtain one galvanometer deflection for the total light flux with the exit-light-reflecting flap closed in order to integrate both the transmitted light and the scattered light. Then obtain a second galvanometer reading with the exit flap open to allow the transmitted light to leave the sphere. The second galvanometer reading is usually made with a shunt-setting for higher sensitivity.

Calculations

21. Calculate the absolute turbidity with the instrument shown in Fig. 4, expressed in percentage decrease, as follows:

$$\text{Absolute turbidity} = \frac{100 \times D_2 S_1 - T}{D_1 \times S_2}$$

---

[5] R. B. Barnes and C. R. Stock, "Apparatus for Transmission Turbidity of Slightly Hazy Materials," *Analytical Chemistry*, Vol. 21, No. 1, Jan., 1949, pp. 181–184.

where:
D_1 = first galvanometer reading,
D_2 = second galvanometer reading,
S_1 = shunt factor for D_1 reading,
S_2 = shunt factor for D_2 reading, and
T = previously determined instrument error, including scattered light from the sample cell.

Report

22. Report the calculated absolute turbidity and the corresponding wavelength and band-width of the incident light, filter number, light source, and solution temperature.

Standard Method for
MEASUREMENT OF BETA PARTICLE RADIOACTIVITY OF INDUSTRIAL WATER AND INDUSTRIAL WASTE WATER[1]

ASTM Designation: D 1890 – 66

ADOPTED, 1966

This Standard of the American Society for Testing and Materials is issued under the fixed designation D 1890; the number immediately following the designation indicates the year of original adoption or, in the case of revision, the year of last revision. A number in parentheses indicates the year of last reapproval.

Scope

1. (a) This method covers the measurement of beta particle activity of industrial water and industrial waste water. It is applicable to beta emitters having maximum energies above 0.1 Mev and at activity levels above 0.5 picocurie per ml of radioactively homogeneous water for most counting systems. The method is not applicable to samples containing radioelements that are volatile under conditions of the analysis.

(b) The method can be used for either absolute or relative determinations. In tracer work, the results may be expressed by comparison with a standard which is defined to be 100 per cent. For radioassay, data may be expressed in terms of a known isotopic standard if the radionuclides concerned are known and no fractionation occurred during processing, or may be expressed arbi-

trarily in terms of some other standard such as strontium-90—yttrium-90. General information on radioactivity and measurement of radiation may be found in the literature.[2]

Summary of Method

2. Beta radioactivity may be measured by one of several types of instruments composed of a detecting device and combined amplifier, power supply, and scaler—the most widely used being proportional or Geiger-Müller counters. Where a wide range of counting rates is encountered (10 to 80,000 counts per minute), the proportional-type counter is preferable due to a shorter resolving time and greater stability of the instrument. The test sample is reduced to the

[2] G. Friedlander and J. W. Kennedy, "Nuclear and Radiochemistry," John Wiley and Sons, Inc., New York, N. Y. (1955).

W. J. Price, "Nuclear Radiation Detection," McGraw-Hill Book Co., Inc., New York, N. Y. (1958).

R. E. Lapp and H. L. Andrews, "Nuclear Radiation Physics", Prentice-Hall Inc., New York, N. Y. (1955).

R. T. Overman and H. M. Clark, "Radioisotope Techniques," McGraw-Hill Book Co., Inc., New York, N. Y. (1960).

[1] Under the standardization procedure of the Society, this method is under the jurisdiction of the ASTM Committee D-19 on Industrial Water. A list of members may be found in the ASTM Year Book.

15–60

minimum weight of solid material having measurable beta activity by precipitation, ion-exchange resin, or evaporation techniques. Beta particles entering the sensitive region of the detector produce ionization of the counting gas. The negative ion of the original ion pair is accelerated towards the anode, producing additional ionization of the counting gas and developing a voltage pulse at the anode. By use of suitable electronic apparatus, the pulse is amplified to a voltage sufficient for operation of the counter scaler. The number of pulses per unit of time is related to the disintegration rate of the test sample. The beta-particle efficiency of the system can be determined by use of prepared standards having the same radionuclide composition as the test specimen and equivalent residual plated solids. An arbitrary efficiency factor can be defined in terms of some other standard such as strontium-90—yttrium-90.

Definitions

3. (*a*) Certain terms in this method that relate specifically to the measurement of radioactivity are defined in accordance with the Definitions of Terms Relating to Industrial Water and Industrial Waste Water (ASTM Designation: D 1129),[3] as follows:

Beta Energy, Maximum.—The maximum energy of the beta-particle energy spectrum produced during beta decay of a given radioactive species.

Note 1.—Since a given beta-particle emitter may decay to several different quantum states of the product nucleus, more than one maximum energy may be listed for a given radioactive species.

Counter Efficiency.—In the measurement of radioactivity, that fraction of the disintegrations occurring in a source which is detected by the counter.

---

[3] Appears in this publication.

Counter Beta-Particle Efficiency.—In the measurement of radioactivity, that fraction of beta particles emitted by a source which is detected by the counter.

Curie.—A unit of radioactivity equivalent to 3.700×10^{10} atomic disintegrations per second or 2.220×10^{12} atomic disintegrations per minute. A microcurie is one millionth of a curie (10^{-6} curie); a picocurie, one millionth of a microcurie (10^{-12} curie).

Counter Background.—In the measurement of radioactivity, the counting rate resulting from factors other than the radioactivity of the sample and reagents used.

Note 2.—Counter background varies with the location, shielding of the detector, and the electronics; it includes cosmic rays, contaminating radioactivity, and electrical noise.

Reagent Background.—In the measurement of radioactivity of water samples, the counting rate observed when a sample is replaced by mock sample salts or by reagent chemicals used for chemical separations.

Note 3.—Reagent background varies with the reagent chemicals and analytical methods used and may vary with reagents from different manufacturers and from different processing lots.

Radioactively Homogeneous Water.—Water in which the radioactive material is uniformly dispersed throughout the volume of water sample and remains so until the measurement is completed, or until the sample is evaporated or precipitating reagents are added to the sample.

(*b*) For definitions of other terms used in this method, refer to Definitions D 1129.

Note 4.—For terms not defined in this method or in Definitions D 1129, reference may be made to other published glossaries, such as the American Standard Glossary of Terms in Nuclear Science and Technology (ASA Designation: N1.1.—1957).

Measurement Variables

4. (a) The relatively high absorption of beta particles in the sample media and any material interposed between source and sensitive volume of the counter results in an interplay of many variables which affect the counting rate of the measurement. Thus, for reliable relative measurements, the variables should be held constant while counting all test samples and standards. For absolute measurements, appropriate correction factors must be applied. The effects of geometry, backscatter radiation, source diameter, self-scatter and self-absorption, absorption in air and detector window for external counters, and counting coincidence losses have been discussed[2] and may be described by the following relation:

$$\text{cpm} = \text{dpm}_b (G_p)(f_{bs})(f_{aw})(f_d)(f_{ssa})(f_c)$$

where:

cpm = recorded counts per minute corrected for background,

dpm_b = disintegrations per minute yielding beta particles,

G_p = point source geometry (defined by the solid angle subtended by the sensitive area of the detector),

f_{bs} = backscatter factor or ratio of cpm with backing to cpm without backing,

f_{aw} = factor to correct for losses due to absorption in the air and window of external detectors. It is equal to the ratio of the actual counting rate to that which would be obtained if there were no absorption by the air and window between the source and sensitive volume of the detector. Expressed in terms of absorption coefficient and density of absorber, $f_{aw} = e^{-\mu x}$, where

μ = absorption coefficient, in square centimeters per milligram, and x = absorber density in milligrams per square centimeter.

f_d = factor to correct a spread source counting rate to the counting rate of the same activity as a point source on the same axis of the system,

f_{ssa} = factor to correct for the absorption and scatter of beta particles within the material accompanying the radioactive element, and

f_c = factor for coincident events to correct the counting rate for instrument resolving time losses and defined by the simplified equation, $f_c = 1 - n\tau$, where n = the observed counts per minute, and τ = instrument resolving time in minutes. Generally, the sample size or source to detector distance is varied to obtain a counting rate that precludes coincident losses. Information on the effect of random disintegration and instrument resolving time on the sample count rate as well as methods for determining the resolving time of the counting system may be found in the literature.

In tracer studies or tests requiring only relative measurements in which the data are expressed as being equivalent to a defined standard, the above correction factors can be simply combined into a counting efficiency factor. The use of a counting efficiency factor requires that sample mounting, density of mounting dish, weight of residue in milligrams per square centimeter, and radionuclide composition, in addition to conditions affecting the above described factors, remain constant throughout the duration of the test and that the comparative standard be prepared for counting in the same manner as the test samples. The data from comparative studies between independent laboratories, when not expressed in absolute units, are more meaningful when expressed as percentage relationships or as the equivalent of a defined standard. Expressing the data in either of these two ways minimizes the differences in counters and other equipment and in techniques used by the laboratories conducting the tests.

(b) The limit of sensitivity for both Geiger-Müller and proportional counters is a function of the background counting rate. Massive shielding or anti-coincidence detectors and circuitry, or both, are generally used to reduce the background counting rate to increase the sensitivity.

Interferences

5. (a) Material interposed between the test sample and the instrument detector, as well as increasing density in the sample containing the beta emitter, produces significant losses in sample counting rates. Liquid samples must be evaporated to dryness in dishes that allow the sample to be "seen" directly by the detector. Since the absorption of beta particles in the sample solids increases with increasing density and varies inversely with the maximum beta energy, plated solids must remain constant between related test samples and should duplicate the density of the solids of the plated standard.

(b) Most beta radiation counters are sensitive to alpha, gamma, and X-ray radiations, with the degree of efficiency dependent upon the type of detector.[2] The effect of these interfering radiations on the beta counting rate is more easily evaluated with external-type counters where appropriate absorbers can be used to evaluate the effects of interfering radiation.

Apparatus

6. (a) Beta Particle Counter, consisting of the following components:

(1) Detector.—The end-window Geiger-Müller tube and the internal or external proportional gas-flow chambers are the two most prevalent commercially available types of detector. The material used in the construction of the detector should be free from detectable radioactivity. When detectors contain windows the manufacturer must supply the window density expressed in milligrams per square centimeter. To establish freedom from undesirable characteristics, the manufacturer shall supply voltage plateau and background counting rate data. The background counting rate data will include ten 10-min counts and one 8-hr or longer count with the detector tube protected by a 2-in. thick lead shield lined with $\frac{1}{8}$-in. thick aluminum. Voltage plateau data shall show the threshold voltage, slope, and length of plateau. The detectors requiring external positioning of the test sample shall be mounted on a tube support of low-density material (aluminum or plastic) and positioned so the center of the window is directly above the center of the test sample. The distance between the detector window and test sample plays an important part in determining the geometry of the system and can be varied for external counters to correspond more favorably with such factors as activity level, source size, sensitivity requirements, energy of beta particles, etc. A convenient arrangement is to combine the tube mount with a sample holder containing slots for positioning the sample at three or four distances from the detector window, varying from approximately 0.2 to 4 in. from tube flange.

(2) Detector Shield.—The detector assembly shall be surrounded by an

external radiation shield of massive metal equivalent to approximately 2 in. of lead and lined with ⅛-in. thick aluminum. The material of construction should be free from detectable radioactivity. The shield shall have a door or port for inserting or removing specimens. Detectors having other than completely opaque windows are light-sensitive. The design of the shield and its openings should eliminate direct light paths to the detector window; beveling of door and opening generally is satisfactory. The percentage of the beta particles scattered from the walls of the shield into the detector can be reduced by increasing the internal diameter of the shield. The use of a detector without a shield must be considered as a non-referee method.

(3) *Scaler.*—Normally the scaler, mechanical register, power supply, and amplifier are contained in a single chassis, generally termed the scaler. The power supply and amplifier sections are matched by the manufacturer with the type of detector to produce satisfactory operating characteristics and to provide sufficient range in adjustments to maintain controlled conditions. The manufacturer shall provide resolving time information for the counting system. The scaler shall have capacity for storing and visually displaying at least 5×10^5 counts with a scaling ratio of 64 or greater (preferably 1000) and with a resolving time no greater than 250 microseconds for use with Geiger-Müller detectors or 5 microseconds for use with proportional detectors. The instrument should have an adjustable input sensitivity matched and set by the manufacturer to that of the detector, and a variable high-voltage power supply with indicating meter.

(b) *Sample Mounting Dishes*, having a flat bottom of a diameter no greater than that of the detector window, preferably having ⅛-in. high side walls with the angle between dish bottom and side equal to or greater than 120 deg to reduce side-wall scattering (Note 5). Dishes should be of a material that will not corrode under the plating conditions and should be of uniform surface density preferably great enough to reach backscatter saturation.[2]

Note 5.—Sample dishes with vertical side walls may be used, but the exact positioning of these dishes relative to the detector is very important. This factor becomes critical for dishes having the same diameter as the detector. Dishes having side walls more than ⅛ in. in height are not recommended.

(c) *Alpha Particle Absorber*, aluminum or plastic, having a uniform density such that total absorbing medium (air plus window plus absorber) between sample and sensitive volume of detector is approximately equal to 7 mg per sq cm of aluminum. The absorber diameter should be equal to or greater than the detector window and should be placed against the window to minimize scattering of the beta particles by the absorber. This absorber should not be used when counting beta particles with maximum energies below 0.35 Mev, due to the high-count rate loss by absorption (about 48 per cent at 0.35 Mev in 7 mg per sq cm of aluminum). The alpha particle absorber is not recommended for use with internal beta particle detectors, especially when either the composition or activity ratios of the radioelements or radioactivity level might vary significantly between samples. Chemical separation of the alpha and beta particle emitters produces a higher degree of accuracy for internal detector measurements. Published information[2] on beta particle absorption should be used as a guide for use of this absorber.

Reagents

7. (a) *Purity of Reagents.*—Reagent grade chemicals shall be used in all tests.

Unless otherwise indicated, it is intended that all reagents shall conform to the specifications of the Committee on Analytical Reagents of the American Chemical Society, where such specifications are available.[4] Other grades may be used, provided it is first ascertained that the reagent is free of radioactivity and of sufficiently high purity to preclude detrimental effects).

Note 6.—Some chemicals, even of high purity, contain naturally occurring radioactive elements, for example, rare earths and potassium compounds. Also, some chemical reagents, including organic compounds, have been found to be contaminated with artificially produced radionuclides. Consequently, when carrier chemicals are used in the analysis of low-radioactivity samples, the radioactivity of the carriers should be determined under identical analytical conditions as used for the sample, including amounts of residual solids in the dish. The radioactivity of the reagents may be considered as background and subtracted from the test sample counting rate. This increased background, of course, reduces the sensitivity of the measurement.

(b) Purity of Water.—Unless otherwise indicated, reference to water shall be understood to mean reagent water conforming to the Specifications for Reagent Water (ASTM Designation: D 1193).[3]

(c) Nitric Acid (sp gr 1.42).—Concentrated nitric acid (HNO_3).

Sampling

8. (a) Collect the sample in accordance with the applicable method of the American Society for Testing and Materials as follows:

D 510—Sampling Industrial Water,[3]
D 860—Sampling Water from Boilers,[3]

---

[4] "Reagent Chemicals, American Chemical Society Specifications," Am. Chemical Soc., Washington, D. C. For suggestions on the testing of reagents not listed by the American Chemical Society, see "Reagent Chemicals and Standards," by Joseph Rosin, D. Van Nostrand Co., Inc., New York, N. Y., and the "United States Pharmacopeia."

D 1496—Sampling Homogeneous Industrial Waste Water.[3]

(b) Preserve the sample in a radioactively homogeneous state.

Note 7.—A sample may be made radioactively homogeneous by addition of a reagent in which the radioelements or compounds of the radioelements present in the sample would be soluble in large concentrations. Addition of acids, complexing agents, or chemically similar stable carriers may be used to obtain homogeneity. Consideration of the chemical nature of the radioelements and compounds present and the subsequent chemistry of the method will indicate the action to be taken. The addition of chemicals corrosive to the mounting dish should be avoided to prevent increased absorption of beta particles by the increased residual solids.

Establishing Counter Controls

9. (a) Put the instrument into operation according to the manufacturer's instructions. Place the counter control standard (Note 8) having an approximate disintegration rate of 10,000 disintegrations per minute in the counting position closest to the detector and turn the "count" switch to "count" position. Slowly increase the high voltage until the first counts are observed and record the "threshold" voltage. Raise the voltage 20 to 25 v (or some other convenient unit) above threshold, turn "count" switch off, reset the scaler to zero, and determine the count rate. Advance the voltage in small equal increments of convenient size (20 or 25 v), determining the count rate at each voltage. The count rate should rise initially, reach an approximately constant value (plateau), and then increase rapidly at the end of the plateau. The operating time at voltages above the plateau should be minimized to avoid extensive arcing of the detector. If the plateau is 150 v in length, additional measurements are not necessary.

Note 8.—The counter control standard may be any available radionuclide having a high percentage of beta particle emission, a half-life sufficiently long to minimize decay corrections, and a maximum beta particle energy above 0.5 Mev. Knowledge of its true beta disintegration rate is not essential. The radionuclide should be fixed permanently to the dish and distributed uniformly over an area preferably smaller than the dish bottom; electrodeposition and flaming of a salt-free solution are the two methods most generally used. The standard may be covered by thin aluminum or plastic of sufficient thickness to exclude any alpha particles originating from the source and to protect against damage. The dish should be securely mounted for reproducible positioning. Any loss of activity in the control standard, other than by natural decay, requires establishment of a new control chart (see Section 10). For external counters, the ratio of control standard source diameter to detector window diameter should not exceed 0.33 to avoid the effect of a spread source on the counting geometry.

(b) Plot the counting rate of the control standard against the indicated voltage. The voltage setting that corresponds to a value approximately 75 v above the "knee" of the curve should be used as the operating voltage, provided this voltage is 50 v below the highest voltage on the plateau; otherwise the operating voltage should be that at approximately the mid-point of the plateau (Note 9). A plateau slope of less than 3 per cent per 100 v is desirable, but slopes between 3 and 6 per cent per 100 v can be tolerated if a stable power supply is used. The voltage plateau and operating voltage of the instrument should be checked on a regular schedule determined by experience and after any repair or major adjustment of the instrument. Shortening of the plateau length or an increase in slope are indications of a deteriorating detector.

NOTE 9.—The counting life of a detector may be shortened by operation at a voltage higher than required for reliable performance. Consequently, the lowest voltage that meets the above conditions and will provide reproducible data should be chosen as the operating voltage.

Control of Instrument Operation

10. (a) Control charts are used to assure uniform daily operation of the instrument. Obtain the background counting rate (N_b) from a 10-min count at the selected operating voltage, using a clean mounting dish in the sample-counting position. Replace the background plate with the control standard, take ten 10-min measurements (N_T), and calculate the average net counting rate $(N_T - N_b)_A$ and average total counts $(N_T)_A$ for a 10-min period. Then calculate the 95 and 99 per cent confidence limits as follows:

$$E = K \frac{\sqrt{(N_T)_A}}{t}$$

where:
$(N_T)_A$ = average total counts for 10-min period,
E = error in a single measurement,
t = length of count, in minutes, and
K = confidence factor (Note 10).

NOTE 10.—The confidence factor, K, is as follows:

Level, per cent	K
68.3	1
90	1.645
95	1.96
99	2.575

(b) On a linear graph of counts per minute versus time in days, plot the average net counts per minute and the upper and lower 95 and 99 per cent confidence limits for the first day and extend lines a short distance to the right at these count rates. Each daily standard measurement or the average of three successive measurements that fall within the 95 per cent confidence limits indicate normal instrument operation. The instrument is suspect of malfunctioning when a standard measurement falls outside the 99 per cent limit and a sufficient number of control and back-

24-24

ground measurements are taken to define operating characteristics. The half-life of the radionuclide of the control standard will dictate the frequency of decay corrections applied to the data of the control chart. The counting rate of the control standard and background must be checked daily, but the operating voltage or new control chart requires determination only if the standard falls outside the described limits or major instrument repairs occur.

Calibration and Standardization for General Measurements

11. Place a known amount of strontium-90—yttrium-90 standard (approximately 5×10^{-3} μc) into a volume of water sufficient to dissolve salts equivalent to those of the test samples and prepare for counting as directed in Section 13. Throughout the experiment, the evaporation, mounting, counting, and density of plate solids of this reference standard must be identical with those of the test samples. Count for a length of time required to produce the desired statistical reliability. The combined efficiency factor is then expressed as a percentage of the disintegration rate of the reference standard.

Calibration and Standardization for Tracer Experiments

12. Add a known quantity of activity of a reference solution of the tracer (approximately 5×10^{-3} μc) to a radioactivity-free standard test sample and process as described in Section 13.

Procedure

13. (a) Place an appropriate volume of the test specimen in a glass beaker, make 0.5 M with HNO_3, and evaporate to 1 to 2 ml. Quantitatively transfer to the mounting dish and evaporate to dryness. The heat should be adjusted carefully to avoid spattering or boiling. A ring heater having a continuously variable voltage control, or adjustable infrared heat lamps, is the preferable heat source for the final evaporation and drying. Uniform spreading of the residual salts is necessary for reliable comparative data. The salts should be thoroughly mixed to assure uniform and homogeneous distribution of the radioactive nuclides in the deposit. Inhomogeneity may result in poor reproducibility. Hygroscopic solids should be cooled in a dry atmosphere and stored in a desiccator until the start of counting. Place the sample in the counter and count for a time interval sufficient to obtain the desired statistical reliability. Record the reading of the register and any other indication of accumulated counts (usually interpolation lights). Transfer of large volume samples to smaller beakers as evaporation nears completion makes for easier transfer of the test specimen to the mounting dish. All transfers should be made with reagent water. The sample size should be chosen with consideration for the absorption of beta particles in the residual solids. Information[2] on the range-energy relationship of beta particles in aluminum should be used as a guide to obtain the desired results.

(b) Precipitation methods may be used to expediently concentrate the radioactive material into small amounts of precipitate. The precipitate is separated and washed free of precipitant by centrifugation or filtration. The method of separation should be chosen that will produce a uniform deposit of precipitate after quantitatively transferring to the mounting dish or filter paper for counting. Calibration of the instrument must be made under counting conditions identical to those of the samples. More detailed information on the techniques and equipment for separation and

24–83

mounting of the precipitate may be found in the literature.[2]

Calculations

14. Results may be expressed in observed counts per minute per milliliter. This method is useful for comparing activities of a group of samples, as in tracer experiments. Results may also be reported in terms of equivalent strontium-90—yttrium-90 activity or other standard radionuclide activity, using the empirical efficiency determined by use of a reference standard. If it is known that only one nuclide is present, its disintegration rate may be determined by use of the efficiency factor determined from a reference standard of that nuclide obtained from the National Bureau of Standards or other supplier. The results may be calculated as follows:

$$\text{Beta activity, cpm} = \frac{A}{t} - B$$

$$\text{Beta activity, cpm per ml} = \frac{1}{V}\left(\frac{A}{t} - B\right)$$

where:

cpm = net counts per minute,
A = total counts accumulated,
B = background, in counts per minute,
t = time of counting, in minutes, and
V = milliliters of test specimen.

Beta activity as equivalent strontium-90—

$$\text{yttrium-90, dpm per ml} = \frac{C}{E_{Sr-Y}}$$

where:

dpm = disintegrations per minute,
E_{Sr-Y} = efficiency of counter for strontium-90—yttrium-90 in equilibrium (fraction), and
C = beta activity of test sample, in counts per minute per milliliter.

Beta activity as radionuclide x, dpm per ml

$$= \frac{C}{E_x}$$

where:

E_x = efficiency of counter for radionuclide x (fraction) and
C = beta activity of test sample, in counts per minute per milliliter.

Conversion of dpm to microcuries:

$$\text{Microcuries per ml} = \frac{\text{dpm per ml}}{2.22 \times 10^6}$$

Precision and Accuracy

15. Precision of counting-rate determinations is given in the literature.[2] Accuracy is calculated from the accuracy of the standard (data furnished by supplier) combined with the precision and accuracy of the method and measurement. The accuracy of any beta measurement is also dependent upon the number of nuclides present combined with the various types of energies of radiation, with the accuracy decreasing as the number of combinations increases.

Standard Method of Test for
HEXANE-EXTRACTABLE MATTER IN INDUSTRIAL WASTE WATER[1]

ASTM Designation: D 1891 – 63

ADOPTED, 1963

This Standard of the American Society for Testing and Materials is issued under the fixed designation D 1891; the final number indicates the year of original adoption as standard or, in the case of revision, the year of last revision.

Scope

1. (*a*) This method covers the gravimetric determination of hexane-extractable matter[2] separated from industrial waste water. The hexane-extractable matter may contain material not normally classified as "oily matter."

(*b*) The method is applicable to the determination of relatively nonvolatile hydrocarbons, hydrocarbon derivatives, grease, and unctuous substances in industrial waste water in the range of from 5 to 1000 ppm.

NOTE 1.—The Joint Committee on Uniformity of Methods of Water Examination has concluded that uniformity of methods for the determination of grease and oily matter is not

---

[1] Under the standardization procedure of the Society, this method is under the jurisdiction of the ASTM Committee D-19 on Industrial Water. A list of members may be found in the ASTM Year Book.

[2] The American Society for Testing and Materials agrees with the conclusion reached in November, 1959, by the Joint Committee on Uniformity of Methods of Water Examination, which states that uniformity of methods for the determination of grease and oily matter is not practicable on the basis of present technical knowledge.

practicable on the basis of present technical knowledge.

Commonly used solvents are hexane, petroleum ether, benzene, chloroform, or carbon tetrachloride. These solvents exert selective extraction of specific greases and oily constituents. In addition, nonoily materials, such as phenolic type material and colloidal sulfur, are selectively extracted to varying degrees by these solvents. The selectivity of extraction is affected by the sample-to-solvent ratio.

Oily matter and grease may be of mineral, animal, or vegetable origin. The solvent action exerted on materials of such different chemical structure will vary to a marked degree. Thus, application of a test method for oily matter or grease to such materials will necessarily produce a variety of results depending on the solvent used. In one case, a solvent may be an excellent extractant of mineral oil and a poor extractant of vegetable oil. In another case, a second solvent may be a poor extractant for mineral oil but excellent for extracting vegetable oil.

The definition of grease and oily matter by necessity is based on the procedure used because of the above considerations. The source of the grease or oily matter, the solvent used, the sample-to-solvent ratio, the pH of the sample, and the inclusion of nonoily matter will dictate the material determined and influence the interpretation of the results obtained.

(*c*) The method is not applicable to the determination of light hydrocarbons

686

that may sustain significant loss by evaporation at temperatures below 80 C. It is also not applicable to the determination of oily matter that may undergo profound, rapid chemical changes by oxidation.

Summary of Method

2. The sample is acidified to a pH of 4 or less. The sample is then extracted with hexane, the solvent evaporated from the separated extract, and the residue weighed.

Definitions

3. For definitions of terms used in this method, refer to the Definitions of Terms Relating to Industrial Water and Industrial Waste Water (ASTM Designation: D 1129).[3]

Apparatus

4. (a) *Condenser.*—West-type, 300-mm, 24/40 standard-taper, outer-ground joint at top and 24/40 standard-taper, inner-ground joint at bottom, with drip tip.

(b) *Distillation Flask.*—A 250-ml, flat-bottom flask, with side arm bent so as to end in a vertical, downward opening, 24/40 standard-taper, inner-ground joint.[4]

(c) *Separatory Funnel.*—Squibb-type, 1000-ml, with standard-taper ground stopper and standard-taper ground stopcock (see Note 3).

(d) *Water Bath.*—Thermostatically controlled at approximately 80 C, and of size and shape such that the separatory funnel described in Paragraph (c) can be immersed to the base of its standard-taper mouth.

Reagents and Materials

5. (a) *Purity of Reagents.*—Reagent grade chemicals shall be used in all tests. Unless otherwise indicated, it is intended that all reagents shall conform to the specifications of the Committee on Analytical Reagents of the American Chemical Society, where such specifications are available.[5] Other grades may be used, provided it is first ascertained that the reagent is of sufficiently high purity to permit its use without lessening the accuracy of the determination.

(b) *Purity of Water.*—Unless otherwise specified, references to water shall be understood to mean reagent water conforming to the Specifications for Reagent Water (ASTM Designation: D 1193).[2]

(c) *n-Hexane.*—Distill an appropriate amount of commercial grade *n*-hexane conforming to the requirements listed in Table I. Discard the first 10 per cent and last 20 per cent of the distillate.

(d) *Hydrochloric Acid (1:4).*—Mix 1 volume of concentrated hydrochloric acid (HCl, sp gr 1.19) with 4 volumes of water.

(e) *Methyl Orange Indicator (0.5 g per liter).*—Dissolve 0.05 g of methyl orange in water and dilute to 100 ml.

(f) *Nitrogen.*—Water-pumped nitrogen. Other inert gases such as carbon dioxide or illuminating gas may be substituted for nitrogen.

Sampling

6. Collect the sample in a weighed, glass-stoppered, 1000-ml, wide-mouth Erlenmeyer flask (Note 2). Rinse the flask with *n*-hexane before taking the

---

[3] Appears in this publication.
[4] An ideal distillation flask assembly may be made of standard, heat-resistant glass parts equivalent to Corning Glass Works' Pyrex No. 5000 flask, No. 9060 connecting tube, No. 7570 stopper, and No. 6710 ground joint with sealed tube for introduction of inert gas during final stages of distillation.

[5] "Reagent Chemicals. American Chemical Society Specifications," Am. Chemical Soc., Washington, D. C. For suggestions on the testing of reagents not listed by the American Chemical Society, see "Reagent Chemicals and Standards," by Joseph Rosin, D. Van Nostrand Co., Inc., New York, N. Y., and the "United States Pharmacopeia."

sample. If the sample is to be obtained through a sample line, flush the line thoroughly. Fill the flask to approximately five eighths its height. Otherwise, collect the sample in accordance with the applicable method of the American Society for Testing and Materials as follows:

D 510—Sampling Industrial Water,[2]
D 860—Sampling Water from Boilers.[2]

NOTE 2.—The sample may be collected in a cork-stoppered flask provided the stopper is wrapped in metal foil. A 2000-ml flask may be used when the concentration of hexane-extractable matter is 5 ppm or less.

Procedure

7. (a) If practical, obtain a sample volume that contains at least 20 mg of extractable matter. Weigh the tared flask and sample to the nearest 1 g. Calculate the sample weight by difference.

(b) Transfer the sample to a 1000-ml separatory funnel and adjust its pH to a maximum of 4, if necessary, by adding HCl (1:4) in the presence of methyl orange indicator.

NOTE 3.—Use a 2000-ml separatory funnel if more than 750 ml of sample was collected in accordance with Note 2.

(c) Rinse the Erlenmeyer flask into the separatory funnel with two 20-ml portions of n-hexane. Stopper the funnel and vigorously shake it for 2 min. Allow the hexane and aqueous phases to separate.

NOTE 4.—Some industrial waste waters form relatively stable emulsions at this point. If this occurs, return as much of the clear aqueous phase to the original sample container as possible. Insert a water-cooled condenser in the mouth of the separatory funnel and immerse the funnel in a water bath held at approximately 80 C. Allow the hexane to reflux for a few minutes to break the emulsion. Remove the separatory funnel from the bath, allow it to cool to room temperature, and then remove the condenser. Proceed as directed in Paragraph (d).

(d) Withdraw as much of the clear, aqueous phase into the original sample container as possible. Gently agitate the material left in the separatory funnel to aid in further separation of the aqueous and hydrocarbon phases. As further separation occurs, continue to remove all but 1 ml of the aqueous phase.

NOTE 5.—Add a few milliliters of n-hexane at this point in the procedure, if necessary, to help break any emulsion. If the sample contains an excessive amount of very viscous or solid grease, add more hexane to the hydrocarbon solution prior to removal of the bulk of aqueous solution.

TABLE I.—REQUIREMENTS FOR
n-HEXANE.

Initial boiling point, min, deg Fahr[a]	150
Dry point, max, deg Fahr[a]	156
Nonvolatile matter, max, g per 100 ml[b]	0.001
Color, Saybolt, min[c]	+30

[a] Determined in accordance with the Method of Test for Distillation of Natural Gasoline (ASTM Designation: D 216).[6]
[b] Determined in accordance with the Methods of Sampling and Testing Volatile Solvents for Use in Paint, Varnish, Lacquer, and Related Products (ASTM Designation: D 268).[7]
[c] Determined in accordance with the Method of Test for Saybolt Color of Petroleum Products (Saybolt Chromometer Method) (ASTM Designation: D 156).[6]

(e) Allow ample time for separation of a clear hexane layer. A cloudy layer indicates the presence of moisture, which might contain water-soluble, hexane-insoluble matter. Withdraw, by means of a pipet or suction tube, approximately two thirds of the hexane phase. Transfer this withdrawn material to a weighed, 250-ml distillation flask by filtering it through a small funnel containing hexane-moistened medium-texture, low-ash filter paper. Wash the filter free of

---

[6] 1967 Book of ASTM Standards, Part 17.
[7] 1967 Book of ASTM Standards, Part 20.

hexane-extractable matter with a few milliliters of normal hexane.

(f) Transfer the aqueous solution, return to the original sample container as described in Paragraph (d), and then to the separatory funnel. Repeat the procedure described in Paragraphs (c), (d), and (e) at least twice. Combine all hydrocarbon solutions in the distillation flask. After the last extraction, draw off and discard all of the aqueous phase and transfer the remaining hexane solution to the distillation flask through the paper filter. Finally, wash the paper filter with two small portions of hexane.

(g) Connect the condenser to the side arm of the distillation flask, stopper the mouth of the flask, and apply heat to the flask by means of the water bath or a heating mantle maintained at approximately 80 C. Distill at a rate of 1 drop per sec until a residue of about 2 ml is left in the flask. Discard the distillate.

(h) Continue heating the flask. Introduce a flow of nitrogen through the mouth of the flask and continue the vaporization of the residue in the flask until all traces of liquid hexane have been removed. When the residue is free of liquid hexane, (10 min heating usually is adequate) disconnect the condenser, remove the flask from the heat source, and lay the flask on its side to cool. Continue the flow of nitrogen to facilitate removal of residual hydrocarbon vapors, until the flask has cooled to ambient temperature.

(i) Discontinue the flow of nitrogen and wipe the outside of the flask first with a damp chamois, then with a dry chamois. Place the flask in a desiccator for 30 min; then weigh.

Calculation

8. Calculate the concentration of the hexane-extractable matter, in parts per million, as follows:

Hexane-extractable matter, ppm

$$= \frac{A - B}{S} \times 1{,}000{,}000$$

where:
A = weight of distillation flask plus residue, in grams,
B = weight of distillation flask, in grams, and
S = weight of sample, in grams.

Precision

9. Agreement between laboratories in results obtained by this method for the concentration range of 5 to 1000 ppm will be within ±2 per cent.

Tentative Method for
OPEN CHANNEL FLOW MEASUREMENT OF INDUSTRIAL WATER AND INDUSTRIAL WASTE WATER BY THE PARSHALL FLUME[1]

ASTM Designation: D 1941 – 62 T

ISSUED, 1962

This Tentative Method has been approved by the sponsoring committee and accepted by the Society in accordance with established procedures, for use pending adoption as standard. Suggestions for revisions should be addressed to the Society at 1916 Race St., Philadelphia 3, Pa.

Scope

1. (*a*) This method covers measurement of the rate of flow of industrial water and industrial waste water in open channels at or near the ground surface, using the Parshall venturi-type flume.[2]

(*b*) Since the flume is self-cleaning, it is particularly applicable to liquid industrial wastes containing settleable solids. It has the lowest loss of head of all the commonly used open-channel flow measuring devices and lends itself to continuous recording of flow or manual measurement. Flumes have been perfected with throat widths from 3 in. to 40 ft that accurately measure flows of 0.02, min, to 1300 million gallons per day, respectively. This method covers flume widths from 3 in. to 8 ft.

[1] Under the standardization procedure of the Society, this method is under the jurisdiction of the ASTM Committee D-19 on Industrial Water. A list of members may be found in the ASTM Year Book.

[2] R. L. Parshall, "Measuring Water in Irrigation Channels with Parshall Flumes and Small Weirs," U. S. Dept. of Agriculture Soil Conservation Service, *Circular No. 834* (1950).

General Principles

2. The Parshall flume (Fig. 1), formerly called the improved venturi flume, is a specially constructed measuring flume so designed that the water for free flow discharge conditions (unsubmerged tail water) is forced to pass through the critical depth within the structure. This provides a means by which a determination of the amount of water passing can be made from a single depth measurement, H_a. Under submerged flow discharge, two depth measurements, H_a and H_b, must be made to calculate the flow through the flume.

NOTE 1.—Since these calculations cannot be made with commercially available instruments, submerged conditions should be avoided if possible.

Description of Terms

3. (*a*) The terms "inlet head, H_a, throat head, H_b, and other terms specific to this method are described as follows:

Inlet Head, H_a.—The depth of the fluid stream measured in feet above the crest (zero point) at the upper third point between the inlet to the flume and the crest.

Throat Head, H_b.—The depth of the fluid stream measured in feet above

downsteam end of the floor of the converging section and the upstream end of the throat floor.

Critical Depth.—The depth for any

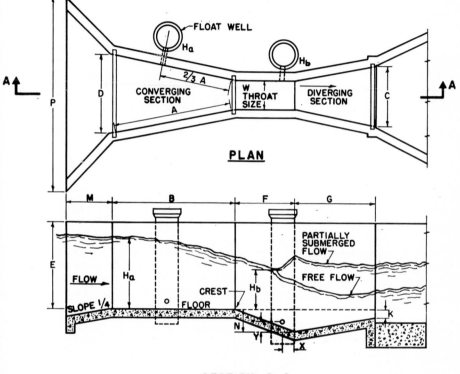

PLAN

SECTION A-A

W—Flume size in inches or feet
A—Length of side wall of converging section
⅔A—Distance back from end of crest to gage point
B—Axial length of converging section
C—Width of downstream end of flume
D—Width of upstream end of flume
E—Depth of flume
F—Length of throat
G—Length of diverging section
H_a—Head above crest at upstream end of flume
H_b—Head above crest at throat section
K—Difference in elevation between lower end of flume and crest
M—Length of approach floor
N—Depth of depression in throat below crest
P—Width between ends of wing walls
X, Y—Horizontal and vertical distances, respectively, from lower end of throat to observation point for H_b.

FIG. 1.—Parshall Measuring Flume.

the crest at a point 2 in. upstream from the junction of the throat and outlet section with exception of the 3 in. flume where this dimension is 1 in.

Crest.—The line of junction of the

particular value of water flow where the specific energy is a minimum.

Free Flow Discharge.—The condition under which the rate of discharge is dependent solely upon the length of crest and depth of water at the gage point H_a in the converging section.

Submerged Flow Discharge.—The condition under which back water develops at H_a and the ratio H_b/H_a exceeds the minimum limit usually 0.6 to 0.7.

(b) For definitions of other terms used in this method, refer to Definitions of Terms Relating to Industrial Water and Industrial Waste Water (ASTM Designation: D 1129).[3]

Apparatus

4. (a) *Parshall Flume (Primary Device)*.—The apparatus consists of the

sunk. Construction should be of reinforced concrete but may be of wood or sheet metal. Stainless steel and plastic liners in concrete or wood flumes are frequently used for extremely corrosive conditions.

NOTE 2.—General economy of construction dictates that the smallest standard throat size be selected provided it is consistent with depth in channel at maximum flow and permissible head loss. Throat widths range from 3 in. to 8 ft. As a general rule, the throat size should be ⅓ to ½ the width of the channel. Downstream elevations should be low enough to maintain free-flow discharge conditions and prevent excessive "backing up" in the diverging section.

TABLE I.—PARSHALL FLUME DIMENSIONS AND CAPACITIES.

W	A	⅔A	B	C	D	E	F	G	K	N	M	P	X	Y	Flume Flow Extremes, million gallons per day	
															Min	Max
					Dimensions in feet and inches											
0-3	1-6⅜	1-¼	1-6	0-7	0-10³⁄₁₆	2-0	0-6	1-0	0-1	0-2¼	1-0	2-6¼	0-1	0-1½	0.02	1.23
0-6	2-7⁄₁₆	1-4⁵⁄₁₆	2-0	1-3½	1-3⅝	2-0	1-0	2-0	0-3	0-4½	1-0	2-11½	0-2	0-3	0.03	2.52
0-9	2-10⅝	1-11⅛	2-10	1-3	1-10⅝	2-6	1-0	1-6	0-3	0-4½	1-0	3-6½	0-2	0-3	0.06	5.75
1-0	4-6	3-0	4-4⅞	2-0	2-9¼	3-0	2-0	3-0	0-3	0-9	1-3	4-10¾	0-2	0-3	0.07	10.41
1-6	4-9	3-2	4-7⅞	2-6	3-4⅜	3-0	2-0	3-0	0-3	0-9	1-3	5-6	0-2	0-3	0.10	15.90
2-0	5-0	3-4	4-10⅞	3-0	3-11½	3-0	2-0	3-0	0-3	0-9	1-3	6-1	0-2	0-3	0.27	21.39
3-0	5-6	3-8	5-4¾	4-0	5-1⅞	3-0	2-0	3-0	0-3	0-9	1-3	7-3½	0-2	0-3	0.39	32.57
4-0	6-0	4-0	5-10⅝	5-0	6-4¼	3-0	2-0	3-0	0-3	0-9	1-6	8-10¾	0-2	0-3	0.84	43.88
5-0	6-6	4-4	6-4½	6-0	7-6⅝	3-0	2-0	3-0	0-3	0-9	1-6	10-1¼	0-2	0-3	1.03	55.32
6-0	7-0	4-8	6-10⅜	7-0	8-9	3-0	2-0	3-0	0-3	0-9	1-6	11-3½	0-2	0-3	1.68	66.89
7-0	7-6	5-0	7-4¼	8-0	9-11⅜	3-0	2-0	3-0	0-3	0-9	1-6	12-6	0-2	0-3	1.94	78.46
8-0	8-0	5-4	7-10⅛	9-0	11-1¾	3-0	2-0	3-0	0-3	0-9	1-6	13-8¼	0-2	0-3	2.26	90.16

Parshall flume, referred to as the primary measuring device, suitably constructed in accordance with standard dimensions given in Table I. The flume should consist of an entrance section with converging walls and level floor, a throat section with parallel walls and down sloping floor, and an exit section with diverging vertical walls and upward sloping floor. The crest should have a smooth, definite edge with all screws and bolts counter-

(b) *Pressure Taps* for instrumentation purposes should be ¾ in. size, horizontal, or sloping downward to stilling or float wells. Taps are made at a point two thirds of the wall length of the converging section upstream from the crest (⅔A as shown in Fig. 1), and at right angles to the wall; they are also made at the downstream end of the throat section. The invert (that is, inside bottom) of the taps should be at the same elevation as the crest and flush with the flume side wall.

---

[3] Appears in this publication.

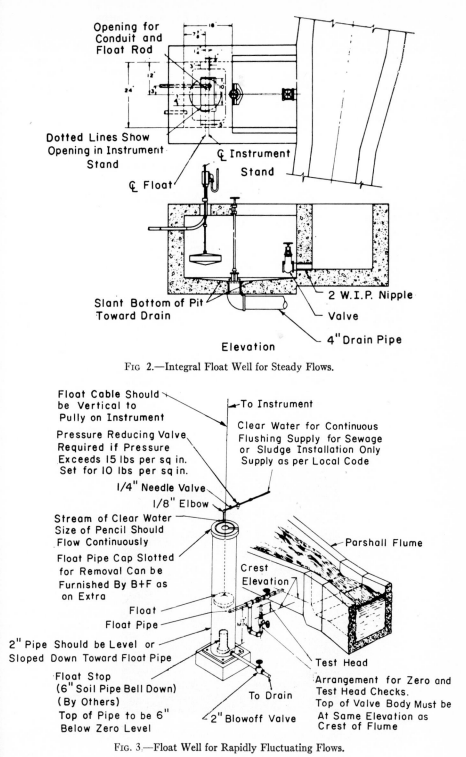

Opening for
Conduit and
Float Rod

Dotted Lines Show
Opening in Instrument
Stand

℄ Instrument
Stand

℄ Float

Slant Bottom of Pit
Toward Drain

2 W.I.P. Nipple

Valve

4" Drain Pipe

Elevation

FIG 2.—Integral Float Well for Steady Flows.

Float Cable Should
be Vertical to
Pully on Instrument

To Instrument

Clear Water for Continuous
Flushing Supply for Sewage
or Sludge Installation Only
Supply as per Local Code

Pressure Reducing Valve
Required if Pressure
Exceeds 15 lbs per sq in.
Set for 10 lbs per sq in.

1/4" Needle Valve

1/8" Elbow

Stream of Clear Water
Size of Pencil Should
Flow Continuously

Parshall Flume

Float Pipe Cap Slotted
for Removal Can be
Furnished By B+F as
on Extra

Crest
Elevation

Float

Float Pipe

Test Head

2" Pipe Should be Level or
Sloped Down Toward Float Pipe

Float Stop
(6" Soil Pipe Bell Down)
(By Others)
Top of Pipe to be 6"
Below Zero Level

To Drain

2" Blowoff Valve

Arrangement for Zero and
Test Head Checks.
Top of Valve Body Must be
At Same Elevation as
Crest of Flume

FIG. 3.—Float Well for Rapidly Fluctuating Flows.

693

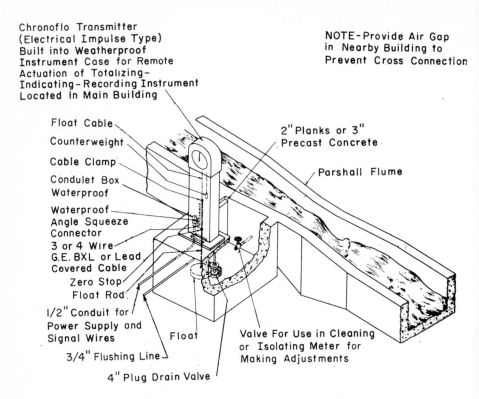

Chronoflo Transmitter
(Electrical Impulse Type)
Built into Weatherproof
Instrument Case for Remote
Actuation of Totalizing-
Indicating- Recording Instrument
Located in Main Building

NOTE-Provide Air Gap
in Nearby Building to
Prevent Cross Connection

Float Cable
Counterweight
Cable Clamp
Condulet Box
Waterproof
Waterproof
Angle Squeeze
Connector
3 or 4 Wire
G.E. BXL or Lead
Covered Cable
Zero Stop
Float Rod
1/2" Conduit for
Power Supply and
Signal Wires
3/4" Flushing Line
4" Plug Drain Valve

Float

2" Planks or 3"
Precast Concrete

Parshall Flume

Valve For Use in Cleaning
or Isolating Meter for
Making Adjustments

FIG. 4.—Typical Installation of Transmitter-Indicator Chronoflo Instruments for Parshall Flumes.

FIG. 5.—Typical Installation of In-Stream Transmitter Chronoflo Instruments for Parshall Flumes

Instrumentation

5. (a) The float well volume should be influenced by the existing conditions of flow, for example, for rapidly varying rates of flow, the volume should be small so that the instrument float can respond quickly to changes in rate (Note 3). For a relatively steady flow, a large volume integral stilling chamber constructed from concrete can be used. Both types are shown in Figs. 2 and 3. The instrument float may be installed directly in the flume as shown in Figs. 4 and 5.

NOTE 3.—To eliminate float lateral drift and consequent metering errors because of cable extension, the diameter of the float well should be only large enough to accommodate the float and allow for its free vertical travel. Suitable drain and shutoff valves should be provided to empty and flush out the float wells. For sewage or sludge-measuring installations, a clear water continuous flushing supply is generally discharged into the float well to prevent solids from accumulating and plugging the tap connections.

(b) Float-actuated measuring instruments should be used to convert liquid levels (sensed variable) from the primary device (Parshall flume) into observable flow information. Indicating, totalizing recording types, or combinations may be considered.

(c) An indicator gage is calibrated in inches of liquid level or flow units directly, that is, in gallons per minute or cubic feet per second for the particular flume.

(d) A totalizing-type measuring instrument meter is equipped with an integrator calibrated to convert the variable (liquid level) in the Parshall flume into gallons and mechanically register the total number of units of flow in gallons. The difference in counter readings over a period of time multiplied by an integrator factor represents the total flow for that period of time.

(e) A recording-type measuring instrument is calibrated to convert the variable (liquid level) in the primary device to gallons and provide a record of changes in conditions throughout a 24-hr period. The recorder chart is linear with scale divisions spaced equally to record the flow rate in gallons.

A totalizer, indicator, recorder-type flowmeter is calibrated to convert the sensed variable (liquid level) in the flume to gallons. The instrument indicates the flow, totalizes the total number of units of flow in gallons and provides a visible record of changes of conditions throughout a 24-hr period.

(f) The choice of instrument will depend upon several factors, including the method used to transmit the sensed variable to the measuring instrument (receiver), relative location of measuring instrument and receiver, the type of information desired, the range of variable, that is, the ratio of maximum to minimum of the variable being measured must be known, whether 4 to 1, 10 to 1, etc., the accuracy desired, and the instrument function as part of a control system.

(g) The motion of a float riding on the liquid surface in the flume or stilling wells of the Parshall flume is generally transmitted to the measuring instrument (receiver) directly by cable, tape, or float rod. A float-rod type directly connected to a transmitter is shown in Figs. 4 and 5. In Fig. 5 the float rides directly in the flume at the proper gaging location to give more rapid response to liquid level changes.

(h) The instrument receiver may be utilized in a location remote from the Parshall Flume, and information may be transmitted from the measuring instrument to the secondary instrument receiver electrically or pneumatically as follows:

Electrical Transmission: The measuring instrument may include an electrical transmitter connected with a remotely located secondary receiver actuated by a timed electrical impulse (Chronoflo Telemeter). The duration of the electrical impulse is proportional to the magnitude of the measured variable; in this case, water level.

Pneumatic Transmission: Transmission by air pressure is effective up to about 1000 ft. The instrument makes use of varying-controlled air pressure

ing discharge. When free flow exists, the rate of discharge can be taken directly from the chart in Fig. 6. When the ratio is greater than these values, the indicated discharge must be lessened because of the effect of submergence. The empirical formulas for the free flow discharge from Parshall flumes are as follows[4]:

$W = 3$ in.—free flow discharge in cubic feet per second $= 0.992\ H_a^{1.547}$

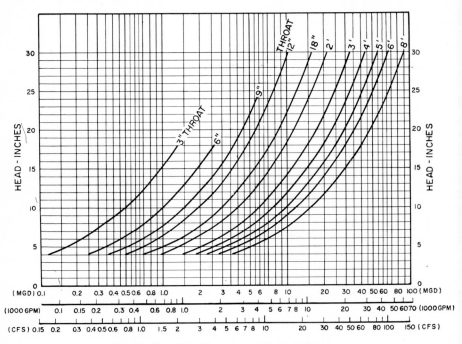

FIG. 6.—Free Flow Capacity for Parshall Flumes

ranging from 3 to 15 psi. Changes in pressure output of the transmitter are proportional to changes in the measured variable level. No wires are used; the output signal (pressure) is continuous and extremely sensitive to change in the measured variable.

Procedure

6. (*a*) A gage reading for water level above the crest (floor of the flume) at point H_a (Fig. 1) is required for comput-

$W = 6$ in.—free flow discharge in cubic feet per second $= 2.06\ H_a^{1.58}$

$W = 9$ in.—free flow discharge in cubic feet per second $= 3.07\ H_a^{1.53}$

$W = 1$ ft to 8 ft—free flow discharge in cubic feet per second $= 4W\ H_a^{1.522L^{.026}}$

$W = 8$ ft and larger—free flow discharge in cubic feet per second $= (3.6875W + 2.5)\ H_a^{1.6}$

where:

$W =$ flume crest width in feet, and

---

[4] See R. L. Parshall, Eq 38 to 42, incl.

Upper Head (Ha, Feet)

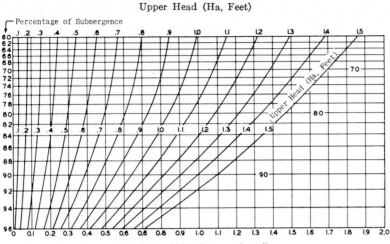

NOTE.—The number of cubic feet per second × 449 = gallons per minute.
FIG. 7.—Rate of Submerged Flow Through a 3-in. Parshall Measuring Flume.

Upper Head (Ha, Feet)

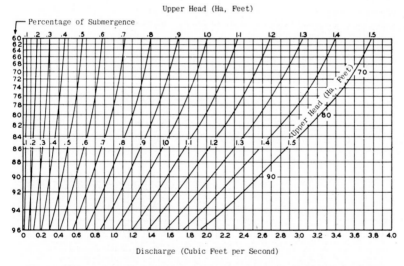

NOTE.—The number of cubic feet per second × 449 = gallons per minute.
FIG. 8.—Rate of Submerged Flow Through a 6-in. Parshall Measuring Flume.

H_a = head above crest upstream from throat in feet.

(b) For submerged flow conditions, readings H_a and H_b upstream and downstream from the throat shall be taken and the ratio H_b/H_a determined. Submerged flow conditions exist when the ratio exceeds 0.6 for the 3 to 9-in. flumes and 0.7 for the 1 to 8-ft flumes. The corrected computed discharges are obtained directly from Figs. 7, 8, and 9 for flumes having 3, 6, and 9-in. throats.

The percentage of submergence is shown on the ordinate. Values for H_a are given on the curves. Discharges in cubic feet per second are given on the abscissa. Figure 10 gives the correction to be subtracted from the free flow discharge for a flume with 1-ft throat operating under submerged conditions. For wider throats, the correction for the 1-ft flume is determined and multiplied by the factor M taken from Table II.[2]

Calibration

7. (*a*) To meet accuracy standards, it is recommended that each Parshall flume be calibrated in place if the discharge can be directly measured by other methods.

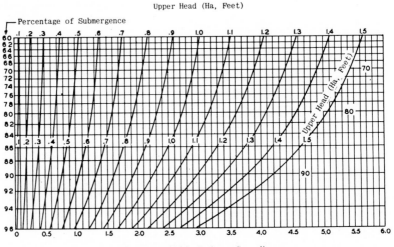

NOTE.—The number of cubic feet per second × 449 = gallons per minute.
FIG. 9.—Rate of Submerged Flow Through a 9-in. Parshall Measuring Flume.

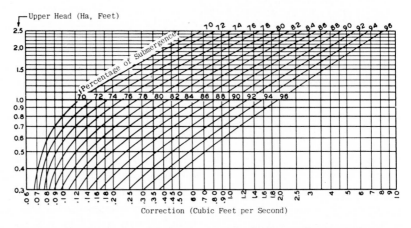

NOTE.—The number of cubic feet per second × 449 = gallons per minute.
FIG. 10.—Correction to Rate of Submerged Flow Through a 1-ft Parshall Measuring Flume.

(b) For calibration purposes, the application of the volumetric method or comparative salt dilution method of flow measurement is recommended. The volumetric method is applicable only when there is available a reservoir of regular form, the volume of which, up to various levels, may be accurately

TABLE II.—CORRECTION FACTORS FOR SUBMERGED FLOWS.

Flume Size, W, ft	Multiplying Factor, M
1	1.0
1.5	1.4
2	1.8
3	2.4
4	3.1
5	3.7
6	4.3
7	4.9
8	5.4

measured within an error of 1.0 per cent. The drawdown during the test run should not cause a variation in head on the flume floor in excess of 4 per cent of the head during any run. The availability of a reservoir of regular form with sufficient storage capacity to meet these conditions places a limit on the

size of flume which can be accurately calibrated by this method to about 1 ft.

(c) For flumes larger than 1 ft in throat width, the comparative salt dilution or chemical method is recommended for calibration purposes. Thorough mixing of the salt solution in the flowing stream and accurate analysis of samples taken at the sampling station downstream from the flume are essential for measurement of flow rates within ±2 per cent.

Accuracy

8. The accuracy of a Parshall flume is directly tied to the accuracy of construction. It is important to keep as close as possible to the dimensions given in Table I. If concrete construction is used, the surfaces should be smooth. Under good construction practices, the accuracy would be about 3 per cent. However, the head relation for a given Parshall flume installation may vary from the indicated relation given in Figs. 4 through 8 by as much as 5 per cent. This is considered well within the accuracy of many flow measuring methods.

Tentative Method of Test for
MORPHOLINE IN INDUSTRIAL WATER[1]

ASTM Designation: D 1942 – 62 T

IssUED, 1962

This Tentative Method has been approved by the sponsoring committee and accepted by the Society in accordance with established procedures, for use pending adoption as standard. Suggestions for revisions should be addressed to the Society at 1916 Race St., Philadelphia 3, Pa.

Scope

1. (a) This method covers a colorimetric procedure for the determination of morpholine in boiler feedwater and steam condensate.

(b) The method may be applied to waters containing morpholine in concentrations from 1 to 5 ppm. Higher concentrations may be determined by dilution.

Summary of Method

2. Carbon disulfide and morpholine react to form a thiocarbamate which reacts with an excess of copper to form an amber to brown compound. The intensity of the color is proportional to the amount of morpholine in the water. In order to obtain the reaction with carbon disulfide, the solution should have a pH of approximately 9.2 to 9.3.

Definitions

3. For definitions of terms used in this method, refer to the Definitions of Terms Relating to Industrial Water and Industrial Waste Water (ASTM Designation: D 1129).[2]

Interferences

4. (a) Substances normally present in boiler feedwater and steam do not interfere with test.

(b) The basic reactions of the test are common to octadecylamine and other long chain aliphatic amines, as well as to short chain primary, secondary, and tertiary amines.

Apparatus

5. (a) *Filter Photometer or Spectrophotometer*, suitable for measurement at a wavelength of 430 mμ (Note 1).

NOTE 1.—Photometers prescribed in this method shall conform to the Recommended Practice for Photometric Methods for Chemical Analysis of Metals (ASTM Designation: E 60).[3]

(b) *Shaker*, reciprocating, adjusted for shaking at the rate of 280 (±5) oscillations per minute with a horizontal stroke of 1 in.

---

[1] Under the standardization procedure of the Society, this method is under the jurisdiction of the ASTM Committee D-19 on Industrial Water. A list of members may be found in the ASTM Year Book.

[2] Appears in this publication.
[3] 1967 Book of ASTM Standards, Part 32.

52-36

Reagents and Materials

6. (a) *Purity of Reagents.*—Reagent grade chemicals shall be used in all tests. Unless otherwise indicated, it is intended that all reagents shall conform to the specifications of the Committee on Analytical Reagents of the American Chemical Society, where such specifications are available.[4] Other grades may be used, provided it is first ascertained that the reagent is of sufficiently high purity to permit its use without lessening the accuracy of the determination.

(b) *Purity of Water.*—Unless otherwise indicated, references to water shall be understood to mean reagent water conforming to the Specifications for Reagent Water (ASTM Designation: D 1193).[2]

(c) *Carbon Disulfide* (CS_2).

(d) *Copper Sulfate Solution (2.0 g per liter).*—Dissolve 2.0 g of copper sulfate ($CuSO_4 \cdot 5H_2O$) in water and dilute to 1 liter.

(e) *Hydrochloric Acid, Standard Solution (0.5 N).*[5]—Add 41.7 ml of concentrated hydrochloric acid (HCl, sp gr 1.19) to 200 ml of water, dilute to 1 liter, and mix well. Determine the exact normality by titration, using methyl orange as an indicator, against sodium carbonate (Na_2CO_3) prepared by heating sodium bicarbonate ($NaHCO_3$) for 2 hr at 270 C.

(f) *Methyl Orange Indicator (0.5 g per liter).*[5]—Dissolve 0.05 g of methyl orange in water and dilute to 100 ml with water.

(g) *Methyl Red Indicator (1 g per liter).*[5]—Dissolve 0.1 g of water-soluble methyl red in water and dilute to 100 ml with water.

(h) *Morpholine, Standard Solution (1 ml = 0.001 g morpholine).*—Weigh 1.099 g of 91 per cent morpholine using a weighing bottle, wash into a 1-liter volumetric flask, and dilute to volume with water. If the morpholine is not 91 per cent, apply the appropriate factor in preparing the standard solution. Check the strength of the undiluted morpholine as follows:

Pipet 50 ml of 0.5 N HCl into a 250-ml Erlenmeyer flask. Add 1 drop of methyl red indicator and from a tared Lunge pipet add up to 2 g of the morpholine directly into the acid. Reweigh the Lunge pipet to determine the sample size. Swirl the flask and observe the color of the solution which should be pink or red; a yellow-colored solution indicates that the sample size is excessive. Heat the solution to boiling and boil gently for approximately 1 min to remove carbon dioxide. Titrate immediately with 0.5 N NaOH to the yellow end point.

Morpholine, per cent

$$= \frac{(A \times a) - (B \times b) \times 8.712}{S}$$

where:

A = milliliters of HCl used,

a = normality of the HCl,

B = milliliters of NaOH required for titration of the sample,

b = normality of the NaOH, and

S = grams of sample used.

(i) *Phenolphthalein Indicator (5.0 g per liter).*[5]—Dissolve 0.5 g of phenolphthalein in 50 ml of 95 per cent ethyl alcohol (Note 2) and dilute to 100 ml with water.

NOTE 2.—Specially denatured ethyl alcohol conforming to Formula No. 3A or 30 of the U. S. Bureau of Internal Revenue may be substituted for 95 per cent ethyl alcohol.

(j) *Sodium Borate Solution (40 g per liter).*—Prepare a solution, saturated at

---

[4] "Reagent Chemicals, American Chemical Society Specifications," Am. Chemical Soc., Washington, D. C. For suggestions on the testing of reagents not listed by the American Chemical Society, see "Reagent Chemicals and Standards," by Joseph Rosin, D. Van Nostrand Co., Inc., New York, N. Y. and the "United States Pharmacopeia."

[5] Reagent used for standardization purposes only.

room temperature, of 40 g of sodium borate ($Na_2B_4O_7 \cdot 10H_2O$) per liter. Adjust the pH of this solution to 9.5 using 0.5 N NaOH.

(k) *Sodium Hydroxide, Standard Solution (0.5 N).*—Prepare a saturated solution by dissolving 162 g of sodium hydroxide (NaOH) in 150 ml of carbon dioxide (CO_2)-free water (Note 3). Cool to 25 C and filter through a gooch crucible, hardened filter paper, or other suitable medium. Pipet 27.25 ml of the filtered solution into a volumetric flask and make up to 1 liter with CO_2-free water. Mix well and store in a polyethylene or heavily waxed bottle; protect the solution by providing a soda-asbestos or soda-lime bulb at the air inlet.

The NaOH may be standardized as follows: Crush 5 g of a National Bureau of Standards certified sample of potassium biphthalate to pass a No. 100 (149-μ) sieve and dry in a glass container at 120 C for 2 hr. Stopper the container and cool in a desiccator. Weigh accurately 1.95 ± 0.05 g of the dried potassium biphthalate and transfer to a 400-ml beaker. Add 100 ml of CO_2-free water, stir gently to dissolve the sample, add 3 drops phenolphthalein indicator, and titrate to a faint pink color with the NaOH solution.

Calculate the normality, N. of the NaOH as follows:

$$N = \frac{A}{0.20433 \times B}$$

where:
A = grams of potassium biphthalate used, and
B = milliliters of NaOH required for titration of the sample.

NOTE 3.—Carbon dioxide-free water may be prepared by heating water contained in a conical flask to boiling and then boiling vigorously for 20 min. The boiled water is cooled in the flask which is stoppered with a 1-hole

rubber stopper fitted to a soda-lime or soda-asbestos tube.

(l) *Wetting Agent Solution.*[6]

Sampling

7. Collect the sample in accordance with the applicable method of the American Society for Testing and Materials, as follows:

D 510 —Sampling Industrial Water,[2]
D 1066—Sampling Steam.[2]

Preparation of Calibration Curve

8. (a) Prepare a series of morpholine standards by dilution with suitable volumes of morpholine-free water. The series should cover the range of 1 to 5 ppm of morpholine.

(b) Treat each reference standard as described in Section 9.

(c) Prepare a calibration curve by plotting the readings on the photometer versus the concentration of morpholine. When the scale of the photometer reads directly in absorbance, plot the results on rectilinear paper. When the scale reads in transmittance, plot the results on semilog paper, using the single cycle log axis to plot transmittance and the linear axis to plot the concentrations.

Procedure

9. (a) Pipet 100 ml of sample into an 8-oz glass bottle having a polyethylene-lined cap and add successively 5 ml of saturated $Na_2B_4O_7$-solution and 0.5 ml of CS_2. Mix thoroughly by shaking 5 min on a shaker and remove.

(b) Add 1 ml of $CuSO_4$ solution; shake vigorously by hand for 30 sec., let stand for 1 min, and then add 1 drop of wetting agent solution from a USP eyedropper having a 3-mm opening.

[6] Triton X-100 manufactured by Rohm & Haas Co., Phila., Pa., and Pluronic L-62 manufactured by Wyandotte Chemicals Corp., Wyandotte, Mich. have been found satisfactory for this purpose.

(c) Mix thoroughly by shaking 4 min on the shaker, remove, and pour contents into a 125-ml separatory funnel. Allow to stand for 1 min, shake vigorously by hand for 15 sec, and let stand for 1 min.

(d) Draw off the sample and read the intensity of the color in a filter photometer or spectrophotometer within 3 to 5 min. Adjust the photometer to zero absorbance or 100 per cent transmittance by using 100 ml of sample and the procedure as described but omit adding 0.5 ml of CS_2.

(e) Determine the morpholine content of the sample directly from the calibration curve prepared as described in Section 8.

Calculation

10. Calculate the concentration of morpholine, in parts per million, as follows:

$$\text{Morpholine, ppm} = \frac{W \times 100}{S}$$

where:

W = parts per million of morpholine read from calibration curve, and

S = milliliters of sample used.

Precision[7]

11. The over-all and single operator precision were determined to be 16 per cent.

[7] Supporting data have been filed at ASTM Headquarters.

Standard Method for

MEASUREMENT OF ALPHA PARTICLE RADIOACTIVITY OF INDUSTRIAL WATER AND INDUSTRIAL WASTE WATER[1]

ASTM Designation: D 1943 – 66

ADOPTED, 1966

This Standard of the American Society for Testing and Materials is issued under the fixed designation D 1943; the number immediately following the designation indicates the year of original adoption or, in the case of revision, the year of last revision. A number in parentheses indicates the year of last reapproval.

Scope

1. (a) This method covers the measurement of alpha particle activity of industrial water and industrial waste water. It is applicable to alpha emitters having energies above 3.9 Mev and at activity levels above 0.5 picocurie per milliliter of radioactively homogeneous water. The method is not applicable to samples containing alpha-emitting radioelements that are volatile under conditions of the analysis.

(b) The method can be used for either absolute or relative determinations. In tracer work, the results may be expressed by comparison with a standard that is defined to be 100 per cent. For radioassay, data may be expressed in terms of alpha disintegration rates after calibration with a suitable standard. General information on radioactivity and measurement of radiation has been published.[2]

Summary of Method

2. The test sample is reduced by evaporation or a suitable chemical method to the minimum weight of material having measurable alpha activity. Alpha radioactivity is measured by an instrument composed of a detecting device, amplifier, power supply, and scaler—the most widely used being proportional and scintillation counters. In the proportional counter, which may be of the windowless or thin-window type, alpha particles entering the sensitive region of the detector produce ionization of the counting gas. The negative ion of the original ion

[2] G. Friedlander and J. W. Kennedy, "Nuclear and Radiochemistry," John Wiley and Sons, Inc., New York, N. Y. (1955).

W. J. Price, "Nuclear Radiation Detection," McGraw-Hill Book Co., Inc., New York, N. Y. (1958).

R. E. Lapp and H. L. Andrews, "Nuclear Radiation Physics," Prentice-Hall Inc., New York, N. Y. (1955).

R. T. Overman and H. M. Clark, "Radioisotope Techniques," McGraw-Hill Book Co., Inc., New York, N. Y. (1960).

[1] Under the standardization procedure of the Society, this method is under the jurisdiction of the ASTM Committee D-19 on Industrial Water. A list of members may be found in the ASTM Year Book.

pair is accelerated towards the anode, producing additional ionization of the counting gas and developing a voltage pulse at the anode. In the scintillation detector, alpha particles interact with the material of the phosphor, transferring some of their energy to electrons. These electrons subsequently lose part of their energy by excitation rather than ionization of atoms, and the excited atoms revert to the ground state by re-emitting energy in the form of light quanta. A suitable light-sensitive device, usually a multiplier phototube, "sees" the resulting flashes of light, and transforms them into voltage impulses. By use of suitable electronic apparatus, the pulse is amplified to a voltage sufficient for operation of the counting scaler. The number of pulses per unit time is related to the disintegration rate of the test sample. The efficiency of the system can be determined by use of a suitable alpha standard having equivalent residual plated solids.

Definitions

3. For definitions of terms used in this method, refer to the Definitions of Terms Relating to Industrial Water and Industrial Waste Water (ASTM Designation: D 1129).[3] For terms not defined in this method or in Definitions D 1129, reference may be made to other published glossaries.[4]

Measurement Variables

4. (a) The relatively high absorption of alpha particles in the sample media affects the counting rate of the measurement. Effects of geometry, back-scatter, source diameter, as well as the purity, pressure variation, and type of flow gas

---

[3] Appears in this publication.
[4] USA Standard Glossary of Terms in Nuclear Science and Technology (USASI Designation N1.1–1957).

used must also be considered. Thus, for reliable relative measurements, the variables should be held constant while counting all test samples and standards. For absolute measurements, appropriate efficiency factors must be applied. If a windowless proportional counter is employed, the sample mount must be electrically conducting.

In tracer studies or tests requiring only relative measurements in which the data are expressed as being equivalent to a defined standard, the above correction factors can be simply combined into a counting efficiency factor. The use of a counting efficiency factor requires that sample mounting, material of mounting dish, and weight of residue (milligrams per square centimeter), in addition to conditions affecting the above described factors, remain constant throughout the duration of the test and that the comparative standard be prepared for counting in the same manner as the test samples. The data from comparative studies between independent laboratories when not expressed in absolute units are more meaningful when expressed as percentage relationships or as equivalent of a defined standard.

(b) The limit of sensitivity for both scintillation and proportional counters is a function of the background counting rate which should be as low as is feasible. Massive shielding is not used for alpha counters. The maximum activity is 100,000 counts per minute or less.

Interferences

5. (a) Solids content in the sample containing the alpha emitter produces significant losses in sample counting rates of about 10 to 15 per cent loss at 1 mg per sq cm. Liquid samples must be evaporated to dryness onto dishes that allow the sample to be "seen" directly by the detector. Solids on the dish must

remain constant in amount between related test samples, and should duplicate the density of the solids of the plated standard.

(b) Most alpha counters are insensitive to beta, gamma, and X-radiations.[2]

Apparatus

6. (a) *Alpha Particle Counter*, consisting of either a proportional detector or a scintillation detector, and a scaler conforming to the following requirements:

(1) *Proportional Detector.*—This may be one of several types commercially available. The material used in the construction of the detector should be free from detectable radioactivity. To establish freedom from undesirable characteristics, the manufacturer shall supply voltage plateau and background counting rate data. Voltage plateau data shall show the threshold voltage, slope, and length of plateau for a particular input sensitivity.

(2) *Scintillation Detector.*—This may be one of several types commercially available. It shall consist of an "activated" zinc sulfide phosphor having a minimum effective diameter of $1\frac{7}{16}$ in. and a superficial density of 10 to 15 mg per sq cm. The phosphor shall be mounted so that it can be attached and optically coupled to a multiplier phototube. Extraneous light shall be excluded from the phosphor either by its being covered with a thin (less than 1 mg per sq cm) opaque window or by enclosing the assembly in a light-proof sample changer. The material used in the construction of the detector should be free from detectable radioactivity. To establish freedom from undesirable characteristics, the manufacturer shall supply voltage plateau and background counting rate data. Voltage plateau data shall show the threshold voltage, slope, and

length of a plateau for a specified scaler sensitivity.

(3) *Scaler.*—Often the scaler, mechanical register, power supply, and amplifier are contained in a single chassis, generally termed the scaler. The power supply and amplifier sections must be matched with the type of detector to produce satisfactory operating characteristics and to provide sufficient range in adjustments to maintain controlled conditions. The manufacturer shall provide resolving time information for the counting system. The scaler shall have capacity for storing and visually displaying at least 5×10^5 counts with a scaling ratio of 64 or greater (preferably 1000) and with a resolving time no greater than 5 μsec. The instrument should have an adjustable input sensitivity that can be matched to the detector and a variable high voltage power supply with indicating meter.

(b) *Sample Mounting Disks or Dishes*, having a flat bottom of a diameter slightly less than the inside diameter of the detector. Flat disks are preferred, but dishes may be used that have $\frac{1}{8}$-in. high side walls with the angle between dish bottom and side equal to or greater than 120 deg. Dishes should be of a material that will not corrode under the plating conditions and should be of uniform surface density; platinum and stainless steel have been used for this purpose.

Reagents

7. (a) *Purity of Reagents.*—Reagent grade chemicals shall be used in all tests. Unless otherwise indicated, it is intended that all reagents shall conform to the specifications of the Committee on Analytical Reagents of the American Chemical Society where such specifications are available.[5] Other grades may be used, provided it is first ascertained that

the reagent is of sufficiently high purity and free from radioactivity to preclude detrimental effects. Some chemicals, even of high purity, contain naturally occurring radioactive elements, for example, uranium, actinium, and thorium. Consequently, when carrier chemicals are used in the analysis of low-radioactivity samples, the radioactivity of the carriers should be determined under identical analytical conditions of the sample including residual dish solids. The radioactivity of the reagents may be considered as background and subtracted from the test sample counting rate.

(b) *Purity of Water.*—Unless otherwise indicated, references to water shall be understood to mean reagent water conforming to the Specifications for Reagent Water (ASTM Designation: D 1193).[3]

(c) *Nitric Acid (sp gr 1.42).*—Concentrated nitric acid (HNO_3).

(d) *Nitric Acid (1:30).*—Mix 1 volume of concentrated HNO_3 (sp gr 1.42) with 30 volumes of water.

Sampling

8. (a) Collect the sample in accordance with the applicable method of the American Society for Testing and Materials, as follows:

D 510—Sampling Industrial Water,[3]
D 860—Sampling Water from Boilers,[3]
D 1496—Sampling Homogeneous Industrial Waste Water.[3]

(b) Preserve the sample in a radioactively homogeneous state. A sample may be made radioactively homogeneous by addition of a reagent in which

---

[5] "Reagent Chemicals, American Chemical Society Specifications," Am. Chemical Soc., Washington, D. C. For suggestions on the testing of reagents not listed by the American Chemical Society, see "Reagent Chemicals and Standards," by Joseph Rosin, D. Van Nostrand Co., Inc., New York, N. Y. and the "United States Pharmacopeia."

the radioelements or compounds of the radioelements present would be soluble in large concentrations. Addition of acids, complexing agents, or stable chemically-similar carriers may be used to obtain homogeneity. Consideration of the chemical nature of the radioelements and compounds present and the subsequent chemistry of the method will indicate the action to be taken.

Establishing Counter Controls

9. (a) Put the instrument into operation according to the manufacturer's instructions. Place the counter control standard in the detector, set the sensitivity control near its maximum and turn the "count" switch to "count" position. Slowly increase the high voltage until the first counts are observed and record the "threshold" voltage. Advance the voltage in increments of convenient size (approximately 25 v) and determine the counting rate at four or more settings of the sensitivity control at each voltage setting. Also measure the background counting rate at each of the settings using an empty sample mounting dish in place of the standard.

The counter control standard may be any available alpha-emitting radionuclide having a half life sufficiently long to eliminate decay corrections. Knowledge of its true disintegration rate is not essential. The radionuclide should be permanently fixed to the dish and uniformly distributed over an area preferably smaller than the dish bottom; electrodeposition and flaming of a salt-free solution are the two methods most generally used. Counter control standards are commercially available.

(b) Plot the gross counting rate of the standard against the voltage. The counting rate should rise initially as the voltage is increased, then, for at least some of the settings of the sensitivity control, reach an approximate constant value, and finally rise again. The "plateau" of the curve should be at least 100 v in length and have a slope less than 2 per cent per 100 v; however, shorter plateaus or one with greater slope may be acceptable if a well-regulated high voltage power supply is available.

(c) Plot the ratio of the square of the net counting rate of the standard to the background counting rate against the voltage for each of the settings of the sensitivity control.

(d) Determine the optimum conditions for operation of the instrument by selecting values for the high-voltage and sensitivity adjustments that correspond to some point lying on the plateau of the counting-rate-versus-voltage plot and near the maximum value of the ratio of the sample-squared-to-background counting rates.

Control of Instrument Operation

10. Use control charts to assure uniform daily operation of the instrument. Obtain the background counting rate from a 10-min count at the selected operating voltage using a clean mounting dish in the sample counting position. Replace the background plate with the control standard, take ten 10-min measurements and calculate the average net counting rate and average total counts for a 10-min period. Then calculate the 95 and 99 per cent confidence limits as follows:

$$E = K \frac{\sqrt{N}}{t}$$

where:
N = average total counts for 10-min period,
E = error in a single measurement,
t = length of count in minutes = 10, and
K = confidence factor, selected from the following:

Level, per cent	K
68.3	1
90	1.645
95	1.96
99	2.575

On a linear graph of counts per minute versus time in days, plot the average net counts per minute and the upper and lower 95 and 99 per cent confidence limits on the first day and extend the lines a short distance to the right at these count rates. Each daily standard measurement (single) or the average of three successive measurements that fall within the 95 per cent confidence limits indicate normal instrument operation. The instrument is suspect of malfunctioning when a standard measurement falls outside the 99 per cent limit and a sufficient number of control and background measurements are taken to define operating characteristics. The counting rate of the control standard and background must be checked daily, but the operating voltage or new control chart require determination only if the standard falls outside the described limits or major instrument repairs occur. Room temperature must be regulated to ±4 F for satisfactory performance.

Calibration and Standardization for General Measurements

11. Place a known amount of alpha standard (approximately 5×10^{-3} μc) into a volume of water sufficient to dissolve salts equivalent to those of the test samples and prepare for counting as directed in Section 13. Throughout the experiment, the evaporation, mounting, counting, and density of plate solids of this reference standard must be identical with those of the test samples. Count for a length of time required to produce the desired statistical reliability. The efficiency factor is then expressed as a percentage of the disintegration rate of the reference standard.

Purified natural uranium, of which

the specific activity is 1.50 disintegrations per minute per microgram (0.676 picocuries per microgram), has been found satisfactory for this purpose. Other alpha-emitter preparations of known disintegration rate, for example, Am^{241} or Np^{237}, may also be used.

Calibration and Standardization for Tracer Experiments

12. Add a known quantity of activity from a reference solution of the tracer (approximately 5×10^{-3} μc) to a radioactivity-free standard test sample and process as directed in Section 13.

Procedure

13. (a) Place an appropriate volume of the test solution in a glass beaker, add 3 ml of concentrated HNO_3 (sp gr 1.42) for each 100 ml of solution, and evaporate to 1 to 2 ml. Quantitatively transfer to the mounting dish and evaporate to dryness. The heat should be adjusted carefully to avoid spattering or boiling. A ring heater having a continuously variable voltage control or adjustable infrared heat lamps are the preferable heat sources for the final evaporation and drying. Uniform spreading of the residual salts is necessary for reliable comparative data. After drying, heat the dish to dull redness for a few seconds, using a burner. Hygroscopic solids should be cooled in a dry atmosphere and stored in a desiccator until the start of counting. Place the sample in the counter and count for a time interval sufficient to attain the desired statistical reliability. Record the reading of the register and any other indication of accumulated counts (usually interpolation lights). Transfer of large volume samples to smaller beakers as evaporation nears completion makes for easier transfer of the test specimen to the mounting dish. All transfers should be made with HNO_3 (1:30). The sample

size should be chosen with consideration for the absorption of alpha particles in the residual solids, and should be such that the density of the deposit on the plate will not exceed 1.0 mg per sq cm.

(b) Precipitation methods may be used expediently to concentrate the radioactive material into small amounts of precipitate. The precipitate is separated and washed free of precipitant by centrifugation or filtration. The method of separation should be chosen that will produce a uniform deposit of precipitate after quantitatively transferring to the mounting dish for counting. Calibration of the instrument must be made under counting conditions identical to those of the samples. More detailed information is published[3] on the techniques and equipment for separation and mounting of the precipitate.

Calculations

14. Results may be expressed in observed counts per minute per milliliter. This method is useful for comparing activities of a group of samples, as in tracer experiments. Results may also be reported in terms of the alpha disintegration rate, using the efficiency determined by use of the calibration standard. The results may be calculated as follows:

$$\text{Alpha activity, cpm} = \frac{A}{t} - B$$

$$\text{Alpha activity, cpm per ml} = \frac{1}{V}\left(\frac{A}{t} - B\right)$$

where:
A = total counts accumulated,
B = background in counts per minute,
t = time of counting in minutes, and
V = milliliters of test specimen used.

$$\text{Alpha disintegration rate, dpm per ml} = \frac{C}{E}$$

where:
E = efficiency of the counter (fraction), and

29–96

C = activity of the test sample in counts per minute per milliliter.

Conversion of disintegrations per minute (dpm) to microcuries:

$$\text{Microcuries per ml} = \frac{\text{dpm per ml}}{2.22 \times 10^6}$$

Precision

15. The precision of the counting rate determinations may be calculated from the equation for random counting error. The precision of the measurement should be determined if nonuniformity of plate solids prevails. In general, a standard deviation of 5 per cent is satisfactory when the evaporation technique is used, but should be determined by the use of standards to assure manipulative competence.

Tentative Method of Test for

RADIOACTIVE STRONTIUM IN INDUSTRIAL WATER AND INDUSTRIAL WASTE WATER[1]

ASTM Designation: D 1944 – 66 T

ISSUED, 1962; REVISED, 1966

This Tentative Method has been approved by the sponsoring committee and accepted by the Society in accordance with established procedures. for use pending adoption as standard. Suggestions for revisions should be addressed to the Society at 1916 Race St., Philadelphia, Pa. 19103.

Scope

1. (*a*) This method covers the measuring of radioactive strontium in industrial water and industrial waste water in concentrations between 10 and 10^6 picocuries per liter. It is limited, by choice of radiation detector and length of time of analysis, to strontium isotopes of mass 89, 90, 91, and 92, which emit beta particles and have half lives longer than two hours. Modifications in nuclear radiation detector and analytical method are included in the method for measuring radioactive strontium in lower and higher concentrations.

(*b*) This method may be used for absolute measurements by calibrating the nuclear radiation detector with a standard strontium radioisotope of the same atomic mass, or for relative measurements by comparing measurements with each other.

Summary of Method

2. (*a*) Radioactive strontium and the added carrier are first precipitated from water to reduce the sample volume, then chemically purified, and finally counted with a beta particle detector.[2] Collection of the initial volume-reducing strontium precipitate is aided by simultaneously precipitating a larger amount of calcium which is added to the sample. Strontium is then purified by scavenging precipitations for insoluble hydroxides and for insoluble chromates at pH 5.5. The main purification step is the precipitation of strontium nitrate from a strong nitric acid solution. A final gravimetric strontium oxalate precipitation is performed, and the chemical yield is computed by comparing the weight of the dried oxalate precipitate with the amount of carrier added initially. The recovery of radioactive strontium is assumed to be equal to the chemical yield.

---

[1] Under the standardization procedure of the Society, this method is under the jurisdiction of the ASTM Committee D-19 on Industrial Water. A list of members may be found in the ASTM Year Book.

[2] G. Friedlander, J. W. Kennedy, and J. M. Miller, "Nuclear and Radiochemistry," 2nd Ed. John Wiley ana Sons, Inc., New York, N. Y. (1964).

30-20

(b) The strontium oxalate precipitate is counted with a beta particle detector. Appropriate corrections are made for counter dead time, chemical yield, and radioactive decay during analysis. If necessary, the fractional count contributed by each isotope is computed. For absolute counting, the final count rate is divided by the counter efficiency for the particular radioisotope. The four beta-emitting radioisotopes of strontium may be identified by the decay characteristics listed in the appendix. Strontium-91 and -92 are eliminated from the sample by storing it for three days, while strontium-90 may be measured by chemically separating its yttrium-90 daughter and counting the latter.[3]

(c) This method is based on a number of methods collected in a review article,[3] and is similar to an already published standard method.[4] The former reference also contains a relatively complete discussion of the chemical behavior of radioactive strontium, and an estimate of interfering radionuclides. For a discussion of beta counting and detection, refer to the Method for Measurement of Beta Particle Radioactivity of Industrial Water and Industrial Waste Water (ASTM Designation: D 1890);[5] decay and absorber measurements have been described in the literature.[2]

Definitions

3. For definitions of terms used in this method, refer to the Definitions of Terms Relating to Industrial Water and Industrial Waste Water (ASTM Designation: D 1129).[5] For terms not defined in the method or in Definitions D 1129, reference may be made to other published glossaries.[6]

Interferences

4. (a) Nonradioactive substances may interfere in the method by preventing the initial precipitation of strontium carbonate, or by causing an overestimation of chemical yield through contamination of the final strontium oxalate precipitate. Precipitation of strontium carbonate from water at a pH above 7 is prevented by a number of complexing agents such as citrate and ethylenedinitrilotetraacetic acid when their molar concentration is of the order of magnitude of that of the combined calcium and strontium. The method is designed to prevent contamination of the oxalate precipitate, but very high concentrations of calcium or barium are not completely separated. Stable strontium in the sample will cause overestimation of chemical yield, and must be compensated for.

(b) The method should not be expected to provide decontamination of more than a million-fold from radionuclides other than strontium. Decontamination from the other alkaline earths, specifically, is somewhat poorer than this.[3] There is no separation from other radioisotopes of strontium, but the beta detector discriminates against the gamma-emitting radioisotope strontium-85 by counting its gamma rays and x-rays less efficiently than beta particles.

Apparatus

5. *Beta Particle Counter.*—The counter is usually a proportional or Geiger-Mueller detector, connected to appropriate amplifier, pulse height discriminator, scaler, and register. Refer to Method D 1890.[5]

[3] D. N. Sunderman and C. W. Townley, "The Radiochemistry of Barium, Calcium, and Strontium," National Academy of Sciences, National Research Council Publication NAS-NS-3010 (1960).

[4] "Standard Methods for the Examination of Water and Waste Water," 11th ed., APHA, Inc., New York, N. Y., p. 448 (1960).

[5] Appears in this publication.

[6] USA Standard Glossary of Terms in Nuclear Science and Technology (USASI Designation: N 1.1.–1957).

Reagents

6. (a) *Purity of Reagents.*—Reagent grade chemicals shall be used in all tests. Unless otherwise indicated, it is intended that all reagents shall conform to the specifications of the Committee on Analytical Reagents of the American Chemical Society, where such specifications are available.[7] Other grades may be used, provided it is first ascertained that the reagent is of sufficiently high purity to permit its use without lessening the accuracy of the determination.

(b) *Purity of Water.*—Unless otherwise indicated, references to water shall be understood to mean reagent water conforming to Specifications for Reagent Water (ASTM Designation: D 1193),[5] referee grade.

(c) *Radioactive Purity* shall be such that the measured radioactivity of blank samples does not exceed the calculated probable error of the measurement,[5] referee grade.

(d) *Acetic Acid (1:2).*—Mix 1 volume of glacial acetic acid with 2 volumes of water.

(e) *Ammonium Acetate Solution (460 g per liter).*—Dissolve 460 g of ammonium acetate ($NH_4C_2H_3O_2$) in water and dilute to 1 liter.

(f) *Ammonium Hydroxide (sp gr 0.90).*—Concentrated ammonium hydroxide (NH_4OH).

(g) *Ammonium Oxalate, Saturated Solution.*—Prepare a solution of ammonium oxalate (($NH_4)_2C_2O_4 \cdot H_2O$) which is saturated at room temperature.

(h) *Barium Nitrate, Carrier Solution (19 g per liter).*—Dissolve 19 g of barium nitrate ($Ba(NO_3)_2$) in water, add 5 ml of concentrated HNO_3 (sp gr 1.42), and dilute to 1 liter. This solution will contain 10 g of Ba^{++} per liter.

(i) *Calcium Nitrate Solution (236 g per liter).*—Dissolve 236 g of calcium nitrate ($Ca(NO_3)_2 \cdot 4H_2O$) in water, add 5 ml of concentrated HNO_3 (sp gr 1.42) and dilute to 1 liter. This solution will contain 40 g of Ca^{++} per liter.

(j) *Ethyl Alcohol (95 per cent).*

(k) *Ethyl Ether.*

(l) *Ferric Nitrate, Carrier Solution (72 g per liter).*—Dissolve 72 g of ferric nitrate ($Fe(NO_3)_3 \cdot 9H_2O$) in water, add 12 ml of HNO_3 (1:19), and dilute to 1 liter. This solution will contain 10 g of Fe^{+++} per liter.

(m) *Nitric Acid (sp gr 1.42).*—Concentrated nitric acid (HNO_3).

(n) *Nitric Acid (1:19).*—Mix 1 volume of concentrated HNO_3 (sp gr 1.42) with 19 volumes of water.

(o) *Nitric Acid (sp gr 1.49).*—Fuming nitric acid (HNO_3).

(p) *Sodium Carbonate Solution (106 g per liter).*—Dissolve 106 g of sodium carbonate (Na_2CO_3) in water and dilute to 1 liter.

(q) *Sodium Chromate Solution (684 g per liter).*—Dissolve 684 g of sodium chromate ($Na_2CrO_4 \cdot 10H_2O$) in water and dilute to 1 liter.

(r) *Sodium Hydroxide Solution (200 g per liter).*—Dissolve 200 g of sodium hydroxide (NaOH) in water and dilute to 1 liter.

(s) *Strontium Nitrate, Carrier Solution (24 g per liter).*—Dissolve 24 g of strontium nitrate ($Sr(NO_3)_2$) in water, add 5 ml of concentrated HNO_3 (sp gr 1.42), and dilute to 1 liter. This solution will contain 10 g of Sr^{++} per liter.

---

[7] "Reagent Chemicals, American Chemical Society Specifications," Am. Chemical Soc., Washington, D. C. For suggestions on the testing of reagents not listed by the American Chemical Society, see "Reagent Chemicals and Standards," by Joseph Rosin, D. Van Nostrand Co., Inc., New York, N. Y. and the "United States Pharmacopeia."

Sampling

7. (a) Collect the sample in accordance with the applicable methods of the American Society for Testing and Materials, as follows:

D   510—Sampling Industrial Water,[5]
D   860—Sampling Water from Boilers.[5]
D 1496—Sampling   Homogeneous   Industrial
Waste Water.[5]

(b) Sample 2 liters, or other suitable volume depending on the expected strontium concentration. The minimum significant count rate of the sample may be calculated as follows:

$$C_m = 1.96 \sqrt{\frac{C_b}{t_b}}$$

where:

C_m = minimum beta count rate in net counts per minute,

C_b = background beta count rate in counts per minute, and

t_b = time of background counts in minutes.

The maximum count rate should not exceed 10^4 counts per min when a Geiger-Mueller counter is used, and 10^5 for a proportional counter. To avoid cross-contaminating less radioactive samples, it is preferable to use the smallest amount of sample giving strontium values of the desired precision.

Calibration and Standardization

8. (a) For absolute counting, the beta detector must be calibrated to obtain the ratio of count rate to disintegration rate for each strontium radioisotope. A standard radioactive strontium solution may be available from the National Bureau of Standards or a commercial supplier; if not, the standard must be prepared by measuring its disintegration rate by a method such as 4π or coincidence counting.[8] In the absence of the appropriate strontium standard, the counter may be calibrated with a radionuclide of known decay scheme that emits beta particles of similar maximum energy. The standard is prepared in the

---

[8] W. B. Mann and H. H. Seliger, "Preparation, Maintenance, and Application of Standards of Radioactivity," National Bureau of Standards, *Circular 594* (1958).

same form as the samples, and is counted in an identical container under the same geometrical conditions.

(b) A strontium-90 standard is prepared by separation from its yttrium-90 daughter with a strontium nitrate precipitation. The strontium is then converted to the oxalate and counted as such. Because of the growth of yttrium-90 into the strontium-90, the count rate of yttrium-90 in the sample must be calculated, and subtracted from the total count rate. The procedure for isolating strontium-90 and preparing the sample for counting is as follows:

(1) Place 5 ml of water, 1 ml of HNO_3 (1:19), 1.0 ml of strontium carrier, and an aliquot of the radioactive strontium standard, containing between 1000 and 10,000 counts per min, in a 50-ml glass centrifuge tube. Stir well.

(2) Add 30 ml of fuming HNO_3 and stir in an ice bath for 10 min. Centrifuge, and discard supernatant solution.

(3) Dissolve the $Sr(NO_3)_2$ precipitate in 5 ml of water, and add 30 ml of fuming HNO_3. Stir in an ice bath for 10 min, centrifuge, and discard the supernatant solution. Note the time of final yttrium-90 separation. Dissolve the precipitate in 10 ml of water.

(4) Add NH_4OH (sp gr 0.90) to make the solution neutral. Add slowly 5 ml of saturated ammonium oxalate and heat almost to boiling.

(5) Filter with suction on a Hirsch funnel. Wash three times each with warm water, 95 per cent ethyl alcohol, and ether. Weigh and count immediately. Record the time of counting. Correct for chemical yield by computing the carrier recovery.

(c) Prepare a strontium-89 standard by following steps (1), (4), and (5). A strontium-91 standard is prepared similarly to strontium-89, and strontium-92 is prepared similarly to strontium-90; in both cases, however, standards of more long-lived radionuclides are more convenient.

(d) The strontium carrier is standardized so that an aliquot of known concentration may be added to each sample. To prepare the carrier, dissolve 24 g of $Sr(NO_3)_2$ in water and dilute to 1 liter. To standardize, pipet 5 ml of this solution into 30 ml of water in a beaker and add 5 ml of saturated ammonium oxalate. Heat almost to boiling, stir well, and filter in a tared, sintered glass crucible. Wash three times each with water, 95 per cent ethyl alcohol, and ethyl ether. Heat in an oven at 110 C for 10 min, let cool in a disiccator, and weigh the strontium oxalate monohydrate. Repeat heating until constant weight is obtained.

Procedure

9. (a) Acidity the sample in a beaker of suitable size. Add 1.0 ml each of barium and strontium carriers (10 mg per ml each) and 2.0 ml of the calcium nitrate solution (40 mg per ml) and mix. Add 50 ml of Na_2CO_3 solution, and stir slowly for $\frac{1}{2}$ hr. Set the beakers aside and let stand 2 hr so that the precipitate settles. Check for complete precipitation by adding a few additional drops of Na_2CO_3 solution.

(b) Decant and discard most of the clear supernatant liquid. Transfer the precipitate quantitatively to a 50-ml glass centrifuge tube with the remaining solution, centrifuge, and discard the supernatant liquid.

(c) Add HNO_3 (sp gr 1.42) dropwise to the precipitate until the carbonate is dissolved (about 2 ml). Heat to boiling, add 1 ml of water, stir, then centrifuge. Transfer the supernatant liquid to a 50-ml glass centrifuge tube. Discard any residual solid, such as silica.

(d) Add 30 ml of fuming HNO_3, cool for 10 min with stirring to precipitate strontium and barium nitrates, and

centrifuge. If necessary, balancing of the centrifuge tubes must be done with fuming nitric acid for all nitrate precipitations to avoid low chemical yields. Discard the supernatant liquid. Invert the tube to drain off the excess HNO_3.

(e) Dissolve the precipitate in 20 ml of hot concentrated HNO_3 (sp gr 1.42). Cool in an ice bath, with stirring, for 20 min. Centrifuge, then discard the supernatant liquid.

(f) Repeat the procedure given in Paragraph (e).

(g) Dissolve the precipitate in 10 ml of water, add 1 ml of $Fe(NO_3)_3$ solution, and precipitate ferric hydroxide $(Fe(OH)_3)$ by making the solution basic with NH_4OH (sp gr 0.90) (phenolphthalein indicator). Heat, stir, centrifuge, and decant the supernatant solution to a 50-ml glass centrifuge tube. Discard the precipitate. Record the time and date of this step which removes the yttrium daughters. The remaining steps should be completed and sample counting started within 90 min of this time.

(h) Add HNO_3 (1:19) dropwise, with stirring, until the solution is neutral. Add 1 ml of acetic acid and 2 ml of $NH_4C_2H_3O_2$ solution to adjust the pH to 5.5. Heat to boiling and add 1 ml of Na_2CrO_4 solution with stirring. Continue stirring for 1 min and then centrifuge. Decant the supernatant lihuid to a 50-ml glass centrifuge tube. Discard the barium chromate $(BaCrO_4)$ precipitate or save for determination of radioactive barium, radium, or lead.

(i) Add 2 ml of NH_4OH (sp gr 0.90) to the solution, heat to boiling, and then add 5 ml of saturated ammonium oxalate solution. Stir, and filter by suction on a weighed filter disk, supported on a Hirsh funnel or other apparatus. Wash three times each with 5-ml portions of water, 5-ml portions of 95 per cent ethyl alcohol, and 5-ml portions of ethyl ether. Transfer the filter and precipitate to a watch glass or counting dish, and weigh; then mount and count the strontium oxalate precipitate.

Calculation

10. (*a*) Calculate the concentration, *D*, of radioactive strontium in microcuries per liter as follows:

$$D = \frac{C}{2.22 \times 10^6 \, EVR}$$

where:
C = beta count rate in net counts per minute,
E = beta counter efficiency in count per disintegration (appropriate average if more than one isotope present),
V = sample volume in liters,
2.22×10^6 = conversion factor from disintegrations per minute to microcuries, and
R = fractional chemical yield for the separation (Section 9 (*h*)).

(*b*) Calculate the decay correction for radioactive strontium as follows:[8]

$$A = A^0 \, e^{-0.693 t_1/T}$$

where:
A = activity at time t_1,
A^0 = activity at time zero,
e = base of natural logarithms,
t_1 = elapsed time between sampling and counting, and
T = half life of radioisotope.

(*c*) Calculate the growth of yttrium daughters of strontium as follows:

$$A_Y = A_{Sr}^0 \left(\frac{1}{1 - T_Y/T_{Sr}} \right) (e^{-0.693 t_2/T_{Sr}} - e^{-0.693 t_2/T_Y}$$

where t_2 = elapsed time between separation of yttrium daughters (Section 9(*f*)) and counting.

Precision

11. Precision depends on the random counting error and on determination of chemical yields. The precision for determining chemical yield by weight is of the order of 2 per cent.

APPENDIX

RADIOACTIVE DECAY CHARACTERISTICS[3],[9] OF STRONTIUM AND YTTRIUM ISOTOPES OF MASS 89, 90, 91, AND 92.

Radioisotope	Half Life	Maximum Beta Energy (Mev)	Gamma Radiation Energy (Mev)	Radioactive Daughter
Sr^{89}........	51 days	1.46	...	...
Y^{89}........	stable	...	...	...
Sr^{90}........	28 years	0.54	...	Y^{90}
Y^{90}........	64 hr	2.26	...	...
Sr^{91}........	9.7 hr	1.09 (33 per cent) 1.36 (29 per cent) 2.67 (26 per cent)	0.64 (11 per cent) 0.75 (19 per cent) 1.02 (22 per cent)	Y^{91m} Y^{91} ...
Y^{91m}........	50 min	...	0.55	Y^{91}
Y^{91}........	58 days	0.36 (0.2 per cent) 1.55 (99.8 per cent)	1.19 (0.2 per cent)	...
Sr^{92}........	2.6 hr	0.55 (90 per cent) 1.5 (10 per cent)	1.37 (92 per cent) 0.44 (4 per cent) 0.23 (4 per cent)	Y^{92}
Y^{92}........	3.5 hr	3.6, weaker	0.94, others	...

[9] D. Strominger, J. M. Hollander, and G. T. Seaborg, "Table of Isotopes," *Reviews of Modern Physics*, Vol. 30, p. 585 (1958).

Tentative Specifications for
DEUTERIUM OXIDE[1]

ASTM Designation: D 2032 – 66 T

ISSUED, 1966

These Tentative Specifications have been approved by the sponsoring committee and accepted by the Society in accordance with established procedures, for use pending adoption as standard. Suggestions for revisions should be addressed to the Society at 1916 Race St., Philadelphia, Pa. 19103.

Scope

1. These specifications cover minimum requirements for deuterium oxide (D_2O) to be used as a moderator in heavy water moderated reactors.[2] Additional requirements may be necessary for specific areas.

Definitions

2. For definitions of terms used in these specifications, refer to the Definitions of Terms Relating to Industrial Water and Industrial Waste Water (ASTM Designation: D 1129).[3]

Requirements

3. Deuterium oxide shall conform to the following requirements:

(a) Isotopic content of deuterium to equal or exceed 99.75 atom per cent (Note),

NOTE.—The isotopic content of deuterium can also be stated as follows:

Atom per cent D, defined as $[D/(H + D)] \times 100$, to equal or exceed 99.75 per cent.

(b) Electrical conductivity not to exceed 15 micromhos per centimeter, measured at 25 C,

(c) Consumption of potassium permanganate not to exceed 1×10^{-5} g per ml,

(d) Turbidity not to exceed the equivalent of 5 nephelos units,

(e) Total solids not to exceed 12 ppm, and

(f) Chlorides not to exceed 0.1 ppm.

Methods of Test

4. (a) *Isotopic Content of Deuterium.*—Determine the isotopic content of deuterium in deuterium oxide in accordance with the Method of Test for Deuterium Oxide (ASTM Designation: D 2184).[3]

(b) *Electrical Conductivity.*—Determine the electrical conductivity in accordance with the Methods of Test for Electrical Conductivity of Industrial Water and

---

[1] Under the standardization procedure of the Society, these specifications are under the jurisdiction of the ASTM Committee D-19 on Industrial Water. A list of members may be found in the ASTM Year Book.

[2] Deuterium oxide may be purchased from the U. S. Atomic Energy Commission.

[3] Appears in this publication.

718

Industrial Waste Water (ASTM Designation: D 1125).[3]

(c) *Consumption of Potassium Permanganate.*—Determine the consumption of potassium permanganate in accordance with the Method of Test for Consumption of Potassium Permanganate by Impurities in Deuterium Oxide (ASTM Designation: D 2033).[3]

(d) *Turbidity.*—Determine the nephelometric turbidity in accordance with the Methods of Test for Turbidity of Industrial Water (ASTM Designation: D 1889).[3] Calibrated commercial standards in sealed tubes are available.

(e) *Total Solids.*—Determine total solids in accordance with the Methods of Test for Particulate and Dissolved Matter in Industrial Waste Water (ASTM Designation: D 1069).[3] No solvent-extractable material should be expected.

(f) *Chloride.*—Determine the chloride content in accordance with the Methods of Test for Chloride Ion in Industrial Water and Industrial Waste Water (ASTM Designation: D 512).[3] When used for the analysis of chlorides in heavy water, standards must be prepared with heavy water.

Tentative Method of Test for

CONSUMPTION OF POTASSIUM PERMANGANATE BY IMPURITIES IN DEUTERIUM OXIDE[1]

ASTM Designation: D 2033 – 64 T

Issued, 1964

This Tentative Method has been approved by the sponsoring committee and accepted by the Society in accordance with established procedures, for use pending adoption as standard. Suggestions for revisions should be addressed to the Society at 1916 Race St., Philadelphia 3, Pa.

Scope

1. This method covers a titrimetric measurement of the consumption of potassium permanganate by impurities in deuterium oxide. It is one of the required methods intended for use in establishing whether the deuterium oxide is of sufficient purity to meet specifications.

Summary of Method

2. A measured amount of deuterium oxide is refluxed with potassium permanganate in an acid medium. Standard oxalic acid is added and the mixture back-titrated with standard potassium permanganate. The consumption of potassium permanganate is calculated after correction is made for a water blank of volume equal in size to that of the deuterium oxide sample.

Definitions

3. For definitions of terms used in this method, refer to the Definitions of Terms Relating to Industrial Water and Industrial Waste Water (ASTM Designation: D 1129).[2]

Reagents

4. (a) *Purity of Reagents.*—Reagent grade chemicals shall be used in all tests. Unless otherwise indicated, it is intended that all reagents shall conform to the specifications of the Committee on Analytical Reagents of the American Chemical Society, where such specifications are available.[3] Other grades may be used, provided it is first ascertained that the reagent is of sufficiently high purity to permit its use without lessening the accuracy of the determination.

(b) *Purity of Water.*—Unless otherwise indicated, references to water shall be understood to mean reagent water con-

---

[1] Under the standardization procedure of the Society, this method is under the jurisdiction of the ASTM Committee D-19 on Industrial Water. A list of members may be found in the ASTM Year Book.

[2] Appears in this publication.
[3] "Reagent Chemicals, American Chemical Society Specifications," Am. Chemical Soc., Washington, D. C. For suggestions on the testing of reagents not listed by the American Chemical Society, see "Reagent Chemicals and Standards," by Joseph Rosin, D. Van Nostrand Co., Inc., New York, N. Y. and the "United States Pharmacopeia."

forming to the Specifications for Reagent Water (ASTM Designation: D 1193).[2]

(c) *Oxalic Acid Solution (0.63 g per liter).*—Dissolve 0.63 g of oxalic acid ($H_2C_2O_4 \cdot 2H_2O$) in water and dilute to 1 liter with water in a volumetric flask.

(d) *Potassium Permanganate, Standard Solution (0.01 N).*—Dissolve 0.316 g of potassium permanganate ($KMnO_4$) in 1 liter of boiling water in a Florence flask. Cover with a beaker and simmer for $\frac{1}{2}$ hr. Cool to room temperature. Filter twice by gravity through a fine fritted-glass filter and store in a dark-colored, glass-stoppered bottle. Pipet triplicate 50-ml aliquots of the 0.01 N sodium oxalate ($Na_2C_2O_4$) solution into 500-ml Erlenmeyer flasks and add 100 ml of water to each. Heat to 90 C and add 10 ml of sulfuric acid (H_2SO_4, 1:4). Titrate rapidly with potassium permanganate solution to a slight pink end point which should persist for 1 min. Calculate the normality of the $KMnO_4$ solution as follows:

$$N = \frac{0.5}{B}$$

where:
N = normality of $KMnO_4$ solution, and
B = milliliters of $KMnO_4$ solution required for the titration.

(e) *Sodium Oxalate, Standard Solution (0.01 N).*—Dry National Bureau of Standards oxidimetric-grade sodium oxalate ($Na_2C_2O_4$) or equivalent, at 105 C for 1 hr and cool in a desiccator. Weigh 0.67 g of the $Na_2C_2O_4$ to the nearest 1 mg, dissolve in water, and dilute to 1 liter. Store in a chemical-resistant borosilicate glass container. Sodium oxalate solutions are subject to deterioration by microorganisms and should be prepared at time of use.

(f) *Sulfuric Acid Solution (1:4).*—Add one volume of concentrated sulfuric acid (H_2SO_4, sp gr 1.84) to four volumes of water and mix. Cool to room temperature and transfer to a glass-stoppered bottle.

Procedure

5. To 100 ml of deuterium oxide (D_2O) in a 300-ml round-bottom flask, add 10 $\pm$ .01 ml of 0.01 N $KMnO_4$ and 5 ml of (1:4) H_2SO_4. Add several boiling chips, insert a reflux condenser, and reflux gently for 1 hr. Cool to not less than 80 C, remove the condenser, and add 40.0 ml of oxalic acid. Shake gently until the color and precipitate have disappeared. Back-titrate with 0.01 N $KMnO_4$ to the first faint pink color of permanganate that persists for 1 min. Using 100 ml of water, repeat the above procedure to provide for a blank correction.

Calculation

6. Calculate the consumption of potassium permanganate as follows:

$KMnO_4$, g per ml

$$= \frac{0.0316 \times N \times [A + B - (C + D)]}{S}$$

where:
A = milliliters of $KMnO_4$ added to the sample,
B = milliliters of $KMnO_4$ required for titration of the sample,
C = milliliters of $KMnO_4$ added to the blank,
D = milliliters of $KMnO_4$ required for titration of the blank,
N = normality of the $KMnO_4$, and
S = milliliters of sample used.

Tentative Method for

OPEN CHANNEL FLOW MEASUREMENT OF INDUSTRIAL WATER AND INDUSTRIAL WASTE WATER BY WEIRS[1]

ASTM Designation: D 2034 - 64 T

ISSUED, 1964

> This Tentative Method has been approved by the sponsoring committee and accepted by the Society in accordance with established procedures, for use pending adoption as standard. Suggestions for revisions should be addressed to the Society at 1916 Race St., Philadelphia 3, Pa.

Scope

1. (*a*) This method covers the measurement of the rate of flow of industrial water and industrial waste water in open channels or streams at or near the ground surface using the triangular (V-notch), rectangular and trapezoidal type weirs having end and bottom contractions.

(*b*) Weirs are particularly applicable where there is low head flow at liquid discharge outlets for relatively clear water containing a minimum of suspended solids which, on low flows, tend to settle out upstream.

General Principles

2. (*a*) The triangular or V-notch weir (Fig. 1) may have an angle of any desired amount, but the 60 and 90-deg notches are most commonly used with the apex pointed downward. The rectangular weir (Fig. 2) has the notch cut in a rectangular shape with level crest and

vertical sides. The trapezoidal weir (Fig. 3) is in reality a combination of the V-notch with the rectangular, a special form being the Cippoletti. (Refer to Table I for an explanation of the dimensions used in Figs. 1, 2, 3 and 4.)

The V-notch weirs give greater heads for a given discharge than does a rectangular notch of the same width at the water surface. They are, therefore, especially recommended for metering flows less than 1 cu ft per sec (cfs) or 450 gal per min (gpm) and are suitable for measuring fluctuating flows up to 10 cfs. Although 60-deg notch wiers are in use, the more common V-notch weir is cut to 90 deg.

(*b*) The rectangular weir is capable of high-capacity metering and is simple and inexpensive to construct.

(*c*) The Cippoletti wier is similar to the rectangular weir, except for sloping sides (one horizontal to four vertical) of the notch. This type has the advantage of a simplified discharge formula which is more convenient to work than that for the rectangular weir.

---

[1] Under the standardization procedure of the Society, this method is under the jurisdiction of the ASTM Committee D-19 on Industrial Water. A list of members may be found in the ASTM Year Book.

(d) When built in accordance with one of the standard designs and used under carefully controlled field conditions, weirs are an accepted means of accurate measurement of the rate of flow.

Description of Terms

3. (a) The terms "Weir," "Weir Notch," and "Crest" used in this method are described as follows:

(b) *Weir.*—A flow measuring device

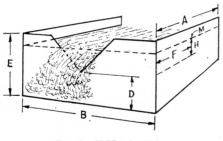

FIG. 1.—V-Notch Weir.

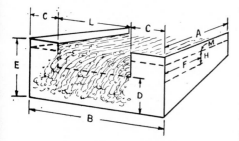

FIG. 2.—Rectangular Weir.

consisting of a dam or other obstruction over which water flows, placed in a pipe, channel or stream.

(c) *Weir Notch.*—The opening cut in the top of a dam through which a stream can flow. In this case, the notch is the weir.

(d) *Crest.*—The weir crest is the level to which water must rise before it can flow over the weir, that is, the top of the dam or the bottom of the notch cut in the dam. The V-notch weir which comes to a point at the bottom has no crest length.

(e) *Nappe.*—The sheet of liquid passing through the notch and falling over the weir crest is called the nappe. When the liquid surface downstream from the weir plate is far enough below the crest so that air has free access beneath the nappe, the flow is said to be free; otherwise, it is submerged. Weir formulas in this method assume free-fall. If this condition is not met, the formulas are not valid.

(f) *Head.*—The head on the weir is the vertical distance from the crest of the weir to the liquid surface. The upstream head, H_a, is measured at a distance of four or more times the maximum value of H_a upstream from the weir plate.

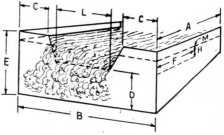

FIG. 3.—Trapezoidal Weir.

(g) *Drawdown.*—Drawdown refers to the curvature of the liquid surface as traced by the intersection of a vertical plane to the weir plate at the mid-point of the crest. The point of observance of the head H_a should be at or beyond the upstream extremity of the curve.

(h) *Contraction.*—A weir which is narrower than the channel in which it is placed is called a contracted weir. When the crest of a weir is constructed as a dam across the full width of the channel, it is known as a suppressed weir, that is, the contractions are suppressed. When the weir is a notch cut in the dam, the horizontal distances from the end of the crest to the side walls are called the end contractions. These end contractions reduce the width of the channel flow as it passes over the weir and provide the

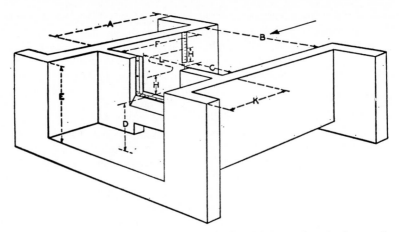

FIG. 4.—Concrete Weir Box with Rectangular Weir Notch Formed by Angle Iron Crest and Sides.

TABLE I.—WEIR BOX DIMENSIONS FOR RECTANGULAR, CIPPOLETTI AND 90-DEG TRIANGULAR NOTCH WEIRS (LETTERS REFER TO DIMENSIONS IN FIGS 1, 2, AND 3).

Approximate Limits of Discharge, cu ft per sec	RECTANGULAR AND CIPPOLETTI WEIRS								
	H	L	A	K	B	E^a	C	D	F
	Maximum Head, ft	Length of Weir Crest, ft	Length of Box Above Weir Crest, ft	Length of Box Below Weir Crest, ft	Total Width of Box, ft	Total Depth of Box, ft	Distance from End of Crest to Side of Box, ft	Distance from Crest to Bottom of Box, ft	Gage Distance, ft
⅒ to 3................	1	1	6	2	4	3	1½	1½	4
⅕ to 6................	1¼	1½	7	3	5	3¼	1¾	1½	4½
¼ to 8................	1¼	2	8	4	6	3½	2	1¾	5
⅓ to 17...............	1½	3	9	5	7	4	2	2	5½
½ to 23...............	1½	4	10	6	9	4	2½	2	6
¾ to 35...............	1½	6	12	6	11½	4½	2¾	2½	6
1 to 50...............	1½	8	16	8	14	4¾	3	2¾	8
1 to 60...............	1½	10	20	8	17	5	3½	3	8
	90-DEG TRIANGULAR NOTCH WEIR								
⅒ to 2½..............	1	...	6	2	5	3	...	1½	4
⅒ to 4⅓..............	1¼	...	6½	3	6½	3¼	...	1½	5

^{a} This distance allows for about 6 in. free board above highest water level in weir box.

needed ventilation. The vertical distance from the crest to the floor of the weir box or bed of the channel is the bottom contraction.

Apparatus

4. *Weir.*—The apparatus shall consist of a partition or dam of timber, concrete, sheet metal, or a weir box placed in a channel or stream over which the liquid flows. With a contracted weir, flow is through a notch of fixed dimensions cut in the top edge of the partition rather than over the full length of the partition.

(a) The recommended form and dimensions of the three types of weirs, 90-

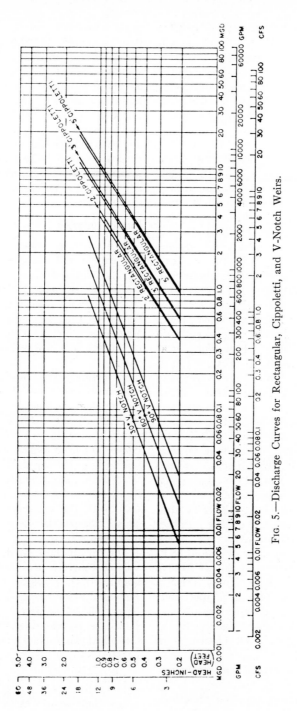

FIG. 5.—Discharge Curves for Rectangular, Cippoletti, and V-Notch Weirs.

deg V-notch, rectangular and Cippoletti, are shown on Figs. 1, 2 and 3 and Table I, respectively. Figure 4 shows a concrete weir box with rectangular weir notch formed by angle-iron crest and sides. Refer to Fig. 5 to determine that the weir chosen will give a usable range of heads at the operating maximum and minimum flows.

(b) The approach channel upstream from the weir should be straight, reasonably level, and free from all disturbing influences for a minimum length 20 times the maximum head on the weir to permit the stream to assume quiet flow. To promote this condition and assure a velocity of approach less than 0.3 ft per sec (fps), a weir box should be installed if practical. Cross-sectional area should be at least six times that at the weir crest.

(c) The weir box dimensions should correspond to the dimensions given in Table I. The crest should be sharp or at least square edged and the plate not more than 1 in. thick. While metal produces the most accurate results because it can be cut to a sharper edge, a thin, straight board will provide sufficient accuracy in most cases. For low heads, a knife-edge crest is necessary. Metal weir plate is usually $\frac{1}{8}$ to $\frac{1}{4}$ in. thick. If properly supported, stiff sheet metal can give results as satisfactory as expensive brass weirs. The weir box size should be selected after approximating the rate of flow by other methods of measurement.

(d) The crest of the weir should be at least 2.5 times the head on the weir above the bottom of the channel so as to reduce velocity of approach to a negligible value.

(e) The weir plate must be correctly centered in the stream and the top of weir plate must be level. The length of the rectangular or Cippoletti weir crest should be at least three times the maximum head.

(f) The head on any weir should be greater than 0.2 ft, but preferably not more than 2 ft. Values below 0.2 ft give a large percentage of errors with small differences in reading. The width of the weir should be chosen so as to permit at least a 0.2-ft head. Heads on the weir greater than 0.2 ft minimize the effects of variation in velocity in the water at different depths as the liquid approaches the weir and thus reduces the error in the results. It is possible to make reliable weir flow measurements with a head between 0.125 and 0.2 ft, if a notched weir is used with extreme care.

Instrumentation

5. (a) For temporary installations, a staff gage should be utilized for measuring the head of the weir.

(b) For permanent installations, a float-actuated measuring instrument should be used to convert liquid levels (sensed variable) from the upstream side of the weir into observable flow information.

(c) Pressure taps for measuring the head on the weir should be installed upstream from the weir at a distance of at least 2.5 and preferably 4 times the maximum head on the weir. For extreme accuracy, the head should be measured in a stilling box. The tap should be above the floor of the channel and approximately 6 in. below the crest level, at right angles, flush with the channel wall and have square, sharp corners free from burrs and other projections.

For certain flow conditions, a large-volume concrete float well, built integrally with the channel, may be utilized. For rapidly fluctuating flows, a separate pipe well of relatively small volume should be employed so that the instrument float can respond quickly to changes in rate (Note 1).

Note 1.—To eliminate float lateral drift and consequent metering errors because of cable extension, the diameter of the float well should be only large enough to accommodate the float and allow for its free vertical travel. Suitable drain and shutoff valves should be provided to empty and flush out the float wells. For sewage or sludge-measuring installation, a clear water, continuous flushing supply should discharge into the float well to prevent solids from' accumulating in the well.

inches of liquid level or flow units directly, that is, gallons per minute or cubic feet per second for the particular weir.

A totalizing-type measuring instrument meter is equipped with an integrator calibrated to convert the variable (liquid level) in the approach channel into gallons and mechanically

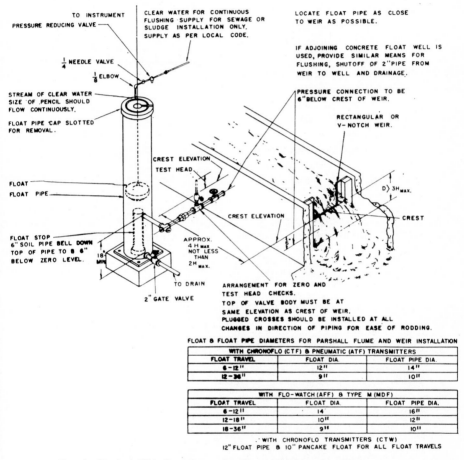

FLOAT & FLOAT PIPE DIAMETERS FOR PARSHALL FLUME AND WEIR INSTALLATION

WITH CHRONOFLO (CTF) & PNEUMATIC (ATF) TRANSMITTERS		
FLOAT TRAVEL	FLOAT DIA.	FLOAT PIPE DIA.
6-12"	12"	14"
12-36"	9"	10"

WITH FLO-WATCH (AFF) & TYPE M (MDF)		
FLOAT TRAVEL	FLOAT DIA.	FLOAT PIPE DIA.
6-12"	14	16"
12-18"	10"	12"
18-36"	9"	10"

.·WITH CHRONOFLO TRANSMITTERS (CTW)
12" FLOAT PIPE & 10" PANCAKE FLOAT FOR ALL FLOAT TRAVELS

FIG. 6.—Typical Weir Installation for Use with Measuring Instruments.

(d) Float-actuated measuring instruments should be used to convert liquid levels (sensed variable) at the gage point in the approach channel into observable flow information. Indicating, totalizing, recording types, or combinations may be considered (Note 2).

NOTE 2.—An indicator gage is calibrated in

register the total number of units of flow in gallons. The difference in counter-readings over a period of time multiplied by an integrator factor represents the total flow for that period of time.

A recording-type measuring instrument is calibrated to convert the variable (liquid level) in the channel to gallons and provide a record of changes in conditions throughout a 24-hr period. The recorder chart is linear with scale divisions spaced equally to record the flow rate in gallons.

A totalizer, indicator, and recorder type flowmeter is calibrated to convert the sensed variable (liquid level) in the channel to gallons. The instruments indicate the flow, totalize the total number of units of flow in gallons and provide a visible record of changes of conditions throughout a 24-hr period.

(e) The choice of instrument will depend upon several factors, including (1) the method used to transmit the sensed variable to the measuring instrument (receiver) (Note 3), (2) relative location of measuring instrument and receiver (Note 4), (3) the type of information desired, (4) the range of variable, that is, the ratio of maximum to minimum of the variable being measured must be known, whether 4 to 1, 10 to 1, etc., (5) the accuracy desired, and (6) the instrument function as part of a control system.

NOTE 3.—*Mechanical actuation:* The motion of a float riding on the liquid surface in a stilling well is generally transmitted to the measuring instrument (receiver) directly by cable, tape, or float rod. A cable type directly connected to a transmitter is shown in Fig. 6. The float rides directly in the well at the proper gaging location to give more rapid response to liquid level changes.

NOTE 4.—The instrument receiver may be utilized in a location remote from the weir and information may be transmitted from the measuring instrument to the secondary instrument receiver electrically or pneumatically as follows:

Electrical transmission: The measuring instrument may include an electrical transmitter connected with a remotely located secondary receiver actuated by a timed electrical impulse (Chronoflow Telemeter). The duration of the electrical impulse is proportional to the magnitude of the measured variable; in this case, water level.

Pneumatic transmission: Transmission by air pressure is effective up to about 1000 ft. The instrument makes use of varying-controlled air pressure ranging from 3 to 15 psi. Changes in pressure output of the transmitter are proportional to changes in the measured variable level. No wires are used; the output signal (pressure) is continuous and extremely sensitive to change in the measured variable.

Procedure

6. (a) Obtain a gage reading of the water level above the weir crest at point M, a distance of F above the crest of the weir. This reading is required for computing discharge. (Refer to Figs. 1, 2, 3, and Table I.) When free flow exists, obtain the rate of discharge in cubic feet per second or gallons per minute by referring to the graph of Fig. 5.

(b) Calculate the free-flow discharge from the three types of weirs as follows:

(1) *Triangular or V-notch weirs:*

$$Vsf = (0.025 + 2.462U)H_a$$

$$(2.5 - 0.0195/0.75U)\dots(1)$$

$$Vsf = 4.28UCH_a^{5/2}\dots\dots(2)$$

(2) Rectangular weirs with full end and bottom contractions:

$$Vsf = 3.08L^{1.022}H_a^{(1.46+0.003L)}\dots\dots(3)$$

(3) Rectangular weirs with complete contractions and negligible velocity of approach:

$$Vsf = 3.33(L - 0.2H_a)H_a^{3/2}\dots\dots(4)$$

(4) Rectangular weirs with or without end contractions and appreciable velocity of approach:

$$Vsf = 3.33(L - 0.1NH_a)$$

$$(H_a + H_v)^{3/2} - H_v^{3/2}\dots(5)$$

(5) Rectangular weirs with end contraction suppressed:

$$Vsf = L(3.228 + 0.4347$$

$$\frac{H_a + 0.0036}{H_t - H_a}\Bigg) (H_a + 0.0036)^{3/2}\dots\dots(6)$$

(6) Cippoletti weirs with full end and bottom contraction:

$$Vsf = 3.08L^{1.022}H_a^{(1.46-0.003L)} + 0.6H_a^{2.6}\dots(7)$$

$$Vsf = 3.367LH_a^{3/2}\dots\dots\dots(8)$$

where:

C = experimentally determined coefficient,

H = head of liquid measured from crest, in feet,

H_a = upper head measured from crest, in feet,

H_t = head of liquid measured from bottom of weir box, in feet,

H_v = velocity head in weir pond, in feet = $V^2/2g$, where V = velocity, in feet per second, and g = acceleration of gravity in feet per second per second,

L = length of crest of weir, in feet,

N = number of end contractions, and

U = slope of sides of notch from vertical or tan θ in which θ is $\frac{1}{2}$ of total included angle of the notch, and

Vsf = rate of flow, in cubic feet per second.

NOTE 5.—Equations 1, 3, and 7 refer to equations appearing in the article by V. M. Cone, "Flow Through Weir Notches with Thin Edges and Full Contractions," *Journal of Agricultural Research*, Vol. 5, 1916, p. 1083. Equations 2 and 8 are from the ASME Fluid Meters Report *Pt 1* (1937) available from American Society of Mechanical Engineers, United Engineering Center, 345 E. 47th St., New York 17, N.Y. Equations 4 and 5 have been taken from the book by James B. Francis, "Lowell Hydraulic Experiments" D. Van Nostrand Co., Inc., New York, N.Y. 5th Ed. (1909). Equation 6 refers to an equation derived by T. Rehbock of the Karlsruhe Hydraulic Laboratory, Germany.

Calibration

7. To meet accuracy standards, it is recommended that each weir be calibrated in place if the discharge can be directly measured by other methods (Note 6).

NOTE 6.—For calibration purposes, the application of the volumetric method or comparative salt dilution method of flow measurement is recommended. The volumetric method is applicable only when there is available a reservoir of regular form, the volume of which, up to various levels, may be accurately measured within an error of 1.0 per cent.

The drawdown during the test run should not cause a variation in head on the weir in excess of 4 per cent of the head during any run. The availability of a reservoir of regular form with

sufficient storage capacity to meet these conditions places a limit on the size of weir which can be accurately calibrated by this method. For weirs larger than 1 ft in crest length, the comparative salt dilution or chemical method is recommended for calibration purposes. Thorough mixing of the salt solution in the flowing stream and accurate analysis of samples taken at the sampling station downstream from the weir are essential for measurement of flow rates within ±2 per cent.

Accuracy

8. The accuracy of a weir measurement is directly related to the following:

(*1*) In the construction of the weir and approach flume, it is important to keep as close as possible to the dimension given in Table I. If concrete construction is used, the surfaces should be smooth.

(*2*) A formula must be used which is based on reliable tests of a weir of similar design and similar range of head.

(*3*) The necessary test measurements, particularly of the head on the weir, must be conducted with the utmost care and precision.

Generally accepted practice in the use of weirs is to limit the maximum head to not more than one third the crest length, but laboratory experiments show that the accuracy of measurement is not impaired by exceeding this limit, especially for crest length of 1 to 4 ft. For a 1-ft weir, either rectangular of Cippoletti, at a head of 1 ft, the rate of discharge agrees within less than 0.5 per cent of the calculated flow; for a 1.5-ft weir, at a head of 1.3 ft, the rate of discharge agrees within less than approximately 0.5 per cent of the calculated flow and for a 3-ft weir, at a head of 1.2 ft, the rate of discharge agrees within about 0.2 per cent of the calculated flow.[2] For accurate measurement, the velocity of the liquid in the weir pond at the head of the weir plate should should not exceed $\frac{1}{3}$ fps.

[2] L. K. Spink, "Principles and Practice of Flow Meter Engineering," The Foxboro Co., Foxboro, Mass.

Tentative Method for

COAGULATION-FLOCCULATION JAR TEST OF INDUSTRIAL WATER AND INDUSTRIAL WASTE WATER[1]

ASTM Designation: D 2035 – 64 T

ISSUED, 1964

This Tentative Method has been approved by the sponsoring committee and accepted by the Society in accordance with established procedures, for use pending adoption as standard. Suggestions for revisions should be addressed to the Society at 1916 Race St., Philadelphia 3, Pa.

Scope

1. (*a*) This method covers the evaluation of conditions required to remove dissolved, suspended, colloidal, and non-settleable matter from industrial water and waste water by chemical coagulation-flocculation, followed by gravity settling.

(*b*) The method provides a systematic evaluation of the variables normally encountered in chemical coagulation flocculation, to achieve a predetermined result.

Summary of Method

2. The chemical coagulation-flocculation jar test is carried out to find the optimum chemicals, dosage, and conditions to achieve the degree of removal required. The primary variables to be investigated using the method include, but are not limited to:

(*a*) Chemical additives,
(*b*) pH,
(*c*) Temperature, and
(*d*) Order of addition and mixing conditions.

Definitions

3. For definitions of terms used in this method, refer to the Definitions of Terms Relating to Industrial Water and Industrial Waste Water (ASTM Designation: D 1129).[2]

Interferences

4. There are some possible interferences that may make the determination of optimum jar test conditions difficult. These include the following:

(*a*) *Temperature Change (During Test)*.—Thermal or convection currents may be set up, interfering with the settling of coagulated particles. This can be prevented by temperature control.

(*b*) *Gas Release (During Test)*.—Flotation of coagulated floc may occur due to

---

[1] Under the standardization procedure of the Society, this method is under the jurisdiction of the ASTM Committee D-19 on Industrial Water. A list of members may be found in the ASTM Year Book.

[2] Appears in this publication.

gas bubble formation caused by super-saturation of gases.

(c) *Testing Period.*—Biological activity or other factors may alter the coagulation characteristics of a water upon prolonged standing. The period between initial and final testing of a given sample should be kept to a minimum and the time recorded.

Reagents

6. (a) *Purity of Reagents.*—Normally commercial grade chemicals and other agents shall be used in this method. However, when comparatively evaluating specific commercial grade reagents by means of the chemical coagulation-flocculation jar test, reagent grade chemicals conforming to the specifications of the Committee

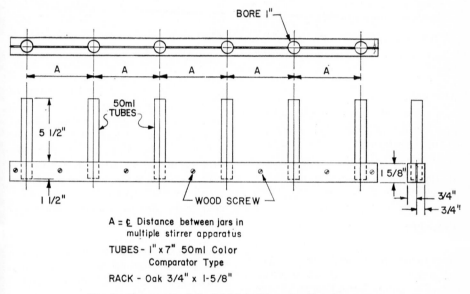

BORE 1"

A = Ȼ Distance between jars in
multiple stirrer apparatus

TUBES - 1"x 7" 50ml Color
Comparator Type

RACK - Oak 3/4" x 1-5/8"

FIG. 1.—Reagent Rack for Multiple Stirrer Jar Test Apparatus.

Apparatus

5. (a) *Multiple Stirrer.*—A multi-position stirrer with continuous speed variation from about 20 to 150 rpm should be used. The stirring paddles should be of light-gage corrosion-resistant material all of the same configuration and size.

(b) *Jars (or Beakers),* all of the same size and shape; 1500-ml Griffin beakers may be used.

(c) *Reagent Racks.*—A means of introducing each test solution to all jars simultaneously. There should be at least one rack for each test solution or suspension. The racks should be similar to that shown in Fig. 1.

on Analytical Reagents of the American Chemical Society shall be used.[3]

(b) *Purity of Water.*—Unless otherwise indicated, references to water shall be understood to mean reagent water conforming to the Specifications for Reagent Water (ASTM Designation: D 1193).[2]

(c) The following are typical test solutions and suspensions used. Those below may be prepared daily by mixing finely-

[3] "Reagent Chemicals, American Chemical Society Specifications," Am. Chemical Soc., Washington, D. C. For suggestions on the testing of reagents not listed by the American Chemical Society, see "Reagent Chemicals and Standards," by Joseph Rosin, D. Van Nostrand Co., Inc., New York, N. Y. and the "United States Pharmacopeia."

ground chemical with water to a concentration of 10 ($\pm$0.1) g per liter (1.0 ml of test solution or suspension when added to 1 liter of sample is equivalent to 10 ppm).

Alum (Al$_2$(SO$_4$)$_3$·14H$_2$O)
Ferric sulfate (Fe$_2$(SO$_4$)$_3$·2H$_2$O)
Ferric chloride (FeCl$_3$·6H$_2$O)
Ferrous sulfate (FeSO$_4$·7H$_2$O)
Lime, hydrated (Ca(OH)$_2$)
Sodium aluminate (NaAlO$_2$)
Sodium carbonate (Na$_2$CO$_3$)
Sodium hydroxide (NaOH)

(d) *Coagulant Aids.*—Prepare and use according to the manufacturer's instructions.

Sampling

7. Collect the water sample under test in accordance with the applicable method of the American Society for Testing and Materials as follows:

D 510—Sampling Industrial Water,[2] and
D 1496—Sampling Homogeneous Industrial Waste Water.[2]

Procedure

8. (a) Measure equal volumes of sample into each of the jars to be used (1000-ml sample into 1500-ml Griffin beakers). As many sample portions may be used as there are positions on the multiple stirrer. Beakers should be located so that the paddles are off center, but clear the beaker wall by about $\frac{1}{4}$ in. Record the sample temperature at the start of the test.

(b) Load the test chemicals in the reagent racks. Use one rack for each series of chemical additions. Make up each tube in the reagent rack to a final volume of 10 ml, with water, before using.

(c) Start the multiple stirrer operating at the "flash mix" speed of approximately 120 rpm. Add test solutions or suspensions, at predetermined dosage levels and sequence. Flash mix for approximately 1 min after the addition of chemicals. Record the flash mix time and speed (rpm).

(d) Reduce speed as necessary, to the minimum required to keep floc particles uniformly suspended throughout the "slow mix" period. Slow mix for 20 min. Record the time for the first visible floc formation. Every 5 min during the slow mix period, record relative floc size and mixer speed (rpm).

(e) After the slow mix period, withdraw the paddles and observe settling of floc particles. Record the time required for vertical particle movement to stop. In most cases this time will be that required for the particles to settle to the bottom of the beaker; however, in some cases there may be interfering convection currents. If so, the recorded settling time should be that at which the particles appear to be moving equally upward and downward.

(f) After 15 min of settling, record the appearance of floc on the beaker bottom, the supernatant color, turbidity, pH, temperature, and other required analyses, determined in accordance with the applicable following methods:

D 1889—Turbidity of Industrial Water,[2] and
D 1293—pH of Industrial Water and Industrial Waste Water.[2]

(g) Repeat steps (a) through (f) until all pertinent variables have been evaluated.

Precision

9. No general statement can be made as to the precision of the method.

Tentative Method of Test for

CYANIDES IN INDUSTRIAL WASTE WATER[1]

ASTM Designation: D 2036 – 64 T

Issued, 1964

This Tentative Method has been approved by the sponsoring committee and accepted by the Society in accordance with established procedures, for use pending adoption as standard. Suggestions for revisions should be addressed to the Society at 1916 Race St., Philadelphia 3, Pa.

Scope

1. This method covers the determination of soluble and insoluble cyanides in industrial waste water by a modified Liebig titration when the cyanide level is known to be greater than 1 mg per liter as CN^-, and by a colorimetric procedure for concentrations less than 1 mg per liter. The procedures do not distinguish between CN^- and CN complexes (Note 1). Furthermore, they do not reveal the cyanogen halide complexes (Note 1), the cyanate compounds (Note 2), and organo-cyanide complexes (Note 3). The method can be used to distinguish between cyanides amenable to oxidation by chlorination and those not amenable by subjecting one portion of the sample to an alkaline chlorination procedure.

Note 1.—Cyanogen chloride is the most common of the cyanogen halide complexes as it is a reaction product and is usually present when chlorinating cyanide-containing industrial water.

The colorimetric procedure described in Section 9(r) through (w) may be used for the direct determination of cyanogen chloride by omitting stabilization of the sample with caustic soda, the distillation step and the addition of Chloramine-T reagent.[2]

Note 2.—The cyanate complexes are decomposed when the sample is acidified in the distillation procedure.[3]

Note 3.—Only those organo-cyanic compounds which hydrolize in water or in an alkaline medium, or are decomposed by mineral acids to simple cyanides, will be revealed.

Summary of Method

2. The method makes use of a distillation procedure for concentrating and removing cyanides by refluxing the sample with dilute sulfuric acid and acid cuprous chloride solution. The liberated HCN is collected in sodium hydroxide solution and its concentration determined by either a titration or colorimetric procedure.

[2] See E. Serfass et al, "Analytical Methods for the Determination of Cyanides in Plating Wastes and in Effluents from Treatment Processes," *Plating*, Vol. 39, p. 267 (1952).

[3] For the determination of cyanates, see B. F. Dodge and W. Zabban, "Analytical Methods for the Determination of Cyanates in Plating Wastes," *Plating*, Vol 39, p. 381 (1952).

[1] Under the standardization procedure of the Society, this method is under the jurisdiction of the ASTM Committee D-19 on Industrial Water. A list of members may be found in the ASTM Year Book.

56-4

Interferences

3. (*a*) Common interferences in the analysis for cyanide include the following: (*1*) sulfides, (*2*) fatty acids and other steam distillable organic compounds, (*3*) glycine, urea, or other substances which hydrolize to form cyanides under analytical conditions, (*4*) substances contributing color or turbidity, and (*5*) oxidizing agents. The first two affect the silver nitrate titration in an adverse manner; (*3*) interferes with color development; (*4*) affects both the titration and colorimetric methods; and (*5*) is likely to result in the destruction of cyanide during manipulation, particularly during the distillation stage.

(*b*) These interfering agents[4] may be removed or treated, or both, as follows:

(*1*) Sulfides shall be removed by treating the portion of the alkaline sample (pH > 11.0) necessary for the CN⁻ determination plus about 25 ml with powdered lead carbonate and mixing. Black lead sulfide precipitates in samples containing sulfides. Repeat this operation until no more lead sulfide forms. Filter the solution through a dry paper into a dry beaker and from the filtrate measure the sample to be used for analysis. Avoid a large excess of lead carbonate and a long time of contact in order to minimize complexation or occlusion of cyanide with the precipitated material.

(*2*) Fatty acids form soaps under alkaline titration conditions which render it difficult or impossible to detect the end point. This type of interference may be removed by an extraction as suggested by Kruse and Mellon.[5] The sample should be acidified with acetic acid to pH 6.0 to 7.0 and extracted with *iso*-octane, hexane, or chloroform (preference in the order named). One extraction with a solvent volume equal to 20 per cent of the sample volume is usually adequate to reduce the fatty acids to a point below the interference level. Avoid multiple extractions or a long contact time at a low pH in order to keep the loss of HCN at a minimum.

(*3*) Oxidizing agents may be removed by the use of ascorbic acid. The use of sulfite reducing agents may result in decomposition products in the distillation procedure which can interfere with the analysis.

(*4*) After the removal of the sulfides, fatty acids, oxidizing agents, and substances capable of producing a color reaction similar to that of cyanides, most other interferences may be removed by distillation.

Apparatus

4. (*a*) *Distillation Apparatus*, including a 1-liter two-neck distilling flask with 19/38 standard taper joints.[6] The side neck shall be fitted with a 19/38 standard taper joint-reduced lower stem of 8 mm inside diameter, which shall be broken off to reach within $\frac{1}{4}$ in. of the bottom of the flask.[7] A cold finger separable-type condenser with 19/38 standard taper joints at inlet and outlet,[8] and a vacuum-type absorber with a medium-porosity gas dispersion tube sealed to the lower end of the 19/38 standard taper inner joint

---

[4] The interferences and some of the procedures for removal are taken from F. J. Ludzack et al, "Analysis of Cyanide in Water and Waste Samples," *Analytical Chemistry*, Vol. 26, p. 1784 (1954).

[5] J. M. Kruse and M. G. Mellon, "Colorimetric Determination of Cyanide, Cyanate and Thiocyanate in Sewage and Plating Wastes," *Sewage and Industrial Wastes*, Vol. 24, p. 1254 (1952).

[6] Flask No. JF3430, obtainable from the Scientific Glass Apparatus Co , Inc., 735 Broad St., Bloomfield, N.J. has been found satisfactory for this purpose.

[7] Stem No. JS8475, obtainable from the Scientific Glass Apparatus Co., has been found satisfactory for this purpose.

[8] Condenser No. JC7800, obtainable from the Scientific Glass Apparatus Co., has been found satisfactory for this purpose.

sealed to the absorber inlet are necessary.[9] The absorber tube should be approximately 200 mm long and 29 mm in diameter. Fit the hose connections to a vacuum source with a screw clamp for flow rate adjustment. Assemble the apparatus as indicated in Fig. 1.

grade chemicals shall be used in all tests. Unless otherwise indicated, it is intended that all reagents shall conform to specifications of the Committee on Analytical Reagents of the American Chemical Society, where such specifications are available.[10] Other grades may be used,

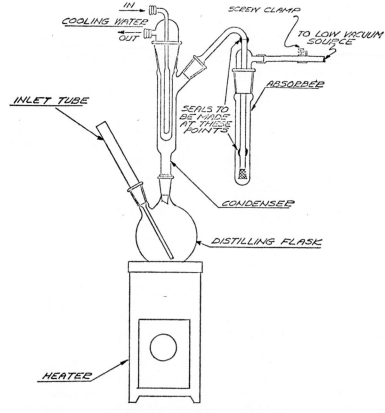

Fig. 1.—Cyanide Distillation Apparatus.

(b) *Microburet*, of 5-ml capacity, for the titration procedure.

(c) *Spectrophotometer or Filter Photometer*, suitable for measurements at 620 mμ, using 1.0-cm absorption cells.

Reagents

5. (a) *Purity of Reagents*.—Reagent

[9] Absorber No. JV8650, obtainable from the Scientific Glass Co., has been found satisfactory for this purpose.

provided it is first ascertained that the reagent is of sufficiently high purity to permit its use without lessening the accuracy of the determination.

[10] "Reagent Chemicals, American Chemical Society Specifications," Am. Chemical Soc., Washington, D. C. For suggestions on the testing of reagents not listed by the American Chemical Society, see "Reagent Chemicals and Standards," by Joseph Rosin, D. Van Nostrand Co., Inc., New York, N Y. and the "United States Pharmacopeia."

(b) *Purity of Water.*—Unless otherwise indicated, references to water shall be understood to mean reagent water conforming to the Specifications for Reagent Water (ASTM Designation: D 1193).[11]

(c) *Acetic Acid (1:9).*—Mix one volume of glacial acetic acid with nine volumes of water.

(d) *Acid Cuprous Chloride Solution.*—Weigh 2 g of finely powdered cuprous chloride (CuCl) into a 250-ml beaker; wash twice, by decantation, with 25-ml portions of sulfuric acid (H_2SO_4, 1:48) and then twice with water. Add about 25 ml of water, then add concentrated hydrochloric acid (HCl, sp gr 1.19) dropwise until the salt dissolves. Dilute to 100 ml with water and store in a tightly-stoppered bottle containing a few pieces of pure copper wire or rod extending from the bottom to the mouth of the bottle. Prepare a large volume of reagent and refill the reagent bottle in use from the stock solution after each use.

Note 4.—Always keep the reagent bottle completely filled. The reagent should be clear; dark discoloration indicates the presence of cupric salts.

(e) *Ascorbic Acid.*

(f) *Bis-Pyrazolone.*[12]—To prepare, dissolve 17.4 g of the pure 1-phenyl-3-methyl-5-pyrazolone[13] in 100 ml of 95 per cent ethanol. Add 25 g of freshly distilled phenylhydrazine and reflux the mixture for at least 4 hr. Filter off the insoluble portion and wash with hot alcohol.

(g) *Calcium Hypochlorite Solution (50 g per liter).*—Dissolve 5 g of calcium hypochlorite ($Ca(OCl)_2$) reagent in 100 ml of water. Store the solution in an amber-colored glass bottle in the dark. Make fresh monthly.

[11] Appears in this publication.
[12] Eastman Kodak Co. Chemical No. 6969 has been found satisfactory for this purpose.
[13] Eastman Kodak Co. Chemical No. 1397 has been found satisfactory for this purpose.

(h) *Chloramine-T (10 g per liter).*—Dissolve 1.0 g of the white-colored, water-soluble grade powder in 100 ml of water. Prepare fresh weekly.

(i) *1-Phenyl-3-Methyl-5-Pyrazolone.*[13]

(j) *Potassium Cyanide, Stock Solution (1 ml = 1 mg CN^-).*—Dissolve 2.51 g of potassium cyanide (KCN) and approximately 2 g of potassium hydroxide (KOH) in 1 liter of water. Standardize against the silver nitrate standard solution by the modified Liebig titration (Section 9(o) through (q) using a 25-ml sample. Prepare the solution fresh every week.

(k) *Potassium Cyanide, Standard Solution (1 ml = 1 µg CN^-).*—Dilute 10 ml of the stock KCN to 1 liter with water. Mix thoroughly and make a second dilution of 10 ml diluted to 100 ml with water. Prepare this solution fresh daily and keep in a glass-stoppered bottle.

(l) *Potassium Iodide—Starch Test Paper.*

(m) *Pyridine.*

(n) *Pyridine-Pyrazolone Reagent.*—Prepare this mixture daily.

Solution A.—Add 0.25 g of 1-phenyl-3-methyl-5-pyrazolone[13] to 50 ml of water. Heat the solution to about 60 C with stirring. Cool to room temperature.

Solution B.—Dissolve 0.01 g of the *bis*-pyrazolone[12] in 10 ml of pyridine. Pour Solution *A* into a filter and catch the filtrate. Then pour Solution *B* through the same filter and catch the filtrate in the same container with Solution *A*. Several minutes of mixing are usually necessary to dissolve the *bis*-pyrazolone[12] in pyridine. The mixed reagent develops a pink color on standing but this does not affect the color production with cyanide if used within 24 hr.

(o) *Rhodanine Indicator (0.2 g per liter).*—Dissolve 0.02 g of *p*-dimethylaminobenzalrhodanine in 100 ml of acetone.

(p) *Silver Nitrate, Standard Solution*

(*1 ml = 1 mg CN⁻*).—Crush approximately 5 g of silver nitrate ($AgNO_3$) crystals and dry to constant weight at 40 C. Dissolve 3.2647 g of crushed, dried crystals in water and dilute to 1 liter with water.

(*q*) *Sodium Hydroxide Solution (50 g per liter).*—Dissolve 50 g of sodium hydroxide (NaOH) in water and dilute to 1000 ml with water.

(*r*) *Sulfuric Acid (1:1).*—Carefully mix 1 volume of concentrated sulfuric acid (H_2SO_4, sp gr 1.84) with 1 volume of water, while stirring constantly. Cool before using.

Sampling

6. (*a*) Collect the sample in accordance with the Methods of Sampling Homogeneous Industrial Waste Water (ASTM Designation: D 1496).[11]

(*b*) If the sample cannot be analyzed immediately, stabilize it by the addition of NaOH to a pH of 12.0 or more and store in a closed bottle.

(*c*) As cyanogen chloride will be hydrolized to cyanate at pH 12 or more, collect a separate sample when an analysis for cyanogen chloride is required. Use a closed container and omit the caustic soda addition. Conduct the analysis as soon as possible after sampling.

Preparation of Sample

7. (*a*) For determination of cyanides amenable to chlorination, divide the sample into two equal parts. Chlorinate one part in accordance with Paragraphs (*b*) and (*c*).

(*b*) Add $Ca(OCl)_2$ dropwise while agitating and maintaining the pH between 11 and 12 by the addition of NaOH solution. Place one drop of the solution on a strip of KI-starch paper. A distinct blue color will indicate the presence of sufficient chlorine. Maintain the excess residual chlorine for 1 hr while agitating. If necessary, add additional $Ca(OCl)_2$.

(*c*) Add approximately 0.5 g of ascorbic acid to reduce the residual chlorine. Test with KI-starch paper. There should not be any color. Again add approximately 0.5 g of ascorbic acid to ensure the presence of excess reducing agent.

Calibration

8. (*a*) From the standard KCN solution (1 ml = 1 μg CN⁻ described in Section 5(*k*), prepare a series of standard samples containing from 1 to 10 μg of cyanide. Treat the samples in accordance with Section 9(*r*) through (*w*).

(*b*) Prepare a calibration curve by plotting the absorbances developed in the standard samples against the concentration in micrograms of cyanide per 50 ml of solution.

(*c*) If the calibration curve appears essentially straight and regular, prepare and process as described in Paragraphs (*a*) and (*b*) standard samples containing less than 1 and over 10 μg of cyanide to determine the limits of concentration measurable with the particular photometer being used.

Procedure

9. (*a*) Use a 500-ml portion of the sample when the cyanide content of the sample is known to be 10 mg per liter or less. If the cyanide is known to be over 10 mg per liter, use a proportionately smaller size sample. In either case, if the cyanide is known to be over 1 mg per liter, distill as described in Paragraphs (*e*) through (*n*) and titrate as described in Paragraphs (*o*) through (*q*).

(*b*) If the cyanide content is known to be less than 1 mg per liter, distill a 500-ml sample as described in Paragraphs (*e*) through (*n*) and determine the cyanide content by the colorimetric procedure as described in Paragraphs (*r*) through (*w*).

(*c*) If the cyanide concentration is unknown, distill a 500-ml sample as described in Paragraphs (e) through (n). Dilute the absorption liquid and washings, obtained in accordance with Paragraphs (e) through (n), to 250 ml. From this liquid take a 200-ml aliquot and titrate as described in Paragraphs (o) through (q). If this titration indicates the cyanide concentration to be less than 1 mg per liter, determine the cyanide concentration colorimetrically on the remaining portion as described in Paragraphs (r) through (w). Should it be desirable to recover cyanide in a more concentrated form than indicated above, a minimum total volume of absorbing solution of 50 ml could be used instead of 250 ml.

(d) For determination of cyanides amenable to chlorination, proceed in accordance with Paragraphs (a), (b), and (c) for both the chlorinated portion and the nonchlorinated portion of the sample. The difference between the cyanide concentration calculated for each of these two portions is equal to the concentration of cyanide amenable to chlorination.

Distillation Procedure

(e) Set up the equipment as shown in Fig. 1 and introduce the sample into the distilling flask. Dilute, if necessary to 250 to 500 ml with water.

(f) Add 50 ml of NaOH solution to the absorber and dilute if necessary with water to obtain an adequate depth of liquid in the absorber.

(g) Start a gentle stream of air bubbling into the sample solution and adjust the suction so that approximately one bubble of air per second enters the boiling flask through the air inlet.

(h) Add 50 ml of H_2SO_4 (1:1), in small increments to the distilling flask.

(i) Pour 10 ml of the acid CuCl solution into the air inlet and wash down by means of a stream of water from a wash bottle.

(j) Gently heat the contents of the distilling flask. Heating should be gradual and at such a rate that a slow refluxing action occurs. Too rapid heating may release dissolved gas too rapidly at first and force sample up into the air inlet.

(k) Continue the refluxing and the passage of air for 1 hr (having an air stream during the entire refluxing procedure is all-important). Turn off the heat, but continue the air flow. After 15 min of cooling, transfer the absorption liquid to a separate container. Thoroughly rinse the absorber and its connecting tube into the container with water.

(l) Refill the absorber with a fresh charge of sodium hydroxide caustic solution and repeat the reflux procedure outlined in Paragraph (g).

(m) If the sample contains readily hydrolyzed cyanides, the absorber liquid from the first reflux will contain all of the available cyanide; if stable complex cyanides are present, a significant yield will appear in the absorber liquid from the second, or from several successive periods, depending upon the degree of stability.

(n) When the optimum time for evolution of cyanide is established for a certain type of sample, distillation may be made on this type of sample for the optimum period, thus eliminating repetition of the reflux procedure outlined in Paragraph (h).

Modified Liebig Titration

(o) Dilute the absorption liquid, or the portion thereof, obtained as described in the distillation procedure given in Section 9 to a convenient volume to be used in all titrations.

(p) Add 0.5 ml of the rhodanine indicator solution.

(q) Titrate with standard silver nitrate solution to the first change in color from a canary yellow to a salmon hue. Titrate a blank containing the same amount of alkali and water. Record the results of the titration and calculate the cyanide concentration in accordance with Section 10(a).

Colorimetric Procedure

(r) Take an aliquot of the absorption liquid obtained from the distillation procedure described in Paragraphs (e) through (n). The volume of this aliquot must be calculated from the estimated cyanide concentration so that it will contain an amount of cyanide measurable with the photometer to be used, as determined in accordance with Section 8.

(s) Place the aliquot of the absorption liquid in a 50-ml beaker and dilute, if necessary, to about 20 ml with water. While mixing constantly, carefully add acetic acid (1:9) from a buret, the tip of which extends well beneath the surface of the solution. A magnetic stirrer will facilitate this addition. Add the acid until the pH of the solution is between 7.0 and 7.5. At no time permit an excess of acid to be present as this would cause loss of cyanide by the evolution of HCN.

(t) Transfer immediately to a 50-ml volumetric flask, add 0.2 ml of chloramine-T solution, and stopper and mix by flask inversion two or three times. Allow 1 to 2 min for the reaction.

(u) Add 5 ml of the mixed pyridine-pyrazolone reagent, dilute to the mark with water, stopper, and mix well by flask inversion and agitation. Allow 20 min for color development.

(v) Measure the absorbance of the developed color with a photometer at 620 mμ and determine the concentration of cyanide in the sample by reference to the calibration curve prepared in accordance with Section 8.

(w) Record the results and make the calculations as shown in Section 10.

Calculations

10. (a) *Modified Liebig Titration (for*

CN⁻ Concentrations Equal to or Greater Than 1 mg per Liter).—Calculate the cyanide concentration as follows:

$$CN^-, \text{ mg per liter} = \frac{(A - B) \times 1000}{C} \times \frac{D}{E}$$

where:

A = milliliters of $AgNO_3$ required for titration of the aliquot,
B = milliliters of $AgNO_3$ required for titration of the blank,
C = milliliters of original sample,
D = milliliters of diluted absorbing solution, and
E = milliliters of aliquot used.

(b) *Colorimetric Procedure (for CN⁻ Concentrations Lower than 1 mg per Liter).*—Calculate the cyanide concentration as follows:

$$CN^-, \text{ mg per liter} = \frac{F \times D}{C \times E}$$

where:
F = micrograms of cyanide determined,
D = milliliters of diluted absorbing solution,
C = milliliters of original sample, and
E = milliliters of aliquot used.

(c) *Cyanide Amenable to Chlorination Treatment.*—Calculate the cyanide concentration as follows:

$$CN^-, \text{ mg per liter} = G - H$$

where:

G = milligrams per liter of CN⁻ in un-chlorinated portion of the sample, and
H = milligrams per liter of CN⁻ in chlorinated portion of the sample.

Report

11. Report the results of analyses in accordance with the Method of Reporting Results of Analysis of Industrial Water and Industrial Waste Water

(ASTM Designation: D 596),[11] Sections 10 and 11.

Precision

12. (*a*) The single laboratory precision of the titrimetric procedure is determined as follows:

$$S_c = 0.002X + 0.02$$

where:

S_c = single laboratory precision, and
X = level of cyanide determined in milligrams per liter.

(*b*) The single laboratory precision of the colorimetric procedure is 0.03 mg at a level of 1 mg per liter of cyanide.

Tentative Method of Test for

EVALUATING INHIBITORY TOXICITY OF INDUSTRIAL WASTE WATERS[1]

ASTM Designation: D 2037 – 64 T

Issued, 1964

This Tentative Method has been approved by the sponsoring committee and accepted by the Society in accordance with established procedures, for use pending adoption as standard. Suggestions for revisions should be addressed to the Society at 1916 Race St., Philadelphia 3, Pa.

Scope

1. (a) This is a non-referee batch method[2] for evaluating the inhibitory toxicity of waste waters to diatoms (see Sections 2(a) and (b)). It can be performed with standard reference water and reference chemicals, and provides information on the toxicity of a sample under prescribed experimental conditions. It is not intended to be a measure of acute toxicity for aquatic life.

(b) The method is applicable to industrial waters and industrial waste waters. Solutions having volatile or readily oxidizable constituents may be tested in accordance with this method (see Section 4(g)).

Summary of Method

2. (a) Samples of waste water are compared to standard control solutions for their inhibitory effect on growth of diatoms in pure culture. The concentration of test material which decreases the amount of growth to 50 per cent of that in the controls within a test period of 7 days is used as a measure of relative toxicity. Where a waste water at its maximal test concentration exhibits insufficient inhibitory toxicity during 7 days for determination of the median inhibitory limit, it is assumed that the substance does not have inhibitory toxicity.

(b) This test with diatoms is similar in concept to the toxicity test for fish but results will differ since it measures inhibitory effects on growth rather than acute toxicity. Research at the Academy of Natural Sciences[3, 4] has shown that the sensitivity of diatoms to industrial wastes is very similar to that of fish in most

[1] Under the standardization procedure of the Society, this method is under the jurisdiction of the ASTM Committee D-19 on Industrial Water. A list of members may be found in the ASTM Year Book.

[2] This method was developed by Dr. Ruth Patrick, Curator of Limnology, Academy of Natural Sciences, Philadelphia, Pa.

[3] R. Patrick, "The Sensitivity of Aquatic Life to Certain Chemicals Commonly Found in Industrial Wastes," U. S. Public Health Service Grant RG-3925 (C2R1), Final Report (1960).

[4] R. Patrick, "Diatoms as Indicators of Changes in Environmental Conditions," Transactions of the Seminar on Biological Problems in Water Pollution, April 23–27. 1956, U. S. Public Health Service (1957).

741

cases. There are exceptions such as with chromates, heavy metals, and radiant-energy absorbing dyes, but in most instances where mixed wastes are concerned, toxicity is similar.

Definitions

3. (*a*) *Diatoms.*—Microscopic unicellular or colonial algae constituting the class Bacillarieae and having silicified cell walls. They are of great importance in the self-purification of natural waters and as food for many other forms of aquatic life.

(*b*) *Inhibitory Toxicity.*—Any direct inhibitory action of pollutants on the rate of reproduction of diatoms which is demonstrable within 7 days or less of testing.

(*c*) *Median Inhibitory Limit* (IL_m).— The concentration of test material which decreases the amount of growth to 50 per cent of that in the controls, within a test period of 7 days. It is the recommended measure or index of relative toxicity. Specifically, it is a concentration value derived by graphical interpolation and is based on the amount of growth made in 7 days in the test flasks as compared with that made in a control.

Interferences

4. (*a*) If the toxic constituent of a waste is volatile, there is a tendency for the toxicity of the test solution to decrease throughout the duration of the test. Unstable substances will decline throughout the test period and the rate of loss will be influenced by the degree of agitation. Agitation by aeration should be avoided when volatile substances are present.

(*b*) Volatile toxic substances may be developed in the test solution as a result of chemical action. For example, when a nonvolatile, strongly acidic substance is dissolved in the dilution water, it reacts with the carbonates naturally present in the water and releases carbon dioxide

which may be injurious either directly, by its toxic action, or by holding in solution other toxic components such as heavy metals. Therefore, acid solutions or solutions containing salts which hydrolyze to form acid solutions must be regarded as volatile substances.

(*c*) Strongly alkaline solutions may exhibit changes similar to those usually attributed to volatility of toxic compounds by absorption of carbon dioxide from the test organism or from the air used for aeration.

(*d*) Substances that are ordinarily considered to be nonvolatile may form toxic volatile products by hydrolysis. For example, the toxic salt sodium cyanide, when in dilute solution, is hydrolyzed in part to hydrocyanic acid. Materials reacting in this manner may have to be considered as volatile, even though the volatility is the property of the secondary product.

(*e*) Certain chemicals, such as phenol, may undergo biological or chemical oxidation. If the oxidation proceeds rapidly, the toxicant may be changed before the toxicity test is performed. If advisable, biological oxidation may be eliminated by carrying out the experiments under sterile conditions. When such toxic material undergoes very rapid oxidation to a nontoxic form, there is little need for concern over inability of the test to measure the toxicity of the material before oxidation, since such toxicity may not present a waste disposal problem.

(*f*) The presence of readily oxidizable constituents may stimulate biological growth except at relatively high concentrations where they may retard growth. Growth inhibition in this case may be due to a depletion of oxygen or other effects; however, the depletion of oxygen only becomes a serious consideration during the nighttime when sunlight is not available since these plants produce their own oxygen.

(g) Some toxic metals form insoluble or only very slightly soluble carbonates or hydroxides and these may form insoluble precipitates when their soluble salts are added to the dilution water used in preparing test solutions. The actual concentration of toxic metals in the test solutions will therefore depend upon the concentration and kind of ions in the dilution water. For example, diatoms can utilize zinc or other heavy metals in the precipitated form and thus become toxic by the presence of precipitants as well as dissolved forms. In this case diatoms are more sensitive to these metals than are fish. Under these conditions, the value obtained for the median inhibitory limit for such a toxic metal may vary with the dilution water used by different investigators. For this reason, the composition of the dilution water must be reported along with the value obtained for the median inhibitory limit. The formation of any precipitate or turbidity during the dilution step also must be recorded.

Apparatus

5. (a) *Compound Microscope.*—A binocular-type compound microscope equipped with a detachable mechanical stage capable of moving all parts of a standard counting cell past the aperture of the objective. The microscope shall also have an adequate combination of oculars and objectives consisting of 7.5 × and 10 × oculars and the following objectives: 4 mm, 16 mm, and water immersion.

(b) *Constant Temperature Room.*—A cabinet or water bath capable of maintaining a temperature within ±1 C of the selected test temperature.

(c) *Counting Cell.*—A Sedgewick-Rafter counting cell of 1-ml capacity, having a rectangular shape with inside dimensions of 20 by 50 mm.

(d) *Cover Glasses* to accompany the Sedgewick-Rafter cell.

(e) *Culturing Vessels.*—Erlenmeyer flasks of 500-ml capacity.

(f) *Hemacytometer.*—Blood counting chamber to be used when diatoms are less than 40 μ in length.

(g) *Lights.*—"Daylight" fluorescent lights to provide approximately 250 to 350 ft-candles.

(h) *Mixing Facilities.*—Compressed filtered air, shaker, or corrosion-resistant mechanical mixer.

(i) *Stage Micrometer.*

(j) *Test Containers.*—Erlenmeyer flasks of 125-ml capacity.

(k) *Whipple Disk Ocular Micrometer.*

Reagents and Materials

6. (a) *Purity of Reagents.*—Reagent grade chemicals shall be used in all tests. Unless otherwise indicated, it is intended that all reagents shall conform to the specifications of the Committee on Analytical Reagents of the American Chemical Society, where such specifications are available.[5] Other grades may be used, provided it is first ascertained that the reagent is of sufficiently high purity to permit its use without lessening the accuracy of the determination.

(b) *Purity of Water.*—Unless otherwise indicated, references to water shall be understood to mean reagent water conforming to specifications of Reagent Water (ASTM Designation: D 1193).[6]

(c) *Aluminum Chloride* ($AlCl_3 \cdot 6H_2O$).

(d) *Ammonium Nitrate* (NH_4NO_3).

(e) *Boric Acid* (H_3BO_3).

(f) *Calcium Carbonate* ($CaCO_3$).

(g) *Calcium Nitrate* ($Ca(NO_3)_2 \cdot 4H_2O$).

(h) *Citric Acid.*

---

[5] "Reagent Chemicals, American Chemical Society Specifications," Am. Chemical Soc., Washington, D. C. For suggestions on the testing of reagents not listed by the American Chemical Society, see "Reagent Chemicals and Standards," by Joseph Rosin, D. Van Nostrand Co., Inc., New York, N. Y. and the "United States Pharmacopeia."

[6] Appears in this publication.

(*i*) *Cobalt Chloride* (CoCl$_2 \cdot$6H$_2$O).

(*j*) *Ferric Citrate* (FeC$_6$H$_5$O$_7 \cdot$3H$_2$O).

(*k*) *Lithium Chloride* (LiCl).

(*l*) *Magnesium Carbonate* (MgCO$_3$).

(*m*) *Magnesium Sulfate* (MgSO$_4$).

(*n*) *Manganese Sulfate* (MnSO$_4$).

(*o*) *Potassium Chloride* (KCl).

(*p*) *Potassium Phosphate, Dibasic* (K$_2$HPO$_4$).

(*q*) *Sodium Bicarbonate* (NaHCO$_3$).

(*r*) *Sodium Metasilicate* (Na$_2$SiO$_3 \cdot$9H$_2$O).

(*s*) *Zinc Sulfate* (ZnSO$_4$).

(*t*) *Dilution Water.*—The purpose of the test will determine the type of dilution water to be used in the preparation of test solutions of the test substance. For actual pollution studies, the most desirable dilution water is that natural water into which the waste effluent is to be discharged. Unless there are specific reasons to the contrary, it is advisable to obtain the dilution water from the receiving body of water at a point where there is no unnatural pollution from any source.

If unpolluted dilution water cannot be obtained from the receiving body of water, water of similar quality, with respect to dissolved mineral content shall be obtained from some other source, or synthesized by adding appropriate chemicals to available natural water of suitable quality. The natural water may first be diluted, if necessary, with reagent water to establish appropriate solute ranges. As a general rule, the calcium, magnesium, sulfate, and total dissolved solids content of the synthesized water, and especially its total alkalinity, should not differ from those of the waste-receiving stream by more than 25 per cent. Nitrates, phosphates and silica are added since batch cultures require greater starting concentrations to account for depletion than would be the case in natural dynamic stream situations.

(*u*) *Standard Reference Water.*—If the purpose of the test is to obtain comparative data from cooperating laboratories using solutions of pure chemical compounds, standard reference waters shall be used for dilution. Since the composition of the dilution water may have a significant effect on the test results, it is advisable to use two reference waters. One should be typical of soft waters and the other typical of hard waters. Almost all waters, because of their low nutrient levels, must have nutrients added to serve as satisfactory culture media. The stock solutions, soil extract, micrometabolic solutions, and ferric citrate solutions listed in Items (*1*) to (*4*) provide essential nutrients.

(*1*) *Stock Solutions for Standard Reference Waters.*—The stock solutions for preparing waters shall be as follows:

Constituent of Stock Solution	Concentration, g per liter	
	Soft Water	Hard Water
Calcium nitrate............	15.226	15.226
Potassium phosphate, dibasic.................	1.6	1.6
Magnesium sulfate........	8.0	20.78
Potassium chloride........	4.0	2.92
Sodium metasilicate.......	70.8	35.4
Calcium carbonate........	2.0	15.33
Sodium bicarbonate........	8.0	5.6
Magnesium carbonate......	...	3.840
Ammonium nitrate........	...	0.729

(*2*) *Soil Extract for Enriching Standard Reference Water.*—To 350 ml of water (boiling) add 35 g of organically enriched soil. Remove from the heat, stir, and let stand for 15 min. Filter through ashless fine-textured filter paper. Pour in a screw top bottle and autoclave. The yield is approximately 225 ml of extract. Use 1 ml of this weak solution per 250 ml of dilution water. Autoclave every time the bottle cap is removed and replaced.

(3) Micrometabolic Solution for Enriching Standard Reference Water:[7]

Constituent	Concentration, mg per liter
Zinc sulfate	20
Manganese sulfate	14
Aluminum chloride	36
Boric acid	20
Lithium chloride	10
Cobalt chloride	10

(4) Ferric Citrate Solution for Enriching Standard Reference Water:

1.820 of ferric citrate
1.30 of citric acid
In most cases use 1 ml per liter.

(v) Standard Reference Water Culture Medium.

—To 1 liter of water distilled from a glass still, add 5 ml of the appropriate soft water or hard water stock solution, 4 ml of soil extract solution, 1 ml of micrometabolic stock solution, and 1 ml of ferric citrate solution.

The culture composition shall be as follows:

Constituent	Soft Water	Hard Water
Calcium nitrate	76.1 mg	76.1 mg
Potassium phosphate	8.0 mg	8.0 mg
Magnesium sulfate	40.0 mg	103.9 mg
Potassium chloride	20.0 mg	14.6 mg
Sodium silicate	354.0 mg	177.0 mg
Calcium carbonate	10.0 mg	76.6 mg
Sodium bicarbonate	40.0 mg	28.0 mg
Magnesium carbonate	...	19.2 mg
Ammonium nitrate	...	3.6 mg
Soil extract solution	4 ml	4 ml
Micro metabolic solution	1 ml	1 ml
Ferric citrate solution	1 ml	1 ml

Sterilize by autoclaving for 20 min at 20 psi and 120 C.

(w) Reference Test Chemical.

—Each investigator may select at his own discretion any pure chemical compound to be used as a reference test chemical. Toxicity tests on this chemical may be run as often as required to provide the investigator with information relative to the reproducibility of the test data with that chemical. It is recommended that a standard reference water culture medium be used as the dilution water for use with the reference chemical.

Test Organism

7. (a) The recommended test organism is a pure culture[8] of the diatom *Nitzschia linearis* W. Sm. for soft water (less than 100 ppm as $CaCO_3$) and *Navicula seminulum* var. *husteditii* Patr. for hard or soft water, and *N. pelliculosa* (*Breb.*) Hilse for hard water.

(b) The organism should be cultured in the laboratory for several weeks before being used in tests. The method of culturing shall be as follows:

(1) To a 500-ml flask containing 250 ml of culture media (soft or hard water culture medium (see Section 6(v))) add with a sterile pipet a 1-ml portion of the pure culture, aerate vigorously, and stopper with a cotton plug. Place the flask in a transparent constant-temperature device so that light is not excluded and maintain the temperature constant at any point between 18 and 28 C throughout the toxicity test. During the daytime, augment the daylight with "daylight" fluorescent lights to provide a total of about 300 ft-candles. Shut off the artificial lights (see Section 5(g)) at the end of each normal working day. At the end of a week withdraw from the flask about 10 ml of solution and add to a fresh supply of culture medium in another 500-ml flask. This new flask shall be placed in the constant-temperature device and aerated. The contents of the flask from which the 10-ml aliquot was drawn may be discarded. Arti-

---

[7] S. P. Chu, "The Influence of the Mineral Composition of the Medium on the Growth of the Planktonic Algae," Part I, Methods and Culture Media, *Journal of Ecology*, Vol. 30 (2), pp. 284–325 (1942).

[8] Pure cultures of these organisms on agar slants may be obtained at nominal cost from Dr. Ruth Patrick of the Academy of Natural Sciences, Philadelphia, Pa.

ficial light shall be supplied to the new flask during the daytime, as in the original exposure. Such transfers to fresh culture medium shall be made weekly for several weeks, or until a normal growth rate is established at which time toxicity tests may be conducted. This procedure shall be continued throughout the duration of the toxicity tests.

(2) Upon the completion of the testing program, the culture may be transferred back to an agar slant containing culture nutrients, allowed to grow for a few days in light, and then stored for 3 to 4 months in a refrigerator before another retransfer is required. Healthy cultures should double their numbers every two to three days. This normally occurs during the logarithmic growth phase. The condition of a culture may be observed by counting cell numbers (Section 10(f)) on several successive days. Cultures should not be used for testing purposes unless a plotting of the results of daily counts shows that the organisms are in the logarithmic phase of growth.

Sampling

8. Collect the sample in accordance with the Methods of Sampling Homogeneous Industrial Waste Water (ASTM Designation: D 1496).[6]

Microscopic Calibration

9. (a) Determine how many intervals on the ocular micrometer are required to cover one of several intervals on the scale of the stage micrometer. This calibration must be repeated for each combination of ocular and objective.

(b) Match a line at one end of the ocular scale with a similar line of the stage micrometer scale. Note the number of stage micrometer divisions between the ocular scale divisions. Since the distance between lines on the stage micrometer is accurately known, the linear value of each ocular division can be deter-

mined. The measurement of each linear distance should be repeated as many times as necessary to provide a reliable average (at least ten measurements). When high-power objectives are calibrated, the stage micrometer lines are magnified to a point where they have appreciable width. As a result the calibration procedure must be modified by placing an ocular line alongside of, rather than end-to-end with the stage micrometer lines.

(c) It is convenient to plot on arithmetic paper the divisions on ocular micrometer versus microns on the stage micrometer. Prepare a different plot for each combination of ocular and objective lenses.

(d) Determine the number of times the area of the ocular micrometer is contained in the area of the counting cell. This determines the number of fields in the cell.

Procedure

10. (a) Make counts at the beginning of the experiment and on the seventh day. Plot the per cent reductions in growth in the various concentrations. From this graph obtain the concentration causing 50 per cent reduction. Obtain points indicating both more and less than a 50 per cent decrease in amount of growth.

Prepare all dilutions required for a single toxicity evaluation from the same sample of waste, portions of which shall be stored until needed at a temperature of 1 to 5 C in completely filled, tightly-stoppered bottles. Hold the duration of such storage to a minimum and report along with the source and nature of the sample.

By agitation, uniformly disperse any undissolved material present in a sample of waste water before a measured portion is withdrawn for mixing with dilution water. Avoid unnecessary exposure of the sample to the atmosphere and violent agitation.

(*b*) Pour 50-ml aliquots of selected dilution into 125-ml Erlenmeyer flasks to ensure relatively large surface-to-volume ratio and thus allow for free exchange of gases between liquid and air when the sample is added to the dilutant.

(*c*) Pour into the selected dilution the volume of sample necessary to produce a given per cent concentration and agi-

TABLE I.—A GUIDE TO THE SELECTION OF EXPERIMENTAL CONCENTRATION BASED ON PROGRESSIVE BISECTION OF INTERVALS ON A LOGARITHMIC SCALE.

Column 1	Column 2	Column 3	Column 4	Column 5
10.0	...	...	...	...
...	...	...	...	8.7
...	...	...	7.5	...
...	...	...	...	6.5
...	...	5.6	...	...
...	...	...	...	4.9
...	...	...	4.2	...
...	...	...	...	3.7
...	3.2	...	...	...
...	...	...	...	2.8
...	...	...	2.4	...
...	...	...	...	2.1
...	...	1.8	...	...
...	...	...	...	1.55
...	...	...	1.35	...
...	...	...	...	1.15
1.0	...	...	...	...

tate the mixture well. Suggested experimental concentrations are described in Tables I and II.

(*d*) Set up two controls, each containing 50 ml of the dilution water selected for the test.

(*e*) For each test, inoculate duplicate test flasks and control flasks (four in all) with exactly 1 ml each of a culture of diatoms which has been well mixed to ensure a uniform inoculum.

(*f*) To inoculate, select the stock culture which shows the most abundant growth of organisms. Pour off the supernatant liquid to leave approximately 100 ml of cells and liquid and thereby con-

centrate the diatoms in the medium. Using a sterile rubber policeman, scrape the organisms from the sides and bottom of the flask, and transfer all of the organisms to a blender[9] which has been previously steam sterilized in an autoclave for 20 min at 120 C and cooled. Use the medium in the blender to rinse the flask several times. Blend organisms 2 to 4 min. Take care that the blender does not become too warm, or the cells will be killed.

TABLE II.—A GUIDE TO THE SELECTION OF EXPERIMENTAL CONCENTRATIONS BASED ON DECILOG INTERVALS.

Concentrations		Log Concentration
Column 1	Column 2	
10.00	...	1.00
...	7.94 (or 7.9)	0.90
6.31 (or 6.3)	...	0.80
...	5.01 (or 5.0)	0.70
3.98 (or 4.0)	...	0.60
...	3.16 (or 3.15)	0.50
2.51 (or 2.5)	...	0.40
...	1.99 (or 2.0)	0.30
1.58 (or 1.6)	...	0.20
...	1.26 (or 1.25)	0.10
1.00	...	0.00

(*g*) Statistically analyze the inoculum count as follows to determine the accuracy of the counting:

(*1*) Determine the standard deviation of the 50 fields using the standard equation as follows:

$$s = \sqrt{\frac{\Sigma (X - \bar{X})^2}{n - 1}}$$

where:
s = standard deviation,
X = an individual score,
n = number of fields counted, and
$\bar{X}$ = arithmetic mean of sample.

---

[9] A Waring blendor has been found satisfactory for this purpose.

(2) Determine $s_{\bar{x}}$ as follows:

$$s_{\bar{x}} = \frac{s}{\sqrt{n}}$$

(3) When $2s_{\bar{x}}/M$ is less than 30 per cent, the count is reliable.

(4) The number of cells per field in a flask at the time of inoculation (Y_0) can be taken as follows:

The number of cells per field as counted on the slide times the dilution factor gives number of cells per field in inoculum, or the cells per field in inoculum divided by total volume of solution in test flask (usually 51 ml).

(h) Maintain the temperature constant (± 1 C) at some point between 18 and 28 C throughout the test period.

(i) Maintain illumination of approximately 250 to 350 ft-candles during 16 hr (day light period) of each test day and keep it at essentially zero illumination during the remaining 8-hr period.

(j) Agitate the samples and controls by aeration with compressed air, by use of a shaker, or by use of a corrosion-resistant mechanical mixer.

(k) Inoculate *accurately* each test flask with 1 ml of organisms by using a sterile bacteriological pipet. Do not touch off the last drop and be consistent in all techniques to ensure reproducibility. Do not inoculate more than 10 flasks without again blending the inoculum for a few seconds. The inoculum must be kept as uniform as possible.

(l) Calculate the number of diatoms introduced into each test flask as follows:

(1) Blend the inoculum as described in Paragraph (f). An undiluted inoculum may be too dense to count. It is difficult to count more than about 20 cells per microscopic field with accuracy. Have ready in test tubes 1.0-ml, 2.0-ml, 3.0-ml, and 4.0-ml portions of sterile culture medium. Use volumetric pipets and always drain them in the same manner. With a sterile 1-ml bacteriological pipet, measure accurately 1 ml of inoculum into the accurately measured volume of medium. Do not touch off the last drop. One of these four dilutions should give a convenient number of cells per field to count.

(2) Count 50 microscopic fields (at a density of 20 cells per field maximum). Do not record fields which contain clusters of cells that cannot be counted accurately. At least 1000 cells should be counted. If results are erratic, 2000 cells should be counted and the number of cells in each field recorded.

(3) Set up a table for recording results as follows:

Field Number	Number of Cells, X	X^2
1...............		
2...............		
3...............		

(m) Measure the pH and make quantitative chemical tests for pertinent constituents of the test solutions at the beginning and end of the test run. In cases of volatile constituents or constituents subject to change in composition, additional analytical tests must be run on the third and fifth days.

(n) After the 7-day test period, scrape the cells from the sides and bottom of the flask with a sterilized rubber policeman. Measure the contents of the flask to be sure the volume is the same as at the start of the 7-day test period. If not, add water to bring it up to volume. Blend the contents of the flask in a blender[9] until it begins to feel warm (usually 5 min). Prepare a slide in the same manner as for inoculum count. Count 100 fields; record the number of cells in groups of 10 fields.

Calculation

11. (a) Count all flasks to be used in determining the amount of growth at a

given concentration and record as follows:

Flask	Cells per 10 Fields (x)	M	Standard Deviation, $n = 10$	$\log\frac{Y_7}{Y_0}$	Number of Divisions
Control:					
1.......					
2.......					
3.......					
4.......					

where:

Y_7 = cells per field after 7 days incubation, and

Y_0 = cells per field at the time of inoculation.

(b) Make a statistical analysis of the final count as follows:

(1) Determine standard deviation of counts from each flask as follows:

$$s = \sqrt{\frac{\Sigma(X - \bar{X})^2}{n - 1}}$$

(2) Determine the range of the number of divisions for each flask by taking the average number of cells per field in the final count and adding or subtracting the standard deviation.

Determine the number of divisions as follows:

$$n = \left[\frac{\log\ (Y_7/Y_0)}{\log 2}\right]$$

where:

n = number of divisions,

Y_7 = number of cells per field at end of 7-day experiment, and

Y_0 = number of cells per field at beginning of experiment.

The cells per field are calculated by dividing the number of cells in ten fields by 10.

Report

12. (a) Record the following test data: temperature, light, dilution water, test organism used, concentration of waste tested, number of divisions in controls, and number of divisions in each of the test flasks after a 7-day test period.

(b) Express the number of divisions in each test flask as a percentage of the divisions in the controls. The concentration causing 50 per cent reduction in growth shall be interpolated graphically (using logarithmic graph paper) from the concentrations tested.

(c) The concentration of any sample which produces a 50 per cent reduction in growth (median inhibitory limit, IL_m) is reported as significant for diatoms. A biologically safe concentration is reported as 0.3 times that concentration at which 50 per cent reduction in growth occurs.

Precision and Accuracy

13. Due to the large number of variables encountered in such tests, no limits for precision and accuracy are given.

Tentative Method of Test for
RADIOACTIVE BARIUM IN INDUSTRIAL WATER AND INDUSTRIAL WASTE WATER[1]

ASTM Designation: D 2038 – 64 T

ISSUED, 1964

This Tentative Method has been approved by the sponsoring committee and accepted by the Society in accordance with established procedures, for use pending adoption as standard. Suggestions for revisions should be addressed to the Society at 1916 Race St., Philadelphia 3, Pa.

Scope

1. (a) This method[2] covers the measurement of radioactive barium contained in industrial water or industrial waste water in concentrations above 10^{-7} curie per liter. It is limited, by length of time of analysis, to barium radioisotopes of masses 139 and 140 which have half-lives longer than 1 hr and are fission products. Modifications in the analytical method are included for measuring radioactive barium in lower concentrations.

(b) The method may be used for absolute measurements by calibrating the nuclear radiation detector with a standard barium radioisotope of the same atomic mass, or for relative measurements by comparing the measurements made.

Summary of Method

2. (a) Radioactive barium and added barium carrier are first precipitated from water to reduce the sample volume, then chemically purified, and finally counted with a gamma counter or beta particle detector. The main purification step is the repeated precipitation of barium chloride from a cold hydrochloric acid-ether mixture, and scavenging with ferric hydroxide. A final precipitation of barium sulfate is made and the chemical yield is computed by comparing the weight of the precipitate to the amount of carrier added originally. The recovery of radioactive barium is assumed to be equal to the chemical yield.

(b) The barium sulfate precipitate is mounted and counted with a beta particle detector[3] or a gamma-ray counter.[3] Corrections are made for counter dead

---

[1] Under the standardization procedure of the Society, this method is under the jurisdiction of the ASTM Committee D-19 on Industrial Water. A list of members may be found in the ASTM Year Book.

[2] This method is based on a previously published method, see D. N. Sunderman and C. W. Townley, "The Radiochemistry of Barium, Calcium, and Strontium," National Academy of Sciences, National Research Council Publication *NAS-NS-3010*, pp. 29 to 32 (1960).

[3] For a discussion of beta counting, refer to the Method for Measurement of Beta Particle Radioactivity of Industrial Water and Industrial Waste Water (ASTM Designation: D 1890), which appears in this publication. For gamma counting, refer to the Method for Measurement of Gamma Radioactivity of Industrial Water and Industrial Waste Water (ASTM Designation: D 1690), which appears in this publication.

750

time, background count, chemical recovery, radioactive decay from sampling time, and growth of daughter activity following separation for the isotope of mass 140. If necessary, the activity contributed by each isotope is calculated. For absolute counting, the observed count rate is divided by the detector efficiency for the isotope concerned. The two isotopes may be distinguished by the characteristics listed in the Appendix.

Definitions

3. For definitions of terms used in this method, refer to the Definitions of Terms Relating to Industrial Water and Industrial Waste Water (ASTM Designation: D 1129)[4] and to other published glossaries.[5]

Interferences

4. (a) Nonradioactive barium present in the sample will interfere in the method causing an overestimation of chemical yield.

(b) The method provides a decontamination of more than 10^5-fold from other radionuclides. Decontamination from strontium and antimony, specifically, is somewhat poorer than for other nuclides but usually exceeds a value of 10^4 for strontium and 10^3 for antimony.[2]

(c) Sulfate ion will precipitate the added carrier and metathesis of this precipitate will be necessary.

Apparatus

5. (a) *Beta Particle Counter.*—Usually a proportional detector with the appropriate amplifier, discriminator, and scaling equipment. (Refer to Method D 1890.)

(b) *Gamma-Ray Counter.*—Preferably a sodium iodide scintillation detector assembly connected to the appropriate amplifier and pulse height analyzer or discriminator. (Refer to Method D 1690.)

Reagents

6. (a) *Purity of Reagents.*—Reagent grade chemicals shall be used in all tests. Unless otherwise indicated, it is intended that all reagents shall conform to the specifications of the Committee on Analytical Reagents of the American Chemical Society, where such specifications are available.[6] Other grades may be used, provided it is first ascertained that the reagent is of sufficiently high purity to permit its use without lessening the accuracy of the determination.

(b) *Purity of Water.*—Unless otherwise indicated, reference to water shall be understood to mean reagent water conforming to the Specifications for Reagent Water (ASTM Designation: D 1193).[4]

(c) *Radioactive purity* shall be such that the measured radioactivity of blank samples does not exceed the expected random counting error of the measurement.

(d) *Ammonium Hydroxide Solution (1:1).*—Mix 1 volume of concentrated ammonium hydroxide (NH_4OH, sp gr 0.90) with 1 volume of water.

(e) *Barium Nitrate, Carrier Solution (19 g per liter).*—Dissolve 19 g of barium nitrate ($Ba(NO_3)_2$) in water and dilute to 1 liter. This solution will contain 10 g of Ba^{++} per liter.

(f) *Ethyl Alcohol* (95 per cent).

(g) *Ethyl Ether.*

(h) *Ferric Nitrate, Carrier Solution (72 g per liter).*—Dissolve 72 g of ferric

---

[4] Appears in this publication.
[5] USA Standard "Glossary of Terms in Nuclear Science and Technology," USASI-N 1.1-1957.

[6] "Reagent Chemicals, American Chemical Society Specifications," Am. Chemical Soc., Washington, D. C. For suggestions on the testing of reagents not listed by the American Chemical Society, see "Reagent Chemicals and Standards," by Joseph Rosin, D. Van Nostrand Co., Inc., New York, N. Y. and the "United States Pharmacopeia."

nitrate ($Fe(NO_3)_3 \cdot 9H_2O$) in water containing 1 ml of concentrated nitric acid (HNO_3, sp gr 1.42) and dilute to 1 liter. This solution will contain 10 g of Fe^{+++} per liter.

tion (30.4 g per liter).—Dissolve 30.4 g of lanthanum nitrate ($La(NO_3)_3 \cdot 6H_2O$) in water and dilute to 1 liter. This solution will contain 10 g of La^{+++} per liter.

(*l*) *Sodium Carbonate Solution (106 g*

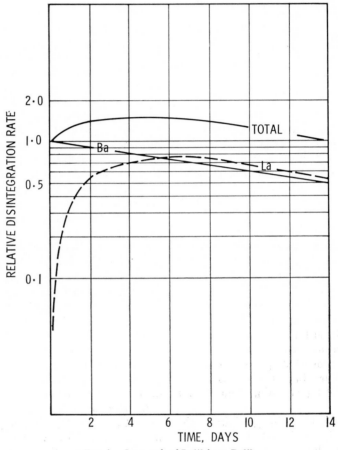

FIG. 1.—Ingrowth of La^{140} from Ba^{140}.

(*i*) *Hydrochloric Acid (sp gr 1.19).*— Concentrated hydrochloric acid (HCl).

(*j*) *Hydrochloric Acid - Ether Reagent.* —Slowly add 500 ml of concentrated hydrochloric acid (HCl, sp gr 1.19) to 100 ml of ethyl ether and mix. Cool in an ice bath before using (Note 1).

NOTE 1: **Caution.**—The hydrochloric acid - ether mixture should be prepared and stored in a fume hood. Naked flames must not be present.

(*k*) *Lanthanum Nitrate, Carrier Solu-*

per liter).—Dissolve 106 g of sodium carbonate (Na_2CO_3) in water and dilute to 1 liter.

(*m*) *Sulfuric Acid Solution (1:4).*— Cautiously mix 1 volume of concentrated sulfuric acid (sp gr 1.84) with 4 volumes of water.

Sampling

7. (*a*) Collect the sample in accordance with the applicable methods of the Amer-

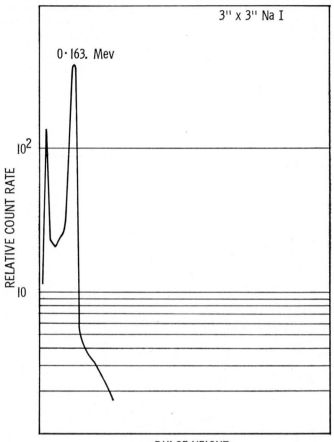

FIG. 2.—Gamma Spectra of 85-Min Ba139.

ican Society for Testing and Materials as follows:

D 510—Sampling Industrial Water (Particularly Sections 32 to 41),[4]
D 860—Sampling Water from Boilers,[4] and
D 1496—Sampling Homogeneous Industrial Waste Water.[4]

(b) Sample 1 liter or less depending on the expected radiobarium concentration. For gamma counting an activity of about 10^{-7} curie is desirable and for beta counting about 10^{-8} curie. The minimum activity measurable will be the smallest amount giving the desired precision for that determination and will be limited by the counter background and efficiency.

Calibration and Standardization

8. (a) For counting barium-140 alone, beta or gamma counting is satisfactory. The lanthanum daughter activity may be measured conveniently by gamma-ray spectrometry. Correction must be made for the equilibrium, or lack of equilibrium between the barium and lanthanum ac-

tivities.[7,8] The ingrowth of lanthanum activity is shown in Fig. 1.

For counting a mixture of the two barium isotopes, either beta or gamma counting may be used. In beta counting, the two activities may be measured by preparing a decay curve or by calcula-

tion using simultaneous equations. Correction must be made for the ingrowth of lanthanum-140 where the barium-140 concentration is high.

A gamma-ray spectrometer may be

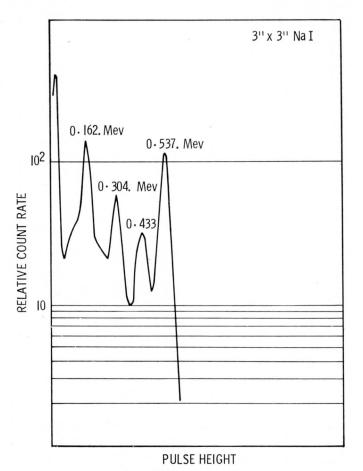

FIG. 3.—Gamma Spectra of 12.8-Day Ba[140].

preparing a decay curve or by calcula-

[7] Finkle and Sugarman, "Radiochemical Studies. The Fission Products," *Paper 116*, McGraw Hill Book Co., Inc. New York, N. Y. (1951).

[8] G. Freedlander and J. W. Kennedy, "Nuclear and Radiochemistry," John Wiley and Sons, Inc., New York, N. Y. (1955).

used to measure barium-139 activity in a mixture of barium-139 and -140 by following the decay of the 0.163 Mev peak. Barium-140 may be counted directly or by counting the 1.6 Mev peak of lanthanum-140 after a suitable decay. Gamma spectra are shown in Figs. 2, 3, and 4.

If absolute values are required, the detector used must be calibrated to obtain the ratio of count rate to disintegration rate for the isotope concerned. A solution may be standardized by a

(b) Barium carrier is standardized so that the chemical yield of the processes completed after the carrier addition may be measured by the amount of precipitate finally recovered. To standardize,

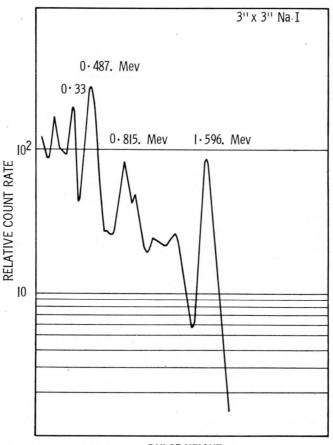

FIG. 4.—Gamma Spectra of 12.8-Day Ba^{140}—40.2-Hr La^{140}

method such as 4π counting, or beta-gamma coincidence counting, and used to prepare standard sources. The sources used for instrument calibration must be prepared in the same form as the samples. In beta counting, backscatter and self-absorption may be significant, and standards[9] should be prepared covering the expected range of chemical yield.

pipet 5 ml of carrier solution into 50 ml of water in a beaker. Add 5 ml of sulfuric acid (1:4) and stir well. Allow to stand for at least 12 hr. Transfer the precipitate to a sintered glass crucible of 5 to 9-μ porosity or tared quantitative

[9] A barium-140 standard is available from the International Atomic Energy Agency, Vienna, Austria.

filter paper, wash with water and alcohol. Dry at 110 C to a constant weight and finally weigh as barium sulfate ($BaSO_4$). The method gives a chemical yield of about 80 per cent.

Procedure

9. (a) Add to the sample in a centrifuge tube, or a beaker in the case of a large sample, 1 ml of barium carrier solution and mix. Then add an excess of Na_2CO_3 solution until a precipitate of barium carbonate forms. Separate this precipitate by centrifugation or by decanting, and by centrifugation in the case of a large sample.

(b) Dissolve the carbonate precipitate in 1 ml of concentrated HCl (sp gr 1.19) and transfer the solution to a 40-ml centrifuge tube. Add 10 ml of ice cold hydrochloric acid-ether mixture (Note 1) and cool in an ice bath for 5 min. Centrifuge the mixture and discard the supernate.

(c) Dissolve the barium chloride ($BaCl_2$) in 1 ml of water and repeat the precipitation as described in Paragraph (b).

(d) Dissolve the $BaCl_2$ in 2 ml of water, add five drops of both iron and lanthanum carriers and an excess of NH_4OH (1:1) to precipitate the hydroxides. Discard the precipitate after washing. Note the time, as this step removes lanthanum activity, and continue as described in Paragraphs (e), (f), and (g) within $\frac{1}{4}$ hr to avoid errors when correcting for the lanthanum-140 ingrowth.

(e) Evaporate the supernate to 2 ml and add 10 ml of hydrochloric acid-ether reagent. Cool and centrifuge to separate the precipitated $BaCl_2$.

(f) Dissolve the $BaCl_2$ in 20 ml of water and add 3 ml of dilute sulfuric acid (1:4). Digest on a hot water bath for 5 min. Centrifuge the mixture and discard the supernatant.

(g) Transfer the precipitate to a tared quantitative filter paper using water. Wash with water, alcohol, and ether. Dry at 110 C for 10 min and weigh as barium sulfate ($BaSO_4$); mount and count the precipitate.

Calculation

10. (a) Calculate the concentration, D, of radioactive barium in curies per liter as follows:

$$D = \frac{C}{2.22 \times 10^{12} EVR}$$

where:

C = count rate of sample, in counts per minute,
E = counter efficiency,
V = liters of sample used,
R = fractional chemical yield for the separation (Section 8(b)), and
2.22×10^{12} = conversion factor from disintegrations per minute to curies.

NOTE 2.—In gamma-ray spectrometry, the counter efficiency, E, in this expression is calculated as follows:

$$E = A \cdot \xi$$

where:
A = fractional abundance of the gamma ray in gammas per disintegration, and
ξ = photopeak detection efficiency in counts per gamma ray.

(b) Calculate the decay correction for radioactive barium as follows:

$$A = A_0 e^{-0.693t/T}$$

where:
A = activity at time t,
A_0 = activity at time zero,
e = base of natural logarithms,
t = elapsed time, in hours, and
T = half-life of radioisotope, in hours.

(c) Calculate the growth of lanthanum-140 in barium-140 samples from:

$$A_{La} = A_{0_{Ba}} \frac{e^{-0.693t/T_{Ba}} - e^{-0.693t/T_{La}}}{(1 - T_{La}/T_{Ba})}$$

or for barium-140 activity from a gamma count of lanthanum

$$A_{0_{Ba}} = A_{La} \frac{(1 - T_{La}/T_{Ba})}{e^{-0.693t/T_{Ba}} - e^{-0.693t/T_{La}}}$$

Precision

11. Precision depends on the random counting error and on determination of chemical yields. Single operator precision is better than ± 2 per cent of the amount of radioactive barium present when the random counting error is less than 1 per cent.

APPENDIX

TABLE I.—RADIOACTIVE DECAY CHARACTERISTICS OF BARIUM AND LANTHANUM ISOTOPES OF MASSES 139 AND 140.[a, b, c]

Radioisotope	Half-Life	Maximum Beta Energy, Mev	Gamma Energy, Mev
Ba^{139}.........	85 min	2.23 (60 per cent) 2.38 (15 per cent) 0.82 (19 per cent)	0.163 (23 per cent)
Ba^{140}.........	12.80 days	1.0 (75 per cent) 0.48 (25 per cent)	0.132 0 162 0.304 0.433 0.537
La^{140}.........	40.2 hr	2.26 (10 per cent) 1.67 (20 per cent) 1.32 (70 per cent) and others (very weak)	0.093 0.33 0.487 0.815 (40 per cent) 1.596 (94 per cent)

[a] See Footnote 2.
[b] D. Strominger, J. M. Hollander, and G. T. Seaborg, "Table of Isotopes," *Review of Modern Physics*, Vol. 30, p. 585 (1956).
[c] Nuclear Data Sheets, published by the National Academy of Sciences.

Tentative Method of Test for
RADIOACTIVE MANGANESE IN INDUSTRIAL WATER AND INDUSTRIAL WASTE WATER[1]

ASTM Designation: D 2039 – 64 T
ISSUED, 1964

This Tentative Method has been approved by the sponsoring committee and accepted by the Society in accordance with established procedures, for use pending adoption as standard. Suggestions for revisions should be addressed to the Society at 1916 Race St., Philadelphia 3, Pa.

Scope

1. (a) This method[2] covers the measurement of radioactive manganese contained in industrial water or industrial waste water in concentrations above 10^{-7} curie per liter. It is limited to the manganese radioisotopes of masses 54 and 56 which are produced in nuclear reactor materials. Modification in the analytical method is included to measure lower concentrations of radioactive manganese.

(b) The method may be used for absolute measurements by calibrating the nuclear radiation detector with a standard manganese radioisotope of the same mass, or for relative measurement by comparing the measurements made.

---

[1] Under the standardization procedure of the Society, this method is under the jurisdiction of the ASTM Committee D-19 on Industrial Water. A list of members may be found in the ASTM Year Book.

[2] This method is based on previously published methods collected in a review article which includes a discussion of the chemical behavior of radioactive manganese, see G. W. Leddicote, "The Radiochemistry of Manganese," National Academy of Sciences, National Research Council Publication NAS-NS-3018 (1960).

Summary of Method

2. (a) Radioactive manganese and the added carrier are first precipitated as manganese dioxide. A final gravimetric precipitation of manganese ammonium phosphate is used to compute the chemical yield of the process.

(b) The final precipitate is mounted and counted with a gamma counter (Note 1) for manganese-54 and -56, or with a beta particle detector (Note 1) for manganese-56 alone. The appropriate corrections are made for counter dead time, chemical yield, and radioactive decay during analysis. If necessary, the fractional count contributed by each isotope is computed and for absolute counting the final count rates are divided by the counter efficiency for that particular radioisotope. The two isotopes may be distinguished by the characteristics given in the Appendix.

NOTE 1.—For a discussion of gamma counting, refer to the Method for Measurement of Gamma Radioactivity of Industrial Water and Industrial Waste Water (ASTM Designation: D 1690).[3] For beta counting, refer to the Method for

---

[3] Appears in this publication.

Measurement of Beta Particle Radioactivity of Industrial Water and Industrial Waste Water (ASTM Designation: D 1890).[3]

Definitions

3. For definitions of terms used in this method, refer to the Definitions of Terms Relating to Industrial Water and Industrial Waste Water (ASTM Designation: D 1129)[3] and to other published glossaries.[4]

Interferences

4. (a) A large excess of chloride ion in the original sample will make the precipitation of manganese dioxide difficult. Stable manganese in the sample will cause overestimation of chemical yield and must be corrected for.

(b) The method provides a decontamination factor of more than 10^5 for radionuclides other than manganese.

Apparatus

5. (a) Beta Particle Counter.—Usually a proportional detector connected to the appropriate amplifier, discriminator, and scaling equipment. (Refer to Method D 1890.)

(b) Gamma-Ray Counter.—Preferably a sodium iodide scintillation detector assembly connected to the appropriate amplifier and pulse height analyzer or discriminator. (Refer to Method D 1690.)

Reagents

6. (a) Purity of Reagents.—Reagent grade chemicals shall be used in all tests. Unless otherwise indicated, it is intended that all reagents shall conform to the specifications of the Committee on Analytical Reagents of the American Chemical Society, where such specifica-

tions are available.[5] Other grades may be used, provided it is first ascertained that the reagent is of sufficiently high purity to permit its use without lessening the accuracy of the determination.

(b) Purity of Water.—Unless otherwise indicated, reference to water shall be understood to mean reagent water conforming to the Specifications for Reagent Water (ASTM Designation: D 1193).[3]

(c) Radioactive Purity.—Radioactive purity shall be such that the measured radioactivity of blank samples does not exceed the calculated probable error of the measurement.

(d) Ammonium Hydroxide Solution (1:1).—Mix 1 volume of concentrated ammonium hydroxide (NH_4OH, sp gr 0.90) with 1 volume of water.

(e) Ammonium Phosphate, Dibasic ($NH_4H_2PO_4$).

(f) Cobalt Chloride, Carrier Solution (20 g per liter).—Dissolve 20 g of cobalt chloride ($CoCl_2 \cdot 6H_2O$) in 100 ml of HCl (1:19), dilute to 1 liter, and store in a polyethylene bottle. This solution will contain 5 g of Co^{++} per liter.

(g) Ethyl Alcohol (95 per cent).

(h) Ethyl Ether.

(i) Ferric Chloride, Carrier Solution (49 g per liter).—Dissolve 49 g of ferric chloride ($FeCl_3 \cdot 6H_2O$) in 100 ml of HCl (1:19), filter, dilute to 1 liter, and store in a polyethylene bottle. This solution will contain 10 g of Fe^{+++} per liter.

(j) Hydrogen Peroxide (30 per cent).—Concentrated hydrogen peroxide (H_2O_2).

(k) Manganese Chloride, Carrier Solution (36 g per liter).—Dissolve 36 g of manganese chloride ($MnCl_2 \cdot 4H_2O$) in

---

[4] USA Standard "Glossary of Terms in Nuclear Science and Technology," USASI-N 1.1 1957.

[5] "Reagent Chemicals, American Chemical Society Specifications," Am. Chemical Soc., Washington, D. C. For suggestions on the testing of reagents not listed by the American Chemical Society, see "Reagent Chemicals and Standards," by Joseph Rosin, D. Van Nostrand Co., Inc., New York, N. Y. and the "United States Pharmacopeia."

water containing 1 ml of concentrated HNO₃ (sp gr 1.42), dilute to 1 liter, and store in a polyethylene bottle. This solution will contain 10 g of Mn⁺⁺ per liter.

(*l*) *Nitric Acid (sp gr 1.42).*—Concentrated nitric acid (HNO₃).

American Society for Testing and Materials as follows:

D 510—Sampling Industrial Water (Particularly Sections 32 to 41),[3]

D 860—Sampling Water from Boilers,[3] and

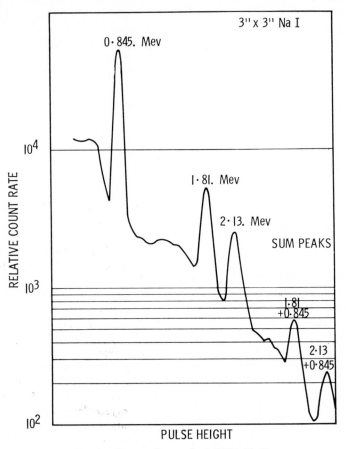

FIG. 1.—Gamma Spectra for 2.58-Hr Mn⁵⁶.

(*m*) *Potassium Bromate* (KBrO₃).

(*n*) *Potassium Chromate, Carrier Solution (37.3 g per liter).*—Dissolve 37.3 g of potassium chromate (K₂CrO₄) in 1 liter of water. This solution will contain 10 g of Cr⁺⁺ per liter.

Sampling

7. (*a*) Collect the sample in accordance with the applicable methods of the

D 1496—Sampling Homogeneous Industrial Waste Water.[3]

(*b*) Sample 1 ml unless the concentration of radioactive manganese is outside the range 10⁻⁷ to 10⁻³ curie per liter. For gamma counting, the optimum activity is about 10⁻⁷ curie, and for beta counting, about 10⁻⁸ curie. The minimum activity detectable would be the smallest amount giving the desired precision for

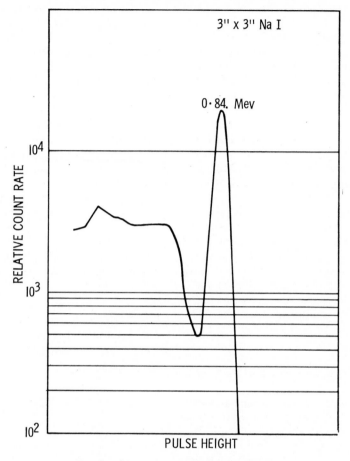

FIG. 2.—Gamma Spectra for 314-Day Mn⁵⁴.

the determination and would be limited by the counter background and efficiency.

Calibration and Standardization

8. (*a*) Gamma-ray spectrometry is recommended for the isotopes included in this method and typical gamma spectra are shown in Figs. 1 and 2. Examination of the gamma spectrum of a sample will show the presence of the short-lived manganese-56 and several counts should be used to construct a decay curve for the 0.84 Mev peak. Analysis of this decay curve gives the counts due to Mn^{56} and

Mn^{54}. In some samples, long decay precludes the presence of Mn^{56} and one count will be sufficient to check the purity of the sample and measure the count rate due to Mn^{54}. If absolute values are required, the gamma spectrometer used may be calibrated with a commercially available Mn^{54} standard.[6] Alternatively, a solution of Mn^{56} can be standardized by 4π beta counting and used to calibrate the gamma detector. The standards used for counting must be prepared

---

[6] Standardized Mn^{54} is available from the Nuclear Chicago Corp., 301 E. Howard Ave., Des Plaines, Ill.

in the same form as the samples and counted on the same detector under identical geometrical conditions.

(b) The manganese carrier solution is standardized so that the chemical yield of the method may be calculated from the amount of precipitate finally obtained for each sample. To standardize, pipet 5 ml of this solution into a 400-ml beaker, dilute to about 200 ml and then add 1 g of $NH_4H_2PO_4$. Heat the solution to boiling and add NH_4OH (1:1) dropwise with stirring until a precipitate begins to form. Continue boiling until the precipitate is crystalline, then check for completeness of the reaction by adding a little ammonia. Cool the solution to about 0 C and let stand for 1 hr. Filter onto a medium-porosity sintered glass filter and wash with very dilute ammonia. Dry at 110 C to constant weight. Weigh as manganese ammonium phosphate ($Mn(NH_4)PO_4 \cdot H_2O$).

Procedure

9. (a) Mix 1 ml of each of the carriers for manganese, cobalt, chromium, and iron in a centrifuge tube (or use an Erlenmeyer flask of suitable volume if a large sample must be taken) and add the sample.

(b) Add 5 ml of concentrated HNO_3 (sp gr 1.42) and boil to remove chlorides until evolution of NO_2 ceases; then add 1 g of $KBrO_3$. Boil the mixture for 10 min and then cool.

(c) Centrifuge the mixture and discard the supernate. Wash the precipitate of manganese dioxide with hot water acidified with HNO_3 until the wash water is colorless.

(d) Dissolve the manganese dioxide in 1 ml of concentrated HNO_3 (sp gr 1.42) and one drop of H_2O_2, boil, and then add 1 ml of iron, chromium, and cobalt carriers.

(e) Repeat the procedure described in Paragraphs (b) and (c).

(f) Dissolve the manganese dioxide in 1 ml of concentrated HNO_3 (sp gr 1.42) and 1 drop of H_2O_2, boil, and then cool. Dilute with 5 ml of water.

(g) Add 4 drops of iron carrier. Add NH_4OH (1:1) to precipitate the iron below a pH of 7. Boil and filter through a fast paper suitable for gelatinous precipitates. Discard the precipitate.

(h) Dilute the solution to 15 ml and add 1 g of $NH_4H_2PO_4$. Boil until a crystalline precipitate forms. Cool in an ice bath for 10 min.

(i) Filter onto a tared quantitative paper. Wash with water, ethyl alcohol, and ether.

(j) Dry at 110 C for 10 min. Weigh as manganese ammonium phosphate ($Mn(NH_4)PO_4 \cdot H_2O$) and mount for counting.

Calculation

10. (a) Calculate the concentration, D, of radioactive manganese in curies per liter as follows:

$$D = \frac{C}{2.22 \times 10^{12} EVR}$$

where:

C = count rate of sample, in counts per minute,
E = counter efficiency,
V = liters of sample used,
R = fractional chemical yield for the separation (Section 8(b)), and
2.22×10^{12} = conversion factor from disintegrations per minute to curies.

Note 2.—In gamma-ray spectrometry, the counter efficiency, E, in this expression is calculated as follows:

$$E = A \, \xi$$

where:

A = fractional abundance of the gamma ray in gammas per disintegration, and,
ξ = photopeak detection efficiency, in counts per gamma ray.

(*b*) Calculate the decay correction for radioactive manganese as follows:

$$A = A_0 e^{-0.693t/T}$$

where:

A = activity at time t,

A_0 = activity at time zero, in same units as A,

e = base of natural logarithms,

t = elapsed time, and

T = half-life of isotope, in same units as t.

Precision

11. Precision depends on the random counting error and on the determination of chemical yields. Precision is poorer if the two isotopes are determined by one count. Single operator precision is better than ±2 per cent of the amount of radioactive manganese present when the random counting error is less than 1 per cent.

APPENDIX

TABLE I.—RADIOACTIVE DECAY CHARACTERISTICS OF MANGANESE
ISOTOPE OF MASSES 54 AND 56.[a, b]

Radioisotope	Half-Life	Maximum Beta Energy, Mev	Gamma Radiation Energy, Mev
Mn^{54}........ ..	314 days	...	0.840 (100 per cent)
Mn^{56}.........	2.58 hr	2.86 (50 per cent) 1.05 (30 per cent) 0.700 (20 per cent)	0.845 (100 per cent) 1.81 (30 per cent) 2.13 (15 per cent)

[a] D. Strominger, J. M. Hollander, and G. T. Seaborg, "Table of Isotopes," *Review of Modern Physics*, Vol. 30, No. 2, Part 2 (1958).
[b] Nuclear Data Sheets, published by the National Academy of Sciences.

Tentative Method of Test for
STRONTIUM-90 IN INDUSTRIAL WATER AND INDUSTRIAL WASTE WATER[1]

ASTM Designation: D 2040 – 64 T
ISSUED, 1964

This Tentative Method has been approved by the sponsoring committee and accepted by the Society in accordance with established procedures, for use pending adoption as standard. Suggestions for revisions should be addressed to the Society at 1916 Race St., Philadelphia 3, Pa.

Scope

1. (a) This method[2,3] covers a procedure for the specific measurement of strontium-90 in the precipitate of strontium oxalate monohydrate obtained in the procedure for measuring gross strontium activity in industrial water and industrial waste water;[4] the measurement is performed after a decay period of approximately two weeks. (The equilibrium between strontium-90 and its daughter product yttrium-90 reaches about 97 per cent of its final value after two weeks.)

(b) The method may be used for absolute measurement by calibrating the nuclear radiation detector with a standard sample of yttrium-90, or for relative measurements of given samples.

Summary of Method

2. (a) The precipitated sample of strontium oxalate monohydrate, mounted for counting,[4] is disintegrated with fuming nitric acid after addition of yttrium carrier. Strontium and yttrium are coprecipitated as a mixture of oxalate and carbonate salts by the addition of excess sodium carbonate. The precipitate is ignited to destroy organic matter. The ignited residue is then dissolved in nitric acid and initial separation of strontium from yttrium is effected by ammoniacal precipitation of yttrium hydroxide. The yttrium hydroxide is dissolved in nitric acid. Strontium carrier is added and the ammoniacal precipitation of yttrium hydroxide is repeated. The yttrium hydroxide precipitate is dissolved in hydrochloric acid, and finally precipitated as yttrium oxalate. The yttrium oxalate is then carefully washed with ethyl alcohol and ethyl ether. The chemical yield is computed by weighing

---

[1] Under the standardization procedure of the Society, this method is under the jurisdiction of the ASTM Committee D-19 on Industrial Water. A list of members may be found in the ASTM Year Book.

[2] Refer to the Method of Test for Radioactive Strontium in Industrial Water and Industrial Waste Water (ASTM Designation: D 1944), which appears in this publication.

[3] This method is based on a number of methods collected in a review article, and is similar to an already published method, see D. N. Sunderman and C. W. Townley, "The Radiochemistry of Barium, Calcium, and Strontium," National Academy of Sciences, National Research Council Publication NAS-NS-3010 (1960); and B. Singer and H. A. Clawson, "Radiochemical Procedures for the PWR Plant," WAPD-CDA-(I)-6 (1957).

[4] See Section 9(h) of Method D 1944.

the oxalate and comparing its yttrium content with that of the carrier added originally.

(b) The yttrium oxalate precipitate is counted with a beta particle detector.[5] Appropriate corrections are made for counter dead time, chemical yield, background, and radioactive decay during analysis. For absolute counting, the final count rate is divided by the counter efficiency for yttrium-90. The storage of untreated samples for three days subsequent to radio-strontium assay[4] will result in the elimination of radioactive yttrium daughter products other than yttrium-90. Strontium-90 is then determined from the equation for equilibrium between strontium-90 and its daughter product yttrium-90.

Definitions

3. For definitions of terms used in this method, refer to the Definitions of Terms Relating to Industrial Water and Industrial Waste Water (ASTM Designation: D 1129)[6] and to other published glossaries.[7]

Interferences

4. Incomplete barium chromate precipitation or separation similar to that described in Section 9(g) of Method D 1944 could allow contamination of oxalate and carbonate precipitate.

Apparatus

5. *Beta Particle Counter.*—Usually a proportional or Geiger-Müller detector, connected to appropriate amplifier, pulse height discriminator, scaler and register. (See Method D 1890.)

Reagents

6. (a) *Purity of Reagents.*—Reagent grade chemicals shall be used in all tests. Unless otherwise indicated, it is intended that all reagents shall conform to the specifications of the Committee on Analytical Reagents of the American Chemical Society, where such specifications are available.[8] Other grades may be used, provided it is first ascertained that the reagent is of sufficiently high purity to permit its use without lessening the accuracy of the determination.

(b) *Purity of Water.*—Unless otherwise indicated, reference to water shall be understood to mean reagent water conforming to Specifications for Reagent Water (ASTM Designation: D 1193).[6]

(c) *Radioactive Purity.*—The radioactive purity shall be such that the measured radioactivity of blank samples does not exceed the expected random counting error of the measurement.

(d) *Ammonium Hydroxide (sp gr 0.90).*—Concentrated ammonium hydroxide (NH_4OH).

(e) *Ammonium Oxalate Solution* ((NH_4)$_2C_2O_4 \cdot H_2O$), saturated solution.

(f) *Ethyl Alcohol (95 per cent).*

(g) *Ethyl Ether.*

(h) *Hydrochloric Acid Solution (1:1).* —Mix 1 volume of concentrated hydrochloric acid (HCl, sp gr 1.19) with 1 volume of water.

(i) *Nitric Acid Solution (2:3).*—Mix 2 volumes of concentrated nitric acid (HNO_3, sp gr 1.42) with 3 volumes of water.

---

[5] For a discussion of beta counting and detection, refer to the Method for Measurement of Beta Particle Radioactivity of Industrial Water and Industrial Waste Water (ASTM Designation: D 1890), which appears in this publication.

[6] Appears in this publication.

[7] USA Standard "Glossary of Terms in Nuclear Science and Technology," USASI-N 1.1-1957.

[8] "Reagent Chemicals, American Chemical Society Specifications," Am. Chemical Soc., Washington, D. C. For suggestions on the testing of reagents, not listed by the American Chemical Society see "Reagent Chemicals and Standards," by Joseph Rosin, D. Van Nostrand Co., Inc., New York, N. Y. and the "United States Pharmacopeia."

(*j*) *Nitric Acid, Fuming* (*sp gr 1.45*).

(*k*) *Sodium Carbonate* (Na_2CO_3), anhydrous.

(*l*) *Sodium Carbonate Solution* (*212 g per liter*).—Dissolve 212 g of sodium carbonate (Na_2CO_3) in water and dilute to 1 liter.

(*m*) *Strontium Nitrate, Carrier Solution* (*24 g per liter*).—Dissolve 24 g of strontium nitrate ($Sr(NO_3)_2$) in water and dilute to 1 liter. This solution contains 10 g of Sr^{+++} per liter.

(*n*) *Yttrium Nitrate, Carrier Solution* (*43 g per liter*).—Dissolve 43 g of yttrium nitrate ($Y(NO_3)_3 \cdot 6H_2O$) in water, add 5 ml of HNO_3 (3:1), and dilute to 1 liter with water. This solution contains 10 g of Y^{+++} per liter.

Sampling

7. The sample shall be collected and treated in accordance with Method D 1944. The strontium oxalate monohydrate precipitate, for use in this method for strontium-90, shall be stored for a period of about two weeks. Record the time of precipitation of strontium oxalate monohydrate.[3]

Calibration and Standardization

8. (*a*) For absolute counting, the beta detector must be calibrated to obtain the ratio of count rate to disintegration rate for yttrium-90. A standard Sr^{90}-Y^{90} solution is commercially available.

(*b*) An yttrium-90 standard is prepared by separation of the radioisotope from its strontium-90 parent by successive yttrium hydroxide precipitations. The procedure for isolating yttrium-90 and preparing the sample for counting is as follows:

(*1*) Pipet 2.0 ml of the standardized yttrium carrier solution into a beaker containing 10 ml of water, 2 ml of the strontium carrier solution, and 1 ml of HNO_3 (2:3). Pipet an aliquot of the standard Sr^{90}-Y^{90} solution containing approximately 10,000 counts per minute.

(*2*) Add concentrated NH_4OH (sp gr 0.90) until yttrium hydroxide precipitates. Add 5 ml in excess. Centrifuge the mixture and discard the supernatant solution. Record the time. Wash the precipitate twice with 10 ml of water.

(*3*) Dissolve the precipitate in HNO_3 (2:3). Add 2 ml of the strontium carrier solution and repeat as described in Step (*2*).

(*4*) Dissolve the precipitate in 2 ml of HCl (1:1) and dilute to 15 ml with water. Heat the solution to near boiling and add 20 ml of the saturated ammonium oxalate solution. Continue heating for 10 min and then cool in an ice bath.

(*5*) Stir, and filter by suction on a weighed filter disk supported on a Hirsch funnel or other apparatus. Wash three times each with 5-ml portions of water, 5-ml portions of 95 per cent ethyl alcohol, and 5-ml portions of ethyl ether. Transfer the filter and precipitate to a watch glass or counting dish and weigh; then mount and count the yttrium oxalate precipitate.

(*c*) The yttrium carrier solution is standardized in order to determine the chemical yield after completion of the chemical procedure. To standardize the solution, pipet 5.0 ml into a beaker containing 20 ml of water, heat to boiling, and add 20 ml of the saturated ammonium oxalate solution. Heat almost to boiling for 10 min, stir well, and cool in an ice bath for 10 min. Filter in a tared, sintered glass crucible. Wash three times each with water, 95 per cent ethyl alcohol, and ethyl ether. Heat in an oven at 110 C for 10 min, allow to cool in a desiccator, and weigh the yttrium oxalate precipitate. Repeat heating until a constant weight is obtained.

Procedure

9. (*a*) Place the filter disk containing the strontium oxalate sample[4] in a

beaker. Add 2.0 ml of standardized yttrium carrier (43 g per liter) and mix. Add 5 ml of fuming HNO_3. Evaporate to near dryness, and cool. Add 2 ml of fuming HNO_3, evaporate to near dryness, and cool.

(b) Add carefully 10 ml of the saturated Na_2CO_3 solution and 1 g of solid Na_2CO_3. Boil for 5 min and cool. Filter using a fine paper. Wash the precipitate with water. Transfer the filter paper containing the precipitate to a porcelain crucible and ignite at 700 C for 1 hr. Cool.

(c) Carefully dissolve the residue in HNO_3 (2:3) and transfer to a beaker with 20 ml of water. Boil for 5 min and cool.

(d) Add concentrated NH_4OH (sp gr 0.90) until yttrium hydroxide precipitates. Add 5 ml in excess and transfer to a centrifuge tube. Centrifuge the mixture and discard the supernatant solution. Wash the precipitate twice with 10 ml of water. Record the time.

(e) Dissolve the precipitate in HNO_3 (2:3). Add 2 ml of the strontium carrier solution and repeat as described in Paragraph (d).

(f) Dissolve the precipitate in 2 ml of HCl (1:1), dilute to 15 ml with water, and transfer to a beaker. Heat the solution to near-boiling and add 20 ml of saturated ammonium oxalate solution. Continue heating for 10 min and then cool in an ice bath.

(g) Stir and filter by suction on a weighed filter disk supported on a Hirsh funnel or other apparatus. Wash three times each with 5-ml portions of water, 5-ml portions of 95 per cent ethyl alcohol, and 5-ml portions of ethyl ether. Transfer the filter and precipitate to a watch glass or counting dish, and weigh; then mount and count the yttrium oxalate precipitate.

Calculations

10. (a) Calculate the concentration, D, of radioactive yttrium-90 in microcuries per liter as follows:

$$D = \frac{C}{2.22 \times 10^6 EVR_1R_2}$$

where:

C = beta count rate, in net counts per minute,

E = beta counter efficiency, in counts per disintegration,

V = volume of original sample, in liters,

R_1 = fractional chemical yield for the separation of yttrium (Section 9(g)),

2.22×10^6 = conversion factor from disintegrations per minute to microcuries, and

R_2 = fractional chemical yield for the separation of strontium given in Method D 1944.

(b) Calculate the decay correction for yttrium-90 as follows:

$$A = A_Y^0 e^{-0.693 t_1/T_Y}$$

where:

A = activity at time sample is counted for yttrium,

A_Y^0 = activity at time of separation of yttrium from strontium (Section 9(d)),

e = base of natural logarithms,

t_1 = elapsed time between counting and separation of yttrium from strontium (Section 9(d) or 8(b)(2), or both), and

T_Y = half-life of yttrium, in same unit as t_1.

(c) Calculate the activity of strontium-90 from the growth and separation of yttrium-90 at the beginning of the decay period of strontium-90 as follows:

$$A_{Sr}^0 = A_Y^0 \left(\frac{1}{1 - e^{-0.693 t_2/T_Y}} \right)$$

where:

A_{Sr}^0 = Sr^{90} activity at the beginning of the decay period of Sr^{90},

A_Y^0 = Y^{90} activity at the time yttrium is separated from Sr^{90} (Section 9(d)), and

l_2 = Sr^{90} decay period as determined in Section 9(d) in same unit as T.

Precision

11. Precision depends on random counting error and on determination of chemical yields. The precision for determining chemical yield by weight is of the order of 2 per cent of the amount of strontium-90 present.

Tentative Method of Test for

DEUTERIUM OXIDE[1]

ASTM Designation: D 2184 – 63 T

Issued, 1963

This Tentative Method has been approved by the sponsoring committee and accepted by the Society in accordance with established procedures, for use pending adoption as standard. Suggestions for revisions should be addressed to the Society at 1916 Race St., Philadelphia 3, Pa.

Scope

1. (a) This method covers the measurement of the isotopic composition of hydrogen in deuterium oxide (heavy water) which is nominally 99.75 atom per cent deuterium (D), equal to $\frac{D}{D+H} \times 100$). The primary use of the heavy water is as a moderator in production, power, or research reactors in which a fissionable nuclide is consumed. In such reactors the percentage of deuterium in the heavy water usually exceeds 95 per cent.

(b) The method is a referee method and is valid also at lower isotopic concentrations of deuterium.

Summary of Method

2. There are numerous physical properties of heavy water that are different in value from the corresponding value for natural water. These properties form the basis of several instrumental methods

of analysis of heavy water. The accepted value for the specific gravity of heavy water is $S^{25}_{25} = 1.10775 \pm 0.00003$ which is roughly 11 per cent greater than the specific gravity of natural water. Measurement of the specific gravity of heavy water is the most precise and accurate method of determining the isotopic concentration of heavy water. The uncertainty of 30 ppm in S^{25}_{25} permits determination of atom per cent deuterium to no better than ±0.03 atom per cent deuterium.

Definitions

3. (a) *Normal Abundance of an Isotope.*—The abundance in atom per cent of the isotopes of an element as it is found in nature.

(b) *Atom Per Cent of an Isotope.*— The atom fraction of the isotope expressed in per cent.

(c) *Atom Fraction of an Isotope.*— The number of atoms of the isotope divided by the total number of atoms of that element in the sample; this ratio is analogous to mol fraction. For example, using the isotopes of oxygen, the atom fraction of O^{18} is $O^{18}/O^{16} + O^{17} + O^{18}$.

---

[1] Under the standardization procedure of the Society, this method is under the jurisdiction of the ASTM Committee D-19 on Industrial Water. A list of members may be found in the ASTM Year Book.

Interferences

4. (a) One or more of the processes for producing heavy water may increase its oxygen-18 content. A change in the concentration of either deuterium or oxygen-18 changes the specific gravity of the water in a nearly linear manner. The heavy water that is sold commercially by the Atomic Energy Commission usually contains oxygen-18 at about 0.4 atom per cent or roughly twice normal abundance. This increase in concentration results from the distillation process because water that contains oxygen-18 has a lower volatility than water that contains oxygen-16.

(b) Determine the correction for oxygen-18 by equilibration with CO_2 and a mass spectrometric analysis of the product CO_2. Bubbling large volumes of gas through the sample is not recommended because traces of moisture would dilute the heavy water with normal water. Therefore, proceed in accordance with Section 8 (e) and (f). Calculate the concentration of oxygen-18 and its contribution to the specific gravity of the sample in accordance with Section 10(a). Calculate the necessary corrections as outlined in Section 10(b).

(c) Exercise extreme care in all steps of the analysis to avoid changing the concentration of deuterium. Avoid contact of the sample with moist air or moist reagents to eliminate dilution effects. Distill to dryness to avoid low results because the vapor pressure of hydrogen deuterium oxide (HDO) is slightly greater than that of deuterium oxide (D_2O). Reduce the risk of dilution by working with quantities of at least 25 ml of the samples. It is not necessary to perform the steps of the analysis in a dry box.

Apparatus

5. (a) *Constant Temperature Bath,* maintained at 25 ± 0.01 C, with a device for shaking the equilibration flasks.

(b) *Distillation Apparatus,* including drying tube with silica gel and receiver with side neck and cap (see Fig. 1).

(c) *Equilibration Flask* (Fig. 1).

(d) *Hypodermic Syringes.*—Two syringes of 50-ml capacity, with large and small bore needles.

(e) *Mass Spectrometer,* for determining the mass-charge ratio, m/e, 44 and 46.

(f) *Precision Pycnometers* (Fig. 1).— Two pycnometers of borosilicate glass, 25-ml capacity; to avoid buoyancy corrections to the empty pycnometers, their weights should be within 2 per cent.

(g) *Rubber Bulb,* on small-bore hypodermic needle with pointed end ground off.

(h) *Thermometers,* graduated in 0.1 C subdivisions and standardized for the ice point; ASTM Kinematic Viscosity Thermometers having ranges of 66.5 to 71.5 F and 74.5 to 79.5 F and conforming to the requirements for thermometers 44F and 45F, respectively, as prescribed in ASTM Specifications E 1 (Note 1).[2]

(i) *Thermometer,* Beckmann Differential, graduated in 0.01 C subdivisions (Note 1).

Note 1.—A standardized platinum resistance thermometer may be used instead of the specified mercury thermometers.

Reagents and Materials

6. (a) *Purity of Reagents.*—Reagent grade chemicals shall be used in all tests. Unless otherwise indicated, it is intended that all reagents shall conform to the specifications of the Committee on Analytical Reagents of the American Chemical Society, where such specifications are available.[3] Other grades may be used, provided it is first ascertained that the reagent is of sufficiently high purity to permit its use without lessening the accuracy of the determination.

[2] 1967 Book of ASTM Standards, Part 30.

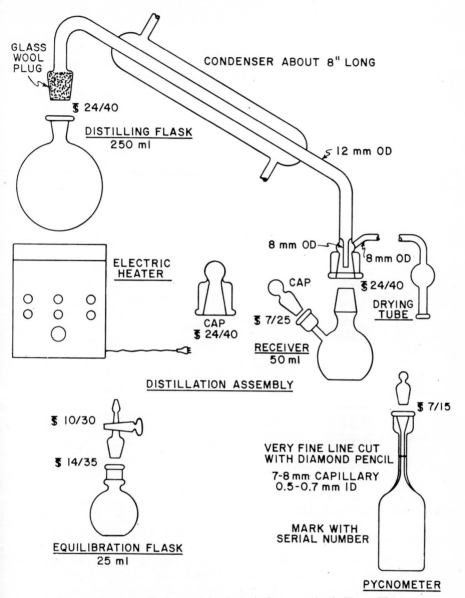

GLASS WOOL PLUG

$ 24/40

DISTILLING FLASK
250 ml

CONDENSER ABOUT 8" LONG

12 mm OD

ELECTRIC HEATER

CAP
$ 24/40

DISTILLATION ASSEMBLY

8 mm OD

8 mm OD

CAP

$ 24/40

DRYING TUBE

CAP
$ 7/25

RECEIVER
50 ml

$ 10/30

$ 14/35

EQUILIBRATION FLASK
25 ml

$ 7/15

VERY FINE LINE CUT
WITH DIAMOND PENCIL

7-8 mm CAPILLARY
0.5-0.7 mm ID

MARK WITH
SERIAL NUMBER

PYCNOMETER

FIG. 1.—Apparatus for Determining Isotopic Concentration in Heavy Water.

(b) *Purity of Water.*—Unless otherwise indicated, references to water shall be understood to mean reagent water conforming to the Specifications for Reagent Water (ASTM Designation: D 1193).[4]

(c) *Carbon Dioxide* (CO_2), gas.
(d) *Silicon Carbide Chips.*
(e) *Glass Wool*, medium.

[3] "Reagent Chemicals, American Chemical Society Specifications," Am. Chemical Soc., Washington, D. C. For suggestions on the testing of reagents not listed by the American Chemical Society, see "Reagent Chemicals and Standards," by Joseph Rosin, D. Van Nostrand Co., Inc., New York, N. Y. and the "United States Pharmacopeia."

[4] Appears in this publication.

(*f*) *Potassium Permanganate,* (KMnO₄), crystal.

(*g*) *Sodium Peroxide* (Na₂O₂).—Use only a freshly opened can because of the hygroscopic property of the material.

Sampling

7. (*a*) Heavy water is normally shipped in 500-lb quantities in stainless steel drums. The exchange reaction is extremely rapid so that uniformity of isotopic composition is attained when the drums are loaded. Avoid excessive contact with humid air. However, isotopic dilution by moisture in the air is not a serious problem when pound quantities are handled.

$$H_2O + D_2O \rightleftharpoons 2HDO$$

(*b*) Open the bung, and lower a 3-ft length of poly(vinyl chloride) (Tygon) or equivalent *dry* plastic tubing having a $\frac{1}{4}$-in. internal diameter into the drum. Close the tubing by pinching, and insert the free end into a clean, dry polyethylene pint bottle. Siphon about 1 lb of heavy water from the drum. Pinch the tube and drain the contents back into the drum. Replace the stopper immediately and then replace the bung. Identify the sample in accordance with the Specification for Equipment for Sampling Industrial Water and Steam (ASTM Designation: D 1192).[4]

Calibration and Standardization

8. (*a*) For precision to the fifth decimal place of a specific gravity determination, the necessary weighings must not be in error by more than 0.1 mg for pycnometer volumes between 25 and 35 ml.

(*b*) Measurements of temperature near 25 C and atmospheric pressure are required within ±0.01 C and ±1 mm respectively. Air temperature in the balance is required within ±1 C. Relative humidities must be determined

within ±3 per cent. The density of the balance weights must be known within ±0.1 g per ml. Note that fractional weights are usually made of a different material from that used in gram weights.

(*c*) Static electricity must be discharged from the pycnometer and tare before weighings are made. Ultraviolet light or a soft source of radioactivity provide a convenient means of discharging the static electricity on glassware.

(*d*) Avoid convection currents of air in the balance by weighing at constant temperature and pressure, preferably in an air-conditioned laboratory. Allow the pycnometer and tare to remain on the balance pans for 20 min to attain temperature equilibrium. Use long-handled tools to place the glassware and weights in the balance. Keep bare hands out of the balance case.

(*e*) Use the mass spectrometer to determine the ratios of masses 46 and 44 in carbon dioxide. Evaluate the performance of the mass spectrometer in accordance with the Recommended Practice for Evaluation of Mass Spectrometers for Use in Chemical Analysis (ASTM Designation: E 137).[5] As a further test of performance, determine the O^{18} content of normal water in accordance with Section 10(*b*). For a correction in the fifth decimal place of the specific gravity, the O^{18} must be determined within 0.01 atom per cent. Since the ratio, R_x, of masses 46 and 44 in CO_2, that has been equilibrated with normal water ($O^{18} = 0.200$ atom per cent) is 0.00418, it follows that this ratio must be determined within 0.0002.

(*f*) *Calibration of Pycnometer.*—Clean and calibrate the pycnometer in accordance with the Method of Test for Density and Specific Gravity of Liquids by Bingham Pycnometer (ASTM Designation: D 1217),[6] except that a tip

[5] 1967 Book of ASTM Standards, Part 30.
[6] 1967 Book of ASTM Standards, Part 17.

condenser is not essential. Calibrations subsequent to the initial three values specified in Method D 1217 need only be made if the weight of the dry pycnometer changes by more than a few tenths of a milligram. A single calibration is sufficient if the new value is within ±0.2 mg of the average of the original three measurements.

Procedure

9. (a) *Determination of Specific Gravity.* —Use clean, dry glassware to assemble the distillation apparatus shown in Fig. 1. Do not use grease on the glass joints. Insert a loosely packed wad of glass wool in the inner glass joint above the distillation flask. Attach a drying tube to the vent above the receiver. In the distillation flask place a few pieces of silicon carbide to prevent bumping and about 50 mg each of $KMnO_4$ and Na_2O_2. Shake the sample thoroughly and withdraw about 35 ml of the sample with a clean, dry syringe. Recap the sample bottle at once. Transfer the aliquot of sample to the distillation flask and immediately connect the flask to the condenser. Distill to dryness at a rate of about 15 to 25 drops per min. Carefully flame the flask and then the neck of the condenser to complete the distillation. Alternately cool and heat the neck of the condenser while keeping the flask hot until no moisture condenses in the neck of the condenser. Remove and cap the receiving flask. Redistill if the distillate shows turbidity or traces of the color of permanganate. Continue in accordance with Method D 1217. Be very careful that the syringe, and the capillary above the mark on the pycnometer are dry. Refer to Section 8(f) and keep the pycnometer full of heavy water until it is required for another analysis.

(b) *Determination of Oxygen-18.*—

Transfer 5 ml of the sample distillate to a 25-ml equilibration flask. Close with a greased ground-joint-stopcock type of cap. Evacuate carefully until the sample forms vapor bubbles, and then fill the flask with carbon dioxide to atmospheric pressure. Equilibrate by shaking in a water bath at 25 C for three hr. Transfer a portion of the gas to the mass spectrometer and measure the ratio of masses 46 and 44 within 0.0002. Record this result as R_x.

Calculations

10. (a) Calculate the contribution of excess oxygen-18 to the specific gravity of the sample from the mass spectrometric result that was obtained from the equilibrated carbon dioxide and the sample as follows:[3]

$$\text{Atom per cent } O^{18} \text{ in sample} = \frac{100 \, R_x}{2.088 + R_x}$$

where $R_x = \dfrac{C^{12}O^{16}O^{18}}{C^{12}O^{16}O^{16}}$

Atom per cent O^{18} in sample − atom per cent O^{18} in tap water = atom per cent O^{18} above normal abundance.
Effect of 0.01 atom per cent O^{18} on specific gravity = 0.000012
(Atom per cent O^{18} above normal abundance) × (0.000012) = correction, ΔS_{25}^{25}, to be deducted from observed specific gravity of the sample.
(b) Calculate the observed value of the specific gravity of the sample in accordance with Method D 1217. Use data on temperature, humidity, and atmospheric pressure to correct observed weights for buoyancy. Reduce the resulting specific gravity, S_{25}^{25}, by the amount of the correction for excess oxygen-18. Finally, subtract the specific gravity of deuterium-free water, 0.999984, from the specific gravity of the sample. Use this difference, ΔS,

directly in the following equation[7] to calculate the atom per cent of deuterium:

$$\text{Atom per cent D} = \frac{924.64 \, \Delta S}{1 - 0.0328 \, \Delta S}$$

Precision

11. The standard deviation of the determination of the deuterium content of heavy water in a single laboratory is 0.02 per cent D.[8] This value is based on

the assumption that the analyst uses care to avoid isotopic dilution, and has performed the determinations enough times to become skillful in each technique of the procedure. Most mistakes in technique cause dilution of the sample, yielding low results. An error of 1 unit in the fifth decimal place of the specific gravity is equivalent to an error of 0.01 per cent.

[7] I. Kirshenbaum, "Physical Properties and Analysis of Heavy Water," National Nuclear Energy Series III-4A, p. 247, McGraw-Hill Publishing Co., New York, N. Y. (1951).

[8] This statement is based on the experience of the control laboratory of the Savannah River Plant of E. I. duPont de Nemours & Co. A round-robin is being organized to collect additional data.

Tentative Method of Test for

RADIOACTIVE COBALT IN INDUSTRIAL WATER AND INDUSTRIAL WASTE WATER[1]

ASTM Designation: D 2185 – 63 T

ISSUED, 1963

This Tentative Method has been approved by the sponsoring committee and accepted by the Society in accordance with established procedures, for use pending adoption as standard. Suggestions for revisions should be addressed to the Society at 1916 Race St., Philadelphia 3, Pa.

Scope

1. (a) This method covers the measurement of radioactive cobalt contained in industrial water and industrial waste water in concentrations between 10^{-7} and 10^{-3} curie per liter. It is limited to the cobalt radioisotopes of masses 58 and 60 produced in nuclear reactors and the isotope of mass 57 which may be used as a cobalt tracer. Modifications in the nuclear radiation detector and analytical method are included in this method for measuring radioactive cobalt in higher and lower concentrations.

(b) The method may be used for absolute measurements by calibrating the nuclear radiation detector with a standard cobalt radioisotope of the same atomic mass, or for relative measurements by comparing the measurements made.

Summary of Method

2. (a) Radioactive cobalt and added

cobalt carrier are separated from other activities, with their added carriers, by ion-exchange chromatography. The separated cobalt is purified and finally counted with a γ counter or β particle detector. An initial concentration may be made by evaporating a large sample to small volume before making the separation. The main purification step is the ion-exchange separation. Two precipitations of potassium cobaltinitrite are performed and the chemical yield is calculated by comparing the weight of the dried final precipitate to the calculated theoretical weight. The recovery of radioactive cobalt is equal to the chemical yield.

(b) The potassium cobaltinitrite precipitate is mounted and counted with a beta particle detector or a gamma ray detector. Corrections are made for counter dead time, background count, chemical recovery, and radioactive decay from sampling time. If necessary, the activity contributed by each isotope is calculated. For absolute counting, the observed count rate is divided by the detector efficiency for the isotope concerned. The isotopes may be distin-

---

[1] Under the standardization procedure of the Society, this method is under the jurisdiction of the ASTM Committee D-19 on Industrial Water. A list of members may be found in the ASTM Year Book.

guished by the characteristics listed in the Appendix.

NOTE 1.—This method is based on a previously published method[2] which contains some comments on the gamma counting of mixtures of the cobalt isotopes of masses 58 and 60. A similar procedure may be used to resolve any two isotopes producing gamma radiation of different energies. For a discussion of beta counting, refer to the Method for Measurement of Beta Particle Radioactivity of Industrial Water and Industrial Waste Water (ASTM Designation: D 1890).[3] For gamma counting refer to the Method for Measurement of Gamma Radioactivity of Industrial Water and Industrial Waste Water (ASTM Designation: D 1690).[3] Typical gamma-ray spectra are shown in a report by Heath[4] and a publication by Crouthamel.[5]

Definitions

3. For definitions of terms used in this method, refer to the Definitions of Terms Relating to Industrial Water and Industrial Waste Water (ASTM Designation: D 1129).[3]

Interferences

4. (a) Nonradioactive cobalt present in the sample will interfere in the method by causing an overestimation of chemical yield and must be corrected for.

(b) The method should not be expected to provide decontamination of more than a million-fold from other radionuclides.

Apparatus

5. (a) Beta Particle Counter, usually a proportional detector connected to the

appropriate amplifier, discriminator, and scaling equipment. Refer to Methods D 1890.[3]

(b) Gamma-Ray Counter, preferably a sodium iodide scintillation detector assembly connected to the appropriate amplifier, pulse height analyzer, or single channel pulse height discriminator. Refer to Methods D 1690.[3]

Purity of Reagents and Materials

6. (a) Reagent grade chemicals shall be used in all tests. Unless otherwise indicated, it is intended that all reagents shall conform to the specifications of the Committee on Analytical Reagents of the American Chemical Society, where such specifications are available.[6] Other grades may be used, provided it is first ascertained that the reagent is of sufficiently high purity to permit its use without lessening the accuracy of the determination.

(b) Unless otherwise indicated, reference to water shall be understood to mean reagent water conforming to the Specifications for Reagent Water (ASTM Designation: D 1193).[3]

(c) Radioactive purity shall be such that the measured radioactivity of blank samples does not exceed the calculated probable error of the measurement.

(d) Acetic Acid (1:2).—Mix 1 volume of glacial acetic acid with 2 volumes of water.

(e) Ammonium Hydroxide (sp gr 0.90).—Concentrated ammonium hydroxide (NH₄OH).

(f) Anion Exchange Resin, 100 to 200 mesh; 4 per cent cross-linked strongly basic resin in chloride form.

[2] L. C. Bogar and C. J. L. Lock, "Radio-chemical Analysis of Corrosion Product Mixtures from High Temperature Pressurized Water Loop Systems," *Talanta*, Vol. 6, p. 133.

[3] Appears in this publication.

[4] R. L. Heath, "Scintillation Spectrometry, Gamma-Ray Spectrum Catalog," IDO 16408.

[5] C. E. Crouthamel, "Applied Gamma-Ray Spectrometry," Pergamon Press, New York, N. Y. (1960).

[6] "Reagent Chemicals, American Chemical Society Specifications," Am. Chemical Soc., Washington, D. C. For suggestions on the testing of reagents not listed by the American Chemical Society, see "Reagent Chemicals and Standards," by Joseph Rosin, D. Van Nostrand Co., Inc., New York, N. Y., and the "United States Pharmacopeia."

(g) Cobalt Chloride Solution, Carrier (5g Co++ per liter).—Dissolve 20 g of cobalt chloride ($CoCl_2 \cdot 6H_2O$) in 100 ml of HCl (1:19), dilute to 1 liter, and store in a polyethylene bottle.

(h) Ethyl Alcohol (95 per cent).

(i) Ethyl Ether.

(j) Ferric Chloride Solution, Carrier (10 g Fe+++ per liter).—Dissolve 49 g of ferric chloride ($FeCl_3 \cdot 6H_2O$) in 100 ml of HCl (1:19), filter, and dilute to 1 liter.

(k) Hydrochloric Acid (sp gr 1.19).—Concentrated hydrochloric acid (HCl).

(l) Hydrochloric Acid (1:1). Mix 1 volume of concentrated hydrochloric acid (HCl, sp gr 1.19) with 1 volume of water.

(m) Hydrogen Peroxide (30 per cent).—Concentrated hydrogen peroxide (H_2O_2).

(n) Manganese Chloride Solution, Carrier (10 g Mn++ per liter).—Dissolve 35.9 g of manganese chloride ($MnCl_2 \cdot 4H_2O$) in 1 liter of water.

(o) Nickel Chloride Solution, Carrier (10 g Ni++ per liter).—Dissolve 40.5 g of nickel chloride ($NiCl_2 \cdot 6H_2O$) in 1 liter of water.

(p) Potassium Chromate Solution, Carrier (10 g Cr++ per liter).—Dissolve 37.3 g of potassium chromate (K_2CrO_4) in 1 liter of water.

(q) Potassium Hydroxide Solution (330 g per liter).—Dissolve 330 g of potassium hydroxide (KOH) in water and dilute to 1 liter.

(r) Potassium nitrite (KNO_2).

(s) Sulfuric Acid (sp gr 1.84).—Concentrated sulfuric acid (H_2SO_4).

(t) Zinc Chloride Solution, Carrier (10 g Zn++ per liter).—Dissolve 10 g of zinc in the minimum of HCl and dilute to 1 liter.

Sampling

7. *(a)* Collect the sample in accordance with the applicable methods of the American Society for Testing and Materials as follows:

D 510—Sampling Industrial Water,[3]
D 860—Sampling Water from Boilers,[3]
D 1496—Sampling Homogeneous Industrial Waste Water.[3]

(b) Take a 1-ml sample unless the concentration of radioactive cobalt is outside the range 10^{-7} to 10^{-3} curies per liter. For gamma counting, the total activity taken should be about 10^{-7} curie, and for beta counting, about 10^{-8} curie. The minimum activity measurable would be the smallest amount giving the desired precision for that determination and would be limited by the counter background.

Calibration and Standardization

8. *(a)* For counting a single cobalt isotope, beta or gamma counting is satisfactory; however, gamma counting is the recommended procedure. If absolute values are required, the detector used must be calibrated to obtain the ratio of sample-disintegration rate to count rate for the isotope concerned. Standards may be prepared by a method such as $4\pi\ \beta$ counting or β-γ coincidence counting. In the absence of the appropriate standard the detector may be calibrated with any standard emitting beta particles or gamma rays of the required energy. The standards must be prepared in the same form as the samples and counted on an identical detector under the same geometric conditions. For counting a mixture of isotopes, γ-ray pulse height analysis is necessary to resolve the components of the mixture.

NOTE 2.—Standardized Co^{60} is available from commercial sources; Co^{57} is available from the National Bureau of Standards, Washington 25, D. C.

NOTE 3.—Heath[4] and Crouthamel[5] provide typical γ spectra for many nuclides and Bogar and Lock[4] illustrate the resolution of mixtures of Co^{58} and Co^{60} using standard gamma spectra prepared from samples of the individual nuclides.

NOTE 4.—In beta counting, the degree of backscattering and self-absorption of beta particles is a function of the precipitate thickness, and hence, chemical yield. With low-energy beta particles this may be quite significant and standards should be prepared covering the expected range of chemical yields.

(b) Cobalt carrier is standardized so that the chemical yield of the processes completed after carrier addition may be calculated from the amount of precipitate finally obtained for each sample. To standardize,[7] pipet 5 ml of the $CoCl_2$ solution into 50 ml of water in a beaker. Add 5 ml of glacial acetic acid and 0.5 g of KNO_2. Heat nearly to boiling, cool, and allow to stand overnight. Filter off the precipitate, wash with water, and then with ethyl alcohol. Dry at 100 C to constant weight and finally weigh as potassium cobaltinitrite $(K_3Co(NO_2)_6 \cdot 3H_2O)$.

Procedure

9. (a) Add to the sample 1 ml of each of the carriers for cobalt, chromium, iron, manganese, nickel, and zinc. Add 5 ml of H_2SO_4 (sp gr 1.84) and digest on a hot plate.

(b) Dilute the solution to 10 ml; add the KOH solution until precipitation is complete. Then add 2 drops of H_2O_2.

(c) Centrifuge, discard the supernate, wash the precipitate with water, and discard the washings.

(d) Dissolve the precipitate in 10 ml of concentrated HCl (sp gr 1.19) and evaporate *just* to dryness. Allow to cool and dissolve the residue in 10 ml of concentrated HCl (sp gr 1.19).

(e) Prepare a column about 1 cm in diameter and 10 cm long, of ion-exchange resin suspended in HCl (sp gr 1.19). Wash with 50 ml of HCl (sp gr 1.19). Do not drain below the top of the resin.

(f) Transfer the solution to the column

[7] Scott and Furman, "Scott's Standard Methods of Chemical Analysis," p. 312, 5th Ed., D. Van Nostrand Co., Inc., New York, N. Y.

and elute with HCl (sp gr 1.19) until the blue cobalt band almost reaches the bottom of the column. Then elute with HCl (1:1) and collect the cobalt fraction. The concentrated hydrochloric acid fraction contains manganese, chromium, and nickel and, if required, may be used for the determination of these activities. Iron remains on the column and may be eluted with HCl (1:19) if required.

(g) Evaporate the cobalt solution to dryness. Add 0.5 ml of HCl (sp gr 1.19) and two drops of H_2O_2. Dilute to 10 ml with water and add NH_4OH (sp gr 0.90) until the solution is basic and a pink-brown color. Add 2 mg of iron carrier, centrifuge, and discard the precipitate. Repeat the iron scavenge.

(h) Add two drops of H_2O_2 to the solution and warm. Add KOH solution dropwise to the solution until a precipitate forms, boil, and cool. Centrifuge and discard the supernate. Wash the precipitate with KOH solution (1:100) and discard the washings.

(i) Dissolve the precipitate in 5 ml of acetic acid (1:2), dilute with water to 10 ml, and add 0.5 g of KNO_2. Heat the mixture almost to boiling and then cool in an ice bath for about 15 min. Centrifuge, decant, wash the precipitate with water, and discard the washings. The addition of a little nitric acid (HNO_3) and H_2O_2 will aid dissolution of the precipitate should this be difficult.

(j) Add 1.0 ml of HCl (sp gr 1.19) to the precipitate and heat until a clear blue solution results. Dilute to 10 ml.

(k) Repeat Steps (h) and (i).

(l) Transfer the precipitate to a tared filter paper. Wash with water, ethyl alcohol, and ethyl ether. Dry at 100 C to a constant weight. Weigh and mount as required for counting.

Calculation

10. (a) Calculate the concentration,

D, of radioactive cobalt in curies per liter as follows:

$$D = \frac{C}{2.22 \times 10^{12} EVR}$$

where:

C = count rate of sample in counts per minute,

E = counter efficiency,

V = liters of sample used,

R = fractional chemical yield for the separation; and

2.22×10^{12} = conversion factor from disintegrations per minute to curies.

Note 5.—In γ-ray spectrometry the efficiency, E, in this expression includes the fractional abundance of the gamma ray A (gammas/decay) and the photopeak detection efficiency e (counts/gamma):

$$E\left(\frac{\text{counts}}{\text{decay}}\right) = A\left(\frac{\text{gammas}}{\text{decay}}\right) \times e\left(\frac{\text{counts}}{\text{gamma}}\right)$$

(*b*) Calculate the decay correction for radioactive cobalt as follows:

$$A = A_0 e^{\frac{-t\,0.693}{T}}$$

where:

A = activity at time t,

A_0 = activity at time zero, in the same units as A,

e = base of natural logarithms,

t = elapsed time, and

T = half-life of radioisotope, in the same units as t.

Precision

11. Precision depends on the random counting error and on the determination of chemical yields. Precision would be poorer if two or more isotopes were determined by one count.

APPENDIX

TABLE I.—RADIOACTIVE DECAY CHARACTERISTICS OF COBALT ISOTOPES OF MASSES 57, 58, AND 60.[8,9]

Radioisotope	Half-Life	Gamma Radiation Energy, Mev	Decay Mode
Cobalt-57.........	270 days	0.136 (10 per cent) 0.122 (88 per cent)	orbital electron capture
Cobalt-58.........	72 days	0.805 ~ (100 per cent)	β^+ emission and electron capture
Cobalt-60.........	5.27 years	1.17 (100 per cent) 1.33 (100 per cent)	β^- emission

---

[8] Dzhelepov and Peker, "Decay Schemes of Radioactive Nucleii," Pergamon Press, New York, N. Y. (1961).

[9] L. C. Bate and G. W. Leddicotte, "The Radiochemistry of Cobalt," NAS-NS-3041, National Research Council Monograph.

APPROVED AS
USA STANDARD Z111.5-1966
BY USA STANDARDS INSTITUTE
UDC 621.013.3:543.064:620.1

Standard Methods of Test for

DEPOSIT-FORMING IMPURITIES IN STEAM[1]

ASTM Designation: D 2186 – 66

ADOPTED, 1966

This Standard of the American Society for Testing and Materials is issued under the fixed designation D 2186; the number immediately following the designation indicates the year of original adoption or, in the case of revision, the year of last revision. A number in parentheses indicates the year of last reapproval.

Scope

1. (*a*) These methods cover the determination of the amount of deposit-forming impurities in steam. Methods A, B, and C give a measure of the amount of total deposit-forming material present; Method D deals with special constituents that may be present. Special precautions and equipment, calculation procedures, and ranges of applicability are described. The following methods are included:

	Sections
Method A (Gravimetric or Evaporative Method)	4 to 10
Method B (Electrical Conductivity)	11 to 17
Method C (Sodium Tracer)	18 to 24
Method D (Silica and Metals)	25 to 27

(*b*) Method A covers gravimetric procedures for determining impurities in concentrations usually not less than 0.1

---

[1] Under the standardization procedure of the Society, these methods are under the jurisdiction of the ASTM Committee D-19 on Industrial Water. A list of members may be found in the ASTM Year Book.

ppm. It is useful for determining impurities that are insoluble or are not detected by other methods. Because of the large sample required and the period of time necessary for evaporating the sample, it is not applicable for transient conditions.

(*c*) Method B depends on the electrical conductance of condensed steam samples to determine the impurity content. The presence of dissolved gases in the condensate samples interferes with conductance measurements even when a mechanical degasser is used, but corrections can be made for some of the more common gases. The method is not recommended for quantitative testing of impurity concentrations less than 3.0 ppm when only mechanical degassing is used; however, its useful range can be extended down to 0.05 ppm if both mechanical and ion-exchange degassers are used. An ion-exchange degasser, which eliminates interferences from basic dissolved gases, is useful for measuring the conductance of cooled steam condensate. A combination of an ion-exchange degasser and mechanical degassers with a conductance measurement at atmospheric boiling-water temperature provides increased sensitivity and precision, and eliminates interference from carbon dioxide.

(*d*) Method C utilizes the element sodium as a tracer to indicate the impurity content of the steam. Because of the high sensitivity of the flame photometric determination of sodium and the lack of interferences, Method C provides the most sensitive measure of impurity content for samples in which sodium represents an appreciable percentage of the impurities. Under favorable conditions, concentrations of impurities as low as 0.0006 ppm can be detected.

(*e*) Method D covers the determination of silica and metals in steam, which are not included in Methods B and C and are not individually determined using Method A.

Definitions

2. For definitions of terms used in these methods, refer to the Definitions of Terms Relating to Industrial Water and Industrial Waste Water (ASTM Designation: D 1129).[2]

Sampling

3. (*a*) Collect the samples in accordance with the applicable methods of the American Society for Testing and Materials, as follows:

D 860—Sampling Water from Boilers,[2]
D 1066—Sampling Steam.[2]

(*b*) The concentrations of sodium and silica in steam samples are usually well below 1 ppm. Because these materials exist in relative abundance in normal plant and laboratory environments, even in atmospheric dust, extreme caution must be used when collecting and handling samples to avoid contamina-

[2] Appears in this publication.

tion. The use of a continuously flowing sample, which eliminates the need for collecting, handling, and storing individual samples, is preferred.

METHOD A

(GRAVIMETRIC OR EVAPORATIVE METHOD)

Application

4. The gravimetric method is recommended for applications for which an average value of impurities over a period of several days or weeks is desired. It is particularly useful for samples in which a large percentage of the impurities are insoluble, do not contain sodium, or do not contribute appreciably to the electrical conductivity of the samples, because the other methods are not satisfactory for these conditions. Examples of such impurities are metals and metal oxides. It is not applicable when short-time trends are of interest or when immediate results are desired. The method is useful for the determination of concentrations of impurities of 0.25 ppm or greater when a previously collected sample is used and for impurities concentrations of 0.1 ppm or greater when continuous sampling is used. Concentrations less than 0.1 ppm can be determined if a continuously flowing sample is evaporated for an extremely long period of time.

Summary of Method

5. This method involves the evaporation of a quantity of steam condensate at a temperature below the boiling point and the weighing of the residue to determine the amount of impurities in the sample. The evaporation process may be carried out on a steam condensate sample previously collected, or the sample may be taken continuously as the evaporation process is continued.

Interferences

6. Possible interferences for these methods are described in the Methods of Test for Particulate and Dissolved Matter in Industrial Water (ASTM Designation: D 1888).[2]

Apparatus

7. Apparatus shall be provided in accordance with Method A of Methods D 1888.

Procedure

8. Proceed in accordance with Method A of Methods D 1888.

Calculation

9. (a) Calculate the percentage of impurities in the sample in accordance with Method A of Methods D 1888.

(b) Dissolved matter and total matter are usually of greatest interest in the determination of impurities in steam. The determination of fixed solids after ignition at some temperature greater than 103 C (217 F) may be of more significance than the measurement taken at 103 C, depending on the type of solids in the sample and the maximum temperature to which the steam is to be heated in the application.

Precision

10. The precision of the analytical results is given in Method A of Methods D 1888. Because of the uncertainties involved in sampling steam, it is not possible to state the over-all precision of this method.

Method B

(Electrical Conductivity)

Application

11. (a) *Mechanical Degasser.*—When electrical conductivity is used in conjunction with an effective mechanical degasser, the relationship between electrical conductivity and impurity concentration in the sample is linear for impurity concentrations down to about 3 ppm. Below this value, the relationship ceases to be linear because of interference from residual dissolved gases not removed by the degasser, and the method is unreliable for impurity concentrations less than about 0.5 ppm. Therefore, this method is recommended for the measurement of impurity concentrations of 3 ppm or greater. The method is not satisfactory for the determination of impurities in steam samples that contain volatile amines, large percentages of insoluble matter, or substances that ionize weakly.

(b) *Ion-Exchange Degasser.*—An ion-exchange degasser consists of an ion-exchange resin that exchanges hydrogen ions for all cations in the sample, thereby eliminating all basic dissolved gases, including volatile amines. By converting mineral salts to their acid forms, it also increases the specific conductance of the impurities. As a result, the linear relationship between conductivity and impurity content is extended to a much lower level, depending on the carbon dioxide content. The method is very useful for measuring low concentrations of impurities in cooled steam condensate, and it is especially useful for indicating small or intermittent changes in impurity content from some normal value. The method is not satisfactory for the determination of impurities in steam condensate samples that contain acidic gases, such as carbon dioxide, large percentages of insoluble matter, or substances that ionize weakly. The sensitivity and accuracy of the method are decreased for samples in which hydroxides represent an appreciable percentage of the impurities, because hydroxides, which contribute to the formation of deposits, are converted to water by the ion-exchange resin. This characteristic is particularly significant when steam is generated at sufficiently high pressure to cause appreciable vaporization of sodium hydroxide from the boiler water.

greater sensitivity afforded by measuring the conductance at atmospheric boiling water temperature extends the linear relationship between conductivity and

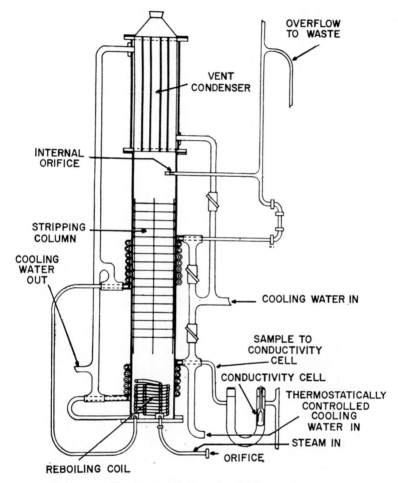

FIG. 1.—Straub Degassing Condenser.

(c) *Mechanical and Ion-Exchange Degasser.*—By combining mechanical and ion-exchange degassing of steam or condensed steam, or both, effective elimination of both acidic and basic dissolved gases is attained. This arrangement has the same advantages and limitations as the ion-exchange degasser alone, except that it will remove acidic gases, and the

the ionized impurity content down to about 0.05 ppm.

Summary of Method

12. (*a*) Because the concentrations of impurities in steam condensate are usually very low, most impurities are assumed to be completely dissolved and completely ionized. Therefore, the elec-

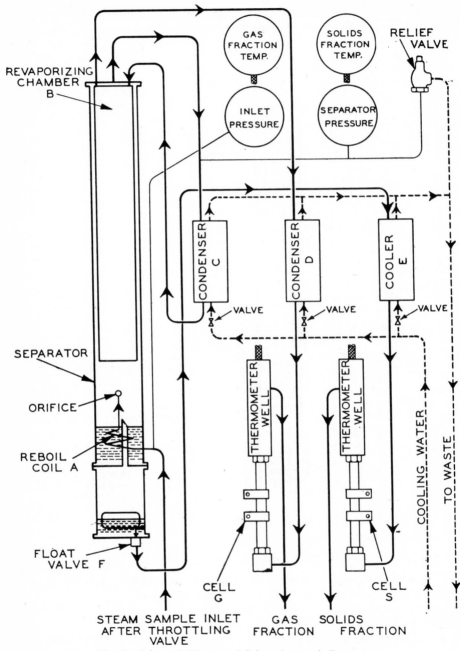

FIG. 2.—Schematic Diagram of Calgon Automatic Degasser.

trical conductivity of the condensate sample is a measure of the concentration of ionized impurities in the sample.

(b) Most steam contains gases from decomposition of certain substances in boiler feedwater and from the addition of chemicals to boiler water or boiler feed-water for the control of corrosion. These gases dissolve and ionize in the condensed steam samples. Since such gases normally do not form deposits, their contribution to conductivity should be eliminated by degassing the sample before its electrical conductivity is measured. Because mechanical degassing is not completely effective, the amount of residual gases must be determined and the measured conductivity value must be corrected for their effect.

(c) Basic dissolved gases, many of which are not effectively removed by mechanical degassing, are converted to water by an ion-exchange degasser. The ion-exchange degasser also converts mineral salts to their acid form by exchanging hydrogen ions for the metallic cations. Since the specific conductance of the acid form is roughly three times that of the original mineral salts at 25 C (77 F), the sensitivity of measurement is increased. If the conductance measurement is made at the atmospheric boiling point (approximately 100 C (212 F)), the specific conductances of the ions are increased and the sensitivity of measurement is improved still further.

Interferences

13. Residual gases remaining in steam condensate samples after mechanical degassing constitute interference with the conductivity measurement. The concentrations of these gases remaining in the samples shall be determined, and appropriate corrections shall be subtracted from the measured conductivity values.

Apparatus

14. (a) Apparatus shall be provided in accordance with the Methods of Test for Electrical Conductivity of Industrial Water and Industrial Waste Water (ASTM Designation: D 1125).[2]

(b) *Mechanical Degasser.*[3]—Mechanical degassers remove dissolved gases from condensed steam samples by combined mechanical agitation and stripping action provided by the counter-flow passage of steam and condensate at saturation temperature. The vapor portion of the sample used for stripping may be discharged to the atmosphere along with the gases or it may be condensed. Typical examples of mechanical degassers are shown in Figs. 1 and 2.

(1) A degasser provides a condensed and cooled sample and, therefore, a separate condensing and cooling coil is not needed. Also, some degassers include conductivity cells and means of measuring sample temperature as integral parts of the units. Such cooling coils, conductivity cells, and temperature indicators shall conform to the applicable ASTM specifications for material, structural design, and performance.

(2) Because of their characteristics, most degassers will accommodate only one sample flow rate. Consequently, the steam-sampling nozzle must be designed for the desired flow rate to provide equal steam velocities entering the sampling nozzle ports and in the pipe from which the sample is taken.

(c) *Ion-Exchange Degasser.*[4]—The ion exchange column shall consist preferably of sulfonated styrenedivinylbenzene resin in a container of plastic or other corrosion-resistant material. A column of approximately 1.5-in. (38-mm) internal diameter and 12 in. (305 mm) in length, containing about 0.6 lb (272 g) of resin, is satisfactory for most applications.

---

[3] The Calgon Degasser, Part No. 483970-3, manufactured by the Calgon Corp., P.O. Box 1346, Pittsburgh, Pa., has been found satisfactory for this purpose.

[4] The Larson-Lane Condensate Analyzer, Model CH-16A, manufactured by Industrial Instruments, Inc., Cedar Grove, N. J., has been found satisfactory for this purpose.

[5] Lumite Woven Swan Fabric No. 1010-000, has been found satisfactory for this purpose.

Woven plastic fabric[5] or similar corrosion-resistant material is required at each end of the column to retain the resin and to permit the condensate sample to enter and leave the column. An example of an ion exchange column, equipped with a conductivity cell, flowmeter, and thermometer, is shown in Fig. 3.

(*d*) *Mechanical-Ion-Exchange Degasser.*[6]—This apparatus consists of a vented condenser in which the steam sample is condensed and mechanically degassed, a

verted to acids. Carbonic acid is driven off as carbon dioxide in the vented reboil chamber. Suitable control valves are required to regulate sample flow rate (Note 2), to adjust cooling water flow rate (Note 3), and to proportion properly the steam sample between the condensing coils in the condenser and in the reboiler. A conductivity cell to measure conductivity of the sample from the reboiler is required (Note 4), and a second conductivity cell to measure conductivity of the

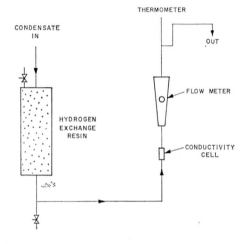

FIG. 3.—Larson-Lane Condensate Analyzer.

cooling coil, a hydrogen ion-exchange bed, and a vented reboil chamber. The vented condenser removes nearly all carbon dioxide and appreciable amounts of other gases. The condensate is cooled in the cooling coil before being transferred to the exchange bed to minimize leaching of the resin (Note 1). The exchange bed exchanges hydrogen ions for all cations in the sample. Thus, hydroxides, ammonia, and alkaline amines are converted to water, carbonates are converted to carbonic acid, and mineral salts are con-

effluent from the condenser is helpful in providing an approximation of the amine concentration, in disclosing the need for resin replacement, and in monitoring the proper operation of the apparatus. Also, thermometers to indicate temperatures of effluent cooling water of the sample entering the resin bed, and of the effluent sample from the reboiler are required to control the apparatus properly. A mechanical-ion-exchange degasser is illustrated in Fig. 4.

[6] The Larson-Lane Steam Purity Analyzer, Model SC-19C, manufactured by Industrial Instruments, Inc., Cedar Grove, N. J., has been found satisfactory for this purpose.

NOTE 1.—Sulfonated styrene, divinylbenzene resin with 8 per cent cross-linkage has proven to be the most stable type and experiences minimum leaching.

NOTE 2.—Commercially available equipment uses the heat from the condensing steam sample to reboil the condensate and to drive off carbon dioxide and other dissolved gases. Such apparatus is designed for a specific condensing pressure which is often considerably less than the pressure of the steam sample. When the steam sample is throttled to condensing pressure, care must be taken to assure that the sample does not become superheated. Even slight superheating can cause deposits of impurities to form at the point of throttling, resulting in a loss of impurity content of the sample. Such superheating can be avoided by providing a sufficiently long uninsulated sampling line before the point of throttling, by providing an auxiliary cooling coil to partially condense the sample upstream of the point of throttling, or by injecting a portion of the condensate sample before the point of throttling. If the condensate injection method is used, the condensate should be obtained from the vented condenser overflow.

NOTE 3.—Commercially available apparatus includes a thermostatic valve for controlling cooling water temperature by automatically adjusting cooling water flow rate and manual flow regulating valves to proportion properly the sample steam to the condenser and to the reboiler.

NOTE 4.—Because conductivity is measured at the constant temperature of atmospheric boiling water, the measuring instrument shall indicate actual conductance at this temperature and shall not include automatic temperature compensation.

Procedure

15. (a) *Mechanical Degasser.*—Place the apparatus in operation for a sufficient length of time to flush away contamination before conductivity measurements are made. Several hours of operation may be required for a new installation to sufficiently reduce contamination. Adjust the degasser to provide adequate venting. A definite plume of steam from the vent is required to provide proper degassing from a degasser that vents to atmosphere. Measure the electrical conductivity of the sample in accordance with Methods D 1125. Determine the concentrations of ammonia and carbon dioxide in the sample in accordance with the applicable methods of the American

Society for Testing and Materials, as follows:

D 513—Total Carbon Dioxide and Calculation of the Carbonate and Bicarbonate Ions in Industrial Water,[2]
D 1426—Ammonia in Industrial Water and Industrial Waste Water.[2]

If the relationship between conductivity and impurity content is not known, determine the concentration of chloride, sulfate, sulfite, phosphate, and hydroxide ions in the boiler water in accordance with the applicable methods of the American Society for Testing and Materials as follows:

D 512—Chloride Ion in Industrial Water and Industrial Waste Water,[2]
D 516—Sulfate Ion in Industrial Water and Industrial Waste Water,[2]
D 1339—Sulfite Ion in Industrial Water,[2]
D 515—Phosphate in Industrial Water,[2] and
D 514—Hydroxide Ion in Industrial Water and Industrial Waste Water.[2]

Also, determine the total matter in the boiler water by evaporation in accordance with Methods D 1888.

(b) *Ion-Exchange Degasser.*—Operate the condensing and cooling coil for a sufficient length of time to remove contamination. Flush condensate through the ion exchange column for at least 5 min. Measure the conductivity of the sample in accordance with Methods D 1125. If the relationship between conductivity and impurity content is not known, determine the composition of the boiler water in accordance with Scheme D 1256. Also, determine the total solids concentration in the boiler water by evaporation in accordance with Methods D 1888.

(c) *Mechanical-Ion-Exchange Degasser.* —Place the apparatus in operation with a sample flow rate of 25 to 75 lb per hr (189 to 567 g per min) and adjust the cooling water control valve to provide a constant cooling water effluent temperature of 40 to 70 C (104 to 158 F). During

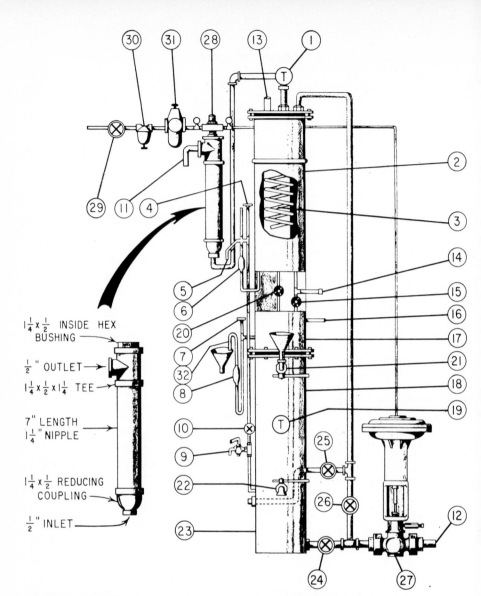

$1\frac{1}{4} \times \frac{1}{2}$ INSIDE HEX BUSHING

$\frac{1}{2}$" OUTLET

$1\frac{1}{4} \times \frac{1}{2} \times 1\frac{1}{4}$ TEE

7" LENGTH $1\frac{1}{4}$" NIPPLE

$1\frac{1}{4} \times \frac{1}{2}$ REDUCING COUPLING

$\frac{1}{2}$" INLET

1—Cooling water effluent thermometer
2—Condensing chamber
3—Condensing coil
4—Alternate location for thermometer (top chamber effluent)
5—Condensing chamber overflow
6—Location for second conductivity cell (top chamber effluent)
7—Effluent thermometer
8—Effluent conductivity cell
9—Sampling cock and drain
10—Throttling valve
11—$\frac{1}{2}$-in. NPT cold water outlet
12—$\frac{1}{2}$-in. NPT cold water inlet
13—Steam vent
14—Steam inlet
15—Inlet reboil chamber steam valve
16—Reboil chamber vent

17—Reboil chamber
18—Resin chamber
19—Resin chamber condensate temperature
20—Outlet reboil chamber steam valve
21—Resin inlet valve
22—Resin outlet valve
23—Condensate cooler
24—Cooling water inlet valve
25—Cooling water outlet valve
26—Cooling water by-pass valve
27—Cooling water control valve
28—Cooling water temperature sensing bulb, well, and air pressure gages
29—Air supply
30—Air filter
31—Air pressure reducing valve and gages
32—Condensate effluent

FIG. 4.—Larson-Lane Steam Purity Analyzer.

initial operation, the condensate cooling coil is by-passed and the condensate leaving the resin is maintained at near boiling water temperature. Operation at this temperature cleans the resin more

6 lb per hr (18.9 to 45.4 g per min) flow from the condensing chamber overflow (Note 5). In order to provide a definite plume of steam from the reboil chamber vent and to provide a condensate efflu-

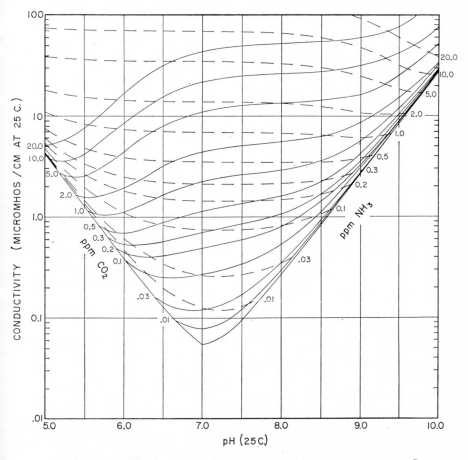

FIG. 5.—Carbon Dioxide, Ammonia, pH, and Conductivity Relationship at 25 C.[7]

quickly. The throttling valve between the condensing chamber and the resin chamber should be adjusted so that $2\frac{1}{2}$ to

ent temperature of approximately 99 C (210 F), open the outlet-reboil-chamber-steam valve completely and throttle the inlet-reboil-chamber-steam valve accordingly. After operating the apparatus for a sufficient length of time, indication that contamination has been completely removed will be shown by a constant conductivity value of about 1.6

[7] See R. W. Lane, C. H. Neff, and T. E. Larson, "A New Method for Increasing the Sensitivity of the Conductivity Measurement of Steam Purity," *Proceedings of the American Power Conference*, Vol. XXIII, pp. 550–558 (1961).

micromhos. Then, cooling of the condensate entering the resin chamber should be initiated by opening the cooling water valves to the condensate cooler and by closing the by-pass valve. It is possible that the cooling water control valve setting may require adjustment to provide an outlet temperature of the resin chamber condensate of 25 to 40 C (77 to 104 F) and to provide a cooling water effluent temperature of 40 to 70 C (104 to 158 F). Readjustment of the reboil chamber steam valves will likely be required. Opening the inlet-reboil-chamber-steam valve completely and gradually closing the outlet-reboil-steam valve, until a definite steam plume is obtained at the reboil chamber vent, is suggested. Measure the electrical conductivity of the sample in accordance with Methods D 1125, except that the conductivity shall not be corrected to 25 C (77 F). The conductivity shall be determined at the temperature of the sample with no correction. If the relationship between conductivity and impurity content is not known, determine the composition of the boiler water in accordance with Scheme D 1256. Also, determine the total matter in the boiler water by evaporation in accordance with Methods D 1888.

NOTE 5.—If condensate is injected into the steam sample before the point of throttling, the condensate should be obtained from the vented condenser overflow. In this case, the flow rate into the instrument should be increased by opening the sample regulating valve; and the throttling valve between the condensing chamber and the resin chamber should be adjusted to provide the additional amount of condensate required for de-superheating in addition to the overflow rate of 2½ to 6 lb per hour.

Calculations

16. (a) *Mechanical Degasser:*

(1) The portion of the measured conductivity contributed by residual dissolved gases shall be determined from Fig. 5. The measured conductivity

shall be corrected by subtracting the conductivity of the dissolved gases.

(2) Some mechanical degassers reject as much as 50 per cent of the original sample as vapor along with the gases stripped from the liquid fraction of the sample, which results in concentration of the impurities in the liquid portion. If an appreciable amount of the sample is rejected as vapor, the corrected conductivity determined in accordance with Item (1) shall be altered, as follows:

$$K = K_m \frac{L}{T}$$

where:

K = true conductivity of the steam sample, in micromhos per centimeter, at 25 C (77 F),

K_m = measured conductivity of the concentrated sample, in micromhos per centimeter, at 25 C (77 F),

L = flow rate of the concentrated sample in pounds per hour, and

T = flow rate of the total sample in pounds per hour.

(3) If the relationship between conductivity and impurity content is known, divide the corrected conductivity value determined in accordance with Item (2) by the ratio of the conductivity to impurity content to determine the concentration of impurities in the sample. (Experience has shown that the ratio of conductivity to impurity concentration for most conditions is approximately two at 25 C (77 F).)

(4) If the relationship between conductivity and impurity content is not known, it shall be determined from the composition of the boiler water, as follows:[8]

---

[8] The values of conductances of the various compounds were taken from A. B. Sisson, F. G. Straub, and R. W. Lane, "Construction and Operation of Larson-Lane Steam Purity and Condensate Analyzers," Symposium on Steam Quality, *ASTM STP No. 192* (1956).

$$F = \frac{3.56\ (Cl^-) + 2.71\ (SO_4^{--}) + 2.41\ (SO_3^{--}) + 3.85\ (PO_4^{---}) + 14.3\ (OH^-)}{T}$$

where:

F = ratio of conductivity (in sodium salt form) to impurity content at 25 C (77 F),

Cl^-, SO_4^{--}, etc. = concentrations of these ions in the boiler water, in parts per million and

T = total matter in the boiler water determined by evaporation, in parts per million.

(b) *Ion-Exchange Degasser:*

(1) If the relationship between conductivity and impurity content is known, divide the measured conductivity value by the ratio of conductivity (in acid form) to impurity content to determine the concentration of impurities in the sample.

(2) If the relationship between conductivity and impurity content is not known, it shall be determined from the composition of the boiler water, as follows:[9]

$$E = \frac{9.2(Cl^-) + 7.9(SO_4^{--}) + 6.4(SO_3^{--}) + 4.5(PO_4^{---})}{T}$$

where:

E = ratio of conductivity (in acid form) to impurity content at 25 C (77 F),

Cl^-, SO_4^{--}, etc., = concentrations of these anions in the boiler water, in parts per million, and

T = total solids in the boiler water determined by evaporation, in parts per million.

(c) *Mechanical-Ion-Exchange Degasser:*

(1) Subtract 0.81 micromhos per centimeter, the theoretical conductivity of pure water at 98.5 C (209.3 F), from

the measured conductivity. (Although the sea-level boiling point of water is 100 C (212 F), a temperature of 98.5 C (209.3 F) is assumed to account for reasonable altitudes above sea level and heat losses from the sample as it flows from the reboil chamber to the conductivity cell.)

(2) If the relationship between conductivity and impurity content is known, divide the corrected conductivity determined in accordance with Item (1) by the ratio of conductivity to impurity content to determine the concentration of impurities in the sample.

(3) If the relationship between conductivity and impurity content is not known, it shall be determined from the composition of the boiler water, as follows:[10]

$$C = \frac{17.0(Cl^-) + 13.6(SO_4^{--}) + 9.6(NO_3^-) + 4.8(PO_4^{---})}{T}$$

where:

C = the ratio of conductivity (in acid form) to impurity content at 98.5 C (209.3 F),

Cl^-, SO_4^{--}, etc., = concentration of these anions in the boiler water, in parts per million, and

T = total solids in the boiler water determined by evaporation, in parts per million.

Precision

17. The precision of the analytical results is given in Methods D 1125. Because of the uncertainties involved in sampling steam, it is not possible to state the over-all precision of the method.

---

[9] The values of the conductances of the various anions (in acid form at 25 C) were taken from R. W. Lane, C. H. Neff, and T. E. Larson, "A New Method for Increasing the Sensitivity of Conductivity Measurement of Steam Purity," *Proceedings of the American Power Conference*, Vol. XXIII, p. 552 (1961).

[10] The values of the conductances of the various anions (in acid form at 98.5 C) were taken from R. W. Lane, C. H. Neff, and T. E. Larson, "A New Method for Increasing the Sensitivity of Conductivity Measurement of Steam Purity," *Proceedings of the American Power Conference*, Vol. XXIII, p. 552 (1961).

Method C

(Sodium Tracer)

Application

18. The principal advantages of the sodium tracer method are its freedom from interferences, its ability to measure extremely small concentrations of impurities, and its rapid response to transient conditions because of the absence of large stagnant sample volumes, such as reboil chambers. Also, it does not require precise control of sample temperature. If the impurities are principally sodium compounds, impurity concentrations as low as 0.0006 ppm can be detected. The sodium tracer method is not recommended for samples having large percentages of impurities that do not contain sodium.

Summary of Method

19. This method utilizes the element sodium as a tracer material to determine the amount of impurities in steam. It is assumed that the ratio of concentrations of sodium-to-impurities in steam is equal to the corresponding ratio in boiler water.

Interferences

20. The types of materials found in steam and their extremely low concentrations render this method free from interferences under ordinary circumstances. Possible interferences in the flame-photometric determination of sodium are described in the Methods of Test for Sodium and Potassium in Industrial Water and Water-Formed Deposits by Flame Photometry (ASTM Designation: D 1428).[2]

Apparatus

21. Apparatus shall be provided in accordance with Methods D 1428.

Procedure

22. (a) Determine the sodium content of both steam and boiler water samples.

(1) The sodium concentration of steam shall be determined either from a continuously flowing sample or from at least ten separately collected samples taken under steady-state conditions. When several separate samples are taken, their sodium concentrations shall be compared to assure that steady-state conditions existed during the sampling period. Samples having sodium contents considerably higher than other samples are generally assumed to be contaminated and shall be discarded.

(2) If the sodium concentration of boiler water samples exceeds 100 ppm, a sufficient amount of sodium-free water shall be added to the samples to dilute their sodium contents to 100 ppm or less. The amount of water added to each sample and the amounts of the original samples shall be measured to enable calculation of the sodium concentrations of the original samples.

(b) Determine the total matter in boiler water samples by evaporation in accordance with Methods D 1888.

Calculation

23. Calculate the impurity concentration of the steam samples, as follows:

$$S_t = S_s \frac{W_t}{W_s}$$

where:

S_t = concentration of impurities in steam, in parts per million,

S_s = concentration of sodium in steam, in parts per million,

W_t = concentration of total matter in boiler water, in parts per million, and

W_s = concentration of sodium in boiler water, in parts per million.

Precision

24. The precision of the analytical results is given in Methods D 1428. Because of the uncertainties involved in sampling steam, it is not possible to

state the over-all precision of the method.

METHOD D
(Silica, Metals, and Metal Oxides)
Application

25. Silica and various metals are impurities that are occasionally found in steam and have definite tendencies to form deposits. Since these substances are not isolated when using Method A and are not detected when using Methods B and C, it is advisable to determine their concentrations separately when they are present in significant quantities.

Procedure

26. Proceed in accordance with the applicable methods of the American Society for Testing and Materials, as follows:

D   857—Aluminum and Aluminum Ion, Total, in Industrial Water[2]
D   859—Silica in Industrial Water and Industrial Waste Water[2]
D 1068—Iron in Industrial Water, and Industrial Waste Water[2]
D 1687—Chromium, Total, in Industrial Water and Industrial Waste Water,[2]
D 1688—Copper in Industrial Water and Industrial Waste Water,[2]
D 1886—Nickel in Industrial Water.[2]

Precision

27. The precision of the analytical results is stated in the appropriate methods listed in Section 26. Because of the uncertainties involved in sampling steam, it is not possible to state the over-all precision of the method.

Tentative Methods of Test for

PHYSICAL AND CHEMICAL PROPERTIES OF ION-EXCHANGE RESINS[1]

ASTM Designation: D 2187 – 66 T

ISSUED, 1963; LAST REVISED, 1966

These Tentative Methods have been approved by the sponsoring committee and accepted by the Society in accordance with established procedures, for use pending adoption as standard. Suggestions for revisions should be addressed to the Society at 1916 Race St., Philadelphia, Pa. 19103.

Scope

1. These methods cover the determination of the physical and chemical properties of ion-exchange resins when used for the treatment of industrial water. They are intended for use in testing both new and used materials. The following five methods are included:

	Sections
Pretreatment	5 to 9
Water Retention Capacity	10 to 15
Backwashed and Settled Density	16 to 21
Particle Size Distribution	22 to 28
Salt-Splitting Capacity of Cation Exchange Resins	29 to 36

Definitions

2. (a) Certain terms in this method that relate specifically to this method are defined as follows:

Ion-Exchange Resin.—A synthetic organic ion-exchange material.

Anion-Exchange Material.—An ion-exchange material capable of the reversible exchange of negatively charged ions.

Cation-Exchange Material.—An ion-exchange material capable of the reversible exchange of positively charged ions.

Mixed Bed.—A physical mixture of anion-exchange material and cation-exchange material.

(b) For definitions of other terms used in this method, refer to the Definitions of Terms Relating to Industrial Water and Industrial Waste Water (ASTM Designation: D 1129).[2]

Purity of Reagents

3. (a) Reagent grade chemicals shall be used in all tests. Unless otherwise indicated, it is intended that all reagents shall conform to the specifications of the Committee on Analytical Reagents of the American Chemical Society, where such specifications are available.[3] Other

---

[1] Under the standardization procedure of the Society, these methods are under the jurisdiction of the ASTM Committee D-19 on Industrial Water. A list of members may be found in the ASTM Year Book.

[2] Appears in this publication.

[3] "Reagent Chemicals, American Chemical Society Specifications," Am. Chemical Soc., Washington, D. C. For suggestions on the testing of reagents not listed by the American Chemical Society, see "Reagent Chemicals and Standards," by Joseph Rosin, D. Van Nostrand Co., Inc., New York, N. Y., and the "United States Pharmacopeia."

grades may be used, provided it is first ascertained that the reagent is of sufficiently high purity to permit its use without lessening the accuracy of the determination.

(b) Unless otherwise indicated, references to water shall be understood to mean non-referee grade reagent water conforming to the Specifications for Reagent Water (ASTM Designation: D 1193).[2]

Sampling

4. (a) Obtain a representative sample either from a shipment of new ion-exchange resin in the manufacturer's original packages or from a bed of used material.

(b) If the complete shipment is indicated by the manufacturer's marking to consist of only one batch or run of resin, the number of packages selected for sampling shall be not less than 10 per cent of the packages in the batch and not less than 3 packages, except that when less than 3 packages are involved a sample shall be taken from each package. Choose at random the packages selected for sampling or, in case the manufacturer has marked the packages to indicate the order in which they were filled from his batch, make the selection with reference to this order of filling if desired by the purchaser. If the shipment consists of more than one batch or run of resin, sample each batch separately and blend the samples of each batch to produce one composite sample for examination.

(c) Carefully open the packages selected making sure that no extraneous contamination is introduced. Insert a sampling device, such as a grain-type sampler, that takes a core not less than $\frac{1}{2}$ in. in diameter into the package being sampled so that it will take a core of the resin from substantially the entire length of the package. Combine the material thus taken from individual packages and thoroughly mix and quarter it until the sample is of the desired size. In the mixing and quartering process, take care to avoid loss of moisture from the sample and to avoid alteration of its physical characteristics. Obtain a minimum of 1 qt for testing. If in using this procedure a large enough sample is not obtained, take more than one core from each package at points well distributed within the package. Take the same number of cores from each package.

(d) Sample beds of used resin by taking cores comprising the full depth of the bed at points well distributed over the bed area. Combine the cores and thoroughly mix and quarter until a minimum sample of 1 qt is obtained. Where beds are too deep or the internal mechanical construction is too complicated to permit use of this procedure, take a sufficient number of samples distributed over the area and throughout the depth of the bed so that a representative sample results.

PRETREATMENT

Scope

5. This method covers the conversion of ion-exchange resins to a known ionic form and is intended for application to both new and used material.

Summary of Method

6. The method consists of chemical pretreatment, rinsing, and removal of water by vacuum filtration.

Apparatus

7. (a) *Pretreatment Apparatus* (Fig. 1):

(1) *Column*, transparent, vertically-supported, 2.5 ± 0.25-cm (1.0 ± 0.1 -in.) inside diameter and approximately 150 cm (60 in.) long. The bottom of the column shall be closed and provided with an outlet of approximately 6-mm

inside diameter. Connections shall be provided at top and bottom for admission and removal of solutions as described in Section 9. Adequate means for measuring

5 cm. Suggested supports are corrosion-resistant screen or porous plate.

(*b*) *Draining Apparatus* (Fig. 2):
(*1*) *Büchner-Type Funnel,* taking a

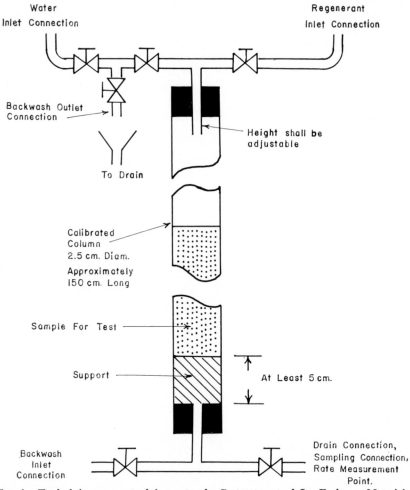

Water
Inlet Connection

Regenerant
Inlet Connection

Backwash Outlet
Connection

Height shall be
adjustable

To Drain

Calibrated
Column
2.5 cm. Diam.
Approximately
150 cm. Long

Sample For Test

Support

At Least 5 cm.

Backwash
Inlet
Connection

Drain Connection,
Sampling Connection,
Rate Measurement
Point.

Fig. 1.—Typical Arrangement of Apparatus for Pretreatment of Ion-Exchange Materials.

and regulating flow shall be provided. Calibrate the column in such a manner that the volume readings required by the method can be made. Make all measurements at 25 ± 5 C.

(*2*) *Support* for the sample, so designed that the distance from the sample to the column outlet is at least

12.5-cm filter paper and supported in a 1-liter suction flask.

(*2*) *Open-Arm Mercury Manometer,* connected by a T-tube to the vacuum train.

(*3*) *Gas-Humidifying Tower* of at least 500-ml capacity, two thirds filled with glass beads or similar material.

(4) Vacuum Pump capable of creating a pressure differential 40 mm of mercury below atmospheric pressure.

Reagents

8. *(a) Hydrochloric Acid (1:4).*—Carefully pour 100 ml of concentrated hydro-

(e) Thymol Blue Indicator.—Dissolve 0.1 g of thymol blue (thymol sulfonphthalein) in 10.75 ml of 0.02 N NaOH. Dilute to 250 ml with water.

(f) Tropaeolin O Indicator.—Dissolve 0.10 g of tropaeolin O (*p*-benzene-sulfonic acid-azoresorcinol) in 50 ml of water

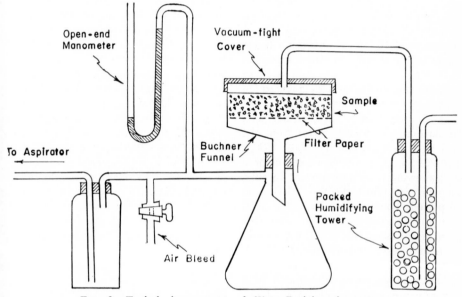

FIG. 2.—Typical Arrangement of Water-Draining Apparatus.

chloric acid (HCl, sp gr 1.19) into 400 ml of water, stirring constantly. Cool to 25 ± 5 C.

(b) Sodium Chloride Solution (100 g per liter).—Dissolve 100.0 g of sodium chloride (NaCl) in 800 ml of water and dilute to 1 liter in a volumetric flask.

(c) Sodium Chloride Solution (240 g per liter).—Dissolve 240 g of sodium chloride (NaCl) in 800 ml of water and dilute to 1 liter in a volumetric flask.

(d) Sodium Hydroxide Solution (40 g per liter).—Carefully add 40.0 g of sodium hydroxide (NaOH) to 800 ml of water. Cool and dilute to 1 liter in a volumetric flask.

and dilute to 100 ml in a volumetric flask.

Procedure

9. *(a)* Adjust the temperature of the water and all solutions to be used in the procedure to 25 ± 5 C and maintain this temperature throughout the test.

(b) Transfer the entire sample as received to a 2-liter beaker using water to rinse out the container. Adjust the water level to the sample level. Let stand a minimum of 1 hr. Mix thoroughly and transfer a representative sample to fill a 400-ml beaker.

(c) Fill the pretreatment column one half full of water. Transfer the entire contents of the 400-ml beaker to the column using additional water if necessary.

(d) Backwash with water using a flow rate that will maintain a 50 per cent expansion of the bed. Adjust the backwash outlet tube to a height above the bed equal to 75 per cent of the bed height. Continue backwashing for a minimum of 10 min or until the effluent is clear. For mixed bed samples proceed in accordance with Paragraph (e). For single component samples proceed in accordance with Paragraph (f).

(e) If the sample is a mixed bed, displace the backwash water from the bed by slowly introducing NaCl (100 g per liter) at the bottom of the column and allowing it to flow upward through the sample. When the water has been displaced, increase the flow rate until the anion-exchange resin is separated from and suspended above the cation-exchange resin. Lower the backwash outlet tube as required to siphon off the anion-exchange resin, collecting it in a separate pretreatment apparatus. Exercise care to prevent the removal of cation-exchange resin in this operation. When the transfer of the anion-exchange resin is complete, discontinue the flow of NaCl. If the separation of anion and cation-exchange resins has not been complete and a mixed band is left in the center, repeat the siphoning procedure to remove this band from the cation-portion of the sample. This mixed material which should not constitute more than 5 per cent of the original sample volume, is not included in subsequent tests. If more than 5 per cent of the sample remains unseparated, the separation should be repeated using NaCl (240 g per liter). In either case proceed

with the separated anion- and cation-components as separate samples as described in Paragraph (f).

(f) Allow the resin to settle, drain until the liquid level is 2 to 3 cm above the top of the bed, and estimate its volume. Pass NaCl (100 g per liter) downflow through the single component sample or the separated components of the mixed bed resin at the approximate rate of 0.133 ml per min per ml of sample for 1 hr. Discontinue the flow of NaCl. Backwash with water for 10 min at a flow rate sufficient to maintain a 50 per cent expansion of the bed. Discontinue the flow of water.

(g) Allow the bed to settle and then drain off the water at a rate of approximately 100 ml per min until the water level is 2 to 3 cm above the top of the bed. Estimate the volume of ion-exchange resin in milliliters.

(h) Determine the amount of reagent and the flow rate required for the initial pretreatment from Table I using the sample volume determined in Paragraph (g).

(i) Pass the specified volume of reagent through the bed at the specified rate until only a 2 to 3-cm layer of liquid remains above the bed. Rinse the bed with 2 sample volumes of water at the same rate.

(j) Determine the amount of reagent and the flow rate required for the second pretreatment from Table II using the sample volume determined in Paragraph (g).

(k) Pass the specified volume of reagent through the bed at the specified rate until only a 2 to 3-cm layer of liquid remains above the bed. Rinse the bed with 1 sample volume of water at the same rate. Increase the rinse rate to 100 ml per min. Rinse for 15 min. Thereafter test successive 100-ml portions of the effluent from anion-exchange resins by adding 2 drops of thymol blue indicator solution. Continue rinsing until a 100-ml portion of the effluent remains yellow (pH > 2.5) on the addition of the indicator. Test the effluent from the cation-exchange resins in the same manner with 2 drops of tropaeolin 0 indicator

with an inlet for air from the water-filled humidifying tower. Apply sufficient suction to maintain a pressure differential of 40 ± 5 mm of mercury below atmospheric pressure. Continue to suck humidified air through the sample for 10 min.

TABLE I.—REQUIREMENTS FOR INITIAL PRETREATMENT.

	Anion-Exchange Resins	Cation-Exchange Resins
Reagent	NaOH	HCl
Concentration	40 g per liter	1:4
Volume required	8 sample volumes	8 sample volumes
Contact time	1 hr	1 hr
Flow rate, ml per min/ml sample	0.133	0.133
Regeneration level:		
lb per cu ft	20.0	42.5
g per liter	320	680

TABLE II.—REQUIREMENTS FOR SECOND PRETREATMENT.

	Anion-Exchange Resins	Cation-Exchange Resins
Reagent	HCl	NaOH
Concentration	1:4	40 g per liter
Volume required	8 sample volumes	4 sample volumes
Contact time	1 hr	0.5 hr
Flow rate, ml per min/ml sample	0.133	0.133
Regeneration level:		
lb per cu ft	42.5	10.0
g per liter	680	160 g per liter

solution. Continue rinsing until a 100-ml portion of the effluent remains yellow (pH < 11.0) on the addition of the indicator.

(*l*) Remove the ion-exchange resin from the pretreatment column eliminating any extraneous material that may have accumulated at the bottom of the bed. Transfer the resin to the Büchner funnel of the draining apparatus which has been fitted with a medium porosity filter paper. Drain the water to the top of the sample using suction if required. Cover the funnel with a suitable vacuum-tight cover, which is fitted

(*m*) Transfer the entire drained sample to a clean, dry, 1-qt, wide-mouthed bottle with a screw top or other vapor-tight closure.

WATER RETENTION CAPACITY

Scope

10. This method covers the determination of the amount of water retained by ion-exchange resins and is intended for testing both new and used materials.

Summary of Method

11. The method consists of the de-

termination of the loss of weight on drying at 110 ± 5 C.

Procedure

12. (*a*) Weigh three approximately 5-g representative samples of material pretreated in accordance with Section 9 to the nearest 1-mg into previously tared weighing vessels.

(*b*) Dry the samples 18 ± 2 hr at 110 ± 5 C.

(*c*) Remove the samples from the oven, cool 30 min in a desiccator, and reweigh.

Calculation

13. Calculate the water retention capacity, in per cent, as follows:

$$\text{Water retained, per cent} = \frac{A - B}{A} \times 100$$

where:

A = grams of wet sample used, and
B = grams of dry sample obtained.

Report

14. Report the per cent water retained as the average of the three values obtained.

Precision

15. The over-all precision of this method is 1.7 per cent of the reported value. The precision of successive runs within a test by a single operator is 0.4 per cent. Since this is a test for materials whose chemical nature cannot be defined, no basis is available for estimation of accuracy.

Backwashed and Settled Density

Scope

16. This method covers the determination of the backwashed and settled density of ion-exchange resin and is intended for testing both new and used material.

Summary of Method

17. The method consists of the determination of the backwashed and settled volume of a known weight of chemically pretreated resin.

Procedure

18. (*a*) Weigh a 200-g sample of resin, pretreated in accordance with Section 9, to the nearest 0.1 g. Transfer it quantitatively to a column that has been calibrated every 5 ml above the 200-ml volume.

(*b*) Backwash with water for 10 min using a slow rate that will maintain a 50 per cent expansion of the bed.

(*c*) Allow the bed to settle and drain at a rate of approximately 100 ml per min until the water level is 2 to 3 cm above the top of the bed. *Do not jar.* Record the volume, in milliliters, of ion-exchange resin. Repeat the 10-min backwash until two successive readings of volume agree within 5 ml.

Calculation

19. (*a*) Calculate the backwashed and settled density, in grams per milliliter as follows:

$$\text{Density} = \frac{A}{B}$$

where:

A = grams of sample used, and
B = volume of sample in milliliters.

(*b*) Calculate the backwashed and settled density in pounds per cubic foot, as follows:

$$\text{Density} = C \times 62.4$$

where C = density, in grams per milliliter.

Report

20. Report the density of the tested material as the average of that calculated from two volumes that agree within 5 ml.

Precision

21. The over-all precision of this method is 3.5 per cent of the reported value. The precision of successive runs within a test by a single operator is 0.5 per cent. Since this is a test for materials whose exact chemical nature cannot be defined, no basis is available for estimation of accuracy.

PARTICLE-SIZE DISTRIBUTION

Scope

22. This method covers the wet sieve analysis of ion-exchange materials.

Summary of Method

23. The method consists of hand-sieving the chemically pretreated resin in water through a series of standard sieves of progressively decreasing size of opening. The volume retained on each of the sieves is measured.

Apparatus

24. (a) Sieves, 8 in. in diameter, conforming to ASTM Specifications E 11, for Sieves for Testing Purposes.[4] A suitable series of such sieves consists of U. S. Standard Numbers 8 (2.38-mm), 12 (1.68-mm), 16 (1.19-mm), 20 (841-μ), 30 (595-μ), 40 (420-μ), 50 (297-μ), 70 (210-μ), and 100 (149-μ).

(b) Water Bath, minimum diameter 12 in.; minimum depth, 6 in.

Procedure

25. (a) Add sufficient water to the

[4] 1967 Book of ASTM Standards, Part 30.

water bath to fill it to the level of the top rim of a sieve placed on the bottom of it.

(b) Fill a 100-ml beaker with a representative portion of the sample pretreated in accordance with Section 9.

(c) Transfer the entire sample onto the sieve with the largest mesh opening using water as required.

(d) Gently raise and lower the sieve through the water interface in the bath so as to alternately lift the particles on the sieve and float them off again. Exercise care that none of the material on the sieve is floated over the edge. Repeat the operation until no further material passes through the screen.

(e) Remove the sieve from the water bath. Transfer the particles in the bath quantitatively to a suitably-sized beaker.

(f) Invert the sieve containing the ion-exchange material in the bath and wash the material from the openings with water. Remove the sieve and transfer the particles quantitatively to a suitably-sized graduated cylinder. Tap the material collected in the graduated cylinder until a constant volume is obtained. Record this volume in milliliters.

(g) Place the sieve of next smaller mesh opening in the bath. Pour the particles which passed the first sieve onto it and adjust the bath level as described in Paragraph (a). Repeat the operation described in Paragraphs (d) through (f) using this smaller mesh sieve.

(h) Repeat the sieving operation with sieves of progressively smaller mesh size until all the sieves in the series have been used. After the final sieving, collect and record the volume of any material remaining in the bath.

Calculation

26. (a) Calculate the percentage of ion-exchange material retained on each sieve as follows:

$$\text{Volume retained, per cent} = \frac{100X}{\Sigma}$$

where:

X = ml retained on a particular sieve, and

Σ = summation of all volumes retained by the sieves used plus the volume passing the smallest sieve.

(b) Calculate the cumulative per cent retained on each sieve by adding to the percentage retained on it the percentages retained on all of the sieves used having larger mesh openings. For example: in a series where U. S. Standard Sieves Nos. 8, 12, 16, 20, 30, 40, 50, 70 and 100 have been used, the cumulative per cent retained on No. 16 equals:

Per cent retained on No. 8 + per cent retained on No. 12 + per cent retained on No. 16

(c) Using normal probability paper, plot the cumulative per cent retained on each sieve as a function of the sieve opening in millimeters. Draw the best straight line through the points giving greater weight to the points representing the largest resin fractions.

(d) On the line drawn as described in Paragraph (c), determine the sieve openings that will retain 40 and 90 per cent of the sample. The sieve opening in millimeters that will retain 90 per cent of the sample is the Effective Size of that sample.

(e) Calculate the Uniformity Coefficient of the sample as follows:

Uniformity Coefficient

$$= \frac{\text{mesh size (mm) retaining 40 per cent of the sample}}{\text{mesh size (mm) retaining 90 per cent of the sample}}$$

Report

27. Report the numbers of the sieves used, and the cumulative per cent re-tained on each. Report also the Effective Size and the Uniformity Coefficient.

Precision

28. (a) For spheroidal materials the over-all precision of the Effective Size is 0.032 and of the Uniformity Coefficient is 0.061.

(b) For one granular material tested, the over-all precision of the Effective Size was 0.052 and of the Uniformity Coefficient was 0.157.

SALT-SPLITTING CAPACITY OF CATION EXCHANGE RESINS

Scope

29. This method covers the determination of the number of milliequivalents of exchangeable hydrogen in a cation-exchange resin sufficiently acidic to split neutral salts.

Summary of Method

30. The method consists of conversion of the sample to the hydrogen form, elution with sodium chloride solution, followed by titration of the hydrogen ion exchanged in this process.

Apparatus

31. (a) *Test Apparatus*, as shown in Fig. 3 shall consist of a filter tube of at least 30-ml capacity having a diameter of at least 2.0 cm containing a sintered glass plate of coarse (A) porosity, a 1-liter separatory funnel and a 1-liter volumetric flask.

(b) *Electrometric pH Measurement Apparatus*, conforming to the requirements given in Section 4 of the Method for Determination of pH of Industrial Water and Industrial Waste Water (ASTM Designation: D 1293).[2]

Reagents

32. (a) *Carbon Dioxide-Free Water*—

Prepare carbon dioxide-free water by heating reagent water, contained in a conical flask, to boiling, and boiling vigorously for 20 min. Cool the boiled water in the flask and then stopper with a 1-hole rubber stopper fitted with a soda-lime or soda-asbestos drying tube.

(b) *Hydrochloric Acid (1:9)*— Carefully pour 100 ml of concentrated hydrochloric acid (HCl, sp gr 1.19) into 500 ml of water, stirring constantly. Cool to 25 ± 5 C and dilute to 1 liter.

(c) *Methyl Orange Indicator (0.5 g/liter)*—Dissolve 0.05 g of methyl orange in water and dilute to 100 ml with water.

(d) *Phenolphthalein Indicator (5.0 g/liter)*—Dissolve 0.5 g of phenolphthalein in 50 ml of 95 per cent ethanol (Note 1). Transfer to a volumetric flask and dilute to 100 ml with water.

NOTE 1—Specially denatured ethyl alcohol conforming to Formula 3A or 30 of the U. S. Bureau of Internal Revenue may be substituted for 95 per cent ethyl alcohol.

(e) *Sodium Chloride Solution (50 g/liter)*—Dissolve 50.0 g of sodium chloride (NaCl) in 800 ml of water and dilute to 1 liter in a volumetric flask.

(f) *Sodium Hydroxide, Standard Solution (0.10 N)*—Prepare a saturated solution by dissolving 162 g of sodium hydroxide (NaOH) pellets in 150 ml of carbon dioxide-free reagent water. Cool to 25 C and filter through a Gooch crucible, hardened filter paper, or other suitable medium. Pipet 5.45 ml of the filtered solution into a volumetric flask and dilute to 1 liter mark with carbon dioxide-free water. Mix well and store in a polyethylene or heavily waxed bottle. Protect the solution by providing an ascarite or soda-lime bulb at the air inlet.

(1) To standardize, dry approximately 10 g of primary standard grade potassium hydrogen phthalate (KHC$_8$-

H$_4$O$_4$) in a glass container at 120 C for 2 hr. Cool in a desiccator. Weigh accurately three 1.00-g samples of the dried potassium hydrogen phthalate and transfer to separate 250-ml conical flasks. Add 100 ml of carbon dioxide-free water and stir gently to dissolve the sample. Titrate with the 0.10 N NaOH electrometrically to a pH of 8.6, or add 2 drops of phenolphthalein indicator and titrate to the first pink that persists for 15 sec with swirling.

(2) Calculate the normality of the NaOH solution as follows:

$$N = \frac{B}{0.20423 \times C}$$

where:

N = normality of the NaOH solution,
B = actual weight of KHC$_8$H$_4$O$_4$ used, and
C = milliliters of NaOH solution used.

Procedure

33. (a) Weigh accurately into separate 100-ml beakers, 10.0-g representative samples of material pretreated in accordance with Section 9.

(b) Rinse the weighed samples with water quantitatively into the filter tubes. Fill the separatory funnel with 1 liter of HCl (1:9). Fill the sample tube with acid and tap to remove air bubbles. Attach the stem of the funnel to the filter tube with a suitable-size rubber stopper. Pass the acid through the sample at a rate of 20 to 25 ml/min, keeping the sample covered with acid at all times. Drain the liquid to the resin level. Discard the effluent.

(c) Rinse the separatory funnel thoroughly with water. Run water through the acid-treated samples at the rate of 20 to 25 ml/min until the effluent is yellow to methyl orange or has a pH above 3.9. Drain to the resin level and discard the effluent water.

(d) Position an acid-free 1-liter volumetric flask under the tip of the filter tube. Fill the separatory funnel with 1 liter of NaCl solution (50 g/liter). Pass the NaCl solution through the sample at a rate of 20 to 25 ml/min keeping the sample covered with solution at all times. Collect the effluent in the volumetric flask. Discontinue the flow of the liquid when 1.0 liter has been collected.

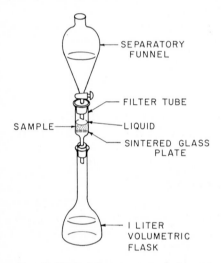

SEPARATORY FUNNEL

FILTER TUBE

SAMPLE

LIQUID

SINTERED GLASS PLATE

I LITER VOLUMETRIC FLASK

FIG. 3—Typical Arrangement of Apparatus for Salt-Splitting Capacity.

(e) Stopper and mix the NaCl effluent thoroughly. Pipet out three 100-ml portions of each sample of effluent. Add 2 drops of phenolphthalein indicator to each and titrate with 0.1 N NaOH solution to the first pink color that will persist on 15-sec swirling, or titrate electrometrically to a pH of 8.6. Record the volume of NaOH used in each titration to the nearest 0.01 ml. Use the average of the three titrations for each sample as "E."

Calculation

34. (a) Calculate the salt-splitting capacity in milliequivalents per wet gram as follows:

$$\frac{\text{Milliequivalents cationic salt-splitting capacity}}{\text{Wet gram}}$$

$$= \frac{E \times N \times 10}{W}$$

where:

E = average milliliters of NaOH required for the titration in Section 33(e),

W = wet weight of the sample, and

N = normality of NaOH used.

(b) Calculate the cationic salt-splitting capacity in milliequivalents per dry gram as follows:

$$\frac{\text{Milliequivalents cationic salt-splitting capacity}}{\text{Dry gram}}$$

$$= \frac{H}{1 - M/100}$$

where:

H = milliequivalents cationic salt-splitting capacity per wet gram, and

M = per cent water retained as determined in accordance with Sections 10 to 15.

(c) Calculate the cationic salt-splitting capacity in milliequivalents per milliliter of back-washed and settled materials as follows:

$$\frac{\text{Milliequivalents cationic salt-splitting capacity}}{\text{Milliliter settled bed}}$$

$$= H \times C$$

where:

H = milliequivalents cationic salt-splitting capacity per wet gram, and

C = wet, settled density, in grams per milliliter, as determined in accordance with Sections 16 to 21.

Report

35. Report the cationic salt-splitting capacity as the average of the results of the three samples.

Precision[5]

36. The over-all precision of this method is 0.075 meq per dry gram. The precision of multiple runs within a test by a single operator is 0.084 meq per dry gram.

[5] Supporting data for these methods have been filed at ASTM Headquarters.

Tentative Method of Test for

PRIMARY AND SECONDARY AMINES IN INDUSTRIAL WATER[1]

ASTM Designation: D 2327 – 65 T

ISSUED, 1965

This Tentative Method has been approved by the sponsoring committee and accepted by the Society in accordance with established procedures, for use pending adoption as standard. Suggestions for revisions should be addressed to the Society at 1916 Race St., Philadelphia, Pa. 19103.

1. Scope

1.1 This method covers a colorimetric procedure for the determination of octadecylamine and dioctadecylamine in steam or steam condensate.

1.2 The method may be applied to waters containing amine in concentrations from 0.2 to 1.75 ppm. Higher concentrations may be determined by dilution.

2. Summary of Method

2.1 Aqueous mixtures of the two amines are analyzed by separate analyses of two portions of the sample. Both octadecylamine and dioctadecylamine react with methyl orange at a pH of 3.4 to 3.6 to form a yellow colored complex soluble in ethylene dichloride. The intensity of color is proportional to the amount of total amine present in the water. The addition of salicyl-

aldehyde to a separate portion of the sample prevents the reaction between octadecylamine and methyl orange and the intensity of the developed color in this latter test is proportional, therefore, to the amount of dioctadecylamine in the water. Octadecylamine is then determined by difference.

3. Definitions

3.1 For definitions of terms used in this method, refer to ASTM Definitions D 1129, Terms Relating to Industrial Water and Industrial Waste Water.[2]

4. Interferences

4.1 Substances normally present in steam or steam condensate do not interfere with the test. Concentrations of morpholine or cyclohexylamine up to 500 ppm do not appreciably interfere.

4.2 The reactions of the test are common to other long chain aliphatic amines or compounds having a long

---

[1] Under the standardization procedure of the Society, this method is under the jurisdiction of the ASTM Committee D-19 on Industrial Water. A list of members may be found in the ASTM Year Book.

[2] Appears in this publication.

chain amine group in the molecule. The quaternaries definitely interfere.

4.3 The presence of polyvalent ions in the steam or steam condensate will cause precipitation in the lines and thus possibly interfere with uniform sampling.

4.4 Ferric iron forms colored compounds that interfere with the test.

5. Apparatus

5.1 *Glass Bottles*, 200-ml capacity, glass-stoppered.

5.2 *Photometer*—A filter photometer or spectrophotometer suitable for measurement at a wavelength of 430 mμ. The photometers and photometric practice prescribed in this method shall conform to ASTM Recommended Practice E 60, Photometric Methods for Chemical Analysis of Metals,[3] and spectrophotometers shall conform to the ASTM Recommended Practice E 275, for Describing and Measuring Performance of Spectrophotometers.[4]

5.3 *Shaker*, reciprocating, adjusted for shaking at the rate of 280 ± 5 oscillations/min with a horizontal stroke of 1 in. for multiple samples. For single samples or for field use, hand shaking is satisfactory.

6. Reagents

6.1 *Purity of Reagents*—Reagent grade chemicals shall be used in all tests. Unless otherwise indicated, it is intended that all reagents shall conform to the specifications of the Committee on Analytical Reagents of the American Chemical Society, where such specifications are available.[5] Other grades may

be used, provided it is first ascertained that the reagent is of sufficiently high purity to permit its use without lessening the accuracy of the determination.

6.2 *Purity of Water*—Unless otherwise indicated, references to water shall be understood to mean reagent water conforming to ASTM Specifications D 1193, for Reagent Water.[2]

6.3 *Acetic Acid, Glacial*—Concentrated acetic acid (CH_3COOH) (99.5 per cent).

6.4 *Acetic Acid (1:49)*—Carefully mix 1 volume of glacial acetic acid with 49 volumes of water.

6.5 *Acid Buffer Solution (pH 3.75)*—Dissolve 125 g of potassium chloride (KCl) and 70 g of sodium acetate trihydrate ($Na_2C_2H_3O_2 \cdot 3H_2O$) in 500 ml of water. Add 300 ml of glacial acetic acid and dilute to 1 liter.

6.6 *Dioctadecylamine, Standard Solution (1 ml = 0.01 mg Dioctadecylamine)*—Dissolve 0.0100 g of commercial dioctadecylamine (Note) in 10 ml of hot isopropyl alcohol. Add this solution with rapid stirring to 50 ml of hot acetic acid (1:49). Cool the solution and dilute to 1 liter with water. Prepare solutions of greater dilution from this standard as required. Before weighing the dioctadecylamine, check its strength by employing ASTM Method D 2073, Test for Total, Primary, Secondary, and Tertiary Amine Values of Fatty Amines by Referee Potentiometric Method,[6] or ASTM Method D 2074, Test for Total, Primary, Secondary, and Tertiary Amine Values of Fatty Amines by Alternate Indicator Method.[6]

NOTE—Commercial dioctadecylamine is quite impure and reagent grade may be difficult to obtain. One crystallization from alcohol will considerably improve its (commercial) quality with respect to primary amines.

[3] *1967 Book of ASTM Standards*, Part 32.

[4] *1967 Book of ASTM Standards*, Part 30.

[5] "Reagent Chemicals, American Chemical Society Specifications," Am. Chemical Soc., Washington, D. C. For suggestions on the testing of reagents not listed by the American Chemical Society, see "Reagent Chemicals and Standards," by Joseph Rosin, D. Van Nostrand Co. Inc., New York, N. Y., and the "United States Pharmacopeia."

[6] *1967 Book of ASTM Standards*, Part 20.

6.7 *Ethylene   Dichloride*   ($CH_2Cl\cdot CH_2Cl$).

6.8 *Isopropyl Alcohol* (($CH_3)_2CHOH$).

6.9 *Methyl Orange Indicator (0.5 g/ liter)*—Dissolve 0.05 g of methyl orange in water and dilute to 100 ml with water. For field use the methyl orange indicator and the acid buffer solution can be combined.

6.10 *Octadecylamine, Standard Solution (1 ml = 0.01 mg Octadecylamine)*— Dissolve 0.0100 g of octadecylamine[7] in 250 ml of hot acetic acid (1:49). Cool the solution and dilute to 1 liter with water. Prepare solutions of greater dilution from this standard solution as required. If purified octadecylamine is not readily obtained use commercially distilled octadecylamine. Before using the commercial product check its strength by employing ASTM Methods D 2073 or D 2074.

6.11 *Salicylaldehyde (1:199)*—Dilute 5 ml of salicylaldehyde[8] (HOC_6H_4CHO) redistilled from its bisulfite compound (melting point 1 to 2 C), to 1 liter with ethylene dichloride. This solution is stable for 1 month.

7. Sampling

7.1 Collect the sample in accordance with ASTM Method D 1066, Sampling Steam.[2]

7.2 Purge the sampling line until several tests indicate equilibrium conditions are reached after the lines are coated with filming amine. Keep the sampling line as short as possible.

7.3 Add 4 ml of acid buffer solution to every 100 ml of sample collected to prevent the amine from plating on the walls of the container.

---

[7] Reagent grade octadecylamine, available from the Armour Chemical Co., has been found satisfactory for this purpose.

[8] Eastman's Catalog No. 225 salicylaldehyde has been found satisfactory for this purpose.

7.4 Determine the amine content as soon as possible after sampling to minimize losses.

8. Calibration

8.1 *Octadecylamine:*

8.1.1 Prepare a series of five octadecylamine standards covering the range of 0 to 1.75 ppm amine by diluting suitable volumes of octadecylamine standard solution to 100 ml with water. Add 4 ml of acid buffer to each standard.

8.1.2 Treat each reference standard as described in 9.1.

8.2 *Dioctadecylamine:*

8.2.1 Prepare a series of five dioctadecylamine standards covering the range of 0 to 1.75 ppm amine by diluting suitable volumes of dioctadecylamine standard solution to 100 ml with water. Add 4 ml of acid buffer to each standard.

8.2.2 Treat each reference standard as described in 9.2.

8.3 Prepare calibration curves in parts per million for both amines by plotting absorbance of the standard solutions against concentration of amine. Determine the absorbance per part per million (specific absorbance) for each amine.

9. Procedure

9.1 *Total Amines:*

9.1.1 Add 2 ml of methyl orange solution and 20 ml of ethylene dichloride to a 104-ml portion of the acid-buffered test sample in a 200-ml glass shaking bottle with ground-glass stopper. Mix thoroughly by shaking 5 min on the shaker. Remove from the shaker, pour the contents of the bottle into a 250-ml separatory funnel equipped with a TFE-fluorocarbon stopcock and allow 3 min for the organic layer to settle.

9.1.2 Draw off the organic layer into a 50-ml beaker, add 0.5 ml of isopropyl alcohol and swirl to remove any turbidity. Read the intensity of the color in a filter photometer or spectrophotometer at a wavelength of 430 mμ and record as absorbance A due to total amine. Adjust the photometer to "zero" absorbance or 100 per cent transmittance by using an ethylene dichloride blank.

9.2 *Dioctadecylamine:*

9.2.1 To another 104-ml portion of the acid-buffered test sample in a 200-ml glass shaking bottle add 20 ml of salicylaldehyde solution. Mix thoroughly by shaking 2 min on the shaker.

9.2.2 Remove from the shaker, loosen the glass stopper, and place the bottle in a 70 ± 3 C water bath for 15 min. Cool the sample in a cold water bath for 10 min to obtain a temperature of 22.5 ± 1.5 C.

9.2.3 Add 2 ml of methyl orange solution and 20 ml of ethylene dichloride and mix thoroughly by shaking 5 min on the shaker. Remove from the shaker, pour the contents of the bottle into a 250-ml separatory funnel, equipped with a TFE-fluorocarbon stopcock, and allow 3 min for the organic layer to settle.

9.2.4 Draw off the organic layer into a 25-ml graduate, adjust the volume to 20 ml with ethylene dichloride, add 0.5 ml of isopropyl alcohol, and swirl to remove any turbidity. Read the intensity of the color in a filter photometer or spectrophotometer at a wave length of 430 mμ and record as absorbance B due to dioctadecylamine. Adjust the photometer as directed in 9.1.2.

10. Calculations

10.1 Calculate the amine concentrations, in parts per million, as follows:

$$\text{Dioctadecylamine, ppm} = \frac{B}{S_2}$$

$$\text{Octadecylamine, ppm} = \frac{A - B}{S_1}$$

where:

A = absorbance determined in accordance with 9.1,

B = absorbance determined in accordance with 9.2,

S_1 = specific absorbance of octadecylamine determined in accordance with 8.3, and

S_2 = specific absorbance of dioctadecylamine determined in accordance with 8.3.

11. Precision[9]

11.1 The precision of this method may be expressed as follows: S_o = 0.042 ppm for octadecylamine and 0.052 ppm for dioctadecylamine, where S_o = single operator precision.

[9] Supporting data for this method have been filed at ASTM headquarters.

Tentative Method of

CORROSIVITY TESTING OF INDUSTRIAL COOLING WATER (COUPON TEST METHOD)[1]

ASTM Designation: D 2328 – 65 T

ISSUED, 1965

This Tentative Method has been approved by the sponsoring committee and accepted by the Society in accordance with established procedures, for use pending adoption as standard. Suggestions for revisions should be addressed to the Society at 1916 Race St., Philadelphia, Pa. 19103.

1. Scope

1.1 This method covers the quantitative measurement of the corrosion and fouling characteristics of cooling water on metal coupons in the absence of heat transfer. The relationship between these measurements and the corrosion and fouling that occurs in the various components in contact with the cooling water must be determined in each instance by inspection of the equipment.

2. Summary of Method

2.1 Carefully prepared metal coupons are installed in contact with flowing cooling water for a measured length of time. After removal from the system, these coupons are examined, cleaned, and reweighed. From the difference in weight, the depth and distribution of pits, and the weight and character of the foreign matter on coupons, the corrosion and fouling characteristics of the water are determined.

3. Definitions

3.1 For definitions of terms used in this method, refer to ASTM Definitions D 1129, Terms Relating to Industrial Water and Industrial Waste Water.[2]

4. Interferences

4.1 Results will be comparable only for the water temperature to which the coupon is exposed, but may be representative for other water temperatures.

4.2 Any deviation in metal composition or surface preparation of the coupons one from another and from the corresponding material of construction in the actual system may cause an error in the results obtained.

4.3 Any deviation in the velocity and direction of flow past the coupons as compared with another and with the velocity and direction of flow in the corresponding components in the actual

---

[1] Under the standardization procedure of the Society, this method is under the jurisdiction of the ASTM Committee D-19 on Industrial Water. A list of members may be found in the ASTM Year Book.

[2] Appears in this publication.

system may cause an error in the results obtained.

4.4 Presence of crevices, deposits, or biological growths in different degrees on the coupons as compared to the corresponding components in the actual system constitutes a source of error in the results obtained.

—Use for attaching the coupon to the phenolic rod. The insulating washer has a sleeve which fits into the coupon hole and around the screw.[3]

5.3 *Phenolic Rod*—Use a 6-in. (152-mm) length of canvas-based 0.5-in. (13-mm) outside diameter phenolic rod attached at one end to a drilled pipe plug,

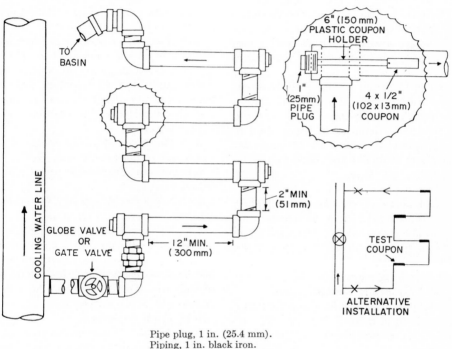

Pipe plug, 1 in. (25.4 mm).
Piping, 1 in. black iron.
"T" connection, 1 in. (25.4 mm).
Flow rate, 8 gpm or
velocity, 3 ft/sec.

FIG. 1—Installation of Corrosion Coupons

4.5 The presence of different metals in close proximity to the coupon (within 3 in.), even if they are insulated from the coupon, constitutes a source of error in the results.

5. Apparatus

5.1 *Coupon Specimens*—Prepare coupons in accordance with 7. Coupon Preparation.

5.2 *Insulating Washer, Screw, and Nut*

and having a flat surface and a hole at the other end suitable for attachment of the coupon.[4]

5.4 *Piping Arrangement*, as illustrated

---

[3] Allied Radio's Extruded Fiber Washer, Part No. 42N773 for a No. 8 screw has been found satisfactory for this purpose.

[4] Phenolic rod meeting the National Electrical Manufacturers Association (NEMA) Grade CE or LE is satisfactory. The pipe plug is marked externally to permit orientation of the coupon as desired.

in Fig. 1 for installation of coupon specimens.

6. Reagents

6.1 *Purity of Reagents*—Reagent grade chemicals shall be used in all tests. Unless otherwise indicated, it is intended that all reagents shall conform to the specifications of the Committee on Analytical Reagents of the American Chemical Society, where such specifications are available.[5] Other grades may be used, provided it is first ascertained that the reagent is of sufficiently high purity to permit its use without lessening the accuracy of the determination.

6.2 *Purity of Water*—Unless otherwise indicated, references to water shall be understood to mean reagent water conforming to ASTM Specifications D 1193, for Reagent Water.[2]

6.3 *Benzene.*

6.4 *Chromic Acid-Phosphoric Acid Solution*—Dissolve 30 g of chromic acid (chromium trioxide, CrO_3) and 36 ml of phosphoric acid (H_3PO_4, sp gr 1.689) in approximately 500 ml of water. Dilute the resulting solution to 1 liter.

6.5 *Chromium Trioxide* (CrO_3).

6.6 *Corrosion Inhibitor*, specific for hydrochloric acid.[6]

6.7 *Corrosion Inhibitor*, specific for sulfuric acid.[6]

6.8 *Hydrochloric Acid* (*sp gr 1.19*)—Concentrated hydrochloric acid (HCl).

6.9 *Hydrochloric Acid* (*1:4*)—Mix one volume of concentrated HCl (sp gr 1.19) with four volumes of water.

6.10 *Hydrochloric Acid* (*1:1.8, Inhibited*)—Mix 357 ml of concentrated HCl (sp gr 1.19) and 5.0 g of inhibitor. Then dilute to 1 liter with water.

6.11 *Isopropyl Alcohol.*

6.12 *Methyl Orange Indicator* (*0.5 g per liter*)—Dissolve 0.05 g of methyl orange in water and dilute to 100 ml with water.

6.13 *Nitric Acid* (*sp gr 1.42*)—Concentrated nitric acid (HNO_3).

6.14 *Nitric Acid-Dichromate Solution*—Mix 224 ml of concentrated HNO_3 (sp gr 1.42) with twice the volume of water. Add 22.75 g of sodium dichromate ($Na_2Cr_2O_7 \cdot 2H_2O$) to the solution and dissolve. Dilute the resulting solution to 1 liter.

6.15 *Phosphoric Acid* (*85 per cent*).—Concentrated phosphoric acid (H_3PO_4).

6.16 *Sodium Dichromate* ($Na_2Cr_2O_7 \cdot 2H_2O$), crystal.

6.17 *Sulfuric Acid* (*sp gr 1.84*)—Concentrated sulfuric acid (H_2SO_4).

6.18 *Sulfuric Acid* (*1:34, Inhibited*)—Slowly add 29 ml of concentrated H_2SO_4 (sp gr 1.84) to approximately 500 ml of water. Add and dissolve 0.5 g of inhibitor. Dilute the resulting solution to 1 liter with water.

6.19 *Trichloroethylene.*

6.20 *Tripoli*—Finely granulated porous siliceous rock. Amorphous silica (SiO_2) soft, porous, and free from sharp edges.

6.21 *Trisodium Phosphate* ($Na_3PO_4 \cdot 12H_2O$). Also available as $Na_3PO_4 \cdot 8H_2O$. Either grade is satisfactory.

6.22 *Vapor Phase Inhibitor Paper.*[7]

7. Coupon Preparation

NOTE—In this procedure, provision is made principally for preparing coupons from sheet metal. However, in a few cases, as with cast iron or cast bronze, it may be necessary to pre-

---

[5] "Reagent Chemicals, American Chemical Society Specifications," Am. Chemical Soc., Washington, D. C. For suggestions on the testing of reagents not listed by the American Chemical Society, see "Reagent Chemicals and Standards," by Joseph Rosin, D. Van Nostrand Co., Inc., New York, N. Y., and the "United States Pharmacopeia."

[6] Rodine 115 and Rodine 213, manufactured by Amchem Products, Inc., Ambler, Pa. have been found satisfactory for this purpose, for sulfuric acid and hydrochloric acid, respectively.

[7] Inhibitor paper manufactured by Orchard Paper Co., 3914 Union Boulevard, St. Louis, Mo., under Code OPC-60 (S) has been found satisfactory for this purpose.

pare coupons from castings; this procedure is also described.

7.1 Use a coupon size of 0.5 by 4.0 by 0.032 in. (13 by 102 by 0.8 mm) for all sheet metals; and a 0.5 by 4.0 by 0.125-in. size (13 by 102 by 3-mm) for cast metals. Other sizes are suitable providing the total area is about 4 in.², the principal requirement being to keep the flat surface area large compared to the edge area.

7.2 *Sheet Metal Coupon Preparation*— Obtain sheet metal of the type desired except for stainless steel; use cold-rolled steel free of rust spots for ferrous metal. Obtain stainless steel with a No. 4 finish.[8]

7.2.1 Shear 20-gage sheet metal material to the dimensions of 0.5 by 4.0 in. (13 by 102 mm).

7.2.2 Drill or punch a $\frac{9}{32}$ in. (7 mm) hole with its center about $\frac{5}{16}$ in. (8 mm) from one end of the coupon.

7.2.3 Deburr all sharp edges on the coupon specimen using a file or emery belt, and deburr the hole with an oversize drill.

7.2.4 Stamp identifying numbers or letters on the small coupon area between the edge and the mounting hole.

7.3 *Cast Metal Coupon Preparation*— Obtain rough castings of the desired metal, measuring about $\frac{3}{4}$ by $4\frac{1}{2}$ by $\frac{1}{4}$ in. (19 by 114 by 6 mm) from a commercial foundry or elsewhere.

7.3.1 Surface grind to the dimensions of 0.5 by 4.0 by 0.125 in. (13 by 102 by 3 mm) and a surface roughness of about 125 μin.

7.3.2 Drill a $\frac{9}{32}$-in. (7-mm) hole with its center about $\frac{5}{16}$ in. (8 mm) from one end of the coupon.

7.3.3 Deburr all sharp edges on the coupon specimen using a file or emery belt, and deburr the hole with an oversize drill.

7.3.4 Stamp identifying numbers or

letters on the small coupon area between the edge and the mounting hole.

7.4 *Cleaning Ferrous Metal Coupons*— Remove oil by immersion in benzene. Dry. Immerse in a solution containing HCl (1:4) for 30 min at room temperature.

7.4.1 Remove acid from the coupon by three rapid successive rinses in separate water baths; the last rinse water bath shall contain methyl orange and must be kept neutral (yellow). The first and second bath must be renewed frequently. Rinse successively in isopropyl alcohol and benzene, and dry with a clean cloth. Store in a desiccator.

7.5 *Cleaning Copper, Brass, and Cupra-Nickel Coupons*—Clean, dry, and store coupons exactly as for ferrous coupons (7.4).

7.6 *Cleaning Stainless Steel Coupons*— Degrease with benzene, dry with a clean cloth, and passivate by immersing in a solution containing 20 per cent HNO_3 (by weight) and 2 per cent $Na_2Cr_2O_7$ by weight at 110 to 120 F (43 to 49 C) for 15 to 30 min; rinse with water, then benzene, dry with a clean cloth, and store in a desiccator.

7.7 *Cleaning Aluminum Coupons*— Degrease with benzene and dry. Immerse in concentrated HNO_3 (sp gr 1.42) for a minimum of 3 min at room temperature. Rinse with water twice, once with isopropyl alcohol, and finally with benzene. Dry with a clean towel. If coupon is not visibly clean, repeat the procedure, using submerged scrubbing with a fiber bristle brush in the water rinse.

7.8 *Cleaning Zinc or Galvanized Steel Coupons*—If the surface is free of oxide, degrease with benzene, dry with a clean towel, and store in a desiccator. If oxide is present, polish with No. (0) emery paper, scrub in isopropyl alcohol using a stiff fiber brush, and rinse in benzene. Dry and store as in 7.7.

[8] See *Metals Handbook*, American Society for Metals, Vol. 1 (1961), p. 430.

8. Procedure

8.1 Weigh clean, dry specimens on an analytical balance to the nearest 0.1 mg.

8.2 After weighing, store the specimens in a desiccator until ready for use. If storing in a desiccator is inconvenient or impractical, use an alternate method for providing a corrosion-free atmosphere.

8.3 Store ferrous metal coupons in separate envelopes made from vapor phase inhibitor impregnated paper.[7] Store nonferrous metal coupons in sealed plastic envelopes or wrapped in plastic film.

8.4 Use an insulating washer to preclude any contact of coupon with the screw and nut assembly. For added protection, attach the specimen to the holder using a screw and nut of the same metal composition as the coupon.

8.5 Install the holder and coupon assembly in a suitable line or in a bypass piping arrangement as shown in Fig. 1.

8.6 Adjust the rate of flow of water in the test piping to a rate that gives a flow velocity which corresponds to the normal flow of water in those parts of the system under prime consideration. Normally, the flow velocity will be in the range of 2 to 6 ft (61 to 183 cm)/sec. Check and readjust the flow as necessary to maintain the desired rate of flow.

8.7 Remove specimens from the system at chosen intervals. Since the corrosion rate will be high initially and then fall to a lower, nearly constant rate, two time series should be chosen.

8.8 Use short time intervals for the first time series in order to establish the rate at which passivity occurs. Remove three or four sets of coupons at 4 to 7-day intervals.

8.9 Use long time intervals for the second time series in order to establish the mean steady state corrosion rate. Remove the first coupons after one month. Remove the remaining coupons at one to three-month intervals.

8.10 Protect the specimen if it cannot be examined, cleaned, and reweighed immediately after removal from the system. Dry between a paper towel. Store the ferrous metal coupons in separate envelopes made from vapor phase inhibitor impregnated paper or wrap carefully in plastic film. For nonferrous metal coupons, wrap carefully in plastic film. The interim period between removal of specimens and reweighing should be kept to a minimum, and in no case may it exceed one week.

8.11 Examine the specimen, and record either by photograph or by words the appearance of the specimen, paying particular attention to the amount and nature of any adherent deposit. Chemical analysis of the adherent deposit may be performed, but this step is optional.

8.12 For ferrous coupons, use one of the following alternate procedures for cleaning the coupon prior to reweighing.

8.12.1 Clean the coupon as well as possible with a plastic knife. Remove oily and greasy deposits by soaking in trichloroethylene. Remove remaining loose corrosion products by brushing with a bristle brush. Immerse the specimen in inhibited acid (two approved methods).

8.12.2 Immerse the specimen in inhibited HCl (1:1.8) for 30 sec.

8.12.3 Immerse the specimen in inhibited H_2SO_4 (1:34) at 160 F (71 C) with a direct current source imposed on the coupon as an anode, and lead as a cathode. The voltage should be 4 to 5 v and the current density 2.5 to 3.0 amp/specimen. Keep the specimens in the bath for 3 to 5 min. Rinse with water after removing specimens from the inhibited acid bath. Rub specimens with Na_3PO_4, then with tripoli. Rinse with water. Rinse with isopropyl alcohol. Dry between paper towels followed by warm air drying.

8.13 For copper or copper alloy coupons, use the following procedure for cleaning prior to reweighing. Clean the coupon as well as possible with a plastic knife. Remove oily or greasy deposits by soaking in trichloroethylene. Immerse the coupon in inhibited HCl (1:1.8) (see 6.10) for 30 sec. Rinse coupons with

cent H_3PO_4 at room temperature for 30 min. Remove and rinse with water, rinse with isopropyl alcohol, and finally, rinse with benzene. Dry between paper towels. Dry in a desiccator for 2 hr.

8.15 Subject a weighed blank coupon to the identical cleaning procedure used and reweigh to determine blank correction factor to be applied to coupon weight losses.

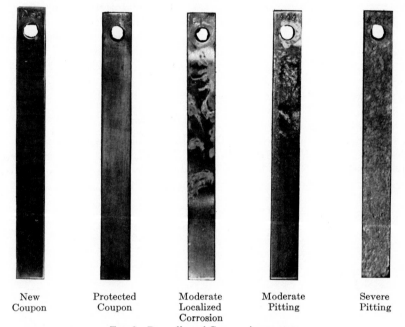

New	Protected	Moderate	Moderate	Severe
Coupon	Coupon	Localized	Pitting	Pitting
		Corrosion		

FIG. 2—Recording of Coupon Appearance.

water, rinse with isopropyl alcohol, and finally, rinse with benzene. Dry coupons between paper towels. Place in a desiccator for 2 hr.

8.14 For aluminum or aluminum alloy coupons, use the following procedure for cleaning prior to reweighing. Clean the coupon as well as possible with a plastic knife. Remove oily or greasy deposits by soaking in trichloroethylene. Immerse the coupon in water solution containing 3 per cent CrO_3 and 5 per

8.16 Reweigh the coupon to nearest 0.1 mg.

8.17 If pitting is apparent on the coupon specimen, measure the thickness of the coupon at the base of each of the five deepest pits. Subtract this value from the thickness of the coupon and record the resultant values as pit depths.

8.18 Record the appearance of the cleaned, weighed coupon as "protected," "moderate localized," "moderate pitting," or "severe pitting," by comparing the coupon with the illustrations given in Fig. 2.

9. Calculations

9.1 Determine the corrosion rate for each coupon as follows (this equation is sufficiently accurate for most corrosion studies):

$$P = \frac{H(W_1 - W_2)}{W_1D} \times 1.825 \times 10^5$$

where:
P = corrosion rate, mils/year,
H = original thickness of the coupon, in.,
W_1 = original weight of the coupon, mg,
W_2 = final weight of the coupon, mg, and
D = exposure time in days.

9.2 In certain systems (usually test installations), where all variables are closely controlled, more precise equations may be used. The corrosion rate equation for a rectangular coupon is given as follows:

$$P = \frac{1}{\left(\dfrac{1}{H} + \dfrac{1}{X} + \dfrac{1}{Y}\right)} \times \frac{W_1 - W_2}{W_1D}$$

$$\times 1.825 \times 10^5$$

where:
H = original thickness of coupon, in.,
X = original length of coupon, in.,
Y = original width of coupon, in.,
W_1 = original weight of coupon, mg,
W_2 = final weight of coupon, mg, and
D = exposure time, days.
The equation given in 9.2 reduces to that given in 9.1 when "X" and "Y" are large compared to "H".

10. Precision

10.1 Precision is a function of each individual system. Therefore, a general statement regarding this property is not practical at this time.

Tentative Method of Test for

BIOCHEMICAL OXYGEN DEMAND OF INDUSTRIAL WATER AND INDUSTRIAL WASTE WATER[1]

ASTM Designation: D 2329 – 65 T

ISSUED, 1965

This Tentative Method has been approved by the sponsoring committee and accepted by the Society in accordance with established procedures, for use pending adoption as standard. Suggestions for revisions should be addressed to the Society at 1916 Race St., Philadelphia, Pa. 19103.

1. Scope

1.1 This method covers a bioassay measurement of biochemical oxygen demand (BOD) of industrial water and industrial waste water. Such oxygen demand is exerted by the following classes of materials:

1.1.1 *Class A*—Carbonaceous organic material usable as a source of food by aerobic organisms,

1.1.2 *Class B*—Oxidizable nitrogen derived from nitrites, ammonia, and organic nitrogen compounds which serve as food for specific bacteria (for example, *nitrosomonas* and *nitrobacter*), and

1.1.3 *Class C*—Certain chemically oxidizable materials (for example, ferrous iron, sulfides, sulfites, etc.) which will react with dissolved oxygen.

1.2 For many waste waters the oxygen demand is due to Class A materials and is determined by the biochemical oxygen demand, commonly abbreviated BOD test, described below. In biologically treated effluents some of the oxygen demand may be due to oxidation of Class B compounds and will also be included in the BOD test. Where Class C materials are present their oxygen demand may not be included in the BOD test unless the test is based upon a calculated initial dissolved oxygen content. All three of these classes will have a direct bearing upon the oxygen balance of the receiving water and must be considered in the discharge of a waste to such a water. (See Appendix A1, Assessing Variables That Affect the 5-day BOD.)

2. Definitions

2.1 The term "biochemical oxygen demand" (BOD) in this method is defined in accordance with ASTM Definitions D 1129, Terms Relating to Industrial Water and Industrial Waste Water,[2] as follows:

2.1.1 *Biochemical Oxygen Demand* is the quantity of oxygen required for the

---

[1] Under the standardization procedure of the Society, this method is under the jurisdiction of the ASTM Committee D-19 on Industrial Water. A list of members may be found in the ASTM Year Book.

[2] Appears in this publication.

biological and chemical oxidation of water-borne substances under conditions of test.

2.1.2 For definitions of other terms used in these methods, refer to Definitions D 1129.

3. Summary of Method

3.1 A sample of industrial water or industrial waste water is incubated at 20 C for 5 days in the presence of a selected biota. Comparison of the oxygen content of the sample at the beginning and at the end of the incubation period provides a measure of the biochemical oxygen demand.

4. Interferences

4.1 Raw and treated domestic sewage usually contains carbonaceous matter readily oxidizable by the broad spectrum of microorganisms present (1).[3] In such cases there is no apparent interference in the application of this procedure. However, many synthetic organic components in industrial waste waters are not amenable to biodegradation by these common organisms. Without special seeding material the effect is manifest as a retardation of aerobic metabolism (no dissolved oxygen depletion) because of either a toxic effect or a deficiency or absence of appropriate microorganisms (2).

4.2 In addition, experience has taught that distilled waters are sometimes contaminated with toxic substances, most often copper, and that some sewage seeds are relatively inactive (3,4). The results obtained with such waters are always low. In such cases, the usual methods of seeding and the standard incubation period of 5 days will fail to assess the effect of such wastes on the actual or potential biochemical oxygen demand of the particular industrial

waste water. (See Appendixes A1 and A2 for comments on nature of some waste waters and Appendix A5. Suggested Test for Toxicity to Seed.)

5. Apparatus

5.1 *Incubation Bottles*, of 250 to 300-ml capacity with ground-glass stoppers.

5.2 *Incubator*—Air or water bath, thermostatically controlled at 20 ± 1 C and so arranged as to exclude light.

6. Reagents

6.1 *Purity of Reagents*—Reagent grade chemicals shall be used in all tests. Unless otherwise indicated, it is intended that all reagents shall conform to the specifications of the Committee on Analytical Reagents of the American Chemical Society, where such specifications are available.[4] Other grades may be used, provided it is first ascertained that the reagent is of sufficiently high purity to permit its use without lessening the accuracy of the determination.

6.2 *Purity of Water*—Unless otherwise indicated, references to water shall be understood to mean reagent water conforming to ASTM Specifications D 1193, for Reagent Water.[2] In addition, water used for these methods shall be free of phenolic compounds, residual chlorine, chloramines, caustic alkalinity, acids, organic materials, and shall contain less than 0.01 ppm of copper.

6.3 *Calcium Chloride Solution (27.5 g/liter)*—Dissolve 27.5 g of anhydrous calcium chloride ($CaCl_2$) in water and dilute to 1 liter.

6.4 *Ferric Chloride Solution (0.25 g/liter)*—Dissolve 0.25 g of ferric chloride

---

[3] The boldface numbers in parentheses refer to the list of references appended to this method.

[4] "Reagent Chemicals, American Chemical Society Specifications," Am. Chemical Soc. Washington, D. C. For suggestions on the testing of reagents not listed by the American Chemical Society, see "Reagent Chemicals and Standards," by Joseph Rosin, D. Van Nostrand Co., Inc., New York, N. Y., and the "United States Pharmacopeia."

(FeCl$_3$·6H$_2$O) in water and dilute to 1 liter.

6.5 *Magnesium Sulfate Solution (22.5 g/liter)*—Dissolve 22.5 g of magnesium sulfate (MgSO$_4$·7H$_2$O) in water and dilute to 1 liter.

6.6 *Phosphate Buffer Solution pH 7.2*—Dissolve 8.50 g of potassium dihydrogen phosphate (KH$_2$PO$_4$), 21.75 g of dipotassium hydrogen phosphate (K$_2$HPO$_4$), 33.40 g of disodium hydrogen phosphate (Na$_2$HPO$_4$·7H$_2$O) and 1.70 g of ammonium chloride (NH$_4$Cl) in approximately 500 ml water and dilute to 1 liter. The pH of this solution should be 7.2 without further adjustment.

6.7 *Seeding Material*—Satisfactory seed may sometimes be obtained or developed by using supernatant liquor from domestic sewage which has been stored at 20 C for 24 to 36 hr or from the receiving water, downstream from the point of discharge.

NOTE 1: **Caution**—See Appendix A2 for comment on acclimated seed types and Appendix A3 on the procedure for development of acclimated seed.

6.8 *Sodium Hydroxide Solution (50 g/liter)*—Dissolve 50 g of sodium hydroxide (NaOH) in 250 ml of water and dilute to 1 liter.

6.9 *Sodium Sulfite Solution (1.575 g/liter)*—Dissolve 1.575 g of anhydrous sodium sulfite (Na$_2$SO$_3$) in 250 ml of water and dilute to 1 liter. This solution is not stable and should be prepared fresh as needed.

6.10 *Sulfuric Acid (1:49)*—Add 20 ml of concentrated sulfuric acid (H$_2$SO$_4$, sp gr 1.84) to 500 ml of water and dilute to 1 liter.

7. Sampling

7.1 Collect the sample in accordance with the applicable method of the American Society for Testing and Materials as follows:

D 510—Sampling Industrial Water,[2] and
D 1496—Sampling Homogeneous Industrial Waste Water.[2]

8. Preservation of Samples

8.1 Because of the possibility of reaction of certain components in industrial waste water with dissolved oxygen, the lapse of time between collection of sample and start of analysis should be kept to an absolute minimum. In addition, samples collected should be protected from atmospheric oxygen.

9. Preparation of Dilution Water (5–7)

9.1 Store the water to be used as dilution water in cotton-plugged bottles for sufficient time to afford saturation with atmospheric oxygen at 20 C. Alternatively, the water may be aerated for immediate use but precautions must be taken to avoid introduction of air-entrained oily matter from the compressed air source. Up to 1 hr may be required for complete aeration of a 5-gal volume of water.

9.2 Add the desired volume of water to a suitable bottle and add 1 ml each of phosphate buffer, magnesium sulfate, calcium chloride, and ferric chloride solutions for each liter of water.

9.3 Seed the dilution water using the seeding material found to be most satisfactory for the particular waste under study. Past experience must be used to determine the actual amount of seeding to be used. Seeded dilution water should be used within 24 hr of its preparation. (See Appendix A4 for comments on preparation of BOD seed from acclimated culture and 11.5 for directions on seed correction control).

9.3.1 The quality of the dilution water, the effectiveness of the seed, and the technique of the analyst should be periodically checked by using pure organic compounds on which the BOD is known or determinable. *If a particular organic compound is known to be present in a given waste it may well serve as a control on the seed used.*

9.3.2 For general BOD work a mixture of glucose and glutamic acid (150 mg of each/liter) is recommended. Glucose has an exceptionally high and variable oxidation rate with relatively simple seeds (8). When used with glutamic acid the oxidation rate is stabilized similar to that obtained with many municipal wastes (k = 0.16 to 0.19).

9.3.3 The standard glucose-glutamic solution should show a BOD of approximately 220 ppm, depending upon the seed used. A variation greater than ± 20 to 30 ppm should not occur more frequently than 5 per cent of the time or the technique used is subject to question. Any appreciable divergence from these results should raise serious questions concerning the quality of the water or the viability of the seeding material.

10. Pretreatment of Samples

10.1 *Samples Containing Acidity or Caustic Alkalinity*—Neutralize to approximately pH 7 with H_2SO_4 (1:49) or NaOH, (50 g/liter) using a pH meter or bromthymol blue as an outside indicator. The pH of seeded dilution water should not be changed by dilution of sample.

10.2 *Samples Containing Residual Chlorine Compounds*—Allow such samples to stand for 1 to 2 hr to permit dissipation of residual chlorine. In the event the foregoing is not effective, use of sodium sulfite solution is indicated. Determine the appropriate quantity of sodium sulfite by adding 10 ml of acetic acid (1:1) or H_2SO_4 (1:49) and 10 ml of 10 per cent potassium iodide (KI) solution to a 1-liter portion of sample. Titrate to starch-iodide end point with sodium sulfite solution. Add to a volume of sample a quantity of sodium sulfite solution indicated by the above tests, mix, and allow 10 to 20 min for reaction time.

Test treated samples for residual chlorine to check the completeness of treatment.

10.3 *Samples Containing Toxic Substances*—Frequently special study and treatment is required to remove or neutralize toxic materials. (See Appendix A5 for comments on suggested test for toxicity to seed.)

10.4 *Samples Supersaturated with Oxygen (Greater than 9.2 ppm at 20 C)*—Such samples may be encountered during winter months or in localities where algae are actively growing. To prevent loss of oxygen during incubation, reduce the oxygen content to saturation by transferring the sample at about 20 C to a partially filled bottle and agitating it by vigorous shaking.

11. Procedure

11.1 Using the technique described in 11.2 to 11.10, prepare one or more dilutions of the sample with seeded dilution water so that at least one dilution will achieve a dissolved oxygen depletion of 1 ppm during the 5-day test period but does not reduce residual dissolved oxygen to less than 1 ppm.

NOTE 2—Although the relationship between chemical oxygen demand (COD) and BOD is not constant, a preliminary COD determination may serve as a guide for estimating the range of the BOD. This is particularly useful in sequential analyses of a given water source.

11.2 Carefully siphon standard seeded dilution water into a graduated cylinder of 1000 to 2000-ml capacity, filling the cylinder half full with no entrainment of air. Add the quantity of carefully mixed sample to desired dilution and fill to the mark with dilution water. Mix well with a plunger-type mixing rod avoiding any entrainment of air. For samples where the range of possible BOD is large it is desirable to prepare a geometric series of dilutions in sufficient number to cover the possible range. (See Appendix A6 for chart showing range of BOD at various dilutions.)

11.3 Siphon, with continued mixing, the diluted sample to fill completely 3 BOD bottles; one for incubation, one for the determination of dissolved oxygen content, and the other for determination of immediate dissolved oxygen demand (IDOD). Insert the stoppers without entrainment of any bubbles.

11.3.1 Preparation of diluted samples may also be done by direct measurement of suitable amounts of sample into BOD bottles of known capacity using a large-tipped volumetric pipet and then filling the bottles with seeded dilution water. Dilutions greater than 1:100 must be made by diluting the waste in a graduated cylinder before measurement into incubation bottles.

11.4 *Seeded Dilution Water Blank*— Prepare one portion of seeded dilution water in a manner similar to that described in 11.3.1, to serve for the determination of initial dissolved oxygen content.

11.5 *Unseeded Dilution Water Blank*— Fill 2 BOD bottles with unseeded dilution water. Stopper and water-seal one of these for incubation. Determine the dissolved oxygen in the other bottle before incubation. The dissolved oxygen results on these two bottles are used as a check on the quality of the unseeded dilution water. The depletion obtained should not be more than 0.2 ppm and preferably not more than 0.1 ppm. Do not use it as a blank correction.

11.6 *Seed Correction Control*—If the dilution water is seeded, determine the oxygen depletion of the seed used in such dilution that will result in a 40 to 70 per cent depletion in 5 days. Use this depletion to calculate the correction due to the small amount of seed in the dilution water. Do not use a seeded blank for seed correction. This method of cor-

rection is preferred because the 5-day seeded dilution water blank is subject to erratic oxidation which is not characteristic in the seeded sample and which is due to the very high dilution of the seed.

11.7 Determine the dissolved oxygen content using ASTM Methods D 1589, Test for Dissolved Oxygen in Industrial Waste Water.[2] In special cases, other modifications may be necessary.

11.8 Water-seal each bottle to be incubated. If special water-sealed bottles are not used, the BOD bottle should be sealed by inversion or complete immersion in a tray of water in the incubator.

11.9 Incubate for 5 days at 20 ± 1 C.

NOTE 3: **Caution**—If the BOD results must be interpreted as pollutional load or as the measure of efficiency of a biological oxidation process, the suitability of 5-day results must be established by the analyst. If the pattern of BOD development is such that the 5-day BOD value is not suitable, the analyst should select the best incubation period. In such cases the incubation period must be reported with the results.

11.10 Determine the final dissolved oxygen content after the incubation period.

12. Calculation

12.1 Calculate the immediate dissolved oxygen demand (IDOD) as follows:

$$\text{IDOD, ppm} = \frac{D_0 - D_1}{P}$$

12.2 Calculate the biochemical oxygen demand (BOD) as follows:

12.2.1 When seeding is not required:

$$\text{BOD, ppm} = \frac{D_1 - D_2}{P}$$

12.2.2 When using seeded dilution water:

$$\text{BOD, ppm} = \frac{(D_1 - D_2) - (B_1 - B_2)f}{P}$$

12.3 Including IDOD, if small or not determined:

$$\text{BOD, ppm} = \frac{D_c - D_2}{P}$$

where:

D_0 = dissolved oxygen (DO) of original dilution water,

D_1 = DO in diluted sample 15 min after preparation,

D_2 = DO of the diluted sample after incubation,

S = DO of original undiluted sample,

D_c = DO available in dilution at zero time = $(D_0 p) + SP$,

p = decimal fraction of dilution water used, and

P = decimal fraction of sample used.

12.4 *Seed Correction*—when dilution water must be seeded, calculate the seed correction as follows:

$$\text{Seed correction} = (B_1 - B_2)f$$

where:

B_1 = DO of the dilution of seed control before incubation,

B_2 = DO of the dilution of seed control after incubation, and

f = ratio of seed in the sample to seed in the control = (per cent seed in D_1)/(per cent seed in B_1).

13. Precision

13.1 The precision of this method cannot be stated because of the numerous variables in the determination. However, the single operator precision of the method has been tested using the standard glucose – glutamic acid solution described in 9.3. Using 8 different types of seed materials, the single operator precision was 11 ppm at an average concentration level of 223 ppm.

APPENDIXES

A1. Assessing Variables That Affect the 5-Day BOD

A1.1 If wastes consisted only of raw or treated domestic sewage, the measurement of the oxygen load upon a receiving water would be simple. Unfortunately, this is not always the case since most wastes are complex in nature and may contain organic compounds not easily amenable to biological oxidation. When such compounds are present the usual methods of seeding and the standard incubation period of 5 days will fail to assess the effect such wastes may have at some point below their point of discharge.

A1.2 Complete stabilization of a given waste may require a period of incubation too long for practical purposes. For this reason the 5-day period is generally used. *For certain organic materials, however, the 5-day period may be misleading unless additional information defining the progress of the oxygen demand is obtained.* Studies with three or more selected incubation periods on a series of dilutions of the test waste will provide information on lag periods, suitability of test inocula, rate of biochemical oxidation, ultimate oxygen demand, and amenability to biochemical self-purification. Such special studies may be used

to indicate biochemical stability or inhibitory effects of a given waste as well as to provide a basis for interpretation of the significance of the 5-day test results in terms of stream data.

A1.3 Two fundamental characteristics are necessary to evaluate the effect of a given waste on a stream. These are the ultimate oxygen demand (L) and the rate of biochemical oxidation (k). Once these have been approximated, a 5-day value can be used along with data on flow, dilution, water temperature, etc., to approximate stream effects (9–12).

A1.4 Studies over a number of years show that the rate (k) rarely has a value of 0.1 but may vary from less than 0.5 to several times this value. BOD data on a given waste water frequently develop in a manner that does not fit a first-order reaction sequence. Generally it is possible to reconcile these data if two or more first-order reactions having relatively larger differences in rates are considered. A reliable estimate of oxidation rate or rates is essential for estimation of the ultimate or long-term oxygen demand

and the rapidity with which dissolved oxygen depression may occur in the receiving water.

A1.5 The following limitations must be applied to interpretation of the results of 5-day BOD tests:

A1.5.1 The 5-day BOD cannot be considered as a quantitative expression without an approxi-mation of the rate of oxidation and the ratio of 5-day to ultimate oxygen demand.

A1.5.2 The 5-day BOD values of different industrial wastes are not additive.

A1.5.3 Efficiency of a biological treatment process may not be accurately determined on the basis of a 5-day BOD of influent and effluent.

A2. ACCLIMATED SEED TYPES AND PREPARATION OF ACCLIMATED SEED (13–16)

A2.1 Many industrial wastes contain organic compounds which are not amenable to oxidation by domestic sewage seed. In these cases, alternate seed materials may be obtained from other sources listed in the order of preference:

A2.1.1 From receiving water below a point of discharge (preferably after several hours have elapsed in time of stream flow) or acclimated seed developed in the laboratory. Seed from re-ceiving water will undoubtedly give the best estimate of the effect of a waste on such water, but it must be collected at a point where a biota has been built up capable of using the particular organic compounds as a food source. With re-current samples of wastes which are not easily susceptible to biochemical oxidation, it is usually more practical to build up and maintain an ac-climated seed in the laboratory.

A3. PROCEDURE FOR THE DEVELOPMENT OF ACCLIMATED MICROORGANISMS AS SEED

A3.1 Obtain at least a 1-liter sample of water from the stream, receiving the waste water at a point downstream where several hours have elapsed in time of stream flow.

A3.2 Neutralize a sample of waste water to pH 7.

A3.3 Add a volume of the waste water sam-ple to the 1 liter of stream water which will re-sult in a COD value for the mixture of approxi-mately 50 ppm or a concentration less than that which causes toxicity problems (determine COD using ASTM Method D 1252, Test for Chemical Oxygen Demand (Dichromate Oxygen Demand) of Industrial Waste Water[2]). Transfer the mix-ture to a jug or bottle and aerate slowly.

A3.4 Add diammonium phosphate in propor-tions of 1 part of nitrogen to 20 parts of COD. If the waste water contains adequate nitrogen and phosphorus the addition of diammonium phos-phate may be omitted. Adequate nitrogen and phosphorus to sustain biological activity is 5 parts of nitrogen and 1 part of phosphorus for every 100 parts of BOD. Incubate the mixture at room temperature and away from light to avoid growth of algae.

A3.5 Make daily observations for signs o bacterial growth as for example: development o turbidity; scum formation on the surface of the liquid; growth attached to the walls, or other changes. Confirm indications of suspected growth by microscopic examinations.

A3.6 When a culture of acclimated organisms has developed it may be continued by feeding on a once-per-day schedule or less often, as needed. A COD of about 50 ppm in the prepared feed is adequate. Discard an appropriate volume of the culture to maintain the original liquid level and salts concentration before adding additional feed.

A3.7 If a culture of microorganisms fails to develop, the stream sample may not have con-tained suitable organisms or inhibitory sub-stances may have been present. Then, other seed sources as sewage, garden soil, etc., should be used to attempt the culture of acclimated micro-organisms. If a culture fails to develop, the waste water may be toxic.

A4. PREPARATION OF BOD SEED FROM ACCLIMATED CULTURE

A4.1 Do not feed the culture for a 14-hr period prior to use as seed.

A4.2 Scrape all attached growth from the wall of the container.

A4.3 Remove the desired volume of the mix-ture to be used as seed and homogenize by vigor-ous shaking in a stoppered bottle or in a me-chanical blender for 30 sec.

A4.4 Pipet the desired volume of homoge-nized seed into each BOD bottle or add the correct volume directly to the dilution water as in 10.3.

A5. Suggested Test for Toxicity to Seed

A5.1 Add the same amount of seed to a series of BOD bottles.

A5.2 Add dilution water to each of the bottles and leave space for the addition of sample.

A5.3 Neutralize the sample, add the desired volume to each bottle, and finish filling the bottles with dilution water.

A5.4 Prepare duplicate bottles in the series of dilutions. Determine the DO of one series of bottles about 15 min after the dilution is prepared. Dilutions of 40, 20, 10, 5, 2.5, 1.0, 0.5, 0.25, 0.12 and 0.06 per cent are suggested.

A5.5 Incubate the second series for a period of 3 days and determine the residual dissolved oxygen.

A5.6 Plot the consumption of dissolved oxygen versus concentration. The magnitude of the oxygen change will depend upon the amount of food available and the toxicity of the wastes. If toxicity is a factor, oxygen consumption will decrease at higher concentration of the waste where toxic conditions are established.

A6. Effective Range of BOD for Corresponding Dilution

A6.1 Figure 1 shows the range of BOD to be expected with volumes of sample ranging from 0.1 to 100 ml when the dilution is made in the conventional 300-ml DO bottle (17).

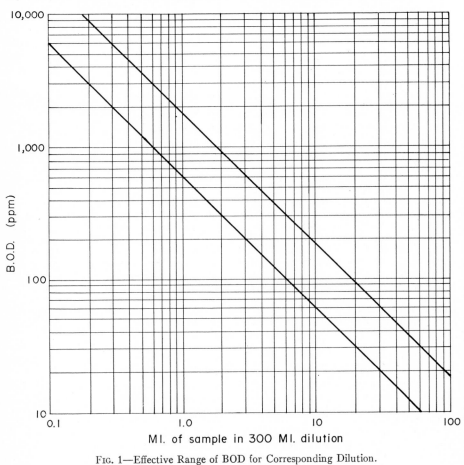

Fig. 1—Effective Range of BOD for Corresponding Dilution.

References

(1) C. N. Sawyer and A. W. Williams, "The Selection of a Dilution Water for the Determination of the BOD of Industrial Wastes." *Sewage Works Journal*, Vol. 14, p. 1000 (1942).

(2) W. L. Lea and M. S. Nichols, "Influence of Phosphorus and Nitrogen on Biochemical Oxygen Demand," *Sewage Works Journal*, Vol. 9, p. 34 (1937).

(3) C. C. Ruchhoft, "Report on the Cooperative Study of Dilution Waters Made for the Standard Methods Committee of the Federation of Sewage Works Associations," *Sewage Works Journal*, Vol. 13, p. 669 (1941).

(4) C. T. Butterfield and W. C. Purdy, "Some Interrelationships of Plankton and Bacteria in Natural Purification of Polluted Water," *Industrial and Engineering Chemistry*, Vol. 23, p. 213 (1931).

(5) E. F. Eldridge, "The BOD of Industrial Wastes," *Michigan State College Engineering Experimental Station Bulletin*, Vol. 78, p. 16 (1938).

(6) W. Rudolfs, G. E. Barnes, G. P. Edwards, H. Heukelekian, E. Hurwitz, C. E. Renn, S. Steinberg, and W. F. Vaughn, "Review of Literature on Toxic Materials Affecting Sewage Treatment Processes, Streams and BOD Determinations," *Sewage and Industrial Wastes*, Vol. 22, p. 1157 (1950).

(7) Subcommittee on Toxicity of Industrial Wastes Research Committee, "Toxicity of Copper and Zinc Ions in the Dilution BOD Test," *Sewage and Industrial Wastes*, Vol. 28, p. 1168 (1956).

(8) E. R. Hermann, "A Toxicity Index for Industrial Wastes," *Industrial and Engineering Chemistry*, Vol. 51, p. 84 (1959).

(9) E. J. Mills, Jr. and V. T. Stack, Jr., "Biological Oxidation Parameter Applied to Industrial Wastes," *Industrial and Engineering Chemistry*, Vol. 48, p. 260 (1956).

(10) E. J. Mills, Jr. and V. T. Stack, Jr., "Acclimation of Microorganisms for the Oxidation of Pure Organic Compounds," Ninth Industrial Waste Conference, Purdue University, *Proceedings*, Vol. 87, p. 492 (1954).

(11) E. J. Mills, Jr. and V. T. Stack, Jr., "Biological Oxidation of Synthetic Organic Chemicals," Eighth Industrial Waste Conference, Purdue University, *Proceedings*, p. 492 (1953).

(12) E. J. Mills, Jr. and V. T. Stack Jr., "Suggested Procedure for Evaluation of Biological Oxidation of Organic Chemicals," *Sewage and Industrial Wastes*, Vol. 27, p. 1061 (1955).

(13) D. G. Ballinger and R. J. Lishka, "Reliability and Precision of BOD and COD Determinations," *Journal of Water Pollution Control*, p. 470, May, 1962.

(14) J. R. Wolf, "Nomograph for Determining Proper Dilution in BOD Test," *Water and Sewage Works*, Vol. 97, p. 122 (1950).

(15) H. M. Gifft, "The Mathematics of BOD Determination," *Water Works and Sewage*, Vol. 90, pp. 8, 313 (1943).

(16) W. N. Grune, "Calculation and Statistical Analysis of the Biochemical Oxygen Demand Velocity Constant," *Public Health Engineering Abstracts*, Vol. 30, pp. 7, 14 (1950).

(17) H. A. Thomas, Jr., "The Slope Method of Evaluating the Constants of the First Stage BOD Curve," *Sewage Works Journal*, Vol. 9, p. 424 (1937).

(18) H. A. Thomas, Jr., "Graphical Determination of BOD Curve Constants," *Water and Sewage Works Journal*, Vol. 97, p. 123 (1950).

Tentative Methods of Test for

ALKYL BENZENE SULFONATE IN INDUSTRIAL WATER AND INDUSTRIAL WASTE WATER[1]

ASTM Designation: D 2330 – 65 T

ISSUED, 1965

These Tentative Methods have been approved by the sponsoring committee and accepted by the Society in accordance with established procedures, for use pending adoption as standard. Suggestions for revisions should be addressed to the Society at 1916 Race St., Philadelphia, Pa. 19103.

1. Scope

1.1 These methods cover the determination of alkyl benzene sulfonate (ABS) in industrial water and industrial waste water. The following methods are included:

	Sections
Method A (Direct Methylene Blue Colorimetric)	5 to 12
Method B (Interference Limited Methylene Blue Colorimetric)	13 to 20

1.2 Method A is a nonreferee, rapid, control procedure suitable for monitoring the effectiveness of a biodegradation or other ABS reduction process. Results must be carefully interpreted since simplification has been made by some sacrifice in specificity.

1.3 Method B is an amplification of Method A in which a series of purification steps are utilized to increase specificity by the elimination of interferences. Method B may be considered the referee method when results obtained are complemented by a knowledge of the composition of the sample matrix or by the utilization of infrared spectroscopy.[2]

1.4 Differentiation between linear and branched-chain ABS, as well as the various positional isomers of either type, is not possible by these methods. It is therefore obvious that, while the methylene blue methods may conveniently be employed to monitor studies designed to measure biodegradibility, they cannot be used to predict this quality.

2. Definitions

2.1 The term "alkyl benzene sulfonate (ABS)" in this method as defined in accordance with the ASTM Definitions D 1129, Terms Relating to Industrial Water and Industrial Waste Water[3] follows:

[1] Under the standardization procedure of the Society, these methods are under the jurisdiction of the ASTM Committee D-19 on Industrial Water. A list of members may be found in the ASTM Year Book.

[2] C. P. Ogden, H. L. Webster, and J. Halliday, "Determination of Biologically Soft and Hard Alkyl Benzene Sulfonates in Detergents and Sewage," *The Analyst*, Vol. 86, 1961, pp. 22-29.

"Determination of Synthetic Detergent Content of Raw Water Supplies (Infrared Process)" *Journal of the American Water Works Association*, Vol. 50, No. 10, October, 1958, pp. 1349–52.

[3] Appears in this publication.

2.2 *Alkyl Benzene Sulfonate* (ABS)[4]— The generic name applied to the neutralized product resulting from the sulfonation of an alkylated benzene.

2.3 For definitions of other terms used in these methods, refer to Definitions D 1129. Refer also to ASTM Definitions E 131, Terms and Symbols Relating to Absorption Spectroscopy.[5]

3. Purity of Reagents

3.1 Reagent grade chemicals shall be used in all tests. Unless otherwise indicated, it is intended that all reagents shall conform to specifications of the Committee on Analytical Reagents of the American Chemical Society, where such specifications are available.[6] Other grades may be used, provided it is first ascertained that the reagent is of sufficiently high purity to permit its use without lessening the accuracy of the determination.

3.2 Unless otherwise indicated, references to water shall be understood to mean non-referee reagent water conforming to ASTM Specifications D 1193, for Reagent Water.[3]

4. Sampling

4.1 Collect the sample in accordance with the applicable method of the

American Society for Testing and Materials, as follows:

D 510—Sampling Industrial Water,[3] and
D 1496—Sampling Homogeneous Industrial Waste Water.[3]

METHOD A

(Direct Methylene Blue Colorimetric)[7]

5. Summary of Method

5.1 The sample is mixed with an acidified, aqueous solution of methylene

TABLE 1—EVALUATION OF POTENTIAL INTERFERENCES IN DIRECT METHYLENE BLUE METHOD.

Added to 1.0 ppm ABS Solution	Concentration, ppm	Indicated ABS, ppm
Acetic acid	100	1.0
Ammonium diethylphosphorodithioate	20	1.1
Benzene sulfonic acid	100	1.3
Cholesterol	100	1.0
2,4-dichlorophenol	100	1.0
Diethanolamine	1000	1.0
Disodium phenylphosphate	10	1.0
Isopropylamine	14	1.0
Leucine	10	1.0
N-1-(naphthylethylenediamine) hydrochloride	100	0.9
Nonyl phenol + 9 EtO	100	1.0
Phenol	100	1.0
Picric acid	5	4.6
Potassium chloride	100	1.0
Potassium cyanate	100	1.0
Potassium nitrate	100	1.0
Potassium thiocyanate	2	1.0
Potassium thiocyanate	100	4.1
Proteins (Knox gelatine)	100	0.9
Sodium dodecyl sulfate	10	14.6
Sodium dodecane sulfonate	5	5.0
Sodium naphthalene sulfonate	5	5.1
Sodium stearate	100	1.0

blue and, any resulting hydrophobic complex, which may be formed, is extracted by serial chloroform washes. The combined chloroform extracts are

---

[4] For a more complete discussion of terms relating to synthetic detergents and their significance, refer to "Syndets and Waste Disposal" by R. E. McKinney *Sewage and Industrial Wastes*, Vol. 29, Part 6, June, 1957, pp. 654-666.

Reference should also be made to ASTM Definitions D 459, Terms Relating to Soaps and other Detergents, *1967 Book of ASTM Standards*, Part 22.

[5] *1967 Book of ASTM Standards*, Part 32.

[6] "Reagent Chemicals, American Chemical Society Specifications," Am. Chemical Soc., Washington, D. C. For suggestions on the testing of reagents not listed by the American Chemical Society, see "Reagent Chemicals and Standards" by Joseph Rosin, D. Van Nostrand Co., Inc., New York, N.Y. and the "United States Pharmacopeia."

[7] Adapted from "Surfactants (Anionic) Methylene Blue Methods," Standard Methods for the Examination of Water and Waste Water, Eleventh Ed. (1960).

washed with an acid solution which hydrolyzes and returns to the aqueous phase the fragments from many of the less stable complexes formed by potentially interfering substances.

5.2 The intensity of the blue color, remaining in the chloroform extract, is measured photometrically at a wavelength of approximately 650 mμ, and related to concentration of ABS by means of a calibration chart.

6. Interferences

6.1 Any compound which will form a chloroform-soluble complex, by a linkage through the bridging nitrogen atom of methylene blue, will interfere by producing high results, unless the complex formed is eliminated by the treatment described in 5.1.

6.2 Any compound, that will selectively combine with the ABS, will inactivate the sulfonate site and block the methylene blue reaction. This negative interference is demonstrated by some amines and has analytical significance in the case of quaternary ammonium compounds.

6.3 An evaluation of the effect of various potential interferences is summarized in Table 1.[8] The listed compounds, in the concentrations indicated, were added to solutions containing 1.0 ppm ABS.

7. Apparatus

7.1 *Filter Photometer or Spectrophotometer*, suitable for measurement at a wavelength of approximately 650 mμ (Note 1).

Note 1—Photometers prescribed in this method shall conform to ASTM Recommended Practice E 60, for Photometric Methods for Chemical Analysis of Metals.[5]

8. Reagents

8.1 *Chloroform* ($CHCl_3$).

[8] Supporting data listing results of cooperative tests are on file at ASTM Headquarters.

8.2 *Methylene Blue Solution*—Dissolve 0.1 g of methylene blue chloride in 100 ml of water. Transfer 30 ml of this solution to a 1-liter volumetric flask and add 500 ml of water. Add 7 ml of concentrated H_2SO_4 (sp gr 1.84) and 50 g of $NaH_2PO_4 \cdot H_2O$. Shake until solution is complete and then dilute to 1 liter with water.

8.3 *Phenolphthalein Indicator Solution (5.0 g/liter)*—Dissolve 0.5 g of phenolphthalein in 50 ml of 95 per cent ethyl alcohol (Note 2) and dilute to 100 ml with water.

Note 2—Specially denatured ethyl alcohol conforming to Formula No. 3A or 30 of the U.S. Bureau of Internal Revenue may be substituted for 95 per cent ethyl alcohol.

8.4 *Sodium Alkyl Benzene Sulfonate (Stock Solution)*—Weigh the amount of reference material[9] necessary to provide the equivalent of 1.0000 g of ABS on a 100 per cent active basis. Dissolve in water and dilute to 1 liter.

8.5 *Sodium Alkyl Benzene Sulfonate, Standard Solution (1.0 ml = 0.01 mg ABS)*—Dilute 10.0 ml of the stock ABS solution to 1 liter with water.

8.6 *Sodium Hydroxide Solution (10 g/liter)*—Dissolve 10 g of sodium hydroxide (NaOH) in water and dilute to 1 liter.

8.7 *Sodium Phosphate, Acidified Wash Solution*—Dissolve 50 g of sodium dihydrogen phosphate monohydrate ($NaH_2PO_4 \cdot H_2O$) in 500 ml of water in a 1-liter volumetric flask. Add 7 ml of concentrated sulfuric acid (H_2SO_4, sp gr 1.84) and dilute to volume with water.

8.8 *Sulfuric Acid (7:993)*—Carefully add 7 ml of concentrated sulfuric acid (H_2SO_4, sp gr 1.84) to water and dilute to 1 liter with water.

[9] Sodium alkyl benzene sulfonate reference material may be obtained from the Soap and Detergent Association, 295 Madison Ave., New York, N.Y. 10017.

9. Calibration

9.1 From a buret, add to a series of 250-ml separatory funnels 0.0, 1.0, 3.0, 5.0, 7.0, 9.0, and 12.0 ml of the standard ABS solution. Dilute to 100 ml with water (Note 3).

Note 3—All glassware used for the determination of ABS should be free of scratches and etch marks, because of the tendency of surface-active materials to adsorb on this type of surface. All volumetric flasks and photometer cells, projected for use in ABS determinations, should, as instructed herein, be preconditioned. Obtain the chloroform extract from 12.0 ml of the standard ABS solution as described in 9. Calibration. Transfer sequentially to each of the volumetric flasks and photometer cells and permit a minimum contact time, in each case, of 5 min. Rinse thoroughly with chloroform and drain.

9.2 Add 3 drops of phenolphthalein solution and just enough NaOH solution to develop a pink color. Add sulfuric acid solution, in small increments, until the pink color is barely discharged.

9.3 Add 25 ml of methylene blue solution and mix. Add 25 ml of chloroform and mix thoroughly by shaking. Permit the phases to separate and then drain the chloroform layer into a second 250-ml separatory funnel. Leave any lacy cuff, at the interface, in the first separatory funnel. Repeat the extraction, serially, with two additional 25-ml portions of chloroform.

9.4 Add 50 ml of phosphate wash solution to the combined chloroform extracts in the second separatory funnel and shake vigorously for 30 sec. Hold the separatory funnel in a vertical position and swirl the contents. Permit settling for 1 min. Filter the chloroform layer through a glass wool plug into a conditioned (Note 3) 100-ml volumetric flask. Add 20 ml of chloroform to the second separatory funnel and repeat the shaking, swirling, and settling steps. Combine the chloroform layer through the glass wool into the volumetric flask. Add additional chloroform as needed to bring the flask to 100 ml and mix thoroughly.

9.5 Using a 40-mm (Note 4) light path, with a wavelength as close to 652 mμ as the available photometer will permit, set the instrument at 100 per cent transmission through the extract of the solution known to contain no ABS (Note 5).

Note 4—If a shorter light path is employed the volumes of standard ABS solution selected for the calibration should be proportionately increased.

Note 5—Because of a tendency to slowly fade, the absorbance of the extracted methylene blue complex should be measured within 30 min after formation.

9.6 Measure the absorbance of each of the extracts and prepare a calibration chart by plotting on rectilinear graph paper, photometer readings against concentration of ABS in milligrams (Note 6).

Note 6—If the scale of the photometer reads in per cent transmittance, plot the results on semilog paper, using the vertical log axis for transmittance and the horizontal linear axis for concentration in millligrams of ABS.

10. Procedure

10.1 Select a volume of sample consistent with the anticipated ABS content (Note 7).

Note 7—If the ABS concentration is not expected to exceed 1 ppm, use a 100-ml sample. For ABS in the 10-ppm range, use a 10-ml sample diluted to 100 ml with water. The sensitivity of the method may be improved in cases of relatively unpolluted waters by concentrating larger sample volumes to 100 ml by evaporation.

10.2 Process the sample and a parallel 100-ml water blank as outlined in 9.2 to 9.6.

11. Calculation

11.1 Calculate the concentration of sodium alkyl benzene sulfonate as fol lows:

$$\text{ABS, ppm} = \frac{W \times 1000}{S}$$

where:

W = milligrams of ABS from the calibration chart, and

S = milliliters of sample selected in 10.1.

12. Precision[8]

12.1 The precision of the method may be expressed as follows:

$$S_t = 0.107X + 0.008$$

where:

S_t = over-all precision, and

X = concentration of ABS, ppm.

TABLE 2—EVALUATION OF POTENTIAL INTERFERENCES IN THE INTERFERENCES LIMITED METHYLENE BLUE METHOD.

Added to 1.0 ppm ABS Solution	Concentration, ppm	Indicated ABS, ppm
Sodium dodecane sulfonate.....	5	3.7
Sodium benzene sulfonate......	100	1.2
Sodium dodecyl sulfate.........	10	0.9
Potassium thiocyanate.........	100	1.0
Picric acid....................	10	1.0

12.2 When the original sample volume is changed by either evaporation or dilution, the calculated precision must be changed accordingly.

METHOD B

(Interference Limited Methylene Blue Colorimetric)[10]

13. Summary of Method

13.1 The selected sample is hydrolyzed by boiling under partial reflux with hydrochloric acid. The residual products are neutralized, to a controlled pH value, and reacted with 1-methylheptylamine. The resulting complexes are extracted into a chloroform phase and evaporated to dryness on a steam

[10] Adapted from E. M. Sallee, J. D. Fairing, et al, "Determination of Trace Amounts of Alkyl Benzene Sulfonates in Water," *Analytical Chemistry*, Vol. 28 (1956), pp. 1822-1826.

bath. The amine component of the complex is removed by boiling in an aqueous alkaline media and the isolated ABS is then determined as described in 9.2 to 9.6.

14. Interferences

14.1 Any compound which will survive the purification steps described in 13. Summary of Method and which, subsequently, will satisfy the limitations imposed in 5.1, will interfere. Current knowledge indicates that such compounds are limited to alkyl sulfonates and, to a much lesser degree, to aryl sulfonates.

14.2 The increased specificity attainable by the use of Method B is illustrated in Table 2.[7] The listed compounds, in the concentrations indicated, were added to solutions containing 1.0 ppm ABS.

15. Apparatus

15.1 The apparatus shall be as described in 7. Apparatus.

15.2 *pH Meter*.

16. Reagents

16.1 See 8. Reagents.

16.2 *Hydrochloric Acid (sp gr 1.19)*—Concentrated hydrochloric acid (HCl).

16.3 *1-Methylheptylamine*.

16.4 *Phosphate Buffer Solution (pH 7.5 ± 0.1)*—Dissolve 10 g of potassium dihydrogen phosphate (KH_2PO_4) in 800 ml of water and adjust the pH value to 7.5 ± 0.1 by adding NaOH solution. Dilute to 1 liter with water.

17. Calibration

17.1 Select the volumes of standard ABS solution suggested in 9.1 and dilute each to 100 ml with water.

17.2 Process each in accordance with 18.1 to 18.6.

18. Procedure

18.1 Select a volume of sample consistent with the anticipated ABS concentration (Note 7) and transfer to a 400-ml beaker. Add a like amount of water to a second 400-ml beaker and process in parallel with the sample (Note 3). Add 30 ml of HCl (sp gr 1.19) and cover with watch glasses. Boil at a slow rate, in a fume hood, so that at least 1 hr is required to reduce the solutions to incipient dryness. Additional water may be added, as required, to satisfy the above limitation.

18.2 Cool and rinse the cover glasses and beaker walls with water from a wash bottle until the residue in the beakers is diluted to approximately 25 ml. Add 3 drops of phenolphthalein solution and make the solutions definitely alkaline by adding NaOH solution. Boil for 2 min, with the cover glasses in place, and then transfer quantitatively, by water washing, to 250-ml separatory funnels. Reserve the beakers for subsequent use.

18.3 Add additional water, if needed, so that the aggregate volume in the separatory funnels is about 100 ml. Carefully add H_2SO_4 (7:993) until the pink phenolphthalein color is barely discharged. Add 10 ml of buffer solution.

18.4 Mix, in 100-ml glass-stoppered graduates, 4 drops of 1-methylheptylamine and 100 ml of chloroform.

18.5 Extract each of the solutions, in the separatory funnels, serially with four 25-ml portions of the amine-chloroform mixture. Shake thoroughly, but not vigorously, for 1 min after each addition. On each occasion allow the chloroform layer to separate and then drain to the respective 400-ml reserved beaker. Leave any lacy cuff, which may persist at the interface, in the separatory funnel with the aqueous phase. Add 5 ml of NaOH solution to the combined chloroform extracts and evaporate the chloroform on a steam bath. Dilute the alkaline residues to about 50 ml with water, cover with watch glasses, and boil for 15 min on a

hot plate. Replace evaporation losses by washing down walls of beakers with water after boiling for 10 min.

18.6 Transfer quantitatively, after cooling, to 250-ml separatory funnels (Note 8). Dilute with water to about 100 ml and add 3 drops of phenolphthalein solution. Add H_2SO_4 (7:993) in small increments, until the pink color is barely discharged. Complete the analysis in accordance with 9.3 to 9.6. Use the processed water blank to set the photometer at 100 per cent transmittance.

Note 8—If the separatory funnels intended for use are the same ones used for the amine extractions, rinse thoroughly with a solution consisting of 1 part HCl (sp gr 1.19) in 10 parts of methanol. Follow with copious water rinses. The same cleaning procedure is effective in removing adsorbed ABS residues and methylene blue stains from glassware.

19. Calculations

19.1 Calculate the concentrations of sodium alkyl benzene sulfonate as follows:

$$\text{ABS, ppm} = \frac{W \times 1000}{S}$$

where:
W = milligrams of ABS from the calibration chart, and
S = milliliters of sample selected in accordance with 18.1.

20. Precision[8]

20.1 The precision of this method may be expressed as follows:

$$S_t = 0.086X - 0.006$$

where:
S_t = over-all precision, and
X = concentration of ABS determined in ppm.

20.2 When the original sample volume is changed by either evaporation or dilution, the calculated precision must be changed accordingly.

Tentative Methods of Test for

COPPER, IRON, AND SILICA IN WATER-FORMED DEPOSITS[1]

ASTM Designation: D 2331 – 65 T

ISSUED, 1965

These Tentative Methods have been approved by the sponsoring committee and accepted by the Society in accordance with established procedures, for use pending adoption as standard. Suggestions for revisions should be addressed to the Society at 1916 Race St., Philadelphia, Pa. 19103.

1. Scope

1.1 These methods cover a group of relatively rapid analytical determinations of one or more constituents of the components of the deposit.[2] Directions are given for the preparation of the sample for analysis, the preliminary examination of the sample, and methods for dissolving the analytical sample or selectively separating constituents of concern.

1.2 The methods include the following:

	Sections
Preparation of the Analytical Sample	6
Preliminary Testing of Analytical Sample	7
Dissolving the Analytical Sample	8
Determination of Copper	9 to 16
Determination of Iron	17 to 24
Determination of Silica	25 to 32

[1] Under the standardization procedure of the Society, these methods are under the jurisdiction of the ASTM Committee D-19 on Industrial Water. A list of members may be found in the ASTM Year Book.

[2] See also ASTM Methods D 1428, Test for Sodium and Potassium in Industrial Water and Water-Formed Deposits by Flame Photometry, which appear in this publication.

2. Definitions

2.1 The term "water-formed deposits" in this method is defined in accordance with the ASTM Definitions D 1129, Terms Relating to Industrial Water and Industrial Waste Water[3] follows:

Water-Formed Deposits—Any accumulation of insoluble material derived from water or formed by the reaction of water upon surfaces in contact with water.

NOTE 1—Deposits formed from or by water in all its phases may be further classified as scale, sludge, corrosion products, or biological deposits. The over-all composition of a deposit or some part of a deposit may be determined by chemical or spectrographic analysis; the constituents actually present as chemical substances may be identified by microscope or X-ray diffraction studies. Organisms may be identified by microscopic or biological methods.

2.2 For definitions of other terms used in this method, refer to Definitions D 1129.

3. Purity of Reagents

3.1 Reagent grade chemicals shall be used in all tests. Unless otherwise in-

[3] Appears in this publication.

dicated, it is intended that all reagents shall conform to the specifications of the Committee on Analytical Reagents of the American Chemical Society where such specifications are available.[4] Other grades may be used, provided it is first ascertained that the reagent is of sufficiently high purity to permit its use without lessening the accuracy of the determination.

3.2 Unless otherwise indicated, references to water shall be understood to mean reagent water conforming to ASTM Specifications D 1193, for Reagent Water.[3]

4. Sampling

4.1 Collect the sample in accordance with ASTM Method D 887, Field Sampling of Water-Formed Deposits.[3]

5. Report

5.1 Methods for reporting analytical results should follow those described in ASTM Method D 933, Reporting Results of Examination and Analysis of Water-Formed Deposits,[3] when applicable.

6. Preparation of Analytical Sample

6.1 *Preliminary Examination*—Examine the sample as collected, using a microscope if available, for structure, color, odor, oily matter, appearance of mother liquor if any, and other characteristics of note (for example, attraction to magnet). Record results for future reference.

6.1.1 Filtration and other steps in the preparation of the analytical sample may frequently be bypassed; for example, a moist sample that contains no separated

water shall be started in accordance with 6.3.1, and a dry sample shall be started in accordance with 6.4, 6.5, or 6.6. Partitioning, 6.4, is not always practical or even desirable. Solvent extraction, 6.5, is unnecessary if the sample contains no oily or greasy matter.

6.2 *Filtration of Sample (Note 2)*— If the sample includes an appreciable quantity of separated water, remove the solid material by filtration. Save the filtrate, undiluted, pending decision as to whether or not its chemical examination is required. Transfer all of the solid portion to the filter, using the filtrate to rinse the sample container if necessary. Air-drying or partial air-drying of the filter is frequently helpful toward effecting a clean separation of the deposit.

NOTE 2—If the sample obviously contains oily matter, its extraction with a suitable solvent (6.4) is essential before filtration or air-drying is attempted.

6.3 *Air-Drying*—Remove the drained solid sample from the filter, being careful to avoid gross contamination with filter paper.

6.3.1 Air dry the entire quantity of solid, spread in a thin layer on a nonreactive, impervious surface. A record of the loss of weight during air-drying is often useful.

6.4 *Partitioning the Sample*—Many samples are obviously heterogeneous. If useful to explain the occurrence of the water-formed deposit, separate clearly defined layers or components, and approximate the relative percentages.

6.4.1 Retain the individual air-dried fractions for separate analysis, preferably storing over an effective desiccant such as anhydrite.

6.5 *Solvent Extraction*—This step is essential only if the air-dried sample smears or agglomerates when tested for pulverization (smears caused by graphite are possible but rare with water-formed deposits). To remove chloroform-

[4] "Reagent Chemicals, American Chemical Society Specifications," Am. Chemical Soc., Washington, D.C. For suggestions on the testing of reagents not listed by the American Chemical Society, see "Reagent Chemicals and Standards," by Joseph Rosin, D. Van Nostrand Co., Inc., New York, N. Y., and the "United States Pharmacopeia."

extractable matter, weigh no more than 10 g of air-dried sample and place this, wrapped in fine-textured filter paper, in a prepared (extracted, dried and weighed) Soxhlet thimble. Paper clips are useful for preventing unfolding of the paper. Extract the thimble and its contents in a Soxhlet apparatus until the solvent (chloroform) in the extraction chamber is colorless. Record the loss in weight of the thimble and contents, dried at 105 C, as chloroform-extracted matter. If important to the solution of the problem, evaporate the solvent and examine the residue.

6.5.1 The extraction may be repeated with other volatile organic solvents if exploratory tests warrant such procedure.

6.6 *Pulverizing*—Whether the sample is dry as received, air-dried, or air-dried and extracted, it must be pulverized to adequate homogeneity. Grind the entire sample, or enough of it to be representative of the whole, to pass a No. 100 (149-μ) sieve (as specified in ASTM Specifications E 11, for Sieves for Testing Purposes).[5] Continue the grinding until all the material passes through the sieve, except for fragments such as splinters of fiber, wood, and metal.

6.6.1 Fragments separated from the sample during grinding should be identified by standard methods if this information is valuable.

6.6.2 Mix the sieved material thoroughly by tumbling in a closed dry container that is no more than two thirds full.

6.6.3 Transfer 5 to 10 g of the thoroughly mixed material to a weighing bottle. This is the analytical sample. Unless the determinations are to be made on an air-dried basis, dry at 105 C and store in a desiccator.

7. Preliminary Testing of Analytical Sample

7.1 Much useful information can be obtained by examining samples of water-formed deposits by one or more of a variety of methods, including spectrography, X-ray diffraction, X-ray fluorescence, microscopy, and ordinary qualitative analysis. Preliminary disclosure of what is present in major, minor, or trace concentrations furnishes an essential guide to planning the determinations that will be made on the sample. The preliminary testing frequently also provides important guidance toward defining problems associated with the deposits

7.2 *Spectrography*—Make a spectrographic analysis by a suitable method agreed upon. A suitable method is outlined in 7.2.2 to 7.2.7.

7.2.1 Although much superior results are obtainable with a spectrograph and associated equipment, data of lesser degree of accuracy can frequently be obtained with less formal equipment such as a visual-arc spectrograph.[6]

7.2.2 Best results are obtained by using a spectrograph having a suitable reciprocal linear dispersion, associated adjuncts and optics, a microphotometer for measuring the transmittances of spectra-line images, and associated equipment for determining intensity ratios.

7.2.3 Mix 50 mg of the pulverized sample, obtained in accordance with 6.6.2, with 900 mg of graphite powder and 250 mg of lithium carbonate, and pack the mixture into graphite-cup electrodes.

---

[5] *1967 Book of ASTM Standards*, Part 30.

[6] "Use of the Spectroscope in the Determination of the Constituents of Boiler Scale and Related Compounds," by A. Gabriel, H. W. Jaffe, and M. J. Peterson, *Proceedings*, Am. Soc. Testing Mats., Vol. 47 (1947), pp. 1111 to 1120.

7.2.4 Record the spectra obtained upon excitation with a d-c arc.

7.2.5 Measure the transmittances of the analytical and lithium lines (internal standards other than lithium are preferred by some operators). From these data determine intensity ratios.

7.2.6 Use the intensity ratios to estimate concentrations from standard analytical curves.

7.2.7 The metallic constituents can frequently be determined within 20 per cent of their content in the deposit, which is sufficiently close for classification as major, minor, or trace.

7.3 *X-ray Diffraction*—Examine the material in accordance with ASTM Method D 934, Identification of Crystalline Compounds in Water-Formed Deposits by X-Ray Diffraction.[3]

7.3.1 The required apparatus shall include a radiation souce, of which more than one may be needed, a camera or other device for sensing or recording radiation intensity, and adjuncts for interpreting the recorded data.

7.3.2 Regrind a portion of the pulverized sample, obtained in accordance with 6.6.2, to pass a No. 270 (53-μ) sieve. Mount the powdered material in the shape or form required for the sensing device that is used.

7.3.3 Make a record on photographic film or its equivalent of the radiation pattern while the mount is exposed to the X-ray beam for the required interval.

7.3.4 The radiation pattern shall be translated into lines and intensities, using the adjuncts available for this purpose, and these shall be compared with standard patterns for known compounds.

7.3.5 Identification of a substance is made when sufficient characteristic lines of a standard pattern occur in the pattern derived from the sample, in essentially the same relative intensity; however, owing to the poor crystallization characteristic of many water-formed deposits, the sensitivity of this evaluation is often much poorer than the 1 per cent usually cited.

7.4 *X-ray Fluorescence*—Make an X-ray fluorescence examination by a suitable method agreed upon and subject to the requirements of 7.4.1 to 7.4.6 (Note 3).

Note 3—An X-ray fluorescence method is under preparation by Committee D-19.

7.4.1 The required apparatus shall include sample preparation equipment, excitation source, devices for housing the sample, a spectrometer assembly, and adjuncts for obtaining and interpreting data.

7.4.2 Regrind the pulverized sample obtained in accordance with 6.6.2 to pass a No. 270 (53-μ) sieve. For order of magnitude determinations the ground sample shall be briquetted to form a wafer (alternately, the powdered sample may be tamped into a specimen holder that is supplied with the apparatus).

7.4.3 More accurate evaluations can be made by fusing the sample with a suitable flux; even higher degrees of precision are often obtainable through chemical pretreatment of the sample to segregate the constituents of major concern.

7.4.4 Irradiate the mount by an X-ray beam of short wavelength (high energy). The characteristic X-rays of each constituent that are emitted or fluoresced upon absorption of the primary or incident X-rays are dispered, and intensities at selected wavelengths measured by sensitive detectors.

7.4.5 The K spectral lines are used to identify elements of atomic number 11 to 50. Whether the K or L lines are used for the elements 51 or higher depends on the available instrumentation.

7.4.6 Detector output (radiation pattern) is related to constituent concentration by calibration curves or charts.

7.5 *Microscopy*—Make a microscopic

examination using ASTM Method D 1245, Examination of Water-Formed Deposits by Chemical Microscopy;[3] ASTM Method D 1128, Identification of Types of Microorganisms and Microscopic Matter in Industrial Water and Industrial Waste Water;[3] ASTM Method D 932, Test for Iron Bacteria in Industrial Water and Industrial Waste Water;[3] and ASTM Methods D 993, Test for Sulfate-Reducing Bacteria in Industrial Water and Water-Formed Deposits.[3]

NOTE 4—Petrography is discussed in Chapter VIII, *Manual on Industrial Water*, Second Edition.

7.5.1 It is preferable to test a portion of the sample as received, so that observations and tests can be made on carefully selected portions.

7.5.2 Thorough preliminary testing with the microscope should include examination in relation to Method D 887, which includes a section on sample description. Much more can be seen of the sample and its outstanding characteristics, such as structure and homogeneity, with the microscopic than with the unaided eye.

7.5.3 Crystals are selected and identified using polarized light and measuring refractive indexes. Amorphous materials may also have optical characteristics that provide a basis for identification under a microscope.

7.5.4 Identification of microorganisms is usually limited to general types as tabulated in Method D 1128. Stains are frequently used to differentiate the organisms from the background. Specific identifications of each species of bacteria, molds, and other organisms can be made by experienced personnel, but this identification is not usually required.

7.5.5 The detection of iron bacteria is frequently significant in relation to corrosion deposits. Method D 932 provides a key to the identification of the several kinds of these bacteria. The method also contains several applications from the field of chemical microscopy that are useful for verification.

7.5.6 Sulfate-reducing bacteria are also important in relation to corrosion problems. ASTM Method D 993 includes referee and nonreferee methods for detecting the presence of such bacteria in deposits, and estimating their relative number by a process of incubation and determination of the amount of hydrogen sulfide formed in the culture.

7.6 *Qualitative Testing*—When optical instruments, such as the microscope and spectroscope, are not readily available, considerable useful information can be disclosed by qualitative tests on the air-dried sample. For example, effervescence with acids would suggest the presence of carbonate, and a white precipitate obtained when barium chloride is added to a hydrochloric acid extract would suggest sulfate. Similar quick tests are available for phosphate and a variety of other constituents, and the deposit probably contains iron if it is attracted by a magnet.

8. Dissolving the Analytical Sample

8.1 *Selective Isolation or Segregation of Constituents*—The preliminary examination (7.1 to 7.6) will disclose which constituents comprise the deposit and provide an estimate of the content of each. A considerable number of quantitative determinations can be made directly on the analytical sample, obtained in accordance with 6.6.3, utilizing special methods of extraction. These solubilizing procedures are generally specific to a particular determination and are included with that determination.

8.2 *Solution in Hydrochloric Acid*—This treatment will dissolve water-formed deposits which do not contain a substantial percentage of stubborn components, including calcium sulfate, various silicates, and some of the more refractory spinels. The use of this solvent is advantageous in that it is not oxidizing, and possible interference from sulfate or nitrate is not introduced.

8.2.1 *Reagents*—The reagents for this solubilizing method are as follows:

8.2.1.1 *Hydrochloric Acid (sp gr 1.19)* —Concentrated hydrochloric acid (HCl).

8.2.1.2 *Hydrochloric Acid (1:4)*—Mix 1 volume of concentrated HCl (sp gr 1.19) with 4 volumes of water.

8.2.1.3 *Hydrochloric Acid (1:9)*—Mix 1 volume of concentrated HCl (sp gr 1.19) with 9 volumes of water.

8.2.3 Weigh approximately 0.5 g of the analytical sample obtained in accordance with 6.6.3, into a 250-ml beaker. Add 50 ml of HCl (1:4) and evaporate to dryness on a hot plate contained in a hood. Add 10 ml of concentrated HCl (sp gr 1.19) and again evaporate to dryness. Add 10 ml of HCl (1:9), bring to a boil, and separate the solution by filtration through a medium-texture, ashless filter paper. Wash the residue and dilute the combined filtrate and washings to a measured volume. Aliquots of this solution shall be used for the analysis of the constituents to be determined.

8.2.4 The residue may be retained for further examination.

8.3 *Solution in Mixed Hydrochloric Acid – Nitric Acid*—This solvent is more effective in eliminating traces of organic material and in dissolving more refractory components which resist hydrochloric acid alone. The nitric acid, however, may interfere with some of the later analytical procedures unless it is thoroughly removed during the dehydration step.

8.3.1 *Reagents*—The reagents for this solubilizing method are as follows:

8.3.1.1 *Hydrochloric Acid (1:1)*—Mix 1 volume of concentrated hydrochloric acid (HCl, sp gr 1.19) with 1 volume of water.

8.3.1.2 *Nitric Acid (sp gr 1.42)*—Concentrated nitric acid (HNO_3).

8.3.2 Add 5 ml of HNO_3 (sp gr 1.42) to approximately 0.5 g of the analytical sample that has been weighed into a 250-ml beaker, and evaporate to near dryness on a hot plate contained in a hood. Add 50 ml of HCl (1:1) and 5 ml of HNO_3 (sp gr 1.42). Evaporate to dryness on a hot plate in a hood. Cool and add 10 ml of HCl (1:1) acid and 1 ml of HNO_3 (sp gr 1.42) and repeat the evaporation. Allow the beaker to cool and then add 50 ml of HCl (1:1). Boil until the volume is decreased to approximately 25 ml and filter through a medium-texture, ashless filter paper. Wash the residue and dilute the combined filtrate and washings to a measured volume. Aliquots of this solution shall be used for the analysis of the constituents to be determined.

8.4 *Solution in Mixed Sulfuric Acid*— The reagents listed in 8.4.1 are considered a good universal solvent for water-formed deposits containing silica, but sulfate and silica must be determined on another portion of the sample.

8.4.1 *Reagents*—The reagents for this solubilizing method are as follows:

8.4.1.1 *Hydrofluoric Acid (48 to 51 per cent)*, HF.

8.4.1.2 *Nitric Acid (sp gr 1.42)*—Concentrated nitric acid (HNO_3).

8.4.1.3 *Sulfuric Acid (1:1)*—Mix carefully 1 volume of concentrated sulfuric acid (H_2SO_4, sp. gr 1.84) with 1 volume of water.

8.4.2 Add 3 ml of H_2SO_4 (1:1) and 10 ml of HF to approximately 0.5 g of the analytical sample, as described in 6.6.3, in a 30-ml platinum crucible; perform these operations in a hood. Evaporate until most of the hydrofluoric acid has been volatilized, then add 1 ml of HNO_3 (sp gr 1.42) and continue heating until strong fumes of sulfur trioxide are evolved. Cool the crucible and contents.

Slowly and cautiously add 15 ml of water and digest for $\frac{1}{2}$ hr. Transfer the contents of the crucible quantitatively to a 250-ml volumetric flask and adjust to volume when cool. Unless the quantity of insoluble matter in the flask is appreciable, it may be ignored (barium, if present, will form barium sulfate).

8.4.3 If alkali metals are to be determined on this solubilized portion, enough of it for these determinations should be withdrawn from the volumetric flask and stored in a plastic bottle.

8.5 *Alkali Fusion*—This method of dissolving the sample is especially useful for the rapid determinations of silica and aluminum.

8.5.1 *Reagents*—The reagents for this solubilizing method are as follows:

8.5.1.1 *Hydrochloric Acid (1:1)*—Mix 1 volume of concentrated hydrochloric acid (HCl, sp gr 1.19) with 1 volume of water.

8.5.1.2 *Sodium Hydroxide (NaOH) pellets* (Do not store in glass bottle).

8.5.2 Add 9 sodium hydroxide pellets (approximately 1.5 g) to a 75-ml nickel crucible. Slowly heat the crucible over a Meker burner until the pellets are molten. Allow the crucible and its contents to cool to room temperature. Weigh 0.05 g of the analytical sample, as described in 6.6.3, and transfer to the crucible containing the sodium hydroxide. Reheat the crucible to remelt the hydroxide and swirl to mix in the weighed material. Use a nickel wire or rod to complete the mixing. Continue heating for 3 min after mixing, then allow the melt to cool. Add 50 ml of water to the crucible and stir the contents of the crucible occasionally until the melt is disintegrated completely (about 1 hr). Transfer the contents to a 1-liter volumetric flask (previously rinsed with HCl (1:1)) containing about 400 ml of water and 20 ml of HCl (1:1) (a plastic funnel with a stem at least 6 in. long should be used so that the strongly alka-line extract will not contact the glass). Police and wash the crucible to ensure complete transfer. Dilute to volume with water.

Determination of Copper

9. Summary of Method

9.1 Copper, free and combined, is selectively extracted from the laboratory sample of the deposit by ammonia containing ammonium persulfate. The copper is determined quantitatively from the color of the extract.

10. Interferences

10.1 No important interferences were evident when the method was applied to a variety of boiler deposits containing from 2 to 54 per cent copper; an off-color (greenish) extract was reported in one instance where the copper was determined in a heater deposit containing about 2 per cent copper and a considerable quantity of hydrated (easily dispersible) iron oxide. Recovery was low for another sample that had a very high organic content. Where either of these interferences is suspected, the weighed portion for analysis should be ignited for 10 min at 500 C before the determination is made (see 14.1).

11. Apparatus

11.1 *Photometer* — Filter photometer suitable for measurements at a wavelength of about 620 mμ (acceptable absorbance measurements can be made in the range of 600 to 700 mμ).

Note 5—Filter photometer and photometric practices described in this method shall conform to ASTM Recommended Practice E 60, for Photometric Methods for Chemical Analysis of Metals.[7]

12. Reagents

12.1 *Ammoniacal Persulfate*—Dissolve 1 g of ammonium persulfate ($(NH_4)_2$

---

[7] *1967 Book of ASTM Standards, Part 32.*

S_2O_8) in 50 ml of water; add 50 ml of ammonia (NH_4OH, sp gr 0.90).

12.2 *Copper Sulfate* ($CuSO_4 \cdot 5H_2O$).

13. Calibration

13.1 *Copper Standards*—Prepare a series of standard solutions of $CuSO_4$ dissolved in the ammoniacal persulfate described in 12.1 to bracket the expected range of copper concentrations.

13.2 Prepare a calibration curve for the photometer by plotting the absorbances of the standard solutions against milligrams of copper per 100 ml of solution.

14. Procedure

14.1 Weigh out 0.1 g of the sample prepared for chemical analysis obtained in accordance with 6.6.3, and transfer to a 150-ml Erlenmeyer flask. Add 75 ml of the ammoniacal persulfate. Allow the mixture to stand at room temperature for 1 hr, stirring at 10-min intervals. Filter through a dense, hard-texture, double-washed filter paper and wash the residue with several small portions of the extractant. Add the wash water to the filtrate and make up to 100 ml in a volumetric flask. Read the absorbance of this extract with the photometer. A quick approximation can be obtained by matching the color of the extract directly with those of the standards.

15. Calculation

15.1 Use the absorbance value to read the copper concentration in milligrams from the calibration curve. Divide by the weight, in milligrams, the portion of the laboratory sample that was taken for analysis and multiply by 100. The result gives the per cent copper in the prepared sample.

16. Precision

16.1 To show repeatability the following results were obtained in some replicate testing of random samples by several laboratories:

Number of Replicates	Average Result, per cent Copper	Range of Results, per cent Copper
8	2.23	2.2 to 2.3
3	2.64	2.60 to 2.66
8	11.6	11.4 to 11.7
7	17.4	17.0 to 18.2
5	21.5	20.9 to 22.0
9	50.8	48.3 to 53.6

DETERMINATION OF IRON

17. Summary of Method

17.1 Ferrous iron, in a solution having a pH of 3.5 to 4.0, reacts quantitatively with ortho-phenanthroline forming an orange-red complex. Color measurement is made at a wavelength of 510 mμ. The iron is reduced with hydroxylamine hydrochloride.

18. Interferences

18.1 Copper, chromium, nickel, and zinc form complexes with orthophenanthroline and thus consume the reagent; the reagent addition made in this method permits a combined concentration equal to at least ten times that of the iron. Bismuth, silver, cadmium, mercury, and molybdenum interfere by forming precipitates. Cyanides must not be present. Phosphates can interfere when present in amounts greatly in excess of the iron.

18.2 When interferences are indicated, the iron shall be separated from the interfering substances (or at least critical concentrations of them) by precipitation with ammonium hydroxide, filtration and re-solution in hydrochloric acid, before making the colorimetric determination.

19. Apparatus

19.1 *Photometer* — Filter photometer suitable for measurements at a wavelength of 510 mμ (Note 5).

20. Reagents

20.1 *Aluminum Nitrate Solution (222 g per liter)*—Dissolve 222 g of aluminum nitrate ($Al(NO_3)_3 \cdot 9H_2O$) in water and dilute to 1 liter with water.

20.2 *Ammonium Acetate Solution (100 g per liter)*—Dissolve 100 g of ammonium acetate ($NH_4C_2H_3O_2$) in 100 ml of water. Add 200 ml of glacial acetic acid ($CH_3 \cdot COOH$), dilute to 1 liter with water, and mix.

20.3 *Ammonium Hydroxide (1:1)*—Mix 1 volume of ammonium hydroxide (NH_4OH, sp gr 0.90) with 1 volume of water.

20.4 *Hydrochloric Acid (1:1)*—Mix 1 volume of hydrochloric acid (HCl, sp gr 1.19) with 1 volume of water.

20.5 *Hydroxylamine Hydrochloride Solution (100 g/liter)*—Dissolve 100 g of hydroxylamine hydrochloride ($NH_2OH \cdot HCl$) in water and dilute to 1 liter with water.

20.6 *Iron, Standard Solution (1 ml = 0.1 mg Fe)*—Dissolve 0.1000 g of clean electrolytic iron wire in 15 ml of H_2SO_4 (1:4) and dilute to 1 liter in a volumetric flask with water.

20.7 *Ortho-phenanthroline (10 g per liter)*—Dissolve 10 g of 1,10-phenanthroline monohydrate in 200 ml of denatured alcohol conforming to Formula No. 30 of the U.S. Bureau of Internal Revenue, and dilute to 1 liter with water.

20.8 *Sulfuric Acid (1:4)*—Carefully mix 1 volume of sulfuric acid (H_2SO_4, sp gr 1.84) with 4 volumes of water.

21. Photometer Calibration

21.1 Prepare a series of standards containing 0, 5, 10, 15, 20 and 25 ml of standard iron solution in 100-ml volumetric flasks. Dilute each to approximately 50 ml with water, treat as described in 22.3 to 22.6, and dilute to 100 ml with water. Measure the transmittance of each standard using the portion containing no added iron as a blank.

21.2 For photometer comparisons, prepare a calibration curve by plotting the transmittance values observed against milligrams of iron (Note 6).

NOTE 6—Cell depth must be 1 cm or less, otherwise the sample aliquot must be additionally diluted with water before the test portion is removed.

22. Procedure

22.1 Prepare the laboratory sample, obtained in accordance with 6.6.3, and use the mixed sulfuric acid method, 8.4, to obtain the solution for analysis.

22.2 Transfer 5 ml of the solubilized sample into a 100-ml volumetric flask and dilute to approximately 50 ml with water.

22.3 Add the following reagents in order, mixing thoroughly after each addition: 4 ml of hydroxylamine hydrochloride, 5 ml of aluminum nitrate, and 10 ml of *ortho*-phenanthroline.

22.4 Add NH_4OH dropwise with thorough agitation after each addition until a slight turbidity persists throughout the solution; avoid an excess. Add HCl dropwise until the turbidity just disappears; again avoid an excess.

22.5 Add 5 ml of ammonium acetate solution, dilute to 100 ml with water, and mix well.

22.6 After 5 min measure the light transmittance of the treated sample using an untreated water blank (Note 7) and determine the iron content of the sample aliquot from the photometer calibration curve.

NOTE 7—The iron content of the reagents is normally well below 0.01 mg and, therefore, not significant in most instances. Each set of reagents should be certified, however. Furthermore, when the amount of iron being measured is very low, a reagent correction can be applied by using a treated blank for maximum accuracy.

23. Calculations

23.1 Calculate the iron, as Fe_2O_3, in the sample as follows:

$$\text{Iron, as Fe}_2\text{O}_3\text{, per cent} = \frac{A}{B} \times \frac{C}{D} \times 143$$

where:
A = weight of iron determined, mg
B = weight of sample, mg
C = volume of sample, ml, and
D = aliquot used, ml.

24. Precision

24.1 To show repeatability the following results were obtained in some replicate testing of random samples in two laboratories:

Number of Replicates	Average Result, per cent	Range of Results, per cent Fe₂O₃
10.........	20.74	20.2 to 21.3
5.........	28.14	28.0 to 28.3
5.........	28.25	28.0 to 28.3
5.........	34.0	34.0 to 34.0
5.........	34.24	34.0 to 34.6
5.........	49.34	49.2 to 49.6
5.........	49.4	49.2 to 49.8

Determination of Silica

25. Summary of Method

25.1 Silica is dissolved from the analytical sample of the deposit by molten sodium hydroxide and the extracted silica is determined colorimetrically. The recommended molybdate-blue method is adapted from ASTM Methods D 859, Test for Silica in Industrial Water and Industrial Waste Water; one of the more elaborate procedures in Method D 859 may be used if more convenient.

26. Interferences

26.1 The dissolution process and the method chosen to evaluate silica are essentially free from interference (assuming that the solution is not turbid or colored); other procedures for silica may be more sensitive to other constituents in the deposit.

27. Apparatus

27.1 *Photometer*—A filter photometer suitable for measurements at a wavelength of 815 mμ (acceptable absorbance measurements can be made in the range of 615 to 815 mμ) (Note 5).

28. Reagents (Note 8)

Note 8—Store all reagents to be used in this method in polyethylene or other suitable plastic bottles.

28.1 *Ammonium Molybdate Solution (100 g/liter)*—Dissolve 10 g of ammonium molybdate $((NH_4)_6Mo_7O_{24} \cdot 4H_2O)$ in water and dilute to 100 ml.

28.2 *Hydrochloric Acid (1:49)*—Mix 2 volumes of concentrated hydrochloric acid (HCl, sp gr 1.19) with 98 volumes of water.

28.3 *Silica, Standard Solution (1 ml = 1 mg SiO₂)*—Dissolve 4.732 g of sodium metasilicate $(Na_2SiO_3 \cdot 9H_2O)$ in water and dilute to 1 liter.

28.4 *Sodium Sulfite Solution (170 g/liter)*—Dissolve 170 g of sodium sulfite (Na_2SO_3) in water and dilute to 1 liter.

29. Calibration

29.1 *Silica Standard*—One milliliter of standard silica solution (1 ml = 1 mg of SiO₂) diluted to 1 liter with water results in a solution of 1 ppm SiO₂ concentration. Prepare a series of standards so that the concentrations of SiO₂ will bracket the anticipated concentration of SiO₂ in the sample.

29.2 *Calibration Curve*—Develop color in the selected series of silica standards by applying the procedure detailed in 30. Procedure using 10-ml aliquots. Simultaneously treat the same volume of water in the same manner (water blank). Zero the photometer with the water blank, then determine the absorbances of the silica standards (at 815 mμ or between 615 mμ and 815 mμ) in accordance with the operating directions provided by the instrument manufacturer. Prepare a graph, plotting absorbance against milligrams of SiO_2, and note the temperature of the solutions used to prepare it. Also, note on this graph the length of light path through the sample, the wavelength or filter designation, and the slit width (if appropriate) that were used when the calibration curve was prepared.

30. Procedure

30.1 Prepare the laboratory sample, obtained in accordance with 6.6.3, and use the alkali fusion method described in 8.5 to obtain the solution for analysis.

30.2 Take 10 ml of the solution prepared in accordance with 30.1 and add, with thorough mixing, 5 ml of HCl (1:49) and 5 ml of ammonium molybdate solution. Allow to stand 1 min; then add 10 ml of Na_2SO_3 solution and mix. Allow this mixture to stand for 5 min. Make sure that its temperature is within 3 C of the value recorded on the calibration curve, zero the photometer with the water blank described in 29.2 and determine the absorbance of the colored solution with the photometer.

30.3 A quick approximation can be obtained by matching the color produced from the solution prepared in accordance with 30.1 directly with colors produced from the standards as described in 29.2.

31. Calculation

31.1 Use the absorbance value to read the silica concentration in parts per million from the calibration curve. Divide by the weight of the material fused with the sodium hydroxide and multiply by 100. The result is the percentage of SiO_2 in the prepared sample.

32. Precision

32.1 To show repeatability the following results were obtained in replicate testing of random samples by an operator who used a referee colorimetric procedure as described in Methods D 859 (the single-operator precision of the referee procedure is reported in parts per billion, and that of the procedure in this method is reported to be 4 per cent of the measured value):

Number of Replicates	Average Result, per cent SiO_2	Range of Results, per cent SiO_2
4...........	1.35	1.3 to 1.4
4...........	14.0	14.0 to 14.0
4...........	27.8	27.5 to 28.0

Tentative Method for

ANALYSIS OF WATER-FORMED DEPOSITS BY X-RAY FLUORESCENCE[1]

ASTM Designation: D 2332 – 65 T

ISSUED, 1965

This Tentative Method has been approved by the sponsoring committee and accepted by the Society in accordance with established procedures, for use pending adoption as standard. Suggestions for revisions should be addressed to the Society at 1916 Race St., Philadelphia, Pa. 19103.

1. Scope

1.1 This method provides for X-ray spectrochemical analysis of water-formed deposits.

1.2 The method is applicable to the determination of elements of atomic number 11 or higher that are present in significant quantity in the sample (usually above 0.1 per cent).

2. Summary of Method

2.1 The sample or its fusion with a suitable flux is powdered and the powder is compacted (mounted). The mount is then irradiated by an X-ray beam of short wavelength (high energy). The characteristic X-rays of the atom that are emitted or fluoresced upon absorption of the primary or incident X-rays are dispersed, and intensities at selected wavelengths are measured by sensitive detectors. Detector output is related to concentration by calibration curves or charts.

2.2 The K spectral lines are used for elements of atomic numbers 11 to 50. Whether the K or L lines are used for the elements numbered 51 or higher depends on the available instrumentation.

3. Definitions

3.1 The term "water-formed deposits" in this method as defined in accordance with ASTM Definitions D 1129, Terms Relating to Industrial Water and Industrial Waste Water[2] follows:

Water-Formed Deposits—Any accumulation of insoluble material derived from water or formed by the reaction of water upon surfaces in contact with water.

NOTE—Deposits formed from or by water in all its phases may be further classified as scale, sludge, corrosion products, or biological deposits. The over-all composition of a deposit or some part of a deposit may be determined by chemical or spectrographic analysis; the constituents actually present as chemical substances may be identified by microscope

[1] Under the standardization procedure of the Society, this method is under the jurisdiction of the ASTM Committee D-19 on Industrial Water. A list of members may be found in the ASTM Year Book.

[2] Appears in this publication.

or X-ray diffraction studies. Organisms may be identified by microscopic or biological methods.

3.2 For definitions of other terms used in this method refer to Definitions D 1129.

4. Apparatus

4.1 *Sample Preparation Equipment:*

4.1.1 *Fusion Crucibles,* prepared from 1-in. (25-mm) commercial-grade graphite rods. The dimensions shall be $1\frac{1}{8}$ in. (29 mm) high, an inside diameter of $\frac{3}{4}$ in. (19 mm), and a cavity $\frac{7}{8}$ in. (22 mm) deep.

4.1.2 *Pulverizers,* including an agate or mullite mortar and pestle, minimum capacity 25 ml.

4.1.3 *Sieves*—No. 100 (149-μ) and No. 270 (53-μ) as specified in ASTM Specifications E 11, for Sieves for Testing Purposes.[3]

4.1.4 *Compactors*—A press, equipped with a gage enabling reproducible pressure, is recommended.

4.2 *Excitation Source (X-ray Tube):*

4.2.1 *Stable Electrical Power Supply* (± 1 *per cent*).

4.2.2 Source of high-intensity, short-wavelength X-rays.

4.3 *Sample Housing (Turret).*

4.4 *Spectrometer*—Best resolution of the spectrometer and best sensitivity are not simultaneously attainable; a compromise is effected to give adequate values for each.

4.4.1 *Collimating System.*

4.4.2 *Spectrogoniometer.*

4.4.3 *Analyzing Crystal and Holder*—The choice of the analyzing crystal is made on the basis of what elements must be determined; for example, a gypsum or an ammonium dihydrogen phosphate crystal can be used for determining magnesium but lithium fluoride is much superior for copper and iron

(high-intensity diffracted secondary rays and consequently greater sensitivity and potential precision). A salt, NaCl, crystal is frequently employed for general use, being applicable over a broad range and producing intense lines and medium broadening.

4.4.4 *Counter-Tube Support.*

4.5 *Evacuating or Flushing System.*

4.6 *Measuring System:*

4.6.1 *Detector* (of which the principal types are the Geiger counter, scintillation counter, and flow-proportional counter).

4.6.2 *Amplifiers (Including Preamplifier), Rate Meter, Recorder, Scaler, and Printout.*

4.6.3 *Zeroing, Gain, and Sequence Controls.*

5. Reagents

5.1 *Purity of Reagents*—Reagent grade chemicals shall be used in all tests. Unless otherwise indicated, it is intended that all reagents shall conform to the specifications of the Committee on Analytical Reagents of the American Chemical Society, where such specifications are available.[4] Other grades may be used, provided it is first ascertained that the reagent is of sufficiently high purity to permit its use without lessening the accuracy of the determination.

5.2 *Purity of Water*—Unless otherwise indicated, references to water shall be understood to mean reagent water conforming to ASTM Specifications D 1193, for Reagent Water.[2]

5.3 *Detector Gas,* usual composition 90 per cent argon, 10 per cent methane

---

[3] *1967 Book of ASTM Standards,* Part 30.

[4] "Reagent Chemicals, American Chemical Society Specifications," Am. Chemical Soc., Washington, D. C. For suggestions on the testing of reagents not listed by the American Chemical Society, see "Reagent Chemicals and Standards," by Joseph Rosin, D. Van Nostrand Co., Inc., New York, N. Y., and the "United States Pharmacopeia."

(other compositions are used); usually used with flow-proportional counter for lines of longer wavelength (2 A or greater).

5.4 *Gallium Oxide*, spectrographic grade (frequently used as a convenient internal standard).

5.5 *Helium Gas*, commercial grade, for the spectrometer flushing system, when vacuum or air paths are not used.

5.6 *Sodium and Lithium Borates* ($Na_2B_4O_7$ and $Li_2B_4O_7$), commonly used as fluxes for the sample.

sample) to present a reproducible surface composition to the X-ray beam.

Note 1—At least semiquantitative results can be obtained more quickly by compacting (mounting) the test portion (7.3 and 7.4) and proceeding in accordance with 8, 9, and 10. The decrease in sample preparation will actually result in improved accuracy in some instances.

7.3 Grind not more than 10 g of the material prepared for X-ray (sample or fusion) to pass a No. 270 (53-μ sieve).

7.4 Make duplicate wafers (or suitable mounts for the particular equipment that

TABLE 1—EMISSION SPECTRA AND RECOMMENDED CRYSTALS.

Element	Recommended Crystal[a]	Wavelength[b]
Aluminum	Gypsum	8.320
Calcium	Lithium fluoride	3.353
Copper	Lithium fluoride	1.539
Iron	Lithium fluoride	1.934
Lead	Lithium fluoride	1.1726[b]
Magnesium	Gypsum	9.869
Phosphorus	Pentaerythritol tetraacetate	6.142
Potassium	Lithium fluoride	3.735
Silicon	Pentaerythritol tetraacetate	7.111
Sodium	Potassium acid phthalate	11.885
Sulfur	Pentaerythritol tetraacetate	5.362
Zinc	Lithium fluoride	1.434

[a] Updated to June, 1964; a production instrument, equipped with mounted crystals, might conveniently use lithium fluoride, pentaerythritol tetraacetate, and potassium acid phthalate.

[b] Emission wavelengths in kX units (1 kX unit = 1.002 A); the wavelength for lead is the L alpha-1 line and the others are averages of the K alpha-1 and -2 lines.

6. Sampling

6.1 Collect the sample in accordance with ASTM Method D 887, Field Sampling of Water-Formed Deposits.[2]

7. Preparation of Sample

7.1 Reduce the entire sample of deposits to about 100 g (drying, degreasing, and crushing if necessary) and grind this subsample to a powder that will pass a No. 100 (149-μ) sieve.

7.2 Mix the powdered sample thoroughly and remove about 10 g for X-ray fluorescence testing (Note 1). Fuse a weighed amount with a weighed amount of a suitable flux (2 to 10 g of flux/g of

will be used) by compacting the powdered sample (precision and accuracy are improved by briquetting). An internal standard is frequently added by fusion to the material to be compacted. Some samples may require a binder (generally organic and added in minimum concentration) for reproducible packing and a smooth surface.

8. Preparation of Apparatus

8.1 Follow the manufacturer's instructions for the initial assembly, conditioning, and preparation of the fluorescent X-ray apparatus.

8.2 Follow the manufacturer's instructions with respect to control settings.

9. Excitation and Exposure

9.1 Position the mounted sample in the special chamber provided for this purpose; avoid touching or otherwise contaminating the sample surface. Produce and record the spectrum at the setting or settings recommended for the instrument. Prepare and analyze duplicate mounts for all samples (make duplicate readings on each mount).

9.2 *Radiation Measurements*—Make radiation measurements for each component of concern using Table 1 as a guide to the frequencies of interest (Note 2).

Note 2—See also Bureau of Mines Information Circular No. 7725, which lists the 2-theta values for characteristic spectral lines when using the analyzing crystals NaCl, LiF, and quartz.

10. Calibration and Standardization

10.1 Semiquantitative evaluations of the concentration of each component may be obtained directly by reference to standardization curves prepared from data obtained by exposing samples containing known quantities of these components.

10.2 More accurate evaluations can be made by preparing special standards containing the same components as the sample in the ratios indicated by the semiquantitative determinations. These special standards can frequently be used to calculate correction factors for the calibration curves to minimize interference effects of the other components of the sample.

10.3 Internal standards may be used to provide direct comparison.

11. Calculations

11.1 Average the results obtained for each component from at least two exposures of each mounted sample. Use these averaged values to read concentrations from prepared calibration curves, charts, or tables.

12. Precision

12.1 *Precision Of Instrument*—The precision of the instrument shall be determined from replicate measurements (10 to 20) on a single prepared sample without moving the sample. This precision shall be reported as the standard deviation of the instrument and is obtained as the usual square root of the summated deviations squared divided by 1 less than the number of replicate measurements.

12.2 *Precision Of Method*—Calculate the standard deviation of the method from duplicate measurements on 10 to 20 samples over at least 3 days, removing and resetting the sample before each new series of measurements. The standard deviation of the method is the square root of the summated deviations squared divided by 4 times the number of analyses.

12.3 Method precision should not differ from instrument precision by more than twice the instrument precision.

12.4 Coefficient of variation of the method is obtained by multiplying the standard deviation by 100 and dividing by the average concentration in per cent.

Tentative Method of Test for

THORIUM IN INDUSTRIAL WATER AND INDUSTRIAL WASTE WATER[1]

ASTM Designation: D 2333 – 65 T

ISSUED, 1965

This Tentative Method has been approved by the sponsoring committee and accepted by the Society in accordance with established procedures, for use pending adoption as standard. Suggestions for revisions should be addressed to the Society at 1916 Race St., Philadelphia, Pa. 19103.

1. Scope

1.1 This method[2,3] covers a colorimetric determination of microgram amounts of thorium in industrial water and industrial waste water. It is sensitive to less than 1×10^{-9} g of thorium in 1 g of water.

1.2 If particulate matter is present in the samples,[4] it can be removed by filtration, treated separately by dissolution procedures, and prepared for the colorimetric method of determination. Interferences from organic compounds that complex thorium are minimized or eliminated by oxidation procedures employing nitric and perchloric acids.

2. Summary of Method

2.1 Particulate matter in the sample is separated by filtration, dissolved in strong oxidizing acids, and the resulting solutions combined with the filtrate. The thorium in the combined solution is co-precipitated with calcium in the form of oxalate salts. These salts are filtered, dissolved in hydrochloric acid, and the thorium determined spectrophotometrically by use of 1-(o-arsonophenylazo)-2-naphthol-3,6-disulfonic acid as the colorimetric reagent. The characteristic wavelength is 545 mμ.

3. Definitions

3.1 For definitions of terms used in this method, refer to ASTM Definitions D 1129, Terms Relating to Industrial Water and Industrial Waste Water.[5]

[1] Under the standardization procedure of the Society, this method is under the jurisdiction of the ASTM Committee D-19 on Industrial Water. A list of members may be found in the ASTM Year Book.

[2] P. F. Thomason, M. A. Perry, and W. M. Byerly, "Determination of Microgram Amounts of Thorium," *Analytical Chemistry*, Vol. 21, p. 1239 (1949).

[3] A. E. Taylor and R. T. Dillon, "Determination of Microgram Quantities of Thorium in Water," *Analytical Chemistry*, Vol. 24, p. 1624 (1952).

[4] Procedures for the analysis of particulate matter conform in part to procedures developed by Petrow, et al, for USAEC under contract AT(30-1)-2470, as given in "Final Report—Part I," Nov. 1, 1960.

[5] Appears in this publication.

4. Interferences

4.1 Among the cationic substances commonly present in appreciable amounts, ferric iron is the primary one which, in high concentrations, might adversely affect this method. Its effect can be minimized by adding hydroxylamine hydrochloride and boiling the test solution to reduce the iron to the ferrous state.

4.2 Anions that complex thorium inhibit the formation of the color complex in the final test solution. Fluorides, oxalates, phosphates, and large amounts of sulfates must be absent or removed. Effects of fluorides can be minimized by adding an excess of aluminum ions and carrying the thorium with a precipitate of a few milligrams of aluminum hydroxide.

5. Apparatus

5.1 *Spectrophotometer*, suitable for measurement at a wavelength of 545 mμ. The photometer and photometric practice prescribed in this method shall conform to ASTM Recommended Practice E 60, for Photometric Methods for Chemical Analysis of Metals,[6] and ASTM Recommended Practice E 275, Describing and Measuring Performance of Spectrophotometers.[7]

5.2 *Filtering Crucible.*

5.3 *Electric Muffle Furnace.*

5.4 *Gooch Filtering Funnels*, with outlets leading into 15 by 125-mm test tubes.

6. Reagents

6.1 *Purity of Reagents*—Reagent grade chemicals shall be used in all tests. Unless otherwise indicated, it is intended that all reagents shall conform to the specifications of the Committee on Analytical Reagents of the American Chemical Society, where such specifica-

tions are available.[8] Other grades may be used, provided it is first ascertained that the reagent is of sufficiently high purity to permit its use without lessening the accuracy of the determination.

6.2 *Purity of Water*—Unless otherwise indicated, references to water shall be understood to mean reagent water conforming to ASTM Specifications D 1193, for Reagent Water.[5] In addition, reagent water shall be thorium-free, and essentially free of fluoride, phosphate, oxalate, and sulfate ions.

6.3 *Aluminum Nitrate Solution (27 g Al/liter)*—Dissolve 375 g of aluminum nitrate ($Al(NO_3)_3 \cdot 9H_2O$) in water and dilute to 1 liter.

6.4. *Ammonium Hydroxide (sp gr 0.90)*—Concentrated ammonium hydroxide (NH_4OH).

6.5 *Ammonium Oxalate Solution* (($NH_4)_2C_2O_4 \cdot H_2O$), saturated.

6.6 *Calcium Carbonate* ($CaCO_3$), solid.

6.7 *Hydrochloric Acid (sp gr 1.19)*—Concentrated hydrochloric acid (HCl).

6.8 *Hydrochloric Acid (1:1)*—Mix 1 volume of concentrated HCl (sp gr 1.19) with 1 volume of water.

6.9 *Hydrofluoric Acid (48 to 51 per cent)*—Concentrated hydrofluoric acid (HF).

6.10 *Hydroxylamine Hydrochloride Solution (100 g/liter)*—Dissolve 10 g of hydroxylamine hydrochloride ($NH_2OH \cdot HCl$) in water and dilute to 100 ml.

6.11 *Nitric Acid (sp gr 1.42)*—Concentrated nitric acid (HNO_3).

6.12 *Perchloric Acid (70 per cent)*—Concentrated perchloric acid ($HClO_4$).

6.13 *Thorin Solution (2 g/liter)*—Dissolve 2 g of Thorin (disodium salt of

---

[6] *1967 Book of ASTM Standards*, Part 32.
[7] *1967 Book of ASTM Standards*, Part 30.

[8] "Reagent Chemicals, American Chemical Society Specifications," Am. Chemical Soc., Washington, D.C. For suggestions on the testing of reagents not listed by the American Chemical Society, see "Reagent Chemicals and Standards" by Joseph Rosin, D. Van Nostrand Co. Inc., New York, N. Y., and the "United States Pharmacopeia."

1-(*o*-arsonophenylazo)-2-naphthol-3, 6-disulfonic acid, molecular weight 576.3) in water and dilute to 1 liter.

6.14 *Thorium, Standard Solution (approximately 1.0 g Th/liter)*—Dissolve 2.4 g of thorium nitrate tetrahydrate (Th·(NO₃)₄·4H₂O) in water and dilute to 1 liter. Standardize by gravimetric determinations employing thorium oxalate precipitation and ignition to thorium oxide.

6.15 *Thorium, Standard Solution (0.01 g Th/liter)*—Prepare by dilution of the standardized solution containing approximately 1.0 g Th/liter.

7. Sampling

7.1 Collect the sample in accordance with the applicable methods of the American Society for Testing and Materials, as follows:

D 510—Sampling Industrial Water,[5]
D 860—Sampling Boiler Water from Boilers,[5] and
D 1496—Sampling Homogeneous Industrial Waste Water.[5]

7.2 Sample 6 liters, or other suitable volume, depending on the expected thorium concentration.

8. Calibration and Standardization

8.1 A standard calibration curve for the spectrophotometer shall be obtained by measuring samples containing known amounts of thorium. Comparisons shall be made by measuring the spectral absorption of an acid solution of the organic colorimetric reagent without thorium present, and of similar acid solutions containing thorium and the reagent. Employing a 1-cm cell, the absorbance has been found to be about 14.853 μg thorium/ml/absorbancy unit.

9. Procedure

9.1 Filter four 1.5-liter samples of the water, using a close-texture, retentive filter paper. If significant amounts of

solids are present, obtain weights and proceed in accordance with 9.2. If no solids are present, proceed in accordance with 9.7.

9.2 Choose the two solids-laden filter papers most closely approximating the average weight and employ each as described in 9.3 through 9.6. Label and save the two corresponding filtrates.

9.3 Place the filter paper in a platinum dish, add 10 ml of HNO₃ (sp gr 1.42) and heat gently until the paper is dissolved and reaction with the HNO₃ has ceased. If necessary, add more HNO₃ to completely dissolve the paper.

9.4 Cool, add 5 ml of HNO₃ , 0.01 ml of the HF solution, and 3 ml of the HClO₄ solution (Note 1). Heat until dense fumes of HClO₄ are driven off, then continue heating until most of the HClO₄ has been volatilized.

NOTE 1: **Caution**—Warm HClO₄ solutions react explosively with organic matter such as oil, paper, starch, wood, etc., the explosive force being directly proportional to the exposed surface area of the organic matter. The presence of HNO₃ prevents this spontaneous reaction and is positive insurance against explosion during evaporations of water samples with HClO₄ , even if they contain organic matter. The preboil with HNO₃ will remove most organic matter; however, if the original samples contain large quantities of organic matter, such as oil films, chunks of wood, or coal dust, the organic matter should be removed by a suitable method before analysis.[9]

9.5 Cool, add 1 ml of concentrated HCl (sp gr 1.19), 5 ml of water, and warm. Filter, wash with 5 ml of water and discard any solids which do not dissolve.

9.6. Transfer the solution containing the dissolved solids, with water washes, from the filter flask to the 1.5-liter volume of the corresponding filtrate.

9.7 Add 10 μg of thorium (approxi-

[9] Precautions for the use of perchloric acid are available in "Chemical Safety Data Sheet SD-11," published by the Manufacturing Chemists' Association of the United States.

mately 1 ml of the standardized thorium nitrate solution) to one sample of the solids-free filtrates (9.1) and also to one sample of the filtrates now containing the dissolved solids (9.6). Add 1 ml of concentrated HCl (sp gr 1.19) and 1 ml of the $Al(NO_3)_3$ solution to each of the four samples.

9.8 Heat to boiling and add 20 ml of hot saturated ammonium oxalate solution. Add NH_4OH (sp gr 0.90) until the solution is about pH 4, or just alkaline to methyl orange. Continue boiling for 1 min and allow to stand at least 20 min, or until the precipitate of calcium oxalate and thorium oxalate has settled.

9.9 Filter, using a filtering crucible. Heat crucibles in an electric muffle furnace at 500 to 635 C to convert the oxalates to carbonates. Weigh the crucibles and contents.

9.10 Place the crucibles in Gooch filtering funnels with the outlets leading into 15 by 125-mm test tubes with graduation marks at volumes of 6 and 10 ml. Add from a pipet 1 ml of concentrated HCl (sp gr 1.19) to each, allowing the acid to run down the sides of the crucibles. Turn on gentle suction and wash each crucible with a fine stream of water until the volume in the test tube is nearly 6 ml. Dry and weigh the crucibles.

9.11 Remove the test tubes from the filtering funnels, add 2 ml of the hydroxylamine hydrochloride solution to each, and boil for 1 min. Add five drops of concentrated HCl (sp gr 1.19), 0.5 ml of the Thorin solution, and dilute with water to 10 ml.

9.12 Prepare a reference solution for use in the spectrophotometer by suspending in 10 ml of water an amount of calcium carbonate equivalent to twice the average weight of calcium carbonate found in the above four samples. Add HCl solution (1:1) dropwise until 10 drops in excess of the amount needed to dissolve the carbonate are present. The

pH should be slightly less than 1.0. Add 4 ml of the hydroxylamine hydrochloride solution, 1 ml of the Thorin solution, and dilute with water to 20 ml.

9.13 Compare in the spectrophotometer the absorbancy of each of the four samples, two of which have 10 μg of added thorium, against the reference solution. Establish cell corrections by comparing the reference solution in different cells. Determine the amount of thorium present by the relative absorbancy of the "thorium-spiked" samples with the plain samples when compared to the reference solution. (Check thorium content in unknowns by reference to the calibration curve as described in 8.1 to evaluate possible effects of unsuspected interferences.)

10. Calculations

10.1 Calculate the quantity of dissolved thorium, from evaluation of results for the two solids-free filtrates, in micrograms per liter, as follows:

$$\text{Thorium (dissolved)} = \frac{W}{S}$$

where:

W = micrograms of thorium found (in filtered samples) in accordance with 9.13, and

S = liters of original sample used.

10.2 Calculate total quantity of thorium, from evaluation of results for the two filtrates to which solution of filterable solids was added, in micrograms per liter, as follows:

$$\text{Thorium (total)} = \frac{W_t}{S}$$

where:

W_t = micrograms of total thorium (dissolved and particulate) found in accordance with 9.13, and

S = liters of original sample used.

10.3 Calculate the quantity of thorium in filtered solids, from evaluation of the results given in 10.1 and 10.2, in micrograms per liter, as follows:

Thorium (solids) = Thorium (total)
              − Thorium (dissolved)

11. Precision

11.1 The precision of this method[4] may be expressed as follows:

$$S_0 = 0.137$$

where S_0 = single operator precision, ppb of thorium.

Tentative Methods of Test for

RADIOACTIVE IODINE IN INDUSTRIAL WATER AND INDUSTRIAL WASTE WATER[1]

ASTM Designation: D 2334 – 65 T

Issued, 1965

These Tentative Methods have been approved by the sponsoring committee and accepted by the Society in accordance with established procedures, for use pending adoption as standard. Suggestions for revisions should be addressed to the Society at 1916 Race St., Philadelphia, Pa. 19103.

1. Scope

1.1 These methods cover the determination of radioactive iodine in industrial water and industrial waste water in concentrations greater than 100 pc/liter. Concentration of the sample can increase the sensitivity of the methods. The methods are given as follows:

	Sections
Method A (Heterogeneous Exchange)	7 to 13
Method B (Distillation)	14 to 20
Method C (Extraction)	21 to 27

1.2 These methods may be used either for absolute measurements by calibrating the nuclear radiation detector with a standard iodine radioisotope of the same atomic mass, or for relative measurements by comparing measurements with each other. The methods are limited by choice of radiation detector and length of analysis to the determination of iodine isotopes of mass 129, 131, 132, 133, 134, and 135 which are fission products. The decay characteristics of the radioiodine isotopes are shown in Appendix A1. The isotopes of mass 124, 125, 126, and 130 which are not fission products will interfere if present, but are rarely encountered.

2. Definitions

2.1 For definitions of terms used in these methods refer to ASTM Definitions D 1129, Terms Relating to Industrial Water and Industrial Waste Water.[2]

3. Counting Instruments and Counting

3.1 *Beta Particle Counter*, usually a proportional or Geiger-Müller detector, connected to appropriate amplifier, pulse-height discriminator, scaler, and register. Refer to ASTM Method D 1890, Measurement of Beta Particle Radioactivity of Industrial Water and Industrial Waste Water.[2]

3.2 *Gamma Counter*, preferably a NaI scintillation detector assembly connected

---

[1] Under the standardization procedure of the Society, these methods are under the jurisdiction of tion the ASTM Committee D-19 on Industrial Water. A list of members may be found in the ASTM Year Book.

[2] Appears in this publication.

to the appropriate amplifier and pulse-height analyzer, or discriminator. Refer to ASTM Method D 1690, Measurement of Gamma Radioactivity of Industrial Water and Industrial Waste Water.[2] Typical gamma-ray spectra are shown in reports by Heath[3] and Crouthamel.[4]

3.3 *Gamma Spectrometer*, preferably multichannel.

3.4 The counting techniques are common to all three methods. The silver iodide precipitate may be counted with a beta particle or gamma detector. A gamma spectrometer is preferred when isotopic identifications are necessary and is required when making absolute measurements when more than one iodine isotope is present. For Methods B and C, the carbon tetrachloride or aqueous solution of the purified iodine isotopes may be counted directly with the gamma counter or spectrometer. Yield determinations can then be made after counting. Corrections are made for counter dead time, background count, and radioactive decay from sampling time. For absolute counting, the observed count rate is divided by the detector efficiency for the isotope concerned. The isotope may be distinguished by the characteristics listed in Appendix A1. Note that I^{132} has a relatively long-lived precursor, 77-hr Te^{132}, and correction should be made after analyzing the sample for Te^{132}. After more than two days decay it could be assumed that all I^{132} in the sample arises from contained Te^{132}.

3.5 The following information is useful in determining the iodine isotopes by gamma spectrometry:

I^{131}—Allow I^{132}, I^{134}, and I^{135} to decay and measure the 0.36 Mev gamma ray.

I^{132}—It is impractical to measure this isotope in equilibrium with other fission product iodine isotopes because of interference from the gamma ray spectra of I^{134} and I^{135}. In the absence of these isotopes measure the 0.67 or 0.78 Mev gamma rays.

I^{133}—After the decay of I^{132} and I^{135}, measure the 0.53 Mev gamma ray.

I^{134}—An approximate analysis can be made by measuring the 0.86 Mev photopeak. The measurement must be made as soon as possible after sampling to minimize interference from I^{132}, I^{133}, and I^{135} gamma rays.

I^{135}—The combined 1.72 to 1.80 Mev photopeak is measured. Interference from I^{132} and I^{134} is minimized by allowing the sample to decay for 6 to 10 hr prior to the measurement.

4. Purity of Reagents

4.1 Reagent grade chemicals shall be used in all tests. Unless otherwise indicated, it is intended that all reagents shall conform to the specifications of the Committee on Analytical Reagents of the American Chemical Society, where such specifications are available.[5] Other grades may be used, provided it is first ascertained that the reagent is of sufficiently high purity to permit its use without lessening the accuracy of the determination.

4.2 Unless otherwise indicated, references to water shall be understood to mean reagent water conforming to ASTM Specifications D 1193, for Reagent Water.[2]

4.3 Radioactive purity shall be such that the measured radioactivity of blank

[3] R. L. Heath, "Scintillation Spectrometry, Gamma Ray Spectrum Catalog," IDO-16408.
[4] C. E. Crouthamel, "Applied Gamma-Ray Spectrometry," Pergamon Press, New York, N.Y. (1960).

[5] "Reagent Chemicals, American Chemical Society Specifications " Am. Chemical Soc., Washington, D.C. For suggestions on the testing of reagents not listed by the American Chemical Society, see "Reagent Chemicals and Standards," by Joseph Rosin, D. Van Nostrand Co., Inc., New York, N. Y., and the "United States Pharmacopeia."

samples does not exceed the calculated probable error of the measurement.

5. Calibration and Standardization

5.1 For absolute counting, the instrument used must be calibrated to obtain the counting efficiency for each iodine isotope present in the sample. Absolute beta counting cannot be accomplished satisfactorily with more than one isotope present. The physiological importance of I^{131} dictates the use of a certified standard for instrument calibration when sample analyses are related to determining environmental hazards. For other cases, radioactive iodine solutions may be standardized by measuring the disintegration rate by 4π beta counting, beta-gamma coincidence counting, or with a calibrated gamma scintillation spectrometer. In the absence of the appropriate standard (other than I^{131}), the detector may be calibrated with other standards of known decay schemes and purity that emit beta particles or gamma rays of similar energy.

5.2 Certified calibrated standard solutions of I^{131} are available at certain times from several vendors. The remaining isotopes of iodine have relatively short half-lives which preclude their availability from a commercial supplier. In addition, the method of formation of those isotopes is from fission, and even with carefully controlled irradiation and decay periods it is not possible to make one of the shorter-lived isotopes free of contamination by significant fractions of the others. Approximate calibration methods must be used. Multichannel gamma spectrometry affords the best resolution into individual isotopes since the relationship of gamma photopeak efficiency to the NaI crystal detector dimensions is known, and gamma energy, as well as half-life can be used for resolution. The major uncertainty of this method is in the decay schemes of the short half-lived radioisotopes since the gamma photopeak disintegration rate relative to the total disintegration rate must be known.

5.3 Successive gamma spectra may be prepared at appropriate intervals and subtracted from each' other using the multichannel analyzer. This method shows the spectrum components lost during the decay and corrects for detector background providing a good approximation to the activity due to the individual iodine isotopes.

5.4 For Methods B and C, the potassium iodide carrier solution is standardized so the chemical yield may be calculated from the weight of the final precipitate. To standardize, pipet 2 ml of the carrier solution into 50 ml of water in a 250-ml beaker. Add 10 ml of silver nitrate ($AgNO_3$) in nitric acid solution (HNO_3 , 1:1) and heat to coagulate the silver iodide (AgI) precipitate. Quantitatively transfer the precipitate to a 100-ml glass centrifuge cone and ensure complete transfer by rinsing the beaker with water. Add 2 or 3 drops of aerosol solution, centrifuge, and discard the supernate. Wash the precipitate with 75 ml of water, add 2 to 3 drops of aerosol, centrifuge, and discard the supernate. Repeat the wash step and then transfer the precipitate to a tared counting dish. Dry under an infrared heat lamp, allow to cool, and weigh as AgI (gravimetric factor = 1.85).

6. Sampling

6.1 Collect the sample in accordance with the applicable methods of the American Society for Testing and Materials as follows:

D 510—Sampling Industrial Water[2] (Particularly Sections 32 to 41),
D 860—Sampling Water from Boilers,[2] and
D 1496—Sampling Homogeneous Industrial Waste Water.[2]

6.2 Sample 1 liter or other suitable

volume depending on the expected iodine concentration. The minimum activity measurable will be the lowest count rate that will result in the desired precision for the determination which will be limited by the counter background and efficiency. The maximum count rate of the aliquot analyzed should not exceed 10^4 counts/min (cpm) for Geiger-Müller counters and 10^5 cpm for proportional counters. For gamma counting, the total activity should be between 10^4 and 10^6 cpm.

METHOD A

(Heterogeneous Exchange)

7. Application

7.1 This method[6] can be used to determine all concentrations above 100 pc/liter in the absence of intolerable interferences. It is particularly useful for rapid analyses of samples since the determination of chemical yield is eliminated.

8. Summary of Method

8.1 This method is based on separation of other activities by cation exchange followed by heterogeneous isotopic exchange of iodide with silver iodide. In order to assure chemical interchange between the several oxidation states of iodine, a complete oxidation reduction cycle is made. Oxidation to periodate is accomplished with alkaline hypochlorite and reduction to iodide with bisulfite in an acid medium.

8.2 The iodine as iodide passes through the cation exchange column and ex-

changes isotopically with preformed silver iodide according to the reaction:

$$\overset{*}{I^-} + AgI \rightleftharpoons A\overset{*}{g}I + I^-$$

No yield determination is required if the sample is known to be free of macro amounts of stable iodine. The recovery is greater than 97 per cent, under this condition.

8.3 The silver iodide precipitate is mounted and counted with a beta particle detector or a gamma detector. A gamma spectrometer is preferred where isotopic identifications are necessary.

9. Interferences

9.1 Stable iodine in the sample would interfere by participating in the exchange reaction and 1 mg of iodine would produce a bias of about minus 5 per cent. Silver isotopes are the only known cation interferences. Silver is removed by absorption on the cation column, but retention may be incomplete. The fission yields of the silver isotopes are very small compared to the iodine yields; however, large amounts of neutron-activated silver ($Ag^{110}M$) could interfere. Large amounts of complexing anions such as cyanide and thiosulfate could result in partial dissolution of the silver iodide, although they probably would be destroyed in the oxidation-reduction cycle.

10. Reagents and Materials

10.1 *Cation Exchange Resin*—Phenol-sulfonic type, 8 per cent crosslinked, 16 to 50 mesh. For high-level samples a smaller size resin of 50 to 100 mesh is suggested for increased surface area when using small columns.

10.2 *Hydrochloric Acid (sp gr 1.19)*—Concentrated hydrochloric acid (HCl).

10.3 *Hydrochloric Acid (1:9)*—Mix 1 volume of concentrated HCl (HCl sp gr 1.19) with 9 volumes of water.

---

[6] This method is based on a previously published method by W. J. Maeck and J. E. Rein, "Determination of Fission Product Iodine, Cation Exchange Purification and Heterogeneous Isotopic Exchange," *Analytical Chemistry*, Vol. 32, p. 1079. Typical gamma-ray spectra are shown in a report of Heath (see Footnote 4), and a publication by Crouthamel (see Footnote 5).

10.4 *Nitric Acid (1:9)*—Mix 1 volume of concentrated nitric acid (HNO_3, sp gr 1.42) with 9 volumes of water.

10.5 *Nitric Acid (1:159)*—Mix 1 volume of concentrated HNO_3 (sp gr 1.42) with 159 ml of water.

10.6 *Potassium Iodide Carrier Solution (8.3 g/liter)*—Dissolve 8.3 g of potassium iodide (KI) in 500 ml of water and dilute to 1 liter.

10.7 *Silica Gel*, 28 to 200 mesh.

10.8 *Silver Nitrate Solution (17 g/liter)*—Dissolve 17 g of silver nitrate ($AgNO_3$) in 500 ml of water and dilute to 1 liter.

10.9 *Sodium Bisulfite Solution (100 g/liter)*—Dissolve 100 g of sodium bisulfite ($NaHSO_3$) in 500 ml of water and dilute to 1 liter.

10.10 *Sodium Carbonate Solution (106 g/liter)*—Dissolve 106 g of sodium carbonate (Na_2CO_3) in 500 ml of water and dilute to 1 liter.

10.11 *Sodium Fluoride Solution (6.3 g/liter)*—Dissolve 6.3 g of sodium fluoride (NaF) in 500 ml of water and dilute to 1 liter.

10.12 *Sodium Hypochlorite (5.25 per cent)*—Commercial grade sodium hypochlorite (NaOCl), household bleach.

10.13 *Wash Solution (Hydrochloric Acid-Sodium Bisulfite)*—Dissolve 1 g of sodium bisulfite ($NaHSO_3$) in 100 ml of water containing 8.5 ml of concentrated HCl (sp gr 1.19), dilute to 1 liter, and mix thoroughly.

11. Procedure

11.1 *Column Preparation:*

11.1.1 Place several grams of the cation exchange resin in a solution of HCl (1:9) and use as a stock supply.

11.1.2 Prepare the column by adding resin to a tube of about 1-cm internal diameter and about 40 cm long with a plug of glass wool at the bottom. After the resin has settled to a volume of 20 ml, add a slurry of 1 ml of silica gel to the top of the column. Wash the column with 20 ml of concentrated HCl (sp gr 1.19) followed by water and finally 25 ml of the eluting solution. DO NOT ALLOW THE COLUMN TO RUN DRY. For high-level activity mixtures, prepare the column as above, except that a smaller mesh size resin to provide a column volume of about 5 ml shall be used.

11.2 *Sample Treatment:*

11.2.1 Transfer the sample to a beaker and make alkaline with Na_2CO_3 solution.

11.2.2 Add 25 ml of NaOCl (1 ml for high-level activity samples), cover with a watch glass, and boil for 5 to 10 min on a hot plate. A heat lamp should be used for the smaller volume high-level samples.

11.2.3 Acidify by adding concentrated HCl (sp gr 1.19) dropwise until the effervescence ceases.

11.2.4 Continue boiling until the evolution of chlorine ceases.

11.2.5 Add 5 ml (2 ml for high-level samples) of $NaHSO_3$ solution and allow to cool.

11.2.6 While the sample is cooling add 2 ml of KI solution and 4 ml of $AgNO_3$ solution to a 100-ml beaker containing 25 ml of HNO_3 (1:9).

11.2.7 Stir until the precipitate coagulates, allow it to settle, and decant the supernate.

11.2.8 Wash twice by decantation with 20-ml portions of HNO_3 (1:9).

11.2.9 Decant the final wash and add 10 ml of NaF solution. Small losses of the precipitate by decantation do not affect either accuracy or precision.

11.2.10 Place a tetrafluoroethylene or glass-coated stirring bar in the beaker and place the beaker on a magnetic stirrer directly under the column.

11.2.11 Transfer the cooled sample to the column, wash the beaker, and transfer the washings to the column. Allow the sample to run through the column into the beaker containing the preformed AgI and follow by running 20 to 30 ml of the wash solution through the column. Maintain constant stirring of the AgI during this step.

11.2.12 Continue stirring the AgI for 10 to 15 min.

11.2.13 Quantitatively filter the AgI onto a suitable filter disk, wash with a minimum amount of HNO_3 (1:159), and suck dry with vacuum.

11.2.14 Mount the filter and count.

12. Calculation

12.1 Calculate the concentration, D, of the iodine isotopes in curies per liter as follows:

$$D = \frac{C}{2.22 \times 10^{12}\, EVR}$$

where:

C = count rate, counts/min,
E = counter efficiency,
V = liters of sample used,
R = fractional chemical yield, and
2.22×10^{12} = conversion factor from disintegrations/min to curies.

12.2 Calculate the counter efficiency, E, for gamma ray spectrometry as follows:

$$E = A\xi$$

where:

A = fractional abundance of the gamma ray, gamma/disintegration, and
ξ = photopeak detection efficiency, counts/gamma ray.

12.3 Calculate decay corrections as follows:

$$A = A_0 e^{-0.693t/T}$$

where:

A = activity at time t,
A_0 = activity at time zero,
e = base of natural logarithms,
t = elapsed time in appropriate units, and

T = half-life of radioisotope in same units as t.

13. Precision

13.1 Single operator precision is 3 to 6 per cent where the random counting error is less than 1 per cent. Precision will decrease when more than one isotope is present in a single sample.

Method B

(Distillation)

14. Application

14.1 This method is applicable to industrial water and industrial waste water with radioiodine concentrations above 100 pc/liter. Concentration of the sample can increase the sensitivity and precision of the method for low-level samples. The method is useful when radioactive interference is encountered with other radioiodine procedures.

15. Summary of Method

15.1 This method is based on the separation of iodine from other activities by distillation of elemental iodine into cold carbon tetrachloride. To assure chemical interchange with the iodine carrier an oxidation-reduction cycle is made. The iodide is oxidized to iodate with permanganate, reduced to iodide with bisulfite, and distilled over as free iodine in the presence of nitrite.

15.2 After washing the carbon tetrachloride with nitric acid, the iodine is reduced with bisulfite and back-extracted into water. Acidified silver nitrate solution is added to precipitate silver iodide. The chemical recovery is used as a measure of radiochemical recovery. Added decontamination from bromine activation product is afforded by the permanganate oxidation step. During this step elemental chlorine and bromine formed are distilled from the reaction flask and swept up the fume hood. High-level radiobromine could be trapped by passing through a caustic solution, if desired.

15.3 The silver iodide precipitate is mounted for counting. Gamma counting of the purified iodine solution can be completed prior to precipitation of the silver iodide, which is then used for determination of the chemical yield.

16. Interferences

16.1 No difficulty has been experienced with interference when using this method. It is possible to conceive of instances of very low iodine concentration in the presence of extremely large amounts of other activation materials wherein the traces carried along physically could present a significant interference. In such a case, repetition of the distillation process or the extraction process prior to precipitation should effect adequate decontamination. It is possible that some species of radioiodine in the +7 valence state might not exchange with the carrier since it is not oxidized to that point. The problem has not been observed, but should be suspected if replicate analyses do not agree. Nonradioactive iodine present in the sample will interfere by causing an overestimation of chemical yield which must be corrected for.

17. Reagents

17.1 *Aerosol Solution (1:100)*—Add 1 ml of 25 per cent aerosol solution to 100 ml of water and mix.

17.2 *Carbon Tetrachloride*—Technical grade carbon tetrachloride (CCl_4).

17.3 *Collodion Solution (1:9)*—Dissolve 8 ml of collodion (USP) in a mixture of 48 ml of ethyl ether (anhydrous) and 24 ml of absolute ethanol.

17.4 *Methyl Orange Indicator (0.5 g/liter)*—Dissolve 0.05 g of methyl orange in water and dilute to 100 ml with water.

17.5 *Nitric Acid Solution (1:9)*—Mix 1 volume of concentrated nitric acid (HNO_3, sp gr 1.42) with 9 volumes of water.

17.6 *Potassium Iodide Carrier Solution (13.08 g/liter)*—Dissolve 13.08 g of potassium iodide (KI) in 500 ml of water and dilute to 1 liter. This solution will contain 10 g of I⁻/liter.

17.7 *Potassium Permanganate Solution (Saturated)*—Dissolve 65 g of potassium permanganate ($KMnO_4$) in 1 liter

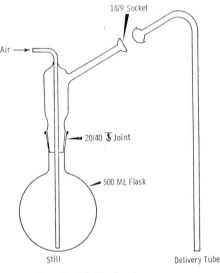

Fig. 1—Distillation Apparatus.

of warm water and let cool (solubility = 6.38 grams/100 ml at 20 C).

17.8 *Silver Nitrate Solution (17 g/liter)*—Dissolve 17 g of silver nitrate ($AgNO_3$) in 300 ml of water and dilute to 1 liter.

17.9 *Sodium Bisulfite Solution (100 g/liter)*—Dissolve 10 g of sodium bisulfite ($NaHSO_3$) in 75 ml of water and dilute to 100 ml. Prepare a new solution when needed, do not store for more than one week.

17.10 *Sodium Hydroxide Solution (200 g/liter)*—Dissolve 200 g of sodium hydroxide (NaOH) in 400 ml of water and dilute to 1 liter.

17.11 *Sodium Nitrite Solution (100 g/liter)*—Dissolve 10 g of sodium nitrite (NaNO₂) in water and dilute to 100 ml.

17.12 *Sulfuric Acid (sp gr 1.84)*—Concentrated sulfuric acid (H₂SO₄).

17.13 *Sulfuric Acid (1:9)*—Slowly, with stirring, add one volume of concentrated H₂SO₄ (sp gr 1.84) to 9 volumes of water.

18. Procedure

18.1 Take a sample aliquot which contains 0.1 to 10 μc of iodine but not to exceed 100 ml.

18.2 Pipet 2.0 ml of KI carrier in the 5 C ml distillation apparatus (Fig. 1). Add the sample, 2 drops of methyl orange indicator, and mix.

18.3 Adjust the pH to the end point with H₂SO₄ (1:9) or NaOH as required. (The color changes from yellow (basic) to red (acidic) or the reverse.)

18.4 Dilute the sample as required to about 70 ml. (Do not adjust the volume if it is already greater than 70 ml.)

18.5 Add 2 ml of concentrated H₂SO₄ (sp gr 1.84) for a 70-ml total volume or increase the amount to yield a final acid concentration of 1:35 for larger samples.

18.6 Add 3 ml of saturated KMnO₄. For volumes greater than 70 ml add 1 ml of saturated KMnO₄ for every 20 ml in the flask. A brown precipitate of manganese dioxide often forms at this step, but there should be sufficient permanganate to color the solution purple. If not, add permanganate solution until a permanent purple color remains.

18.7 Boil gently for 10 min. Cool to room temperature. (Bromine and chlorine are volatilized during boiling.)

18.8 Add NaHSO₃ solution dropwise while stirring until the purple color of permanganate and brown of iodine and manganese dioxide just disappear. Avoid an excess of bisulfite. Add the reagent as

rapidly as possible to avoid loss of iodine by volatilization.

18.9 Place 40 ml of CCl₄ in a 100-ml graduated cylinder. Place the cylinder in a 1-liter beaker used as an ice water bath and allow the CCl₄ to cool.

18.10 Place the top on the distilling apparatus and connect it to a delivery tube which has been placed in the CCl₄. Lubricate the ball socket joint with concentrated H₂SO₄ and clamp. Connect an air line to the inlet and adjust the flow rate to about 2 bubbles/sec.

18.11 Open the still and add about 2 ml of NaNO₂ solution. *Close the still immediately.*

18.12 Boil gently with a bunsen burner until all of the color in the still fades and then continue boiling for 1 min longer. Continue the air sparge for an additional 5 min.

18.13 Disconnect the delivery tube and rinse with water, catching the rinse in the CCl₄ trap.

18.14 Transfer the CCl₄ trap contents to a 250-ml separatory funnel. Drain the CCl₄ to a 250-ml beaker and discard the upper aqueous phase. Transfer the CCl₄ back into the separatory funnel, rinsing the beaker with 50 ml of HNO₃ (1:9). Shake and let the phases separate.

18.15 Drain the CCl₄ back into the 250-ml beaker and discard the upper aqueous phase.

18.16 Transfer the CCl₄ back into the separatory funnel. Rinse the beaker with 50 ml of water and add to the separatory funnel. Add 3 to 5 drops of fresh NaHSO₃ as needed and shake until all color is gone from the organic phase.

18.17 Discard the CCl₄ to organic waste in a ventilated fume hood. The aqueous phase may be gamma-counted if desired.

18.18 Transfer the aqueous phase to the 250-ml beaker, add 1 ml of HNO₃ (1:9) and stir. Add 10 ml of the AgNO₃ solution and heat until the AgI precipitate coagulates.

18.19 Transfer the precipitate to a 100-ml glass centrifuge cone using water to rinse the beaker contents into the cone. Add 2 or 3 drops of the 1 per cent aerosol solution, centrifuge, and discard the supernate.

18.20 Wash the precipitate with 75 ml of water, add 2 or 3 drops of the 1 per cent aerosol solution, centrifuge, and discard the supernate.

18.21 Repeat the procedure given in 18.20.

18.22 Transfer the precipitate to a tared counting dish. Dry under an infrared heat lamp.

18.23 Weigh the precipitate. Apply 4 or 5 drops of dilute collodion to fix the precipitate while counting and determine the count rate.

19. Calculations

19.1 See 12. Calculations.

20. Precision

20.1 Single operator precision is within 3 per cent when the random counting error is less than 1 per cent. Precision will decrease when more than one iodine isotope is present in a single sample.

METHOD C

(Solvent Extraction)

21. Application

21.1 This method is applicable to industrial water with radioiodine concentrations above 100 pc/liter.

22. Summary of Method

22.1 This method[7] is based on the separation of iodine isotopes from other

radiosotopes by extraction into carbon tetrachloride. To assure chemical interchange with the iodine carrier, an oxidation-reduction cycle is made. The iodine is oxidized to periodate in the presence of sodium hypochlorite and then reduced to iodide with sodium bisulfite in acid medium.

22.2 Iodide in the aqueous solution is oxidized, by sodium nitrite, to free iodine which is extracted into carbon tetrachloride. After the organic phase is washed with water, the free iodine is extracted into an aqueous phase by shaking with a sodium bisulfite solution. This extraction cycle is repeated to provide high decontamination.

22.3 Silver nitrate is added to precipitate silver iodide and the precipitate is mounted for counting. In some cases gamma counting of the purified aqueous iodine solution may be made prior to the precipitation of the silver iodide which is then used for determination of the yield.

23. Interferences

23.1 Nonradioactive iodine present in the sample will interfere in the method by causing an overestimation of chemical yield and must be corrected for.

24. Reagents

24.1 *Carbon Tetrachloride*—Technical grade carbon tetrachloride (CCl_4).

24.2 *Ethyl Alcohol (95 per cent)*.

24.3 *Nitric Acid (sp gr 1.42)*—Concentrated nitric acid (HNO_3).

24.4 *Nitric Acid (1:9)*—Mix 1 volume of concentrated HNO_3 (sp gr 1.42) with 9 volumes of water.

24.5 *Potassium Iodide Carrier Solution (13.08 g/liter)*—Dissolve 13.08 g of potassium iodide (KI) in 500 ml of water and dilute to 1 liter. This solution will contain 10 g of I^-/liter.

24.6 *Silver Nitrate Solution (17 g/liter)*—Dissolve 17 g of silver nitrate ($AgNO_3$) in 300 ml of water and dilute to 1 liter.

---

[7] This method is based on previously published methods by L. E. Glendenin and R. P. Metcalf, *National Nuclear Energy Series*, Vol. 9, Book 3, p. 1625; and G. J. Hunter and M. Perkins, "The Determination of Radioiodine," AERE-AM 64, (1960).

24.7 *Sodium Bisulfite Solution (100 g/liter)*—Dissolve 10 g of sodium bisulfite ($NaHSO_3$) in 75 ml of water and dilute to 100 ml. (Keep only a small stock and re-make weekly.)

24.8 *Sodium Hypochlorite (5.25 per cent)*—Commercial grade sodium hypochlorite (NaOCl), household bleach.

24.9 *Sodium Hydroxide Solution (200 g/liter)*—Dissolve 200 g of sodium hydroxide (NaOH) in 400 ml of water and dilute to 1 liter.

24.10 *Sodium Nitrite Solution (100 g/liter)*—Dissolve 10 g of sodium nitrite ($NaNO_2$) in 100 ml of water.

25. Procedure

25.1 Transfer 100 ml of sample to a beaker, add 10 ml of KI carrier solution, and make basic with NaOH solution.

25.2 Add 20 ml of NaOCl solution, sufficient water for a total volume of 100 ml for small samples, boil gently for 10 min, and allow to cool to room temperature.

25.3 Acidify by adding concentrated HNO_3 (sp gr 1.42) dropwise, add 5 ml of $NaHSO_3$ solution, and allow to stand 5 min.

25.4 Transfer the sample to a separatory funnel, add 50 ml of CCl_4, 1 ml of $NaNO_2$ solution, shake for 2 min, and allow phase to separate.

25.5 Transfer the lower organic phase to a clean separatory funnel, add 25 ml of CCl_4 to the aqueous phase, shake for 1 min, allow the phases to separate, combine the organic phases, and discard the aqueous phase.

25.6 Add 50 ml of HNO_3 (1:9), shake for 1 min, allow the phases to separate, and transfer the organic phase to a clean separatory funnel.

25.7 To the organic phase, add 50 ml of water and sufficient $NaHSO_3$ solution to discolor the organic phase. Shake and allow the phases to separate. Discard the organic phase.

25.8 Repeat the procedure given in 25.3 through 25.7.

25.9 Drain the aqueous phase into a clean 250-ml beaker containing 3 ml of HNO_3 (1:9) and boil gently for 1 min to expel SO_2. The aqueous sample may be gamma-counted if desired.

25.10 Precipitate AgI by adding 10 ml of $AgNO_3$ solution and heat until the precipitate coagulates.

25.11 Collect the AgI on a tared filter and wash with 5 ml of water. Wash twice with 5-ml portions of alcohol (95 per cent) and dry for 15 min in a 125-C oven.

25.12 Weigh and mount for counting.

26. Calculations

26.1 See 12. Calculations.

27. Precision

27.1 The single operator precision is within 5 per cent when the random counting error is 1 per cent or less. The precision decreases when more than one iodine isotope is present in a single sample.

APPENDIX A1

DECAY CHARACTERISTICS OF RADIOIODINE [a,b,c]

Radio-isotope	Half-Life	Maximum Beta Energy, Mev	Gamma Decay, Mev	Radioactive Daughter
I^{129}....	1.56×10^7 yr	>99 per cent, 0.150	0.0376 (Xe^{129})	Xe^{129} (stable)
I^{131}....	8.05 days	9 per cent, 0.250 9 per cent, 0.335 81 per cent, 0.608 1 per cent, 0.812	0.080 (Xe^{131}) 0.177 (Xe^{131}) 0.284 0.364 0.51 (Xe^{131}) 0.639 0.724	Xe^{131m_2} (0.7 per cent) Xe^{131m_1} (6.3 per cent) Xe^{131} (stable)(93 per cent)
I^{132}....	2.5 hr	15 per cent 0.73 20 per cent, 0.9 23 per cent, 1.16 24 per cent 1.53 18 per cent, 2.12	0.528 0.624 0.673 0.777 0.96 1.16 1.40 1.96 2.2	Xe^{132} (stable)
I^{133}....	20.8 hr	9 per cent, 0.65 91 per cent, 1.3	0.53 0.85 1.4	Xe^{133m} (2.4 per cent) Xe^{133} (97.6 per cent)
I^{134}....	54.0 min	70 per cent, 1.6 30 per cent, 2.8	0.12 0.20 0.86 1.10 1.78 >2.3	Xe^{134} (stable)
I^{135}....	6.75 hr	35 per cent, 0.47 40 per cent, 1.0 25 per cent, 1.4	0.42 0.86 1.04 1.14 1.28 1.46 1.72 1.80	Xe^{135m} (30 per cent) Xe^{135} (70 per cent)

[a] Nuclear Data Sheets, National Academy of Sciences, National Research Council. Available from Superintendent of Documents.

[b] W. H. Sullivan, Trilinear Chart of the Nuclides, ORNL for USAEC. Available from Superintendent of Documents.

[c] D. Strominger J. M. Hollander, and G. T. Seaborg, "Table of Isotopes." *Review of Modern Physics*, Vol. 30 No. 2, Part II (1958)

Tentative Method of Test for

RADIUM-226 IN INDUSTRIAL WATER AND INDUSTRIAL WASTE WATER[1]

ASTM Designation: D 2335 – 65 T

ISSUED, 1965

This Tentative Method has been approved by the sponsoring committee and accepted by the Society in accordance with established procedures, for use pending adoption as standard. Suggestions for revisions should be addressed to the Society at 1916 Race St., Philadelphia, Pa. 19103.

1. Scope

1.1 This method covers the determination of radium-226 in industrial water and industrial waste water. The lower limit of concentration to which this method is applicable is 1 pc (10^{-6} μc)/ liter. It may be applied to any higher concentration by modification of sample size. This method is not applicable to the determination of other radium isotopes.

1.2 This method may be used for absolute measurements by calibrating with radium-226 or for relative measurements by comparing measurements with each other.

2. Summary of Method

2.1 The method is based on the volatilization and scintillation counting of radon-222 produced from radium-226.

2.2 Radium-226 is collected from water by precipitation as carbonate in the presence of barium salt as carrier.

The radium is dissolved in acid and any existing radon is removed (de-emanation). The radium solution is then stored while radon is produced. After a suitable storage period, the radon which has formed is transferred to an alpha scintillation counter, kept 3 hr for growth of the daughters (polonium-218, lead-214, bismuth-214, and polonium-214), and the alpha activity measured. Radium-226 content is calculated from the alpha count rate. Radioactive decay characteristics of radium-226 and its immediate daughters are listed in Table 1.

3. Definitions

3.1 For definitions of terms used in this method, refer to ASTM Definitions D 1129, Terms Relating to Industrial Water and Industrial Waste Water.[2] For terms not defined in Definitions D 1129, reference may be made to other published glossaries.[3]

---

[1] Under the standardization procedure of the Society, this method is under the jurisdiction of the ASTM Committee D-19 on Industrial Water. A list of members may be found in the ASTM Year Book.

[2] Appears in this publication.

[3] USA Standard "Glossary of Terms in Nuclear Science and Technology" (USASI Designation: N 1.1—1957).

TABLE 1—RADIOACTIVE DECAY CHARACTERISTICS OF RADIUM-226
AND ITS DAUGHTERS.

Radionuclide	Half-Life	Radiation	
		Type	Energy, Mev
Radium-226	1622 years	alpha	4.78
Radon-222..............	3.82 days	alpha	5.49
Polonium-218	3.05 min	alpha	6.00
Lead-214..............	26.8 min	beta	1.03 (6 per cent); 0.73 (71 per cent) 0.67 (23 per cent)
		gamma	0.35; 0.30; 0.24
Bismuth-214...........	19.7 min	beta (>99 per cent)	3.26 (19 per cent); 1.88 (9 per cent); 1.51 (40 per cent); 1.0 (23 per cent); 0.4 (9 per cent)
		alpha (0.04 per cent)	5.52; 5.44
		gamma	0.61; 1.12; 1.76; 1.38; 1.24; 0.77; 2.20; others
Polonium-214..........	160 μsec	alpha	7.68
Thallium-210[a].........	1.32 min	beta	1.9
Lead-210..............	19.4 years	beta	0.061 (15 per cent); 0.017 (85 per cent)
		gamma	.047

[a] Minor chain member.

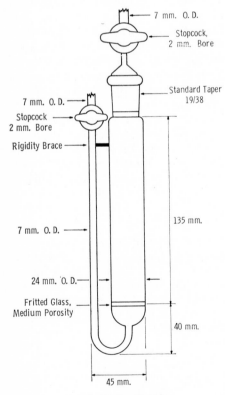

FIG. 1—Radon Bubbler.

7 mm. O. D.
Stopcock, 2 mm. Bore
Standard Taper 19/38
7 mm. O. D.
Stopcock 2 mm. Bore
Rigidity Brace
7 mm. O. D.
135 mm.
24 mm. O. D.
Fritted Glass, Medium Porosity
40 mm.
45 mm.

4. Interferences

4.1 There are no radioactive interferences with this method.

4.2 The interference of any materials, such as chelating agents, which decrease the precipitation of barium and radium carbonates is eliminated by determination of the chemical yield of barium and correcting accordingly.

4.3 If the barium content of the sample exceeds 1 mg/liter, the barium content of a separate portion of the water must be determined and a suitable correction made.[4]

5. Apparatus

5.1 *Radon Bubbler* (Fig. 1).

5.2 *Radon Scintillation Chamber*[5] (Fig. 2).

[4] N. Howell Furman, Editor, *Standard Methods of Chemical Analysis*, 6th Ed., D. Van Nostrand Co., Inc., Princeton, N. J., Vol. 1, pp. 138–159 (1962).

F. Feigl, *Spot Tests in Inorganic Analysis*, 5th Ed., Elsevier Publishing Co. (1958).

[5] H. F. Lucas, *Review of Scientific Instruments*, Vol. 28, pp. 680–683 (1957). Chambers obtained from William H. Johnston Laboratories, Baltimore, Md. have been found satisfactory for this purpose.

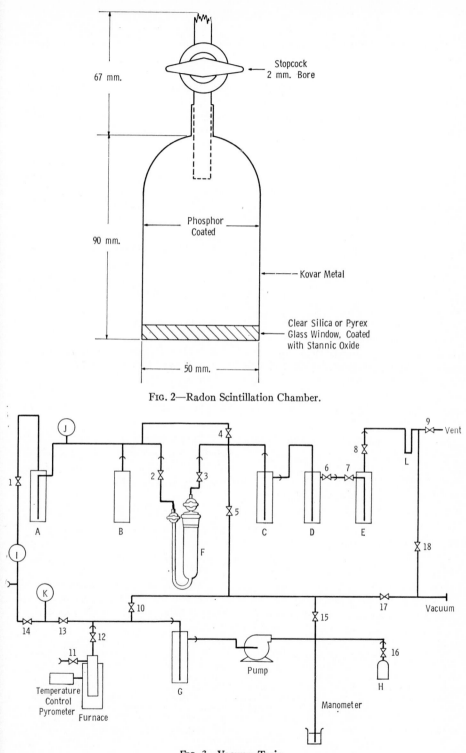

FIG. 2—Radon Scintillation Chamber.

FIG. 3—Vacuum Train.

5.3 *Vacuum Train*, including water and charcoal traps (Fig. 3). The vacuum train may be made of glass, stainless steel, or copper. *A* and *E* are charcoal traps containing 7 g each of activated coconut charcoal. *B* is a safety trap about $\frac{3}{4}$ in. in diameter by 6 in. long; *C*, *D*, and *G* are water traps. *F* is the radon bubbler (Fig. 1). *H* is the radon scintillation chamber (Fig. 2). *I* is a flowmeter, *J* and *K* are vacuum-pressure gages, and *L* is a vacuum gage capable of measuring down to 20 μ. Numbers 1 through 18 are vacuum valves or stopcocks. The helium reservoir is the tubing between valves 13 ind 14 which is 15 cm³, including the volume in the gage.

5.4 *Furnace*, tube-type, about $1\frac{1}{4}$ in. ID.

5.5 *Alpha Scintillation Counter*—For a suitable alpha scintillation counter refer to ASTM Method D 1943, Measurement of Alpha Particle Radioactivity of Industrial Water and Industrial Waste Water.[2] For this method the multiplier phototube must be at least 2 in. in diameter. The alpha scintillation counter must not have an integral alpha phosphor.

6. Reagents and Materials

6.1 *Purity of Reagents*—Reagent grade chemicals shall be used in all tests. Unless otherwise indicated, it is intended that all reagents shall conform to the specifications of the Committee on Analytical Reagents of the American Chemical Society, where such specifications are available.[6] Other grades may be used, provided it is first ascertained that the reagent is of sufficiently high purity

to permit its use without lessening the accuracy of the determination.

6.2 *Purity of Water*—Unless otherwise indicated, references to water shall be understood to mean reagent water conforming to ASTM Specifications D 1193, for Reagent Water.[2]

6.3 *Radioactive Purity* shall be such that the measured radioactivity of blank samples does not exceed the calculated probable error of the measurement.

6.4 *Ammonium Hydroxide (sp gr 0.90)* —Concentrated ammonium hydroxide (NH_4OH), carbonate-free.

6.5 *Barium Nitrate Carrier Solution (19 g/liter)*—Dissolve 19 g of barium nitrate ($Ba(NO_3)_2$) in water and dilute to 1 liter. This solution will contain 10 g of Ba^{++}/liter.

6.6 *Coconut Charcoal, Activated* (6 to 14 mesh).

6.7 *Dry Ice*, commercial grade.

6.8 *Ethyl Alcohol (95 per cent)*.

6.9 *Ethyl Ether*.

6.10 *Helium*.

6.11 *Isopropyl Alcohol*, commercial grade.

6.12 *Perchloric Acid Solution (1:1)*— Add 1 volume of perchloric acid ($HClO_4$, 70 to 72 per cent) to 1 volume of water and mix thoroughly.

NOTE 1: **Caution**—Warm $HClO_4$ solutions react explosively with organic matter. Precautions in the use of $HClO_4$ are available.[7]

6.13 *Radium, Standard Solution (10 pc/ml)*.[8]

6.14 *Sodium Carbonate Solution (212 g/liter)*—Dissolve 212 g of sodium carbonate (Na_2CO_3) in water and dilute to 1 liter.

[6] "Reagent Chemicals, American Chemical Society Specifications," Am. Chemical Soc., Washington, D. C. For suggestions on the testing of reagents not listed by the American Chemical Society, see "Reagent Chemicals and Standards," by Joseph Rosin, D. Van Nostrand Co., Inc., New York, N. Y., and the "United States Pharmacopeia."

[7] Precautions for the use of perchloric acid are available in "Chemical Safety Data Sheet SD-11," published by the Manufacturing Chemists' Association of the United States.

[8] Standardized radium solution, $RaCl_2$, 10 pc/ml, available from the National Bureau of Standards, Catalog No. 4950, has been found satisfactory for this purpose.

6.15 *Sulfuric Acid (1:1)*—Cautiously add 1 volume of concentrated sulfuric acid (H_2SO_4, sp gr 1.84) to 1 volume of water and mix thoroughly.

7. Sampling

7.1 Collect the sample in accordance with the applicable methods of the American Society for Testing and Materials, as follows:

D 510—Sampling Industrial Water[2] (especially to Sections 32 to 41),

D 860—Sampling Water from Boilers,[2] and

D 1496—Sampling Homogeneous Industrial Waste Water.[2]

8. Calibration and Standardization

8.1 *Counter Efficiency*—Place 1 ml of the standardized radium solution (10 pc/ml) in the bubbler, add 1 ml of $HClO_4$ (1:1), 25 ml of water, and pass 3 liters of helium through the solution at a rate of 100 ml/min, venting to the atmosphere. Close the stopcocks and store 14 days for ingrowth of radon. Transfer the accumulated radon to the charcoal trap as in 9.5, then to the scintillation counter as in 9.6 through 9.11, let stand 3 hr, and count as described in 9.12. The counter calibration factor F (counts per minute per picocurie) may be calculated as follows:

$$F = \frac{A - B}{10 \times 0.921}$$

where:

A = gross count rate, counts/min,

B = the background count rate, counts/min.

10 = the number of picocuries of the radium-226 activity taken for the calibration, and

0.921 = the ingrowth factor for radon-222 from radium-226 for 14 days' storage.

8.2 *Reagent Blank*—Carry out the entire procedure (9. Procedure), substitut-

ing 1 liter of reagent water for the sample. Calculate the radium-226 content of the reagents.

9. Procedure

9.1 Take for analysis 1 liter of sample or a convenient smaller volume provided that it contains at least 100 pc of radium-226. Add to this 10 ml of $Ba(NO_3)_2$ solution and 10 ml of $HClO_4$ (1:1). Heat to boiling (**CAUTION,** see 6.12). Allow to cool; add NH_4OH until the solution is definitely alkaline, and add 50 ml of Na_2CO_3 solution. Digest 30 min or more. Collect the precipitate on a fine ashless filter paper or fine fritted-glass filter crucible and discard the filtrate.

9.2 Dissolve the precipitate from the filter paper or filter crucible in 5 ml of $HClO_4$ (1:1), catching the solution in a tube. Wash the filter twice with 5-ml portions of water, catching the washes in the same tube. Transfer the solution and washes to the radon bubbler. The total volume, including any water used in the transfer, should not exceed 30 ml.

9.3 Pass 3 liters of helium through the solution, at a rate of 100 ml/min, venting to the atmosphere. Close the stopcocks on the bubbler and record the time.

9.4 Store the solution in the radon bubbler for 14 days. The bubbler need not be attached to the vacuum train during this storage period (Note 2).

NOTE 2—Other storage periods may be used if mutually agreeable. For other storage periods, the concentration of radon in the solution will be a different fraction of the equilibrium concentration than 0.921. A suitable correction should be applied using the build-up factors of Table 2.

9.5 Attach the radon bubbler and charcoal trap E to the vacuum system. Evacuate the system to the bubbler stopcocks by opening valves 4, 6, 7, 8, and 18. Valves 1, 2, 3, 5, 9, and 17 should be closed. Cool traps A, C, D, and E

with a dry ice-isopropyl alcohol mixture. When the traps have reached dry ice temperature, shut off the pump and open valve 1 slowly to allow the system to fill with helium to atmospheric pressure. Open valve 9 and pass helium through at a rate of 100 ml/min. Then close valve 18, open valves 2 and 3, and close valve 4. Maintain a flow rate of 100 ml/min for 30 min for a total flow of 3 liters. Close valves 1, 2, 7, and 9. Evacuate trap E to 20 μ through valve 18. Close valves 8 and 18. The dry ice may now be removed and the traps allowed to warm.

9.6 Open valve 9 and transfer the charcoal trap E to the furnace. Open valves 10, 13, 15, 16, and 17 and make sure that valves 18, 5, 11, 12, and 14 are closed. Evacuate the system. Cool trap G with dry ice-isopropyl alcohol mixture.

9.7 When trap G has reached temperature, close valves 10, 13, and 15, open valves 12 and 16, and raise the temperature of the furnace to 500 C.

9.8 While maintaining the furnace at 500 C, pump the system into the scintillation cell H with the peristaltic pump.

9.9 Open valve 14 until a pressure of 2 psig is obtained; then close valve 14 and open valve 13. When the pressure has become steady, close valve 13 and pump the system into cell H with the peristaltic pump.

9.10 Flush the system twice more with helium gas by repeating the procedure outlined in 9.9.

9.11 Close valve 16 and remove cell H from the vacuum system.

9.12 Let the scintillation cell stand 3 hr; then place it on the photomultiplier tube of the counting system, and measure the alpha activity as described in Method D 1943.

9.13 Quantitatively transfer the solution from the radon bubbler to a beaker, heat to boiling, and add 5 ml of sulfuric acid (H_2SO_4, 1:1). Keep the solution hot for about 5 min, and let stand 30 min or longer. Collect the precipitate on a filter crucible (Gooch-type) with a fine fritted-glass disk; wash with hot water, and discard the filtrate and wash water before washing the precipitate with ethyl alcohol, and finally with ether. Dry at 110 C then weigh. From the weight of barium sulfate, calculate the chemical yield.

TABLE 2—GROWTH OF RADON IN PURE RADIUM-226.[a]

Time, Days	Rn-222/Ra-226	Time, Days	Rn-222/Ra-226
0........	0.0000	16.......	0.9449
1........	0.1657	17.......	0.9541
2........	0.3040	18.......	0.9617
3........	0.4193	19.......	0.9680
4........	0.5156	20.......	0.9733
5........	0.5950		
6........	0.6628	21.......	0.9777
7........	0.7187	22.......	0.9814
8........	0.7653	23.......	0.9846
9........	0.8042	24.......	0.9871
10........	0.8367	25.......	0.9892
11........	0.8637	26.......	0.9910
12........	0.8863	27.......	0.9925
13........	0.9052	28.......	0.9937
14........	0.9209	29.......	0.9948
15........	0.9340	30.......	0.9956

[a] H W. Kirby, *Analytical Chemistry*, Vol. 26, p. 1067 (1954).

10. Calculation

10.1 Calculate the concentration, D, of radium-226 in picocuries per liter as follows:

$$D = \frac{(A - B)}{V R S F}$$

where:

A = gross alpha count rate, counts/min,

B = background count rate, counts/min,

F = calibration factor, counts/min/pc (see 8.1),

V = volume of original sample, liters,

R = fractional chemical yield for the separation, and

S = buildup factor = 0.921 (or other suitable value from Table 2 if solution is stored for a period other than 14 days).

10.2 *Correction for Reagent Blank*— Subtract the reagent blank, as obtained in 8.2 from the concentration D obtained in 10.1 to obtain the corrected radium concentration of the sample.

11. Precision

11.1 Precision depends on random counting error and on determination of chemical yield.

Tentative Method for

FLOW MEASUREMENT OF INDUSTRIAL WATER AND INDUSTRIAL WASTE WATER BY THE VENTURI METER TUBE[1]

ASTM Designation: D 2458 – 66 T

Issued, 1966

This Tentative Method has been approved by the sponsoring committee and accepted by the Society in accordance with established procedures, for use pending adoption as standard. Suggestions for revisions should be addressed to the Society at 1916 Race St., Philadelphia, Pa. 19103.

1. Scope

1.1 This method covers the measurement of the rate of flow of industrial water and industrial waste water in pipelines using the Herschel Standard Venturi meter tube.

1.2 Venturi[2] meter tubes are applicable for the measurement of industrial water flow and particularly for slurries or similar nonhomogeneous liquids containing large concentrations of suspended solids. Individually calibrated, the Venturi tube is used as a standard of measurement for acceptance tests on pumping and similar equipment. Pressure losses through Venturi tubes are less than for other primary flow measuring devices installed in pipelines. Thus, substantial savings in pumping power consumption can be realized by its use.

2. Description of Terms

2.1 *Head, H*—The energy (capacity to do work) possessed by a liquid because of its elevation, velocity, pressure, or any combination of these. Each source of energy may be expressed in terms of equivalent head in feet, inches of water, or pounds per square inch, and each can be converted into the other two.

2.2 *Differential Head, H_D*—The difference in pressure head H_D in Fig. 2 between the inlet and the throat of the Venturi tube.

2.3 *Loss of Head*—The difference in line pressure at the inlet end and just downstream from the Venturi tube. It is also termed "nonrecoverable head."

2.4 *Hydraulic Gradient*—A line in any selected plane, connecting all points representing pressure head in any system.

2.5 *Beta Ratio*—The ratio of throat diameter, *d*, to the inlet diameter, *D*.

---

[1] Under the standardization procedure of the Society, this method is under the jurisdiction of the ASTM Committee D-19 on Industrial Water. A list of members may be found in the ASTM Year Book.

[2] The principle of the Venturi meter was first stated in 1797 by J. B. Venturi, an Italian, and was first applied by Clemens Herschel to the measurement of flow in pipes in 1887.

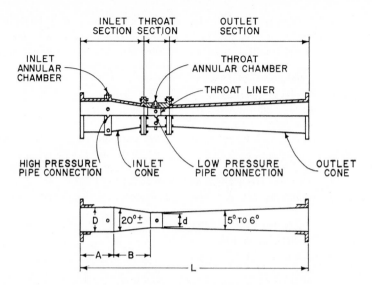

Fig. 1—Elements of Herschel Standard (Long) Venturi Meter Tube.

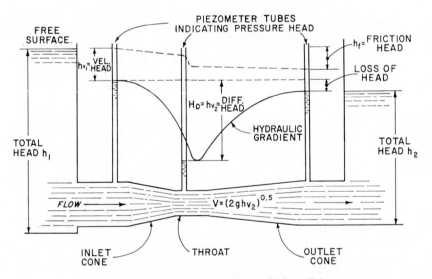

Fig. 2—Diagram of Theory of Venturi Meter Tube.

The quantity d/D is expressed as a decimal and represented by the Greek letter Beta.

3. General Principles

3.1 The standard (long-type) Herschel[3] Venturi meter tube is a specially constructed primary differential producer and flow-measuring device which is installed between two flanges in a pipe-

[3] Clemens Herschel, "Fluid Meters: Their Theory and Application," Report of Special Research Committee on Fluid Meters, ASME, 1924.

line to form a constricted section (Fig. 1). The device operates on the principle that when a fluid passes through a reduced cross sectional area, an increase in velocity and a corresponding decrease in pressure (head) will occur (Fig. 2). This reduction in pressure is a simple function of the rate of flow. Two pressure measurements are made, one each at the high-pressure inlet point and at the low-pressure throat section. The difference in head, H_D (h_{v_2}), expressed either as inches of water column or feet of water, is a measure of velocity, which is a measure of rate of flow, with the flow varying as the square root of the differential.

3.1.1 The increase in velocity is given as follows:

$$V = C(2gh_{v_2})^{0.5}$$

where:

V = velocity, theoretical, ft/sec,
C = discharge coefficient (average value = 0.98),
g = acceleration constant of gravity = 32.16 ft/sec/sec, and
h_{v_2} = velocity head, theoretical, ft of water.

3.1.2 The fluid flow formulas for the Venturi tube are derived from this basic relationship. The flow formula then becomes the following:

$$Q = AC(2gh_{v_2})^{0.5}$$

where:

Q = cu ft per unit time, and
A = area of pipe, ft.^{2}

3.2 In addition to the simple determination of the differential head, H_D, there are two factors to be considered in measurement with a Venturi tube. These are the velocity of approach and friction. Flowing fluid in a pipeline as it reaches the inlet section of the Venturi tube has a certain velocity of approach. At the throat section, the fluid has a velocity due to the constriction plus the original velocity. Observed differential

head must be corrected for this velocity of approach factor. This correction is made through a table of values related to the Beta ratio d/D. The factor is expressed as $1/[(1 - B^4)^{0.5}]$.

3.2.1 When the throat-to-inlet ratio, B, is less than 0.3, the velocity of approach factor correction amounts to less than 1 per cent and may be disregarded in other than exact calculations.

3.2.2 Values of the velocity of approach factor $1/[(1 - B^4)^{0.5}]$ for B ratios greater than 0.350 are as follows:

B or $\dfrac{d}{D}$	$\dfrac{1}{(1 - B^4)^{0.5}}$	B or $\dfrac{d}{D}$	$\dfrac{1}{(1 - B^4)^{0.5}}$
0.350	1.008	0.600	1.072
0.400	1.013	0.650	1.103
0.500	1.033	0.750	1.209
0.550	1.049	...	...

3.2.3 The friction factor causes the apparent value of the flow to be lower than the theoretical value indicated by the observed differential. Each Venturi tube, therefore, has a discharge coefficient, C, to correct the observed differential value to the actual value. Depending on throat velocity and measuring range, the value of C for various sizes of Venturi tubes will be between 0.96 and 0.99 with an average value of 0.98 generally used.

3.3 The formula for Venturi tube measurement evolved from consideration of the concept of flow, pressure, velocity, and the necessary correction factors becomes:

$$Q = AC\left(\frac{1}{(1 - B^4)^{0.5}}\right) \times (2gH_D)^{0.5}$$

where Q = ft^3 per unit of time. By the use of proper additional numerical factors, this formula can be converted into gallons per unit of time.

4. Apparatus

4.1 *Venturi Meter Tube* (*Primary Device*)—The apparatus shall consist of the

Venturi meter tube referred to as the primary measuring device suitably constructed in accordance with standard dimensions selected to give accurately measurable differential pressures over the entire required variation of quantity flow. At no time should the throat pressure drop below atmospheric. The Venturi tube should consist of inlet, throat, and outlet sections (Fig. 1). The inlet section shall consist of a short cylinder, A, and a truncated cone, B, of about 20 deg total angle equipped with piezometer ring or annular chamber which circumscribes the section and serves as a means of obtain-

The diameter of the throat is usually between one-third and three-fourths of the entrance of pipeline diameter.

Note 1—When a Venturi tube is to be used for metering liquids containing large concentrations of suspended solids or sludge, the annular ring is eliminated and replaced by single hole taps at the inlet and throat and these are flushed continuously with clean water.

4.1.3 The outlet section follows the throat section and is essentially a long truncated cone of about 5 to 7-deg angle which gradually returns to the original pipeline size. Construction is generally of high-tensile cast iron, tar-coated on the

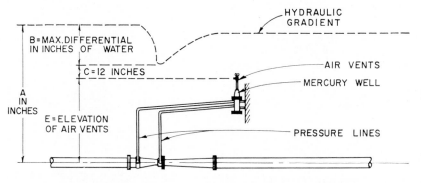

Fig. 3—Location of Air Vents on Mercury Wells of Instruments.

ing the average pressure of fluid at the upstream point.

4.1.1 The fluid pressure enters the annular chamber through equally spaced vent holes drilled through the inner wall of the chamber. The outside wall of the annular chamber contains one or more tapped holes, to one of which is connected the "high-pressure" line to the metering instrument.

4.1.2 The throat section, the most constricted part, follows the inlet section and is surrounded by an annular chamber to serve as a means of obtaining the average pressure at that point. Reamed holes through the liner admit fluid pressure to the annular chamber. The outside wall is tapped for the "low-pressure" line to the metering instrument (Note 1).

outer and inner surfaces, except for the throat liner of bronze or other corrosion material as conditions require. The liner is carefully finished to specified diameter and profile, since accuracy of metering depends largely upon the shape, dimensions, and surface finish of this tube section. Complete linings of bronze, rubber, vitreous enamel, or glass are frequently used for extremely corrosive conditions.

5. Instrumentation

5.1 Two small pressure lines should connect at either side on the horizontal axis of the annular chambers of a Venturi tube with the metering instrument employed. In laying out the pressure lines, it is important that air locks or accumulations of sediment be avoided. The lines should slope in one direction only with a minimum pitch of $\frac{1}{2}$ in./ft or be vertical as shown in Fig. 3.

5.2 When metering liquids carrying solids in suspension, it is important that the suspended material be prevented from entering the annular chambers and pressure connections to the instrument. Con-

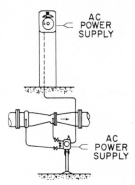

FIG. 4—Electric Operation.

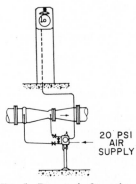

FIG. 5—Pneumatic Operation.

tinuous flushing is recommended and is achieved by attaching a clear water supply to each instrument pressure pipe and maintaining a small but continuous flow of water into the annular chambers of the Venturi tube. The flushing water pressure should exceed the maximum line pressure by at least 10 psi. Flows should be equal, continuous, and held to a small quantity to prevent any measurable pressure differential which would be reflected in the metering instrument.

5.3 Mercury-well instruments must be

located so that air vents on the wells are at least the maximum differential of instruments, plus 12 in. (30.5 cm) below the minimum hydraulic grade of the pipeline at the inlet of the Venturi tube. Referring to Fig. 3, "E", the elevation of the air vents above the center line of the tube equals the elevation "A" of the hydraulic grade of the tube minus "B" minus 12 in. (30.5 cm).

5.4 Since the minimum elevation of the hydraulic grade in a pipeline varies widely under differing conditions of flow, a careful study should be made whenever an instrument is to be installed under "borderline" conditions. Special

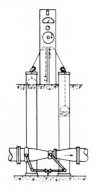

FIG. 6—Water Column Operation.

applications of standard devices and instrument layouts have been developed to meet the problems imposed by low hydraulic grade as follows:

5.4.1 *Electrical   Transmission*—The measuring instrument may include an electrical transmitter connected by a simple two-wire circuit or by means of leased telephone wires with a remotely located recording, indicating or totalizing instrument, or both, as shown in Fig. 4.

5.4.2 *Pneumatic Transmission*—In installations where air-operated instruments are desired and where the distance from the Venturi tube to the meter instrument does not exceed 1000 ft (304.8 m), an air transmitter, located at the

Venturi tube, may be employed as shown in Fig. 5. This air transmitter is a differential unit with pressure connections to the Venturi tube as described in 5.1 and 5.2. The rate of flow is indicated or recorded on an air-operated receiver connected to the transmitter by one pneumatic pressure tube. Changes in the pressure output signal, which vary from 3 to 15 psi, are proportioned to changes on the measured variable, rate of flow.

5.4.3 *Water Columns*—With a low hydraulic grade and only moderate fluctuation in head, a float-operated instrument with water columns (float wells) can be used as shown in Fig. 6. In this case, differential pressure is represented by the difference in water level in the two columns.

6. Calibration

6.1 To meet accuracy standards, it is recommended that each Venturi be calibrated in place if the discharge can be directly measured by other methods.

Note 2—For calibration purposes, the application of the volumetric method or comparative salt dilution method of flow measurement is recommended.

6.2 The volumetric method is applicable only when there is available a reservoir of regular form, the volume of which, up to various levels, may be accurately measured within an error of 1.0 per cent.

6.3 The drawdown during the test run should not cause a variation in head on the Venturi in excess of 4 per cent of regular form with sufficient storage capacity to meet these conditions. This places a limit on the size of the Venturi which can be accurately calibrated by this method.

6.4 For Venturis larger than 1 ft (30.5 cm) in throat diameter, the comparative salt dilution or chemical method is recommended for calibration purposes. Thorough mixing of the salt solution in the flowing stream and accurate analysis

of samples taken at the sampling station downstream from the Venturi are essential for measurement of flow rates with ± 2 per cent.

7. Procedure

7.1 A Venturi tube may be installed in a horizontal, vertical, or inclined position in a pipeline, provided it is at all times full of the fluid being metered.

7.2 It is essential that the fluid entering a Venturi tube be of uniform turbulence, free from helical flow and from local high or low-pressure areas. Therefore, long uninterrupted runs of straight pipe upstream from the Venturi location are essential for accurate fluid metering (Note 3).

Note 3—Suppliers of Venturi metering tubes or the ASME Power Test Codes and Supplements recommend the straight runs of pipe between the upstream locations of elbows, gate, and globe valves, decreasers and increasers and the tube.

7.2.1 If ideal conditions can not be achieved and little or no straight pipe run upstream is available, a straightening vane assembly is required consisting of four vanes in the form of a cross, one pipe diameter long, installed preceding the Venturi tube. Conditions downstream from the Venturi tube have practically no effect on its performance.

7.3 For purposes of calculating rates of flow through a Venturi tube when indicating and recording flowmeters are not available, it is necessary to obtain a head reading, H_D, in feet of water or h_d in the inches of water column which expresses the differential in pressure heads at the inlet and throat of the metering tube (Note 4).

Note 4—In order to ensure dependable, accurate metering over long periods under normal operating conditions, it is recommended that the differential in pressure heads at the lowest flow rate that is to be accurately metered be not less than 1 in. (2.54 cm) of water for installations metering the flow of water; 2 in.

(5.1 cm) of water for sewage; and 3 in. (7.6 cm) of water for sludge or other liquids having a higher percentage of settleable solids.

7.4 Where the magnitude of pressure heads at the metering tube inlet and throat does not permit the use of open water columns, a water differential can be obtained using a mercury manometer. Then each 1.00 in. of mercury deflection will equal 12.57 in. or 1.0475 ft (30.5 cm) of water differential.

8. Calculations

8.1 The rate of flow in terms of cubic feet per second or gallons per minute may be calculated using each of following formulae, respectively:

$$Q_A = 8.02 \times A_2 \times C_f \times C_R \times H_D{}^{0.5}$$

where:

Q_A = volume of rate of flow, actual, ft³/sec,

A_2 = area of Venturi tube throat cross section, ft,²

C_f = discharge coefficient = 0.98 average value,

C_R = velocity of approach factor = $1/[(1 - B^4)^{0.5}]$, and

H_D = effective differential head, ft of water.

$$GPM = 7.22 \times a \times C_f \times C_R \times h_d{}^{0.5}$$

where:

GPM = volume rate of flow, actual, gal/min,

a = area of Venturi tube throat cross section, in.,² and

h_d = effective differential head, in. of water.

8.2 For other flow rates per unit of time, the constant in the equations may be converted to obtain the desired volumes.

NOTE 5—The differential head measured should be corrected for variations in temperature between the manometer fluid and the fluid flowing through the Venturi nozzle. The correction is as follows:

$$\frac{\text{Head} \times \text{Specific Gravity of Manometer Fluid}}{\text{Specific Gravity of Fluid Flowing}}$$

9. Precision

9.1 With standard Venturi tubes having annular chambers at the inlet and throat, the error due to poor installation conditions will rarely exceed 3 per cent except in cases of severe helical flow or where the tube is preceded by an increaser or a partially closed valve.

9.2 The precision of the Venturi tube will normally be in the range of ±2 per cent, but greater precision can be obtained if the tubes are calibrated at a hydraulic laboratory associated with a university or technical college. For reliable measurements, it is essential that the Venturi tube should not follow immediately after a valve, elbow, or other irregularity in the pipeline, which would tend to cause great turbulence or set up permanent crosscurrents or whirls. It should be preceded by a length of five or more diameters of straight pipe in which the flow may steady down after any cause of disturbance. When it is impractical to provide a sufficient straight run of pipe, the flow should be steadied by straightening vanes consisting of a sheet metal cross one or two diameters long inserted in the pipe ahead of the Venturi tube.

9.3 Manufacturers of Venturi tubes generally will guarantee accuracy of uncalibrated tubes to ±¾ of 1 per cent of actual flow over a range the limits of which are governed by size and proportion of the tube.

Tentative Method of Test for

GAMMA SPECTROMETRY OF INDUSTRIAL WATER AND INDUSTRIAL WASTE WATER[1]

ASTM Designation: D 2459 – 66 T

Issued, 1966

This Tentative Method has been approved by the sponsoring committees and accepted by the Society and by the Institute of Petroleum in accordance with established procedures, for use pending adoption as standard. Suggestions for revisions should be addressed to the Society at 1916 Race St., Philadelphia, Pa. 19103.

1. Scope

1.1 This method covers the measurement by means of gamma spectrometry of gamma radioactivity of industrial water and industrial waste water. It is applicable to nuclides emitting gamma rays with energies greater than 0.1 Mev. The count rate of the sample to be counted should be in the range from 10^5 counts per minute to twice the background count rate.

1.2 The method can be used for either absolute or relative determinations. In tracer work, the results may be expressed by comparison with an initial concentration of a given nuclide which is taken as 100 per cent. For radioassay the results may be expressed in terms of known nuclidic standards if the radionuclides are known. In addition to the quantitative measurement of gamma radioactivity, gamma spectrometry can be used for the identification of specific

gamma emitters in a mixture of radionuclides. General information on radioactivity and measurement of radiation has been published (1).[2] Information on specific application of gamma spectrometry is also available in the literature (2).

2. Summary of Method

2.1 Gamma spectra are measured with a gamma-ray spectrometer. The spectrometer assembly is used to analyze the gamma spectra of radionuclides in a manner similar in general to the analysis of emission spectra of elements with the emission spectrograph. The sensing unit required for the detection of the emitted gamma radiation is the thallium-activated sodium iodide crystal. Gamma photons penetrating the crystal have a high probability of interacting with it. Interaction of a single gamma photon with the atoms in a crystal results in a transfer of some or all of the energy of the photon to one or more electrons in the crystal. The energetic electrons col-

---

[1] Under the standardization procedure of the Society, this method is under the jurisdiction of the ASTM Committee D-19 on Industrial Water. A list of members may be found in the ASTM Year Book.

[2] The boldface numbers in parentheses refer to the list of references appended to this method.

lide with bound electrons, and the bound electrons are removed from the ground state orbits of the atoms. As the ground state orbits are subsequently filled, energy is released in the form of photons

2.2 One method of analysis of the pulse spectra is by use of a pulse-height analyzer, either multiple or single channel. The multiple-channel (or multi-channel) analyzer determines the ampli-

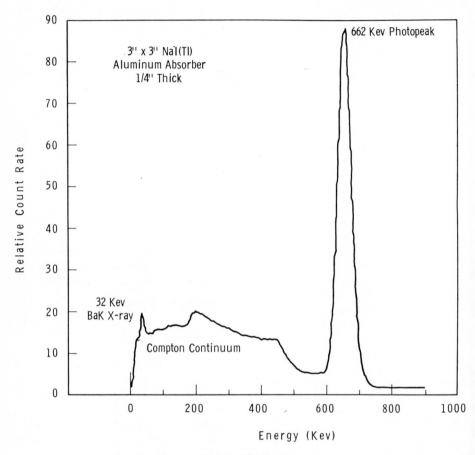

Fig. 1—Cesium-137 Spectrum.

in the visible region which can be detected by a multiplier phototube.

2.1.1 The current output from the multiplier phototube anode is directly proportional to the energy lost by the incident gamma photon. These current pulses are fed into an amplifier of sufficient gain to produce voltage output pulses in the amplitude range typically from 0 to 10 or 0 to 100 v.

tude of each pulse produced in the multiplier phototube and accumulates in a memory the number of pulses in each amplitude band (or channel) in a given counting time. The single-channel analyzer similarly classifies pulses according to amplitude but passes on to a scaler or ratemeter only those pulses falling within a single pre-set amplitude range, the rest being discarded. Some single-channel analyzers are equipped with a motor-driven potentiometer and can scan the complete pulse distribution and register the counting rate on a strip chart recorder.

2.3 The frequency distribution of the amplitudes (pulse heights) of the pulses can be separated into two principal components. One of these components has a Gaussian distribution and is the result of total absorption of the gamma energy by the sodium iodide crystal. This peak is normally referred to as the full-energy peak or photopeak. The other component is a continuous one lower in energy than that of the photopeak. The continuous curve is referred to as the Compton continuum and is due to interactions wherein the gamma photons lose only part of their energy to the crystal. These two portions of the curve are shown in Fig. 1. Other peaks, such as backscatter or X-rays from shields, are often superimposed on the Compton continuum. In the plot of pulse height versus count rate, the location of the photopeak on the pulse-height axis is proportional to the gamma energy of the incident photon and is the basis for the qualitative application of the gamma-ray spectrometer. The area under the photopeak is related to the number of gamma photons interacting with the crystal and is the basis for the quantitative application of the gamma-ray spectrometer. The Compton continuum serves no useful purpose in photopeak analysis and must be corrected for when a mixture of gamma emitters is analyzed.

3. Definitions

3.1 *Resolution, Gamma*—The ratio (expressed as per cent) of the width in energy units of the observed photopeak of a gamma emitter at half the maximum count rate to the average energy of the photopeak.

3.2 For definitions of other terms used

in this method, refer to ASTM Definitions D 1129, Terms Relating to Industrial Water and Industrial Waste Water.[3]

3.3 For terms not defined in this method or in Definitions D 1129, reference may be made to other published glossaries.[4]

4. Interferences

4.1 In complex mixtures of gamma emitters, the degree of interference of one nuclide in the determination of another is governed by several factors. If the nuclides are present in approximately equal proportion radiometrically, interference will occur when the photopeaks are not completely resolved, or in general whenever the difference in energies between principal photopeaks is 10 per cent or less. A method of predicting the gamma resolution of a crystal detector if given in the literature (3). If the nuclides are present in the mixture in unequal proportions radiometrically, and nuclides of higher gamma energies are predominant, there is serious interference with interpretation of minor, less energetic gamma photopeaks. The density of the sample is another factor that can cause interference through absorption of gammas with energies between 0.1 and 0.2 Mev. Interference from this source can be avoided by preparing standards for calibration in solutions with density comparable to the sample under analysis.

5. Apparatus

5.1 *Gamma Ray Spectrometer*, consisting of the following components:

5.1.1 *Detector Assembly*—A sodium iodide crystal "activated" with about 0.1 per cent thallium iodide, cylindrical, with or without an inner sample well, 2

---

[3] Appears in this publication.

[4] Reference may be made to the "USA Standard Glossary of Terms in Nuclear Science and Technology" (USASI Designation: N1.1-1957).

to 4 in. (5.1 to 10.2 cm) in diameter, $1\frac{3}{4}$ to 4 in. (4.4 to 10.2 cm) high, and hermetically sealed in an opaque container with a transparent window. The crystal shall contain less than 5 ppm of potassium, and shall be free of other radioactive materials. In order to establish freedom from other radioactive materials, the manufacturer shall supply the gamma spectrum of the background of the crystal, between 0.08 and 3 Mev. The crystal shall be attached and optically coupled to a multiplier phototube. (The multiplier phototube requires a preamplifier or a cathode follower compatible with the amplifier.) The resolution of the assembly for the photopeak of cesium-137 shall be 9 per cent or less. The detector assembly shall be surrounded by an external radiation shield made of massive metal, equivalent to 2 to 4 in. (5.1 to 10.2 cm) of lead. It is desirable that the inner walls of the massive shield be at least 5 in. (12.7 cm) distant from the crystal surfaces. If the shield is made of lead or a lead liner and if there are less than 10 in. (25.4 cm) between shield and detector, then the massive shield shall have a graded inner shield of $\frac{1}{16}$ in. (1.6 mm) of cadmium or tin lined with 15 mils of copper on the surface nearer the detector. The shield shall have a door or port for inserting and removing specimens.

5.1.2 *Power Supply*, high-voltage, of range (usually from 500 to 1500 v) sufficient to operate the multiplier phototube. The power supply shall be regulated to 0.1 per cent with a ripple of not more than 0.01 per cent. Line noise caused by calculators and other equipment shall be removed with rf filters and additional regulators.

5.1.3 *Amplifier*, compatible with the pre-amplifier or cathode follower and with the pulse-height analyzer.

5.1.4 *Pulse-Height Analyzer*—Single channel with continuous discriminator drive or step discriminator drive or multichannel.

5.1.5 *Readout:*

5.1.5.1 *Single-Channel Pulse-Height Analyzer*—To record the counts or count rate per discriminator window width, a scaler or a count rate meter and a strip chart recorder must be provided. The strip chart recorder drive mechanism is synchronized with the continuous discriminator drive on the analyzer. The scaler should have a scaling ratio of at least 512, preferably 1000; capacity of 9×10^5 counts; and a resolving time no longer than 5 μsec. If the pulse-height analyzer is equipped with a step discriminator drive, the scaler should be equipped with a digital printer. A count rate meter must be used to couple a strip chart recorder to the single-channel analyzer. A count rate meter is useful for locating rapidly the peaks in the sample.

5.1.5.2 *Multichannel Analyzer*—Many different readout devices are available. They include strip chart recorder, XY plotter, digital printer, typewriter, magnetic tape recorder, and paper tape punch. For most applications a strip chart recorder or XY plotter and a digital printer or typewriter will be adequate. Magnetic and paper tapes are used if the calculations are performed on a computer.

5.2 *Container for Test Specimen*—A polyethylene container having an inside diameter at the base approximately equal to or less than the diameter of the crystal or the well in the crystal with the absorber in place.

5.3 *Absorber*—Aluminum, $\frac{1}{4}$ in. (6.4 mm) in thickness, with a diameter, equal to or greater than the diameter of the crystal; or (for a well crystal) lead, $\frac{1}{16}$ in. (1.6 mm) in thickness, cylindrical, and having an outer diameter slightly less than the diameter of the well. The absorber should be kept on top of the crystal or in the sample well at all times.

6. Calibration and Standardization

6.1 *General Measurements:*

6.1.1 Put the instrument into operation according to the manufacturer's instructions. Place an appropriate volume of a standard solution of a radionuclide (10^{-2} to 10^{-3} microcuries per ml) in a container, and place the container on the detector or in the well. The standard solution should give about 10^4 counts per minute. In all measurements, volumes of samples and standards, as well as the container must be identical. If precipitates or residues from evaporated samples are to be analyzed then the standards must be evaporated on the same type of mount as the sample.

6.1.2 *Energy   Calibration*—Calibrate the energy response of the analyzer and detector with standards containing known nuclides. The standards should be sealed and should emit gammas from about 0.1 Mev to 2 or 3 Mev. Some commercially available nuclides suitable for energy calibration are: cerium-141, 0.14 Mev; tin-113, 0.39 Mev; chromium-51, 0.32 Mev; cesium-137, 0.66 Mev; manganese-54, 0.84 Mev; sodium-22, 0.51 and 1.28 Mev; cobalt-60, 1.17 and 1.33 Mev; and radium, 0.35, 0.61, 1.13 and 1.76 Mev. The radionuclidic purity of the standards should be verified periodically to ensure against accidental contamination or the presence of long lived impurities by comparing the observed spectra with the spectra published in the literature (4). The energy calibration should include four different energies and should cover the range from 0.1 to 2.0 Mev.

6.1.2.1 The single-channel analyzer shall be calibrated to cover the range from 0.1 to 2.0 Mev. The gain of the system, including the multiplier phototube and the amplifier gains, shall be adjusted until the cesium-137 photopeak is about one-third full scale of the baseline potentiometer. The position of the photopeak shall be found by turning on the scaler, strip chart recorder, or count rate meter and slowly rotating the discriminator potentiometer from full scale toward zero until a maximum count rate is observed. For precise results the position of the photopeak shall be found by a stepwise, manual adjustment of the baseline discriminator potentiometer and a window width of about one per cent full scale until the maximum count rate is observed. The value of the baseline potentiometer setting shall be recorded along with the gamma energy of the photopeak. The values of the baseline potentiometer settings for at least three other photopeaks shall be found in a similar manner.

6.1.2.2 The   multichannel   analyzer shall be calibrated to cover the range from 0.1 to 2.0 Mev. The gain of the system, amplifier and multiplier phototube, shall be adjusted until the cesium-137 photopeak is about one-third full scale. Locate the channel containing the maximum count rate and record the gamma energy and the channel number of the middle of the photopeak. Leaving the gain constant, locate at least three other photopeaks of different energies and record the channel numbers of the middle of the photopeaks and the corresponding gamma energies.

6.1.2.3 Plot on rectangular coordinate paper the gamma energy versus the channel number or baseline potentiometer seting of each photopeak. A linear relationship will be observed if the equipment is operating properly. Samples should not be analyzed if there is a nonlinear relationship. Calculate the slope and intercept of the line by using the graph or by making a least squares calculation. On each day during which samples will be counted repeat the above sequence of operations with at least two of the four gamma energies. If the slope and intercept of the linear plot are essentially unchanged, the calibration data remain valid. If an appreciable change in slope is evident, then the entire calibration procedure must be rerun. A report giving more information on the routine testing and calibration procedures for multichannel analyzers has been published (5).

6.1.3 *Photon Detection Efficiency*—The photon detection efficiency is a function of the gamma energy. A curve of this function can be constructed provided at least four nuclides, disintegrating with known photon emission rates, each nuclide emitting only one gamma, are counted. The photon detection efficiency is the ratio of the observed count rate to the known photon emission rate. The photon detection efficiency may be calculated for the photopeak of a given gamma energy, the total observed count rate, or any desired fraction of the total count rate. The photon detection efficiency versus the gamma energy shall be plotted on rectangular coordinate paper. Other methods of determining the counter efficiency are given in the literature (6).

6.1.4 In order to calculate the count rate of each nuclide in the mixture, the count rate of that nuclide in a characteristic energy region and the interference from the other nuclides present in that region must be known. One method of choosing the energy regions is given in the literature (7). The characteristic energy region for a nuclide is usually the full energy peak, but the presence of another full energy peak nearby will influence the choice. It is not essential that the portions chosen have common boundaries, but it is essential that no boundaries overlap.

6.1.4.1 Obtain a pure solution of each gamma-emitting nuclide present in the sample. Place the solution containing one of the nuclides in the container and ad-

just the total volume to that of the sample. Analyze the gamma spectrum and find the baseline potentiometer settings or the channel numbers for the boundaries for each of the portions of the spectrum to be used in the calculations. For example, if there are five gamma-emitting nuclides present in the sample, then there must be five portions of the spectrum used in the calculations. Obtain the count rate, corrected for background, for each portion of the spectrum and the total count rate. Calculate the ratio of the count rate of each portion to the total count rate. The ratios are used as the coefficients in the equations used for calculating the amount of each nuclide present in a mixture. Repeat this procedure for each nuclide in order to obtain coefficients for each nuclide. If there are "n" nuclides in the mixture it is necessary to determine "n^2" coefficients. Once the coefficients have been determined, it is unnecessary to redetermine them as long as the resolution of the analyzer or the geometry of the system does not change. If the gain of the analyzer changes, it is necessary to recalculate the locations of the boundaries, channel numbers, or discriminator potentiometer settings.

6.2 *Tracer Experiments:*

6.2.1 Place an appropriate volume of a reference solution of the tracer (10^{-2} to 10^{-3} μc/ml) in a container and place the container on the detector or in the well. Throughout an experiment, volumes must be kept constant. Determine proper settings of voltage and gain and the count rate as directed in 6.1.4.

7. Procedure

7.1 Place the test specimen in a container and place the container on the detector or in the well. Determine the pulse spectrum. From the positions of the photopeaks and from the history of the specimen, identify the nuclides present in the sample. If the evidence is insufficient to permit identification of all nuclides in the mixture, decay studies, chemical separation of the constituents, or both, may be necessary. Procure appropriate standards and determine the counter efficiencies for the additional photopeaks. A background count should be taken at the beginning and at the conclusion of the experiment and an average value taken in computing results. The energy calibration should also be rerun at the conclusion of the experiment.

8. Calculations

8.1 The concentration of each of the "n" components in the sample must be expressed in terms of "n" simultaneous equations and the equations must be solved. The use of matrices and the solution of sets of linear simultaneous equations are described in the literature (8). A small analog computer designed especially for solving the equations from mixtures containing up to nine nuclides has been reported (9). An example of a matrix and the solution is given in the Appendix.

8.2 In order to convert the calculated gamma count rate of each nuclide to a photon emission rate, it is necessary to know the photon detection efficiency of the analyzer for each nuclide. The determination of the photon detection efficiency is given in 6.1.3. The disintegration rate of a nuclide is a function of the photon detection efficiency of the detector and of the number of photons of a given energy emitted each disintegration of the nuclide. This rate is calculated as follows:

$$\mathrm{dpm} = \frac{C}{A \times \zeta}$$

where:
dpm = disintegrations per minute,
C = observed counts per minute,
A = fractional abundance of the gamma ray, gammas per disintegration, and
ζ = photon detection efficiency, counts per gamma ray.

9. Precision

9.1 The precision of the counting-rate determination may be calculated by published methods reported elsewhere (10). The precision error includes the errors associated with the determination of each coefficient used in the calculation, those of the observed count rates of the sample within the boundaries, those of the background, and those due to instability of the counting equipment during the counting time. The precision error due to the count rates can be calculated while those due to the equipment are unknown and can be determined experimentally by multiple counts of a known mixture. In general, the major constituent of a mixture can be determined with a precision of about 5 per cent. However, the precision of the determination of minor components (less than 10 per cent of the total counts) will be poor if the major constituents emit gammas of higher energy. Accuracy and precision both suffer if the boundaries of the photopeaks are close together compared to the width of the peak. Boundaries should be as wide as possible without including large numbers of counts of other nuclides. Highly sophisticated methods of solving the equations are of value only if the counting equipment is stable and if the precision errors due to the count rates are small. Generally, the use of punched cards or tape and large computers are desirable primarily for the speed and ease of making the calculations and not to increase the precision of the method. Computers do not decrease the over-all precision errors, but may make meaningful estimates of the precision by the use of appropriate programs.

References

(1) G. Friedlander and J. W. Kennedy, *Nuclear and Radiochemistry*, John Wiley and Sons, Inc., New York, N. Y., 1964.
W. J. Price, *Nuclear Radiation Detection*, McGraw-Hill Book Co., Inc., New York, N. Y., 1964.
K. Seigbahn, *Alpha-, Beta-, and Gamma-Ray Spectroscopy*, North Holland Publishing Co., Amsterdam, 1965.

(2) C. E. Crouthamel, *Applied Gamma-Ray Spectrometry*, Pergamon Press, New York, N. Y., 1960.
R. E. Connally, "Instrumental Methods of Gamma-Ray Spectrometry," *Analytical Chemistry*, Vol. 28, 1956, pp. 1847–1853.

(3) D. De Soete and J. Hoste, "Predicting Gamma Resolution," *Nucleonics*, 20, No. 4, April, 1962, pp. 72–76.

(4) R. L. Heath, "Scintillation Spectrometry Gamma-Ray Spectrum Catalogue," *IDO-16880*, Clearing House for Federal Scientific and Technical Information, U. S. Department of Commerce, Springfield, Va. 22150.
D. Strominger, J. M. Hollander, and G. T. Seaborg, "Table of Isotopes," *Reviews of Modern Physics*, Vol. 30, No. 2, Part II, 1958.
R. C. Hawkins, W. J. Edwards, E. M. McLeod, "Tables of Gamma Rays from the Decay of Radionuclides," *AECL-1225*, Scientific Document Distribution Office, Atomic Energy of Canada Limited, Chalk River, Ontario, Canada, 1961.
M. H. Wachter, W. H. Ellett, and G. L. Brownell, "Absorption of Gamma Radiation in NaI Well Crystals," *Review of Scientific Instruments*, Vol. 31, 1960, pp. 626–630.

(5) D. F. Crouch and R. L. Heath, "Routine Testing and Calibration Procedures for Multichannel Pulse Analyzers and Gamma-Ray Spectrometers," *IDO-16923*, Clearing House for Federal Scientific and Technical Information, U. S. Department of Commerce, Springfield, Va. 22150.

(6) J. B. Ashe and J. H. McCrary, "Method for Determining Photopeak Efficiency of Scintillation Counters," *Review of Scientific Instruments*, Vol. 32, No. 2, 1961, pp. 205–206.
G. A. Brinkman, A. H. W. Aten, Jr., and J. Th. Veenboer, "Absolute Standardization with a NaI (Tl) Crystal—I. Calibration by Means of a Single Nuclide." *International Journal of Applied Radiation and Isotopes*, Vol. 14, 1963, pp. 153–157. "Absolute Standardization with a NaI (Tl) Crystal—II. Determination of the Total Efficiency," *International Journal of Applied Radiation and Isotopes*, Vol. 14, 1963, pp. 433–437.
W. Zimmerman, "Evaluation of Photopeaks in Scintillation Gamma-Ray Spectroscopy", *Review of Scientific Instruments*, Vol., 32, No. 2, 1961, pp. 1063–1065.

(7) G. R. Hagee, G. J. Karches, and A. S. Goldin, "Determination of I^{131}, Cs^{137}, and Ba^{140} in Fluid Milk by Gamma Spectroscopy," *Talanta*, Vol. 5, 1960, p. 36.

(8) P. S. Dwyer, *Linear Computations*, John Wiley and Sons, Inc., New York, N. Y., 1951.
R. F. Overman, "Normalizing Gamma Spectra for Data Processing," *DP-751*, Clearing House for Federal Scientific and Technical Information, U. S. Department of Commerce, Springfield, Va. 22150.
A. J. Ferguson, "A Program for the Analysis of Gamma Ray Scintillation Spectra Using the Method of Least Squares," *AECL-1398*, Scientific Document Distribution Office, Atomic Energy of Canada Limited, Chalk River, Ontario, Canada, 1961.
W. B. Strickfaden and R. M. Kloepper, "IBM 704 Programs for Unfolding Complex Gamma Ray Spectra," *LA-2461*, Clearing House for Federal Scientific and Technical Information, U. S. Department of Commerce, Springfield, Va. 22150.
"Applications of Computers to Nuclear and Radiochemistry," *NAS-NS-3107*, Clearing House for Federal Scientific and Technical Information, U. S. Department of Commerce, Springfield, Va. 22150.

(9) R. C. Propst and R. F. Overman, "An Analog Computer for the Solution of Linear Simultaneous Equations," *DP-846*, Clearing House for Federal Scientific and Technical Information, U. S. Department of Commerce, Springfield, Va. 22150.

(10) G. Friedlander and J. W. Kennedy, *Nuclear and Radiochemistry*, John Wiley and Sons, Inc., New York, N. Y., 1955, pp. 252–269.
R. T. Overman and H. M. Clark, *Radioisotope Techniques*, McGraw-Hill Book Co., Inc., New York, N. Y., 1960, pp. 98–130.
A. A. Jarrett, "Statistical Methods Used in

the Measurement of Radioactivity," *AECU-262*, Clearing House for Federal Scientific and Technical Information, Springfield, Va. 22150.

P. R. Rider, *An Introduction to Modern Statistical Methods*, John Wiley and Sons, Inc., New York, N. Y., 1939.

P. G. Hoel, *Introduction to Mathematical Statistics*, 2nd Ed., John Wiley and Sons, Inc., New York, N. Y., 1954.

APPENDIX

A1. Solution of a Five Component Mixture

A1.1 The method of calculation is given by the following example. The coefficients given in Table A1 are expressed as per cent of the total count rate and therefore the solutions are given as the total gamma count rates of the nuclides present. The values of the coefficients are valid for only one particular counting arrangement and are shown only to illustrate the calculations.

TABLE A1—COEFFICIENTS OF NU-CLIDES (STANDARDS) (EXPRESSED AS PER CENT OF TOTAL).

Energy Boundaries, kev	Nuclide				
	Ce^a	Cr^{51}	Ru^{103}	$Zr\text{-}Nb^{95}$	Co^{60}
64–144	31.2	5.01	8.33	7.54	3.76
256–400	14.7	81.3	10.1	11.6	6.97
401–576	9.09	0.20	66.6	9.86	8.01
676–900	9.66	0.00	0.37	54.2	10.4
1024–1444	2.71	0.00	0.23	0.11	40.8

a The Ce is a mixture of Ce^{144} and its daughter Pr^{144}.

A1.2 The simultaneous equations can be arranged in the form of a matrix:

$$C_{11}N_1 + C_{12}N_2 + C_{13}N_3 + C_{14}N_4 + C_{15}N_5 = M_1$$
$$C_{21}N_1 + C_{22}N_2 + C_{23}N_3 + C_{24}N_4 + C_{25}N_5 = M_2$$
$$C_{31}N_1 + C_{32}N_2 + C_{33}N_3 + C_{34}N_4 + C_{35}N_5 = M_3$$
$$C_{41}N_1 + C_{42}N_2 + C_{43}N_3 + C_{44}N_4 + C_{45}N_5 = M_4$$
$$C_{51}N_1 + C_{52}N_2 + C_{53}N_3 + C_{54}N_4 + C_{55}N_5 = M_5$$

where:

C = coefficient given in the table, expressed as per cent,

N = total gamma count rate of a nuclide, and

M = observed count rate of the sample between the given energy boundaries.

A1.3 Substituting the values for C into the equations:

$$31.2\ N_1 + 5.01\ N_2 + 8.33\ N_3 + 7.54\ N_4 + 3.76\ N_5 = M_1 \ldots (1)$$
$$14.7\ N_1 + 81.3\ N_2 + 10.1\ N_3 + 11.6\ N_4 + 6.97\ N_5 = M_2 \ldots (2)$$
$$9.09\ N_1 + 0.20\ N_2 + 66.6\ N_3 + 9.86\ N_4 + 8.01\ N_5 = M_3 \ldots (3)$$
$$9.66\ N_1 + 0.00\ N_2 + 0.37\ N_3 + 54.2\ N_4 + 10.4\ N_5 = M_4 \ldots (4)$$
$$2.71\ N_1 + 0.00\ N_2 + 0.23\ N_3 + 0.11\ N_4 + 40.8\ N_5 = M_5 \ldots (5)$$

where:

N_1 is Ce

N_2 is Cr^{51}

N_3 is Ru^{103}

N_4 is $Zr\text{-}Nb^{95}$, and

N_5 is Co^{60}.

A1.4 If the following count rates are observed between the given energy boundaries for an unknown sample then the five equations are solved for the total count rate, N, of each nuclide.

Observed count rate:

M_1 = 11.17 counts per minute

M_2 = 24.93 counts per minute

M_3 = 18.83 counts per minute

M_4 = 15.05 counts per minute, and

M_5 = 9.14 counts per minute.

A1.5 After solving the equations and multiplying the values of N by 100, since the coefficients are expressed as per cent of total, the following count rates are found:

Ce, N_1 = 20 counts per minute

Cr^{51}, N_2 = 20 counts per minute

Ru^{103}, N_3 = 20 counts per minute

$Zr\text{-}Nb^{95}$, N_4 = 20 counts per minute, and

Co^{60}, N_5 = 20 counts per minute.

Tentative Method of Test for

RADIONUCLIDES OF RADIUM IN INDUSTRIAL WATER AND INDUSTRIAL WASTE WATER[1]

ASTM Designation: D 2460 – 66 T

Issued, 1966

This Tentative Method has been approved by the sponsoring committee and accepted by the Society in accordance with established procedures, for use pending adoption as standard. Suggestions for revisions should be addressed to the Society at 1916 Race St., Philadelphia, Pa. 19103.

1. Scope

1.1 This method covers a procedure for the separation of dissolved radium from industrial water and industrial waste water for the purpose of measuring its radioactivity. While all radium isotopes are included, the method is limited to alpha-emitting radioisotopes by choice of radiation detector. The most important of these isotopes are radium-223, radium-224, and radium-226. The lower limit of concentration to which this method is applicable is 1 pc/liter; it may be applied to higher concentration by reduction of sample size.

1.2 This method may be used for absolute measurements by calibrating with a suitable alpha emitting radioisotope such as radium-226, or for relative methods by comparing measurements with each other. Mixtures of radium isotopes may be reported as equivalent radium-226. Information is also provided from which the relative contributions of radium isotopes may be calculated.

2. Summary of Method

2.1 Radium is collected from the water by coprecipitation with mixed barium and lead sulfates. The carriers are added to a solution containing alkaline citrate, which prevents precipitation until interchange has taken place. Sulfuric acid is then used to precipitate sulfates, which are purified by nitric acid washes. The precipitate is dissolved in ammoniacal EDTA, and the barium and radium sulfates are reprecipitated by addition of acetic acid, thus separating from lead and other radionuclides. The precipitate is dried on a plate, weighed to determine chemical yield, and alpha-counted to determine the total disintegration rate of radium isotopes. This procedure is based upon a published one.[2,3]

[1] Under the standardization procedure of the Society, this method is under the jurisdiction of the ASTM Committee D-19 on Industrial Water. A list of members may be found in the ASTM Year Book.

[2] A. S. Goldin, "Determination of Dissolved Radium," *Analytical Chemistry*, Vol. 33 (1961), pp. 406–409.

[3] P. F. Hallbach (ed.), "Radionuclide Analysis of Environmental Samples," Method RC-88A, USPHS Report *R59-6* (1959).

3. Significance

3.1 Radium is the most radiotoxic of the elements. Its isotope of mass 226 is the most hazardous, and a separate method is provided for the determination of this isotope. Refer to ASTM Method D 2335, Test for Radium-226 in Industrial Water and Industrial Waste Water.[4] The isotopes 223 and 224, though not so hazardous, are of some concern in appraising the quality of water.

3.2 The isotopes other than that of mass 226 may be determined by difference if 226 is measured separately. It should be noted that one finds radium-226 and -223 together in variable proportions,[5,6] but radium-224 does not normally occur with them. Thus radium-223 may often be determined by simply subtracting the radium-226 content from the total; and if radium-226 and -223 are low, radium-224 may be determined directly. The determination of a single isotope in a mixture is less precise than if it occurred alone.

4. Definitions

4.1 For definitions of terms used in this method, refer to ASTM Definitions D 1129, Terms Relating to Industrial Water and Industrial Waste Water.[4] For terms not included in Definitions D 1129, reference may be made to other published glossaries.[7]

5. Interferences

5.1 Content of barium in the sample exceeding 0.2 mg will cause a falsely high chemical yield.

---

[4] Appears in this publication.
[5] H. G. Petrow and R. J. Allen, "Estimation of the Isotopic Composition of Separated Radium Samples," *Analytical Chemistry*, Vol. 33 (1961), pp. 1303–1305.
[6] E. R. Ebersole, et al., AEC Report *TID-7616* (1962), pp. 147–175.
[7] "USA Standard Glossary of Terms in Nuclear Science and Technology" (USASI Designation: N1.1-1957).

6. Apparatus

6.1 For suitable gas flow or scintillation alpha counting equipment, refer to ASTM Method D 1943, Measurement of Alpha Particle Radioactivity of Industrial Water and Industrial Waste Water.[4]

7. Reagents

7.1 *Purity of Reagents*—Reagent grade chemicals shall be used in all tests. Unless otherwise indicated, it is intended that all reagents shall conform to the specifications of the Committee on Analytical Reagents of the American Chemical Society, where such specifications are available.[8] Other grades may be used, provided it is first ascertained that the reagent is of sufficiently high purity to permit its use without lessening the accuracy of the determination.

7.2 *Purity of Water*—Unless otherwise indicated, references to water shall be understood to mean referee grade reagent water conforming to ASTM Specifications D 1193, for Reagent Water.[4]

7.3 *Radioactive Purity* shall be such that the measured radioactivity of blank samples does not exceed the calculated probable error of the measurement.

7.4 *Acetic Acid, Glacial (sp gr 1.05)*.

7.5 *Ammonium Hydroxide (sp gr 0.90)*—Concentrated ammonium hydroxide (NH_4OH).

7.6 *Ammonium Hydroxide (1:1)*—Mix one volume of concentrated ammonium hydroxide (NH_4OH, sp gr 0.90) with one volume of water.

7.7 *Barium Nitrate Carrier Solution (11.2 g $Ba(NO_3)_2$/liter)*—Dissolve 11.2 g of barium nitrate ($Ba(NO_3)_2$) in water and dilute to 1 liter. This solution will contain 10 g Ba^{++}/liter.

---

[8] "Reagent Chemicals, American Chemical Society Specifications," Am. Chemical Soc., Washington, D. C. For suggestions on the testing of reagents not listed by the American Chemical Society, see "Reagent Chemicals and Standards," by Joseph Rosin, D. Van Nostrand Co., Inc., New York, N. Y., and the "United States Pharmacopeia."

7.8 *Citric Acid Solution (350 g/liter)*— Dissolve 350 g of citric acid monohydrate in water and dilute to 1 liter.

TABLE 1—GROWTH OF ALPHA ACTIVITY IN RADIUM-226.

Time, hr	Correction, F
0	1.0000
1	1.0160
2	1.0363
3	1.0580
4	1.0798
5	1.1021
6	1.1238
24	1.4892
48	1.9054
72	2.2525

7.9 *Lead Nitrate Carrier Solution (166 g/liter)*—Dissolve 166 g of lead nitrate ($Pb(NO_3)_2$) in water and dilute to 1 liter.

7.10 *Methyl Orange Indicator*—Dissolve 1.0 g of methyl orange in water and dilute to 1 liter.

7.11 *Nitric Acid (sp gr 1.42)*—Concentrated nitric acid (HNO_3).

7.12 *Sodium Ethylenediamine Tetraacetate Solution (EDTA) (93 g/liter)*—Dissolve 93 g of sodium ethylenediamine tetraacetate dihydrate in water and dilute to 1 liter.

7.13 *Sulfuric Acid (1:1)*—Cautiously add with stirring one volume of concen-

TABLE 2—RADIUM ISOTOPES AND DAUGHTERS.[a]

Nuclide		Radiation		Half-Life	Common Name
Parent	Daughters	Type[b]	Energy[c]		
Ra^{226}		α	4.78 (95 per cent) 4.59 (5 per cent)	1.6 × 10^3 years	radium
	Rn^{222}	α	5.48	3.8 days	radon
	Po^{218}	α	6.00	3 min	radium A
	Pb^{214}	β (γ)		27 min	radium B
	Bi^{214}	β (γ)		20 min	radium C
	Po^{214}	α	7.68	1.6 × 10^{-4} sec	radium C′
Ra^{224}		α	5.68 (95 per cent) 5.44 (5 per cent)	3.6 days	thorium X
	Rn^{220}	α	6.28	54 sec	thoron
	Po^{216}	α	6.78	0.16 sec	thorium A
	Pb^{212}	β (γ)		10.6 hr	thorium B
	Bi^{212}	β (64 per cent) (γ)		60 min	thorium C
		α (36 per cent)	6.09 (27 per cent) 6.05 (70 per cent) others		
	Po^{212}	α	8.78	0.3 μsec	thorium C′
	Ti^{208}	β (γ)		3.1 min	thorium C″
Ra^{223}		α (γ)	5.71 (50 per cent) 5.60 (24 per cent) others	11.7 days	actinium X
	Rn^{219}	α (γ)	6.81 (82 per cent) 6.55 (13 per cent) 6.42 (5 per cent)	4 sec	actinon
	Po^{215}	α	7.36	0.002 sec	actinium A
	Pb^{211}	β (γ)		36 min	actinium B
	Bi^{211}	α (γ)	6.62 (83 per cent) 6.27 (17 per cent)	2.2 min	actinium C
	Tl^{207}	β		4.8 min	actinium C″

[a] Daughters with half-lives less than 30 days.
[b] Gamma indicated only when more than 5 per cent and greater than 0.1 Mev.
[c] Energy indicated for alpha radiation only.

trated sulfuric acid (H_2SO_4, sp gr 1.84) to one volume of water.

8. Sampling

8.1 Collect the sample in accordance with the applicable methods of the American Society for Testing and Materials, as follows:

are available from the National Bureau of Standards. Two or more portions of such a solution, containing known disintegration rates shall be analyzed as described in 10.1 through 10.7. After counting, the measured activity shall be corrected for chemical yield, and the efficiency, E (see 11.1 and 11.2), shall be

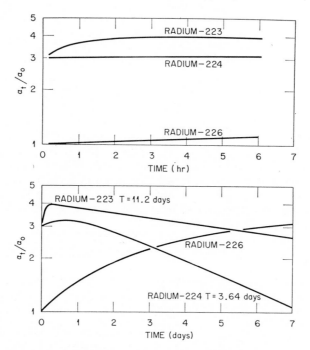

Fig. 1—Growth of Alpha Activity into Pure Radium Isotopes.

D   510—Sampling Industrial Water,[4]
D   860—Sampling Water from Boilers,[4] and
D 1496—Sampling Homogeneous Industrial Waste Water.[4]

8.2 Sample 1 liter, or a smaller volume, provided it contains from 100 to 10,000 pc of radium. Add 10 ml of HNO_3 per liter of sample.

9. Calibration and Standardization

9.1 For absolute counting the alpha detector must be calibrated to obtain the ratio of count rate to disintegration rate. Standardized solutions of radium-226

calculated as the ratio of the observed counting rate to the known disintegration rate.

10. Procedure

10.1 Add to the sample 5 ml of citric acid and make alkaline with NH_4OH. Add 2 ml of lead carrier and 1.00 ml of barium carrier.

10.2 Heat to boiling and add 10 drops of methyl orange indicator. With stirring, add H_2SO_4 (1:1) until the solution becomes pink, then add 5 drops in excess.

10.3 Digest hot for 10 min. Let cool and collect the precipitate in a centrifuge tube. If large volumes are handled, collection will be facilitated by initial decanting. Centrifuge, then discard the supernatant liquid.

10.4 Wash the precipitate twice with 10-ml portions of HNO_3 and discard the washings. Dissolve the precipitate in 10 ml of water, 10 ml of EDTA, and 4 ml of NH_4OH (1:1). Warm if necessary to effect dissolution.

10.5 Reprecipitate barium sulfate ($BaSO_4$) by dropwise addition of acetic acid, adding 3 drops in excess. Note the time. Centrifuge then discard the supernatant liquid. Add 10 ml of water, mix well, centrifuge, and discard the supernatant liquid.

10.6 Transfer the precipitate to a suitable alpha plate, previously flamed and weighed. Dry the precipitate, flame, and weigh to determine chemical yield.

10.7 Count in an appropriate alpha counter, noting the time.

11. Calculation

11.1 Calculate the concentration D of alpha-emitting radium radionuclides as radium-226 in picocuries of radium per liter as follows:

$$D = \frac{C}{2.22\,EVRF}$$

where:

C = alpha counting rate, net counts per minute,

E = counter alpha-particle efficiency, counts per disintegration,

V = sample volume, liters,

2.22 = conversion factor from disintegrations per minute to picocuries,

R = fractional chemical yield for the separation, and

F = correction for daughter growth between separation (see 10.5 and Table 1) and counting.

11.2 The relative contribution of various radium isotopes, if desired, may be obtained by alpha spectroscopy.[9] Otherwise, repeated measurements of the activity permit estimation of the isotopic composition. Table 2 lists the alpha-active radium isotopes and their daughters. Figure 1 shows characteristic growth and decay curves[2] for the three important isotopes, and equations and tables have been published.[10]

12. Precision

12.1 Precision depends on the random counting error and on determination of chemical yield. The observed single operator precision is about 10 per cent.[2]

---

[9] R. H. Gatrousis and C. E. Crouthamel, "Progress in Nuclear Energy," Series IX (*Analytical Chemistry*), Vol. 2, C. E. Crouthamel, Ed. Pergamon Press, N. Y. (1961) pp. 44–65.

[10] H. W. Kirby, "Decay and Growth Tables for the Naturally Occurring Radioactive Series," *Analytical Chemistry*, Vol. 26 (1954) p. 1064.

Tentative Method of Test for

RADIOACTIVE IRON-59 IN INDUSTRIAL WATER AND INDUSTRIAL WASTE WATER[1]

ASTM Designation: D 2461 – 66 T

ISSUED, 1966

This Tentative Method has been approved by the sponsoring committee and accepted by the Society in accordance with established procedures, for use pending adoption as standard. Suggestions for revisions should be addressed to the Society at 1916 Race St., Philadelphia, Pa. 19103.

1. Scope

1.1 This method covers the measurement of radioactive iron contained in industrial water and industrial waste water in concentrations above 0.1 μc/liter. It is limited by choice of radiation detector to the iron radioisotope of mass 59 produced in nuclear reactors and which may also be used as a tracer. Modifications in the analytical method are included for measurement at higher and lower concentrations.

1.2 This method may be used for absolute measurements by calibrating the nuclear radiation detector with a standard iron-59 solution, or for relative measurements by comparing the measurements made.

2. Summary of Method

2.1 Radioactive iron and added iron carrier are separated from other activities by hydroxide precipitation, liquid-liquid extraction, and ion exchange. The separated iron is counted with a gamma counter or spectrometer, or a beta particle detector.

NOTE 1—This method is adapted from Procedures 1 and 3 of a previously published monograph.[2] The decay scheme of iron-59 is given in the Appendix, Table A1. For a discussion of beta counting, refer to ASTM Method D 1890, Measurement of Beta Particle Radioactivity in Industrial Water and Industrial Waste Water.[3] For gamma counting, refer to ASTM Method D 1690, Measurement of Gamma Radioactivity in Industrial Water and Industrial Waste Water.[3] Gamma-ray spectrometry is described in a report by Heath[4] and a publication by Crouthamel.[5] Gamma-ray spectrometry is also described in ASTM Method D 2459, Test for Gamma Spectrometry of Industrial Water and Industrial Waste Water.[3]

3. Significance

3.1 Iron-59 is formed by neutron irradiation of iron in nuclear reactor structures, or in solution or suspension in

[1] Under the standardization procedure of the Society, this method is under the jurisdiction of the ASTM Committee D-19 on Industrial Water. A list of members may be found in the ASTM Year Book.

[2] J. M. Nielson, "The Radiochemistry of Iron," National Academy of Sciences, National Research Council Report NAS-NS-3017, 1960.

[3] Appears in this publication.

[4] R. L. Heath, "Scintillation Spectrometry, Gamma-Ray Spectrum Catalog," AEC Report IDO 16880, 1964.

[5] C. E. Crouthamel, "Applied Gamma-Ray Spectrometry," Pergamon Press, New York, N. Y., 1960.

cooling water exposed to neutron irradiation. Its determination is therefore of importance in evaluating the potential radioactive hazard of the cooling water, and in some instances, in locating the source of corrosion products in the cooling water.

3.2 Some samples may require decontamination greater than that furnished by this method. If so, Procedure 7 of the monograph[2] may be used, or the liquid-liquid extraction steps of this method may be repeated.

4. Definitions

4.1 For definitions of terms used in this method, refer to ASTM Definitions D 1129, Terms Relating to Industrial Water and Industrial Waste Water.[3]

4.2 For terms not defined in Definitions D 1129, reference may be made to other published glossaries.[6]

5. Interferences

5.1 Nonradioactive iron present in the sample will interfere in the method by causing an overestimation of chemical yield and must be corrected for if its amount exceeds 0.2 mg in the sample taken.

5.2 Substances such as tartrate will interfere by preventing the initial precipitation of iron as hydroxide.

5.3 Excessive amounts of iron-55, a 2.7-year emitter of manganese x-rays, may interfere in beta counting. If this interference occurs, correction may be determined by use of a standardized iron-55 preparation.

5.4 The method should not be expected to provide decontamination of more than a million-fold from other radionuclides.

6. Apparatus

6.1 *Beta Particle Counter*—This counter is usually a proportional detector connected to the appropriate amplifier, discriminator, and scaling equipment. Refer to ASTM Method D 1890, Measurement of Beta Particle Radioactivity in Industrial Water and Industrial Waste Water.[3]

6.2 *Gamma Counter*—This counter is preferably a NaI scintillation detector assembly connected to the appropriate amplifier, pulse-height analyzer, or single-channel pulse-height discriminator. Refer to ASTM Method D 1690, Measurement of Gamma Radiation in Industrial Water and Industrial Waste Water.[3]

6.3 *Ion-Exchange Column*—Glass column approximately 17 cm long by 0.9-cm I.D., with a 50-ml reservoir at the top and a 2-mm bore stopcock at the bottom. A loose glass wool plug shall be inserted in the bottom.

7. Reagents and Materials

7.1 *Purity of Reagents*—Reagent grade chemicals shall be used in all tests. Unless otherwise indicated, it is intended that all reagents shall conform to the specifications of the Committee on Analytical Reagents of the American Chemical Society, where such specifications are available.[7] Other grades may be used, provided it is first ascertained that the reagent is of sufficiently high purity to permit its use without lessening the accuracy of the determination.

7.2 *Purity of Water*—Unless otherwise indicated, references to water shall be understood to mean referee grade reagent water conforming to ASTM Specifications D 1193, for Reagent Water.[3]

7.3 *Radioactive Purity* shall be such that the measured radioactivity of

---

[6] "USA Standard Glossary of Terms in Nuclear Science and Technology" (USASI Designation: N1.1-1957).

[7] "Reagent Chemicals, American Chemical Society Specifications," Am. Chemical Soc., Washington, D.C. For suggestions on the testing of reagents not listed by the American Chemical Society, see "Reagent Chemicals and Standards," by Joseph Rosin, D. Van Nostrand Co., Inc., New York, N. Y., and the "United States Pharmacopeia."

blank samples does not exceed the calculated probable error of the measurement.

7.4 *Ammonium Hydroxide (sp gr 0.90)* —Concentrated ammonium hydroxide (NH_4OH).

7.5 *Anion Exchange Resin*—Make a slurry with water and transfer to the column (6.3) until a layer of resin[8] about 12 cm deep is formed. Wash with 50 ml of water and 50 ml of concentrated HCl (sp gr 1.19) before each use.

7.6 *Ferric Chloride Carrier Solution (49 g/liter)*—Dissolve 49 g of ferric chloride ($FeCl_3 \cdot 6H_2O$) in 100 ml of HCl (1:19), filter, and dilute to 1 liter. This solution contains 10 g Fe^{+++}/liter. Standardize by precipitation of hydroxide, filtering, and igniting to ferric oxide (Fe_2O_3).[9]

7.7 *Hydrochloric Acid (sp gr 1.19)*— Concentrated hydrochloric acid (HCl).

7.8 *Hydrochloric Acid (1:1)*—Mix one volume of hydrochloric acid (sp gr 1.19) with one volume of water.

7.9 *Hydrochloric Acid (1:19)*—Mix 1 volume of concentrated hydrochloric acid (HCl, sp gr 1.19) with 19 volumes of water.

7.10 *Hydrogen Peroxide (30 per cent)*— Concentrated hydrogen peroxide (H_2O_2).

7.11 *Nitric Acid (sp gr 1.42)*—Concentrated nitric acid (HNO_3).

7.12 *Nitric Acid-Hydrofluoric Acid Mixture*—Mix one volume of concentrated HNO_3 (sp gr 1.42), one volume of hydrofluoric acid (HF, sp gr 1.19), and 98 volumes of water.

7.13 *Nitric Acid-Hydrogen Peroxide Mixture*—Mix five volumes of HNO_3 (sp gr 1.42), two volumes of H_2O_2 (30 per cent), and thirteen volumes of water.

7.14 *Thenoyltrifluoroacetone (TTA)-*

---

[8] Dowex 2-X8 chloride-form resin, 200 to 400-mesh, obtainable from the Dow Chemical Co., has been found satisfactory for this purpose.

[9] N. H. Furman, ed., "Scott's Standard Methods of Chemical Analysis," D. Van Nostrand Co., Inc., New York, N. Y., 1962.

Xylene (111 g/liter)—Dissolve 111 g of TTA in xylene and dilute to 1 liter.

7.15 *Xylene.*

8. Sampling

8.1 Collect the sample in accordance with the applicable methods of the American Society for Testing and Materials as follows:

D 510—Sampling Industrial Water.[3]
D 860—Sampling Water from Boilers,[3] and
D 1496—Sampling Homogeneous Industrial Waste Water.[3]

8.2 For gamma counting, the total iron-59 activity taken should be about 0.1 μc, and for beta counting, about 0.01 μc. The minimum activity measurable would be the smallest amount giving the desired precision for that determination and would be limited by the counter background.

9. Calibration

9.1 For absolute measurement the detector must be calibrated to obtain the ratio of count rate to disintegration rate. Standardized solutions of iron-59 are available from one or more suppliers. Two or more portions of such a solution, containing known disintegration rates, shall be analyzed as described in 10.1, 10.2, 10.11. After counting, the measured activity shall be corrected for chemical yield, and the efficiency, E, (see 11.1) shall be calculated as the ratio of the observed counting rate to the known disintegration rate.

10. Procedure

10.1 Make the sample just acidic with concentrated HCl (sp gr 1.19) and add 2 ml in excess. Add 1.00 ml of $FeCl_3$ carrier. Boil 2 min to ensure solution of all the iron (see ASTM Method D 1068, Test for Iron in Industrial Water and Industrial Waste Water.[3])

10.2 Add excess NH₄OH. Collect the precipitate in a centrifuge tube by initial settling (if large volume) and centrifugation. Discard the supernatant solution and wash the precipitate with 15 ml of water, discarding the wash.

10.3 Add to the precipitate 3 ml of water and 10 ml of concentrated HNO_3 (sp gr 1.42). Stir to dissolve and add 1 ml of H_2O_2. Mix.

10.4 In the following procedure, use a suitable extraction apparatus. A separatory funnel may be employed as usual, or a centrifuge tube may be used, removing unwanted phases by transfer pipet. Add 15 ml of TTA-xylene and extract for 5 min. Discard the aqueous (lower) phase. Wash the extract and vessel walls with several milliliters of water and discard the wash. If necessary for high decontamination, transfer the extract in this and the next three steps to clean vessels.

10.5 Add 15 ml of nitric acid-hydrogen peroxide mixture, shake 1 min, and discard aqueous phase.

10.6 Wash the extract with 15 ml of nitric acid-hydrofluoric acid mixture. Discard the aqueous phase.

10.7 Add 5 ml of concentrated HCl (sp gr 1.19). Mix until the organic phase is essentially decolorized. Discard the organic phase and wash the aqueous phase and vessel with several milliliters of xylene. Discard the xylene.

10.8 Evaporate just to dryness (do not bake), and take up in 20 ml of concentrated HCl (sp gr 1.19). Pass through the prepared resin in the column. Discard the effluent. Wash with 40 ml of concentrated HCl (sp gr 1.19).

10.9 Wash with 40 ml of HCl (1:1).

Elute iron from the resin with 30 ml of water.

10.10 Precipitate with excess NH₄OH. Filter on ashless paper designed for gelatinous precipitates. Dry and ignite to Fe_2O_3 in a porcelain crucible. Weigh to determine chemical yield.

10.11 Mount the Fe_2O_3 and count beta or gamma radiation.

11. Calculation

11.1 Calculate the concentration, A, of iron-59 in microcuries per milliliter as follows:

$$A = \frac{C}{2.22 \times 10^6 \, E}$$

where:
C = corrected count rate of sample, counts per minute per milliliter,
E = counter efficiency, and
2.22×10^6 = conversion factor from disintegrations per minute to microcuries.

11.2 Calculate the decay correction for iron-59 as follows:

$$A = A_0 e^{(-0.693 t_d/45)}$$

where:
A = activity at time of measurement,
A_0 = activity at time zero, that is, reference time, and
t_d = elapsed time, days, between measurement and reference time.

12. Precision

12.1 Precision depends on random counting error and on determination of chemical yield. The single operator precision is within 3 per cent when the random counting error is 1 per cent or less.

APPENDIX

TABLE A1—RADIATIONS OF IRON-59.[a]

Half-Life	Beta		Gamma	
	Energy, Mev	%	Energy, Mev	%
45 Days	0.27	46	0.19	3
	0.46	54	1.10	57
			1.29	43

[a] D. Strominger, J. M. Hollander, and G. T. Seaborg, "Table of Isotopes," *Reviews of Modern Physics*, Vol. 30, No. 2, Part II, 1958.

Tentative Method for

MEASUREMENT OF DELAYED NEUTRON-EMITTING FISSION PRODUCTS IN NUCLEAR REACTANT COOLANT WATER DURING REACTOR OPERATION[1]

ASTM Designation: D 2470 – 66 T

ISSUED, 1966

This Tentative Method has been approved by the sponsoring committee and accepted by the Society in accordance with established procedures, for use pending adoption as standard. Suggestions for revisions should be addressed to the Society at 1916 Race St., Philadelphia, Pa. 19103.

1. Scope

1.1 This method covers the detection and measurement of delayed neutron-emitting fission products contained in nuclear reactor coolant water while the reactor is operating, and is limited to the measurement of the delayed neutron-emitting bromine isotope of mass 87 and the delayed neutron-emitting iodine isotope of mass 137. The other delayed-neutron-emitting fission products could not in all cases be accurately distinguished by this method from the delayed neutron-emitting nitrogen isotope of mass 17 formed under some reactor conditions by neutron irradiation of the coolant water molecules.

1.2 This method may be used for absolute measurement of the concentration of the combined bromine-87 and iodine-137 fission products on a continuous basis by calibrating the delayed neutron detector readings with a standard delayed neutron-emitting solution. This method may be used for relative measurements of the delayed neutron level by comparing detector readings with the base level readings obtained with no fission products present in the water to provide a means of detecting fissionable material in contact with the coolant, or by comparing the detector readings of coolant from various channels with the mixed coolant readings to provide a means for locating the position of the exposed fissile material. General information on the occurrence of delayed neutron emission, neutron measurement, and application of delayed neutron measurement to the detection and location of fissionable material have been published.[2]

---

[1] Under the standardization procedure of the Society, this method is under the jurisdiction of the ASTM Committee D-19 on Industrial Water. A list of members may be found in the ASTM Year Book.

[2] R. A. Dewes and J. C. Childs, "Delayed Neutron Detection Methods Applied to the Detection and Location of Reactor Fuel Element Failures," *Communications and Electronics*, Jan., 1960.

2. Summary of Method

2.1 The neutron activity in a flowing sample of the nuclear reactor cooling water is measured when the reactor is in operation, with special delayed neutron measurement equipment. The elapsed time of the coolant sample after leaving the operating reactor core is adjusted to 1 to 2 min by control of the sampling flow rate. This delay time is large enough to reduce the delayed neutron emission from the 4.14-sec half-life nitrogen isotope of mass 17 produced by neutron irradiation of the oxygen in water molecules and all of the delayed neutron-emitting fission products except bromine-87 and iodine-137 to insignificant levels, thereby providing a means for measuring the neutron emission from the bromine-87 and iodine-137 fission products without interference.

2.2 The delayed neutron particles are measured with special proportional counters filled with boron trifluoride gas enriched in the boron isotope of mass 10. The neutron particles emitted by the coolant sample enter the sensitive region of the detector and react with the boron atoms of mass 10 to produce alpha particles and lithium atoms. The alpha particles in turn produce ionization of the counting gas and are measured as voltage pulses by a counting scaler as in the proportional alpha counting described in ASTM Method D 1943, Measurement of Alpha Particle Radioactivity of Industrial Water and Industrial Waste Water.[3] The number of pulses per unit time is related to the disintegration rate of the bromine-87 and iodine-137 in the test sample. The efficiency of the system can be determined by passing a standard delayed neutron-emitting solution through the system as described in 10. Sample Measurement Procedure.

3. Significance

3.1 The presence and level of delayed neutron-emitting fission products can only be measured in coolant coming from an operating nuclear reactor because of the short-life of the delayed neutron-emitting fission products.

3.2 This method cannot be used to distinguish between the iodine-137 and bromine-87 nuclides because of the closeness of their half-lives. A measure of the total delayed neutron emission from the mixture of the two nuclides results from this method.

3.3 The neutron counters are not sensitive to other radiation except when the gamma and beta radiation levels are sufficiently large to cause a pile up or summation of many small pulses with a resulting pulse having an amplitude greater than the sensitivity control setting. Beta and gamma radiation levels of this size normally will not be encountered in this measurement.

4. Definitions

4.1 For definitions of terms used in this method refer to ASTM Definitions D 1129 Terms Relating to Industrial Water and Industrial Waste Water.[3]

4.2 For terms not defined in this method or in Definitions D 1129, reference may be made to other published glossaries.[4]

5. Measurement Variables

5.1 During this method of continuous measurement, the short half-life delayed neutron-emitting fission products are constantly being formed by fission in the reactor and are circulated in the coolant as they are formed and then decay. A separate by-pass stream of different flow velocity is removed from the system for the purpose of measurement. The re-

---

[3] Appears in this publication.

[4] "USA Standard Glossary of Terms in Nuclear Science and Technology" (USASI Designation: N 1.1-1957).

sulting equilibrium concentration of the delayed neutron-emitting fission products which is being measured will be affected by a number of operating variables which must be accurately measured and corrected for in the fission product measurement. These operating variables are: the coolant flow rate

5.2 In tests requiring only relative measurement of fission product delay neutrons above a previously established background or normal level as in detecting a fuel element cladding failure, all of the variables listed in 5.1 should be held constant and should be the same as for the background or normal level

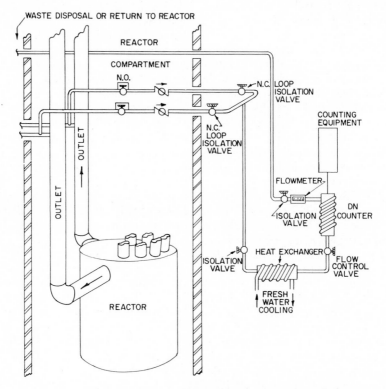

Fig. 1—Typical Fuel Element Failure Detection System Installation.

through the reactor, the time decay of the coolant after leaving the neutron flux until it is measured in the delayed neutron measurement equipment, the coolant recirculation time if the reactor coolant is recirculated rather than once through, the thermal neutron flux in the reactor, and the detector efficiency which is affected by the detector geometry, source volume, and characteristics of the gas-filled detectors used.

measurement. In tests requiring determination of the actual level of the delayed neutron-emitting fission products as in determining the amount of fissile material exposed to the coolant, the variables described must be accurately known. The efficiency of the delayed neutron-measurement equipment for registering counts on the scaling equipment of the delayed neutrons being given off by the coolant sample entering the equipment is best determined experimentally by passing a standard solution containing a known level of delayed neutron-emitting isotopes through the measurement equipment. This is described in detail in 9. Calibration and Standardization.

5.3 The limit of sensitivity for the measurement is a function of the background counting rate (without flow through the detector) and the electronic noise produced by the electrical equipment. The use of borate hydrogenous or hydrogenous-cadmium shielding to minimize the detection of stray neutrons from the reactor will aid in reducing the background counting rate.

6. Interferences

6.1 If the sample has not decayed sufficiently when it has reached the delayed neutron detector, the delayed neutron emanation from nitrogen-17 which is not a fission product will interfere with the measurement of fission product level. Other shorter-lived delayed neutron emitting fission products such as bromine-89 will also interfere with the quantitative estimation of the iodine-137 and bromine-87 nuclides if the sample decay is too short.

7. Apparatus

7.1 *Neutron Particle Detection and Counting Equipment*, consisting of the following components (see Fig. 1):

7.1.1 *Helical Source Coil* for containing the coolant and concentrating the source of delayed neutrons. The volume of the coil should be in the order of 150 to 500 cm³ depending on the length of the neutron counters used. It should be constructed of metal to decrease beta and alpha particle detection.

7.1.2 *Boron Trifluoride Proportional Counters* enriched in boron of mass 10 located in proximity to the source coil to measure delayed neutron emission

from the coil. There are several types commercially available. To establish freedom from undesirable characteristics, the manufacturer shall supply voltage plateau and background counting rate data. Voltage plateau data shall show the threshold voltage, slope, and length of plateau for a particular input sensitivity. The counters should have a matched operating voltage to allow them to be used in parallel with a single preamplifier and voltage supply. From three to twelve of these counters should be used within or around the source coil, or both, depending on the geometric arrangement. Three tubes inside the source coil are generally equivalent to a larger number outside the coil.

7.1.3 *Cylindrical Container and Shield* filled with water, paraffin, or polyethylene or combinations of the three with an optional cadmium shield for containing the source coil and neutron counters. The function of the shield is to moderate the 0.013 mev and 0.67 mev delayed neutrons to thermal neutron energy, where they are more efficiently counted, and to shield the neutron counters from ambient neutrons leaking through the reactor shield. Holes for the gas-filled proportional counters and for a neutron-emitting calibration source are required in the container and shield.

7.1.4 *Electrical Amplification and Counting Equipment* consisting of a high-voltage power supply, amplifier, a discriminator circuit, a digital pulse counter (scaler), and an elapsed time indicator. A preamplifier should be employed if more than 6 in. (15.2 cm) of cable are used to connect the neutron counters to the amplifier and counting equipment. The input sensitivity of the amplifier should be variable by a factor of 10 with the amplifier gain control. A variable discriminator circuit should be present at the amplifier output to eliminate gamma pulses and electronic noise. This discriminator should be variable over at least 10 per cent of the output range. Often the scaler, mechanical register, power supply, amplifier, and discriminator are contained in a single chassis, generally termed the scaler. The power supply and amplifier sections must be matched with the type of detector to produce satisfactory operating characteristics and to provide sufficient range in adjustments to maintain controlled conditions. The manufacturer shall provide resolving time information for the counting system. The scaler shall have capacity for storing and visually displaying at least 5×10^5 counts with a scaling ratio of 64 or greater (preferably 1000) and with a resolving time no greater than 5 μ sec. The instrument should have an adjustable input sensitivity that can be matched to the detector and a variable high-voltage power supply with indicating meter.

7.2 *Sampling and Circulating System* to circulate reactor cooling water through the neutron detector made up of a flow-regulating valve, flow meter, isolation valves, sample cooler, if required, and pipe or tubing to make up the typical circuit shown in Fig. 1. The equipment should be selected to give controllable and measurable sample flow rates to and through the source coil equivalent to the required one to two-min sample delay time, and an ambient temperature at the neutron counters below 150 F (65.5 C). The equipment should also meet the applicable sampling equipment requirements in ASTM Specifications D 1192, for Equipment for Sampling Industrial Water and Steam.[3]

8. Sampling

8.1 Continuous sampling is required for this measurement with the reactor in operation. The flushing, sampling, and sample disposal should be in accordance with Sections 32 to 41 of ASTM Methods D 510, Sampling Industrial Water.[3]

8.2 The sample points and sample rate should be selected so that the delay time of the coolant sample from the reactor outlet to the center of the coolant source coil is 1 to 2 min.

9. Calibration and Standardization

9.1 Put the instrument into operation according to the manufacturer's instructions. Place the neutron calibration source, nominally 5 mc of polonium-beryllium in the calibration hole.

9.2 Set the amplifier gain and discriminator (pulse-height selector) controls at approximately the center of their ranges. Turn the "count" switch to "count" position. Raise the voltage until a count rate of about 300 counts per minute is obtained. Advance the voltage in increments of 25 to 50 v and determine the counting rate at each of these voltage settings (count for 1 min at each setting). Determine the counting rate at four or more settings of the discriminator (pulse-height selector) at each voltage setting. Also measure the background counting rate at each of the settings with the calibration source removed. The reactor should be operating with the same neutron flux as for the sample measurement described in 10 to give proper background measurement.

9.3 Plot the net counting rate against the various voltage settings. The curve should rise sharply and then reach an approximately constant value (plateau) and finally rise again. A voltage about midway on the plateau of the curve should be selected. Plot the net count rate against the various discriminator settings, using the previously selected voltage that was on the voltage plateau. The curve should rise initially as the discriminator setting is decreased, level off, and then rise sharply again. The setting of the discriminator that corresponds to a value near the shoulder of the curve, but definitely on the pulse height plateau, should be used. The counting rate of the source and background must be checked with 10-min counts whenever delayed neutrons are to be measured, but the plateaus require redetermination only if source and background rates change appreciably.

10. Sample Measurement Procedure

10.1 With the equipment calibrated, background determined, and equipment in operation in accordance with 9. Calibration and Standardization, initiate continuous sample flow through the coolant source coil by opening the isolation valves and adjusting the flow-regulating valve to give a flow rate as measured on the flow meter equivalent to a holdup time of 1 to 2 min. Where high-temperature coolant is being sampled, care should be taken that the sample cooler is performing satisfactorily since high ambient temperature will damage the neutron counters.

10.2 Turn the "count" switch to "count" position and proceed to make ten 10-min measurements. After a sufficient number of counting intervals have been recorded, stop the sample flow by closing the isolation valves. Subtract the background from the count rate as described in 12.1.

11. System Efficiency Determination

11.1 The absolute counting efficiency of the delayed neutron measuring system is best determined experimentally by passing a solution with a known delayed neutron emission through the system. Three ways that this can be done are as follows:

11.1.1 Continuous recirculation of water containing a known concentration of uranium of mass 235 through the counting system and an operating reactor (usually a test reactor) to give about 250,000 neutron disintegrations per minute at the counter. The solution can be contained and circulated in plastic tubing with a suitable holdup chamber in the reactor, reactor flux measuring equipment, and coolant flow-measuring equipment.

11.1.2 Utilization of the nitrogen-17 delayed neutron-emitting isotope in a reactor system where there is no significant fissile material in contact with the coolant, as the standard for determining the efficiency. In this method, the delay time of the sample from the reactor outlet to the counter must be reduced to about 4 sec and the reactor neutron flux and flow rates carefully measured.

11.1.3 Insertion of a fixed area, nominally 0.1 per cent of the reactor core area, plated with a known amount of uranium-235 per unit area in a known thermal neutron flux in the flowing reactor coolant when no other fissile material is in contact with the coolant. The system is operated in the same manner as for measurement of unknown delayed neutron levels.

11.2 The counting efficiency, E, of the delayed neutron measuring system can be found by the relation:

$$E = \frac{\text{count rate observed}}{\text{total delayed neutron emission rate}}$$

11.3 The expression used for calculating the total delayed neutron emission rate in the measuring system is as follows:

$$D = \frac{\phi \sigma V r W L Y_1 f_1 (1 - e^{-\lambda_1 T_a}) e^{-\lambda_1 T_d}}{v M (1 - e^{-\lambda_1 T_c})}$$
$$+ \frac{\phi \sigma V r W L Y_2 f_2 (1 - e^{-\lambda_2 T_a}) e^{-\lambda_2 T_d}}{v M (1 - e^{-\lambda_2 T_c})}$$

where:

A = total delayed neutron activity in the detector station, neutrons/min,

V = DN detection station volume, cm^3,

r = fission product release factor = 1.0 (for dissolved U^{235}),

ϕ = thermal neutron flux density, neutron/sec-cm^2,

σ = fission cross section of U^{235}, cm^2,

W = mass of U^{235} in system, g,

L = Avogadro's number = 6.023 $\times$ 10^{23} atoms/mole,

Y_1 = fission yield of Br^{87} (0.02),

Y_2 = fission yield of I^{137} (0.06),

f_1 = neutron transition fraction of Br^{87} (0.27),

f_2 = neutron transition fraction of I^{137} (0.049),

v = system volume, liters,

M = gram molecular weight of U^{235},

λ_1 = decay constant of Br^{87} (0.0125 sec^{-1}),

λ_2 = decay constant of I^{137} (0.0315 sec^{-1}),

T_a = activation time, sec,

T_c = cycle time, sec, and

T_d = delay time, sec.

12. Calculations

12.1 Results may be expressed in observed counts per minute at a given reactor neutron flux after the background has been subtracted. This method is useful for comparing the combined bromine-87 and iodine-137 delayed neutron activity of each of a group of samples, measured under the same conditions, as in locating a fuel cluster containing a defect or in following the change with time of these fission products in the coolant. The counting equipment is responding to each sample in the same manner. Results may also be reported in terms of the combined bromine-87 and iodine-137 neutron disintegration rate in the source coil if the efficiency of the neutron measurement system has been determined as described in 11. System Efficiency Determination. The results may be calculated as follows:

Br^{87} and I^{137} delayed neutron activity,

$$C \text{ cpm} = \frac{N}{t} - B$$

Br^{82} and I^{137} neutron disintegration rate,

$$\text{dpm/ml} = \frac{1}{EV} \times C$$

where:

N = total counts accumulated,

B = background, counts/min,

t = time of counting, in min,

V = milliliters of active volume in source coil being counted by the neutron counters, and

E = efficiency of the counting system (fraction).

12.2 The approximate area of exposed fissionable material in the reactor core or circulating in the coolant can be determined by solving the relationship given in 11. System Efficiency Determination for the desired quantity after making the required changes in the parameters. For release of fission products from a defective fuel element in the recoil fraction, r would vary from 0.5 to 0.25 depending on the geometry. The fraction of uranium-235 in the fuel alloy, the density of the fuel alloy, and the fission fragment range (8.15 $\times$ 10^{-4} cm for iodine-137 and 10.5 $\times$ 10^{-4} cm for bromine-87) must be substituted for the weight of the dissolved uranium-235.

13. Precision

13.1 The precision of the counting rate determination may be calculated by published methods reported elsewhere.[5]

[5] G. Friedlander and J. Kennedy, "Nuclear and Radio-chemistry," John Wiley & Sons, Inc., New York, N. Y., 1955, pp. 252–269.

Tentative Method of Test for

MEASUREMENT OF TRITIUM RADIOACTIVITY OF INDUSTRIAL WATER AND INDUSTRIAL WASTE WATER[1]

ASTM Designation: D 2476 – 66 T

Issued, 1966

This Tentative Method has been approved by the sponsoring committee and accepted by the Society in accordance with established procedures, for use pending adoption as standard. Suggestions for revisions should be addressed to the Society at 1916 Race St., Philadelphia, Pa. 19103.

1. Scope

1.1 This method covers the measurement of tritium radioactivity contained in industrial water and industrial waste water and fixed as T_2O or THO in concentrations above 10 pc/ml. The lower limit of the analysis is dependent upon the efficiency of the scintillator solution and cosmic rays. The upper limit of analysis without dilutions, 0.3 μc/ml, is dependent upon the efficiency of the scintillator solution and overloading level of the instrument. It is limited to liquid scintillation counting and to the hydrogen isotope of mass 3.

1.2 The method can be used for either absolute or relative determinations. In tracer work, the results may be expressed by comparison with a standard that is defined to be 100 per cent. For radioassay, data may be expressed in terms of disintegration rates after calibration with a tritium standard. General information on liquid scintillation counting has been published.[2]

2. Summary of Method

2.1 The scintillator solution, mixed with the radioactive sample, is excited by beta particles and emits light pulses by a molecular de-excitation process. The number of pulses per unit time is proportional to the quantity of activity present. Multiple solutes are used in the scintillator to provide the best combination of wavelength and pulse height for this application. The pulse height is enhanced by cooling the sample to 35 F (1.7 C). Cooling below this temperature will solidify the scintillator solution and sample. Cooling of the photomultiplier tubes also reduces the background caused by thermionic emission. These pulses are detected by two multiplier phototubes connected in coin-

[1] Under the standardization procedure of the Society, this method is under the jurisdiction of the ASTM Committee D-19 on Industrial Water. A list of members may be found in the ASTM Year Book.

[2] C. G. Bell, Jr. and F. N. Hayes, Editors, *Liquid Scintillation Counting*, Pergamon Press, New York, N. Y., 1958.

cidence and converted to electric signals. The amplified pulses are recorded and the count rate is measured. The efficiency of the system can be determined by use of prepared tritiated water standards having the same density and color as the sample.

3. Definitions

3.1 For definitions of terms used in this method, refer to ASTM Definitions D 1129, Terms Relating to Industrial Water and Industrial Waste Water.[3]

3.2 For terms not defined in this method or in Definitions D 1129, reference may be made to other published glossaries.[4]

4. Interferences

4.1 Quenching, the reduction in emitted light and hence the attenuation of pulse heights, causes significant reduction in the absolute counting efficiency. Quenching may be caused by impurities in the scintillator solution which inhibits the transfer of energy or by color in the sample which absorbs the emitted light. Quenching may be corrected for by adding a known amount of tritiated water standard to the sample after it has been counted. The sample shall then be recounted and the increment in count, together with the amount of added radioactivity, shall be used to compute the counting efficiency of the individual sample.

4.2 Samples or scintillator stock solutions exposed to daylight or fluorescent lighting must be dark-adapted for a minimum of 2 hr or erratic results will occur.

4.3 Any ionizing radiation may interfere in the tritium analysis; therefore,

it may be desirable to distill the sample prior to analysis.

4.4 Even low potassium-40 content glass or quartz sample vials will produce a higher background, 2.5 times and 0.5 times respectively, than polyethylene vials.[5]

4.5 The count rate of the sample should be less than 2.9×10^5 counts/min else the electromechanical registrar will become overloaded.

4.6 Sample vial optics should be reproduced from one sample to another or erratic results will occur.

4.7 Fission gases may be removed from the sample by refluxing.

5. Apparatus

5.1 *Liquid Scintillation Counter* consisting of the following components:

5.1.1 *Amplifier,*

5.1.2 *Counting Chamber,* contained within freezer,

5.1.3 *Freezer,*

5.1.4 *High-Voltage Power Supply,* 1500 v,

5.1.5 *Matched 2-in. Multiplier Photo-tubes in Coincidence,*

5.1.6 *Preamplifier,*

5.1.7 *Pulse-Height Discriminator,* and

5.1.8 *Scaler,* 10^6 counts, or printout, 10^6 counts, or both.

5.2 *Sample Vials,* polyethylene, of suitable size to fit the counting chamber and to contain 20 to 25 ml.

6. Reagents

6.1 *Purity of Reagents*—Reagent grade chemicals shall be used in all tests. Unless otherwise indicated, it is intended that all reagents shall conform to the Specifications of the Committee on Analytical Reagents of the American Chemical Society, where such specifica-

---

[3] Appears in this publication.
[4] "USA Standard Glossary of Terms in Nuclear Science and Technology" (USASI Designation: N1.1-1957).

[5] F. E. Butler, "Determination of Tritium n Water and Urine," *Analytical Chemistry,* Vol. 33, March, 1961, p. 409.

tions are available.[6] Other grades may be used, provided it is first ascertained that the reagent is free of radioactivity and of sufficiently high purity to permit its use without lessening the accuracy of the determination.

6.2 *Purity of Water*—Unless otherwise indicated, references to water shall be understood to mean referee grade reagent water conforming to ASTM Specifications D 1193, for Reagent Water.[3]

6.3 *Scintillator Stock Solution*—(If prepared in the presence of daylight or fluorescent light, store in a dark place 2 days before use.) Dissolve 120 g of naphthalene, 0.05 g of *p-bis* (2-(5-phenyloxazolyl)) benzene (POPOP), and 4 g of 2,5-diphenyloxazole (PPO), in 1 liter of *p*-dioxane.[5] Store in an amber-colored bottle. This solution must be standardized initially before use.

NOTE 1: CAUTION—*p*-Dioxane, the solvent in the scintillation solution, is flammable and its vapors are toxic. Preparation of the scintillation solution should be carried out in a hood away from heat or flames.[7]

7. Sampling

7.1 Collect the sample in accordance with the applicable method of the American Society for Testing and Materials, as follows:

D 510—Sampling Industrial Water,[3] especially Sections 32 to 41,
D 860—Sampling Water from Boilers,[3]
D 1066—Sampling Steam,[3] and
D 1496—Sampling Homogeneous Industrial Waste Water.[3]

---

[6] "Reagent Chemicals, American Chemical Society Specifications," Am. Chemical Soc., Washington, D. C. For suggestions on the testing of reagents not listed by the American Chemical Society, see "Reagent Chemicals and Standards," by Joseph Rosin, D. Van Nostrand Co., Inc., New York, N. Y., and the "United States Pharmacopeia."

[7] N. Irving Sax, *Dangerous Properties of Industrial Materials*, Reinhold Publishing Corp., 1962.

8. Standardization and Calibration

8.1 *Standardized Scintillator Solution*—Transfer 16 ml of the scintillator stock solution into each of two 20-ml polyethylene sample vials. Pipet 4 ml of tritiated water standard solution[8] containing 4000 to 5000 dpm/ml into one vial and 4 ml of water into the remaining vial (Note 2). Mix. The latter will serve as a blank. Place the vials in position in the freezer and allow to cool a minimum of 30 min, preferably 2 hr, to reduce the background. Count the blank and standard and calculate the efficiency factor for the scintillator mixture as follows:

$$\text{Tritium activity, } C = \frac{1}{V}\left(\frac{N}{t} - B\right)$$

where:
N = number of counts accumulated,
B = background of blank, counts per minute (cpm),
C = net counts per minute per milliliter (cpm/ml),
t = time of counting, min, and
V = milliliters of test specimen used.

$$\text{Tritium efficiency (fraction), } E\,{}_{{}^{3}H} = \frac{C}{D}$$

where: D = disintegration rate, disintegrations per minute per milliliter (dpm/ml)

Tritium efficiency factor, $F(\mu c/cpm)$

$$= \frac{1}{E\,{}_{{}^{3}H} \times 2.22 \times 10^6}$$

where: 2.22×10^6 = conversion from disintegrations per minute to microcuries

NOTE 2—If the sample vial is of such size as to contain 25 ml, use 20 ml of scintillator stock solution and 5 ml of sample.

---

[8] A tritiated water standard from the National Bureau of Standards, Washington, D. C., has been found satisfactory for this purpose.

9. Procedure

9.1 Filter the sample through a membrane filter if turbid.

9.2 Distill the sample if ionizing radiation other than tritium is present. The distillate must be redistilled if any ionizing radiation other than tritium is carried over during the previous distillation.

9.3 Transfer a 4- (or 5-)ml sample aliquot into a polyethylene sample vial and add 16 (or 20) ml of previously standardized scintillator solution. Mix.

9.4 Prepare a blank having the same density and color as the sample using 4 (or 5) ml of water.

9.5 Place the sample and blank in the freezer and allow to cool for 30 min (preferably 2 hr) (Note 3).

9.6 Count the sample for the length of time to give the desired reliability.

NOTE 3—The same sample blank may be used for a number of samples provided the same scintillator solution is used for each and the blank has the same density and color as the samples.

10. Calculations

10.1 Calculate the tritium radioactivity in microcuries per milliliter as follows:

$$\text{Tritium activity, } A, \ (\mu c/ml) = FC$$

where:

F = tritium efficiency factor determined in 8.1, and

C = net counts per minute per milliliter (as determined in 9.6).

11. Precision

11.1 Precision of counting rate determinations may be calculated by published methods reported elsewhere.[9] Single operator precision is ± 3 per cent.

---

[9] G. Friedlander, J. W. Kennedy, and J. Miller, *Nuclear and Radiochemistry*, John Wiley and Sons, Inc., New York. N. Y., 2nd Ed., 1964.

Tentative Method of Test for

pH OF AQUEOUS SOLUTIONS WITH THE GLASS ELECTRODE[1]

ASTM Designation: E 70 – 52 T

Issued, 1946; Revised, 1952

This Tentative Method has been approved by the sponsoring committee and accepted by the Society in accordance with established procedures, for use pending adoption as standard. Suggestions for revisions should be addressed to the Society at 1916 Race St., Philadelphia 3, Pa.

[In accordance with the Society's policy that tentatives should not be continued indefinitely, this tentative will be discontinued in May, 1968, unless some other definitive action is taken with respect to it prior to that time.]

Scope

1. This method covers the definition of pH and the apparatus and procedure for the electrometric measurement of pH values of aqueous solutions or extracts with the glass electrode. It does not deal with the manner in which the solutions or extracts are prepared.

Definition of pH

2. The pH of an aqueous solution or extract is defined in terms of E, the electromotive force between the glass and calomel electrodes when immersed in the solution or extract, and E_s, the electromotive force obtained when the electrodes are immersed in a standard solution (whose assigned pH is designated pH_s), by the following equation (Note 1):

$$pH = pH_s + \frac{(E - E_s)\, F}{2.3026\, RT}$$

where:

F = the faraday,
R = the gas constant, and
T = the absolute temperature, $t\ C +$ 273.16.

Note 1.—Values of $F/(2.3026\ RT)$ are given in Table I.

Description of Terms

3. For the purpose of this method, the term "meter" shall apply to the instrument used for the measurement of potential (either in millivolts or in terms of pH units), the term "electrodes" to the glass electrode and the saturated calomel reference electrode, and the term "assembly" to the combination of the meter and the electrodes. The performance of the meter shall be differentiated from that of the electrodes.

Standard Solutions

4. (a) The pH_s of six recommended standard solutions at several temperatures is listed in Table II. The buffer solutions shall be prepared from highly

---

[1] Under the standardization procedure of the Society, this method is under the jurisdiction of the ASTM Committee E-1 on Methods of Testing. A list of members may be found in the ASTM Year Book.

907

purified materials sold specifically as pH standards (Note 2), and the solution of hydrochloric acid shall be prepared from concentrated hydrochloric acid conforming to the specifications of the American Chemical Society. Potassium hydrogen phthalate and the two phosphate salts shall be dried at 110 C for 1 hr before use, but borax should not be heated above room temperature, while potassium hydrogen tartrate need not be dried before preparing the saturated solution specified in Paragraph (d). The five

TABLE I.—VALUES OF $F/(2.3026\ RT)$.

Temperature, deg Cent	$F/(2.3026\ RT)$, volts^{-1}
0	18.452
5	18.120
10	17.800
15	17.492
20	17.193
25	16.905
30	16.626
35	16.356
40	16.095
45	15.842
50	15.597
55	15.359
60	15.129

standards with pH less than 9.5 shall be preserved in bottles of chemically resistant glass or polyethylene. The alkaline phosphate solution shall be preserved in glass bottles coated on the inside with paraffin. These standards shall be replaced at an age of three months.

Note 2.—The five buffer salts can be obtained in the form of standard samples from the National Bureau of Standards. These standard samples are numbered as follows:

Buffer Salt	Standard Sample Number
Potassium hydrogen tartrate	188
Potassium hydrogen phthalate	185
Potassium dihydrogen phosphate	186—I
Disodium hydrogen phosphate	186—II
Borax	187

(b) *Distilled Water.*—The specific conductance of the distilled water shall not exceed 2×10^{-6} ohm^{-1} cm^{-1}. For the preparation of the tartrate, phthalate, and hydrochloric acid solutions, the water need not be freed of dissolved carbon dioxide. The water used for the two phosphate standards and the borax standard shall be boiled for 15 min or purged with air free of carbon dioxide

TABLE II.—pH OF STANDARD SOLUTIONS.[a]

Temperature, deg Cent	0.1 M Hydrochloric Acid	Saturated Tartrate Solution	0.05 M Phthalate Solution	0.025 M Phosphate Solution	0.01 M Borax Solution	0.01 M Alkaline Phosphate Solution
0	1.10	...	4.01	6.98	9.46	...
10	1.10	...	4.00	6.92	9.33	...
20	1.10	...	4.00	6.88	9.22	...
25	1.10	3.56	4.01	6.86	9.18	11.72
30	1.10	3.55	4.01	6.85	9.14	...
35	1.10	3.54	...	...	...	11.38
40	1.10	3.54	4.03	6.84	9.07	...
50	1.11	3.55	4.06	6.83	9.01	...
60	1.11	3.57	4.10	6.84	8.96	...

[a] For a discussion of the manner in which these pH values were assigned, see the paper by G. G Manov, "Standard Buffer Solutions," Symposium on pH Measurement, *Proceedings* Am. Soc. Testing Mats., Vol. 46 (1946).

and shall be protected with a soda-lime tube or equivalent (Note 3) while cooling and in storage. The pH of the carbon dioxide-free water shall be between 6.5 and 7.5 at 25 C.

Note 3.—Precautions shall be taken to prevent contamination of the distilled water with traces of the material used for protection against carbon dioxide.

(c) *Standard Hydrochloric Acid (0.1 M, pH$_s$ = 1.10 at 25 C).*—Prepare a solution slightly more concentrated than 0.1 M, standardize, and dilute to 0.1 M.

(d) *Standard Tartrate Solution (saturated near 25 C, pH$_s$ = 3.56 at 25 C).*— Shake vigorously an excess of potassium hydrogen tartrate ($KHC_4H_4O_6$) with 100 to 300 ml of distilled water in a glass-stoppered bottle. Filter, if necessary, to remove suspended salt. Add a crystal of thymol (about 0.1 g) as a preservative.

(e) *Standard Phthalate Solution* (0.05 M, pH_8 = 4.01 at 25 C).—Dissolve 10.21 g of potassium hydrogen phthalate ($KHC_8H_4O_4$) in distilled water and dilute to 1 liter.

(f) *Standard Neutral Phosphate Solution* (0.025 M with respect to each phosphate salt, pH_8 = 6.86 at 25 C).—Dissolve 3.40 g of potassium dihydrogen phosphate (KH_2PO_4) and 3.55 g of anhydrous disodium hydrogen phosphate (Na_2HPO_4) in distilled water and dilute to 1 liter.

(g) *Standard Borax Solution* (0.01 M, pH_8 = 9.18 at 25 C).—Dissolve 3.81 g of sodium tetraborate decahydrate ($Na_2B_4O_7 \cdot 10H_2O$) in distilled water and dilute to 1 liter.

(h) *Standard Alkaline Phosphate Solution* (0.01 M trisodium phosphate, pH_8 = 11.72 at 25 C).—Dissolve 1.42 g of anhydrous disodium hydrogen phosphate (Na_2HPO_4) in 100 ml of a 0.1 M carbonate-free solution of sodium hydroxide and dilute to 1 liter with distilled water.

pH Meters

5. There shall be two permissible types of meter, designated types I and II. The choice of meter will depend upon the desired precision of the measurement. For referee work or in case of dispute, meters of type I shall be used. The two types are differentiated on the basis of their electrical characteristics. These requirements are listed in Table III.

Calomel and Glass Electrodes

6. (a) The saturated calomel electrode shall be used in each assembly (Note 4). A few crystals of solid potassium chloride shall be present within the chamber surrounding the calomel, at each temperature. The design of the electrode shall permit a fresh liquid junction between the solution of potassium chloride and the buffer or test solution to be formed for each test and shall allow

traces of solution to be readily removed by washing.

(b) The pH response of the glass electrode shall conform with the requirements set forth in Section 7. If glass electrodes are used outside the electrode compartment of the meter, the leads shall be shielded from the effects of body capacitance.

TABLE III.—ELECTRICAL CHARACTERISTICS OF METERS.

	Type I Meter	Type II Meter
Vacuum-tube operation....	yes	yes
Type of measuring circuit.	potentiometric	calibrated direct deflection meter
Method for detection of balance..............	null indicator (ammeter, galvanometer, or electron-ray tube)	direct deflection
Maximum grid current drawn from glass electrode during measurement.................	2×10^{-12} amp	5×10^{-11} amp
Standard cell for calibration of working battery.................	yes	no
Scale: Units shown............	millivolts, pH, or both	millivolts, pH, or both
Minimum range, pH.....	0 to 13	0 to 13[a]
Minimum range, mv.....	0 to ±1100	0 to ±400
Maximum value of smallest ruled interval..................	0.1 pH 10 mv	0.1 pH 10 mv
Asymmetry potential compensator..............	yes	yes
Automatic or manual temperature compensator	yes	optional[b]
Minimum range, deg Cent..................	10 to 40	10 to 40
Maximum value of smallest graduation, deg Cent..............	2	2
Power supply, batteries or 110-v ac..............	either	either

[a] A double scale may be provided.
[b] If a temperature compensator is not provided, the instrument shall be furnished with suitable charts giving corrections for each degree from 10 to 40 C for various pH readings.

(c) If the assembly is in intermittent use, the ends of the electrodes shall be immersed in distilled water between measurements. The high-alkalinity type of glass electrode shall be stored in the borax buffer solution. For prolonged storage, glass electrodes may be allowed to become dry, and calomel electrodes shall be capped to prevent undue evaporation (Note 5).

Note 4.—Other reference electrodes of constant potential may be used, provided no difficulty is experienced in standardizing the assembly as described in Section 8.

Note 5.—New glass electrodes and those that have been stored dry shall be conditioned as recommended by the manufacturer. Requirements for the physical dimensions and shape of the electrodes and the composition of the internal reference solution are not considered part of this method.

Performance Tests of Meter and Electrodes

Note 6.—Except for measurements of the highest precision, it will usually be unnecessary to perform the tests described in Section 7. In the usual pH measurement, the stability of the meter, the accuracy of the scale reading, and the pH response of the glass electrode over the range of the measurements are verified by checking the assembly with a series of standard buffer solutions.

7. (*a*) *Assembly.*—The assembly shall be judged to be performing satisfactorily if it furnishes, within acceptable limits of accuracy, the correct pH values for the standard buffer solutions listed in Table II. When the electrodes are immersed in a buffer solution, the measured potential difference shall be substantially constant, and the cause of any instability shall be determined.

(*b*) *Meter.*—The meter shall be brought to electrical balance in accordance with the manufacturer's instructions. The performance shall then be tested by applying a known variable potential through a resistance of approximately 200 megohms to the terminals of the meter, the high-resistance lead being connected to the terminal corresponding to the glass electrode. The source of potential may be a precision-type potentiometer with a range of 1100 mv or more and a limit of error not greater than 0.1 mv. The 200 megohm resistor shall be properly

shielded to avoid capacity pickup. Commencing with a value of zero, the applied potential shall be increased in increments of 100 mv, and the readings of the dial of the meter at balance shall be noted. The process shall be extended to cover the entire range of the meter. In no case shall the difference between the applied voltage and that indicated by the meter differ by more than 1 mv per increment of applied voltage (Note 7).

Note 7.—If the cumulative error at the end of the scale exceeds $\pm$ 3 mv for type I meters and $\pm$ 6 mv for meters of type II, a calibration curve for the meter shall be constructed and corrections applied to each measurement of electromotive force or pH. Differences of electromotive force (volts) are converted to corresponding differences of pH by multiplying by $F/(2.3026\ RT)$ (Table I). Inasmuch as the meter is made to read correctly at the pH of the standard, the calibration correction to be applied to a pH measurement is the difference between the scale corrections at the pH of the standard and that of the unknown, with due regard for sign.

(*c*) *Glass Electrodes.*—The difference of potential between the glass electrode and the standard hydrogen gas electrode shall be measured when both electrodes are immersed in the same portion of various buffer solutions over the pH range in which the glass electrode is to be used. For these comparisons the cell shall be placed in a water bath thermostatically controlled to ± 0.1 C near 25 C. The solutions used for this test shall be those listed in Section 4. The standards of pH 9.18 and below (at 25 C) shall be used to test electrodes of the general-purpose type. The borax and trisodium phosphate standards shall be used to test the high-alkalinity type of electrode. These buffer solutions shall be supplemented by a 0.1 M carbonate-free solution of sodium hydroxide, the pH of which is approximately 12.8 at 25 C. The difference of potential between the general-purpose glass electrode and the hydrogen electrode shall be independent, within ± 2 mv, of pH changes in the range 1.10 to 9.18 pH. The difference of potential between the hydrogen electrode and a glass electrode of the high-alkalinity type shall be the same, within ± 5 mv, at pH 12.8 as at pH 9.18.

Standardization of the Assembly

8. (a) The instrument shall be turned on, allowed to warm up thoroughly, and brought to electrical balance in accordance with the manufacturer's instructions. The glass and calomel electrodes and the sample cup shall be washed three times with distilled water and dried gently with clean absorbent tissue. A fresh liquid junction shall be formed. The temperature of the test (unknown) solution shall be noted and the temperature dial of the meter adjusted to the proper setting.

(b) If the anticipated pH of the test solution is less than 9.18, two standard solutions shall be selected (Note 8) to bracket this pH, if possible, and these standards shall be warmed or cooled as necessary to match within 2 C the temperature of the unknown. The sample cup shall then be filled with the first standard and the electrodes immersed. In type I meters, the dial of the meter shall be set to the pH of the standard (pH_s) at the appropriate temperature as read from Table II or interpolated in the data therein. The operating button shall be engaged and the standardizing knob or asymmetry potential knob rotated until the meter is brought to balance. In type II meters the operating button shall be engaged, or range switch turned to the proper position, and the asymmetry potential knob rotated until the reading of the dial corresponds to the known pH of the standardizing buffer solution. The sample cup shall be filled repeatedly with additional portions of the standard solution until the instru-

ment remains in balance within ± 0.02 pH unit for two successive portions without a change in the position of the asymmetry potential knob. If the temperature of the electrodes differs appreciably from that of the solutions, several portions of solution shall be used and the electrodes immersed deeply to assure that both electrodes and standard are at the desired temperature. In order to reduce the effects of thermal and electrical hysteresis, the temperature of electrodes, standard solutions, and wash water should be kept as close to that of the unknowns as possible.

The electrodes and sample cup shall then be washed three times and a fresh liquid junction formed. The second standard shall be placed in the sample cup, the instrument adjusted to the new balance point, and the pH read from the dial. The setting of the asymmetry potential knob shall not be changed. Additional portions of the second standard shall be used until successive readings of the pH agree within 0.03 unit for type I meters and 0.05 unit for type II meters. The assembly shall be judged to be operating satisfactorily if the reading obtained for the second standard agrees with the assigned pH_s of that standard within these limits of error.

NOTE 8.—The assembly shall always be calibrated with two buffer solutions to check the linearity of the response of the electrode at different pH values and to detect a faulty glass electrode or incorrect temperature compensation. The presence of a faulty electrode is indicated by failure to obtain a reasonably correct value for the pH of the second standard solution when the meter has been standardized with the first. A cracked electrode will often yield pH values that are essentially the same for both standards.

(c) If the anticipated pH of the test solution is greater than 10.0, the high-alkalinity type of electrode shall be used and the manufacturer's instructions observed. The borax solution shall be used for initial standardization of the assembly. The second standard shall be the alkaline phosphate solution, if the temperature of measurement is between 25 and 38 C. The assembly shall be judged to be operating satisfactorily if the reading obtained for the second standard agrees with the assigned pH of this standard (Note 9) within 0.1 unit.

Note 9.—The change of pH_S with change of temperature is large for the alkaline phosphate standard. Hence, the temperature of this standard shall be noted to the nearest degree C and used to obtain pH_S by interpolation in the data of Table II. If the temperature of measurement is below 25 C or above 38 C and the pH greater than 10.0, the instrument shall be standardized with the borax solution alone. Correct functioning of the high-alkalinity electrode should be demonstrated by use of the two standards at some temperature between 25 and 38 C.

(d) If only an occasional pH determination is made, the assembly shall be standardized each time it is used. In a long series of measurements, initial and final standardizations shall be supplemented by a check at intervals of 30 min to 1 hr, or longer, if little or no change is found between successive standardizations.

Determination of pH of Test Solutions

9. (a) After the meter has been standardized with two standard solutions (Section 8), the electrodes and the sample cup shall be washed and dried as described in Section 8 (a). The cup shall then be filled with a portion of the test solution, a fresh liquid-junction formed, and a preliminary value obtained for pH. In the case of well-buffered test solutions, one to three portions will usually be sufficient to yield pH values reproducible to ±0.03 or ±0.05 unit for meters of type I or type II, respectively, and that show drifts of less than ±0.02 unit in 1 or 2 min.

(b) The pH of distilled water and slightly buffered solutions that are in equilibrium with the air shall be measured as described in Paragraph (a), except that the pH of successive portions of water or test solutions shall be measured, with vigorous agitation, until the observed results for two successive portions agree within 0.1 unit. Six or more portions may be necessary. The flow cell may also be used (see Section 10 (c)). If the water sample or the slightly buffered test solution is not in equilibrium with the carbon dioxide of the atmosphere, the measurements shall be made with external electrodes in a wide-mouth flask that has been flushed with carbon dioxide-free air, and the contents of the flask shall be protected from exposure to air during the measurement.

Determination of pH with a Flow Cell

10. Flow cells and electrode units for immersion in flow channels are an important feature of industrial pH control. In conjunction with electronic recorders and recorder-controllers, they provide the continuous measurements necessary for fully automatic regulation of pH. The flow cell is particularly advantageous for the determination of the pH of water or of sparingly buffered solutions. Simple dip measurements without agitation are subject to appreciable errors due to inadequate washing of the electrodes, solubility of the glass, and absorption of carbon dioxide during the measurement. A rapid flow of solution past the electrode maintains a clean glass interface, retards the tendency for fine solids to collect at the surface, minimizes errors resulting from solubility of the glass, and protects the sample from atmospheric contaminants.

(a) Flow Cell.—The flow unit may be of metal, glass, rubber, or plastic. If metal pipe connections are employed, they shall all be of the same metal. The volume of the unit shall be small, to permit a high rate of flow. If the cell is not provided with a resistance thermometer for automatic temperature compensation (or if it is used in conjunction with a meter not equipped to utilize this feature), arrangements for monitoring the temperature of the solutions shall be provided. The unit and the leads shall be free from the effects of body capacity.

(b) *Standardization and pH Determination.*—If the assembly is in continuous use, it shall be standardized daily in accordance with the instructions given in Section 8. Two standards shall be used in order to check the proper functioning of the electrodes. For a precision of ±0.1 pH unit below pH 9, the temperature of the standard should be within 2 C of that of the flowing solution. For the measurement of pH, the instructions furnished by the manufacturer of the meter or recorded shall be carefully observed.

(c) *pH of Water and Slightly Buffered Solutions.*—A flow rate sufficient to change the solution in the cell five times per minute shall be maintained. The pH of water or of a slightly buffered solution shall not be read until the flow of water or test solution has been continued for at least 15 min following immersion of the electrodes in the standard buffer solution, or until a drift of less than 0.1 pH unit in 2 min is observed. If the pH of the flowing solution is changing, the glass electrode measurement may lag considerably behind the true pH.

Report

11. The pH values obtained for the test solutions shall be reported to the nearest 0.05 or 0.1 unit, depending on the type of meter used and the requirements of the test. The probable limit of error of the measurements shall be estimated from the known errors of the instrument and electrodes (Section 7) and the reproducibility of duplicate tests. The estimated error shall not be smaller than the following limits:

	Estimated Error, pH units	
	pH 9.18 and Under	pH Over 9.18
Buffered solutions, type I meter	± 0.04	± 0.08
Buffered solutions, type II meter	± 0.05	± 0.10
Buffered solutions, flow cell	± 0.08	± 0.10
Water or unbuffered solutions	± 0.10	...

Tentative Methods for

PREPARATION, STANDARDIZATION, AND STORAGE OF STANDARD SOLUTIONS FOR CHEMICAL ANALYSIS[1]

ASTM Designation: E 200 – 65 T

ISSUED, 1962; LAST REVISED, 1965

These Tentative Methods have been approved by the sponsoring committee and accepted by the Society in accordance with established procedures for use pending adoption as standard. Suggestions for revisions should be addressed to the Society at 1916 Race St., Philadelphia 3, Pa.

Scope

1. (*a*) These methods cover procedures for the preparation, standardization, and storage of the standard volumetric solutions and reagent testing solutions commonly used in chemical analyses.

(*b*) The methods are given as follows:

Significance

2. The accuracy of many analytical measurements is dependent upon the manner in which the standard solutions are prepared and stored, and the accuracy with which they are standardized. Combining the methods recommended for the preparation and handling of such solutions into one method eliminates the necessity for covering such details in all of the methods wherein the solutions are used.

Definition

3. *Standard Volumetric Solution.*—A solution of accurately determined concentration used in the quantitative analysis of chemicals and other products. The concentration of such solutions is

[1] Under the standardization procedure of the Society, these methods are under the jurisdiction of the ASTM Committee E-15 on Analysis and Testing of Industrial Chemicals. A list of members may be found in the ASTM Year Book.

usually expressed in terms of normality or molarity.

Apparatus

4. (a) *Volumetric Glassware.*—The use of ordinary volumetric glassware will meet the accuracy requirements of many test methods.

NOTE 1.—For dependable accuracy, volumetric glassware meeting the requirements for Class A items of Federal Specification DD-V-581a should be used. These requirements are identical with those given in "Testing of Glass Volumetric Apparatus," *Circular 602*, Nat. Bureau Standards, April 1, 1959. While for normal work apparatus meeting these spec-

TABLE I—TEMPERATURE CORRECTION FACTORS (F).

Approximate Normality	Solute	ΔN/deg C for 20 to 30 C
1.0............	NaOH, HCl, H_2SO_4	0.00035
0.5............	NaOH, HCl, H_2SO_4	0.00014
0.1............	all aqueous	0.00002
0.05...........	all aqueous	0.00001
0.01...........	all aqueous	0.00000
0.5 (in methanol).	NaOH	0.00045
0.1 (in 1 N H_2SO_4)........	$Ce(SO_4)_2$	0.000035

ifications can be used without calibration corrections, it is preferable that such calibration corrections be used in standardizing volumetric solutions. Such corrections may be of significance when the volumetric ware is frequently used with alkali solutions, for the corrosive effect of the alkali upon the glass may result in changes in the apparent volume. It is recommended, therefore, that volumetric glassware, particularly burets and transfer pipets, be recalibrated at 3-month intervals if it is frequently used to measure alkali solution volumes.

(b) *Buret.*—A calibrated 50-ml buret,[2] or any standard 50-ml buret calibrated by either the National Bureau of Standards or by the user. Alternatively, a calibrated 100-ml buret[3] with a 50-ml bulb

[2] MCA Type 1 buret has been found satisfactory for this purpose.
[3] MCA Type 3 buret has been found satisfactory for this purpose.

at the top and a 50-ml stem below, may be used. For use with alkali solutions, burets equipped with TFE-fluorocarbon stopcock plugs are preferable.[4]

Temperature Effects

5. Volumetric solutions are often used at temperatures differing from those at which the standardization was carried out. Significant errors may be introduced when the solutions are used at these other temperatures. Values for the change of normality with temperature (ΔN/deg C) have been established for the volumetric solutions described herein, and are listed in Table I. When warranted by the desired accuracy of the work, normalities of standard solutions may be corrected to the temperature at which they are used as follows:

$$N_{t_2} = N_{t_1} + (t_1 - t_2)(F)$$

where:

N_{t_1} = normality of solution when standardized,

N_{t_2} = normality of solution when used,

t_1 = temperature of solution (Centigrade) during standardization,

t_2 = temperature of solution (Centigrade) during use, and

F = factor to correct for thermal expansion of the solution (ΔN/deg C values from Table I).

From the above equation it will be seen that the correction is to be added to the normality of the solution when standardized if the temperature of use is lower than the temperature of standardization while the correction is to be subtracted if the temperature of use is higher than the temperature of standardization.

[4] Directions for the calibration of burets and other volumetric glassware are given in "Testing of Glass Volumetric Apparatus," *Circular 602*, Nat. Bureau Standards, April 1, 1959, and in many textbooks on quantitative analysis; see I. M. Kolthoff and E. B. Sandell, "Quantitative Inorganic Analysis," 3rd Ed., MacMillan Co., New York, N. Y., pp. 511–513 (1953).

Measurements

6. (a) *Weighings.*—When it is directed that a chemical be "accurately weighed," the weighing is to be performed in a manner so as to limit the error to 0.1 per cent or less. Where a specific weight of substance is designated in a procedure, it is intended, unless otherwise specified in the individual procedure, that a quantity within ±5 per cent of the designated weight be used, and that this quantity be "accurately weighed" as defined in these Methods (Note 2).

Note 2.—In weighing primary standards to be used in standardizing volumetric solutions many laboratories customarily weigh to the nearest 0.1 mg even though such increased accuracy of weighing does not improve the accuracy or precision of the standardization.

(b) *Buret Readings.*—When buret readings are specified, or when the procedure infers that a specific volume be measured from a buret, the reading is to be estimated to one fifth of the smallest volume subdivision marked on the buret. In reading a 50-ml buret having subdivisions of 0.10 ml, therefore, the reading should be estimated to the nearest 0.02 ml.

(c) *Expression of Results.*—It is customary to express the normality of standard solutions to 1 part in 1000.

Reagents

Note 3.—Additional information on reagents is given in the Recommended Practices for Apparatus, Reagents, and Safety Precautions for Chemical Analysis of Metals (ASTM Designation: E 50).[5]

7. (a) *Purity of Reagents.*—Reagent grade chemicals shall be used in preparing and standardizing all solutions. Unless otherwise indicated, it is intended that all reagents shall conform to the current specifications of the Committee on Analytical Reagents of the American Chemical Society, where such specifica-

---

[5] 1967 Book of ASTM Standards, Part 32.

tions are available.[6] Other grades may be used, provided it is first ascertained that the reagent is of sufficiently high purity to permit its use without lessening the accuracy of the determination.

(b) *Purity of Water.*—Unless otherwise indicated, references to water shall be understood to mean reagent water conforming to the Specifications for Reagent Water (ASTM Designation: D 1193).[7] Where specified, carbon dioxide-free water is to be prepared by heating distilled water to boiling in a conical flask, and boiling for 20 min. The boiling water is cooled in the flask which is stoppered with a 1-hole rubber stopper fitted to a soda lime-ascarite drying tube. For larger (10 to 20-liter) volumes of carbon dioxide-free water, the absorbed carbon dioxide may be removed by inserting a fritted-glass gas-dispersion tube to the bottom of the container and bubbling nitrogen through the water for 1 or 2 hr.

(c) *Primary Standards.*—The National Bureau of Standards offers for sale certified standard samples of arsenic trioxide, benzoic acid, potassium hydrogen phthalate, potassium dichromate, and sodium oxalate. Where specified, these samples, or samples of commercially available primary standards, are to be used in standardizing the volumetric solutions.

Concentration of Solutions

8. Directions are given for the preparation of the most commonly used concentrations of the standard volumetric solutions. Stronger or weaker solutions are prepared and standardized in the same general manner as described, using

---

[6] "Reagent Chemicals, American Chemical Society Specifications," Am. Chemical Soc., Washington, D. C. For suggestions on the testing of reagents not listed by the American Chemical Society, see "Reagent Chemicals and Standards," by Joseph Rosin, D. Van Nostrand Co., Inc., New York, N. Y., and the "United States Pharmacopeia."

[7] Appears in this publication.

proportionate amounts of the reagents. Similarly, if quantities larger than 1 liter are to be prepared, proportionate amounts of the reagents should be used.

Mixing of Solutions

9. When quantities of solution larger than 1 or 2 liters are prepared, special problems are encountered in being sure that they are well mixed before being standardized. While blade stirrers with glass or metal shafts are suitable for many solutions, they are not suitable in every case. In those cases where contact of a glass or metal stirrer with the solution would be undesirable it may be possible to use a sealed polyolefin-coated stirrer. In those cases where only contact of the solution with metal must be avoided, the solution can be mixed by inserting a fritted-glass gas-dispersion tube to the bottom of the container and bubbling nitrogen through the solution for 1 or 2 hr.

Storage of Solutions

10. (a) Glass containers are suitable for the storage of most of the standard solutions, although the use of polyolefin containers is recommended for alkali solutions.

(b) When large quantities of solutions are prepared and standardized, it is necessary to provide protection against changes in normality due to absorption of gases or water vapor from the laboratory air. As volumes of solution are withdrawn from the container, the replacement air should be passed through a drying tube filled with equal parts of 8 to 20-mesh soda lime, oxalic acid, and 4 to 8-mesh anhydrous calcium chloride, each product being separated from the other by a glass wool plug.

Preparation and Standardization of Solutions

11. Methods of standardization are given for each volumetric solution even though the methods of preparation for some of these solutions specify that they be prepared on a determinate basis. Since it is not possible to prepare large volumes of solutions on a determinate basis, a method of standardization is provided for those solutions that are prepared in such large volumes that accurate measurements of the solution volumes cannot be made.

STANDARD VOLUMETRIC SOLUTIONS

SODIUM HYDROXIDE, 0.02 TO 1.0 N

Preparation of 50 Per Cent NaOH Solution and of Standard Solutions

12. (a) Dissolve 162 g of sodium hydroxide (NaOH) in 150 ml of carbon dioxide-free water. Cool the solution to 25 C and filter through a Gooch crucible, hardened filter paper, or other suitable medium. Alternatively, commercial 50 per cent NaOH solution may be used.

(b) To prepare a 0.1 N solution, dilute 5.45 ml of the clear solution to 1 liter with carbon dioxide-free water, mix well, and store in a tight polyolefin container.

(c) For other normalities of NaOH

TABLE II.—SODIUM HYDROXIDE DILUTION REQUIREMENTS.

Desired Normality	Grams of NaOH Required per 1 liter of Solution	Volume of 50 per cent NaOH Solution (25 C) Required per 1 liter of Solution, ml
0.02.............	0.8	1.09
0.04.............	1.6	2.18
0.05.............	2.0	2.73
0.1.............	4.0	5.45
0.2.............	8.0	10.90
0.25.............	10.0	13.63
0.5	20.0	27.25
1.0	40.0	54.54

solution, use the requirements given in Table II.

Standardization

13. (a) Crush 10 to 20 g of primary standard potassium hydrogen phthalate ($KHC_8H_4O_4$) to 100-mesh fineness, and dry in a glass container at 120 C for 2 hr. Stopper the container and cool in a desiccator.

(b) To standardize a 0.1 N solution, weigh 0.95 $\pm$ 0.05 g of the dried $KHC_8H_4O_4$, and transfer to a 500-ml conical flask. Add 100 ml of carbon dioxide-free water, stir gently to dissolve the sample, add 3 drops of a 1.0 per cent solution of phenolphthalein in alcohol, and titrate with NaOH solution

TABLE III.—WEIGHTS OF DRIED POTASSIUM HYDROGEN PHTHALATE.

Normality of Solution	Weight of Dried KHC₈H₄O₄ to be Used, g[a]
0.02	0.19 $\pm$ 0.005
0.04	0.38 $\pm$ 0.005
0.05	0.47 $\pm$ 0.005
0.1	0.90 $\pm$ 0.005
0.2	1.90 $\pm$ 0.05
0.25	2.35 $\pm$ 0.05
0.5	4.75 $\pm$ 0.05
1.0	9.00 $\pm$ 0.05

[a] The listed weights are for use when a 50-ml buret is to be used. If a 100-ml buret is to be used, the weights should be doubled.

to a color that matches that of an end point color standard.

(c) The weights of dried $KHC_8H_4O_4$ suitable for other normalities of NaOH solution are given in Table III.

pH 8.6 End Point Color Standard

14. Mix 25 ml of a solution 0.2 M in boric acid (H_3BO_3) and 0.2 M in potassium chloride (KCl), with 6 ml of 0.2 M NaOH solution, add 3 drops of a 1.0 per cent solution of phenolphthalein in alcohol, and dilute to 100 ml with carbon dioxide-free water.

Calculation

15. Calculate the normality of the NaOH solution, as follows:

$$A = \frac{B}{0.20423 \times C}$$

where:

A = normality of the NaOH solution,
B = grams of $KHC_8H_4O_4$ used, and
C = milliliters of NaOH solution consumed.

Precision[8]

16. (a) Sodium Hydroxide (1.0N):

(1) Repeatability.—The average difference between two results (each the average of duplicate determinations), obtained by the same analyst on different days, will approximate 0.00064 normality units, absolute. Two such values should be considered suspect (95 per cent confidence level) if they differ by more than 0.0020 normality units, absolute.

(2) Reproducibility.—The average difference between two results (each the average of duplicate determinations), obtained by analysts in different laboratories, will approximate 0.0011 normality units, absolute. Two such values should be considered suspect (95 per cent confidence level) if they differ by more than 0.0035 normality units, absolute.

(3) Checking Limits for Duplicates.—At the 95 per cent confidence level, duplicate results which agree within 0.0019 normality units, absolute, are acceptable for averaging.

(b) Sodium Hydroxide (0.1N):

(1) Repeatability.—The average difference between two results (each the average of duplicate determinations), obtained by the same analyst on different days, will approximate 0.00012 normality units, absolute. Two such values should

[8] The Recommended Practice for Developing Precision Data on ASTM Methods for Analysis and Testing of Industrial Chemicals (ASTM Designation: E 180), which appears in the 1967 Book of ASTM Standards, Part 22, was used in developing these precision estimates. Supporting data giving results of cooperative tests have been filed at ASTM Headquarters.

be considered suspect (95 per cent confidence level) if they differ by more than 0.00036 normality units, absolute.

(2) *Reproducibility.*—The average difference between two results (each the average of duplicate determinations), obtained by analysts in different laboratories, will approximate 0.00020 normality units, absolute. Two such values should be considered suspect (95 per cent confidence level) if they differ by more than 0.00066 normality units, absolute.

(3) *Checking Limits for Duplicates.*—At the 95 per cent confidence level, duplicate results which agree within 0.00029 normality units, absolute, are acceptable for averaging.

NOTE 4.—Precision data have not been obtained for concentrations other than those listed in Section 16.

Stability

17. The use of polyolefin containers eliminates some of the difficulties attendant upon the use of glass containers, and their use is recommended. Should glass containers be used, the solution must be standardized frequently if there is evidence of action on the glass container, or if insoluble matter appears in the solution.

HYDROCHLORIC ACID, 0.02 TO 1.0 N

Preparation

18. (a) To prepare a 0.1 N solution, measure 8.3 ml of concentrated hydrochloric acid (HCl, sp gr 1.19) into a graduated cylinder and transfer it to a 1-liter volumetric flask. Dilute to the mark with water, mix well, and store in a tightly closed glass container.

(b) For other normalities of HCl solution, use the requirements given in Table IV.

Standardization[9]

19. (a) Transfer 2 to 4 g of anhydrous sodium carbonate (Na_2CO_3) to a platinum dish or crucible, and dry at 250 C for 4 hr.[10] Cool in a desiccator.

(b) To standardize a 0.1 N solution, weigh accurately 0.22 ± 0.01 g of the dried Na_2CO_3, and transfer to a 500-ml conical flask. Add 50 ml of water, swirl to dissolve the carbonate, and add 2 drops of a 0.1 per cent solution of methyl red in alcohol. Titrate with the HCl solution to the first appearance of a red color, and boil the solution carefully, to avoid

TABLE IV.—HYDROCHLORIC ACID DILUTION REQUIREMENTS.

Desired Normality	Volume of HCl to be Diluted to 1 liter, ml
0.02	1.66
0.04	3.32
0.1	8.3
0.2	16.6
0.5	41.5
1.0	83.0

TABLE V.—WEIGHTS OF DRIED SODIUM CARBONATE.

Normality of Solution	Weight of Dried Na_2CO_3 to be Used, g
0.02	0.088 ± 0.001[a]
0.04	0.176 ± 0.001[a]
0.1	0.22 ± 0.01[b]
0.2	0.44 ± 0.01[b]
0.5	1.10 ± 0.01[b]
1.0	2.20 ± 0.01[b]

[a] A 100-ml buret should be used for this standardization.

[b] The listed weights are for use when a 50-ml buret is used. If a 100-ml buret is to be used, the weights should be doubled.

loss, until the color is discharged. Continue the titration, alternating the addition of HCl solution and the boiling, to the first appearance of a faint red color that is not discharged on further heating.

(c) The weights of dried Na_2CO_3

[9] A buret having a bent delivery tube is helpful in carrying out this standardization procedure.

[10] A primary standard grade of anhydrous sodium carbonate (Na_2CO_3) is available from Mallinckrodt Chemical Works, P.O. Box 5439, St. Louis, Mo. 63160.

suitable for other normalities of HCl solution are given in Table V.

Calculation

20. Calculate the normality of the HCl solution, as follows:

$$A = \frac{B}{0.053 \times C}$$

where:

A = normality of the HCl solution,
B = grams of Na_2CO_3 used, and
C = milliliters of HCl solution consumed.

Precision[8]

21. (*a*) *Hydrochloric Acid (1.0N):*

(*1*) *Repeatability.*—The average difference between two results (each the average of duplicate determinations), obtained by the same analyst on different days, will approximate 0.0007 normality units, absolute. Two such values should be considered suspect (95 per cent confidence level) if they differ by more than 0.0021 normality units, absolute.

(*2*) *Reproducibility.*—The average difference between two results (each the average of duplicate determinations), obtained by analysts in different laboratories, will approximate 0.0015 normality units, absolute. Two such values should be considered suspect (95 per cent confidence level) if they differ by more than 0.0050 normality units, absolute.

(*3*) *Checking Limits for Duplicates.*— At the 95 per cent confidence level, duplicate results which agree within 0.0011 normality units, absolute, are acceptable for averaging.

(*b*) *Hydrochloric Acid (0.1N):*

(*1*) *Repeatability.*—The average difference between two results (each the average of duplicate determinations), obtained by the same analyst on different days, will approximate 0.00012 normality units, absolute. Two such

values should be considered suspect (95 per cent confidence level) if they differ by more than 0.00038 normality units, absolute.

(*2*) *Reproducibility.*—The average difference between two results (each the average of duplicate determinations), obtained by analysts in different laboratories, will approximate 0.00022 normality units, absolute. Two such values should be considered suspect (95 per cent confidence level) if they differ by more than 0.00074 normality units, absolute.

(*3*) *Checking Limits for Duplicates.*— At the 95 per cent confidence level, duplicate results which agree within 0.00044 normality units, absolute, are acceptable for averaging.

NOTE 5.—Seventy-two results from nine laboratories were considered in establishing the precision data for each of the two concentrations listed herein.

NOTE 6.—Precision data have not been obtained for concentrations other than those listed in Section 21.

Stability

22. Restandardize monthly.

SULFURIC ACID, 0.02 TO 1.0 *N*

Preparation

23. (*a*) To prepare a 0.1 *N* solution, measure 3.0 ml of concentrated sulfuric acid (H_2SO_4, sp gr 1.84) into a graduated cylinder and slowly add it to one half the desired volume of water in a 600-ml beaker. Rinse the cylinder into the beaker with water. Mix the acid-water

TABLE VI.—SULFURIC ACID
DILUTION REQUIREMENTS.

Desired Normality	Volume of H_2SO_4 to be Diluted to 1 liter, ml
0.02	0.60
0.2	6.0
0.1	3.0
0.5	15.0
1.0	30.0

mixture, allow it to cool, and transfer to a 1-liter volumetric flask. Dilute to the mark with water, mix well, and store in a tightly closed glass container.

(b) For other normalities of the H_2SO_4 solution, use the requirements given in Table VI.

Standardization[9]

24. (a) Transfer 2 to 4 g of anhydrous sodium carbonate (Na_2CO_3) to a platinum dish or crucible, and dry at 250 C for 4 hr.[10] Cool in a desiccator.

(b) For standardization of a 0.1 N solution, weigh accurately 0.22 ± 0.01 g of the dried Na_2CO_3 and transfer to a 500-ml conical flask. Add 50 ml of water, swirl to dissolve the Na_2CO_3, and add 2 drops of a 0.1 per cent solution of methyl red in alcohol. Titrate with the H_2SO_4 solution to the first appearance of a red color, and boil the solution carefully, to avoid loss, until the color is discharged. Continue the titration alternating the addition of H_2SO_4 solution and the boiling, to the first appearance of a faint red color that is not discharged on further heating.

(c) The weights of dried Na_2CO_3 suitable for other normalities of H_2SO_4 solution are given in Table V.

Calculation

25. Calculate the normality of the H_2SO_4 solution, as follows:

$$A = \frac{B}{0.053 \times C}$$

where:

A = normality of the H_2SO_4 solution,
B = grams of Na_2CO_3 used, and
C = milliliters of H_2SO_4 solution consumed.

Precision[8]

26. (a) *Sulfuric Acid (1.0N):*
　　(1) *Repeatability.*—See Section 21(a) (1).

(2) *Reproducibility.*—See Section 21(a)(2).
(3) *Checking Limits for Duplicates.*— See Section 21(a)(3).

(b) *Sulfuric Acid (0.1N):*
　　(1) *Repeatability.*—See Section 21(b)(1).
　　(2) *Reproducibility.*—See Section 21(b)(2).
　　(3) *Checking Limits for Duplicates.*— See Section 21(b)(3).

Stability

27. Restandardize monthly.

Hydrochloric Acid, Special 1 N

Note 7.—This solution is not for general use but is designed to satisfy the special requirements of ASTM Committee E-15, Subcommittee B-2 on Alkalies.

Preparation

28. Measure 83.0 ml of concentrated hydrochloric acid (HCl, sp gr 1.19) into a graduated cylinder and transfer it to a 1-liter volumetric flask. Dilute to the mark with water, mix well, and store in a tightly closed glass container.

Standardization

29. (a) Transfer 5 g of anhydrous sodium carbonate (Na_2CO_3) to a platinum dish or crucible, and dry at 250 C for 4 hr (Note 8).[10] Cool in a desiccator. Weigh accurately 2.2 ± 0.1 g of the dried Na_2CO_3, and transfer to a 500-ml conical flask. Add 75 ml of water, swirl to dissolve the Na_2CO_3, and add 3 drops of a 0.1 per cent solution of methyl orange. Titrate with HCl solution to a pink color.

Note 8.—The specified weight of Na_2CO_3 is suitable when a 50-ml buret is used for the acid solution. If a 100-ml buret is to be used, the specified weight of Na_2CO_3 should be doubled.

(b) Methyl orange modified with xylene cyanole FF, suitable for use in this procedure, is described in Section 75 (*p*).

Calculation

30. Calculate the normality of the HCl solution, as follows:

$$A = \frac{B}{0.053 \times C}$$

where:

A = normality of the HCl solution,
B = grams of Na_2CO_3 used, and
C = milliliters of HCl solution consumed.

Precision

31. (a) *Repeatability.*—The average difference between two results (each the average of duplicate determinations), obtained by the same analyst on different days, will approximate 0.00093 normality units, absolute. Two such values should be considered suspect (95 per cent confidence level) if they differ by more than 0.0028 normality units, absolute.

(b) *Reproducibility.*—The average difference between two results (each the average of duplicate determinations), obtained by analysts in different laboratories, will approximate 0.0020 normality units, absolute. Two such values should be considered suspect (95 per cent confidence level) if they differ by more than 0.0064 normality units, absolute.

(c) *Checking Limits for Duplicates.*—At the 95 per cent confidence level, duplicate results which agree within 0.0031 normality units, absolute, are acceptable for averaging.

NOTE 9.—Seventy-six results from ten laboratories were considered in establishing these precision data.

Stability

32. Restandardize monthly.

SULFURIC ACID, SPECIAL 1 N

(See Note 7)

Preparation

33. Measure 30.0 ml of concentrated sulfuric acid (H_2SO_4, sp gr 1.84) into a graduated cylinder, and slowly add it to one half the desired volume of water in a 600-ml beaker. Rinse the cylinder into the beaker with water. Mix the acid-water mixture, allow it to cool, and transfer to a 1-liter volumetric flask. Dilute to the mark with water, mix well, and store in a tightly closed glass container.

Standardization

34. (a) Transfer 5 g of anhydrous sodium carbonate (Na_2CO_3) to a platinum dish or crucible, and dry at 250 C for 4 hr (Note 8).[10] Cool in a desiccator. Weigh accurately 2.2 $\pm$ 0.1 g of the dried Na_2CO_3, and transfer to a 500-ml conical flask. Add 75 ml of water, swirl to dissolve the Na_2CO_3, and add 3 drops of a 0.1 per cent solution of methyl orange. Titrate with H_2SO_4 solution to a pink color

(b) Methyl orange modified with xylene cyanole FF, suitable for use in this procedure, is described in Section 75 (p).

Calculation

35. Calculate the normality of the H_2SO_4 solution, as follows:

$$A = \frac{B}{0.053 \times C}$$

where:

A = normality of the H_2SO_4 solution,
B = grams of Na_2CO_3 used, and
C = milliliters of H_2SO_4 solution consumed.

Precision

36. (a) *Repeatability.*—See Section 31(a).

(b) *Reproducibility.*—See Section 31(b).

(c) *Checking Limits for Duplicates.*—See Section 31(c).

Stability

37. Restandardize monthly.

Silver Nitrate (0.1N)

Preparation

38. Dry 17.5 g of silver nitrate ($AgNO_3$) at 105 C for 1 hr. Cool in a desiccator. Transfer 16.99 g of the dried $AgNO_3$ to a 1-liter volumetric flask. Add 500 ml of water, swirl to dissolve the $AgNO_3$, dilute to the mark with water, and mix. Store the solution in a tightly-stoppered amber-glass bottle.

Note 10.—If desired the solution may also be prepared on a determinate basis by weighing the dried silver nitrate accurately and diluting the solution carefully to volume.

Standardization

Note 11: Caution—Nitrobenzene, used in this section, is extremely hazardous when absorbed through the skin or when its vapor is inhaled. Such exposure may cause cyanosis; prolonged exposure may cause anemia. Do not get in eyes, on skin, or on clothing. Avoid breathing vapor. Use only with adequate ventilation.

39. (a) Transfer 0.3 g of sodium chloride (NaCl) to a platinum dish, and dry at 105 C for 2 hr. Cool in a desiccator. Weigh accurately 0.28 ± 0.01 g of the dried NaCl and transfer to a 250-ml glass-stoppered conical flask. Add 25 ml of water, swirl to dissolve the NaCl, and add 2 ml of nitric acid (HNO_3). Add, from a volumetric pipet, 50 ml of the $AgNO_3$ solution, mix, and add 1 ml of ferric ammonium sulfate solution ($FeNH_4(SO_4)_2$, 80 g per liter) and 5 ml of nitrobenzene. Stopper the flask and shake vigorously to coagulate the precipitate. Rinse the stopper into the flask with a few milliliters of water and titrate the excess of $AgNO_3$ with ammonium thiocyanate solution (NH_4SCN) until the first permanent reddish-brown color appears and persists after vigorous shaking for 1 min. Designate the volume of NH_4SCN solution required for the titration as Volume I.

(b) Using the same volumetric pipet used in Paragraph (a), transfer 50 ml of the $AgNO_3$ solution to a clean, dry, 250-ml, glass-stoppered conical flask. Add 25 ml of water, 2 ml of HNO_3, 1 ml of $FeNH_4(SO_4)_2$ solution (80 g per liter), and 5 ml of nitrobenzene (Caution, see Note 11), stopper the flask, and shake vigorously. Rinse the stopper into the flask with a few milliliters of water and titrate the $AgNO_3$ solution with NH_4SCN solution until the first permanent reddish-brown color appears and persists after vigorous shaking for 1 min. Designate the volume of NH_4SCN solution consumed as Volume II.

(c) Measure accurately, from either a buret or a volumetric pipet, 2.0 ml of the $AgNO_3$ solution, designate the exact volume as Volume III, and transfer to a 100-ml, glass-stoppered conical flask. Add 25 ml of water, 2 ml of HNO_3, 1 ml of $FeNH_4(SO_4)_2$ solution (80 g per liter), and 5 ml of nitrobenzene, stopper the flask, and shake vigorously. Rinse the stopper into the flask with a few milliliters of water and titrate the $AgNO_3$ solution with NH_4SCN solution until the first permanent reddish-brown color appears and persists after vigorous shaking for 1 min. Designate the volume of NH_4SCN solution consumed as Volume IV.

Note 12.—The ammonium thiocyanate titrant used in the three titrations must be from the same, well-mixed solution. The nitrobenzene used in each titration must also be from the same, well-mixed container.

Calculation

40. Calculate the normality of the $AgNO_3$ solution as follows:

$$A = \frac{B}{0.05845 \times (C - D)}$$

where:
A = normality of the $AgNO_3$ solution,
B = grams of NaCl used,
C = volume of $AgNO_3$ solution consumed by the total chloride =

$$50 - \left(\text{Volume I} \times \frac{50}{\text{Volume II}} \right),$$

and

$D =$ volume of $AgNO_3$ solution consumed by any chloride ion in the nitrobenzene $=$ Volume III $-$

$$\left(\text{Volume IV} \times \frac{50}{\text{Volume II}} \right).$$

Precision

41. (a) *Repeatability.*—The average difference between two results (each the average of duplicate determinations), obtained by the same analyst on different days, will approximate 0.0004 normality units, absolute. Two such values should be considered suspect (95 per cent confidence level) if they differ by more than 0.0010 normality units, absolute.

(b) *Reproducibility.*—The average difference between two results (each the average of duplicate determinations), obtained by analysts in different laboratories, will approximate 0.0005 normality units, absolute. Two such values should be considered suspect (95 per cent confidence level) if they differ by more than 0.0014 normality units, absolute.

(c) *Checking Limits for Duplicates.*—At the 95 per cent confidence level, duplicate results which agree within 0.00074 normality units, absolute, are acceptable for averaging.

NOTE 13.—Seventy-nine results from ten laboratories were considered in establishing these precision data.

Stability

42. Restandardize monthly.

AMMONIUM THIOCYANATE (0.1N)

Preparation

43. Transfer 7.8 g of ammonium thiocyanate (NH_4SCN) to a flask, add 100 ml of water, and swirl to dissolve the NH_4SCN. When solution is complete,

filter through a Gooch crucible, hardened filter paper, or other suitable medium. Dilute the clear filtrate to 1 liter with water and mix. Store the solution in a tightly-stoppered glass bottle.

Standardization

44. Measure accurately about 40 ml of freshly standardized 0.1N silver nitrate ($AgNO_3$), and transfer to a 250-ml conical flask. Add 50 ml of water, swirl to mix the solution, and add 2 ml of nitric acid (HNO_3) and 1 ml of ferric ammonium sulfate solution ($FeNH_4$-($SO_4)_2$, 80 g per liter). Titrate the $AgNO_3$ solution with the NH_4SCN solution until the first permanent reddish-brown color appears and persists after vigorous shaking for 1 min.

Calculation

45. Calculate the normality of the NH_4SCN solution, as follows:

$$A = \frac{B \times C}{D}$$

where:

$A =$ normality of the NH_4SCN solution,

$B =$ milliliters of $AgNO_3$ solution used,

$C =$ normality of the $AgNO_3$ solution, and

$D =$ milliliters of NH_4SCN solution required for titration of the solution.

Precision (See Note 13)

46. (a) *Repeatability.*—The average difference between two results (each the average of duplicate determinations), obtained by the same analyst on different days, will approximate 0.0004 normality units, absolute. Two such values should be considered suspect (95 per cent confidence level) if they differ by more than 0.0011 normality units, absolute.

(b) *Reproducibility.*—The average difference between two results (each the average of duplicate determinations), obtained by analysts in different laboratories, will approximate 0.0005 normality units, absolute. Two such values should be considered suspect (95 per cent confidence level) if they differ by more than 0.0014 normality units, absolute.

(c) *Checking Limits for Duplicates.*—At the 95 per cent confidence level, duplicate results which agree within 0.00028 normality units, absolute, are acceptable for averaging.

Stability

47. Restandardize monthly.

IODINE (0.1N)

Preparation

48. Transfer 12.7 g of iodine and 60 g of potassium iodide (KI) to an 800-ml beaker, add 30 ml of water, and stir until solution is complete. Dilute with water to 500 ml, and filter through a sintered-glass filter. Wash the filter with about 15 ml of water, transfer the combined filtrate and washing to a 1-liter volumetric flask, dilute to the mark with water, and mix. Store the solution in a glass-stoppered, amber-glass bottle in a cool place.

Standardization

49. Transfer 1 g of arsenic trioxide (As_2O_3) to a platinum dish, and dry at 105 C for 1 hr.[11] Cool in a desiccator. Weigh accurately 0.20 ± 0.01 g of the dried As_2O_3 and transfer to a 500-ml conical flask. Add 10 ml of sodium hydroxide solution (NaOH, 40 g per liter), and swirl to dissolve. When solution is complete, add 100 ml of water and 10 ml of sulfuric acid (H_2SO_4, 1:35), and mix. Slowly add sodium bicarbonate ($NaHCO_3$) until effervescence ceases, add 2 g of $NaHCO_3$ in excess, and stir

---

[11] A primary standard grade of arsenic trioxide (As_2O_3) is available from the National Bureau of Standards, Washington 25, D. C

until dissolved. Add 2 ml of starch solution (10 g per liter) and titrate with the iodine solution to the first permanent blue color.

Calculation

50. Calculate the normality of the iodine solution, as follows:

$$A = \frac{B}{0.049455 \times C}$$

where:

A = normality of the iodine solution,
B = grams of As_2O_3 used, and
C = milliliters of iodine solution required for titration of the solution.

Precision (see Note 9)

51. (a) *Repeatability.*—The average difference between two results (each the average of duplicate determinations), obtained by the same analyst on different days, will approximate 0.00014 normality units, absolute. Two such values should be considered suspect (95 per cent confidence level) if they differ by more than 0.00040 normality units, absolute.

(b) *Reproducibility.*—The average difference between two results (each the average of duplicate determinations), obtained by analysts in different laboratories, will approximate 0.00021 normality units, absolute. Two such values should be considered suspect (95 per cent confidence level) if they differ by more than 0.00069 normality units, absolute.

(c) *Checking Limits for Duplicates.*—At the 95 per cent confidence level, duplicate results which agree within 0.00030 normality units, absolute, are acceptable for averaging.

Stability

52. (a) Restandardize sealed bottles monthly.

(b) Restandardize open bottles weekly.

SODIUM THIOSULFATE (0.1N)

Preparation

53. Dissolve 25 g of sodium thiosulfate $(Na_2S_2O_3 \cdot 5H_2O)$ in 500 ml of freshly boiled and cooled water, and add 0.11 g of sodium carbonate (Na_2CO_3). Dilute to 1 liter with freshly boiled and cooled water, and let stand for 24 hr. Store the solution in a tightly-closed glass bottle.

Standardization

54. Pulverize 2 g of potassium dichromate $(K_2Cr_2O_7)$,[12] transfer to a platinum dish, and dry at 120 C for 4 hr. Cool in a desiccator. Weigh accurately 0.21 ± 0.01 g of the dried $K_2Cr_2O_7$, and transfer to a 500-ml glass-stoppered conical flask. Add 100 ml of water, swirl to dissolve, remove the stopper, and quickly add 3 g of potassium iodide (KI), 2 g of sodium bicarbonate $(NaHCO_3)$, and 5 ml of hydrochloric acid (HCl). Stopper the flask quickly, swirl to ensure mixing, and let stand in the dark for 10 min. Rinse the stopper and inner walls of the flask with water and titrate with the $Na_2S_2O_3$ solution until the solution has only a faint yellow color. Add 2 ml of starch solution (10 g per liter), and continue the titration to the disappearance of the blue color.

Calculation

55. Calculate the normality of the $Na_2S_2O_3$ solution, as follows:

$$A = \frac{B}{0.04904 \times C}$$

where:

A = normality of the $Na_2S_2O_3$ solution,
B = grams of $K_2Cr_2O_7$ used, and
C = milliliters of $Na_2S_2O_3$ solution required for titration of the solution.

[12] A primary standard grade of potassium dichromate $(K_2Cr_2O_7)$ is available from the National Bureau of Standards, Washington 25, D. C.

Precision

56. (a) *Repeatability.*—The average difference between two results (each the average of duplicate determinations), obtained by the same analyst on different days, will approximate 0.00013 normality units, absolute. Two such values should be considered suspect (95 per cent confidence level) if they differ by more than 0.00040 normality units, absolute.

(b) *Reproducibility.*—The average difference between two results (each the average of duplicate determinations), obtained by analysts in different laboratories, will approximate 0.00023 normality units, absolute. Two such values should be considered suspect (95 per cent confidence level) if they differ by more than 0.00076 normality units, absolute.

(c) *Checking Limits for Duplicates.*— At the 95 per cent confidence level, duplicate results which agree within 0.00026 normality units, absolute, are acceptable for averaging.

NOTE 14.—Seventy-eight results from ten laboratories were considered in establishing these precision data.

Stability

57. Restandardize weekly.

POTASSIUM PERMANGANATE (0.1N)

Preparation

58. Dissolve 3.2 g of potassium permanganate $(KMnO_4)$ in 100 ml of water and dilute the solution with water to 1 liter. Allow the solution to stand in the dark for two weeks and then filter through a fine-porosity sintered-glass crucible. *Do not wash the filter.* Store the solution in glass-stoppered, amber-colored glass bottles.

NOTE 15.—Do not permit the filtered solution to come into contact with paper, rubber, or other organic material.

Standardization[13]

59. (a) Transfer 2 g of sodium oxalate[14] ($Na_2C_2O_4$) to a platinum dish and dry at 105 C for 1 hr. Cool in a desiccator. Weigh accurately 0.30 ± 0.01 g of the dried $Na_2C_2O_4$ and transfer to a 500-ml glass container. Add 250 ml of sulfuric acid (H_2SO_4, 1:19) that was previously boiled for 10 to 15 min and then cooled to 27 ± 3 C, and stir until the sample is dissolved. Add 39 ml of the $KMnO_4$ solution at a rate of 30 ± 5 ml per min, while stirring slowly, and let stand for about 45 sec until the pink color disappears. Heat the solution to 60 C, and complete the titration by adding $KMnO_4$ solution until a faint pink color persists for 30 sec. Add the final 0.5 to 1.0 ml dropwise, and give the solution time to decolorize before adding the next drop.

(b) Carry out a blank determination on a second 250-ml portion of the H_2SO_4 (1:19), and make sure that the pink color at the end point matches that of the standardization solution. Correct the sample titration volume as shown to be necessary.

NOTE 16.—The specified 0.30 g sample of $Na_2C_2O_4$ should consume about 44.8 ml of 0.1N $KMnO_4$.

NOTE 17.—If the pink color of the solution persists more than 45 sec after the addition of the first 39 ml of $KMnO_4$ solution is complete, discard the solution and start over with a fresh solution of the $Na_2C_2O_4$, but add less of the $KMnO_4$ solution.

NOTE 18.—The blank correction usually amounts to 0.03 to 0.05 ml.

Calculation

60. Calculate the normality of the $KMnO_4$ solution, as follows:

$$A = \frac{B}{0.06701 \times C}$$

[13] A buret having a bent delivery tube is helpful in carrying out this standardization procedure.

[14] A primary standard grade of sodium oxalate ($Na_2C_2O_4$) is available from the National Bureau of Standards, Washington, 25, D. C.

where:

A = normality of the $KMnO_4$ solution,
B = grams of $Na_2C_2O_4$ used, and
C = milliliters of $KMnO_4$ solution required for titration of the solution.

Precision

61. (a) *Repeatability.*—The average difference between two results (each the average of duplicate determinations), obtained by the same analyst on different days, will approximate 0.0001 normality units, absolute. Two such values should be considered suspect (95 per cent confidence level) if they differ by more than 0.00033 normality units, absolute.

(b) *Reproducibility.*—The average difference between two results (each the average of duplicate determinations), obtained by analysts in different laboratories, will approximate 0.0002 normality units, absolute. Two such values should be considered suspect (95 per cent confidence level) if they differ by more than 0.00045 normality units, absolute.

(c) *Checking Limits for Duplicates.*— At the 95 per cent confidence level, duplicate results which agree within 0.00031 normality units, absolute, are acceptable for averaging.

NOTE 19.—Eighty results from ten laboratories were considered in establishing these precision data.

Stability

62. Restandardize weekly.

POTASSIUM DICHROMATE (0.1N)

Preparation

63. Transfer 6 g of potassium dichromate ($K_2Cr_2O_7$)[12] to a platinum dish and dry at 120 C for 4 hr. Cool in a desiccator. Place 4.9 g of the dried $K_2Cr_2O_7$ in a 1-liter volumetric flask, and add 100 ml of water. Swirl to dissolve and when solution is complete, dilute to the mark with water and mix. Store the solution in a glass-stoppered bottle.

Standardization

64. Place 40 ml of water in a 250-ml glass-stoppered conical flask, and add 40 ml, accurately measured, of the $K_2Cr_2O_7$ solution. Stopper the flask, swirl to mix, remove the stopper, and add 3 g of potassium iodide (KI), 2 g of sodium bicarbonate ($NaHCO_3$), and 5 ml of hydrochloric acid (HCl). Stopper the flask quickly, swirl to ensure mixing, and let stand in the dark for 10 min. Rinse the stopper and inner walls of the flask with water and titrate with freshly standardized sodium thiosulfate solution ($Na_2S_2O_3$) until the solution has only a faint yellow color. Add 2 ml of starch solution (10 g per liter), and continue the titration to the disappearance of the blue color.

Calculation

65. Calculate the normality of the $K_2Cr_2O_7$ solution, as follows:

$$A = \frac{B \times C}{D}$$

where:

A = normality of the $K_2Cr_2O_7$ solution,

B = milliliters of $Na_2S_2O_3$ solution required for titration of the solution,

C = normality of the $Na_2S_2O_3$ solution, and

D = milliliters of $K_2Cr_2O_7$ solution used.

Precision (see Note 19)

66. (a) *Repeatability.*—The average difference between two results (each the average of duplicate determinations), obtained by the same analyst on different days, will approximate 0.0002 normality units, absolute. Two such values should be considered suspect (95 per cent confidence level) if they differ by more than 0.00046 normality units, absolute.

(b) *Reproducibility.*—The average difference between two results (each the average of duplicate determinations), obtained by analysts in different laboratories, will approximate 0.0003 normality units, absolute. Two such values should be considered suspect (95 per cent confidence level) if they differ by more than 0.00083 normality units, absolute.

(c) *Checking Limits for Duplicates.*—At the 95 per cent confidence level, duplicate results which agree within 0.00020 normality units, absolute, are acceptable for averaging.

NOTE 20.—The precision data obtained for the standardization of the sodium thiosulfate solution were considered in the analysis of the potassium dichromate standardization results.

Stability

67. Restandardize monthly.

METHANOLIC SODIUM HYDROXIDE SOLUTION (0.5N)

Preparation

68. Dilute 28 ml of clear 50 per cent NaOH solution (see Section 12(a)) with 71 ml of water, add 900 ml of absolute methanol, and mix thoroughly in a hard glass container having a vented closure. Store the solution in a light-resistant hard glass bottle fitted with a delivery tube and a guard tube containing a carbon dioxide absorbent.

NOTE. 21.—Mixing of the solution may be accompanied by liberation of considerable air and should be done with a vented system.

Standardization

69. See Section 13(a), but use 4.75 ± 0.05 g of the dried $KHC_8H_4O_4$.

pH 8.6 End Point Color Standard

70. See Section 14.

Calculation

71. See Section 15.

Precision

72. (a) *Repeatability.*—The average difference between two results (each the average of duplicate determinations) obtained by the same analyst on different days, will approximate 0.00069 normality units, absolute. Two such values should be considered suspect (95 per cent confidence level) if they differ by more than 0.0018 normality units, absolute.

(b) *Reproducibility.*—The average difference between two results (each the average of duplicate determinations) obtained by analysts in different laboratories, will approximate 0.0015 normality units, absolute. Two such values should be considered suspect (95 per cent confidence level) if they differ by more than 0.0040 normality units, absolute.

(c) *Checking Limits for Duplicates.* — At the 95 per cent confidence level, duplicate results which agree within 0.0010 normality units, absolute, are acceptable for averaging.

NOTE 22.—Seventy-two results from nine laboratories were considered in establishing these precision data.

Stability

73. The solution must be standardized frequently if there is evidence of action on the glass container, or if insoluble matter appears in the solution.

CERIC SULFATE, 0.1 N (in 1 N H_2SO_4)

Preparation

74. To 60 g of ceric ammonium nitrate $[(NH_4)_2Ce(NO_3)_6]$ add 30 ml of concentrated sulfuric acid (H_2SO_4, sp gr 1.84), and stir until a smooth slurry is formed. Add, cautiously and with constant stirring, 100 ml of water, and stir for 2 min when addition is complete. Add 600 ml of additional water in three portions, adding the water slowly, and stirring for 2 min after each 200 ml is added. Dilute with water to 900 ml, cool, filter through a fine-porosity, sintered-glass crucible covered with a layer of asbestos, and let the filtrate stand undisturbed in a tightly-closed glass container for 2 or 3 days. If any insoluble matter precipitates during the standing, filter through a fine-porosity, sintered-glass crucible covered with a layer of asbestos, and dilute the filtrate with water to 1 liter. If the solution is clear after standing, dilute it with water to 1 liter. Store the solution in tightly-closed glass containers.

Standardization

NOTE 23: **Caution**—The preparation of the osmium tetroxide solution used in this procedure should be carried out in a well-ventilated hood because of the poisonous and irritating vapors given off by this compound.

75. Transfer about 1 g of arsenic trioxide (As_2O_3)[11] to a platinum dish, and dry at 105 C for 1 hr. Cool in a desiccator. Weigh accurately 0.20 ± 0.01 g of the dried As_2O_3 and transfer to a 500-ml conical flask. Rinse the walls of the flask with 25 ml of water containing 2 g of sodium hydroxide (NaOH), and swirl to dissolve. When solution is complete, dilute with 100 ml of water, add 10 ml of sulfuric acid (H_2SO_4, 1:1), 3 drops of a solution of 0.01 M osmium tetroxide (OsO_4) (**Caution,** see Note 23) in 0.1 N H_2SO_4, and 2 drops of 0.025 M 1,10-phenanthroline ferrous sulfate indicator solution. Titrate slowly with the ceric sulfate solution to the sharp color change from pink to very pale blue. Record the temperature of the ceric sulfate solution so that temperature corrections can be made if the solution is later used at a temperature different from that of standardization (see Table I, Section 5).

Calculation

76. Calculate the normality of the ceric sulfate solution, as follows:

$$A = \frac{B}{0.049460 \times C}$$

where:

A = normality of the ceric sulfate solution,

B = grams of As_2O_3 used, and

C = milliliters of ceric sulfate solution required for titration of the solution.

Precision

77. (a) *Repeatability.*—The average difference between two results (each the average of duplicate determinations), obtained by the same analyst on different days, will approximate 0.00012 normality units, absolute. Two such values should be considered suspect (95 per cent confidence level) if they differ by more than 0.00031 normality units, absolute.

(b) *Reproducibility.*—The average difference between two results (each the average of duplicate determinations), obtained by analysts in different laboratories, will approximate 0.00017 normality units, absolute. Two such values should be considered suspect (95 per cent confidence level) if they differ by more than 0.00047 normality units, absolute.

(c) *Checking Limits for Duplicates.*—At the 95 per cent confidence level, duplicate results which agree within 0.00033 normality units, absolute, are acceptable for averaging.

NOTE 24.—Sixty results from nine laboratories were considered in establishing these precision data.

Stability

78. Restandardize monthly.

REAGENT TESTING SOLUTIONS

Standard Ion Solutions

79. (a) *Arsenic, Standard Solution (1 ml = 0.001 mg As).*—Dissolve 0.1320 g of arsenic trioxide (As_2O_3) in 10 ml of sodium hydroxide solution (NaOH, 100 g per liter), neutralize with sulfuric acid (H_2SO_4, 1:15), add 10 ml of the acid in excess, and dilute with water to 1 liter. To 10 ml of this solution (1 ml = 0.1 mg As) add 10 ml of H_2SO_4 (1:15), and dilute with water to 1 liter.

(b) *Chloride, Standard Solution (1 ml = 0.005 mg Cl⁻).*—Dissolve 0.1650 g of sodium chloride (NaCl) in water, and dilute to 1 liter. Dilute 5 ml of this solution to 1 liter.

(c) *Iron, Standard Solution (1 ml = 0.01 mg Fe).*—Dissolve 0.1000 g of iron in 10 ml of hydrochloric acid (HCl, 1:1) and 1 ml of bromine water. Boil until the excess bromine is removed. Add 200 ml of HCl, cool, and dilute to 1 liter in a volumetric flask. Dilute 100 ml of this solution to 1 liter.

(d) *Lead, Standard Solution (1 ml = 0.01 mg Pb).*—Dissolve 0.160 g of lead nitrate ($PbNO_3$) in 100 ml of nitric acid (HNO_3, 1:99), and dilute to 1 liter. Dilute 100 ml of this solution with HNO_3 (1:99) to 1 liter. Prepare the dilute solution immediately before use.

(e) *Sulfate, Standard Solution (1 ml = 0.01 mg SO₄⁻⁻).*—Dissolve 0.148 g of anhydrous sodium sulfate (Na_2SO_4) in water, and dilute to 100 ml. Dilute 10 ml of this solution to 1 liter.

Nonstandardized Reagent Solutions

80. (a) *Acetic Acid Solution (1:19).*—Dilute 50 ml of glacial acetic acid with 950 ml of water, and mix.

(b) *Ammonium Acetate Solution (100 g per liter).*—Dissolve 100 g of ammonium acetate (CH_3COONH_4) in about 750 ml of water, filter, and dilute to 1 liter.

(c) *Ammonium Acetate — Acetic Acid Solution.*—Dissolve 100 g of ammonium acetate (CH_3COONH_4) in about 600 ml of water, filter, add 200 ml of glacial acetic acid to the filtrate, and dilute to 1 liter.

(d) *Ammonium Hydroxide Solution (1:1).*—Dilute 500 ml of ammonium hydroxide (NH_4OH) with 500 ml of water, and mix.

(e) *Ammonium Molybdate — Sulfuric Acid Solution (50 g per liter).*—Transfer 50 g of ammonium molybdate (($NH_4)_6$ $Mo_7O_{24}\cdot4H_2O$) to a 1-liter flask, add 800 ml of $1N$ H_2SO_4, shake to dissolve the salt, and dilute with $1N$ H_2SO_4 to 1 liter.

(f) *Ammonium Thiocyanate Solution (300 g per liter).*—Dissolve 300 g of ammonium thiocyanate (NH_4CNS) in about 750 ml of water, filter, and dilute to 1 liter.

(g) *Barium Chloride Solution (120 g per liter).*—Dissolve 120 g of barium chloride ($BaCl_2\cdot2H_2O$) in about 750 ml of water, filter, and dilute to 1 liter.

(h) *Bromine Water (Saturated).*—To 1 liter of water in a glass-stoppered bottle add bromine and shake until no more bromine is dissolved by the solution. Keep a few drops of bromine on the bottom of the bottle, and use only the clear water solution.

(i) *Ferric Ammonium Sulfate Indicator Solution (80 g per liter).*—Dissolve 80 g of clear crystals of ferric ammonium sulfate ($FeNH_4(SO_4)_2\cdot12H_2O$) in about 750 ml of water, filter, add a few drops of sulfuric acid (H_2SO_4), if necessary, to clear the solution, and dilute to 1 liter.

(j) *Hydrogen Sulfide Solution (Saturated).*—Saturate water with hydrogen sulfide gas by bubbling the gas through the water. The solution must be freshly prepared.

(k) *Hydroxylamine Hydrochloride Solution (100 g per liter).*—Dissolve 100 g of hydroxylamine hydrochloride (NH_2-$OH\cdot HCl$) in about 600 ml of water, filter, and dilute to 1 liter.

(l) *Hydroxylamine Hydrochloride Solution (300 g per liter).*—Dissolve 300 g of hydroxylamine hydrochloride (NH_2-$OH\cdot HCl$) in about 600 ml of water, filter, and dilute to 1 liter.

(m) *Mercuric Acetate Solution (25 g per liter).*—Dissolve 25 g of mercuric acetate ($Hg(CH_3COO)_2$) in about 500 ml of water, filter, and dilute to 1 liter.

(n) *Mercuric Chloride Solution (50 g per liter).*—Dissolve 50 g of mercuric chloride ($HgCl_2$) in about 750 ml of water, filter, and dilute to 1 liter.

(o) *Methyl Orange Indicator Solution (1 g per liter).*—Dissolve 0.1 g of methyl orange in 100 ml of water and filter if necessary.

(p) *Methyl Orange Indicator Solution, Modified.*—Dissolve 0.1 g of methyl orange and 0.14 g of xylene cyanole FF dye in 100 ml of water and filter if necessary.

(q) *Methyl Red Indicator Solution (1 g per liter).*—Dissolve 1 g of methyl red in 1 liter of ethanol (95 per cent) (Note 25).

Note 25.—In most cases certain denatured alcohols such as specially denatured Formula Nos. 3A, 30, or 2B may be substituted for ethanol.

(r) *Methyl Red Indicator Solution (5 g per liter).*—Dissolve 5 g of methyl red in 1 liter of ethanol (95 per cent) (Note 25).

(s) *Osmium Tetroxide Solution (0.01 M) (in 0.1 N H_2SO_4).*—Dissolve 0.25 g of osmium tetroxide (OsO_4) in 100 ml of 0.1 N H_2SO_4 (**Caution,** see Note 26).

Note 26: **Caution**—The preparation of the osmium tetroxide solution should be carried out in a well-ventilated hood because of the poisonous and irritating vapors given off by this compound.

(t) *1,10-Phenanthroline (o-Phenanthroline) Ferrous Sulfate Indicator Solution (0.025 M).*—Dissolve 1.485 g of ortho-phenanthroline monohydrate in 100 ml of 0.025 M ferrous sulfate solution. The 0.025 M ferrous sulfate solution is prepared by dissolving 0.695 g of $FeSO_4 \cdot 7H_2O$ in 100 ml of water.

(*u*) *1,10-Phenanthroline (o-Phenanthroline) Solution (3 g per liter)*. —Dissolve 3 g of *ortho*-phenanthroline monohydrate in 500 ml of water, add 1 ml of hydrochloric acid (HCl), mix, filter, and dilute to 1 liter.

(*v*) *Phenolphthalein Indicator Solution (10 g per liter)*.—Dissolve 1 g of phenolphthalein in 100 ml of ethanol (95 per cent) (see Note 25).

(*w*) *Phenolphthalein Solution in Pyridine (10 g per liter)*.—Dissolve 10 g of phenolphthalein in pyridine and dilute with pyridine to 1 liter.

(*x*) *Potassium Iodide Solution (100 g per liter)*.—Dissolve 100 g of potassium iodide (KI) in about 750 ml of water, filter, and dilute to 1 liter.

(*y*) *Potassium Iodide Solution (300 g per liter)*.—Dissolve 300 g of potassium iodide (KI) in about 750 ml of water, filter, and dilute to 1 liter.

(*z*) *Silver Nitrate Solution (17 g per liter)*.—Dissolve 17 g of silver nitrate ($AgNO_3$) in water, mix, dilute to 1 liter, and store in a light-resistant glass container.

(*aa*) *Sodium Diethyldithiocarbamate Solution (1 g per liter)*.—Dissolve 1 g of sodium diethyldithiocarbamate in 750 ml of water, filter if necessary, and dilute to 1 liter.

(*bb*) *Sodium Hydroxide Solution (4 g per liter)*.—Dissolve 4 g of sodium hydroxide (NaOH) in water and dilute to 1 liter.

(*cc*) *Stannous Chloride Solution (20 g per liter)*.—Dissolve 20 g of stannous chloride ($SnCl_2 \cdot 2H_2O$) in 500 ml of hydrochloric acid (HCl), filter, if necessary, through a sintered-glass filter, and dilute with HCl to 1 liter.

(*dd*) *Starch Indicator Solution (10 g per liter)*. —Mix 1 g of soluble starch with 5 mg of red mercuric iodide (HgI_2) and enough cold water to make a thin paste, and pour slowly, with constant stirring, into 100 ml of boiling water. Boil the mixture while stirring until a thin, translucent fluid is obtained. Cool before use.

ABBREVIATED METHOD OF TEST FOR ACIDITY AND ALKALINITY IN WATER SUPPLIES IN THE EVAPORATIVE INDUSTRY*

Committee D-19 recommends to the Society the publication as information only of the following abbreviated method of test for acidity and alkalinity. The method has been prepared at the request of the chairman of the Chemical Section, Subcommittee on the Care of Pressure Vessels in Service, of the Boiler Code Committee of The American Society of Mechanical Engineers, for inclusion in a subsequent revision of Section 7 on the Care of Power Boilers, of the ASME Boiler Test Code.

PROPOSED NON-REFEREE METHOD OF TEST FOR ACIDITY AND ALKALINITY IN INDUSTRIAL WATER[1]

Scope and Application

1. This method is intended for the routine titrimetric measurement of acidity or alkalinity in industrial water except that which (*1*) is highly polluted with industrial wastes, (*2*) contains buffering materials at the end point, or (*3*) contains materials that will interfere with the titration by reason of color, precipitation, etc. It is particularly applicable to boiler and service waters and to the analysis of those samples incidental to the control of water treating systems.

Interferences

2. Industrial waste materials in highly polluted water may interfere chemically with the titration by destroying the indicator. Appreciable natural coloration of the sample or formation of a precipitate during titration may mask or otherwise interfere with detection of the color change.

Reagents

3. (*a*) *Hydrochloric or Sulfuric Acid Standard (0.02 N).*—Add 1.70 ml of hydrochloric acid (HCl, sp gr 1.19) or 0.56 ml of sulfuric acid (H_2SO_4, sp gr 1.84) to 100 ml of reagent water, dilute to 1 liter, and standardize by any of the accepted procedures.

(*b*) *Methyl Orange Indicator.*—Dissolve 1 g of methyl orange in 1 liter of reagent water.

(*c*) *Methyl Purple Indicator.*—Proprietary compound.[2]

(*d*) *Phenolphthalein Indicator.*—Dissolve 5 g of phenolphthalein in 1 liter of

* Published as information only, June, 1957.
[1] This method is based on, and is a simplification of, Non-Referee Method B of the Methods of Test for Acidity and Basicity (Alkalinity) in Industrial Water and Industrial Waste Water (ASTM Designation: D 1067). For details not presented herein, refer to Method D 1067, which appears in this publication, and Table I of the Report of Committee D-19, *Proceedings*, Am. Soc. Testing Mats., Vol. 53 (1953).

[2] Available as a prepared reagent from most chemical supply houses.

a 50 per cent solution of ethyl alcohol[3] in water.

(e) *Sodium Hydroxide, Standard Solution (0.02 N).*—Dissolve 4.0 g of sodium hydroxide (NaOH) in approximately 50 ml of reagent water. Dissolve 0.2 g of barium hydroxide $(Ba(OH)_2)$ in the NaOH solution. Transfer the solution to a 100-ml volumetric flask and dilute to the mark with reagent water. Stopper the flask and allow to stand over night. Without disturbing any solids that may

TABLE I.—DETERMINATION OF
ACIDITY OR ALKALINITY.

Indicator	Acid	Alkaline
Methyl orange......	pink	orange
Methyl purple......	purple	green
Phenolphthalein[a]....	colorless	pink

[a] When using phenolphthalein it is important that the analyst always use the same amount of indicator, since the pH of the end point depends somewhat on the quantity added.

have settled to the bottom, pipet 20 ml of the clear, supernatant liquid into a 1000-ml volumetric flask and dilute to volume with freshly boiled reagent water. Standardize the diluted NaOH solution against the standard acid solution using methyl orange (or methyl purple) as the indicator. Store in a heavily waxed bottle and protect the air inlet with a soda-asbestos or soda-lime tube.

Procedure

4. (a) Transfer a 100-ml portion of the sample into a 250-ml, narrow-mouth Erlenmeyer flask (Note 1).

NOTE 1.—If the sample requires more than 10 ml of standard acid or NaOH solution for its titration, use a correspondingly smaller sample aliquot.

(b) Add five drops of the desired indicator and mix thoroughly. The sample

---

[3] Specially denatured ethyl alcohol, Formula No. 30, has been found satisfactory for this purpose.

will immediately acquire a color as indicated in Table I, the color depending on the acidity or alkalinity of the sample and the type of indicator employed.

(c) Titrate with standard acid (for alkaline samples) or standard NaOH solution (for acid samples) until a permanent color change as shown in Table I is observed (Note 2). Add the standard solution in small, uniform increments, swirling the flask vigorously after each addition (Note 3). As the end point of titration is approached, a momentary change in color will be noted in the portion of the sample with which the reagent first mixes. From this point on, make dropwise additions of the acid or alkali.

NOTE 2.—It is mandatory that inexperienced analysts become acquainted with the behavior of the several indicators before attempting to titrate samples. This is particularly true with methyl orange, especially when titrations must be made in locations having poor illumination. Acidity and alkalinity determinations made with methyl purple indicator give very nearly the same values as those with methyl orange. Because of the more readily detectable end point, use of methyl purple in preference to methyl orange is strongly recommended.

NOTE 3.—When titrations are to be made repeatedly, a magnetic-type stirrer is desirable.

Calculations

5. Calculate the acidity or alkalinity as follows:

$$\text{Acidity, or alkalinity, epm} = \frac{A \times N \times 1,000}{S}$$

Acidity, or alkalinity, ppm, as $CaCO_3$

$$= \frac{A \times N \times 50,000}{S}$$

where:

A = milliliters of standard acid or NaOH solution required for the titration,

N = normality of the standard acid or NaOH solution, and

S = milliliters of sample used.

TABLE II.—PRECISION AND ACCURACY.

	Precision	Accuracy
Methyl orange (or methyl purple)........	0.05 epm (2.5 ppm CaCO₃) or 2 per cent, whichever is greater.	±0.10 epm (5 ppm CaCO₃) or 4 per cent, whichever is greater.
Phenolphthalein......................	0.01 epm (0.5 ppm CaCO₃) or 0.5 per cent, whichever is greater.	±0.05 epm (2.5 ppm CaCO₃) or 2 per cent, whichever is greater.

Report

6. Report the results as acidity (or alkalinity) to the nearest 0.05 epm (or 2.5 ppm $CaCO_3$), naming the indicator used in the titration.

Precision and Accuracy

7. Provided the sample contains no materials acting as buffers at the end point selected, the precision and accuracy of this method are as shown in Table II.

ABBREVIATED METHODS FOR THE ANALYSIS OF WATER SUPPLIES IN THE EVAPORATIVE INDUSTRY*

Committee D-19 on Industrial Water recommends to the Society the publication as information only of the following abbreviated methods for hardness, hydroxide ion, nitrate ion, and sulfite ion. These methods are based on, and represent simplifications of, the corresponding ASTM methods of test. The committee has been requested to prepare simplified and abbreviated procedures by the chairman of the Chemical Section, Subcommittee on the Care of Pressure Vessels in Service, of the Boiler Code Committee of The American Society of Mechanical Engineers, for inclusion in a subsequent revision of Section 7, on the Care of Power Boilers, of the ASME Boiler Test Code.

PROPOSED NON-REFEREE METHOD OF TEST FOR HARDNESS IN INDUSTRIAL WATER [1,2]

Application

1. This method is intended primarily for routine testing of low-pressure boiler water, and is not suitable for highly colored waters which obscure the color change of the indicator. It is applicable to concentrations covering the range of 0.1 to 24 epm, and is capable of differentiating between calcium and magnesium hardness.

Interferences

2. The substances listed in Table I of the Methods of Test for Hardness in Industrial Water (ASTM Designation: D 1126)[3] do not interfere with this determination if they are present in concentrations not in excess of those indicated.

Reagents[4]

3. (a) *Buffer Solution.*—Prepare the buffer solution in three steps as follows:

(*1*) Dissolve 40 g of sodium tetraborate ($Na_2B_4O_7 \cdot 10H_2O$) in 800 ml of water.

(*2*) Dissolve 10 g of sodium hydroxide (NaOH), 10 g of sodium sulfide (Na_2S), and 10 g of potassium sodium tartrate ($KNaC_4H_6O_6 \cdot 4H_2O$) in 100 ml of water.

---

* Published as information only, June, 1954.
[1] This method is based on, and is a simplification of, Non-Referee Method A of the Methods of Test for Hardness in Industrial Water (ASTM Designation: D 1126). For details not presented herein, refer to Methods D 1126, which appear in this publication.
[2] By publication of this method, neither the American Society for Testing and Materials nor the American Society of Mechanical Engineers undertakes to insure anyone utilizing the method against liability for infringement of Letters Patent nor assumes any such liability, and such publication should not be construed as a recommendation of any patented or proprietary reagents or procedure that may be involved.

[3] Appears in this publication.
[4] All reagents listed are available from chemical suppliers.

(3) Cool and mix the two solutions; then dilute to 1 liter with water.

(b) *Hardness Indicator Solution.*—Dissolve 1.0 g of Chrome Black T, color index 203, in 30 ml of water containing 1 ml of sodium carbonate (Na_2CO_3) solution (30 g per liter). Adjust the solution to pH 10.5 with the Na_2CO_3 solution; then dilute to 100 ml with methanol. Store the hardness indicator solution in a polyethylene, plastic, or hard rubber bottle.

(c) *Hardness Titrating Solution.*—Dissolve 4.0 g of disodium ethylenediamine tetraacetate dihydrate in 800 ml of water. Adjust the solution to pH 10.5 with NaOH solution (40 g per liter), adding the NaOH dropwise while stirring, and using indicator paper or a pH meter to measure the pH. Adjust the strength of solution to equal that of calcium chloride solution prepared as follows:

Dissolve 1 g of calcium carbonate ($CaCO_3$) in dilute hydrochloric acid (one volume HCl (sp gr 1.19) plus three volumes water) and evaporate to dryness. Add 5 ml of water, and again evaporate to dryness. Repeat the addition of water and evaporation to dryness several times to insure complete expulsion of free acid. Dissolve the residue in water, and dilute to 1 liter in a volumetric flask.

Store the hardness titrating solution in a polyethylene, plastic, or hard rubber bottle.

(d) *Sodium Hydroxide Solution.*—Dissolve 40 g of sodium hydroxide (NaOH) in water, and dilute to 1 liter. Store the sodium hydroxide solution in a polyethylene, plastic, or hard rubber bottle.

(e) *Calcium Indicator.*—Mix 0.20 g of ammonium purpurate and 100 g of sodium chloride (NaCl) by grinding them together to a 40- to 50-mesh size.

Procedure

4. (a) *Total Hardness.*—Measure 50 ml of clear sample into a 250-ml white porcelain evaporating dish. Adjust the sample, if necessary, to a pH range of 7 to 10 with dilute ammonium hydroxide (one volume NH_4OH (sp gr 0.90) plus three volumes water) or dilute hydrochloric acid (one volume HCl (sp gr 1.19) plus three volumes water), using indicator paper to measure the pH. Add 0.5 ml of buffer solution and stir Add two or three drops of hardness indicator solution and stir. If hardness is present, the solution will be red in color, in which case titrate the sample with hardness titrating solution until the color of the sample being titrated changes to blue and the red tinge disappears. Record the amount of hardness titrating solution added as C (see Calculation, Section 5).

(b) *Calcium Hardness.*—Measure 50 ml of clear sample into a 250-ml white porcelain evaporating dish. Add 2 ml of the NaOH solution and stir. Add 0.2 g of calcium indicator (a calibrated dipper is sufficiently accurate) and stir. If calcium hardness is present, the solution will be salmon pink in color, in which case titrate the sample with hardness titrating solution until the color of the sample being titrated changes to orchid purple without further color change. Record the amount of hardness titrating solution added as D (see Section 5).

Calculation

5. (a) Calculate the hardness in terms of chemical equivalents per million, epm, as shown in Eq 1, or in parts of $CaCO_3$ per million parts of sample, ppm, as shown in Eq 2.

$$\text{Hardness, epm} = 0.4 \times C \ldots\ldots(1)$$
$$\text{Hardness, ppm} = 20 \times C \ldots\ldots(2)$$

where:

C = milliliters of hardness titrating

solution added in accordance with Section 4(a).

(b) Calculate the calcium hardness in terms of chemical equivalents per million, epm, as shown in Eq 3, or in parts of $CaCO_3$ per million parts of sample, ppm, as shown in Eq 4.

Calcium hardness, epm = 0.4 × D...(3)
Calcium hardness, ppm = 20 × D...(4)

where:

D = milliliters of hardness titrating solution added in accordance with Section 4(b).

(c) Calculate the magnesium hardness in terms of chemical equivalents per million, epm, as shown in Eq 5, or in parts of $CaCO_3$ per million parts of sample, ppm, as shown in Eq 6.

Magnesium hardness, epm = 0.4 (C − D)..(5)
Magnesium hardness, ppm = 20 (C − D)..(6)

where:

C = milliliters of hardness titrating solution added in accordance with Section 4(a), and

D = milliliters of hardness titrating solution added in accordance with Section 4(b).

Precision and Accuracy

6. (a) Results for hardness, calcium hardness, and magnesium hardness should be reproducible to within 0.002 epm (0.1 ppm), or 1 per cent of the amount present, whichever is the greater.

(b) This method is accurate to within 0.04 epm (2.0 ppm) or 2 per cent of the hardness present, whichever is the greater, in the absence of interfering ions in excess of the amounts indicated in Method D 1126, and in the hardness range of 0.10 to 24 epm (5 to 1200 ppm.)

PROPOSED NON-REFEREE METHOD OF TEST FOR HYDROXIDE ION IN INDUSTRIAL WATER[1]

Application

1. This method is applicable to industrial water such as boiler water, and is suitable for routine testing purposes.

Interferences

2. Organic matter and acid-consuming ions, such as silicate and chromate, that are not precipitated by strontium chloride, interfere with this determination to some extent but are not usually present in boiler water in appreciable concentrations.

Reagents

3. (a) *Strontium Chloride Solution.*—Dissolve 4.5 g of strontium chloride $(SrCl_2 \cdot 6H_2O)$ in 1 liter of water.

(b) *Phenolphthalein Indicator Solution.*[2]—Dissolve 5 g of phenolphthalein in 1 liter of a mixture of equal parts of ethanol[3] and water.

(c) *Standard Acid Solution.*[2]—Dilute 1.71 ml of hydrochloric acid (HCl, sp gr 1.18) or 0.55 ml of sulfuric acid (H_2SO_4, sp gr 1.84) to 1 liter with water. Standardize the acid solution by any authoritatively recognized procedure

Procedure

4. Measure 100 ml of clear sample into a 250-ml Erlenmeyer flask. Add 1 ml of $SrCl_2$ solution for each 10 ppm of carbonate and phosphate ions present in the sample, then add an excess of 4 ml. Place a rubber stopper loosely in the mouth of the flask and heat the

---

[1] This method is based on, and is a simplification of, the Standard Method of Test for Hydroxide Ion in Industrial Water and Industrial Waste Water (ASTM Designation: D 514). For details not presented herein, refer to Method D 514, which appears in this publication.

[2] Phenolphthalein indicator solution and 0.02 N standard hydrochloric or sulfuric acid solutions are available from chemical suppliers.

[3] Specially denatured ethyl alcohol, formula 30, may be used if desired.

flask contents to boiling. Boil not longer than 3 sec. Let the hot flask stand for 2 or 3 min, then cool with the stopper in place to prevent entrance of CO_2. Remove the stopper, add two or three drops of phenolphthalein indicator solution and, swirling the flask contents continuously, titrate immediately with standard acid solution until the pink color just disappears.

Note.—If the sample contains more than 150 ppm of hydroxide ion, use a proportionately smaller size sample than 100 ml, and dilute it to 100 ml with water.

Calculation

5. Calculate the concentration of hydroxide ion in terms of parts per million, as follows:

$$\text{Hydroxide, ppm} = \frac{17,000 \times N \times V}{S}$$

where:
S = milliliters of sample used,
N = normality, expressed decimally, of standard acid solution, and
V = milliliters of standard acid solution added.

PROPOSED NON-REFEREE METHOD OF TEST FOR NITRATE ION IN INDUSTRIAL WATER[1]

Application

1. This method is applicable to routine testing of colorless boiler water in the range of 0 to 50 ppm of nitrate ion.

Interferences

2. (a) Nitrite ion interferes with the nitrate ion determination in proportion to its concentration in the sample, but generally is not present in boiler water.

(b) Organic matter in the form of tannin extract interferes to a varying extent, depending on the type of photometer used. Satisfactory results have been obtained in the presence of 100 ppm of organic matter as quebracho tannin.

Apparatus

3. Commercial photoelectric filter photometer or spectrophotometer suitable for measurements at 470 mμ.

Reagents

4. (a) *Standard Potassium Nitrate Solution (1 ml = 1 mg nitrate ion).*— Dry potassium nitrate (KNO_3) in an

[1] This method is based on, and is a simplification of, Standard Method of Test for Nitrate Ion in Industrial Water (ASTM Designation: D 992). For details not presented herein, refer to Method D 992, which appears in this publication.

oven at 105 ± 1 C (220 ± 2 F) for 24 hr. Weigh out 1.631 g, dissolve in approximately 20 ml of water, and dilute to 1 liter with water in a volumetric flask.

(b) *Brucine Alkaloid Solution.*—Dissolve 5 g of pure brucine alkaloid crystals (**Caution,** see Note 1) in approximately 20 ml of chloroform, and dilute to 100 ml with chloroform.

Note 1: **Caution.**—Brucine is a very poisonous alkaloid and care should be taken in handling it.

(c) *Sulfuric Acid (sp gr 1.84).*

Calibration

5. Prepare a series of solutions of known nitrate concentrations in the range of the samples to be tested, by diluting various volumes of standard KNO_3 solution to 1000 ml. Each milliliter of standard solution in 1 liter equals 1 ppm of nitrate ion. Treat these solutions as prescribed in Section 6, measure their color absorbances with the photometer, and plot NO_3^- concentration versus color absorbance.

Procedure

6. Measure 5.0 ml of sample into each of two dry 125-ml Erlenmeyer flasks.

Add with a dropper (not a pipet) 15 drops of brucine alkaloid solution to one of the flasks, followed by 10 ml of H_2SO_4 from a buret to each of the flasks. Add the acid rapidly but cautiously to avoid spattering, and mix thoroughly. Allow the flasks to stand for at least 3 min, then add 10 ml of water to each. Mix and cool to room temperature by immersing the flasks in cool water. Transfer the solution without brucine alkaloid to a photometer cell, place the cell in the photometer, and adjust the instrument to the zero reference point. Replace the cell with one containing the brucine-treated sample, and determine the photometer reading.

Calculation

7. Read the nitrate concentration equivalent to the observed absorbance from the calibration curve prepared in Section 5.

Accuracy

8. In the range of nitrate concentrations from 0 to 50 ppm as NO_3, a precision of 0.5 ppm can be obtained. In the absence of interfering substances, the accuracy is of approximately the same order.

NOTE 2.—This method gives greatest accuracy on samples having up to about 20 ppm of nitrate as NO_3. Above 50 ppm, the method is less accurate, so that it is preferable to dilute as necessary, to keep below 50 ppm.

PROPOSED NON-REFEREE METHOD OF TEST FOR SULFITE ION IN INDUSTRIAL WATER[1]

Application

1. This method is applicable to industrial water, and is particularly suitable for routine testing of boiler water where the sulfite content is 3 ppm or more.

Interferences

2. Catalysts, such as copper, cause rapid oxidation of the sulfite when the sample is exposed to air. This action is hastened by increase in temperature. Other reducing agents, such as sulfides and certain heavy metal ions, will react like sulfite.

Reagents

3. (a) Starch Solution.—Make a paste of 1 g of arrowroot starch or soluble iodometric starch with cold water. Pour the paste into 100 ml of boiling water and boil for several minutes. Store in a glass-stoppered bottle in a cold place. Starch

solution, prepared in this manner, will remain chemically stable for 2 to 3 days.

(b) Hydrochloric Acid (1:3).—Mix one volume of hydrochloric acid (HCl, sp gr 1.19) with three volumes of water.

(c) Potassium Iodide Solution (50 g KI per liter).—Dissolve 50 g of potassium iodide (KI) in 1 liter of freshly boiled and cooled water.

(d) Standard Titrating Solution (1 ml = 1 mg Na_2SO_3).—Dissolve 0.566 g of potassium iodate KIO_3, dried at 120 C, and 0.5 g of sodium bicarbonate (Na-HCO_3) in water, and dilute to 1 liter in a volumetric flask.

Sampling

4. Collect a cooled (15 to 20 C), fresh, air-free sample in accordance with the applicable method of the American Society for Testing Materials, as follows:

D 510—Sampling Industrial Water,[2]
D 860—Sampling Water from Boilers,[2]
D 1066—Sampling Steam.[2]

Procedure

5. Pour 5 ml of HCl (1:3) into a 250-ml wide-mouth Erlenmeyer flask. Rapidly

---

[1] This method is based on, and is a simplification of, the Tentative Method of Test for Sulfite Ion in Industrial Water (ASTM Designation: D 1339). For details not presented herein, refer to Method D 1339, which appears in this publication.

[2] Appears in this publication.

pipet 100 ml of fresh sample into the acid, keeping the pipet tip below the surface. Add 1 ml of starch solution and 5 ml of KI solution. Immediately add titrating solution dropwise from a buret while shaking the flask, until the first persistent blue color appears in the sample. Record the volume of titrating solution used as S. Repeat the test, using 100 ml of pure water (distillate or demineralized water) instead of sample, and record the volume of titrating solution as B.

Calculation

6. Calculate the concentration of sulfite, in parts per million, as follows:

Sulfite as SO_3^{--}, ppm $= (S - B) \times 6.35$

Sulfite as Na_2SO_3, ppm $= (S - B) \times 10$

where:

$S =$ milliliters of titrating solution required for the sample, and

$B =$ milliliters of titrating solution required for pure water.

ABBREVIATED METHOD OF TEST FOR ORTHOPHOSPHATE IN WATER SUPPLIES IN THE EVAPORATIVE INDUSTRY*

Committee D-19 recommends to the Society the publication as information only of the following abbreviated method of test for orthophosphate. The method has been prepared at the request of the Chemical Section, Subcommittee on the Care of Pressure Vessels in Service, of the Boiler Code Committee of the American Society for Mechanical Engineers for inclusion in a subsequent revision of Section 7 on the Care of Power Boilers, of the ASME Boiler Test Code.

PROPOSED NON-REFEREE METHOD OF TEST FOR TOTAL ORTHOPHOSPHATE IN INDUSTRIAL WATER[1]

Application

1. This method covers the colorimetric determination of orthophosphate in industrial water, except water that is highly polluted. It is intended primarily as a control procedure when high precision is not required.

Interference

2. High concentrations of ferric ions and chromate ions interfere with the test; however such concentrations generally are not present in the water for which this method is intended. Color and turbidity, which would interfere if present, are removed prior to color development.

Apparatus

3. Use one of the following means for color evaluation:

(a) *Matched Nessler Tubes*, 50-ml capacity.

(b) *Commercial Color Comparator*, with permanent standards.

(c) *Photometer.*—Spectrophotometer or filter photometer suitable for measurements at 620 mμ.

Reagents

4. (a) *Ammonium Molybdate Solution.* —Add 280 ml of sulfuric acid (H_2SO_4, sp gr 1.84) to about 700 ml of water. To this acid solution add slowly, and with constant stirring, 25 g of ammonium heptamolybdate ((NH_4)$_6$Mo$_7$O$_{24}$·4H$_2$O). Warm the mixture slightly, if necessary, to complete solution; then dilute to 1 liter with water.

(b) *Decolorizing Carbon.*—Analytical grade that will not add significant phosphate to the sample.[2]

(c) *Standard Phosphate Solution (1 ml = 0.1 mg PO$_4$).*—Dissolve 0.1433 g of oven-dried potassium phosphate, monobasic (KH$_2$PO$_4$) in water and dilute to 1 liter.

(d) *Stannous Chloride Solution.*— Dissolve 2.38 g of stannous chloride

---

[1] This method is based on, and is a simplification of, Non-Referee Method C of the Tentative Methods of Test for Phosphate in Industrial Water (ASTM Designation: D 515). For details not presented herein, refer to Method D 515, which appears in this publication.

[2] Nordite A, manufactured by American Nordite Co., Inc., Jacksonville, Fla., has been found satisfactory for this purpose.

($SnCl_2 \cdot 2H_2O$) in 25 ml of hydrochloric acid (HCl, sp gr 1.19) and store the solution in a dark glass or painted dropping bottle.

Calibration

5. (a) Prepare a series of phosphate standards covering PO_4^{---} concentrations from 0 to 5 ppm, in 1-ppm increments, by diluting 1 ml of the standard phosphate solution prepared in accordance with Section 4(c) to 100 ml with water, 2 ml of the standard phosphate solution to 100 ml with water, etc. Each additional milliliter of standard phosphate solution so diluted results in a solution having 1 ppm additional phosphate ion.

(b) Develop the colors of the series of standards as described for the sample in Section 6 (b).

(c) Determine the absorbance at 620 mμ for each standard with the photometer. Prepare a calibration curve plotting PO_4^{---} concentration against absorbance.

Procedure

6. (a) If the sample is turbid or colored, add two 0.25-g increments of decolorizing carbon to 200 ml of sample in an Erlenmeyer flask, shaking it vigorously for 1 min after each addition. Filter through a dry, medium-texture filter paper.[3]

(b) If the PO_4^{---} concentration is anticipated to be 5 ppm or less, pour 100 ml of clear, colorless sample into a 250-ml Erlenmeyer flask. If the concentration is anticipated to be more than 10 ppm, dilute a correspondingly smaller volume to 100 ml with water and pour the diluted sample into the Erlenmeyer flask. Add 4 ml of ammonium molybdate solution and mix by shaking the flask. Add 1 ml of $SnCl_2$ solution and shake the flask again.

(c) If visual comparison is to be made, transfer 50 ml of the sample solution to a Nessler tube and compare the color of the solution with the color of 50 ml of the standards prepared in accordance with Section 5 (a) and (b), and which are contained in a series of similar Nessler tubes. Record the PO_4^{---} concentration of the standard that most nearly matches the sample solution in color.

(d) If a commercial color comparator is to be used, treat the clear, colorless sample as directed in the instructions supplied by the comparator manufacturer, using the reagents provided with the comparator. Make color comparisons between the sample solution and the permanent standards with which the comparator is equipped. Record the PO_4^{---} concentration as directed by the comparator manufacturer.

(e) If photometric measurement is to be made, transfer part of the sample solution to the same size sample cell as was used in preparing the calibration curve in Section 5 (c). Determine the absorbance at 620 mμ with the photometer as directed in the instructions supplied with the photometer being used. Record the PO_4^{---} concentration indicated by the calibration curve as being equivalent to the absorbance determined.

Calculation

7. Calculate the concentration of orthophosphate, PO_4^{---}, in parts per million, as follows:

$$PO_4^{---}, \text{ppm} = \frac{C \times 100}{S}$$

where:

C = parts per million phosphate ion indicated by the matching standard or by the calibration curve, and

S = milliliters of sample tested directly or diluted before testing.

---

[3] Whatman No. 40 filter paper has been found satisfactory for this purpose.

Precision and Accuracy

8. (a) *Precision.*—Duplicate results should not differ by more than the following:

Concentration Range, ppm	By Nessler Tubes or Commercial Comparator, Difference, ppm	By Photometer, Difference, ppm
0 to 10	4	2
10 to 25	4	2
25 to 100	10	4
100 to 200	20	10

(b) *Accuracy.*—Average results should not differ from the true concentration by more than the following:

Concentration Range, ppm	By Nessler Tubes or Commercial Comparator, Difference, ppm	By Photometer, Difference, ppm
0 to 10	±2	±1
10 to 25	±2	±1
25 to 100	±5	±2
100 to 200	±10	±5

PROPOSED METHODS OF TEST FOR APPEARANCE PROPERTIES OF INDUSTRIAL WATER[1, 2]

These are proposed methods of test and are published as information only. Comments are solicited and should be addressed to the American Society for Testing and Materials, 1916 Race St., Philadelphia 3, Pa.

Scope

1. (a) Methods are presented herein for measuring the following optical properties of industrial water:

	Sections
Light Transmittance, T	4 to 8
Absorbance (Optical Density) log b/T.	9 to 12
Geometric Light-Scattering Pattern	13 to 15

(b) The optical properties of a liquid are interrelated and, wherever possible, the interrelationship is indicated.

Definitions

2. (a) *Transmittance.*—Transmittance, T, is defined as the ratio of the amount of light, I, of known characteristics passing through a column of liquid containing a soluble colorant, to the amount of light, I_o, from the same source transmitted through an optically identical liquid-filled sample system not containing the colorant.

$$T = I/I_o$$

Better accuracy and less interference result as more nearly monochromatic light is used. The absolute intensity of the light source and the partial light reflection from the transparent walls of the sample container cancel out leaving the "transmittance ratio" free of transmission losses common to both measurements.

---

[1] These proposed methods are under the jurisdiction of the ASTM Committee D-19 on Industrial Water. A list of members may be found in the ASTM Year Book.

[2] Published as information, June, 1956. Revised in June, 1961 by the deletion of former Sections 13 to 22 on turbidity, now published as the Methods of Test for Turbidity of Industrial Water (ASTM Designation: D 1889), which appear in this publication.

(b) *Absorbance (Optical Density).*—Absorbance, A, which is also sometimes referred to as optical density, is defined as the negative logarithm of the transmittance.

$$A = \log b/T = K'Cb = KC$$

where:

C = concentration, and

b = path length (held constant here).

The numerical values of K' and K are characteristics of the optical system and can be determined by measuring the transmittance or absorbance of a known concentration of the colorant.

Suspended matter should be removed by centrifugation prior to transmittance measurements.

(c) *Geometric Light-Scattering Pattern.*—A polar diagram of the scattered light from a transparent cylindrical cell at various angles relative to the narrow incident beam, with appropriate corrections for size of volume viewed and for extraneous light.

Applications

3. (a) *Transmittance, T, or Absorbance, A.*—This photoelectric method is useful in the measurement of colored constituents in solution (and of soluble constituents that develop color with reagents) when such colorants exhibit specific wavelength regions of light absorption. The nature of the sample must also be such that the transmittance responds only to changes in the constituent being determined. The method is especially useful in the rapid and accurate laboratory determination of many light-absorbing substances that are present in extremely dilute solution, and are otherwise not suitable for titration or precipitation tests. Many colori-

metric determinations are possible with any instrument that can accurately measure transmittance.

(*c*) *Geometric Light-Scattering Pattern.*— In some industrial research and control applications, it is desirable to know the dissymmetry of the light-scattering at various angles in order to determine the average linear dimensions of the particles. The equipment shown in Fig. 5 of the Methods of Test for Turbidity of Industrial Water (ASTM Designation: D 1889)[2a] is particularly useful in the study and control of polymers, colloidal solutions, and large-molecule organic substances that can exist in liquid

(*a*) A light source of constant intensity. This requires a suitable voltage regulator system if alternating current is used.

(*b*) Equipment for isolating approximately monochromatic light from the source, such as:

(*1*) A set of selected "monochromatic" light filters of known filter response in the particular photometer in which they are used,

(*2*) A diffraction grating and calibrated angulation system, or

(*3*) A refraction prism and calibrated angulation system.

(*c*) Optically identical (matched) sample

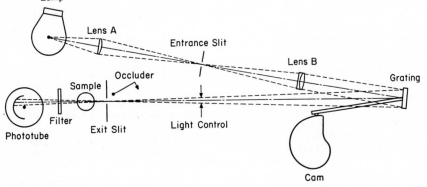

Courtesy of Baush & Lomb Optical Co

FIG. 1.—Transmittance Instrument Diagram Showing Path of Light as Viewed from a Point Directly Above the Instrument.

solutions. The equipment is not intended for measuring the Raman effect, which involves light-scattering at wavelengths other than the wavelength of the incident light, and is not useful for determining the chemical composition of solutions that are more complicated than binary solutions.

TRANSMITTANCE

Apparatus

4. Various instruments for measuring transmittance are commercially available. The schematic diagram shown in Fig. 1 indicates one such instrument. Accurate photoelectric transmittance measurements require the following:

[2a] Appears in this publication.

cells, or the same sample cell must be used for both solutions.

(*d*) An adequate photoelectric detecting and measuring system for the particular wavelength of monochromatic light being used. Photochemical, photographic, and visual comparison systems also exist, but are not detailed in this method. See Fig. 2 showing a hand spectroscope for making visual-transmittance comparisons without the use of photoelectric equipment.[3]

Checking Transmittance Instrument Performance

5. (*a*) With filter photometers use a filter having peak transmittance at designated wavelength.

(b) Preparation of Solutions for Checking Wavelength Scale Setting:

(1) Hydrochloric Acid (1:99).—Into a 1-liter volumetric flask place approximately 400 ml of distilled water. Add 10-ml of concentrated ACS grade HCl. Mix and make to volume with distilled water.

(2) Cobalt Chloride Stock Solution.—Into a 1-liter volumetric flask place 22 to

(c) Checking Wavelength Scale Setting of Spectrophotometric Instruments at 510 ± 5mμ:

(1) Set the wavelength of the instrument at 500 mμ with the sample holder empty. Adjust the dark current for "0" on transmittance scale or "∞" on optical density scale. With distilled water in the sample holder, set the instrument to read 100 per cent transmittance or "0" density.

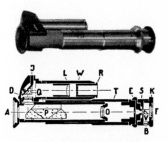

Longitudinal cross-section showing slit tube *T* which contains dust-guard window *F*, slit *S* adjustable by knurled ring *E*, comparison prism *V* and aperture *B* which are controlled by knurled ring *K*; also prism tube *A* which contains Amici prism *P* and focusing magnifier *O*; and side tube which contains draw tube *R* with wavelength scale *W*, focusing lens *L*, deflection prism *Q* with adjustment screw *J*, and magnifying lens *D*.

Courtesy of Arthur H. Thomas Co.

FIG. 2.—Zeiss-Winkel Hand Spectroscope.

23-g of ACS grade $CoCl_2$. Dissolve in HCl (1:99). Make to volume with HCl (1:99).

[3] For more complete discussions of photometers and spectrophotometers, reference may be made to the following:

A. Weissberger, "Physical Methods of Organic Chemistry," Interscience Publishers, Inc., New York, N. Y., Part II (1949).

M. G. Mellon, Ed., "Analytical Absorption Spectroscopy," John Wiley and Sons, Inc. (1950).

W. G. Berl, Ed., "Physical Methods in Chemical Analysis," Vol. I (Section on Spectrophotometry and Colorimetry, by Wallace R. Brode, pp. 194–252), Academic Press, Inc. (1950).

Willard, Merritt, and Dean, "Instrumental Methods of Analysis," Second Edition, D. Van Nostrand Co., Inc., New York, N. Y. (1951).

Chapter II.—"Photoelectric Colorimeters and Fluorescence Meters."

Chapter IV.—"Spectrophotometry and Flame Photometry."

Harley and Wiberley, "Instrumental Analysis" (Chaps. 3, 4, and 7), John Wiley and Sons, Inc. (1954).

TABLE I.—WAVELENGTHS OF VISIBLE MERCURY LINES.

Angstroms	Region
4047	violet
4078	violet
4339	blue
4348	blue
4358	blue
4916	blue-green
5461	green
5770	yellow
5791	yellow

(2) Replace the distilled water with a sample of the undiluted stock cobalt solution (Paragraph *(b)*, Item *(2)*) and record the percentage transmittance or optical density.

(3) Repeat steps *(1)* and *(2)* until read-

ings have been recorded at wavelength settings of 500, 505, 510, 515, and 520 mμ.

(4) Wavelength scale is adjusted properly when maximum absorption occurs at a wavelength between 505 and 515 mμ.

(5) When a more accurate check is desired, the wavelength setting can be recalibrated by an experienced person

(d) *Checking Transmittance or Optical Density Scale:*

(1) At least two samples of $CoCl_2$ solution are required.

(2) Set the optical density scale at "∞." Set the wavelength scale of the instrument at 510 mμ or use a 525-mμ filter. With distilled water in the sample

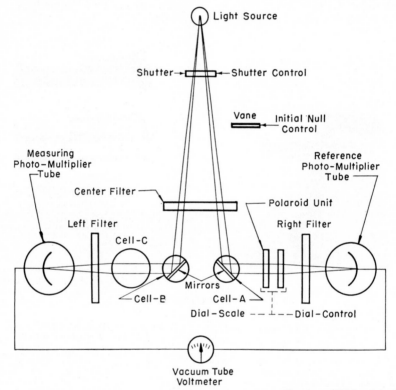

Courtesy of Fisher Scientific Co.

Note.—Dashed lines indicate mechanical connections to panel control.

Fig. 3.—Simplified Schematic Diagram of Fisher Nefluoro Photometer.

using a mercury lamp. The visible mercury lines are shown in Table I.

Note 1.—An alternate method of checking the wavelength calibration is by mapping the transmittance of didymium glass. Because of the unsymmetrical form of some of the absorption bands and the width of the absorption bands, the plot will depend on the slit width and the instrument used.[4]

---

[4] Table of Maximum and Minimum Transmittancies for Didymium is given on p. 210 of "Analytical Absorption Spectroscopy," Edited by M. G. Mellon, John Wiley and Sons, Inc.

holder set the instrument to read 100 per cent transmittance or "0" optical density.

(3) Replace the distilled water with a sample of the undiluted stock cobalt solution and record the optical density reading.

(4) Dilute the sample with equal volume of distilled water. Repeat step (2) and then measure the optical density of the diluted sample.

(5) The optical density reading of the diluted sample should be one half that of the stock solution.

(6) Mix the diluted sample with an equal volume of distilled water. Repeat step (2) and measure the optical density of the new sample.

(7) The optical density of the twice-diluted sample should be one half that obtained in step (4) and one fourth of the optical density of the stock solution.

"dark current." Carefully clean the liquid cells. Measure the intensity of the exit beam with the solvent-filled reference cell in position at nearly full-scale reading. Then measure the exit-beam intensity with the sample cell containing the unknown in position, using the same incident-light intensity adjustment. Repeat the two readings until a

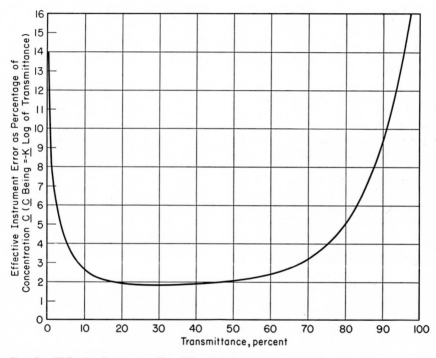

Fig. 4.—"Effective Instrument Error" for Colorimetric Analysis Showing Reason for Limiting Transmittance Measurements to the 10 to 60 per cent Range.

Procedure

6. (a) The wavelength of the monochromatic light must be suitable for the characteristic absorption band of the constituent to be measured. The nature of the sample must also be such that the transmittance responds only to changes in the constituent to be measured.

(b) Follow the manufacturer's instructions in detail for the available instrument. For high-intensity lamps, operate the light source at least 5 min to stabilize it before starting the readings. Balance the measuring system mechanically and electrically for

constant ratio is obtained. The transmittance is the ratio of the two readings.

$$\text{Transmittance ratio} = \frac{R_s}{R_r}$$

where:
R_s = sample light intensity, and
R_r = reference light intensity.

(c) For instruments using two polarizing units and null balancing electrical circuits, obtain the readings in terms of the angle between the polarizing units. For such instruments, the transmittance = $K \cos^2 \theta$, where K is a constant and Θ is the smaller angle between the axes of polarization. Such instruments usually have dials calibrated directly in percentage transmission or optical density, or both (see Fig. 3).

Errors

7. (*a*) Errors due to improper positioning of the galvanometer index and due to instrument limitations and errors of the operator in reading the galvanometer scale, together constitute the "absolute error," a value entirely independent of the nature of the analytical method and of the manipulative skill of the chemist. The effect of the "absolute error" on the precision of an analysis is called the "effective instrument error." Others[5] have defined the "Relative Analysis Error" (RAE) as the effective error for a 1 per cent "Absolute Photometric Error." The magnitude of the "effective error" corresponding to a given "absolute error" value, is mathematically dependent on the transmittance of the sample, and as a consequence, the efficiency of an analytical procedure may depend as much on the dilution ratio, the cell-path length, and the wavelength and band-width selected, as on the verity of the chemical reactions involved. This is a fact too frequently disregarded in the development of new procedures. Figure 4 illustrates the "effective error" corresponding to an "absolute error" of 0.5 per cent, and indicates the folly of conducting colorimetric analysis at either low- or high-transmittance values. Note that the minimum effective error is obtained at a transmittance reading of 36.8 per cent and that readings in the 20 to 60 per cent transmittance range are to be preferred.

(*b*) Transmittancy measurements of fluorescent solutions present some difficulties, particularly with instruments in which the solution is placed between the exit slit of the monochromator and the photoelectric receiver. The absorption cell should be kept as far as possible from the photocell. If a lens is placed between the absorption cell and the receiver to project an image of the exit slit at an additional diaphragm in front

[5] See G. H. Ayres, "Evaluation of Accuracy in Photometric Analysis," *Analytical Chemistry*, Vol. 21, p. 652 (1949).

of the receiver of such a size as barely to transmit the image, most of the fluorescent light is blocked. Another solution to the problem is to add a suitable filter to the system just in front of the photocell, which will pass the light of the absorption band but will absorb the fluorescent light. It is also necessary to use filters to avoid difficulties with other second-order effects from diffraction and refraction monochromators.

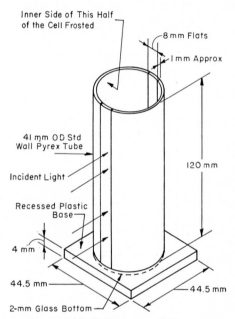

Courtesy of L. P. Witnauer and H. J. Scherr.

Fig. 5.—Diagram of Cylindrical Light-Scattering Cell.

Reporting Results

8. The wavelength and effective band-width of the monochromatic light or the filter designation, light source and solution temperatures should always be reported with the transmittance value.

Absorbance (Optical Density)

Apparatus

9. See Sections 4 and 5.

Procedure

10. See Section 6.

Calculating Results

11. Absorbance or optical density is usually read directly from a second scale of the instrument, or may be calculated from the transmittance. See definition, Section 2 (*b*).

Reporting Results

12. See Section 8.

Geometric Light-Scattering Pattern

Apparatus

13. The geometric light-scattering pattern is measured by a goniophotometer as shown in Fig. 5 of Methods D 1889. Liquid sample cells must be cylindrical with axis aligned parallel to the light slit and perpendicular to the path of the light. If the geometric scattering pattern is to be measured only at 45 deg, 90 deg, and 135 deg, a six-sided cell may be used as shown in Fig. 5 of Methods D 1889. If a more complete scattering pattern is to be measured, it is desirable to use a circular sample cell with flat incident and exit light windows as shown in Fig. 5. The advantage of the more complete light-scattering pattern that can be obtained with the circular sample cell over the pattern that can be obtained by a six-sided or eight-sided sample cell will be apparent after referring to Figs. 2 and 3 of Methods D 1889.

Procedure

14. For details, see manufacturer's instructions.

Reporting Results

15. In addition to the polar diagram of the scattered light, also report the wave band of the monochromatic light and its filter number and the light source. A report on the solution temperature may also be important in some instances.

APPENDIXES

APPENDIX I

REFERENCE TABLES AND CURVES

ATOMIC WEIGHTS OF THE MORE COMMON ELEMENTS[a]

Element	Symbol	Atomic Weight	Valence
Aluminum	Al	26.9815	3
Barium	Ba	137.34	2
Boron	B	10.811	3
Bromine	Br	79.909	1, 3, 5, 7
Cadmium	Cd	112.40	2
Calcium	Ca	40.08	2
Carbon	C	12.01115	2, 4
Chlorine	Cl	35.453	1, 3, 5, 7
Chromium	Cr	51.996	2, 3, 6
Cobalt	Co	58.9332	2, 3
Copper	Cu	63.54	1, 2
Fluorine	F	18.9984	1
Hydrogen	H	1.00797	1
Iodine	I	126.9044	1, 3, 5, 7
Iron	Fe	55.847	2, 3
Lead	Pb	207.19	2, 4
Magnesium	Mg	24.312	2
Manganese	Mn	54.9380	2, 3, 4, 6, 7
Mercury	Hg	200.59	1, 2
Molybdenum	Mo	95.94	3, 4, 6
Nickel	Ni	58.71	2, 3
Nitrogen	N	14.0067	3, 5
Oxygen	O	15.9994	2
Phosphorus	P	30.9738	3, 5
Potassium	K	39.102	1
Silicon	Si	28.086	4
Silver	Ag	107.870	1
Sodium	Na	22.9898	1
Sulfur	S	32.064	2, 4, 6
Tin	Sn	118.69	2, 4
Zinc	Zn	65.37	2

[a] Based on international atomic weights, 1961, published in the *Chemical and Engineering News*, November 20, 1961, p. 43.

CHEMICAL CONVERSION FACTORS: RESIDUE TO PERTINENT ELEMENT OR RADICAL

Weighed	Sought	Factor
Al_2O_3....................	Al	0.529
$BaSO_4$...................	Ba	0.588
$BaSO_4$...................	SO_4	0.412
CaO......................	Ca	0.715
CdS......................	S	0.778
CO_2....................	CO_3	1.364
CuO......................	Cu	0.799
Fe_2O_3...................	Fe	0.699
$KMnO_4$..................	Mn	0.348
$Mg_2P_2O_7$..............	Mg	0.219
$Mg_2P_2O_7$..............	PO_4	0.853
$Mn_2P_2O_7$..............	Mn	0.387
$(NH_4)_3PO_4 \cdot 12MoO_3$........	P	0.0022
Ni-glyoxime.............	Ni	0.203
PbO_2...................	Pb	0.866
SnO_2...................	Sn	0.788
TiO_2...................	Ti	0.60
ZnO.....................	Zn	0.803

DISSOLVED OXYGEN (SATURATION VALUES)

Temperature, deg C	ppm, by weight
10......................	11.33
15......................	10.15
20......................	9.17
25......................	8.38
30......................	7.63
35......................	7.1
40......................	6.6
45......................	6.1
50......................	5.6

DENSITY AND VISCOSITY OF WATER

Temperature, deg C	Density, lb per cu ft	Viscosity, centipoises
10..............	62.40960	1.3077
15..............	62.37205	1.1404
20..............	62.31640	1.0050
25..............	62.24414	0.8937
30..............	62.15676	0.8007
35..............	62.05585	0.7225

IONIC EQUIVALENT CONDUCTANCE
AT 25 C

Ion	$\lambda_0{}^a$
K^+	73.52
Na^+	50.11
H^+	349.82
$NH_4{}^+$	73.4
$\frac{1}{2} Ca^{++}$	59.5
$\frac{1}{2} Mg^{++}$	53.06
Cl^-	76.34
$NO_3{}^-$	71.44
$\frac{1}{2} SO_4{}^{--}$	79.8
OH^-	198
$HCO_3{}^-$	44.48
$\frac{1}{2} CO_2{}^{--}$	83
HS^-	72
$HSO_3{}^-$	71
$\frac{1}{2} SO_3{}^{--}$	80
$H_2PO_4{}^-$	29
$\frac{1}{2} HPO_4{}^{--}$	60
$\frac{1}{3} PO_4{}^{---}$	78

$^a \lambda_0$ = Ionic equivalent conductance at infinite dilution.

TEMPERATURE CONVERSION FORMULAS

Deg C = 5/9 (deg F − 32)

Deg F = 9/5 deg C + 32

BICARBONATE, CARBONATE, AND HYDROXIDE RELATIONSHIPS

	Bicarbonate	Carbonate	Hydroxide
$P = 0$	M	0	0
$P < \frac{1}{2} M$	$M - 2P$	$2P$	0
$P = \frac{1}{2} M$	0	$2P$	0
$P > \frac{1}{2} M$	0	$2(M - P)$	$2P - M$
$P = M$	0	0	M

M = Methyl orange alkalinity.

P = Phenolphthalein alkalinity.

Multiply	By	To Obtain
Acres..................................	43,560	square feet
Acre-feet..............................	325,851	gallons
Centimeters............................	0.394	inches
Centimeters............................	0.01	meters
Centimeters............................	10	millimeters
Cubic feet.............................	1728	cubic inches
Cubic feet.............................	7.48	gallons
Cubic feet.............................	28.32	liters
Cubic feet per minute..................	62.43	pounds of water per minute
Cubic feet per second..................	0.646	million gallons per day
Cubic feet per second..................	448.83	gallons per minute
Cubic inches...........................	16.39	cubic centimeters
Feet...................................	30.48	centimeters
Feet of water..........................	0.8826	inches of mercury
Feet of water..........................	62.43	pounds per square foot
Feet of water..........................	0.4335	pounds per square inch
Gallons................................	3785	cubic centimeters
Gallons................................	0.1337	cubic feet
Gallons................................	231	cubic inches
Gallons................................	3.785	liters
Gallons, Imperial......................	1.2	gallons, U. S.
Gallons of water.......................	8.345	pounds of water
Grains.................................	0.0648	grams
Grains per gallon......................	17.12	parts per million
Grains per gallon......................	142.86	pounds per million gallons
Grams..................................	15.43	grains
Grams..................................	0.001	kilograms
Grams..................................	1000	milligrams
Grams..................................	0.0021	pounds
Grams per liter........................	58.42	grains per gallon
Grams per liter........................	8.345	pounds per 1000 gallons
Grams per liter........................	1000	parts per million
Inches.................................	2.54	centimeters
Inches of mercury......................	1.133	feet of water
Inches of mercury......................	0.4912	pounds per square inch
Inches of water........................	0.0736	inches of mercury
Inches of water........................	0.036	pounds per square inch
Kilograms..............................	2.205	pounds
Kilograms..............................	1000	grams
Kilometers.............................	3281	feet
Kilometers.............................	0.6214	miles
Liters.................................	1000	cubic centimeters
Liters.................................	0.0353	cubic feet
Liters.................................	61.02	cubic inches
Liters.................................	0.2642	gallons
Meters.................................	100	centimeters
Meters.................................	3.281	feet
Meters.................................	39.37	inches
Milligrams.............................	0.001	grams
Milliliters............................	0.001	liters
Milligrams per liter...................	1	parts per million
Million gallons per day................	1.547	cubic feet per second
Ounces.................................	437.5	grains
Ounces.................................	28.35	grams
Parts per million......................	0.0584	grains per gallon
Parts per million......................	8.345	pounds per million gallons
Pounds.................................	7000	grains
Pounds.................................	453.6	grams
Pounds per cubic foot..................	0.016	grams per cubic centimeter
Pounds per square inch.................	2.31	feet of water
Pounds per square inch.................	2.036	inches of mercury
Square miles...........................	640	acres
Tons, long.............................	2240	pounds
Tons, metric...........................	2205	pounds
Tons, short............................	2000	pounds

TABLE I.—ANALYSES OF TYPICAL PUBLIC WATER SUPPLIES IN THE UNITED STATES.

(From U. S. Geological Survey Water-Supply Papers 1299 and 1300.)

Water Supply[a]	1	2	3	4	5	6	7	8
Date of Collection	4/9/52	5/12/49	6/4/52	2/6/52	6/30/52	2/11/52	Average 1950 to 51 Year	June 1949
Silica (SiO_2), ppm	2.1	...	2.5	8.6	6.6	17	12	7.5
Iron (Fe), ppm	0.21	0.0	0.03	0.24	0.00	0.0	...	0.02
Manganese (Mn), ppm	0.00	...	0.00	...	...	0.00	...	0
Calcium (Ca), ppm	36	67	5.3	23	31	12	31	13
Magnesium (Mg), ppm	10	26	1.7	9.2	6.1	3.6	12	5.6
Sodium (Na), ppm	3.4	} 14	1.4	} 2.7	8.0	139	189	11
Potassium (K), ppm	0.7		0.6			0.4	3	...
Bicarbonate (HCO_3), ppm	135	163	10	25	79	317	121	66
Carbonate (CO_3), ppm	0	...	0	0	0	0	12	0
Sulfate (SO_4), ppm	17	137	11	64	39	5.6	290	13
Chloride (Cl), ppm	6.3	20	2.6	6.6	7.0	56	83	10
Fluoride (F), ppm	0.1	...	0.1	0.0	1.0	0.8	0.4	0.1
Nitrate (NO_3), ppm	...	...	0.3	5.9	2.6	0.0	0.2	0.0
Dissolved solids, ppm	150	461	34	147	156	388	692	93
Hardness as $CaCO_3$, ppm	131	274	20	95	102	45	315	54
Noncarbonate hardness as $CaCO_3$, ppm	20	140	6	75	38	0	197	1
Specific conductance, micromhos at 25 C	225	...	53.4	228	236	660	1040	152
pH	8.2	7.4	6.9	8.1	7.5	7.8	8.4	7.9
Color	3	...	1	5	3	10	...	...
Turbidity	14	...	1.9	...	...	...	...	...
Temperature, deg Fahr	37	...	54	50	...	...	...	...

[a] Water supplies are identified as follows:
1. Chicago, Ill. Lake Michigan: Chicago Avenue pumping station.
2. Jacksonville, Fla. Well supply (finished).
3. New York, N. Y. Catskill supply (finished).
4. Philadelphia, Pa. Schuylkill River supply (finished).
5. Washington, D. C. Potomac River (finished).
6. Houston, Tex. Scott Street well 4; depth, 1756 ft.
7. Los Angeles, Metropolitan District of Southern California. Colorado River (finished).
8. San Francisco, Calif. Crystal Spring lines (finished).

TABLE II.—ANALYSES BY U. S. GEOLOGICAL SURVEY OF TYPICAL SURFACE WATERS OF THE UNITED STATES.

Surface Waters[a]	1			2			3			4		
Date of Collection	Max	Min	Avg	Max	Min	Avg	Max	Min	Avg	Max	Min	Avg
	Oct. 1 to 9, 1953	May 11 to 20, 1954	1953 to 1954	Jan. 1 to 10, 1954	May 1 to 10, 1954	1953 to 1954	Aug. 1 to 3, 5 to 10, 1955	March 1 to 10, 1955	1954 to 1955	Jan. 4 to 14, 1953	June 10 to 13, 1953	1952 to 1953
Silica (SiO_2), ppm	4.9	5.4	5.8	1.3	0.3	3.6	5.1	6.2	6.7	...	...	...
Iron (Fe), ppm	0.03	0.02	0.03	0.01	0.03	0.02	0.01	0.48	0.08	...	...	...
Manganese (Mn), ppm	...	...	...	...	...	...	0.00	0.32	0.18	...	...	...
Calcium (Ca), ppm	25	8.7	15	26	18	20	62	20	40	80	56	62
Magnesium (Mg), ppm	9.8	1.5	4.6	5.0	2.7	3.4	15	4.9	10	26	12	18
Sodium (Na), ppm	6.8	5.9	5.7	9.5	3.6	5.0	43	4.9	21	73	39	59
Potassium (K), ppm				1.5	1.0	1.1	4.1	1.6	2.6	...	...	...
Bicarbonate (HCO_3), ppm	68	22	38	84	57	66	29	26	26	265	167	191
Carbonate (CO_3), ppm	0	0	0	0	0	0	0	0	0	0	0	0
Sulfate (SO_4), ppm	38	16	24	15	11	11	201	48	120	211	119	177
Chloride (Cl), ppm	12	3.0	7.2	16	4.4	7.8	52	8.0	29	26	9.5	16
Fluoride (F), ppm	0.2	0.1	0.1	0.4	0.2	0.2	0.5	0.1	0.3	...	...	...
Nitrate (NO_3), ppm	5.8	1.8	3.3	0.4	1.7	1.3	3.8	4.5	3.3	3.7	3.8	3.3
Dissolved solids, ppm	156	55	97	121	74	90	409	120	259	589	348	462
Hardness as $CaCO_3$, ppm	103	28	58	86	55	64	219	69	141	306	189	229
Noncarbonate hardness as $CaCO_3$, ppm	47	10	26	17	9	10	195	49	20	89	52	72
Specific conductance, micromhos at 25 C	251	94.0	158	214	129	153	648	185	408	878	538	697
pH	7.6	7.2	...	7.2	7.2	...	6.9	6.8	...	7.9	7.4	...
Color	9	3	4	5	2	9	3	27	...	...	...	...
Temperature, deg Fahr	...	...	...	...	...	...	85	45	...	...	...	...

Surface Waters[a]	5			6			7			8		
	Max	Min	Avg	Max	Min	Avg	Max	Min	Avg	Max	Min	Avg
Date of Collection	Oct. 5, 1953	May 29, 1954	1953 to 1954	Nov. 7, 1953	July 31, 1954	1953 to 1954	Sept. 21 to 30, 1953	June 21 to 30, 1953	1952 to 1953	March 11 to 20, 1952	June 11 to 20, 1952	1951 to 1952
Silica (SiO$_2$), ppm	...	...	...	28	6.4	15	11	14	15	15	9.6	13
Iron (Fe), ppm	...	...	...	...	...	...	0.12	0.23	0.14	0.14	0.03	0.06
Manganese (Mn), ppm	...	...	...	...	...	...	...	...	...	...	...	...
Calcium (Ca), ppm	137	38	94	70	...	34	144	64	95	26	17	20
Magnesium (Mg), ppm	40	5.4	24	13	...	4.7	57	15	31	8.1	4.4	6.0
Sodium (Na), ppm	810	45	340	628 }	...	75	208	28	101	10	4.9	6.9
Potassium (K), ppm	...	...	...		...	...	12	4.6	6.8	1.8	1.7	1.9
Bicarbonate (HCO$_3$), ppm	235	121	209	216	41	105	260	212	243	106	69	85
Carbonate (CO$_3$), ppm	5	0	...	0	0	...	0	0	0	0	0	0
Sulfate (SO$_4$), ppm	280	30	180	136	21	40	553	79	262	23	12	15
Chloride (Cl), ppm	1280	62	497	892	...	95	194	24	86	5.8	2.0	3.9
Fluoride (F), ppm	...	...	...	...	...	...	0.5	0.3	0.4	0.4	0.2	0.3
Nitrate (NO$_3$), ppm	11	5.2	6.8	22	2.8	4.0	3.4	1.4	2.7	1.3	1.1	1.1
Dissolved solids, ppm	2770	285	1300	1900	82	342	1310	335	719	147	91	111
Hardness as CaCO$_3$, ppm	505	117	333	228	36	104	594	221	364	98	60	75
Noncarbonate hardness as CaCO$_3$, ppm	304	18	162	51	2	18	381	48	166	11	4	5
Specific conductance, micromhos at 25 C	4720	470	2230	3170	154	568	1930	541	1100	234	147	177
pH	8.3	8.2	...	8.2	7.6	...	7.5	7.5	...	7.7	7.3	...
Color	...	...	...	...	...	...	...	...	...	15	25	...

[a] Surface waters are identified as follows:
1. Delaware River at Trenton, N. J.
2. Tennessee River at Kentucky Dam, near Paducah, Ky. (WSP-1350).
3. Ohio River at Ravenswood, W. Va. (Water Quality and Flow Variations in the Ohio River 1951–55. Ohio River Valley Sanitation Commission.)
4. Missouri River at Nebraska City, Nebr. (WSP-1291).
5. Arkansas River at Arkansas City, Kans. (WSP-1352).
6. Trinity River at Romayor, Tex. (WSP-1352),
7. Colorado River near Grand Canyon, Ariz. (WSP-1293).
8. Columbia River at Maryhill Ferry near Rufus, Ore. (WSP-1253).

TABLE III.—ANALYSES OF GROUND WATER FROM REPRESENTATIVE
AQUIFERS IN THE UNITED STATES.

(From U. S Geological Survey Water-Supply Papers 1299 and 1300.)

Aquifers[a]	1	2	3	4	5	6	7	8
Date of Collection	1/16/52	10/20/51	4/2/51	1/17/52	5/24/51	5/14/52	1/29/49	10/4/48
Silica (SiO_2), ppm	7.0	11	13	12	21	14	19	27
Iron (Fe), ppm	0.09	0.19	0.43	0.80	1.6	0.00	...	0
Manganese (Mn), ppm	...	0.00	0.0	0.13	...	0.00	0	0
Calcium (Ca), ppm	49	3.0	8.2	72	62	62	56	12
Magnesium (Mg), ppm	9.1	0.8	4.6	28	11	17	12	7.7
Sodium (Na), ppm	} 9.6	104	17	5.5	56	7.1	71	9.4
Potassium (K), ppm		1.4	1.7	1.0	2.1	1.2	...	...
Bicarbonate (HCO_3), ppm	165	211	85	294	255	244	243	56
Carbonate (CO_3), ppm	0	9	0	0	0	0	0	...
Sulfate (SO_4), ppm	31	9.3	3.7	65	54	15	67	8.9
Chloride (Cl), ppm	9.0	28	2.5	8.0	36	12	51	9.5
Fluoride (F), ppm	0.1	0.9	0.1	0.1	0.3	0.2	...	0
Nitrate (NO_3), ppm	0.2	1.1	0.4	0.7	1.8	5.4	3.5	17
Dissolved solids, ppm	197	274	94	340	370	259	399	115
Hardness as $CaCO_3$, ppm	160	11	39	295	200	225	189	61
Noncarbonate hardness as $CaCO_3$, ppm	24	0	0	54	0	25	0	16
Specific conductance, micromhos at 25 C	342	443	137	565	595	449	...	...
pH	7.7	8.6	6.9	7.6	7.3	7.6	7.7	7.1
Color	2	3	7	2	0	0	...	0
Turbidity	...	2	2	...	...	0	...	...
Temperature, deg Fahr	...	68	...	52	...	78	...	...
Depth, ft	58 to 71	636	400 to 600	108	90 to 265	avg 900	180 to 640	378

[a] Aquifers are identified as follows:
1. Schenectady, N. Y. Wells.
2. Montgomery, Ala. Well 31.
3. Memphis, Tenn. Parkway well field.
4. South Bend, Ind. Well 2, North Station.
5. Wichita, Kans. Wells.
6. San Antonio, Tex. Brackenridge Park well field
7. Glendale, Calif. Grandview wells.
8. Tacoma, Wash. Well 5A.

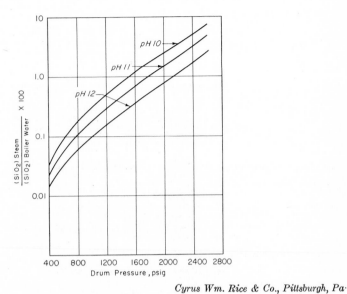

Cyrus Wm. Rice & Co., Pittsburgh, Pa·

FIG. 1.—Percentage of Silica in Steam versus Boiler Drum Pressure at Selected Boiler Water pH.

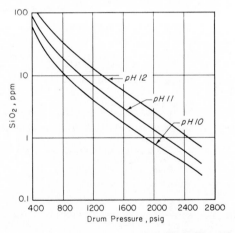

Cyrus Wm. Rice & Co., Pittsburgh, Pa.

FIG. 2.—Maximum Boiler Water Silica Concentration versus Drum Pressure at Selected Boiler Water pH. (Based on maintaining 0.02 ppm SiO_2 maximum in steam.)

TABLE IV.—INDUSTRIAL WATER REQUIREMENTS.

The amounts of water or steam required per unit of product in many industrial operations are tabulated below. All cited sources for the values are listed together at the end of the table.

	Water	Steam
Acetic acid from carbide..........		7300 lb per ton HAc (3)
Acetic acid from pyroligneous acid.	100,000 gal per ton HAc (3)[a]	15,700 lb per ton HAc (3)
Acetic acid from pyroligneous liquor............................	240 M gal per ton HAc (3)	64,000 to 74,000 lb per ton HAc (3)
Acetic acid, direct (Othmer process)............................		54,200 lb per ton HAc (3)
Alcohol, industrial...............	120 gal per gal 100 proof alcohol (5)	50 lb per gal 190 proof alcohol (3)
	52 gal per gal 190 proof alcohol (3)	
	100 gal per gal alcohol (2)	
	20,000 gal per ton grain (1)	
	600,000 gal per 1000 bu grain mashed (5)	
Alumina (Bayer process)..........	6300 gal per ton Al$_2$O$_3$·3H$_2$O (3)	15,000 lb per ton Al$_2$O$_3$·3H$_2$O (3)
Ammonia, synthetic...............	31,000 gal per ton liquid NH$_3$ (1, 3)	
Ammoniated superphosphate......	27 to 30 gal per ton ammoniated superphosphate (3)	
Ammonium sulfate...............	200,000 gal per ton salt (1)	
Buna S..........................	173,000,000 gal per day for 100,000 tons Buna S per year (3)	
Butadiene.......................	320,000 gal per ton butadiene (2)	
Calcium metaphosphate..........	4000 gal per ton Ca(PO$_3$)$_2$	
Carbon dioxide..................	23,000 gal per ton CO$_2$ (1)	20,000 lb per ton solid CO$_2$ from 18 per cent flue gas (3)
	20,000 gal per ton solid CO$_2$ from 18 per cent flue gas (3)	
Casein (grain-curd process)........		2400 lb per ton casein
Caustic soda (lime-soda process)...	18,000 lb per ton NaOH in 11 per cent solution (3)	2700 lb per ton NaOH in 11 per cent solution (3)
	21,000 lb per ton NaOH in 11 per cent solution (1)	
Caustic soda (electrolytic).........		20,000 lb per ton 76 per cent NaOH (3)
Cellulose nitrate.................	50 gal per lb cellulose nitrate (3)	
	10,000 gal per ton cellulose nitrate (1)	
Charcoal and wood chemicals......	65,000 gal per ton crude CaAc$_2$ (3)	64,000 lb per ton crude CaAc$_2$ (3)
Cottonseed oil...................	20 gal per gal oil (3)	15 lb per gal oil (3)
	0.6 gal per gal hardened oil (3)	0.5 lb per gal hardened oil (3)
Coumarin (synthetic).............		3000 lb per ton coumarin or 0.75 ton salicylaldehyde (3)
Cuprammonium rayon.............	90,000 to 160,000 gal per ton 11 per cent moisture rayon (3)	
Fatty acid refining, continuous....		1390 lb per ton stock charged (3)
Gelatin..........................		400 lb per ton gelatin (3)
Glycerine........................	1100 gal per ton glycerine (1)	8000 lb per ton glycerine (3)
Gunpowder......................	200,000 gal per ton gunpowder (1) or explosives (2)	
Hydrochloric acid (salt process)...	2900 gal per ton 20 Bé HCl (3)	
Hydrochloric acid (synthetic process)............................	500 to 1000 gal per ton 20 Bé HCl (3)	
Hydrogen........................	660,000 gal per ton H$_2$ (1)	
Lactose (milk sugar)..............	200,000 to 220,000 gal per ton lactose (1, 3)	80,000 lb per ton lactose (3)
Magnesium carbonate, basic.......	4320 gal per ton basic MgCO$_3$ (3)	18,000 lb per ton basic MgCO$_3$ (3)
	39,000 gal per ton MgCO$_3$ (1)	
Magnesium hydroxide from sea water and dolomite..............	Sea water 58,000 gal and fresh water 500 gal per ton Mg(OH)$_2$ (3)	800 lb per ton Mg(OH)$_2$ (3)
Oxygen, liquid..................	2000 gal per 1000 cu ft O$_2$ (3)	
Phenol, synthetic................		4000 lb per ton phenol (3)
Phosphoric acid (blast furnace)....	75,000 gal per ton 100 per cent H$_3$PO$_4$ (3)	
Phosphoric acid (Dorr strong-acid process)........................	7500 gal per ton 35 per cent P$_2$O$_5$ acid (1, 3)	780 lb per ton 35 per cent P$_2$O$_5$ acid (3)
Potassium chloride from Sylvinite..	40,000 to 50,000 gal per ton KCl (3)	2500 lb per ton KCl (3)
Soap, laundry...................	230 gal per ton soap (3)	4000 lb per ton soap (3)
	500 gal per ton soap (2)	
Soda ash (ammonia-soda process)..	15,000 to 18,000 gal per ton 58 per cent soda ash (1, 3)	
Sodium bichromate...............		6000 lb per ton sodium bichromate (3)
Sodium chlorate..................	60,000 gal per ton sodium chlorate (3)	11,000 lb per ton sodium chlorate (3)
Sodium silicate...................	160 gal per ton 40 Bé water glass (3)	1040 lb per ton 40 Bé water glass (3)
Sodium sulfate, natural...........		3650 lb per ton anhydrous Na$_2$SO$_4$ (95 + per cent) (3)
Stearic acid and red oil...........		18,000 lb per ton stearic acid (3)
Sulfur dioxide, liquid.............	18,000 gal per ton liquid SO$_2$ (3)	6800 lb per ton liquid SO$_2$ (3)
Sulfuric acid (chamber process)....	2500 gal per ton 100 per cent H$_2$SO$_4$ (3)	

[a] The boldface numbers in parentheses refer to the list of references appended to this section of the appendix.

	Water	Steam
Sulfuric acid (contact process).....	4000 gal per ton 100 per cent H₂SO₄ (3) 5000 gal per ton H₂SO₄ (2)	
Trisodium orthophosphate.........		150 lb per ton Na₃PO₄·12H₂O (3)
Vanillin (synthetic)..............		30,800 lb per ton vanillin (3)
Viscose rayon....................	180,000 to 200,000 gal per ton viscose yarn (3)	140,000 lb per ton viscose yarn (3)
FOOD INDUSTRY		
Bread..........................	500 to 1000 gal per ton bread (4)	600 to 1000 lb per ton bread (4)
Brewing		
Beer........................	470 gal per bbl beer (5)	
Whiskey.....................	80 gal per gal whiskey (5)	
Canning		
Apricots.....................	8000 gal per 100 cases No. 2 cans (5)	
Asparagus...................	7000 gal per 100 cases No. 2 cans (1, 5)	
Beans		
Green....................	3500 gal per 100 cases No. 2 cans (1, 5)	
Lima....................	25,000 gal per 100 cases No. 2 cans (1, 5)	
Pork and beans..............	3500 gal per 100 cases No. 2 cans (1)	
Beets........................	2500 gal per 100 cases No. 2 cans (5)	
Corn........................	2500 gal per 100 cases No. 2 cans (5)	
Cream or whole..............	4000 gal per 100 cases No. 2 cans (1)	
Peas........................	3000 gal per 100 cases No. 2 cans (1)	
Sauerkraut...................	300 gal per 100 cases No. 2 cans (1, 5)	
Spinach.....................	16,000 gal per 100 cases No. 2 cans (1, 5)	
Succotash....................	12,500 gal per 100 cases No. 2 cans (5)	
Tomatoes		
Products....................	7000 gal per 100 cases No. 2 cans (1)	
Whole.....................	750 gal per 100 cases No. 2 cans (1)	
Corn refining....................	333 gal per ton corn (1)	
Edible gelatin...................	13,200 to 20,000 gal per ton gelatin (4)	
Edible oil	22 gal per gal oil (3)	
Meat packing		
Packing house.................	55,000 gal per 100 hog units (1, 5)	
Poultry......................	4400 gal per ton live weight (1)	
Slaughter house...............	16,000 gal per 100 hog units (1, 5)	
Stockyards...................	160 gal per acre (5)	
Milk and milk products		
Butter.......................	5000 gal per ton butter (1)	
Cheese.......................	4000 gal per ton cheese (1, 5)	
Dairies......................	3 gal per qt milk (2)	
Receiving and bottling.........	450 gal per 100 gal milk (1, 5)	
Creamery....................	220 gal per ton raw (5)	
Restaurants....................	0.5 to 4.0 gal per meal (2, 5)	
Sugar		
Beet.......................	2160 gal per ton refined sugar (3) 20,000 to 25,000 gal per ton sugar (1) 2600 to 3200 gal per ton beets (1)	
Refined cane..................	1000 gal per ton sugar (2) Condensing 4800 to 8400 gal per ton (3) Pure water 1400 gal per ton refined sugar	3500 lb per ton refined sugar (3)
Vegetable dehydration		
Beets........................	37,400 gal per ton product (1)	
Cabbage......................	15,000 gal per ton product (1)	
Carrots......................	31,600 gal per ton product (1)	
Potatoes.....................	11,200 to 25,000 gal per ton product (1)	
Rutabagas....................	30,400 gal per ton product (1)	
Sweet potatoes................	18,000 gal per ton product (1)	
TEXTILE INDUSTRY		
Cotton		
Bleaching....................	25 to 38 gal per yd (2)	
Dyeing......................	1000 to 2000 gal per 100 lb goods (1)	
Finishing....................	10 to 15 gal per yd (2)	
Processing...................	3800 gal per 100 lb goods (1)	
Knit goods, bleaching............	16,000 gal per ton goods (2)	
Linen..........................	200,000 gal per ton goods (1)	
Rayon		
Cuprammonium yarn...........	160,000 gal per ton yarn (1)	
Dissolving pulp...............	190,000 gal per ton pulp (1)	
Viscose yarn.................	200,000 gal per ton yarn (1)	
Silk, hosiery dyeing..............	6000 to 8000 gal per ton goods (2)	
Wool		
Scouring.....................	2000 to 15,000 gal per 100 lb raw wool (1)	
Scouring and bleaching........	40,000 gal per ton goods (2)	
MISCELLANEOUS INDUSTRIES		
Air conditioning.................	6000 to 15,000 gal per person per season (1)	
Aluminum......................	1,920,000 gal per ton aluminum (2)	
Buildings, office................	27 to 45 gal per day per capita (2, 5)	
Cement, portland................	750 gal per ton cement (2, 3)	
Cement rock, beneficiation........	720 gal per ton raw rock (3)	

TABLE IV.—*Concluded*

	Water	Steam
Coal		
By-product coke	1430 to 2860 gal per ton coke (3)	570 to 860 lb per ton coke (3)
Carbonizing	3500 gal per ton coal carbonized (1)	
Washing	125 gal per ton coal (1)	
Electricity	80 gal per kw electricity (2, 5)	
	120,000 gal per ton coal burned (1)	
Hospitals	135 to 350 gal per day per bed (2, 5)	
Hotels	300 to 525 gal per day per guest room (2, 5)	
Laundries		
Commercial	8600 to 11,400 gal per ton "work" (2, 5)	
Institutional	6000 gal per ton "work" (2, 5)	
Leather tannery	375 gal per ton vegetable tan (3)	
	600 gal per ton chrome tan (3)	
	6000 to 16,000 gal per ton leather (2)	
	16,000 gal per ton hides (1)	
Petroleum		
Airplane engine (to test)	125,000 gal per airplane engine (2)	
Gasoline	7 to 10 gal per gal gasoline (2)	
Gasoline, aviation	25 gal per gal aviation gasoline (2)	
Gasoline, natural	20 gal per gal gasoline (3) and 2000 cu ft stripped gas at 150 lb pressure	6 lb per gal gasoline (3) and 2000 cu ft stripped gas at 150 lb pressure
Gasoline, polymerization	34 gal per gal polymer gasoline (3)	2.7 lb per gal polymer gasoline (3)
Oil, Fischer-Tropsch synthesis	150,000 gal per 100 bbl oil (7)	
Oil fields	18,000 gal per 100 bbl crude oil (1)	
Oil refinery	77,000 gal per 100 bbl crude oil (1)	
Pulp and paper mills	50,000 to 150,000 gal per ton pulp (2)	
De-inking paper	38,000 gal per ton paper (1)	
Paper board	14,000 gal per ton paper board (1)	
Soda pulp		13,000 lb per ton dried soda pulp (3)
Strawboard	26,000 gal per ton strawboard (1)	
Sulfate pulp (Kraft)		10,000 lb per ton dried sulfate pulp (3)
Sulfate pulp bleaching	60,224 gal to bleach 1 ton (3) dry pulp of 80 to 85 G.E. brightness	3120 lb to bleach 1 ton (3) dry pulp of 80 to 85 G.E. brightness
Sulfate pulp		5000 to 7000 lb per ton dried pulp (3)
Rock wool	4000 to 5000 gal per ton rock wool (1, 3)	3000 lb per ton rock wool (3)
Rubber (auto tire)		120 lb per auto tire (3)
Steel plant	20,000 to 35,000 gal per ton steel (1)	
Fabricated steel	42,000 gal per ton steel (2)	
Ingot steel	18,000 gal per ton steel (2)	
Pig iron	4000 gal per ton pig iron (1)	
Sulfur mining	3000 gal per ton sulfur (1)	

References

(1) G. E. Symons, "Treatment of Industrial Wastes," *Water and Sewage*, Vol, 82, No. 11, November, 1944, p. 44.
(2) *Journal*, Am. Water Works Assn., Vol. 37, No. 9, September, 1945, p. 4.
(3) Chemical and Metallurgical Engineering Flow Sheets, 4th Ed. (1944).
(4) Food Industries Flow Sheets of the Food Producing Industry, 2nd Ed. (1947).
(5) H. E. Jordan, "Industrial Requirements for Water," *The Johnson National Drillers' Journal*, July–August, 1948, p. 7.
(6) W. L. Faith, "Plant Location in Agricultural Process Industries," *Chemical Engineering Progress*, Vol. 45, May, 1949, p. 313.
(7) W. C. Schroeder, "Comparison of Major Processes for Synthetic Liquid Fuels," *Chemical Industries*, Vol. 62, No. 4 p. 577 (1948).
(8) S. T. Powell and L. G. von Lossberg, "Relation of Water Supply to Chemical Plant Location," *Chemical Engineering Progress*, Vol. 45, May, 1949, pp. 289–300.

GLOSSARY

Technical terms not in ordinary use, and words used in the Manual in a special sense, are defined below. Definitions given in Standard D 1129[1] are not repeated here.

Absorption—Assimilation of molecules of other substances into the physical structure of a liquid or solid without chemical reaction.

Absorption, radiation—1. The process whereby the number of particles or photons emerging from a body is reduced relative to the number entering, as a result of interactions of the particles with the body.

2. The process whereby part or all of the energy of a particle or of electromagnetic radiation is lost while traversing a body of matter.

Absorption tower—A vertical structure for carrying out an absorption process.

Acid—A compound which dissociates in water solution to furnish hydrogen ions.

Acid anhydride—An oxide which will form an acid when united with water.

Acid mine drainage—Acidic drainage from bituminous coal mines, containing a high concentration of acidic sulfates, especially ferrous sulfate.

Acid radical—The anion in equilibrium with the hydrogen ion of an acid.

Acidify—To make acidic by the addition of acid or acid salt.

Acidimetry—The art of determining the acidity of aqueous solutions.

Activation—The process of inducing radioactivity in a material through nuclear bombardment, especially by neutrons.

Activation analysis—A method of chemical analysis, especially for trace quantities, based on the detection of characteristic radionuclides following nuclear bombardment.

Adsorption—Physical adhesion of molecules to the surfaces of solids without chemical reaction.

Aerobic—Living only in the presence of free oxygen.

---

[1] Appears in this publication.

Agglomerate—To gather together into a larger mass or cluster; to coalesce.

Albuminoid—Any of a number of substances resembling the true proteins such as collagen and keratin. A protein in its broad sense.

Algae—Simple forms of aquatic plant life which multiply only by division, but contain chlorophyll and use sunlight for photosynthesis.

Aliquot—A measured fraction of the known total volume of a solution.

Amorphous—Structure without crystalline components; having no determinate shape.

Amperometrically—Determined by measurement of electric current flowing or generated, rather than by voltage measurement.

Anaerobic—Living in the absence of free oxygen.

Analysis, chemical—Determination of the chemical elements or constituents of a compound or mixture. Also a statement of the results of such a determination.

Angstrom unit—A measurement of length usually applied to light or other radiation wavelengths—0.0001 μ, cm/10^8.

Anion—A negatively charged ion resulting from dissociation of molecules in aqueous solution.

Anode—The positive pole in an electrolytic cell which attracts negatively charged particles or ions (anions).

Anthrax—A malignant infectious disease of cattle, sheep, and other animals, and of man, caused by *Bacillus anthracis*.

Arc, visible—An electrical discharge in which radiation of wavelengths discernible by the normal human eye is produced.

Arthropods—Animals with articulate body and limbs.

Ascarite—A proprietary absorbent for carbon dioxide consisting of asbestos fibers impregnated with dehydrated sodium hydroxide.

Aspirator—A type of suction pump operated from a laboratory water tap.

Autotrophs—Microorganisms which utilize inorganic materials for energy and obtain carbon from the carbon dioxide of the atmosphere.

Background, instrument—Undesired counts or responses due to cosmic rays, local contaminating radioactivity, electronic noise, and the like. Background is sometimes used to refer to the radiation causing the undesired response.

Backwash—Reversed flow of liquid for cleaning or the discharge from such an operation.

Bacteria—One-celled microscopic organisms.

Bacteria, iron—Bacteria which assimilate iron and excrete its compounds in their life processes, thereby contributing to corrosion.

Bacteria, non-pathogenic—Bacteria which do not induce disease in man or the higher animals.

Bacteria, pathogenic—Microorganisms that produce disease.

Bacteria, sulfate-reducing—Bacteria which assimilate oxygen from sulfate compounds, thereby reducing them to sulfides.

Bacteriophage—A viral agent that dissolves specific bacterial cells.

Balance, water—A material account of the weight of water entering and leaving an industrial installation or process.

Basic—Alkaline.

Beam trap—A device on an X-ray-diffraction camera for absorbing the undiffracted primary X-ray beam after it has passed through the sample.

Biota, stream—The collective animal and plant life of a stream.

Birefringence—The difference between the maximum and minimum index of refraction of a crystal.

Blanket—A layer of material outside the core of a reactor in which fissionable materials are produced through neutron activation.

Blowdown—Draining off a portion of the liquid in a vessel, usually to reduce the concentration of the remaining liquid.

BOD—Biochemical oxygen demand of a water— the oxygen required for oxidation of the soluble organic matter by bacterial action in the presence of oxygen.

Bovine tuberculosis—An infectious disease affecting any of various tissues of the body due to the tubercle bacillus and characterized by the production of tubercles.

Brine—Concentrated solution, especially of chloride salts.

Bromination—Chemical treatment with bromine.

Brucellosis—Infection with bacteria of the Brucella group, frequently causing abortions in animals and undulant fever in man.

Buffer—A substance which tends to resist changes in pH of a solution.

Buffered water—Water containing dissolved or suspended material which resists changes in the pH of the water.

Calibration—The process of standardizing.

Carbonate hardness—That hardness in a water

caused by bicarbonates and carbonates of calcium and magnesium.

Carryover—Entrainment of liquid or solid particles from the boiling liquid in the evolved vapor; also the particles so entrained.

Cathode—The negative pole of an electrolytic cell which attracts positively charged particles or ions (cations); the negative electrode of a vacuum tube.

Cathodic protection—Reduction or prevention of corrosion of a metal surface by making it cathodic by use of sacrificial anodes or impressed currents.

Cation—A positively charged ion resulting from dissociation of molecules in solution.

Cavitation—The formation of cavities in a liquid by rapid movement over confining or impelling surfaces and the subsequent collapse of these cavities; the destruction of metal surfaces as a result of cavitation in the liquid.

Centrifuge—A device for separating the lighter and heavier portions of a fluid by centrifugal force.

Chamber, ionization—An instrument whose response to radiation is due only to collection of the ions formed by the interaction of the radiation with the chamber materials.

Chelating agents—Chemical compounds which have the property of withdrawing ions into soluble complexes.

Chlorinator—A machine for feeding either liquid or gaseous chlorine to a stream of water.

Coagulation—The coalescence of fine particles to form larger particles.

Collimator tube—A device for defining the path of rays, such as light or X-rays.

Colloidal—Matter of very fine particle size, usually in the range of 10^{-5} to 10^{-7} cm in diameter.

Colorimeter—A device for measuring or comparing colors or colored solutions.

Colorimeter, photoelectric-cell—A colorimeter which measures the light transmitted through a solution by the response of a photoelectric cell.

Colorimetric determination—An analytical procedure based on measurement, or comparison with standards, of color naturally present in samples or developed therein by addition of reagents.

Combinations, molecular—Possible mutual arrangements of the known proportions of anions and cations present in a mixture.

Combinations, probable—The most likely manner, in the judgment of the analyst, in which the ions of a solution or the constituents of a deposit are combined into compounds in the original sample.

Combining weight—The relative or equivalent weight of an element or compound which enters into combination with another element or compound.

Comparator—A device for comparing colored or turbid solutions against standard solutions' light filters under favorable lighting conditions.

Complexes—Compounds formed by the union of two or more simple salts.

Composition, elemental—Describing a substance in terms of atoms of which it is composed.

Concentration—The process of increasing the dissolved solids per unit volume of solution, usually by evaporation of the liquid; the amount of material dissolved in a unit volume of solution.

Concentration, maximum permissible—The concentration of a specific radionuclide, or a mixture of radionuclides, allowed in an environmental medium, such as air or water.

Condensate—Liquid (water) obtained by evaporation and subsequent condensation.

Condenser—An apparatus for removing heat from a gas (steam) so as to cause the gas to revert to the liquid state (water).

Cooling coil—A coil of pipe or tubing to contain a flowing stream of hot liquid which is cooled by heat transfer to a cold liquid outside.

Cooling tower—Hollow, vertical structure with internal baffles to break up falling water so that it is cooled by upward-flowing air and evaporation from the extended surface of the water.

Corrosion—Chemical attack, as of metals, by which the metal is converted to a compound and thus deteriorated.

Corrosion, electrochemical—Corrosion resulting from the flow of an imposed or self-induced electric current.

Counter, proportional—An instrument whose response to radiation is based upon the collection of the ions formed by the interaction of the radiation with the counter materials, *plus* a proportionate number of secondary ions formed by gas amplification.

Cross-section—The probability, per unit flux and per unit time, that a given nuclear reaction will occur.

Crustaceae—Aquatic animals having a shell.

Culture—Any organic growth which has been intentionally developed by use of a suitable food and environment.

Culture medium—A food substance for growing organic life for study.

Curie—The unit of quantity of radioactive material, defined as that quantity of a nuclide in which the number of disintegrations is 3.7×10^{10} per second.

Deaeration—The process of removing air from a liquid in which it is dissolved.

Decantation—Separation of a liquid from solids, or from a higher density liquid, by carefully pouring off the upper layer after the heavier material has settled.

Decay, heat—The heat produced in or by radioactive material through absorption of the disintegration energy.

Decay, radioactive—Radioactive disintegration.

Decompose—To separate into simpler substances or to change the form or quality of a substance by chemical action; to decay or rot.

Degas—To remove a gas from a liquid or solid.

Dehydrated—Freed from, or lacking, water.

Dehydration—Process of removing water, such as roasting, desiccation, etc.

Dendrite—A tree-like crystalline structure within a solid material.

Density—Weight per unit volume.

Deposit, water-formed—Material formed or deposited on the walls of a water-containing vessel.

Descale—To remove a solid scale layer from its supporting surface.

Desuperheating—Removing sensible heat from a gas (steam) to reduce its temperature.

Detergent—A cleansing and dispersing agent which, like soap, removes a film from its supporting structure by other means than solvent or chemical action.

Diaphragm—A flexible partition between two chambers.

Diatom—Single-celled marine animal having a coating or sheath consisting principally of silica.

Diatomaceous—Made up of the skeletal remains of diatoms.

Diatomaceous earth—A fine, siliceous earth consisting mainly of the cell walls of diatoms.

Diffraction—Bending a beam of light, and so separating it into its colored components, by passing it through a medium of different density or by grazing it across a grating.

Diffraction, angle of—The angle through which a beam of light is bent as it passes through a substance of different density.

Diffractor—A prism or grating which will cause light rays to bend.

Digestion—Prolonged solution of, or reaction with, a solid by a liquid.

Dilution—The addition of more solvent to a solution.

Disintegration, radioactive—A spontaneous nuclear transformation characterized by the emission of energy from the nucleus.

Dissolved matter—The material in solution in a liquid.

Dolomitic lime—Lime containing 30 to 50 per cent magnesium and 70 to 50 per cent calcium oxide as contrasted with a lime containing 95 to 98 per cent calcium oxide.

Dose—A measure of the amount of radiation energy absorbed per unit mass.

Dosimeter—Any instrument which measures radiation dose, especially a small ionization chamber in which accumulated electrical charge, rather than current or events, is measured.

Dry pipe—The horizontal pipe within a boiler through which generated steam is discharged. By multiple changes in direction of steam flow, it serves to separate water droplets from the steam.

Eductor—A mechanical device combining a high-velocity fluid jet, a venturi, and a side arm for pumping gas or liquid in through the side arm and discharging it with the effluent jet; frequently used as a vacuum pump.

Efficiency, detector—A measure of the probability that an event will be recorded when a radiated particle or photon passes into a detector. It is usually measured by the fraction or per cent recorded.

Efficiency, over-all—The response of a detector to a radiation source, defined as the fraction of emitted radiation particles or quanta recorded by the detector.

Effluent—A liquid, solid, or gaseous product, frequently waste, discharged or emerging from a process.

Electrolyte—A substance which dissociates into two or more ions when it is dissolved in water.

Electrolyze—To decompose a compound, either liquid, molten, or in solution, by an electric current.

Embrittlement, caustic—Intergranular failure of boiler steel resulting from the combination of a stress beyond the yield point of the steel and attack by a concentrated caustic solution.

Encrusting—Capable of forming a hard coating or scale.

Encrusting solids—Dissolved solids which, when concentrated by evaporation, will precipitate as a hard coating or scale on heat-transfer surfaces.

End point—The stage in a titration when equivalence is attained as revealed by a change that can be observed or measured such as color development, formation of precipitate, or attainment of specified pH.

End point, electrometric—The stage in a titration when equivalence is reached as revealed by attainment of a specified pH or change in current flow measured by a glass electrode.

End point, methyl-orange—The stage in an acid-base titration when equivalence is attained as revealed by change in color of methyl-orange indicator.

End point, phenolphthalein—The stage in an acid-base titration when equivalence is attained as revealed by change in color of phenolphthalein indicator.

Energy, disintegration—The energy released in radioactive decay.

Entrainment—The carrying over of drops of liquid from an evaporator or boiler due to the vapor velocity being greater than the rate of settling of the drops.

Enzyme—A catalyst produced by living cells.

Equalizing basin—A holding basin in which, by retention, variations in flow and composition of a liquid are averaged out.

Equivalent, chemical—The weight in grams of a substance which combines with or displaces one gram of hydrogen, obtained by dividing the formula weight by the valence.

Erosion—The wearing away of a solid substance by repeated impact action of a solid, liquid, or gas.

Etiologic agent—Causative agent, such as a bacterium which induces a specific disease.

Evaporated—A liquid converted to its vapor by the application of heat or reduced pressure.

Evaporator—An apparatus in which a solution is converted to a vapor and a more concentrated solution, the relatively pure vapor usually being condensed for re-use.

Evaporator, single-effect—An evaporator in which the liquid is subjected to only one evaporating step.

Evaporator, multiple-effect—A series of single-effect evaporators so connected that the vapor from one effect is the heating medium for the next.

Evaporator salines—The concentrated solution effluent from evaporators; also the salts in such a solution.

Evapotranspiration—Transfer of moisture to the atmosphere by plant life, occurring as a result of the processes of evaporation and photosynthesis.

Evolution—The escape or liberation of a gas.

Excited—Stimulated, by applied energy, into an unstable or metastable state, such as in the formation of ions from neutral atoms.

Extraction—The process of dissolving and separating out specific constituents of a sample by treatment with solvents specific for those constituents.

Eyepiece—The lens or lens system to which an observer applies his eye in using an optical instrument.

Fallout—Radioactive débris, usually from a nuclear detonation, which has been deposited on the earth after having been air-borne. Special forms of fallout are "dry fallout" (or "dustout"), "rainout," and "snowout."

Fauna—Animals, or animal life.

Ferrobacillus ferrooxidans—An autotrophic bacterium which oxidizes ferrous iron under acid conditions.

Filamentous—Having the shape of a fine thread-like body or structure.

Film badge—An appropriately packaged photographic film for detecting radiation exposure of personnel.

Filter plant—The portion of a plant containing the equipment employed to strain water for the removal of suspended solids.

Filtrate—The liquid which has passed through a filter.

Filtration—The process of separating solids from a liquid by means of a porous substance through which only the liquid passes.

Fission—The splitting of a nucleus into two more or less equal fragments, usually as a result of the capture of a bombarding particle, especially a neutron. In addition to the two fragments, neutrons and gamma rays are usually emitted during fission.

Fission products—The nuclides produced by the fission of a heavy element nuclide such as uranium-233, uranium-235, or plutonium-239.

Flame photometer—Apparatus for giving a reproducible amount of emitted light for a given concentration of element in the test solution, and for determining the intensity of such emission as a function of concentration of the element without excessive interference from other emitted light.

Flashing—The conversion of a portion of a hot liquid under pressure to its vapor by release of the pressure.

Floc—A felted mass formed in a liquid medium by the aggregation of a number of fine suspended particles.

Flora—Plants, or plant life.

Flow cells—A sensing element or combination of elements, such as electrodes, immersed in a flowing liquid or gas for the purpose of measuring continuously some property of the fluid, such as electrical conductivity.

Flow diagram—The diagrammatic representation of a works process, showing the sequence and interdependence of the successive stages.

Flumed—The transportation of solids by suspension or flotation in flowing water.

Fluorescence—The absorption of radiation at one wavelength or range of wavelengths and its re-emission as radiation of longer, visible wavelengths.

Flux—The number of particles or photons passing through a surface per unit time; for electromagnetic radiation, the energy passing through a surface per unit time.

Fluxing—Addition of a low-melting compound to a substance to decrease fusion temperature of the mixture.

Geiger-Mueller tube—A gas-filled chamber with electrodes operated at a voltage such that a discharge triggered by a primary ionization event will increase until stopped by reduction of the electric field. The size of the response is independent of the unit amount of primary ionization.

Geometry—The average solid angle at the source subtended by the aperture or sensitive volume of a detector, divided by 4π. Geometry is frequently (but loosely) used to denote over-all counting efficiency.

Glass electrode—An electrode consisting of a thin glass membrane separating solutions of known and unknown pH value, the potential difference between the two sides being measured for determining the pH of the unknown.

Grain per gallon—A measure of solution concentration—17.1 ppm.

Grating—A band of equidistant, parallel, straight lines ruled on a suitable surface for systematically dispersing polychromatic light into its separate wavelength components.

Gravimetric—Measured by weight.

Ground water—Water derived from wells or springs, not surface water from lakes or streams.

Gases, half-bound—Gases, such as carbon dioxide, which are evolved by decomposition of unstable ions upon heating.

Half-life—The average time required to reduce the amount of a particular radionuclide to half its original value through radioactive disintegration.

Heat exchanger—A mechanical device by which heat is transferred from a flowing fluid within tubes to another outside the tubes.

Heat transfer—The process of removing heat from a hot body or fluid to another, usually through an intervening wall.

Heater, feedwater—A heat exchanger for raising the temperature of feedwater.

Heterotrophs—Microorganisms which must obtain carbon from organic compounds.

Homogeneous—Of uniform composition throughout.

Hot-well, condenser—Reservoir at the bottom of a condenser shell for collecting condensed water.

Humidity—The concentration of water vapor in an atmosphere.

Hydrazine—An ammonium compound, N_2H_4, which is used as an oxygen scavenger in boiler water.

Hydrometer—A buoyant instrument with graduated stem for measuring the specific gravity of liquids.

Hydroponics—Growth of plants in nutrient solution rather than in earth.

Hygroscopic—Tending to absorb moisture from the atmosphere.

Hypochlorite solution—Bleaching or sterilizing solution containing (O Cl)⁻ ion.

Incubation—Maintenance of viable organisms in nutrient solution at constant temperature for controlled growth or reproduction.

Index of refraction—Ratio of the velocity of light in the substance in question to the velocity of light in a vacuum.

Indicator—Substance which gives a visible change, usually of color, at a desired point in a chemical reaction.

Inoculate—To introduce a small amount of substance into a solution for observation of its effect such as growth or crystal formation.

Intensity, line-spectra—Intensity of the characteristic lines in the spectrum of an excited element.

Interfering substances—Materials which restrict or prevent a desired reaction, or contaminate the product.

Iodimetry—Measurement by consumption or reaction of iodine, usually in solution.

Ion—An atom or radical in solution carrying an integral electrical charge either positive (cation) or negative (anion).

Ion exchange—A process by which certain ions of given charge may be absorbed from solution and replaced in the solution by other ions of similar charge from the absorbent.

Isotropic—Having the same optical properties in all directions.

Kjeldahl determination—The chemical determination of nitrogen by which organic material is decomposed and its nitrogen converted to ammonia.

Latent energy—The energy (heat) required for a change of state at constant temperature, as the thawing of ice into water or the evaporation of water into steam.

Lattice—The uniform, three-dimensional arrangement of atoms or ion groups in a crystal.

Leach—To dissolve certain constituents from a larger mass by a slow washing operation.

Lignin—The major non-cellulose constituent of wood.

Macro—Large, as compared with micro (small).

Macro sample—One large enough to be weighed accurately on an analytical balance.

Macrochemical—On a normal scale of weights and volumes, as opposed to microchemical.

Membrane, porous—A barrier, usually thin, which permits the passage only of particles up to a certain size or of special nature.

Metabolism—The process by which food is used and wastes are formed in living matter.

Methemoglobinemia—Condition resulting from intake of excessive quantities of nitrate (blue babies).

Microbiological—Pertaining to very small living matter and its processes.

Microbiota—Microscopic plants and animals.

Microchemical—Chemical reactions on a very small scale.

Microorganism—Minute living matter.

Microscopic—Minute, very small; pertaining to a microscope.

Microscopy, chemical—Identification by microscopic observation of both chemical reactions and optical properties.

Moderator—Material used in a nuclear reactor to slow neutrons from the high energies at which they are released. Moderators are usually materials of high scattering cross-section, low atomic weight, and low absorption cross-section.

Molds—Filamentous fungi composed of many cells.

Monitoring, radioactive—Periodic or continuous determination of the amount of ionizing radiation or radioactive contamination present in any area, as a safety measure for health protection.

Mother liquor—A solution substantially freed from undissolved material by filtration, decantation, or centrifuging.

MPC—Maximum permissible concentration. See Concentration, maximum permissible.

Nephelometry—Measurement of the light scattered by turbid liquids.

Nessler tubes—Matched cylinders with strain-free, clear-glass bottoms for comparing color density or opacity.

Nesslerization—A process for determining ammonia by its reaction with a mercury complex in alkaline solution.

Neutralization—Reaction of acid or alkali with the opposite reagent until the hydrogen ions are approximately equal to the hydroxyl ions in the solution.

Neutron activation analysis—Activation analysis using neutrons as the bombarding particle.

Nitrobacter—A genus of bacteria that oxidize nitrite to nitrate.

Nitrogen, organic—Nitrogen combined in organic molecules such as proteins, amines, and amino acids.

Nitrosomonas—A genus of bacteria that oxidize ammonia to nitrite.

Noncarbonate hardness—Hardness in water caused by chlorides, sulfates, and nitrates of calcium and magnesium.

Non-condensable—Gaseous matter not liquefied or dissolved under the existing conditions.

Non-referee—A method of test featuring speed

and practical usefulness rather than high accuracy, which is used for process control and general information rather than in settlement of disputed test results.

Nuclide—A species of atoms with a given nuclear constitution, described by the number of protons Z, the total number of nucleons (protons plus neutrons) A, and (if necessary) the energy state. Usually only atoms capable of existing for a time of the order of 10^{-10} seconds or longer are considered to be nuclides.

Nutrient—Food.

Objective—The lens, or set of lenses, opposite the eyepiece in a microscope, which forms an image of the specimen.

Occlusion—An absorption process in which one material adheres strongly to another, usually a solid.

Opacity—The ratio of transmitted to incident light.

Orientation—The relative position of particles with respect to one another or to a reference point.

Orientation, crystal—The geometric relationship between the optical axes and an external reference.

Orifice—A restricted opening of known dimensions, usually for limitation or measurement of fluid flow.

Oxidation—Reaction of a substance with oxygen; loss of electrons by one element to another element.

Oxide—A chemical compound of a metal, or group of elements which act in common as a metal, with oxygen.

Oxide, basic—An oxide which forms hydroxide on reaction with water.

Oxygen demand—Oxygen required for oxidation of inorganic matter, or for stabilization of decomposable organic matter by aerobic bacterial action.

Pathogenic—Causing disease.

Pathogens—Pathogenic or disease-producing organisms.

Photometer—An instrument which measures the intensity of light or degree of light absorption.

Photon—The smallest unit of electromagnetic radiation. The term *photon* is most commonly used in reference to the particulate aspect of electromagnetic radiation. A photon of radiation frequency v has an energy hv and a momentum hv/c, where c is the velocity of light *in vacuo*.

Photosynthesis—Formation of chemical compounds in chlorophyll-containing tissues of plants exposed to light.

Physical tests—Determinations based on observation or measurement of physical properties.

Pollution—The result of discharging normally foreign material into ground or surface water.

Polyphosphate—Molecularly dehydrated orthophosphate.

Precipitate—An insoluble compound formed by chemical reaction between two or more normally soluble compounds in solution.

Priming—A carry-over of water with a sudden generation of steam, like the bumping which sometimes occurs when water is boiled in an open vessel.

Process, hot-flow—Addition of chemicals to hot water (200–212 F) passing slowly through a reaction tank.

Proliferation—The growth or production by multiplication of parts as in budding or cell division.

Protozoa—Microscopic, one-celled animals.

Purity, steam—An inverse measure of the non-water (salts, solids, oil) constituents of steam.

Quality, steam—An inverse measure of the entrained, unevaporated moisture in steam.

Qualitative—Pertaining to the nature of component parts rather than to the amount of such components present.

Quench—To cool a material suddenly; halt abruptly a process or reaction.

Radiation—The emission and propagation of energy through space or through a material medium; also the energy so propagated.

Radioactivity—Spontaneous nuclear disintegration with emission of particulate or electromagnetic radiations.

Radionuclide—A radioactive nuclide.

Radiotracer—A tracer which is detected by means of its radioactivity.

Rainout—See Fallout.

Reactant—A substance which undergoes chemical change in contact with another substance.

Reactor—An assembly capable of sustaining a fission chain reaction.

Reconstitution—The restoration of the original characteristics of a specific water.

Recycled—Having flowed more than once through the same series of processes, pipes, or vessels.

Referee method—A method of test, usually of the highest accuracy available, which is used by mutual consent of contracting parties for establishing an acceptable value or quality in settlement of disputed test results.

Refractory—Heat-resistant; fusible with difficulty.

Regeneration—Restoration of water-treating power to an ion exchanger.

Rehydration—Recombination of water with a molecule of a chemical compound.

Reprecipitation—Dissolving a precipitate and then re-forming it by repetition of the previous procedure. (Used as a purification step in analysis.)

Residue—That which remains after a part has been separated or otherwise treated.

Resolving power—Capacity of an optical system to distinguish adjacent images.

Riparian—Of, pertaining to, or situated, or dwelling on the bank of a river or other body of water.

Rotifera—Minute, many-celled aquatic animals.

Runoff—Water flowing to a stream as a result of rainfall or melting snow.

Saprophytic organism—Any organism living on dead or decaying matter.

Scintillation—The production of light photons by the interaction of radiation with a suitable material.

Sedimentation—Gravitational settling of solid particles in a liquid system.

Self-absorption—The absorption of radiation particles or photons in the source itself.

Sequester—To form a stable, water-soluble complex.

Settling basin—Reservoir receiving water after chemical mixing to permit settling of the floc.

Shielding—Material used to prevent or reduce the passage of radiation particles or photons.

Slimes—Substances of viscous organic nature, frequently derived from microbiological growth.

Sludge blanket—A horizontal layer of solids hydrodynamically suspended within an enclosed body of water.

Softener, base-exchange—Water softener using an ion-exchange material.

Softener, lime-soda—Water softener using calcium hydrate and sodium carbonate as the reacting chemicals.

Solubility—Degree to which a substance will dissolve in a particular solvent.

Solutes—Substances which are dissolved in a liquid.

Solid solution—Mixture of two or more isomorphous substances in a single crystal form.

Species—A classification group having only minor details of difference among themselves.

Specific gravity—Ratio of the weight of any volume of a substance to the weight of an equal volume of water at 4 C.

Spectrograph—Instrument used for photographing a spectrum.

Spectrophotometry—Quantitative measurement with a photometer of the quantity of light of any particular wavelength absorbed by a colored solution, or emitted by a sample subjected to some form of excitation such as a flame, arc, or spark.

Spectroscope—Instrument used to view spectra emitted by bodies or substances.

Spectroscopy—Application of spectroscope to investigation of chemical composition.

Spore—A minute resistant body within bacteria, considered as a resting stage of bacteria.

Spray ponds—Ponds or basins in which cooling water is pumped and sprayed through nozzles, thereby reducing the water temperature by evaporation.

Stage, mechanical—The device used to manipulate a specimen under the lens of a microscope for examination.

Standardization—The manipulations necessary to bring a preparation to an established or known quality; for example, the preparation and adjustment of a standard solution in volumetric analysis.

Staphylococci—A genus of sphere-shaped, pusforming bacteria.

Statistical uncertainty—That portion of the uncertainty of a radioactivity determination due to the random variation in the disintegration process.

Stoichiometric—The fixed weight ratios in which elements combine into chemical compounds.

Streptococci—A genus of sphere-shaped bacteria forming chains of cells; produce pus.

Strongly basic acid absorber—An ion-exchange resin in which the hydroxyl ion exhibits a very low exchange potential.

Sulfuritic material—Compounds of sulfur and iron represented by the formula FeS_2.

Superheater—A heat exchanger in which steam is heated above the equilibrium temperature corresponding to the operating pressure.

Supernatant—The liquid standing above a sediment or precipitate.

Survey meter—A portable instrument for detecting and measuring radiation under varied physical conditions.

Thermal shock—A stress-strain condition set up by a sudden change in temperature.

Titration—The determination of a constituent in a solution by the measured addition of a reactive, standard solution of known strength until the reaction is completed.

Titer—The concentration of a dissolved substance as determined by titration.

Tracer—A foreign substance mixed with or attached to a given substance to enable the distribution or location of the latter to be determined subsequently.

Tritium—A radioactive hydrogen isotope of atomic weight 3.

Tube bank—A large number of metal tubes set parallel and close together, as in a boiler.

Tube failure—Leakage or bursting of tubes resulting from corrosion, overheating, etc.

Tuberculation—A type of corrosion in which the corrosion products form blisters or nodules.

Turbidimeter—Instrument for determining the quantity of matter, in the form of fine suspended particles, in a liquid.

Turbidity—The reduction of transparency of a liquid due to the scattering of light by suspended particles.

Undulant fever—An irregular, relapsing fever, with swelling of joints, spleen, and rheumatic pains caused by Brucella organisms.

Vacuum deaeration—Equipment operating under vacuum to remove dissolved gases from water in the cold.

Vacuum-return system—A system whereby a vacuum is applied to the return pipes to facilitate the flow of condensate back to the boiler.

Viable—Living and potentially reproductive.

Virus—Submicroscopic infectious agent.

Volatile—Capable of being readily evaporated at relatively low temperature.

Volatilize—To convert into a gas or vapor.

Volumetric—Pertaining to measurement by volume, as opposed to gravimetric.

Waste—Any material which is of no further utility to the particular process involved.

Water of crystallization—Water which is an integral constituent of crystals or hydrated salts.

Water hammer—A sharp, hammer-like blow caused by the sudden stoppage of water flow in a long pressure conduit due to the rapid closing of valves. It may also be caused by the sudden collapse of steam bubbles upon entering cold water.

Weakly basic acid absorber—An ion-exchange resin in which the hydroxyl ion exhibits an exceedingly high exchange potential.

Weir boxes—Dams over which, or through a notch in which, the liquid carried by a horizontal open channel is constrained to flow for measurement.

Westphal—A type of weighing balance for determining the specific gravity of liquids and solids.

X-ray diffraction—A method of identifying crystalline substances by means of the scattering of X-rays by the constituent atoms to form characteristic patterns.

Yeasts—Broad group of fungal microorganisms causing fermentation.

Zeolite—A group of hydrated aluminum complex silicates, either natural or synthetic, with cation-exchange properties.

Zeolite, regenerating—A zeolite capable of being regenerated or converted to its original form by brine treatment.

Zeolite softeners—Equipment containing zeolite for softening water.

LIST OF ASTM SYMPOSIUMS AND TECHNICAL PAPERS ON INDUSTRIAL WATER

Committee D-19 has sponsored many symposiums and discussions of various phases of the use of industrial water. The resulting papers have been published at several times and different places. For convenience in locating this literature relating to the subject of this Manual, a complete listing is given below.

1934

M. C. Schwartz and W. B. Gurney, "The Determination of Traces of Dissolved Oxygen by the Winkler Method," *Proceedings*, Vol. 34, Part II, p. 796 (1934).

Sheppard T. Powell, "Water as an Engineering and Industrial Material," ninth Edgar Marburg Lecture, presented at 1934 Annual Meeting of A.S.T.M. in Atlantic City, N. J., June, 1934; *Proceedings*, Vol. 34, Part II, p. 3 (1934).

1936

Alfred H. White, Claude H. Leland, and Dale W. Button, "Determination of Dissolved Oxygen in Boiler Feed Water," *Proceedings*, Vol. 36, Part II, p. 697 (1936).

W. C. Schroeder, A. A. Berk, and Everett P. Partridge, "Effect of Solution Composition on the Failure of Boiler Steel Under Static Stress at 250 C.," *Proceedings*, Vol. 36, Part II, p. 721 (1936).

R. M. Hitchens and R. W. Towne, "The Rate of Reaction of Sodium Sulfite with Oxygen Dissolved in Water," *Proceedings*, Vol. 36, Part II, p. 687 (1936).

W. C. Schroeder, A. A. Berk, and Everett P. Partridge, "The Use of Solubility Data to Control the Deposition of Sodium Sulfate or Its Complex Salts in Boiler Waters," *Proceedings*, Vol. 36, Part II, p. 755 (1936).

1937

R. T. Sheen and C. A. Noll, "Determination of Hardness in Water by Direct Titration," *Proceedings*, Vol. 37, Part II, p. 609 (1937).

Everett P. Partridge, "Some Applications of the Polarizing Microscope to Water-Conditioning Problems," *Proceedings*, Vol. 37, Part II, p. 600 (1937).

T. H. Daugherty, "Technique in the Determination of Dissolved Oxygen," *Proceedings*, Vol. 37, Part II, p. 615 (1937).

1938

Baker Wingfield, W. H. Goss, Walter J. Hamer, and S. F. Acree, "The Need for pH Standards," ASTM Bulletin, No. 90, January, p. 15 (1938).

Frederick G. Straub and T. A. Bradbury, "A Method for the Embrittlement Testing of Boiler Waters," *Proceedings*, Vol. 38, Part II, p. 602 (1938).

J. B. Romer, W. W. Cerna, and H. F. Hannum, "The Estimation of Sodium in Water Supplies by an Indirect Method," *Proceedings*, Vol. 38, Part II, p. 638 (1938).

P. G. Bird, "Removal of Dissolved Salts from Water by Exchange Filters," *Proceedings*, Vol. 38, Part II, p. 631 (1938).

1939

R. C. Ulmer, "Determination by the Evaporation Method of Small Amounts of Dissolved Solids in Water Such as Condensed Steam from Boilers," *Proceedings*, Vol. 39 p. 1221 (1939).

A. M. Amorosi and J. R. McDermet, "The Calculation of the Distribution of Carbon Dioxide Between Water and Steam," *Proceedings*, Vol. 39, p. 1204 (1939).

D. S. McKinney, "The Calculation of Equilibria in Dilute Water Solutions," *Proceedings*, Vol. 39, p. 1191 (1939).

Richard C. Corey and Thomas J. Finnegan, "The pH Dissolved Iron Concentration and Solid Product Resulting from the Reaction Between Iron and Pure Water at Room Temperature," *Proceedings*, Vol. 39, p. 1242 (1939).

1940

Symposium on Problems in the Classification of Natural Water Intended for Industrial Use, *Proceedings*, Vol. 40, pp. 1305 to 1353 (1940):

Robert C. Adams, "Reporting the Results of Water Analysis."

V. V. Kendall, "A Review of Data on the Relationship of Corrosivity of Water to Its Chemical Analysis."

Everett P. Partridge and G. B. Hatch, "Measuring the Scale-Forming and Corrosive Tendencies of Water by Short-Time Tests."

J. H. Walker, "A Method of Measuring Corrosiveness."

1941

Boiler Feedwater Studies. Report of Joint Research Committee, ASTM Bulletin, No. 111, August, p. 56 (1941).

Symposium on Problems and Practice in Determining Steam Purity by Conductivity Methods, *Proceedings,* Vol. 41, pp. 1261 to 1338 (1941):
A. R. Belyea and A. H. Moody, "The Sampling of Steam and Boiler Water."
S. F. Whirl and W. A. Lower, "Experimental Methods for Determining Conductivity Corrections for Dissolved Gases in Steam Condensate."
D. S. McKinney, "Calculation of Corrections to Conductivity Measurements for Dissolved Gases."
P. B. Place, "The Degasification of Steam Samples for Conductivity Tests."
A. R. Mumford, "A New Type of Conductivity Apparatus for Use with Boiler Waters and Steam Samples."
C. E. Kaufman, "Conductivity Cells and Electrical Measuring Instruments."

1942

Round-Table Discussion on the Solvent Action of Water Vapor at High Temperature and Pressure, *Proceedings,* Vol. 42, pp. 977 to 1020 (1942):
George W. Morey, "Solubility of Solids in Water Vapor."

1943

ROBERT C. ADAMS, ROBERT E. BARNETT and DANIEL E. KELLER, JR., "Field and Laboratory Determination of Dissolved Oxygen," *Proceedings,* Vol. 43, p. 1240 (1943).
R. C. ULMER, J. M. REYNAR, AND J. M. DECKER, "Applicability of the Schwartz-Gurney Method for Determining Dissolved Oxygen in Boiler Feedwater and Modification of the Method to Make It Especially Applicable in the Presence of Such Impurities as Are Encountered in Power Plants," *Proceedings* Vol. 43, p. 1258 (1943).
Symposium on the Identification of Water-Formed Deposits, Scales, and Corrosion Products by Physico-Chemical Methods, *Proceedings,* Vol. 43, pp. 1269 to 1308 (1943):
C. E. Imhoff and L. A. Burkardt, "X-ray Diffraction Methods in the Study of Power Plant Deposits."
Everett P. Partridge, R. K. Scott, and P. H. Morrison, "Diagnosis of Water Problems at Limbo Station."
J. A. Holmes and A. O. Walker, "The Interpretation of Analyses and Problems Encountered in Water Deposits."

1944

Boiler Feedwater Studies Joint Research Committee, *Proceedings,* Vol. 44, p. 504 (1944).
Round-Table Discussion on Organizing the Classification of Industrial Waters, *Proceedings.* Vol. 44, pp. 1051 to 1082 (1944):
W. D. Collins, "Typical Water Analyses for Classification with Reference to Industrial Use."
Lewis B. Miller, "The Use of Selected Waters in Pulp and Paper Manufacture."

R. E. Hall, "Treatment of Various Types of Waters for Operating Pressures Above 400 psi."
J. A. Holmes, "Classification of Feedwater for Boilers Operating Between 100–400 psi."

1947

Round Table Discussion on Water-Formed Deposits, *Proceedings,* Vol. 47, pp. 1088 to 1117 (1947):
Michael Fleischer, "Some Problems in Nomenclature in Mineralogy and Inorganic Chemistry."
Alton Gabriel, Howard Jaffe, and Maurice Peterson, "Use of the Spectroscope in the Determination of the Constituents of Boiler Scale and Related Compounds."
J. F. SEBALD, "An Evaluation of Test Methods for the Oxygen in Deaerated Boiler Feedwater, "*Proceedings,* Vol. 47, p. 1121 (1947).

1948

Panel Discussion on Corrosion of Pressure Vessels, *Proceedings,* Vol. 48, pp. 897 to 926 (1948):
R. B. Donworth, "Station Design and Composition of Materials as Factors in Boiler Corrosion."
Richard C. Corey, "Corrosion of High-Pressure Steam Generators: Status of Our Knowledge of the Effect of Copper and Iron Oxide Deposits in Steam Generating Tubes."

1949

Round Table Discussion on Standards for Water-Borne Wastes, ASTM BULLETIN, No. 16, December (1949):
George D. Beal and S. A. Braley, "Analysis of Water-Borne Industrial Wastes: The Need for Uniformity in Methods of Analysis and Reporting."
Charles F. Hauck, "Gaging and Sampling Water-Borne Industrial Wastes."

1950

Max Hecht, "Industrial Water and Water-Borne Industrial Waste," ASTM BULLETIN, No. 168, September, p. 31 (1950).

1951

Symposium on Flame Photometry, STP 116, Am. Soc. Testing Mats. (1951): R. K. Scott, W. M. Marcy, and J. J. Hronas, "The Flame Photometer in the Analysis of Water and Water-Formed Deposits."

1952

Symposium on Continuous Analysis of Industrial Water and Industrial Waste Water, *STP 130,* Am. Soc. Testing Mats. (1952):
M. F. Madarasz, "Automatic Sampling of Industrial Water and Industrial Waste Water."
Robert Rosenthal, "Some Practical Aspects of the Measurement of pH, Electrical Con-

ductivity and Oxidation-Reduction Potential of Industrial Water."

A. E. Griffin, "Continuous Recording of Chlorine Residuals and Determination of Chlorine Demand."

F. C. Staats, "Measurement of Color, Turbidity, Hardness, and Silica in Industrial Waters."

J. K. Rummel, "Continuous Measurement of Dissolved Gases in Water."

1955

Symposium on High-Purity Water Corrosion, *STP 179*, Am. Soc. Testing Mats. (1955):

F. N. Alquist, "The Preparation and Maintenance of High-Purity Water."

H. W. Huntley and S. Untermyer, "The Use of Water in Atomic Reactors."

Donald M. Wroughton, James M. Seamon, and Paul E. Brown, "Influence of Water Composition on Corrosion in High-Temperature, High-Purity Water."

A. H. Roebuck, "Effect of Material Composition in High-Temperature Water Corrosion."

R. U. Blaser and J. J. Owens, "Special Corrosion Study of Carbon and Low Alloy Steels."

1956

Symposium on Steam Quality, *STP 192*, Am. Soc. Testing Mats. (1956):

W. B. Gurney, "Measurement and Purification of Steam to 0.01 ppm Total Dissolved Solids."

E. E. Coulter and T. M. Campbell, Jr., "Steam Purity Determination by Tracer Techniques."

R. O. Parker and R. J. Ziobro, "Comments on Corrections to Steam Conductivity Measurements."

A. B. Sisson, F. G. Straub, and R. W. Lane, "Construction and Operation of Larson-Lane Steam Purity and Condensate Analyzers."

Symposium on Industrial Water and Industrial Waste Water, *STP 207*, Am. Soc. Testing Mats (1956):

Claude K. Rice, "Three is a Vital Number." (The relations of the Public, Government and Industry in the measurement and abatement of stream pollution.)

T. C. Wilson, "Industrial Waste Problems in Southern California."

Carl B. Johnston, "Water Pollution Control in the Los Angeles Area."

Robert C. Adams, "Committee D-19: The First Quarter Century."

O. M. Elliott, "Sea Water Purification."

J. K. Rice, "The Use of Organic Flocculants and Flocculating Aids in the Treatment of Industrial Water and Industrial Waste Water."

1957

Everett P. Partridge, "Your Most Important Raw Material—Water," thirty-first Edgar Marburg Lecture, presented at 1957 Annual Meeting of ASTM in Atlantic City, N. J., June, 1957.

Symposium on Determination of Dissolved Oxygen in Water, *STP 219*, Am. Soc. Testing Mats. (1957):

K. G. Stoffer, "A Study of the Accuracy of Methods of Testing for Dissolved Oxygen in High-Purity Water."

W. W. Eckenfelder, Jr. and Conrad T. Burris, "Polarographic Measurement of Dissolved Oxygen."

Thomas Finnegan and Ross C. Tucker, "The Beckman Dissolved Oxygen Analyzer."

A. J. Ristaino and A.A. Dominick, "Evaluation of Hartmann and Braun Dissolved Oxygen Recorder for Boiler Feedwater."

H. A. Grabowski, "Determination of Dissolved Oxygen by Means of a Cambridge Analyzer."

1958

Symposium on Radioactivity in Industrial Water and Industrial Waste Water, *STP 235*, Am. Soc. Testing Mats. (1958):

A. R. Belyea, "Introduction."

A. Louis Medin, "Radioactivity and Purity Control of APPR Primary Water."

S. F. Whirl and J. A. Tash, "Radioactive Waste Processing Control, Shippingport Atomic Power Station."

C. J. Munter, "Test Methods for Radioactivity Hazards in Industrial Waters."

B. Kahn, D. W. Moeller, T. H. Handley, and S. A. Reynolds, "Analysis for Radionuclides in Aqueous Wastes from an "Atomic" Plant."

D. L. Reid, "Analysis of Environmental Samples for Radionuclides."

L. R. Setter, G. R. Hagee, and C. P. Straub, "Analysis of Radioactivity in Surface Waters."

J. M. Seamon, "Summation."

L. R. Setter, G. R. Hagee, and C. P. Straub, "Analysis of Radioactivity in Surface Waters," ASTM BULLETIN, No. 227, January, p. 35 (1958).

1959

Symposium on Identification of Water-Formed Deposits, *STP 256*, Am. Soc. Testing Mats. (1959):

J. K. Rice, "Deposit Identification—First Step Toward Understanding a Water Problem."

C. H. Anderson, "The Application of Emission Spectroscopy to the Analysis of Water-Formed Deposits."

C. M. Maddin and R. B. Rosene, "Identification by Instrumental Methods of Chemical Compounds in Water-Formed Deposits."

E. A. Gulbransen and T. P. Copan, "Electron Microscopy and Electron Diffraction Studies of Oxide Films on Iron in Water and Oxygen Atmospheres."

J. V. Smith, "Correlation of Elemental Analysis and Phase Identification as Viewed by a Mineralogist."

R. K. Scott, "Summary."

Symposium on Technical Developments in the Handling and Utilization of Water and Industrial Waste Water, *STP 273*, Am. Soc. Testing Mats. (1959):

William L. Lamar, "Introduction."

L. C. Schwendiman, R. E. Brown, J. F. Honstead, C. E. Linderoth, and D. W. Pearce, "Disposal of Industrial Radioactive Waste Waters at Hanford."

Franklin B. Barker, "Determination of Radioactive Materials in Water."

Joseph J. Finnerty, "Utilization of Cooling Towers in Conservation and Pollution Control."

R. B. Richman, "Improvements in Water Treatment for Once-Through Reactor Cooling."

James M. Morris, Jr., "Disposal of Oil-Field Brines in the Central Valley of California."

L. V. Wilcox, "Effect of Industrial Wastes on Water for Irrigation Use."

William E. Katz, "Operation of Batch-Type and Continuous Electric Membrane Demineralizers."

R. P. Lappala, L. I. Yaeger, and J. A. Bjorksten, "Solar Distillation of Saline Water with Particular Regard to Materials Problems."

1960

Frank E. Clarke, "Old Wine in New Bottles," ASTM BULLETIN, No. 243, January, p. 17 (1960).

1961

Symposium on Impurities in Steam, *Proceedings*, Vol. 61, pp. 1369–1423 (1961):

M. M. Rubright, "The Stoichiometry of the Vaporous Carry-Over of Sodium Chloride from High-Pressure Boiler Water" (ASTM sponsored research report).

R. V. Cobb and E. E. Coulter, "The Prevention of Errors in Steam Purity Measurement Caused by Deposition of Impurities in Sampling Lines."

R. C. Ulmer and H. A. Klein, "Impurities in Steam from High-Pressure Boilers."

1962

Symposium on Water and Industrial Waste Water, *STP 337*, Am. Soc. Testing Mats. (1962):

J. E. Kinney, "The Political Puppet Called Purity."

S. Sussman, I. L. Portnoy, and J. Jacobson, "Handling and Analysis of Routine Water Samples in Volume."

A. C. Muller, "Water—Raw Material for Utilities Steam Generation."

R. D. Hoak, "Thermal Loading of Streams."

R. A. Baker, "Chromatographic Analyses of Organics in Aqueous Solutions."

L. E. Lancy and Walter Zabban, "Analytical Methods and Instrumentation Used for the Determination of Some Cyanogen Compounds."

E. Goldman, "A Discussion and Comparison of Two Methods for the Determination of Nitrates in Water."

R. C. Allen, "Continuous Automatic Boiler Water Silica Analyses."

INDEX

The word "water," if not qualified, stands for industrial water in this index. The word "deposits" stands for water-formed deposits.

38-52

APPLICATION FOR ASTM ORGANIZATIONAL MEMBERSHIP

PLEASE PRINT OR TYPE

Extracts from Charter and Bylaws and Dues Schedule on REVERSE SIDE of this application

Application is made for membership in the American Society for Testing and Materials in the class of (check one):

☐ **SUSTAINING MEMBER**   ☐ **INDUSTRIAL MEMBER**   ☐ **INSTITUTIONAL MEMBER**

and if elected the applicant agrees to be governed by the Charter and Bylaws of the Society, and to further its objectives as laid down therein. (This membership includes: opportunities for participation of the Official Representative of the membership in the general and District activities of the Society, and for him [or others in the member organization whom he designates] to make application for participation on its technical committees; subscription(s) to *Materials Research & Standards*; parts of the *Book of Standards*; other publications; member discounts on publications; and other benefits and privileges.)

Parent Firm or Organization ....

Division, Plant or Subsidiary..
(In which membership is to be held, if applicable)

Major Product...
(Or service performed by firm or organization)

Official Representative..
(Name of individual who will exercise membership privileges)

Official Representative's Title...Dept..

Address for Mail (Please follow carefully the instructions and sample below)

Representative's Major Field of Interest.........................Specific Application of Effort.............................
Examples: chemical research/civil engineering   Examples: polymer plastics/construction

Representative's Date of Birth: Month..........................Day........................Year...........................

Representative is Graduate of, or attended,
☐ High School   ☐ Vocational School   ☐ Technical Institute   ☐ College or University

Representative is Graduate of, or attended (Name of College or University)..

Year...................Degree, or Course...................Representative's Highest Degree Attained............................

PERSON AUTHORIZED TO APPLY FOR MEMBERSHIP	Membership Proposed By (Signature of Two Members)*

Name..   ....
(Signature)

Position..

Address..   *For assistance with signatures, send application with request for aid to the ASTM Executive Secretary

---

INSTRUCTIONS FOR PROVIDING ADDRESS FOR MAIL

To help provide prompt delivery of mail, please provide the address of the Official Representative in the block above as illustrated in the sample. The equipment which processes mailing labels limits addresses to four lines of 30 spaces each. Please PRINT. Place the last name of the Official Representative first. Leave a space between words. Use no punctuation marks or special characters, except the ampersand (&). Use initials and abbreviations where necessary. Include your ZIP CODE if you have one.

⟜ **START HERE**   **SAMPLE**

Name (Organization)	`AM SOC FOR TESTING & MATERIALS`
Name (Representative)	`LAUGHLIN P H JR DATA PROC MGR`
Mail Address	`1916 RACE STREET`
	`PHILADELPHIA PA 19103`

MAIL TO: American Society for Testing and Materials,
1916 Race St., Philadelphia, Pa. 19103

(Do NOT pay dues or order publications now. See instructions on reverse side.)

D-19, 2nd Ed.   989   C55–29

INFORMATION ON ORGANIZATION MEMBERSHIP

Extract From Charter:

1. The name of the corporation is the "American Society for Testing and Materials."

2. The corporation is formed for the promotion of knowledge of the materials of engineering, and the standardization of specifications and the methods of testing.

Extract From Bylaws:

ARTICLE 1. Members and Their Election

Sec. 1. The corporate membership of the Society shall consist of Personal Members, Institutional Members, Industrial Members, Sustaining Members, Associate Members, Senior Associate Members, and Honorary Members elected from a corporate category of membership. In addition there shall be Student Members, and Honorary Members elected from non-members of the Society. The rights of membership of Institutional, Industrial, and Sustaining Members shall be exercised by the individual who is designated as the official representative of that membership.

Sec. 3. An Institutional Member shall be a public library, educational institution, a nonprofit professional, scientific or technical society, government department or agency at the federal, state, city, county or township level, or separate divisions thereof, meeting the qualifications established by the Board of Directors for this classification.

Sec. 4. An Industrial Member shall be a plant, firm, corporation, partnership, or other business enterprise, or separate divisions thereof, trade association, or research institute meeting the qualifications established by the Board of Directors for this classification.

Sec. 5. A Sustaining Member shall be a person, plant, firm, corporation, society, department of government or other organization, or separate divisions thereof, electing to give greater support to the Society's activities through the payment of larger dues.

DUES SCHEDULE
(Membership is for the calendar year.)

Classes of Membership	Book of Standards Benefits	Annual Dues[a]
	(Information on additional publication benefits provided on membership will be sent to applicants)	(Entrance fee eliminated)
SUSTAINING MEMBER	Up to ONE complete set of the current Book of Standards (on request)	$500.00[b] minimum
INDUSTRIAL MEMBER	Up to FOUR parts (on request)	$125.00
INSTITUTIONAL MEMBER	Up to THREE parts (on request)	$ 35.00

NOTE: Benefits of membership and prices of publications are subject to change without notice.

[a]Of the Annual dues $5.00 is for each subscription to *Materials Research & Standards*. (Not deductible.)

[b]Organizations wishing to provide increased support for the Operation of the Society may supplement the minimum Sustaining Membership dues by an additional amount in the form of annual payments in such amounts and for such periods as the organization may choose or in the form of a lump sum in anticipation of annual payments of such additional dues.

PAYMENT OF DUES
Do NOT pay dues or order publications now

When notified of election to membership, the Official Representative of the membership will receive an invoice for the dues payment required to establish the membership for the calendar year. At that time he will also receive the opportunity to apply for participation in the activities of the Society, and to request the publications the membership will be entitled to receive. The election to membership shall be voided if payment of dues is not made within three months of election to membership.

SELECTION OF AN OFFICIAL REPRESENTATIVE: Careful attention should be given the selection of the Official Representative of an organizational membership. He should be qualified to exercise the rights and privileges of membership to enhance the overall interests of the organization. This would involve balloting on highly technical matters, and might include participation on technical committees, and selection of other participants for committee work.

VOTING RIGHTS: The Official Representative of each organizational membership shall be privileged to cast one ballot in Society matters.

PUBLICATION ORDERS AND SHIPMENTS: Orders for publications at member prices must come from the address in which the membership is held. All free publications, notices, ballots, etc. will be directed to the Official Representative of the membership, including the second free subscription to *Materials Research & Standards* furnished an Industrial Member. A Sustaining Member, however, may request the five additional subscriptions to *MR&S* for other mailing addresses prepared in accordance with the instructions.

APPLICATION FOR ASTM INDIVIDUAL MEMBERSHIP†

PLEASE PRINT OR TYPE

Extracts from Charter and Bylaws and Dues Schedule on REVERSE SIDE of this application

The undersigned hereby applies for membership in the American Society for Testing and Materials in the class of (check one):

☐ **PERSONAL MEMBER**   ☐ **SENIOR ASSOCIATE MEMBER‡**   ☐ **ASSOCIATE MEMBER**

and if elected the applicant agrees to be governed by the Charter and Bylaws of the Society, and to further its objectives as laid down therein. (This membership includes: opportunities for the participation of the member in the general and District activities of the Society, and for him to make application for participation on its technical committees; subscription to *Materials Research & Standards;* part(s) of the *Book of Standards;* other publications; member discounts on publications; and other benefits and privileges.)

Last Name..First Name................................Middle Initial................

Title..Department................................

Parent Firm or Organization..

Division, Plant or Subsidiary..
(In which you are employed, if applicable)

Address..

City..State................................ Zip Code

Major Product..
(Or service performed by your firm or organization)

Address for Mail (Please follow carefully the instructions and sample below)

<table>
<tr><td></td><td></td><td></td><td></td><td></td><td></td><td></td><td></td><td></td><td></td><td></td><td></td><td></td><td></td></tr>
<tr><td></td><td></td><td></td><td></td><td></td><td></td><td></td><td></td><td></td><td></td><td></td><td></td><td></td><td></td></tr>
<tr><td></td><td></td><td></td><td></td><td></td><td></td><td></td><td></td><td></td><td></td><td></td><td></td><td></td><td></td></tr>
<tr><td></td><td></td><td></td><td></td><td></td><td></td><td></td><td></td><td></td><td></td><td></td><td></td><td></td><td></td></tr>
</table>

Major Field of Interest................................Specific Application of Effort................
Examples: chemical research/civil engineering   Examples: polymer plastics/construction

Date of Birth: Month................................Day................................Year................

Graduate of, or attended,

☐ High School ☐ Vocational School ☐ Technical Institute ☐ College or University

Graduate of, or attended (Name of College or University)................................

Year................Degree, or Course................Highest Degree Attained................

MEMBERSHIP POLICY: An industrial organization desiring to participate in the technical activities of the Society and/or obtain publications of the Society at membership discount prices is expected to maintain at least one Sustaining or Industrial membership. This may be supplemented by Personal and Associate memberships as desired.

Membership Proposed By
(Signature of Two Members)*

....

....

*For assistance with signatures, send application with request for aid to the ASTM Executive Secretary.
‡Please outline your prior ASTM affiliation.
†Application forms for Student Membership available on request.

....
Applicant's Signature

INSTRUCTIONS FOR PROVIDING ADDRESS FOR MAIL

To help provide prompt delivery of mail, please provide your address in the block above as illustrated in the sample. The equipment which processes mailing labels limits addresses to four lines of 30 spaces each. Please PRINT. Place your last name first. Leave a space between words. Use no punctuation marks or special characters, except the ampersand (&). Use initials and abbreviations where necessary. Include your ZIP CODE if you have one.

⇨ START HERE   SAMPLE

Name	A	R	M	S	T	R	O	N	G		R	O	B	E	R	T		S		J	R		
Mail Address	L	A	W	T	O	N		E	N	G	R	G		&		M	F	G		C	O	R	P	
(Home or Company)	1	2	3	4		M	A	I	N		B	L	V	D									
	F	A	C	T	O	R	Y	T	O	W	N			I	N	D		1	0	2	3	7	

**MAIL TO: American Society for Testing and Materials,
1916 Race St., Philadelphia, Pa. 19103**

(Do NOT pay dues or order publications now. See instructions on reverse side.)

D-19, 2nd Ed.   991   C55–36

INFORMATION ON INDIVIDUAL MEMBERSHIP

Extract From Charter:

1. The name of the Corporation is the "American Society for Testing and Materials."
2. The corporation is formed for the promotion of knowledge of the materials of engineering, and the standardization of specifications and the methods of testing.

Extract From Bylaws:

ARTICLE 1. Members and Their Election

Sec. 1. The corporate membership of the Society shall consist of Personal Members, Institutional Members, Industrial Members, Sustaining Members, Associate Members, Senior Associate Members, and Honorary Members elected from a corporate category of membership. In addition there shall be Student Members, and Honorary Members elected from non-members of the Society. The rights of membership of Institutional, Industrial, and Sustaining Members shall be exercised by the individual who is designated as the official representative of that membership.

Sec. 2. A Personal Member shall be a person meeting the qualifications established by the Board of Directors for this classification. ("The basic qualification . . . shall be that he is interested in the Society's field of activities.")

Sec. 6. An Associate Member shall be a person less than thirty years of age. He shall have the same rights and privileges as a Personal Member, except that he shall not be eligible for office. An Associate Member shall not remain in this category beyond the end of the calendar year in which his thirtieth birthday occurs.

Sec. 8. A Senior Associate Member shall be a retired person who has reached the age of 65 or is disabled, who has been a member of the Society and/or a participant in an activity of the Society for a total of ten years, not necessarily continuously, and who elects to continue his association with the Society through the payment of reduced dues. He shall have the same rights and privileges as a Personal Member, except as may be limited by the Board of Directors for this classification.

DUES SCHEDULE
(Membership is for the calendar year.)[a]

Classes of Membership	Book of Standards Benefits	Annual Dues[b]
	(Information on additional publications benefits provided on membership will be sent to applicants)	(Entrance fee eliminated)
PERSONAL MEMBER	Up to TWO parts of the current Book of Standards (on request)	$20.00
SENIOR ASSOCIATE MEMBER	ONE part (on request)	$10.00
ASSOCIATE MEMBER	ONE part (on request)	$10.00

NOTE: Benefits of membership and prices of publications are subject to change without notice.

[a]Members elected after six months of any membership year shall have expired may elect to pay only one-half of the amount of dues for that year; but if they do so, Personal Members may receive ONLY ONE FREE PART of the Book of Standards, and Senior Associate and Associate Members receive NO FREE PARTS. Half year members are also not entitled to receive publications distributed prior to July 1.

[b]Of the Annual dues, $5.00 is for subscription to *Materials Research & Standards*. (Not deductible.)

PAYMENT OF DUES
Do NOT pay dues or order publications now

When notified of his election to membership, the applicant will receive an invoice for the dues payment required to establish the membership for the calendar year. At that time he will also receive the opportunity to apply for participation in the activities of the Society, and to request the publications he will be entitled to receive as a member. The election to membership shall be voided if payment of dues is not made within three months of election to membership.

VOTING RIGHTS: Each corporate member shall be privileged to cast one ballot in Society matters.

PUBLICATION ORDERS AND SHIPMENTS: Orders for publications at member prices must come from the address in which the membership is held. All free publications, notices, ballots, etc. must be directed to the member at the address for mail.